St. Patrick School
P9-CQQ-089

M E R R I L L

PHYSICAL SCIENCE

GLENCOE

Macmillan/McGraw-Hill

New York, New York Columbus, Ohio Mission Hills, California Peoria, Illinois

A GLENCOE PROGRAM

MERRILL PHYSICAL SCIENCE

Student Edition
Teacher Wraparound Edition
Teacher Resource Package
Study Guide, Student Edition
Reinforcement, Student Edition
Enrichment, Student Edition
Transparency Package
Laboratory Manual
Laboratory Manual, Teacher Annotated Edition
Spanish Resources
Chapter Review Software
Computer Test Bank
Videodisc Correlation

REVIEWERS

Richard A. Boolootian, Ph.D.
Director of Science Curriculum
Mirman School
Los Angeles, California

Theodore L. Boydston, III
Science Coordinator
Dade County Public Schools Region V
Miami, Florida

Robert C. Cambric
Science Dept. Chairperson
St. Francis Academy
Joliet, Illinois

Stephen A. Clark
Chemistry and Physics Teacher
Elbert County Comprehensive High School
Elberton, Georgia

Billie R. Easley
Science Dept. Head
Thackerville High School
Thackerville, Oklahoma

Elder Harrison, Jr.
Instructor
Chicago Public Schools
Chicago, Illinois

Mathew Keller
Physical Science and Chemistry Teacher
Rancho Cotate High School
Rohnert Park, California

Lillie B. Kelly
Science Dept. Chairperson
Shades Mountain Christian School
Birmingham, Alabama

Sr. Mary Ita O'Donnell
Science Dept. Chairperson
St. Joseph High School
Brooklyn, New York

Sandra McMillen Pace
Science Dept. Chairperson
Southeast High School
Macon, Georgia

Dominic Salinas
Assistant Principal
Parkway High School
Bossier City, Louisiana

Cover Photograph: Neon Tubes by Jim Osborn

Copyright © 1993 by the Glencoe Division of Macmillan/McGraw-Hill School Publishing Company. All rights reserved. Except as permitted under the United States Copyright Act, no part of this publication may be reproduced or distributed in any form or by any means, or stored in a database or retrieval system, without prior written permission of the publisher.

Send all inquiries to:
GLENCOE DIVISION
Macmillan/McGraw-Hill
936 Eastwind Drive
Westerville, OH 43081

ISBN 0-675-16776-0

Printed in the United States of America.

7 8 9 10 11 12 13 14 15 VH/MC 03 02 01 00 99 98 97 96 95

AUTHORS

Richard G. Smith has been teaching chemistry at the high school level for 25 years. He received a regional outstanding teacher award from the American Chemical Society and has participated in NSF summer institutes in chemistry. Mr. Smith graduated Phi Beta Kappa with a B.S. degree in Education from Ohio University and earned his M.A.T. in Chemistry from Indiana University. He is a member of the American Chemical Society and the National Science Teachers Association as well as other national professional organizations.

Jack T. Ballinger is a chemistry professor at St. Louis Community College in St. Louis, Missouri, where he has taught for 21 years. He received his B.S. degree in chemistry at Eastern Illinois University and his M.S. degree in organic chemistry at Southern Illinois University. He is a member of the American Chemical Society, the St. Louis Society of Analysts, and the National Education Association.

Marilyn Thompson teaches physics, chemistry, and physical science at Center Senior High School in Kansas City, Missouri. Ms. Thompson holds a B.A. degree in chemistry with an emphasis in physics and education from Carleton College, Northfield, Minnesota. She is a member of the American Association of Physics Teachers and the National Science Teachers Association.

CONSULTANTS

Senior Consultant, Physics:
John D. McGervey
Professor of Physics
Case Western Reserve University
Cleveland, Ohio

Physics:
Patrick Hamill, Ph.D.
Professor of Physics
San Jose State University
San Jose, California

Chemistry:
Robert C. Smoot, M.S.
Chemistry Teacher and Rollins Fellow in Science
McDonogh School
McDonogh, Maryland

Reading:
Barbara Pettegrew, Ph.D.
Director of Reading/Study Center
Assistant Professor of Education
Otterbein College
Westerville, Ohio

Safety:
Robert Tatz, Ph.D.
Instructional Lab Supervisor
Department of Chemistry
The Ohio State University
Columbus, Ohio

Special Features:
Stephen C. Blume
Elementary Science Specialist
St. Tammany Public School System
Slidell, Louisiana

Charles McLaughlin
Coordinator of Science Education
St. Joseph Public Schools
St. Joseph, Missouri

John R. Grube
High School Science Coordinator (former)
Eastside Union High School District
San Jose, California

Gifted and Mainstreamed:
Barbara Murdock
Elementary Consultant For Instruction
Gahanna-Jefferson Public Schools
Gahanna, Ohio

Judy Ratzenberger
Middle School Science Instructor
Gahanna Middle School West
Gahanna, Ohio

CONTENTS

14

6 C Carbon 12.011

14 Si Silicon 28.0855

32 Ge Germanium 72.59

50 Sn Tin 118.710

82 Pb Lead 207.2

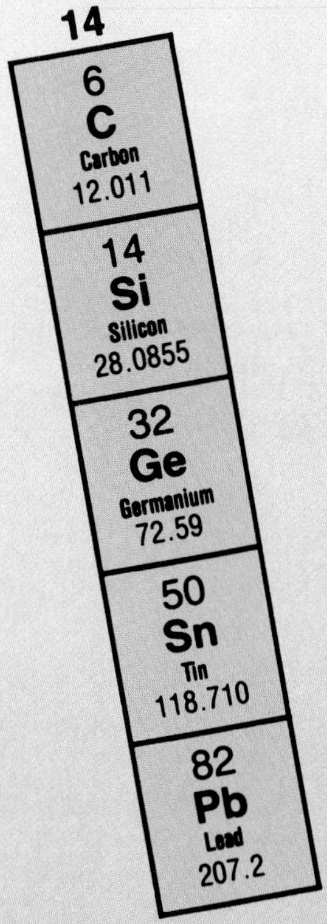

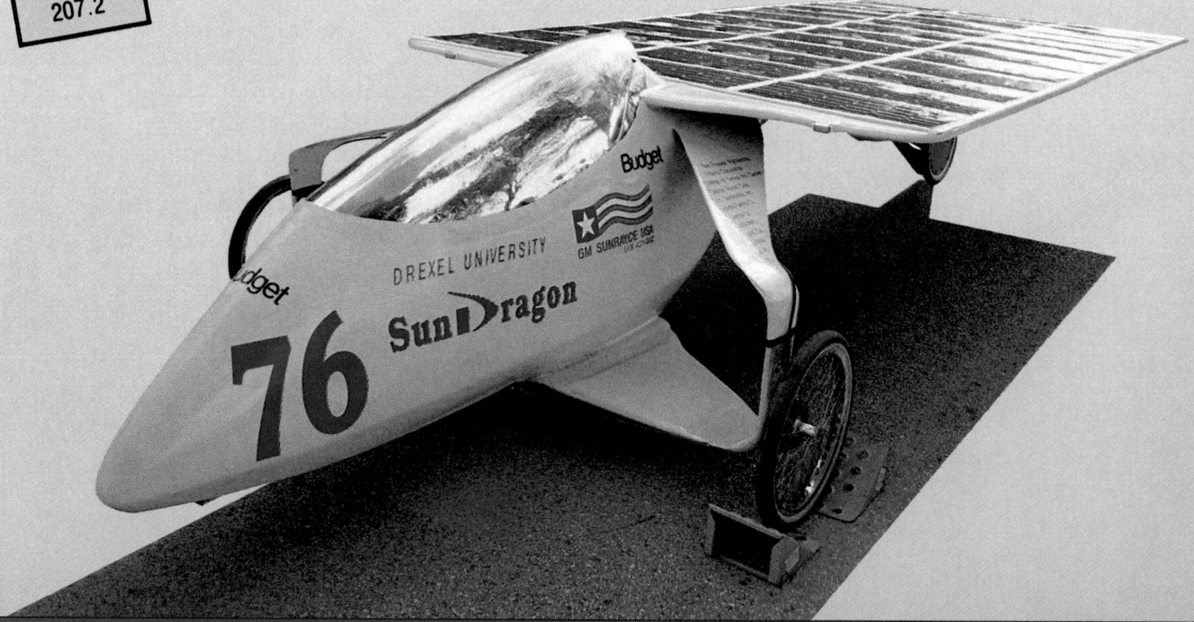

ACTIVITIES

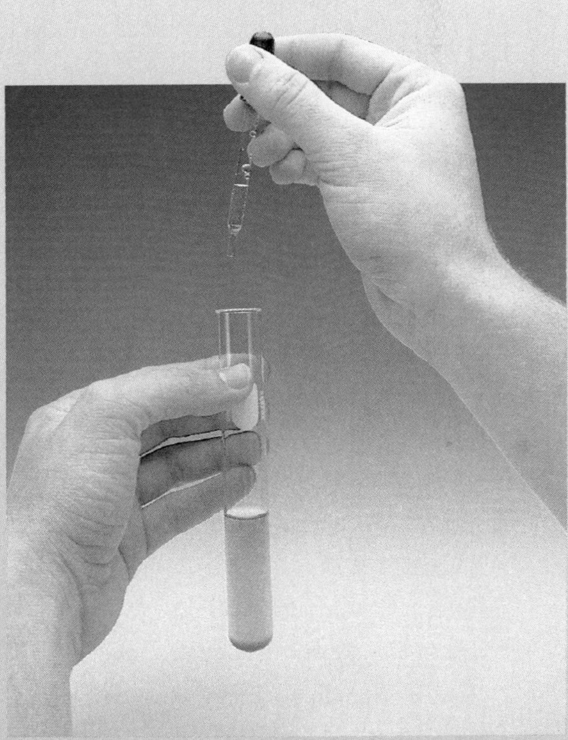

MINI-Labs

PROBLEM SOLVING

TECHNOLOGY

SKILL BUILDERS

GLOBAL CONNECTIONS

CAREERS

SCIENCE AND LITERATURE/ART

USING MERRILL PHYSICAL SCIENCE

Physical Science is an everyday experience. It's a subject you're familiar with because every part of your day is based upon physical science principles...the simple act of walking involves gravity, which holds you to Earth, friction between the soles of your shoes and the ground, which allows you to overcome inertia, accelerate forward, make turns, and even stop. Depending on temperature, the morning drizzle may have left a puddle or an icy spot for you to cross. What you see, hear, touch, and smell along your walk all involve physical science principles. **Merrill Physical Science** will help you understand science principles and recognize their applications to everyday life.

a quick tour of your textbook

What's happening here? Have you ever considered what allows gum to be stretched? Each unit begins with thought-provoking photographs that will make you wonder. The unit introduction then explains what is happening in the photographs and how the two relate to each other and to the content of the unit. What allows gum to be stretched? Read the opener to Unit 4 to find out.

UNIT 4 KINDS OF SUBSTANCES

What's Happening Here?

Even after you think *you're* done with a piece of chewing gum, look again—it still has plenty of stretch and give for the shoe of the next passerby. Chewing gum gets its stretch from its structure—a special arrangement of atoms called a polymer. A gum drop model of the chewing gum polymer is shown below. In this unit you'll learn about polymers and many other kinds of substances—metal, nonmetal, organic, biological—and the special properties of each. But hey, next time put your gum in the trash.

UNIT CONTENTS

296

297

It's clearly organized to get you started and keep you going.

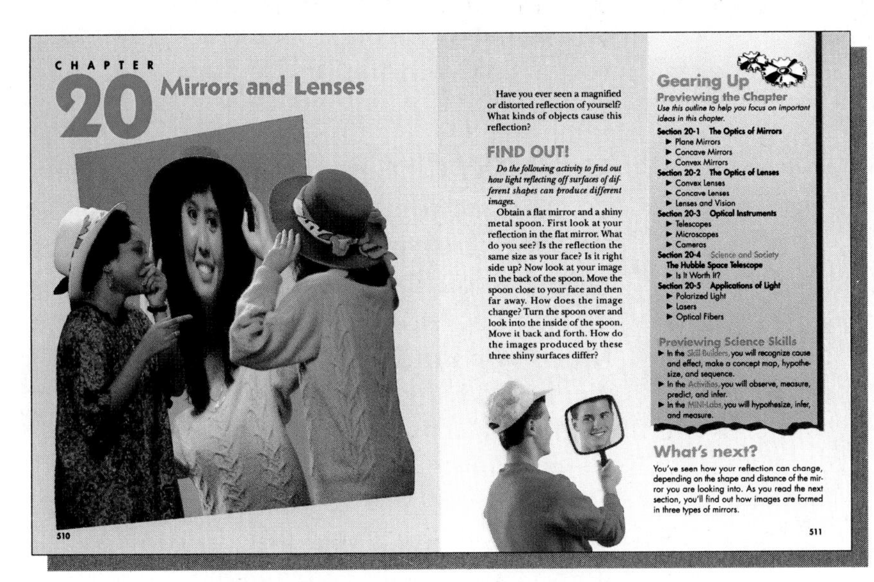

CHAPTER 20 Mirrors and Lenses

510

Have you ever seen a magnified or distorted reflection of yourself? What kinds of objects cause this reflection?

FIND OUT!

Do the following activity to find out how light reflecting off surfaces of different shapes can produce different images.

Obtain a flat mirror and a shiny metal spoon. First look at your reflection in the flat mirror. What do you see? Is the reflection the same size as your face? Is it right side up? Now look at your image in the back of the spoon. Move the spoon close to your face and then far away. How does the image change? Turn the spoon over and look into the inside of the spoon. Move it back and forth. How do the images produced by these three shiny surfaces differ?

Gearing Up

Previewing the Chapter

Use this outline to help you focus on important ideas in this chapter.

Section 20-1 The Optics of Mirrors
- Plane Mirrors
- Concave Mirrors
- Convex Mirrors

Section 20-2 The Optics of Lenses
- Convex Lenses
- Concave Lenses
- Lenses and Vision

Section 20-3 Optical Instruments
- Telescopes
- Microscopes
- Cameras

Section 20-4 Science and Society **The Hubble Space Telescope**
- Is It Worth It?

Section 20-5 Applications of Light
- Polarized Light
- Lasers
- Optical Fibers

Previewing Science Skills
- In the Skill Builders, you will recognize cause and effect, make a concept map, hypothesize, and sequence.
- In the Activities, you will observe, measure, predict, and infer.
- In the MINI-Labs, you will hypothesize, infer, and measure.

What's next?

You've seen how your reflection can change, depending on the shape and distance of the mirror you are looking into. As you read the next section, you'll find out how images are formed in three types of mirrors.

511

As you begin each new chapter, use the **Gearing Up** to preview what topics are covered and how they are organized. You will also preview the skills you will use in this chapter.

After you've performed the **FIND OUT** activity and previewed the chapter, you're ready to further explore the topics ahead. Read **What's next** to see what's ahead.

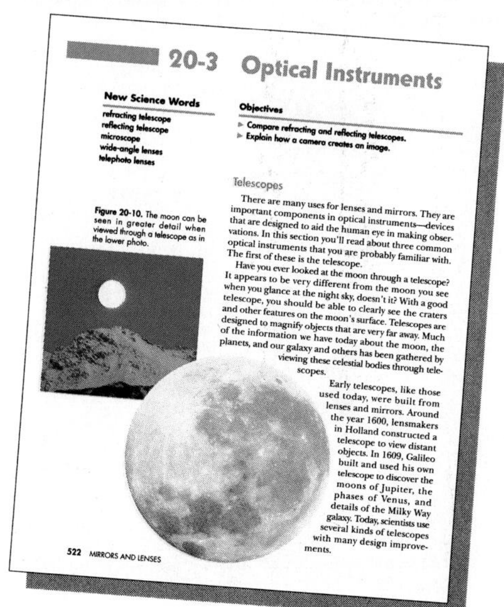

20-3 Optical Instruments

New Science Words

refracting telescope
reflecting telescope
microscope
wide-angle lenses
telephoto lenses

Objectives
- Compare refracting and reflecting telescopes.
- Explain how a camera creates an image.

Telescopes

There are many uses for lenses and mirrors. They are important components in optical instruments—devices that are designed to aid the human eye in making observations. In this section you'll read about three common optical instruments that you are probably familiar with. The first of these is the telescope.

Have you ever looked at the moon through a telescope? It appears to be very different from the moon you see when you glance at the night sky, doesn't it? With a good telescope, you should be able to clearly see the craters and other features on the moon's surface. Telescopes are designed to magnify objects that are very far away. Much of the information we have today about the moon, the planets, and our galaxy and others has been gathered by viewing these celestial bodies through telescopes.

Early telescopes, like those used today, were built from lenses and mirrors. Around the year 1600, lensmakers in Holland constructed a telescope to view distant objects. In 1609, Galileo built and used his own telescope to discover the moons of Jupiter, the phases of Venus, and details of the Milky Way galaxy. Today, scientists use several kinds of telescopes with many design improvements.

Figure 20-10. The moon can be seen in greater detail when viewed through a telescope as in the lower photo.

522 MIRRORS AND LENSES

Chapters are organized into three to five numbered sections. The **Objectives** at the beginning of the numbered section tell you what major topics you'll be covering and what you should expect to learn about them. The **New Science Words** are also listed in the order in which they appear in the section.

Experience science by observing, experimenting, and asking questions.

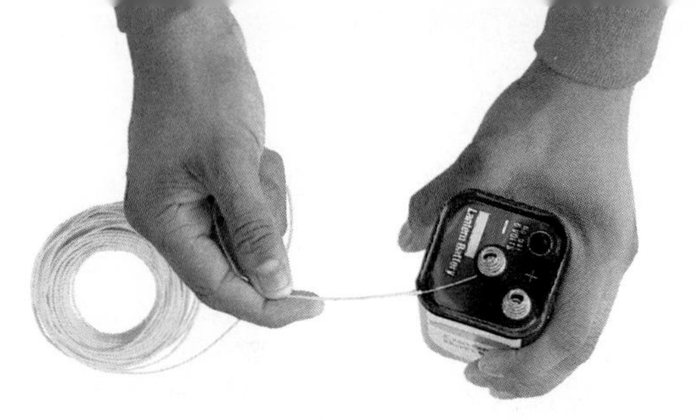

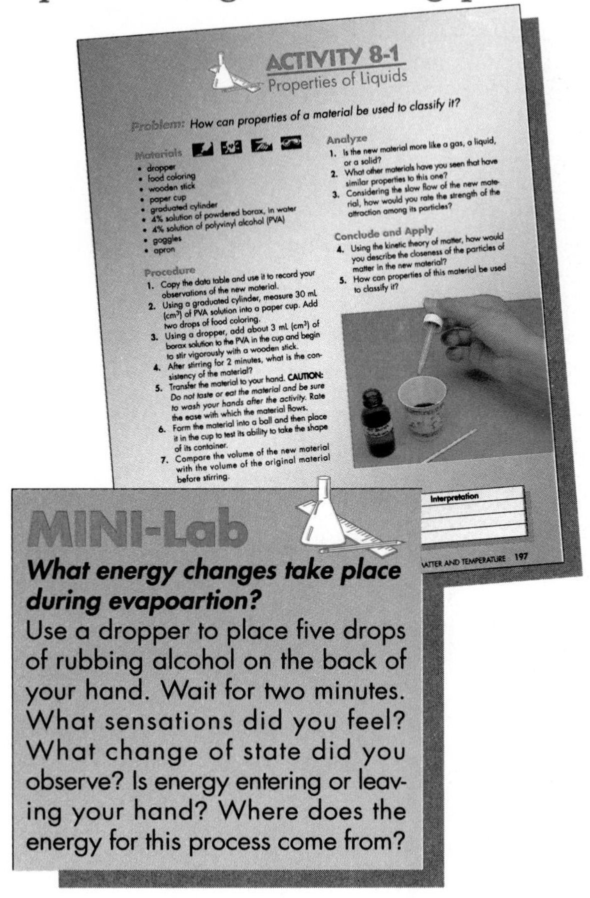

ACTIVITY 8-1
Properties of Liquids

Problem: *How can properties of a material be used to classify it?*

Materials

- dropper
- food coloring
- wooden stick
- paper cup
- graduated cylinder
- 4% solution of powdered borax, in water
- 4% solution of polyvinyl alcohol (PVA)
- goggles
- apron

Procedure

1. Copy the data table and use it to record your observations of the new material.
2. Using a graduated cylinder, measure 30 mL (cm^3) of PVA solution into a paper cup. Add two drops of food coloring.
3. Using a dropper, add about 3 mL (cm^3) of borax solution to the PVA in the cup and begin to stir vigorously with a wooden stick.
4. After stirring for 2 minutes, what is the consistency of the material?
5. Transfer the material to your hand. **CAUTION:** *Do not taste or eat the material and be sure to wash your hands after the activity.* Rate the ease with which the material flows.
6. Form the material into a ball and then place it in the cup to test its ability to take the shape of its container.
7. Compare the volume of the new material with the volume of the original material before stirring.

Analyze

1. Is the new material more like a gas, a liquid, or a solid?
2. What other materials have you seen that have similar properties to this one?
3. Considering the slow flow of the new material, how would you rate the strength of the attraction among its particles?

Conclude and Apply

4. Using the kinetic theory of matter, how would you describe the closeness of the particles of matter in the new material?
5. How can properties of this material be used to classify it?

Interpretation

ATTER AND TEMPERATURE 197

MINI-Lab

What energy changes take place during evapoartion?

Use a dropper to place five drops of rubbing alcohol on the back of your hand. Wait for two minutes. What sensations did you feel? What change of state did you observe? Is energy entering or leaving your hand? Where does the energy for this process come from?

Science is more than words in a book. The two Activities and the MINI-Labs in each chapter give you the chance to further explore and investigate the science topics covered in your textbook.

In the **Activities,** you'll use household items and laboratory equipment as you follow the easy, step-by-step procedure. At the end of each Activity are questions that ask you to analyze what you've done.

Most **MINI-Labs** are designed so you can do them on your own or with friends outside of the science classroom using materials you find around the house. Doing a MINI-Lab is an easy and fun way to further your knowledge about the topics you're studying.

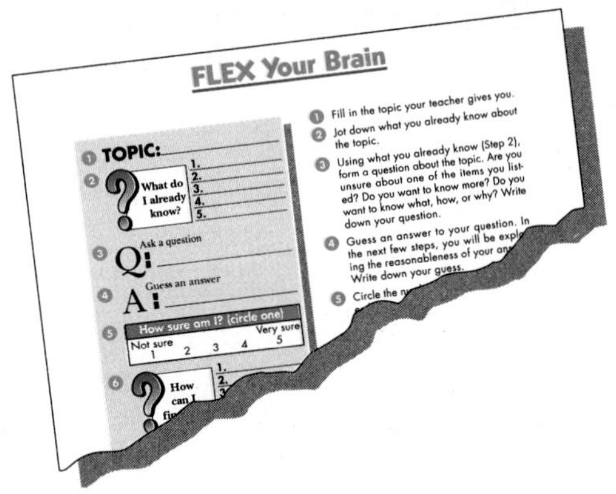

FLEX Your Brain

1 TOPIC:

2 What do I already know? 1. 2. 3. 4. 5.

3 Ask a question Q:

4 Guess an answer A:

5 How sure am I? (circle one) Not sure 1 2 3 4 5 Very sure

6 How can I fi...

1. Fill in the topic your teacher gives you.
2. Jot down what you already know about the topic.
3. Using what you already know (Step 2), form a question about the topic. Are you unsure about one of the items you listed? Do you want to know more? Do you want to know what, how, or why? Write down your question.
4. Guess an answer to your question. In the next few steps, you will be exploring the reasonableness of your an... Write down your guess.
5. Circle the n...

Flex Your Brain is a unique activity you can use to sharpen your critical thinking skills. Starting from what you already know about a science topic, you will apply a simple ten-step procedure to extend your knowledge about the topic from a perspective that interests you.

Each **Problem Solving** feature gives you a chance to solve a real world problem or understand a science principle.

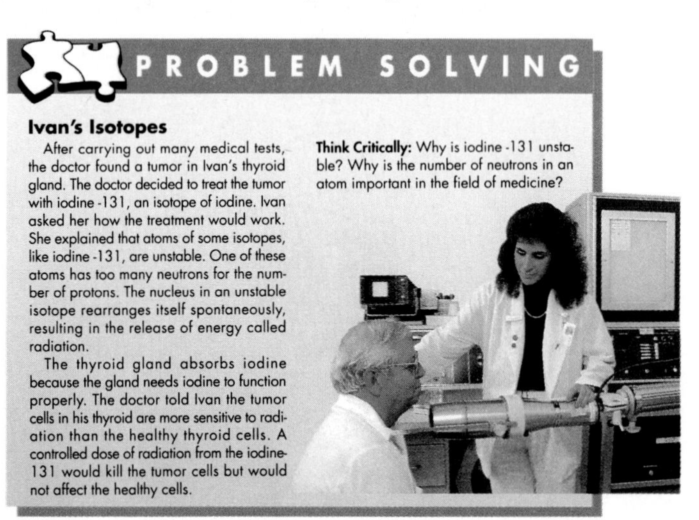

PROBLEM SOLVING

Ivan's Isotopes

After carrying out many medical tests, the doctor found a tumor in Ivan's thyroid gland. The doctor decided to treat the tumor with iodine-131, an isotope of iodine. Ivan asked her how the treatment would work. She explained that atoms of some isotopes, like iodine-131, are unstable. One of these atoms has too many neutrons for the number of protons. The nucleus in an unstable isotope rearranges itself spontaneously, resulting in the release of energy called radiation.

The thyroid gland absorbs iodine because the gland needs iodine to function properly. The doctor told Ivan the tumor cells in his thyroid are more sensitive to radiation than the healthy thyroid cells. A controlled dose of radiation from the iodine-131 would kill the tumor cells but would not affect the healthy cells.

Think Critically: Why is iodine-131 unstable? Why is the number of neutrons in an atom important in the field of medicine?

Explore news-making issues, concerns about the environment, and how science shapes your world through technology.

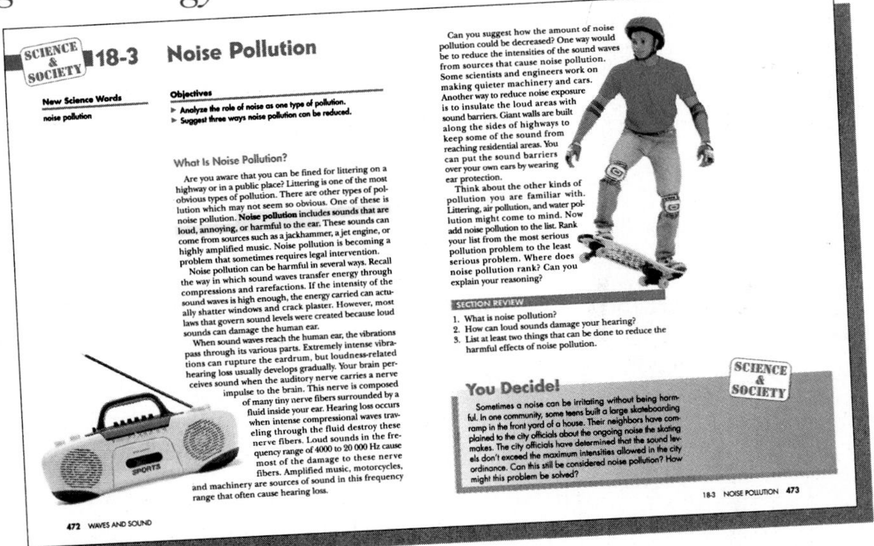

SCIENCE & SOCIETY **18-3** **Noise Pollution**

New Science Words

noise pollution

Objectives

- Analyze the role of noise as one type of pollution.
- Suggest three ways noise pollution can be reduced.

What Is Noise Pollution?

Are you aware that you can be fined for littering on a highway or in a public place? Littering is one of the most obvious types of pollution. There are other types of pollution which may not seem so obvious. One of these is noise pollution. **Noise pollution** includes sounds that are loud, annoying, or harmful to the ear. These sounds can come from sources such as a jackhammer, a jet engine, or highly amplified music. Noise pollution is becoming a problem that sometimes requires legal intervention.

Noise pollution can be harmful in several ways. Recall the way in which sound waves transfer energy through compressions and rarefactions. If the intensity of the sound waves is high enough, the energy carried can actually shatter windows and crack plaster. However, most laws that govern sound levels were created because loud sounds can damage the human ear.

When sound waves reach the human ear, the vibrations pass through its various parts. Extremely intense vibrations can rupture the eardrum, but loudness-related hearing loss usually develops gradually. Your brain perceives sound when the auditory nerve carries a nerve impulse to the brain. This nerve is composed of many tiny nerve fibers surrounded by a fluid inside your ear. Hearing loss occurs when intense compressional waves traveling through the fluid destroy these nerve fibers. Loud sounds in the frequency range of 4000 to 20 000 Hz cause most of the damage to these nerve fibers. Amplified music, motorcycles, and machinery are sources of sound in this frequency range that often cause hearing loss.

Can you suggest how the amount of noise pollution could be decreased? One way would be to reduce the intensities of the sound waves from sources that cause noise pollution. Some scientists and engineers work on making quieter machinery and cars. Another way to reduce noise exposure is to insulate the loud areas with sound barriers. Giant walls are built along the sides of highways to keep some of the sound from reaching residential areas. You can put the sound barriers over your own ears by wearing ear protection.

Think about the other kinds of pollution you are familiar with. Littering, air pollution, and water pollution might come to mind. Now add noise pollution to the list. Rank your list from the most serious pollution problem to the least serious problem. Where does noise pollution rank? Can you explain your reasoning?

SECTION REVIEW

1. What is noise pollution?
2. How can loud sounds damage your hearing?
3. List at least two things that can be done to reduce the harmful effects of noise pollution.

You Decide! SCIENCE & SOCIETY

Sometimes a noise can be irritating without being harmful. In one community, some teens built a large skateboarding ramp in the front yard of a house. Their neighbors have complained to the city officials about the ongoing noise the skating makes. The city officials have determined that the sound levels don't exceed the maximum intensities allowed in the city ordinance. Can this still be considered noise pollution? How might this problem be solved?

472 WAVES AND SOUND

18-3 NOISE POLLUTION 473

The impact of science on society directly affects you. In the **Science and Society** section in each chapter, you'll learn about an issue that's affecting the world around you. The topics you'll read about are controversial, and you'll explore them from several sides. Then, you'll have a chance to express your opinion in the You Decide feature that follows.

In the **Technology** feature in each chapter, you'll read about recent discoveries, newly developed instruments, and applications of technology that have shaped our world and furthered our knowledge.

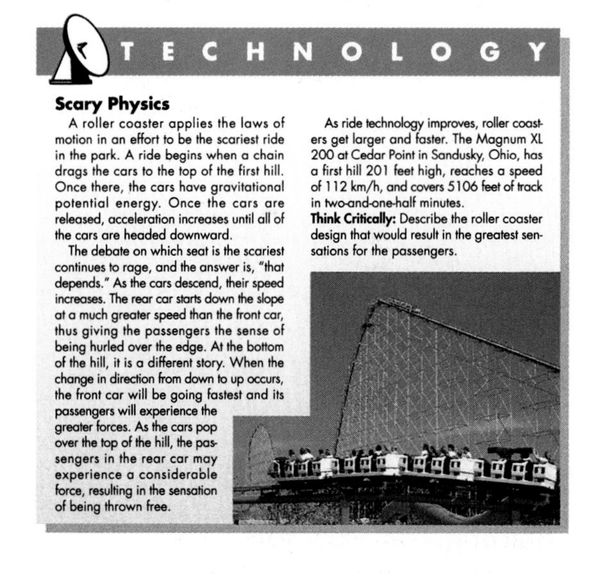

TECHNOLOGY

Scary Physics

A roller coaster applies the laws of motion in an effort to be the scariest ride in the park. A ride begins when a chain drags the cars to the top of the first hill. Once there, the cars have gravitational potential energy. Once the cars are released, acceleration increases until all of the cars are headed downward.

The debate on which seat is the scariest continues to rage, and the answer is, "that depends." As the cars descend, their speed increases. The rear car starts down the slope at a much greater speed than the front car, thus giving the passengers the sense of being hurled over the edge. At the bottom of the hill, it is a different story. When the change in direction from down to up occurs, the front car will be going fastest and its passengers will experience the greater forces. As the cars pop over the top of the hill, the passengers in the rear car may experience a considerable force, resulting in the sensation of being thrown free.

As ride technology improves, roller coasters get larger and faster. The Magnum XL 200 at Cedar Point in Sandusky, Ohio, has a first hill 201 feet high, reaches a speed of 112 km/h, and covers 5106 feet of track in two-and-one-half minutes.

Think Critically: Describe the roller coaster design that would result in the greatest sensations for the passengers.

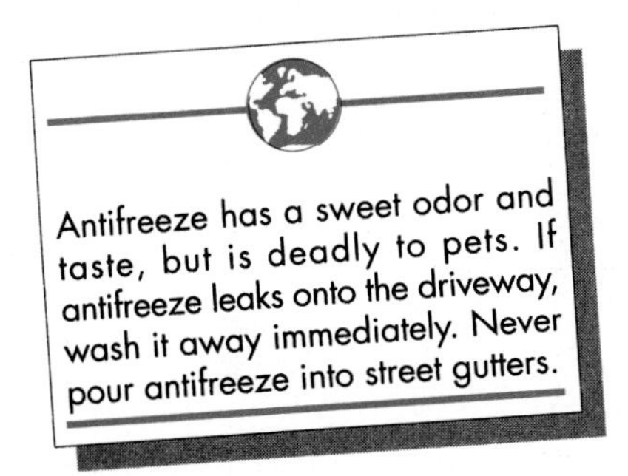

Antifreeze has a sweet odor and taste, but is deadly to pets. If antifreeze leaks onto the driveway, wash it away immediately. Never pour antifreeze into street gutters.

Each **EcoTip** suggests a simple step you can take to help improve the environment. EcoTips explain how you can get involved in making Earth a better place to live.

SKILL HANDBOOK

Organizing Information

Sequencing

Think about going to a grocery store to purchase a loaf of bread. As you walk down the aisles, you notice that canned fruits are in one section, boxed cereals are in another, and the bread you are looking for is in yet another. What would happen if different food items were placed randomly on the shelves? It would be difficult for people to locate the food items they wanted. Just like the grocery store, much of the world around you has been put into order to make it easier to understand. Sequencing and outlining are two methods scientists use to organize information.

One method of organizing information is to create a sequence. A sequence is an arrangement of things or events in a particular order. In some of your classes, the students may have been seated in alphabetical order. By organizing students alphabetically, teachers find it easier to remember students' names and to match papers with names in their grade books.

Think about baking chocolate chip cookies. Certain steps have to be followed for the cookies to taste good. If you skip a step in order, the cookies will not turn out right. Baking chocolate chip cookies is an example of the arrangement of events in a particular order.

When you are asked to sequence things or events, you must first identify what comes first. You then decide what should come second. Continue to choose things or events until they are all accounted for and in order. Then, go back over the sequence to make sure each thing or event logically leads to the next.

Suppose you wanted to watch a movie that just came out on videotape. What sequence of events would you have to follow to watch the movie? You would first turn the television set to channel 3 or 4. You would then turn the videotape player on, insert the tape, and press the "play" button. Once the tape had started playing, you would adjust the sound and picture. Then, when the movie was over, you would rewind the tape.

676

measurement?

2. In SI, the base unit of mass is the gram. What would you call 0.1 gram? 1000 grams?
3. **Apply:** Make a list of measuring tools you have used in the past month. For each example, tell what units you used to make your measurements.

Skill Builder — **Sequencing**

Using the data in Table 2-1, arrange the following units in order, from largest to smallest: centigram, gram, milligram, kilogram, decigram. If you need help, refer to Sequencing in the **Skill Handbook** on page 676.

32 PHYSICAL SCIENCE METHODS

Discover that you can apply what you've learned as you answer questions and practice your science skills.

At the end of each section are several Section Review questions that help you test your knowledge. The last question challenges you to think critically and **Apply** what you've learned.

The **Skill Builder** feature lets you sharpen your science skills using only paper and pencil. If you need help with these skills, refer to the **Skill Handbook** at the back of the book. Here, you can find complete information about each type of skill covered in the Skill Builders.

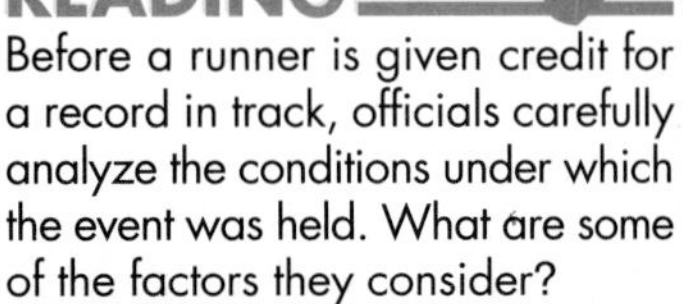

Science is related to every other subject you study. The **Science And** features challenge you to solve math problems, read literature excerpts, and to write about topics you're studying as you make the connections between science and other disciplines.

The **Chapter Review** starts with a summary so you can review the major concepts from each section. Then, you'll apply your knowledge and practice thinking skills as you answer the questions that follow.

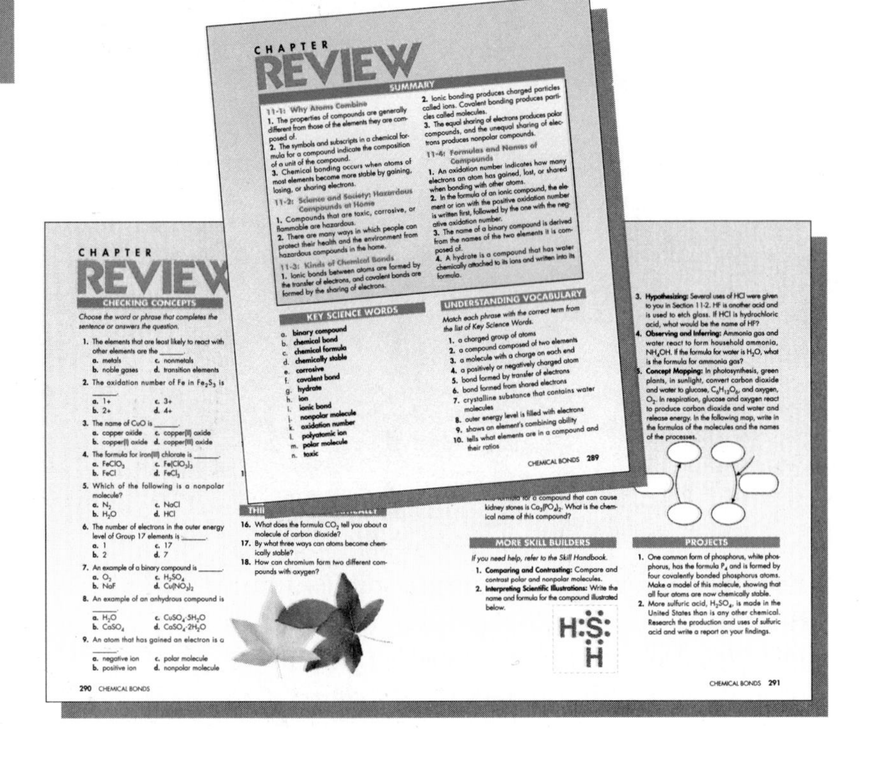

CHAPTER REVIEW

SUMMARY

11-1: Why Atoms Combine

1. The properties of compounds are generally different from those of the elements they are composed of.
2. The symbols and subscripts in a chemical formula for a compound indicate the composition of a unit of the compound.
3. Chemical bonding occurs when atoms of most elements become more stable by gaining, losing, or sharing electrons.

11-2: Science and Society: Hazardous Compounds at Home

1. Compounds that are toxic, corrosive, or flammable are hazardous.
2. There are many ways in which people can protect their health and the environment from hazardous compounds in the home.

11-3: Kinds of Chemical Bonds

1. Ionic bonds between atoms are formed by the transfer of electrons, and covalent bonds are formed by the sharing of electrons.
2. Ionic bonding produces charged particles called ions. Covalent bonding produces particles called molecules.
3. The equal sharing of electrons produces polar compounds, and the unequal sharing of electrons produces nonpolar compounds.

11-4: Formulas and Names of Compounds

1. An oxidation number indicates how many electrons an atom has gained, lost, or shared when bonding with other atoms.
2. In the formula of an ionic compound, the element or ion with the positive oxidation number is written first, followed by the one with the negative oxidation number.
3. The name of a binary compound is derived from the names of the two elements it is composed of.
4. A hydrate is a compound that has water chemically attached to its ions and written into its formula.

KEY SCIENCE WORDS

a. binary compound
b. chemical bond
c. chemical formula
d. chemically stable
e. corrosive
f. covalent bond
g. hydrate
h. ion
i. ionic bond
j. nonpolar molecule
k. oxidation number
l. polyatomic ion
m. polar molecule
n. toxic

UNDERSTANDING VOCABULARY

Match each phrase with the correct term from the list of Key Science Words.

1. a charged group of atoms
2. a compound composed of two elements
3. a molecule with a charge on each end
4. a positively or negatively charged atom
5. bond formed by transfer of electrons
6. bond formed from shared electrons
7. crystalline substance that contains water molecules
8. outer energy level is filled with electrons
9. shows an element's combining ability
10. tells what elements are in a compound and their ratios

CHEMICAL BONDS 289

CHAPTER REVIEW

CHECKING CONCEPTS

Choose the word or phrase that completes the sentence or answers the question.

1. The elements that are least likely to react with other elements are the ______.
   a. metals c. nonmetals
   b. noble gases d. transition elements
2. The oxidation number of Fe in Fe_2S_3 is ______.
   a. 1+ c. 3+
   b. 2+ d. 4+
3. The name of CuO is ______.
   a. copper oxide c. copper(II) oxide
   b. copper(I) oxide d. copper(III) oxide
4. The formula for iron(III) chlorate is ______.
   a. $FeClO_3$ c. $Fe(ClO_3)_3$
   b. FeCl d. $FeCl_3$
5. Which of the following is a nonpolar molecule?
   a. N_2 c. NaCl
   b. H_2O d. HCl
6. The number of electrons in the outer energy level of Group 17 elements is ______.
   a. 1 c. 17
   b. 2 d. 7
7. An example of a binary compound is ______.
   a. O_2 c. H_2SO_4
   b. NaF d. $Cu(NO_3)_2$
8. An example of an anhydrous compound is ______.
   a. H_2O c. $CuSO_4 \cdot 5H_2O$
   b. $CaSO_4$ d. $CaSO_4 \cdot 2H_2O$
9. An atom that has gained an electron is a ______.
   a. negative ion c. polar molecule
   b. positive ion d. nonpolar molecule

290 CHEMICAL BONDS

16. What does the formula CO_2 tell you about a molecule of carbon dioxide?
17. By what three ways can atoms become chemically stable?
18. How can chromium form two different compounds with oxygen?

kidney stones is $Ca_3(PO_4)_2$. What is the chemical name of this compound?

MORE SKILL BUILDERS

If you need help, refer to the Skill Handbook.

1. **Comparing and Contrasting:** Compare and contrast polar and nonpolar molecules.
2. **Interpreting Scientific Illustrations:** Write the name and formula for the compound illustrated below.

3. **Hypothesizing:** Several uses of HCl were given to you in Section 11-2. HF is another acid and is used to etch glass. If HCl is hydrochloric acid, what would be the name of HF?
4. **Observing and Inferring:** Ammonia gas and water react to form household ammonia, NH_4OH. If the formula for water is H_2O, what is the formula for ammonia gas?
5. **Concept Mapping:** In photosynthesis, green plants, in sunlight, convert carbon dioxide and water to glucose, $C_6H_{12}O_6$, and oxygen, O_2. In respiration, glucose and oxygen react to produce carbon dioxide and water and release energy. In the following map, write in the formulas of the molecules and the names of the processes.

PROJECTS

1. One common form of phosphorus, white phosphorus, has the formula P_4 and is formed by four covalently bonded phosphorus atoms. Make a model of this molecule, showing that all four atoms are now chemically stable.
2. More sulfuric acid, H_2SO_4, is made in the United States than is any other chemical. Research the production and uses of sulfuric acid and write a report on your findings.

CHEMICAL BONDS 291

Discover how physical science topics relate to people and places all over the world.

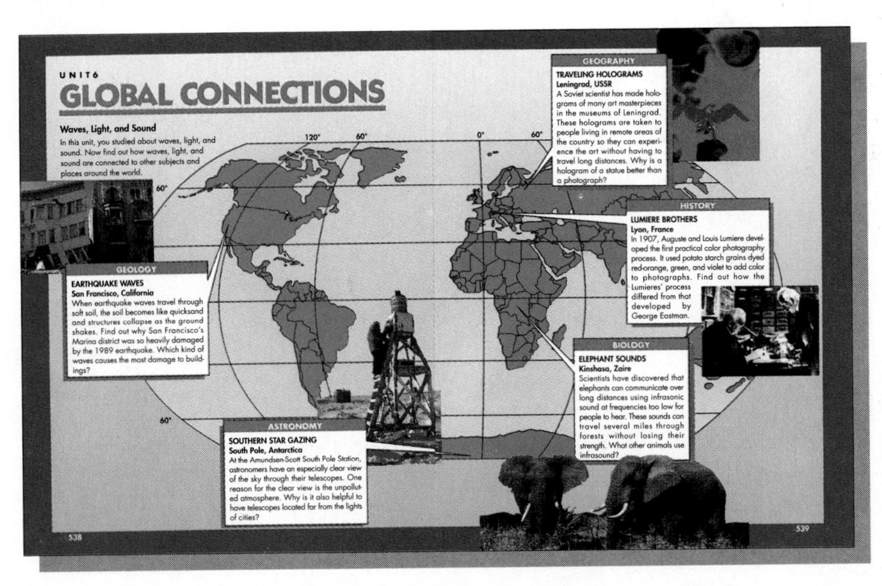

UNIT 6

GLOBAL CONNECTIONS

Waves, Light, and Sound

In this unit, you studied about waves, light, and sound. Now find out how waves, light, and sound are connected to other subjects and places around the world.

GEOLOGY

EARTHQUAKE WAVES
San Francisco, California
When earthquake waves travel through soft soil, the soil becomes like quicksand and structures collapse as the ground shakes. Find out why San Francisco's Marina district was so heavily damaged by the 1989 earthquake. Which kind of waves causes the most damage to buildings?

ASTRONOMY

SOUTHERN STAR GAZING
South Pole, Antarctica
At the Amundsen-Scott South Pole Station, astronomers have an especially clear view of the sky through their telescopes. One reason for the clear view is the unpolluted atmosphere. Why is it also helpful to have telescopes located far from the lights of cities?

GEOGRAPHY

TRAVELING HOLOGRAMS
Leningrad, USSR
A Soviet scientist has made holograms of many art masterpieces in the museums of Leningrad. These holograms are taken to people living in remote areas of the country so they can experience the art without having to travel long distances. Why is a hologram of a statue better than a photograph?

HISTORY

LUMIERE BROTHERS
Lyon, France
In 1907, Auguste and Louis Lumiere developed the first practical color photography process. It used potato starch grains dyed red-orange, green, and violet to add color to photographs. Find out how the Lumieres' process differed from that developed by George Eastman.

BIOLOGY

ELEPHANT SOUNDS
Kinshasa, Zaire
Scientists have discovered that elephants can communicate over long distances using infrasonic sound at frequencies too low for people to hear. These sounds can travel several miles through forests without losing their strength. What other animals use infrasound?

538 539

Global Connections help you to see how physical science is related to other sciences as well as social studies, history and health.

Also at the end of each unit you will find two **Careers** that relate to the material in the unit you just read. What jobs may be related to waves, light, and sound? Read the careers at the end of Unit 6 to find out.

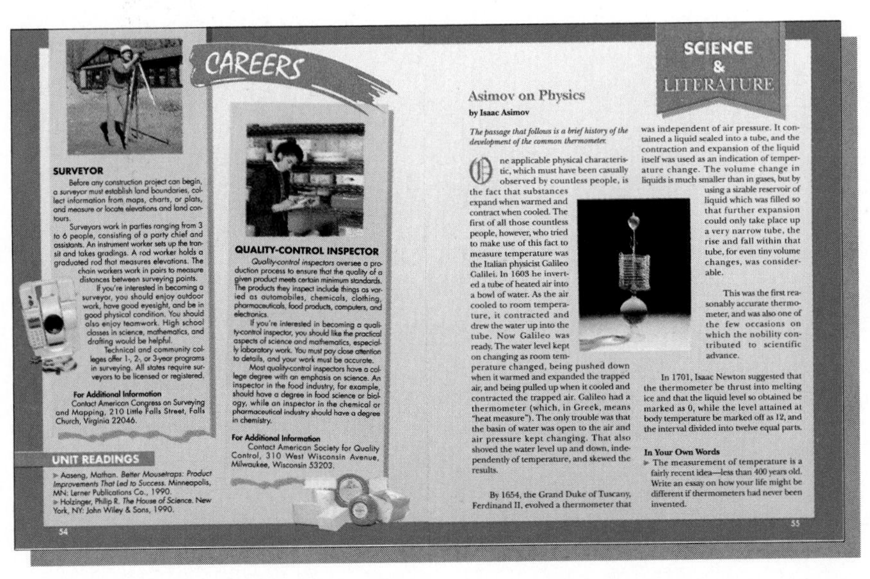

CAREERS

SURVEYOR

Before any construction project can begin, a *surveyor* must establish land boundaries, collect information from maps, charts, or plats, and measure or locate elevations and land contours.

Surveyors work in parties ranging from 3 to 6 people, consisting of a party chief and assistants. An instrument worker sets up the transit and takes gradings. A rod worker holds a graduated rod that measures elevations. The chain workers work in pairs to measure distances between surveying points.

If you're interested in becoming a surveyor, you should enjoy outdoor work, have good eyesight, and be in good physical condition. You should also enjoy teamwork. High school classes in science, mathematics, and drafting would be helpful.

Technical and community colleges offer 1-, 2-, or 3-year programs in surveying. All states require surveyors to be licensed or registered.

For Additional Information

Contact American Congress on Surveying and Mapping, 210 Little Falls Street, Falls Church, Virginia 22046.

QUALITY-CONTROL INSPECTOR

Quality-control inspectors oversee a production process to ensure that the quality of a given product meets certain minimum standards. The products they inspect include things as varied as automobiles, chemicals, clothing, pharmaceuticals, food products, computers, and electronics.

If you're interested in becoming a quality-control inspector, you should like the practical aspects of science and mathematics, especially laboratory work. You must pay close attention to details, and your work must be accurate.

Most quality-control inspectors have a college degree with an emphasis on science. An inspector in the food industry, for example, should have a degree in food science or biology, while an inspector in the chemical or pharmaceutical industry should have a degree in chemistry.

For Additional Information

Contact American Society for Quality Control, 310 West Wisconsin Avenue, Milwaukee, Wisconsin 53203.

UNIT READINGS

- Aaseng, Mathan. *Better Mousetraps: Product Improvements That Led to Success.* Minneapolis, MN: Lerner Publications Co., 1990.
- Holzinger, Philip R. *The House of Science.* New York, NY: John Wiley & Sons, 1990.

54

SCIENCE & LITERATURE

Asimov on Physics

by Isaac Asimov

The passage that follows is a brief history of the development of the common thermometer.

One applicable physical characteristic, which must have been casually observed by countless people, is the fact that substances expand when warmed and contract when cooled. The first of all those countless people, however, who tried to make use of this fact to measure temperature was the Italian physicist Galileo Galilei. In 1603 he inverted a tube of heated air into a bowl of water. As the air cooled to room temperature, it contracted and drew the water up into the tube. Now Galileo was ready. The water level kept on changing as room temperature changed, being pushed down when it warmed and expanded the trapped air, and being pulled up when it cooled and contracted the trapped air. Galileo had a thermometer (which, in Greek, means "heat measure"). The only trouble was that the basin of water was open to the air and air pressure kept changing. That also shoved the water level up and down, independently of temperature, and skewed the results.

By 1654, the Grand Duke of Tuscany, Ferdinand II, evolved a thermometer that was independent of air pressure. It contained a liquid sealed into a tube, and the contraction and expansion of the liquid itself was used as an indication of temperature change. The volume change in liquids is much smaller than in gases, but by using a sizable reservoir of liquid which was filled so that further expansion could only take place up a very narrow tube, the rise and fall within that tube, for even tiny volume changes, was considerable.

This was the first reasonably accurate thermometer, and was also one of the few occasions on which the nobility contributed to scientific advance.

In 1701, Isaac Newton suggested that the thermometer be thrust into melting ice and that the liquid level so obtained be marked as 0, while the level attained at body temperature be marked off as 12, and the interval divided into twelve equal parts.

In Your Own Words

- The measurement of temperature is a fairly recent idea—less than 400 years old. Write an essay on how your life might be different if thermometers had never been invented.

55

What do physical science and literature have in common? A lot, as you'll discover when you read the unit close to Unit 1. Each unit is closed with a reading from literature or an example of art that makes a connection with physical science.

UNIT 1 PHYSICAL SCIENCE BASICS

What's Happening Here?

Does the large photograph belong in a science lab or in an art exhibit? It was shot by a physical scientist. A physical scientist is curious about the way matter behaves and how energy interacts with matter. Because of this curiosity, the scientist has learned how glass and water can bend and reflect light and how chemicals act on film to give these beautiful results. What does it take to be a scientist? Only curiosity and a desire to investigate the world around you. If you are curious, you too can be a scientist.

UNIT CONTENTS

CHAPTER

1 The Nature of Science

Isn't it frustrating when something doesn't work the way you'd like it to? Sometimes that feeling of frustration can lead to ideas for improvements or new inventions.

FIND OUT!

Do this exercise to explore some ways of solving problems.

Working with a partner, think of something in your school that doesn't work as well as it could. You may choose a device, like a pencil sharpener or window shade, or a system, such as the cafeteria line or the grading process.

Without showing each other your work, you and your partner each make a list of ways you could improve the device or system you chose. Then write down the steps you would go through to make these improvements.

Now show each other your lists. How are they different? Why do you think you and your partner came up with different approaches to the same problem? Would your answers have been different if you had worked together? Is there any way to find out whether one approach would work better?

Gearing Up

Previewing the Chapter

Use this outline to help you focus on important ideas in the chapter.

Section 1-1 Physical Science and You
- Applying Science
- Physical Science

Section 1-2 Problem Solving
- What Is a Problem?
- Problem-Solving Strategies
- Critical Thinking
- Problem Solving in Science

Section 1-3 Science and Society
Problems? What Problems?
- Research or Action?

Section 1-4 Exploring Science
- Experimentation
- Safety

Previewing Science Skills

- In the **Skill Builders**, you will observe and infer, outline, and make a concept map.
- In the **Activity**, you will observe, predict, and control variables.
- In the **MINI-Lab**, you will observe and infer.

What's next?

You have identified a problem and attempted to work out a solution to the problem. Now find out how your approach to problem solving compares with the approach used by scientists.

1-1 Physical Science and You

New Science Words

technology
physical science

Objectives

- ▶ Compare and contrast "pure" science and technology.
- ▶ Define *physical science.*
- ▶ Discuss some of the topics covered in physical science.

Applying Science

How are scientific discoveries made? Do scientists, with a specific goal in mind, conduct experiments until they reach that goal? The answer is "Sometimes, but not always." Read the brief true accounts that follow.

A scientist forgot to rinse out a flask. It was later discovered that a coating left on the inside of the flask kept the flask from shattering when dropped. This discovery led to the invention of safety glass, similar to that used in automobile windshields.

While studying data from a radio telescope, an astronomy student noticed that a particular star seemed to be emitting short, regular pulses of energy. Her observation led to the discovery of pulsars, stars that are as massive as the sun, but are only the size of a large mountain.

As these accounts show, the path to scientific discovery is not always a direct one. But the processes of science are always the same—observing, questioning, exploring, and seeking answers. Scientists are always trying to understand the world around them—from processes in their own bodies to reactions in the laboratory; from the burning of paper to the explosion of a star.

Figure 1-1. Scientists seek to learn more about Earth by studying the stars.

In their search for knowledge, scientists often make surprising discoveries. Not every discovery will have common, everyday applications. For example, the discovery of pulsars did not lead to the development of any consumer products. However, it did open up a whole new field of investigation. Scientists have learned about how matter behaves under the special condition that exists inside the very dense stars. Someday this information may help them to learn more about matter here on Earth.

Other scientific discoveries, such as the shatterproof glass flask, lead directly to practical and useful everyday applications. The application of scientific knowledge to improve the quality of human life is called **technology.**

There is no sharp boundary between science and technology. Scientific discoveries lead to technological inventions. Inventions, in turn, may lead to further discoveries. Science includes both "pure" science, for the advancement of knowledge, and "applied" science, or technology.

MINI-Lab

How can patterns help explain complicated systems?

Make a froth of bubbles by adding a few drops of dishwashing detergent to a small amount of water in the bottom of a large glass. Use a soda straw to blow air into the solution until the glass is full of bubbles. Observe the bubble system closely and try to describe what you see. Make your task easier by examining the shape and structure of a single bubble. What can you find in one bubble that is just like all the other bubbles around it? What is the shape of a bubble wall? How many walls come together to form an edge? Are there any exceptions?

What is technology?

Figure 1-2. By applying their scientific knowledge, scientists and engineers develop products that make our lives easier.

Physical Science

Physical science is the study of matter and energy. Everything in the universe is either matter or energy. Plants and animals, rocks and clouds, eggs and elephants are all examples of matter. And lightning, thunder, heat, and sunlight are all examples of energy.

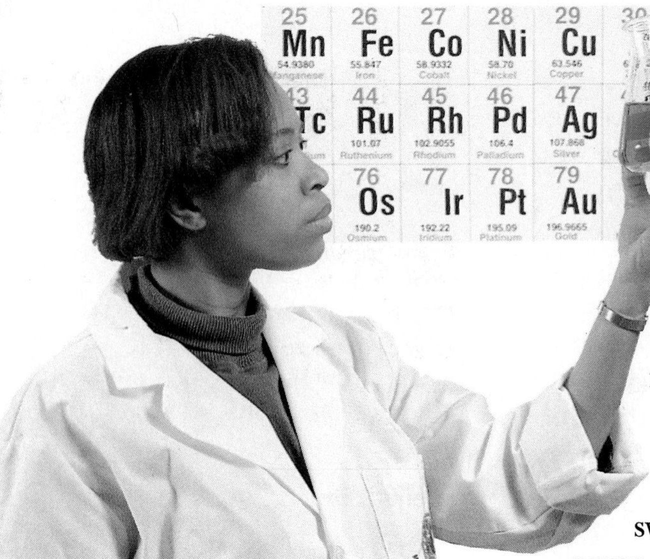

Figure 1-3. In the laboratory, scientists test their own ideas and check the work of other scientists.

Physical science deals with the composition and properties of matter. Composition has to do with what matter is made up of. Properties have to do with what matter is like and how it behaves. You're already familiar with some properties of different kinds of matter. You know that rocks are hard, wax melts at low temperatures, and sugar tastes sweet. Hardness, melting point, and taste are some of the properties of matter.

In physical science, you'll learn how matter and energy are related. You'll discover how energy is transferred through matter, as when the sound from a stereo reaches your ears. You'll find out how refrigerators stay cold and why a down jacket keeps you warm.

As you learn about electricity, sound, heat, and light, you'll discover how energy is used to do work. In the study of force and motion, you'll learn why acorns fall to Earth while satellites remain in orbit.

As you study physical science, be on the lookout for patterns. Observe how things and ideas are organized into systems, and how different parts of a system interact. Your observations are bound to lead you to ask questions. The rest of this chapter will help you find out how to go about answering those questions.

Look through the table of contents for this book to find out what subjects a physical scientist studies. Then find a book in the library that lists such careers, such as The Occupational Outlook Handbook. Select a career that relates to physical science and describe it in a brief oral report to your class.

SECTION REVIEW

1. What is the difference between science and technology? Give an example of each.
2. Define *physical science.*
3. **Apply:** Pose three questions that you think could be answered by the activities of physical science.

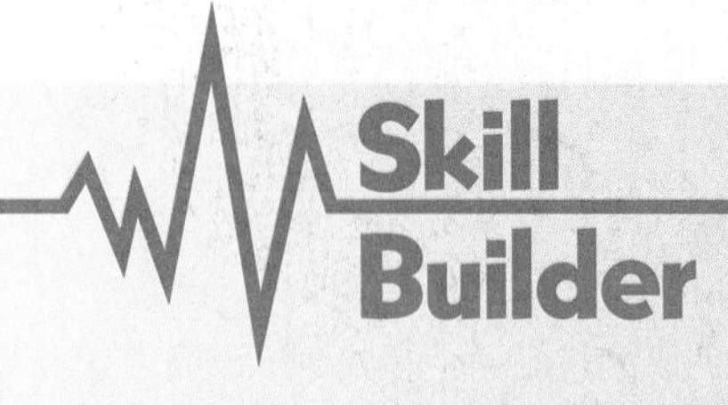

Observing and Inferring

Bring in a newspaper or magazine article related to physical science. Summarize the article and explain whether it deals with a scientific discovery or a technological development. If you need help, refer to Observing and Inferring in the **Skill Handbook** on page 678.

Problem Solving

1-2

Objectives

- ▶ Distinguish between problems and exercises.
- ▶ Evaluate approaches for solving problems.
- ▶ Compare and contrast hypothesis, theory, and scientific law.

New Science Words

model
critical thinking
observation
hypothesis
theory
scientific law

What Is a Problem?

How can astronauts be kept safe and healthy on long space missions? Is Earth's climate warming up? What's the best way to make recorded music sound like the real thing? Each of these questions suggests a problem that can be approached scientifically. They are considered problems because their solutions are not obvious. Some crucial information is missing.

What do all problems have in common?

Solving a problem involves finding missing information, but sometimes it's not clear at first what kind of information is needed. For example, to find out whether the temperature of Earth's troposphere is increasing, where should temperature readings be made? Many weather stations throughout the world are in or near cities, but temperatures in cities generally are higher than temperatures in unpopulated areas. Scientists must decide whether temperature readings from cities should be included in their data. They also must decide how many years back they should go. Should they check temperatures starting at 1950? 1900? or even further back? As you can see, there are a lot of "problems" in deciding how to go about solving a problem.

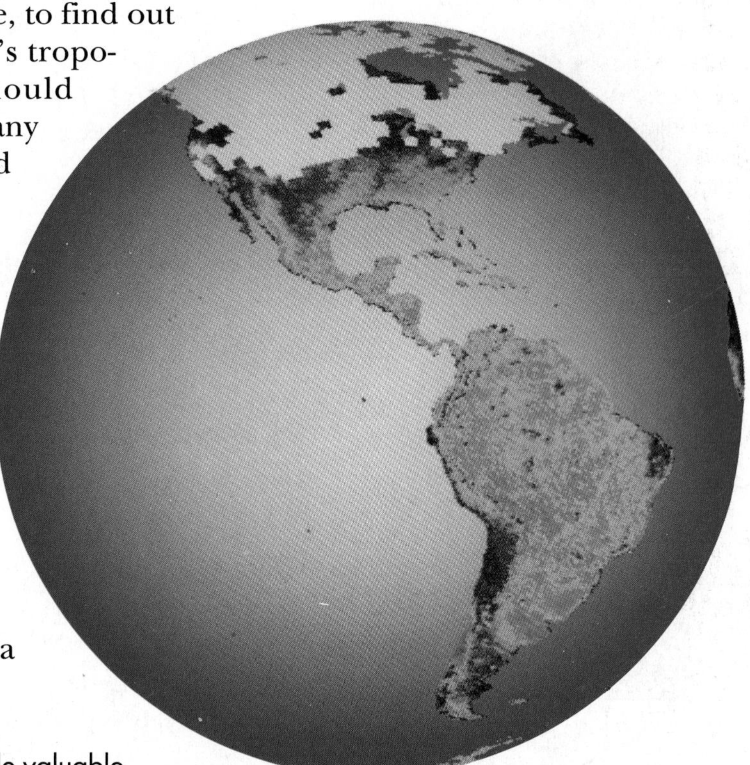

Figure 1-4. Infrared satellite images provide valuable information about temperatures at Earth's surface.

Figure 1-5. Thomas Edison was an inventor who perfected the technique of applying scientific discoveries to develop and improve hundreds of products.

Solving problems always involves uncertainty. So, it's not surprising that scientists sometimes make false starts or end up on dead-end paths before they arrive at solutions. Solving problems sometimes involves trial-and-error and the ability to learn from mistakes. For example, in the process of inventing the light bulb, Thomas Edison tried more than 100 materials before he found one that would work as the filament of the bulb.

A problem for one person may not be a problem for someone else. For a stranger, finding a certain building downtown is a problem that requires using a map and reading street signs. For someone who passes the building on the way to work every day, finding the building is not a problem.

There's a difference between a problem and an exercise. In an exercise, the steps required to find the solution are usually obvious. For example, finding the average weight of five classmates is an exercise if you know how to calculate averages. If you don't know how to find averages, you are faced with a problem.

Figure 1-6. Maps and street signs can help a stranger find an address.

Problem-Solving Strategies

Before you can solve a problem, you need to understand exactly what the problem is. That may sound obvious, but people often have trouble solving problems because they don't know where to start. Sometimes that's because they haven't defined the problem clearly enough.

Suppose a friend asks you to help fix a broken bicycle. How will you proceed? Maybe you'll look over the bike and ask your friend a lot of questions. Is something wrong with a tire? Is there a problem with the gears? Does the bicycle rattle? Your questions and observations will help you pinpoint the specific problem. You'll progress from knowing only that the bicycle is broken to knowing, for example, that the gears don't shift properly. The more precisely you can define the problem, the less time you'll waste looking for solutions.

What is the first step in solving a problem?

Once you've defined the problem, there's no single "right" way to start looking for answers. The important thing is to be systematic. Proceed in logical steps from what you know to what you don't know. Keep track of your steps, so that if something doesn't work, you can move on to something else instead of trying the same thing over again.

Here are some ways to try solving problems:

- Use what you know about the problem to predict a solution and try it. If your effort fails, think about why it didn't work. Then make another prediction and try that. Keep eliminating possibilities until you find the one that works. You've probably used this method to search for something you've lost. You think about when you last saw the item, and where you've been since then. This helps you to direct your search. Then you consider where you may have left the item, and you look there. If you don't find it, you look in the next logical place.

What is a model?

• Look for patterns that will help you make predictions about the problem. Suppose you occasionally break out in a rash. If you pay attention to what you eat, touch, and wear every day, you may find a pattern that helps you discover what's causing the rash. Putting information into a table or graph or making a drawing sometimes can help you find patterns.

• Develop a model. When your problem deals with something complicated or difficult to see, it may help to develop a model. A **model** is an idea, system, or structure that represents whatever you're trying to explain. The model is never exactly like the thing being explained, but it is similar enough to allow comparisons.

To find out how the shape of an airplane can affect performance, scientists and engineers make model airplanes of different shapes. These models are based on theories that describe how moving air behaves. They then test the different models under various conditions to find out which shape works best. They might also create different computer models, which are programs that predict the outcomes of different designs under various conditions.

Figure 1-7. The wind tunnel is used to test the effects of wind on the airplane model.

TECHNOLOGY

Driving Smart

The time spent sitting in traffic is expected to increase fourfold by the year 2000. In an effort to improve safety and traffic flow, scientists and engineers are working on systems that use traffic monitoring, navigation equipment, and radio links. Early efforts are directed at helping motorists avoid traffic jams. Traffic sensors embedded in the road transmit data about traffic volume and speed to a central computer. This computer analyzes the data to predict the locations of traffic jams. This information is then transmitted by radio to an onboard computer in an individual car. The location of pending traffic jams and possible alternate routes are then projected on the car's video screen to help the driver choose the best route.

Another line of research involves vision-enhancement systems originally developed for the military. These systems could be linked to vehicle control to provide automatic speed control and emergency braking. Improvement of the sensory apparatus of a car would enable more vehicles to travel closer together, safely, at high speeds.

Think Critically: What problems exist with a system that provides drivers alternate routes around a traffic jam?

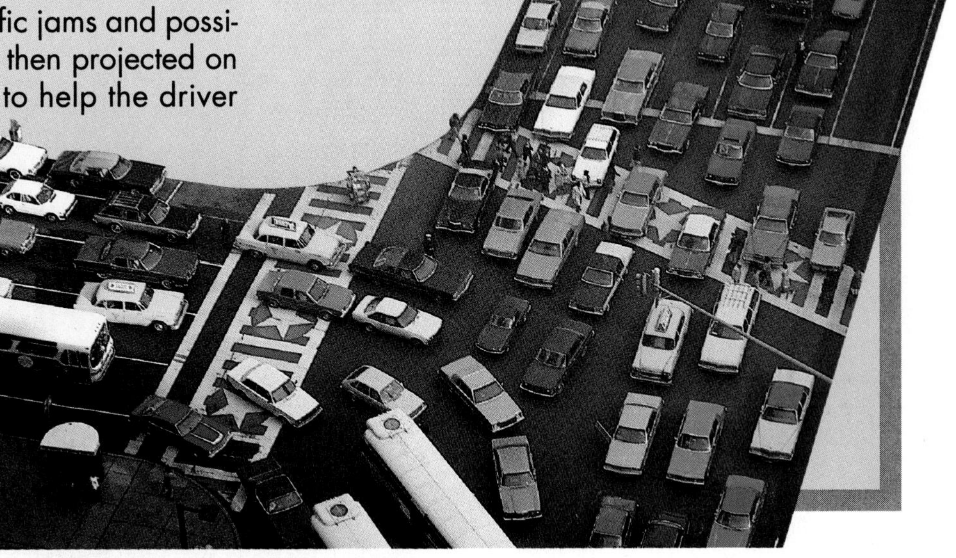

• Break the problem down into smaller, simpler problems. Sometimes it's hard to see what needs to be done when the problem is complicated. Look for ways to solve it step-by-step.

If one problem-solving approach doesn't work, try another. As you search for solutions, keep thinking about what you first knew about the problem and what you've learned about from each problem-solving attempt. When you find a solution, think again about the problem and ask yourself if your solution makes sense.

Critical Thinking

What is critical thinking?

Imagine that you have just made a batch of chili, and it just doesn't taste right. It tastes bland. What could have gone wrong? Did you follow the recipe? Did you cook it at the right temperature for the proper length of time? After thinking about it, you decide that you may have left out an essential ingredient—chili powder. How did you arrive at this conclusion? Without being aware of it, you probably used some aspect of critical thinking.

Critical thinking is a process that uses certain skills to solve a problem. Let's see how you may have used critical thinking to solve the "great chili problem." First you identified the problem—the bland taste—by mentally comparing the taste of your chili with that of other batches of chili you've eaten. Next you may have separ-ated important information from unimportant information by deciding that the temperature and cooking time of the chili had little to do with its flavor. Finally, you examined your assumption that you had followed the recipe correctly. This seemed like the best bet. You looked at the recipe again and concluded that you had left out the chili powder.

You probably went one step further and analyzed your conclusion. You asked if leaving the chili powder out would make the chili bland. If the answer was "yes," then you may have solved the problem.

"Flex Your Brain," as seen on the next page, is an activity that can be used throughout this book. This activity will help you to think about and examine your thinking. "Flex Your Brain" is a way to keep your thinking on track when you are investigating a topic. Each activity takes you through a series of steps, starting with what you already know and believe, and leading to new conclusions and awareness. Then, it encourages you to review and discuss the steps you took.

The "Flex Your Brain" activities, and other features of this book, are designed to help you improve your critical thinking skills. You'll become a better problem solver, and your next batch of chili will taste great.

FLEX Your Brain

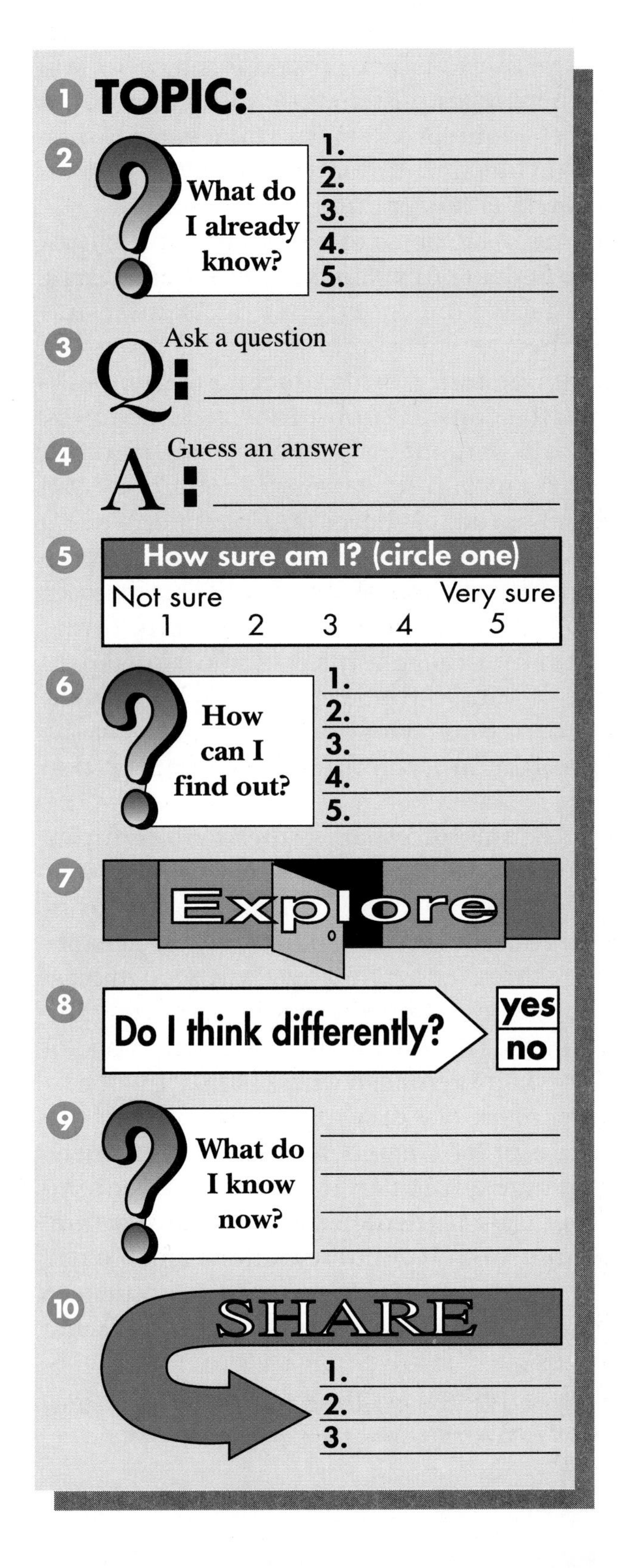

1. Fill in the topic your teacher gives you.
2. Jot down what you already know about the topic.
3. Using what you already know (Step 2), form a question about the topic. Are you unsure about one of the items you listed? Do you want to know more? Do you want to know what, how, or why? Write down your question.
4. Guess an answer to your question. In the next few steps, you will be exploring the reasonableness of your answer. Write down your guess.
5. Circle the number in the box that matches how sure you are of your answer in Step 4. This is your chance to rate your confidence in what you've done so far and, later, to see how your level of sureness affects your thinking.
6. How can you find out more about your topic? You might want to read a book, ask an expert, or do an experiment. Write down ways you can find out more.
7. Make a plan to explore your answer. Use the resources you listed in Step 6. Then, carry out your plan.
8. Now that you've explored, go back to your answer in Step 4. Would you answer differently? Mark one of the boxes.
9. Considering what you learned in your exploration, answer your question again, adding new things you've learned. You may completely change your answer.
10. It's important to be able to talk about thinking. Choose three people to tell about how you arrived at your response in every step. For example, don't just read what you wrote down in Step 2. Try to share how you thought of those things.

Figure 1-8. Observations of the simple cocklebur led to the idea for the "zipperless" fastener.

Problem Solving in Science

The steps to solving a scientific problem are similar to those you use to solve any problem. The first step is observation. **Observation** is the process of using your senses to gather information. To fix your friend's bicycle, you examined the bicycle and listened for clues that would help you zero in on the problem. In science, tools such as microscopes, rulers, thermometers, and clocks can help make your observations more precise.

Good observations lead to testable predictions about how to solve a problem or explain how something works. In science, a testable prediction is called a **hypothesis.**

What is a hypothesis?

How do you find out if a hypothesis is right? You test it. A hypothesis can be tested by conducting experiments and making further observations. In a later section of this chapter, you'll find out more about experiments. If one hypothesis turns out to be wrong, another one can be proposed and tested. It's never possible to prove that a hypothesis is absolutely right. However, you can keep ruling out different possibilities until you settle on one you think is most likely to be right. It may take many experiments and many different kinds of data to thoroughly test a hypothesis. The more results you obtain that support the hypothesis, the more confident you can be that it's correct.

Scientists use the information they gather during experimentation to form a theory. A **theory** is an explanation based on many observations supported by experimental results. A theory is the most logical explanation of why things work the way they do. Theories may lead the way to more experiments. As new information is collected, a theory may need to be revised or discarded and replaced with another theory.

Over many years, scientists have observed that matter is never created nor destroyed in chemical changes. It is stated as the law of conservation of mass. A **scientific law** is a "rule of nature" that sums up related observations and experimental results to describe a pattern in nature. Generally, laws predict what

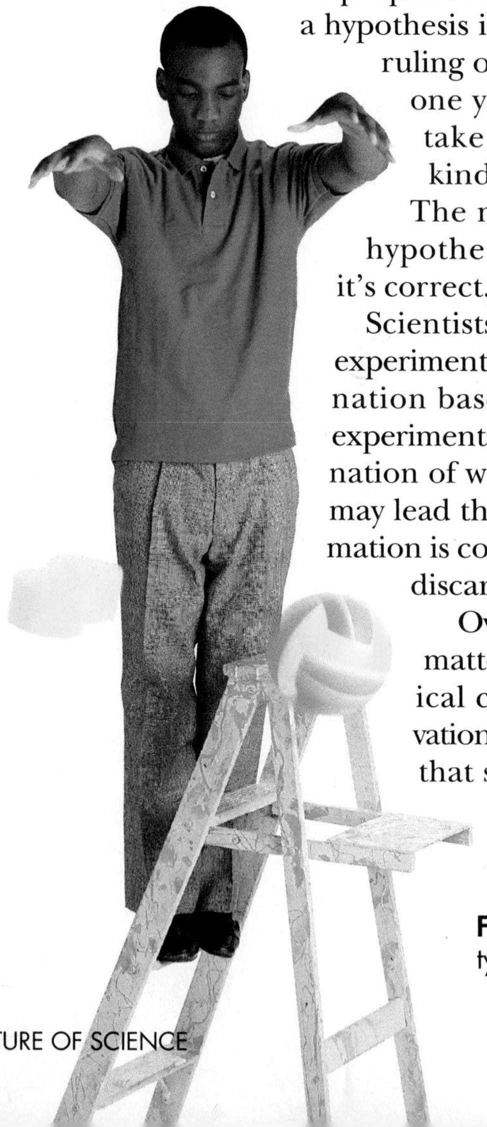

Figure 1-9. You can learn something about gravity by observing how different objects fall.

Figure 1-10. A simple event, such as the falling of an apple, inspired Isaac Newton to investigate gravity. This study eventually led to the development of an entirely new field of physics.

will happen in a given situation, but don't explain why. Theories may serve as explanations of laws. Like theories, laws may be changed or discarded if new observations show them to be incorrect.

Whether you're puzzling over a physical science mystery in the classroom or just trying to figure out where you left your homework, you can use what you've learned about problem solving to lead you to a solution.

SECTION REVIEW

1. Explain the difference between an exercise and a problem. Give an example of each.
2. Compare and contrast these terms: *hypothesis, theory, scientific law.*
3. **Apply:** Develop a model to describe how you decide what to wear to school every day. Could someone who doesn't know you use the model to predict what you'll wear tomorrow?

Outlining

Skill Builder

Think of a problem you solved or tried to solve recently. Outline the steps you followed in searching for the solution. If you need help, refer to Outlining in the **Skill Handbook** on page 677.

1-3 Problems? What Problems?

New Science Words

greenhouse effect
ozone layer

Objectives

- Describe some of the environmental issues presently being studied by scientists.
- Examine how scientific controversies arise.

Research or Action?

Is Earth's environment changing? You may have heard a lot about such problems as global warming, ozone depletion, and acid rain. But did you know that scientists disagree about the extent of these problems and what should be done about them?

What is the greenhouse effect?

The **greenhouse effect**, heating Earth by the atmosphere's trapping the sun's energy, is necessary to provide an environment in which life as we know it can exist. But the burning of fossil fuels adds increased amounts of carbon dioxide to the atmosphere, and this heating may be happening at a faster-than-usual rate, causing global warming.

In the 1970s, scientists began to worry about damage to the ozone layer. The **ozone layer** is a part of the atmosphere that protects life on Earth from the damaging effects of ultraviolet radiation from the sun. Scientists suggested that continued use of chlorofluorocarbons (KLOR uh floor uh kar bunz) (CFCs), chemicals used in refrigerators and air conditioners and in manufacturing plastic foam products, would destroy the ozone layer.

Around the same time, other scientists warned that sulfur and nitrogen oxides released when fossil fuels burn were making precipitation very acidic. This precipitation, called acid rain, was harmful to trees, crops, and aquatic life.

Figure 1-11. The trees in this forest show the effects of acid rain.

Since these predictions were made, scientists have gathered data by taking measurements, creating models, doing experiments, and using other problem-solving techniques. Some scientists say their data show that the problems are serious and need immediate action. Others say the data are flawed and that more research is needed before drastic action is taken to solve problems that could be minor. Just about everyone agrees that changes that are taking place in the atmosphere today may have harmful effects far beyond what is presently suspected. At the very least, we must reduce those activities that continue to add acids and carbon dioxide to the atmosphere.

SECTION REVIEW

1. Think of a topic on which you think more scientific research needs to be done. How would you decide what kind of research should be done next?
2. Does it ever make sense to start trying to solve a problem before you've learned everything you can about it?

You Decide!

If you were a scientist studying the greenhouse effect, ozone depletion, or acid rain, how would you decide when enough research had been done and when action should be taken? How would you know what action to take? Who should make these decisions, scientists doing the research, government, or the public? Would your answers be the same if you were considering a smaller scientific problem that would not affect the health of a whole planet and its inhabitants?

1-4 Exploring Science

New Science Words

experiment
control
constant
independent variable
dependent variable

Objectives

- Appreciate the importance of following guidelines in doing experiments.
- Define *independent variable* and *dependent variable.*
- Understand laboratory safety rules.

Experimentation

You've learned that problem solving in science involves making observations, forming a hypothesis, and testing the hypothesis with experiments. Now you'll learn just how to conduct an experiment.

An **experiment** is an organized procedure for testing a hypothesis. When scientists conduct experiments, they usually are seeking new information. Classroom experiments often demonstrate and verify information that already is known but may be new to you.

When doing an experiment, it is important to follow certain guidelines to reduce the chance of reaching wrong conclusions. Suppose you want to know whether storing microwave popcorn in a freezer will make it pop better. You store a package of popcorn in the freezer for a day or two, pop the corn, and count the unpopped kernels. Could you draw a meaningful conclusion from this "experiment?" No, because you don't have anything to compare your results with. Maybe you'd get the same number of unpopped kernels with corn stored at room temperature. But you don't know, because you didn't test any unfrozen popcorn.

To draw a conclusion, you need a control—a standard for comparison. In an experiment, a **control** shows that your result is related to the condition you're testing and not to some other condition.

To find out if storing popcorn in the freezer makes a difference, you need to test popcorn stored at room temperature, as a control. All other conditions should be the same for both batches of popcorn. The popcorn should be the same brand, equally fresh, stored for the same period of time, and popped in the same microwave oven, at the same power, for the same length of time. Only one condition, the place of storage, should differ between the two batches. All of the other factors are constants. A **constant** is a factor that doesn't vary in an experiment.

EcoTip

Design an experiment to test for smog outside your house. HINT: Rubber bands left outside in a very polluted area will break easily in a few weeks.

Can you be confident in conclusions based on the results of popping just one bag of popcorn stored each way? What if one of the bags happened to be defective? To be sure of your conclusions, you should repeat the experiment several times with different bags of popcorn, storing half of each bag in the freezer and half at room temperature.

What are dependent and independent variables?

If your experiment shows that storing microwave popcorn in the freezer makes it pop better, you may want to do another experiment to find out if the length of time the popcorn is stored makes a difference. You could store different batches of popcorn for different lengths of time. Length of time stored would be the **independent variable,** the factor adjusted by the experimenter. The measure of popping success—the number of unpopped kernels—would be the dependent variable. A **dependent variable** depends on the value of the independent variable. What factors would be constants?

Keeping an orderly procedure for an experiment will help you to draw conclusions and decide what to do next in your investigation. It will also allow others to duplicate your investigation. Although scientists agree that there is no one way to solve a problem, their scientific methods often include the following steps:

Determine the problem. What do you want to find out?

Make a hypothesis. What prediction do you want to test?

Test your hypothesis. What steps can you take to reach a conclusion about your hypothesis? What measurements should you record?

Analyze the results. What happens during your experiment?

Draw conclusions. Do your observations and data suggest that your hypothesis is correct? If not, do you think your hypothesis is wrong, or do you need to change your experimental procedure?

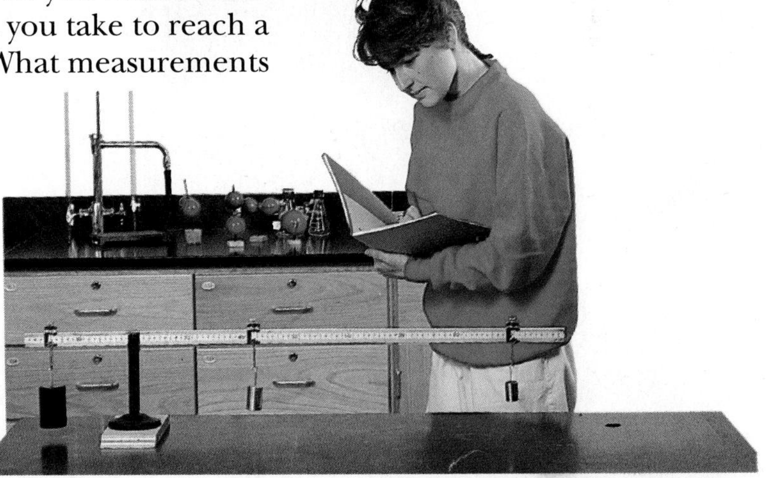

Figure 1-12. Keeping accurate records is an important part of scientific experimentation.

Safety

When working in the physical science laboratory, you'll handle glass, hot objects, sharp objects, and chemicals. A few rules will help you carry out experiments and activities safely.

PROBLEM SOLVING

Lauren's Experiment

Lauren walked for about 40 minutes every morning before school. During her walk, she used headphones to listen to a tape player attached to her belt.

Lauren found that she had to replace the carbon dry cell batteries in the tape player about every two and one-half weeks. So, she decided to conduct an experiment to find out whether alkaline dry cells, which cost more, would be less expensive to use than carbon dry cells. She hypothesized that, over a period of time, using alkaline dry cells would save her money.

She purchased two alkaline dry cells for $2.04 and two carbon dry cells for $1.38. She tested the dry cells on her morning walks, keeping track of the amount of time the tape player was in operation using each pair of dry cells. To keep the test fair, she played the same tape and kept the volume of the player constant throughout the experiment.

Two alkaline dry cells lasted 16 hours and 15 minutes, whereas two carbon dry cells lasted only eight and one-half hours. Lauren then divided the cost of the dry cells by the number of hours to determine which dry cells were less expensive to use. Which dry cells were the better buy?

Think Critically: What problem-solving methods did Lauren use in the experiment?

First, know what you're supposed to do before you begin. Read and follow all directions carefully and pay attention to any cautions.

Dress appropriately to reduce the chance of accidents. Avoid clothing with large, floppy sleeves. Remove dangling jewelry, such as chains and bracelets, and tie back or cover long hair.

Think about what you're doing. Handle glass carefully, and don't touch hot objects with your bare hands. To be on the safe side, treat all equipment as if it were hot. Wear safety glasses and a protective apron.

Be sure you understand the safety symbols explained in Appendix B on page 674. They will be used throughout the textbook to alert you to possible laboratory dangers.

Learn the proper way to clean up spills and clean them up immediately.

Your workspace should contain only those materials you need for your experiment. Keep books and other objects out of the way. Arrange your equipment so that you won't have to reach over burners or across equipment that could be knocked over.

Watch closely when your teacher demonstrates how to handle equipment, how to dispose of materials, and any other safety practices.

Make sure you know the location and proper operation of safety equipment, such as fire extinguishers.

Did You Know?

Alfred Nobel, the man who left his fortune to fund the Nobel Prizes, was the inventor of dynamite.

SECTION REVIEW

1. What is the function of a control in an experiment?
2. You are doing an experiment to find out how the temperature of water affects the rate at which sugar dissolves. What factors should remain constant? What factors will vary?
3. **Apply:** Design an experiment to determine the fastest route from your home to school.

Concept Mapping

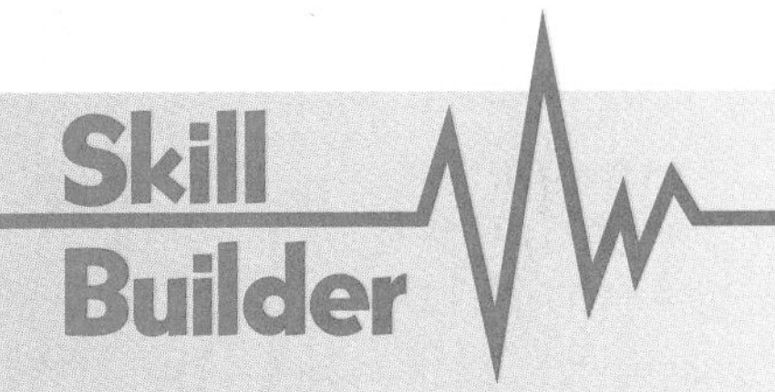

Arrange these steps in organizing a scientific experiment to make an events chain concept map: *draw conclusions, make a hypothesis, determine the problem, analyze the results, test your hypothesis.* If you need help, refer to Concept Mapping in the **Skill Handbook** on pages 684 and 685.

ACTIVITY 1-1
Identifying and Controlling Variables

Problem: *How do variables help solve problems?*

Materials 

- string, 1.5 meters
- identical weights (3)
- smaller weight (1)
- metric ruler
- ring stands (2)
- scissors
- stopwatch

CAUTION: *Refer to page 674 in Appendix B for an explanation of safety symbols.*

Procedure

1. Cut the string into one 60-cm length and three 30-cm lengths.
2. Tie one 30-cm string to each of the identical weights.
3. Tie the long string between the two ring stands and attach the short strings as shown. Use knots that can be easily untied.
4. Swing one of the weights and observe what happens to the other weight. Measure distances and times as precisely as possible. Record this information.
5. Make a list of variables, such as length of string and amount of weight, that may affect the movements of the weights.
6. Adjust the identified variables one at a time. Measure and record the response of the swinging weights.
7. When all variables have been tested, predict the effect of adding a third string and weight. Test your prediction.

Analyze

1. How do the two swinging weights affect each other?
2. What variables did you identify?
3. Which variable has the greatest effect and which has the least?

Conclude and Apply

4. Why is it important to change only one variable at a time?
5. Is adding the third weight the same as one variable or is it more than one? Explain.

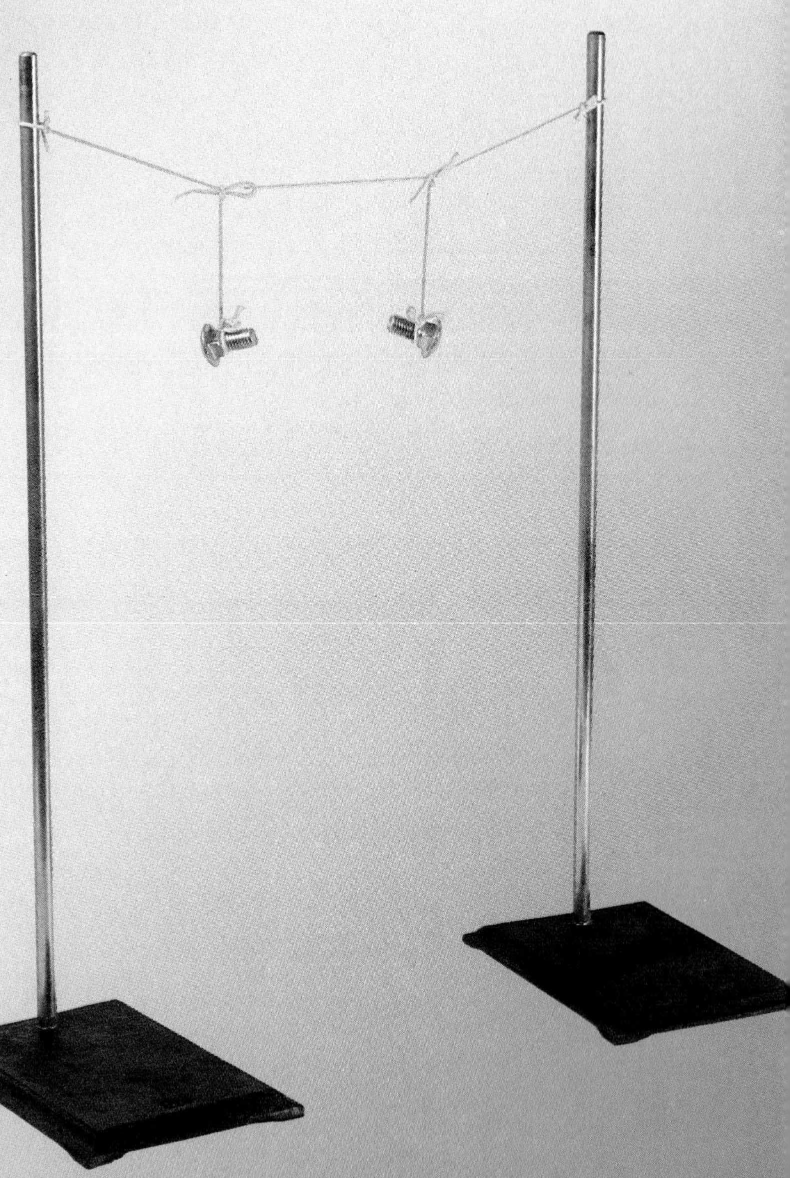

CHAPTER

REVIEW

SUMMARY

1-1: Physical Science and You

1. Science includes both "pure" science, which is study for the purpose of advancing human knowledge, and technology, which is applying science to improve the quality of human life.

2. Physical science is the study of matter and energy.

3. Some physical science topics include the composition of matter, the types of energy, and the interactions of matter and energy.

1-2: Problem Solving

1. A problem and an exercise both involve finding missing information. With an exercise, the method for finding the information is known. With a problem, the method must be developed as the solution is sought.

2. In solving a problem, a systematic series of steps should be followed, always leading from known information to unknown information.

3. A hypothesis is a testable prediction. A theory is an explanation based on many observations supported by experimental results. A scientific law describes a pattern in nature.

1-3: Science and Society: Problems? What Problems?

1. Some environmental issues being studied by scientists include global warming, ozone depletion, and acid rain.

2. Different interpretations of the same observations often lead to different conclusions.

1-4: Exploring Science

1. In conducting a scientific experiment, certain guidelines should be followed to ensure that the purpose of the experiment is met and the results of the experiment are valid.

2. All experiments involve certain variables. An independent variable is determined by the experimenter. A dependent variable depends on the value of the independent variable.

3. Certain safety rules and procedures must be followed in the science laboratory at all times.

KEY SCIENCE WORDS

a. **constant**
b. **control**
c. **critical thinking**
d. **dependent variable**
e. **experiment**
f. **greenhouse effect**
g. **hypothesis**
h. **independent variable**
i. **model**
j. **observation**
k. **ozone layer**
l. **physical science**
m. **scientific law**
n. **technology**
o. **theory**

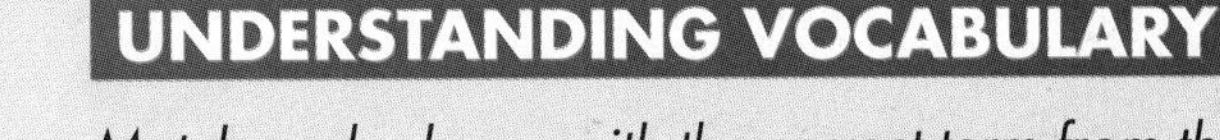

UNDERSTANDING VOCABULARY

Match each phrase with the correct term from the list of Key Science Words.

1. the study of matter and energy
2. applying science to improve quality of life
3. an idea, system, or structure that can be used to solve a problem
4. a testable prediction
5. the use of human senses to gather information
6. an organized method of testing a hypothesis
7. describes but doesn't explain a pattern in nature
8. a factor that doesn't change in an experiment
9. warming Earth's atmosphere by trapping energy from the sun
10. factor in an experiment that is adjusted by the experimenter

CHAPTER

REVIEW

CHECKING CONCEPTS

Choose the word or phrase that completes the sentence or answers the question.

1. Study of science for the sole purpose of advancing our knowledge is called ______ science.
   a. experimental **c.** theoretical
   b. pure **d.** technological
2. Physical science would involve the study of all of the following except ______.
   a. the melting point of wax
   b. the composition of wax
   c. the behavior of bees producing wax
   d. energy released by burning wax
3. A(n) ______ is used as a standard for comparison in an experiment.
   a. control **c.** independent variable
   b. theory **d.** constant
4. A ______ is an explanation supported by experimental results.
   a. conclusion **c.** scientific law
   b. theory **d.** model
5. It is believed that chlorofluorocarbons are responsible for ______.
   a. the greenhouse effect
   b. acid rain
   c. global warming
   d. ozone depletion
6. Which of these is not a safety rule to be followed in the laboratory?
   a. follow all directions carefully
   b. clean up all spills immediately
   c. wear rubber-soled shoes at all times
   d. know the location of the fire extinguisher
7. The ______ shields Earth from the damaging effects of ultraviolet radiation.
   a. troposphere **c.** nitrogen oxide
   b. carbon dioxide **d.** ozone
8. The ______ describes the steps followed in conducting an experiment.
   a. problem **c.** conclusion
   b. procedure **d.** data
9. A scientific ______ is sometimes called a "rule of nature."
   a. theory **c.** model
   b. law **d.** hypothesis
10. Which is the final step in an experiment?
    a. reach a conclusion
    b. state the problem
    c. set up a procedure
    d. record data

UNDERSTANDING CONCEPTS

Complete each sentence.

11. ______ is the application of scientific knowledge to improve the quality of life.
12. The greenhouse effect is produced by increased amounts of ______ present in the atmosphere.
13. A(n) ______ is an organized procedure for testing a hypothesis.
14. In an experiment involving popcorn, the brand name would be a ______.
15. ______ is a process that uses certain skills to solve a problem.

THINK AND WRITE CRITICALLY

16. Why is it usually easier to find the solution to an exercise than it is to find the solution to a problem? Include examples in your answer.
17. Describe how a hypothesis, a theory, and a scientific law are related.

18. Discuss the importance of recording all observations and data when conducting a science experiment.
19. Describe four safety precautions to be followed in the science laboratory.
20. Describe one current environmental issue that is controversial and explain why scientists disagree on the issue.

APPLY

21. In a study of the sun, what questions might a pure scientist ask? What questions might an applied scientist ask? How might the two sets of questions be related?
22. What aspects of the following items would a physical scientist be interested in?
    a. an electric guitar **b.** a piece of coal
23. Which problem-solving approach would you use to solve the following problems? Explain your choice in each case.
    a. solving a complex word problem in math
    b. figuring out a secret code
    c. predicting how a skyscraper would be affected by an earthquake
24. Design an experiment to determine how the temperature of water affects the time it takes sugar to dissolve in it. Identify the variables, constants, and control, if any.
25. Explain this statement: Scientists often learn as much from an incorrect hypothesis as they do from one that is correct.

MORE SKILL BUILDERS

If you need help, refer to the Skill Handbook.

1. **Comparing and Contrasting:** Compare and contrast the methods used to complete an exercise and to solve a problem.
2. **Hypothesizing:** Propose a hypothesis to explain why a balloon filled with air weighs more than a deflated balloon.
3. **Interpreting Scientific Illustrations:** The following are safety symbols used in two different experiments. Using Table B-2 on page 674 in Appendix B, describe the safety precautions that should be taken in each experiment.

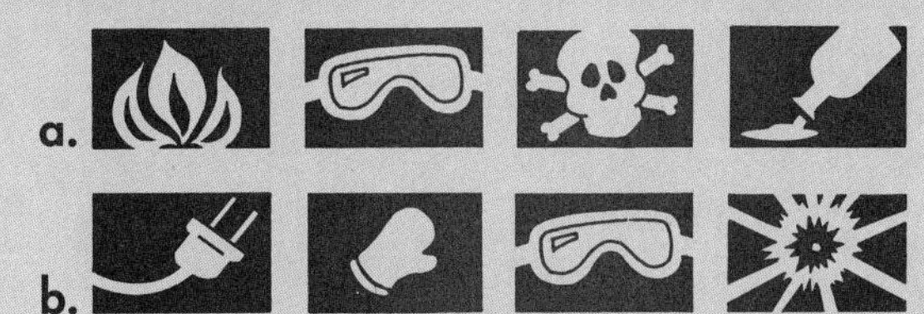

4. **Using Variables, Constants, and Controls:** Do some objects fall faster than others? Design an experiment to find out. State your hypothesis and describe your procedure for testing it. Identify your controls, constants, and variables.

PROJECTS

1. Make a poster illustrating laboratory safety techniques.
2. Make a scrapbook of recent newspaper or magazine articles dealing with the scientific debate surrounding the greenhouse effect, the ozone layer, and/or acid rain. Read the articles carefully and include at the end of your scrapbook a short essay explaining your position on the problem.

CHAPTER 2 Physical Science Methods

Look around your classroom. In order to build the room and produce all the things inside it, such as the desks, chairs, shelves, and chalkboards, many measurements had to be made. Think about some of the things that were measured and the tools used to measure them.

FIND OUT!

Do this simple activity to find out how measurements are made.

Imagine that measuring tools have not been invented. Pick something in your classroom to use as a tool for measuring length. It can be an object from your desk; a hand, foot, or arm; or anything else that can easily be used.

Working with a partner, measure a distance in the room with your measuring device. Now have your partner measure the same distance, first using his or her own measuring device, then using yours. Which measurements can you compare? How similar are they? How could you improve your measuring devices?

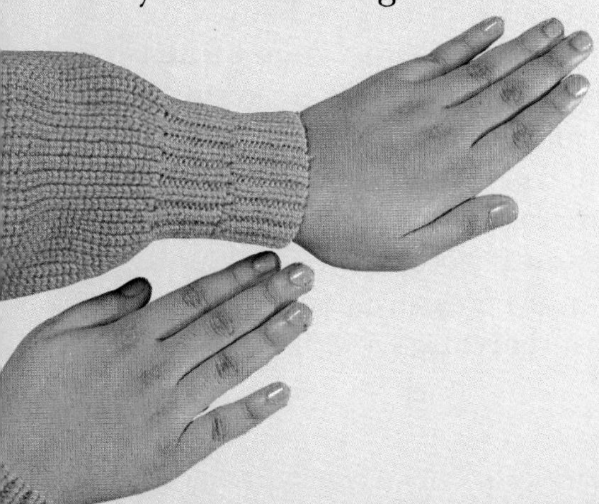

Gearing Up

Previewing the Chapter

Use this outline to help you focus on important ideas in this chapter.

Section 2-1 Standards of Measurement
- Units and Standards
- International System of Units

Section 2-2 Using SI Units
- SI Units and Symbols
- Length
- Volume
- Mass
- Density
- Time and Temperature

Section 2-3 Graphing
- Using Graphs
- Line Graphs
- Bar Graphs
- Pie Graphs

Section 2-4 Science and Society
Metrics for All?
- Metrics in the United States

Previewing Science Skills

- In the Skill Builders, you will sequence, make a concept map, and make and use graphs.
- In the Activities, you will observe, collect and organize data, and measure in SI.
- In the MINI-Labs, you will measure in SI, make inferences, and make and use graphs.

What's next?

Now that you have compared measurements made with your own measuring devices, find out what a measurement standard is. Once you know why standards are so important in making measurements, learn to use the system of measurement that is used by scientists throughout the world.

2-1 Standards of Measurement

New Science Words

standard
SI

Objectives

- **Define standard of measurement.**
- **Recognize the need for standards of measurement.**
- **Name the prefixes used in SI and tell what multiple of ten each represents.**

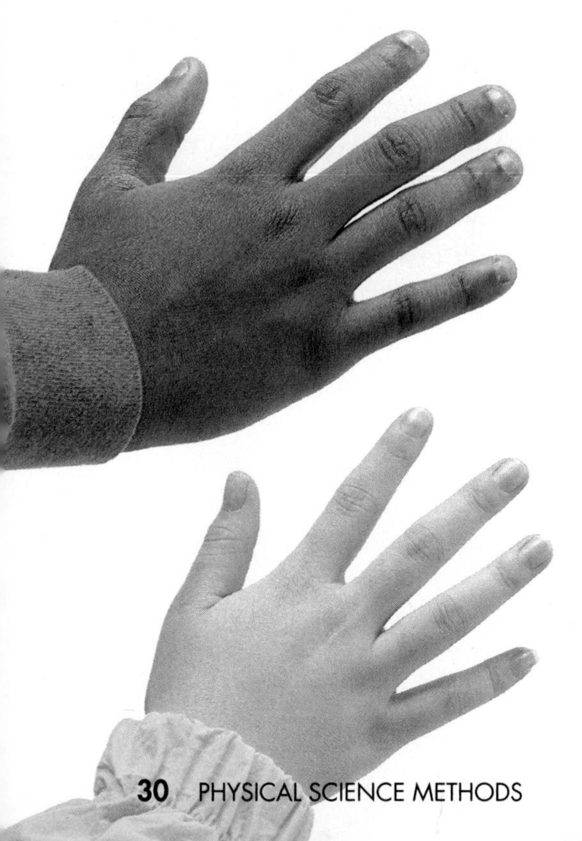

Units and Standards

How wide is your desk? At what temperature does ice cream start to melt? How fast does sugar dissolve? In order to answer any of these questions, some measurement must be made.

Measuring is an important skill. It is especially important in science. In order for a measurement to be useful, a measurement standard must be used. A **standard** is an exact quantity that people agree to use for comparison. When all measurements are made using the same standard, the measurements can be compared to each other.

Suppose you and a friend want to make some measurements to find out if a desk will fit through a doorway. You have no ruler, so you decide to use your hands as measuring tools. Using the width of his or her hands, your friend measures the doorway and says it is 8 "hands" wide. Using the width of your hands, you measure the desk and find it is 7-3/4 "hands" wide. Will the desk fit through the doorway? You can't be sure. What if your hands are wider than your friend's hands? Then the distance equal to 7-3/4 of your hands might be greater than the distance equal to 8 of your friends hands.

What mistake did you make? Even though you both used your hands to measure, you didn't check to see if your hands were the same width as your friend's hands. In other words, you didn't use a measurement standard, so you can't compare measurements.

International System of Units

Suppose the label on a ball of string indicates that the length of the string in the ball is "150." Can you tell how much string is in the ball? No. It could be 150 feet, 150 meters, or 150 of some unit you've never heard of. In order for a measurement to make sense, it must include a number and a unit.

Your family probably buys lumber by the foot, milk by the quart, and potatoes by the pound. These measurement units are part of the English system of measurement, which is most commonly used in the United States. Most other nations use a system of measurement based on multiples of ten. The first such system of measurement, called the metric system, was devised by a group of scientists in the late 1700s. The system was based on a set of standards established and agreed to by the scientists.

What system of measurement is used in the U.S.?

In 1960 an improved version of the metric system was devised. Known as the International System of Units, this system is often abbreviated SI, from the French *Le Système Internationale d'Unités*. **SI** is the standard system of measurement used worldwide. All SI standards are universally accepted and understood throughout the scientific community.

In SI, each type of measurement has a base unit, such as the meter, which is the base unit of length. In the next section, you will learn the units used to measure length, mass, time, temperature, volume, and density.

Figure 2-1. The standard kilogram mass, composed of a platinum-iridium alloy, is kept at the International Bureau of Weights and Measures in Sevres, France.

The system is easy to use because it is based on multiples of ten. Prefixes are used with the names of the base units to indicate what multiple of ten should be used with the base unit. For example, the prefix *kilo-* means 1000. So a *kilometer* is 1000 meters. The most frequently used prefixes are shown in Table 2-1. Based on information from the table, how long is a centimeter?

Table 2-1

IMPORTANT SI PREFIXES

Prefixes	Symbol	Multiplying factor
kilo-	k	1000
deci-	d	0.1
centi-	c	0.01
milli-	m	0.001
micro	μ	0.000 001
nano-	n	0.000 000 001

PROBLEM SOLVING

Nonstandard Measurement Units

As the students in Mr. Craig's science class entered the classroom, everyone noticed a long strip of tape on the chalkboard. Mr. Craig informed the students that they would be measuring the length of the tape.

The students were divided up into two teams. One team was to measure the length of the tape in cubits, the distance from the elbow to the end of the middle finger. The other team was given a piece of wood and a ball of string. Each student was to cut a piece of string exactly as long as the piece of wood, and then use the string to measure the tape.

Although the students in each group made their measurements carefully, each student using cubits came up with a different number of units for the length of the tape. The students using pieces of string all came up with the same number of units.

Why were the measurements in cubits all different, but those made with string all the same?

Think Critically: Why is it important to use a system of measurement based on standard units?

SECTION REVIEW

1. What are some advantages of using the International System of measurement over the English system of measurement?
2. In SI, the base unit of length is the meter. What would you call 0.1 meter? 1000 meters?
3. **Apply:** Make a list of measuring tools you have used in the past month. For each example, tell what units you used to make your measurements.

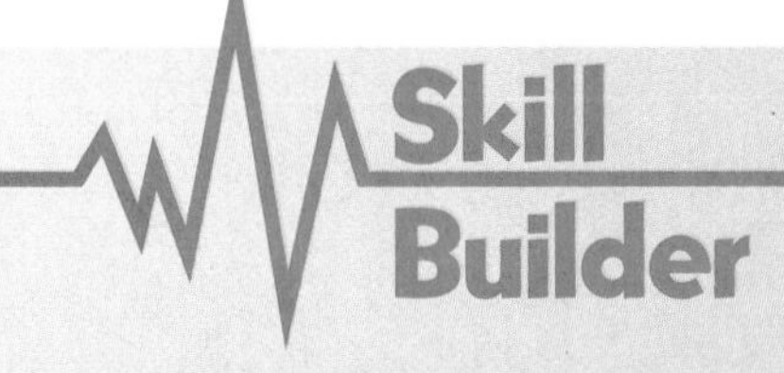

Sequencing

Using the data in Table 2-1, arrange the following units in order, from largest to smallest: centigram, gram, milligram, kilogram, decigram. If you need help, refer to Sequencing in the **Skill Handbook** on page 676.

ACTIVITY 2-1
Scales of Measurement

Problem: *Can you invent your own system of measurement?*

Materials
- string 1 m long
- scissors
- masking tape

Procedure
1. Cut your piece of string to match the length, width, or height of some object in the room.
2. Cut a narrow strip of masking tape and fasten it to one end of the string. Mark the tape "0."
3. Cut a second strip of tape and fasten it to the other end of the string. Mark this strip "1."
4. Fold the string in half and use tape to mark the halfway point "1/2."
5. Fold the string again and mark the "1/4" positions. Repeat again for the "1/8" positions.
6. Cut a second piece of string the same length as the first. Devise a way to divide the string into 1/3, 1/6, and 1/12 segments.
7. Repeat Step 6 to divide a third piece of string into 1/5 and 1/10 segments.
8. Select two objects in the room to measure, one larger than the string and one smaller.
9. Have each team member use one of the strings to measure both objects. Record all measurements on a data sheet.

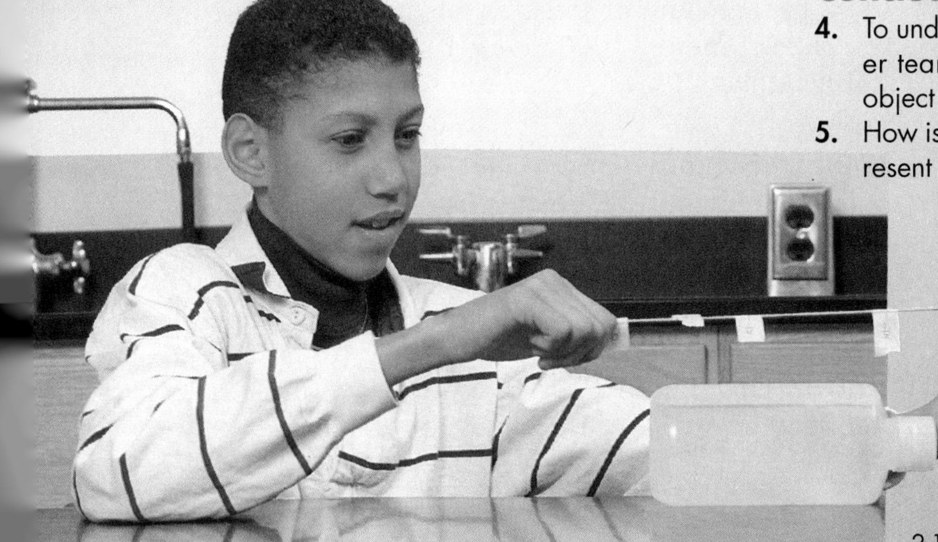

Data and Observations

String*	Object measured	Object length
1/8		
1/8		
1/12		
1/12		
1/10		
1/10		
*Object used to determine length of string: ______		

Analyze
1. Which of the three scales is most likely to provide the most accurate measurement of a small object? Why?
2. Which of the three scales is easiest to record in decimal numbers?
3. Which scale is easiest to make and which is easiest to use?

Conclude and Apply
4. To understand measurements made by another team, why is it important to know what object matched the length of their string?
5. How is it possible for different numbers to represent the same length?

2-2 Using SI Units

New Science Words

meter
volume
derived units
liter
mass
kilogram
density
time
second
kelvin

Objectives

- ▶ Identify SI units and symbols for length, volume, mass, density, time, and temperature.
- ▶ Define *derived unit.*
- ▶ Demonstrate an ability to convert related SI units.

SI Units and Symbols

Every type of measurement in SI has a base unit and a symbol for that unit. These names and symbols are shown in Table 2-2.

Table 2-2

SI BASE UNITS		
Measurement	**Unit**	**Symbol**
Length	Meter	m
Mass	Kilogram	kg
Time	Second	s
Electric current	Ampere	A
Temperature	Kelvin	K
Amount of substance	Mole	mol
Intensity of light	Candela	cd

What is the SI unit of length?

Length

The word *length* is used in many different ways. For example, the length of a novel is the number of pages it contains. The length of a movie is the number of hours and minutes it runs.

In scientific measurement, length is the distance between two points. That distance may be the diameter of a period on this page or the distance from Earth to the moon. The SI unit of length is the **meter** (m). A baseball bat is about 1 meter long. Metric rulers and metersticks are used to measure length.

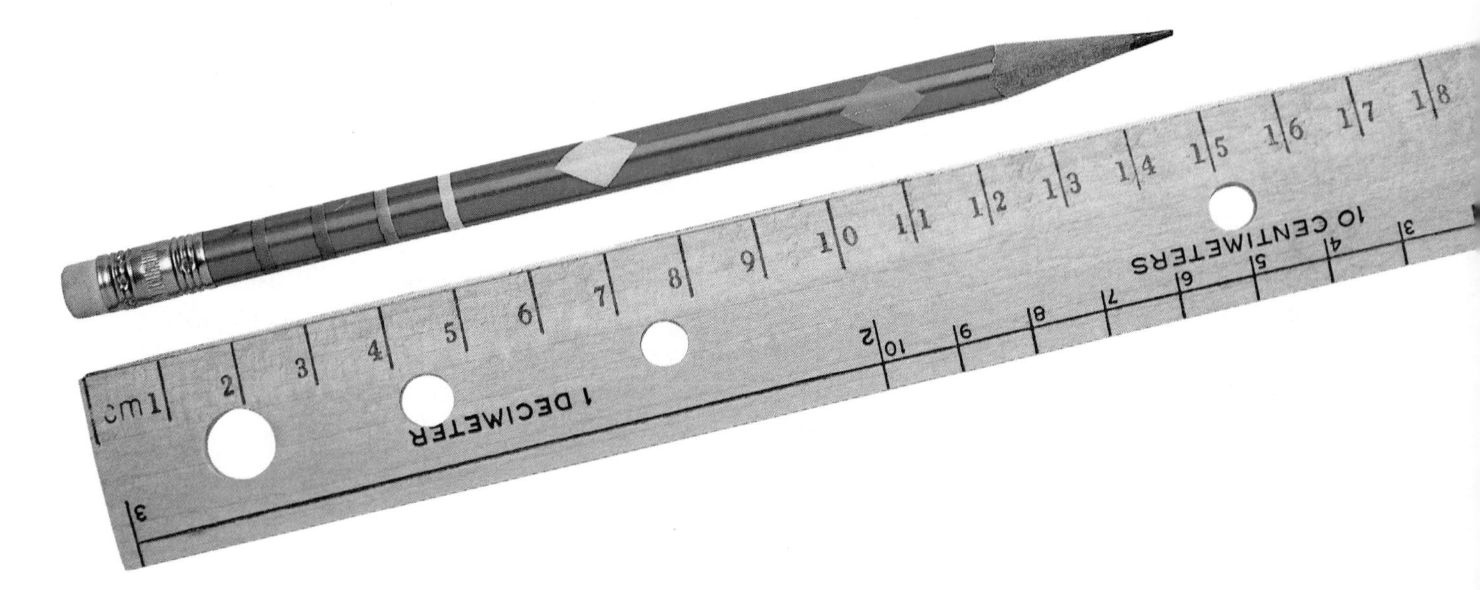

Figure 2-2. A metric ruler is used to measure the length of small objects, such as a pencil.

Recall that measurement in SI is based on multiples of ten. The prefix *deci-* means 1/10, so a decimeter is one-tenth of a meter. Similarly, a centimeter (cm) is one-hundredth of a meter. The diameter of a shirt button is about 1 cm.

$$100 \text{ cm} = 10 \text{ dm} = 1 \text{ m}$$

How many centimeters are in 1 decimeter?

Centimeters can be divided into smaller units called millimeters (mm). A millimeter is 1/1000 of a meter. One tooth along the edge of a postage stamp is about 1 mm long.

The size of the unit you select to make a measurement will depend on the size of the item being measured. For example, you would probably use the centimeter to measure the length of your pencil and the meter to measure the length of your classroom. What unit would you use to measure the distance from your home to school? You would probably want to use a unit larger than a meter. The kilometer (km), which is 1000 meters, is used to measure long distances. One kilometer is about ten football fields long.

Suppose you know the length of something in meters and want to change, or *convert,* the measurement to centimeters. Because 1 m = 100 cm, you can convert from meters to centimeters simply by multiplying by 100. Because SI is based on multiples of ten, any unit can be converted to a related unit by multiplying or dividing it by the appropriate multiple of ten.

If you follow these "rules," conversion will be easy:

- When converting from larger to smaller units, multiply—move the decimal to the right.
- When converting from smaller to larger units, divide—move the decimal to the left.
- Move the decimal point as many places as there are zeros in the multiple of ten you are using.

For example, to convert 532 cm to meters, you divide because you're converting from smaller (cm) to larger (m) units. Because 100 cm = 1 m, move the decimal point two places to the left. So, 532 cm = 5.32 m.

Another way to convert units is to multiply by one. For example, 1 meter = 100 centimeters. Therefore,

$$\frac{1 \text{ meter}}{100 \text{ centimeters}} = \frac{100 \text{ centimeters}}{100 \text{ centimeters}} = 1$$

To convert 532 cm to meters, write

$$532 \text{ cm} \times \frac{1 \text{ m}}{100 \text{ cm}} = \frac{532 \text{ m}}{100} = 5.32 \text{ m}$$

The cm label is cancelled, because it appears in both the numerator and the denominator.

EXAMPLE PROBLEM

Problem Statement:

How many centimeters are in 1.98 meters?

Known Information:

Strategy Hint: Think about which way you should move the decimal point.

1 m = 100 cm
When converting from larger to smaller units, multiply.
Because 1 m = 100 cm; move the decimal two places to the right.

Solution:

1.98 m = 198 cm

PRACTICE PROBLEMS

Strategy Hint: First change kilometers to meters; then change meters to centimeters.

1. How many centimeters are in 253.8 kilometers?

Strategy Hint: Remember the meanings of the prefixes.

2. A bookshelf is 75 cm wide. How many dm is this? How many m would this be?

TECHNOLOGY

Space Spheres

The space shuttle *Challenger* served as the manufacturing site for one of the latest reference materials produced by the National Bureau of Standards. The reference material is a polystyrene sphere that measures 10 micrometers across. The head of a pin could hold 18 000 of these spheres. The spheres will be packaged in a 5-mL vial containing about 30 million spheres in water. These spheres can be used as a reference for manufacturers and researchers who need to calibrate instruments to check particle size in products such as cosmetics, paint pigments, flour, toner used in photocopiers, and so on. The spheres can also be used to improve microscopic measurements made in areas such as medicine and electronics.

The *Challenger* was chosen as the manufacturing site because of its gravity-free environment. Spheres produced by conventional processes on Earth tend to float or sink during their formation. This results in spheres with a variation in diameter that is too great for use as a standard. The reduced gravity of space allows the production of spheres that are very uniform in size and shape.

Think Critically: Name some products that you use or encounter daily that had to be calibrated to ensure their proper operation.

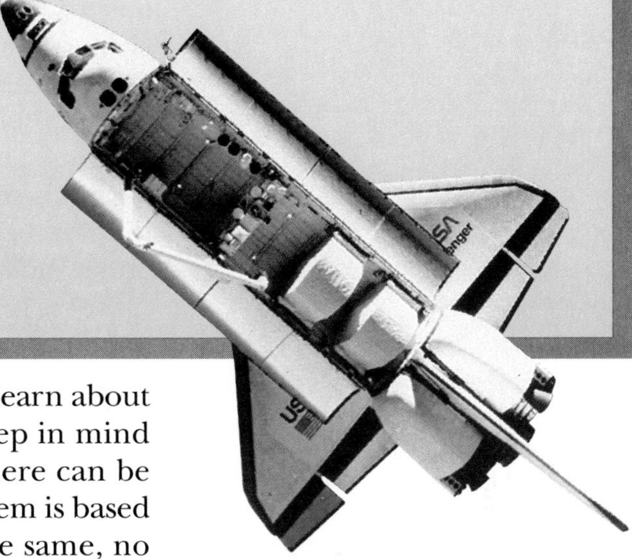

As you move ahead in this section, you will learn about several different types of measurements. Keep in mind that the conversion "rules" you have used here can be used with any base unit in SI, because the system is based on multiples of ten. The prefixes remain the same, no matter what base unit you may be using.

Volume

The amount of space occupied by an object is called its **volume.** If you wanted to know the volume of a solid object, such as a building brick, you would measure its length, width, and height, and multiply the three figures together. For the brick, your measurements would be in centimeters, and the volume would be expressed in cubic centimeters (cm^3). For a larger object, such as a truck, your measurements would be in meters and the volume in cubic meters (m^3).

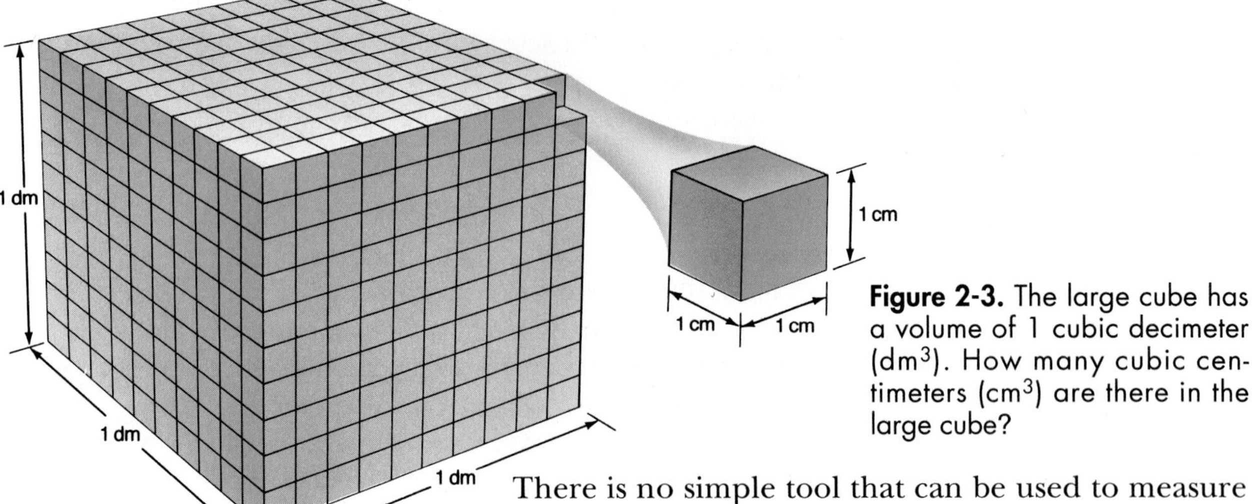

Figure 2-3. The large cube has a volume of 1 cubic decimeter (dm^3). How many cubic centimeters (cm^3) are there in the large cube?

What is a derived unit?

There is no simple tool that can be used to measure the volume of an object directly. Volume units are obtained by combining other SI units. Units obtained this way are called **derived units.**

How do you measure the volume of a liquid? A liquid has no "sides" to measure. In measuring a liquid's volume, you indicate the capacity of a container that holds that amount of liquid. Liquid volumes are sometimes expressed in cubic centimeters, as in doses of medicine. The most common units for expressing liquid volumes are liters and milliliters. A **liter** occupies the same volume as a cubic decimeter (dm^3). That is, a liter is the same volume as a cube that is 1 dm (10 cm) on each side. A liter is slightly larger than a quart of milk. The liter is not an SI unit, but it is used with that system.

One liter (L) is equal to 1000 milliliters (mL). A cubic decimeter (dm^3) is equal to 1000 cubic centimeters (cm^3). So, because $1 \text{ L} = 1 \text{ dm}^3$, $1 \text{ mL} = 1 \text{ cm}^3$.

Suppose you wanted to convert a measurement in liters to cubic centimeters. The same "rules" you used for converting length can be used for any SI unit.

EXAMPLE PROBLEM

Problem Statement: How many liters of gasoline are in 538 cm^3?

Known Information:
Strategy Hint: 1 L = 1000 cm^3. Change cm^3 to mL.

$1 \text{ cm}^3 = 1 \text{ mL}$
$1 \text{ L} = 1000 \text{ mL}$; therefore, $1 \text{ L} = 1000 \text{ cm}^3$.
Because you are converting from smaller to larger units, you divide. Move the decimal point three places to the left.

Solution: $538 \text{ cm}^3 = 0.538 \text{ L}$

To measure volume in the laboratory, you will use a slender glass container called a graduated cylinder. The volumes are marked on a scale along the cylinder, as shown in Figure 2-4.

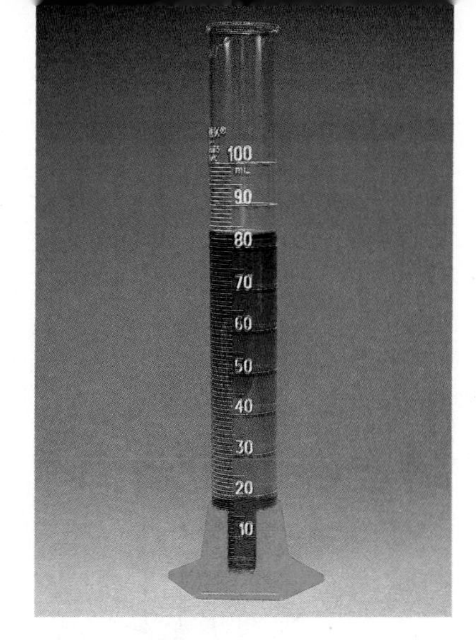

Figure 2-4. To read the volume of a liquid, look along the bottom of the curved surface of the liquid.

Mass

A table tennis ball and a golf ball have about the same volume. But if you pick them up, you notice a difference. The golf ball has more mass. **Mass** is the amount of matter in an object. The SI unit of mass is the **kilogram** (kg). For measuring objects of small mass, the gram (g) is used. How many grams are there in 1 kilogram?

In the laboratory, mass is measured with a balance. There are several different types of balances, but they all operate on the same principle. You use something of known mass to balance something else of unknown mass.

Figure 2-5. Although the two balls are about the same size, the ball on the left has more mass.

Density

If you were to take a cube of polished aluminum and a cube of silver the same size, they would look quite similar. And they would have the same volume. But the cube of silver would have more mass. The mass and volume of an object can be used to find the density of the material it is made of. **Density** is the mass per unit volume of a material.

Like volume, density is a derived unit. You can find the density of an object by dividing its mass by its volume. For example, the density of an object having a

Did You Know?

The mass of the Milky Way galaxy is more than 100 million times that of the sun.

MINI-Lab

What is the density of a pencil?
Use a balance to measure the mass of a pencil in grams. Then put 90.0 mL of water into a 100-mL graduated cylinder. Lower the pencil, eraser end down, into the cylinder until the pencil floats. Read the new volume number at the water's surface. How many mL did the water level rise? How does this compare with the mass of the pencil? Continue to push the pencil point down until it is completely underwater. Read the new volume. Calculate the pencil's density by dividing its mass by the change in mL of the water level when the pencil is completely underwater.

Table 2-3

DENSITIES OF SOME MATERIALS

Material	Density (g/cm^3)	Material	Density (g/cm^3)
Hydrogen	0.000 09	Quartz	2.6
Oxygen	0.0013	Aluminum	2.7
Cork	0.24	Iron	7.9
Water	1.0	Copper	8.9
Glue	1.27	Lead	11.3
Sugar	1.6	Mercury	13.6
Table salt	2.2	Gold	19.3

mass of 10 g and a volume of 2 cm^3 is 5 g/cm^3. This value is expressed as 5 grams per cubic centimeter. Notice that both the mass and volume units are used to express density.

Sometimes the density of an object can help you to identify the material it's made of. Table 2-3 lists the densities of some familiar materials.

Time and Temperature

When working in the laboratory, it is often necessary to keep track of how long it takes for something to happen, or whether something heats up or cools down. These measurements involve time and temperature.

Time is the interval between two events. The SI unit for time is the **second.** In the laboratory, you will use a stopwatch or a clock with a second hand to measure time.

Figure 2-6. The stopwatch (left) and the atomic clock (above) both measure the same thing—time.

You will learn the scientific meaning of temperature in a later chapter. For now you can think of temperature as a measure of how "hot" or how "cold" something is. The temperature of a material is measured with thermometer that has a scale marked on it.

Figure 2-7. A Celsius Thermometer

For most scientific work, temperature is measured on the Celsius (C) scale. On this scale, the freezing point of water is zero degrees (0°C), and the boiling point of water is one hundred degrees (100°C). Between these points, the scale is divided into 100 equal divisions. Each one represents 1 Celsius degree. On the Celsius scale, normal human body temperature is 37°C and a comfortable room temperature is 25°C.

The SI unit of temperature is the **kelvin** (K). Zero on the Kelvin scale (0 K) is the coldest possible temperature. This temperature is also known as absolute zero. On the Celsius scale, 0 K is approximately −273°C. That is 273 degrees below the freezing point of water—very cold indeed!

Most laboratory thermometers are marked only with the Celsius scale. Because the divisions on the two scales are the same size, the Kelvin temperature can be found by adding 273 to the Celsius reading. So, on the Kelvin scale, water freezes at 273 K and boils at 373 K. Notice that degree signs are not used with the Kelvin scale.

Science and MATH

You probably know how much you weigh in pounds. Find your mass in kilograms. HINT: 1 pound has a mass of 0.454 kg.

SECTION REVIEW

1. Make the following conversions.
   a. 100 cm to meters
   b. 2.3 dm^3 to liters
   c. 27°C to K
2. Explain why density is a derived unit.
3. **Apply:** How many examples of the use of SI units can you find? Observe road signs and outside thermometers and check labels of products in your home.

Concept Mapping

Skill Builder

Make a network tree concept map to show the SI base units used to measure length, mass, time, and temperature. If you need help, refer to Concept Mapping in the **Skill Handbook** on pages 684 and 685.

2-3 Graphing

New Science Words

graph

Objectives

- ▶ Identify three types of graphs and explain the correct use of each type.
- ▶ Distinguish between dependent and independent variables.
- ▶ Interpret graphs.

Using Graphs

What happens when heat is applied to an ice cube? Did you answer, "The ice cube melts"? Most people would. However, suppose this were a scientific investigation. You would measure and record mass, temperature, temperature changes, changes in state, and the time intervals involved. At the end of the investigation, you would describe the procedure and results in both words and numbers.

Often it is helpful to be able to show what happens during the course of an investigation. This can be done with a graph. A **graph** is a visual display of information or data. A graph of the ice cube investigation would look something like Figure 2-8.

Graphs are not only used in science. They are useful for displaying information in business, sports, and many everyday situations. Different kinds of graphs are appropriate for displaying different types of information. It is important to use the correct kind of graph for the data you are presenting.

MINI-Lab

How can a graph help you observe change?

Place a thermometer in a plastic foam cup of hot water. Measure and record the temperature every 30 seconds for 5 minutes. Make a line graph of the changing temperature showing time on the *x*-axis and temperature on the *y*-axis. Repeat the experiment, starting with freshly heated water. This time, cover the cup with a plastic lid. Plot the curve on the same grid as before. List all the information this graph tells you about the two cups.

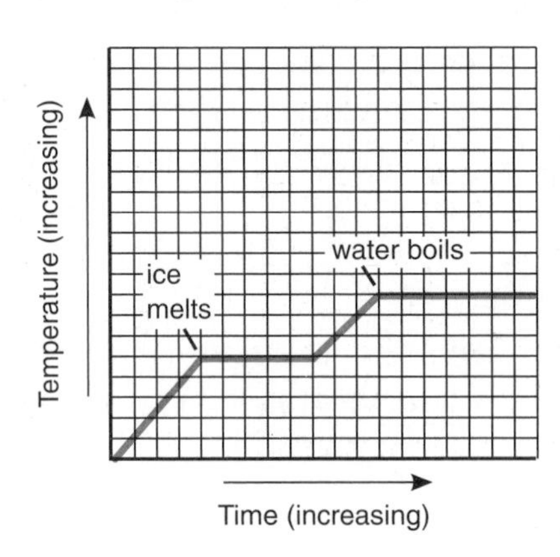

Figure 2-8. The graph shows what happens when water is heated over a period of time.

Three of the most commonly used kinds of graphs are line graphs, bar graphs, and pie graphs. The section on Making and Using Graphs, on page 687 in the **Skill Handbook,** is a step-by-step guide to constructing each of these kinds of graphs. Study this material when you have finished reading this section.

Line Graphs

Line graphs are used to show trends or continuous change. Suppose you want to show how the temperature of a room changes after you switch on the heat one chilly morning. Taking temperature readings in the room every five minutes, you might collect information that looks like that shown in Table 2-4. If you look closely at the data, you can see how temperatures changed over time. But the relationship is easier to see in the graphs shown in Figure 2-9. Both graphs show that temperature increased for the first 15 minutes, then stayed constant. Do the graphs tell you anything about what made the temperature change?

In this example, two things are changing, or varying—time and temperature. Time is the independent variable. Its value does not depend on changes in the value of the other variable, temperature. Temperature is the dependent variable. Its value depends on changes in the time. In a line graph, the dependent variable always is plotted on the vertical *y*-axis, and the independent variable is plotted on the horizontal *x*-axis.

Both graphs in Figure 2-9 show the same information. Notice, however, that the temperature scales along the vertical axes are different. In the graph on the left, each square represents 1°C. What does each square represent in the graph on the right? The hatch marks on the

Table 2-4

ROOM TEMPERATURE	
Time (minutes after turning on heat)	Temperature (°C)
0	16
5	17
10	19
15	20
20	20
25	20

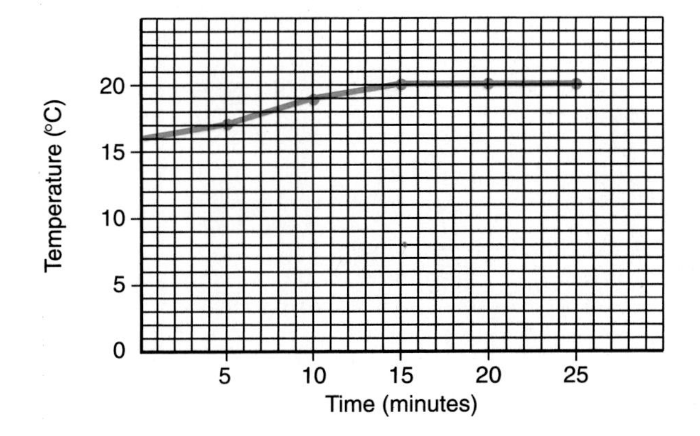

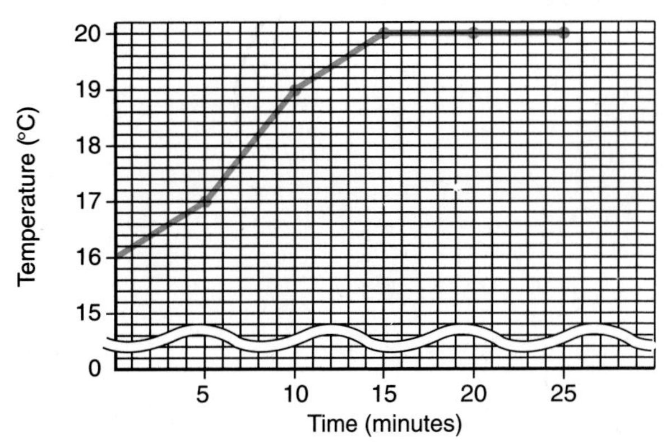

Figure 2-9. Two Graphs of the Same Room Temperature Data

vertical axis between the 0 and the 15 mean that numbers between 0 and 15 have been left out to save space. Compare the two graphs in Figure 2-9. Which graph shows a bigger temperature change over the same time period? Be careful! The two graphs show exactly the same information, but because there is more space between the numbers on the vertical axis in the graph on the right, the change looks larger.

Bar Graphs

Table 2-5

TEMPERATURE OF CLASSROOMS	
Temperature (°C)	**Number of Classrooms**
16	1
17	3
18	3
19	2
20	3
21	5
22	5
23	3

A bar graph is useful for showing information collected by counting. For example, suppose you measured the temperature in every classroom in your school and organized your data in a table like Table 2-5. You could show these data in a bar graph like the one shown in Figure 2-10. The height of each bar corresponds to the number of rooms at a particular temperature.

In a line graph, adjacent points are connected with a straight or curving line. In a bar graph, the bars are not connected. Do you see why? If the bars corresponding to 20°C and 21°C were connected, for example, the graph would suggest that a number of rooms had temperatures between 20°C and 21°C, when actually, no rooms had such temperatures.

Figure 2-10. A typical bar graph shows comparisons, but does not indicate trends.

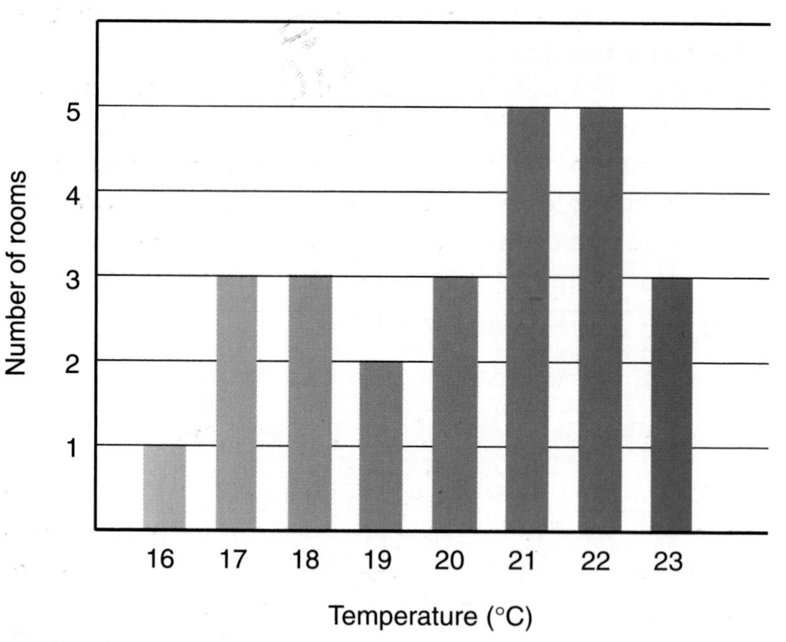

Pie Graphs

A pie graph is used to show how some fixed quantity is broken down into parts. The circular "pie" represents the total, and the "slices" represent the parts. The slices usually are represented as percentages of the total.

Figure 2-11 shows how a pie graph could be used to show the percentage of buildings in a neighborhood using each of a number of fuels in their heating systems. You can see at a glance that more buildings use gas heat than any other kind of system. What else does the graph tell you?

When you use graphs, think carefully about the conclusions you can draw from them. Can you infer cause and effect from looking at a graph? How might the scale of the graph affect your conclusions? Is any information missing or improperly connected?

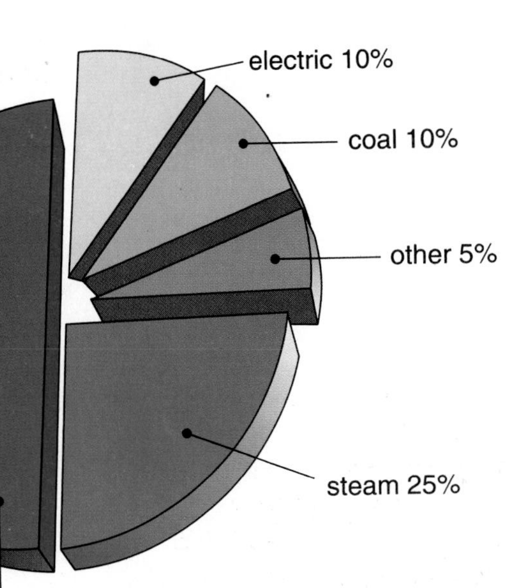

Figure 2-11. A pie graph shows the different parts of a whole quantity.

SECTION REVIEW

1. Your class does an experiment to show how the volume of a gas changes with changes in temperature. You are asked to make a line graph of the results. What are the dependent and independent variables?
2. Explain why points are connected in a line graph, but not in a bar graph.
3. **Apply:** Suppose you take a survey to find out how 150 adults in your neighborhood get to work. Your survey shows that 75 ride the bus; 45 drive their own cars; 15 carpool; 9 walk, ride bikes, or ride motorcycles; and the rest use different methods on different days. What kind of graph would be best for displaying your results at a neighborhood meeting?

EcoTip

The following percentages show water usage in a typical U.S. home: Toilet flushing, 33%; laundry, 26%; bathing, 20%; dishwashing, 3%; miscellaneous, 18%.

Making and Using Graphs

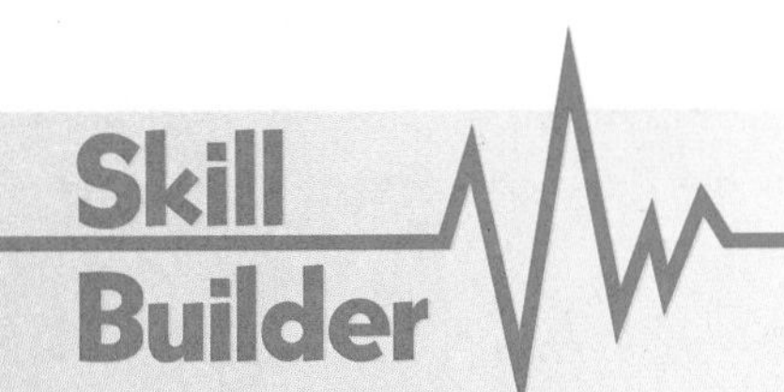

Find a graph in a newspaper or magazine. Tell what kind of graph you found and write an explanation of what the graph shows. If you need help, refer to Making and Using Graphs in the **Skill Handbook** on page 687.

2-4 Metrics for All?

Objectives

- **Analyze the benefits and drawbacks of universal use of the SI system.**
- **Give examples of SI units used in the United States.**

Metrics in the United States

In the United States, athletes compete on courses that are measured in meters, medicine is sold in milligrams and milliliters, and many automobile parts are measured in SI units. But carpenters still buy lumber measured in feet and inches, farmers measure their land in acres and their crops in bushels, fabric is sold by the yard, and highway signs give distances in miles and speed limits in miles per hour.

For nearly 100 years, advocates of the metric system have argued for widespread adoption of the system in the United States. But opponents have argued just as vigorously against it.

Representatives of industry say such a changeover would require them to replace or convert their machinery—a costly process. But people in favor of the change point out that machinery is often replaced anyway, and the cost would be a one-time expense that would produce lasting benefits. Switching to SI units would make trade easier with other countries, most of which use the SI system. And because SI is based on multiples of ten, it makes calculations and conversions much easier. Using the system might reduce calculation errors and save time.

Many citizens resist the switch to SI units because they have grown up using such units as feet, pounds, and gallons, and they feel more comfortable continuing to use them. However, most people do not really know very much about these units, especially how units relate to one another. For example, do you know how many cubic inches there are in a fluid ounce? Do you know how many ounces there are in a pound, or how many inches are in a mile? For that matter, do you know that there are two different kinds of miles—the nautical mile and the statute mile? How many feet are in each? How many yards? How many square feet make up an acre?

These are just a few of the questions that arise in using our present system. Look up the information needed to answer them. Then think about how easy such measurement conversions would be in a system like SI.

SECTION REVIEW

1. Write a list of different units used to measure length in the United States. Then show the calculations necessary to convert from one unit to another. Do the same thing using SI units for length. Which is easier?
2. Write a one-page essay summarizing your position on the adoption of SI in the United States.

You Decide!

Should the United States switch to using SI measurements exclusively? If so, how could the switch be accomplished?

ACTIVITY 2-2
Metric Munchies

Problem: *What is involved in converting from English to metric measure?*

Materials
- balance
- graduated cylinder, 100-mL
- munchie ingredients
- measuring cup
- measuring teaspoon
- measuring tablespoon
- plastic container, 1 quart
- hot plate

Procedure
1. Copy the data table and the list of munchie ingredients.
2. Use the English measuring cup or spoon to measure out the proper amount of munchie ingredient assigned to your team.
3. Use the balance or graduated cylinder to determine the metric value of the measured ingredient. Convert solid measure to grams. Convert liquid measure to milliliters.
4. Write the metric equivalent in your data table. Also write it on the metric ingredients list posted in the classroom.
5. Copy the completed list of metric measures.
6. At the direction of the teacher, place your ingredient in the cooking pot.
7. Watch how the teacher cooks the munchies and write cooking instructions.

Data and Observations

Ingredient	Object measured	Metric
Margarine	1/4 pound	
Sugar	2 cups	
Cocoa	6 tablespoons	
Milk	1/2 cup	
Rolled oats	3 cups	
Vanilla	1 teaspoon	
Nuts	1/2 cup	

Analyze
1. The volume ratio of sugar to oatmeal is 2 to 3. What is their mass ratio?
2. Which recipe, English or metric, requires the use of the most measuring devices?
3. Which kind of measure tends to be more accurate, volume or mass?

Conclude and Apply
4. English measured recipes tend to use whole numbers and simple fractions. How could you simplify the metric recipe?
5. How would kitchen equipment change if all recipes were metric?
6. What benefits and problems can you see in changing all recipes to metric?

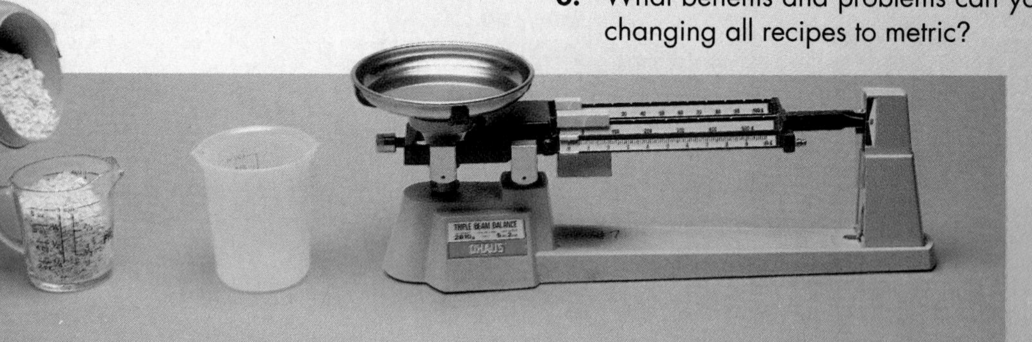

CHAPTER

REVIEW

SUMMARY

2-1: Standards of Measurement

1. A standard of measurement is an exact quantity that people agree to use as a basis of comparison.

2. When a standard of measurement is established, all measurements are compared to the same exact quantity—the standard. Therefore, all measurements can be compared with one another.

3. In SI, prefixes are used to make the base units larger or smaller by multiples of ten. The most common prefixes and their values are: *kilo-* 1000, *deci-* 0.1, *centi-* 0.01, *milli-* 0.001, *micro-* 0.000 001, and *nano-* 0.000 000 001.

2-2: Using SI Units

1. The most commonly used units in SI and their symbols include: length—meter, m; volume—cubic decimeter, dm^3; mass—kilogram, kg; density—grams per cubic centimeter, g/cm^3; time—second, s; and temperature—kelvin, K. Liter and degree Celsius are also commonly used for volume and temperature, respectively.

2. A derived unit is one that is obtained by combining other SI units. Volume and density units are derived units.

3. Any SI unit can be converted to any other related SI unit by multiplying or dividing by the appropriate multiple of ten.

2-3: Graphing

1. Different kinds of graphs are appropriate for displaying different types of information. Three commonly used types of graphs are line graphs, bar graphs, and pie graphs.

2. In a line graph, the independent variable is always plotted on the horizontal *x*-axis; the dependent variable is always plotted on the vertical *y*-axis.

3. Many different kinds of data can be interpreted from graphs.

2-4: Science and Society: Metrics for All?

1. There are many benefits and drawbacks to the adoption of the SI system.

2. SI units are already in wide use on consumer goods and distance signs throughout the United States.

KEY SCIENCE WORDS

a. **density**
b. **derived units**
c. **graph**
d. **kelvin**
e. **kilogram**
f. **liter**
g. **mass**
h. **meter**
i. **second**
j. **SI**
k. **standard**
l. **time**
m. **volume**

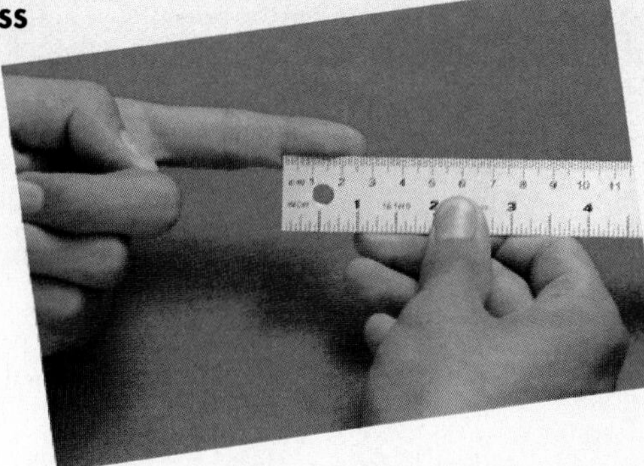

UNDERSTANDING VOCABULARY

Match each phrase with the correct term from the list of Key Science Terms.

1. the modern version of the metric system
2. the amount of space occupied by an object
3. an agreed-upon quantity to be used for comparison
4. the amount of matter in an object
5. obtained by combining other SI units
6. a visual display of data
7. the SI unit of mass
8. the SI unit of length
9. a metric unit of volume
10. mass per unit volume

CHAPTER

REVIEW

CHECKING CONCEPTS

Choose the word or phrase that completes the sentence or answers the question.

ALL

1. A meaningful measurement must have ______.
   a. a number only
   b. a unit only
   c. a number and a unit
   d. a prefix and a unit
2. The ______ is an example of an SI unit.
   a. foot
   b. second
   c. pound
   d. gallon
3. The system of measurement used by scientists around the world is the ______.
   a. SI
   b. Standard system
   c. English system
   d. Kelvin system
4. SI is based on ______.
   a. inches
   b. multiples of five
   c. English units
   d. multiples of ten
5. The SI prefix that means 1/1000 is ______.
   a. *kilo-*
   b. *nano-*
   c. *cent-*
   d. *milli-*
6. The symbol for deciliter is ______.
   a. dL
   b. dcL
   c. dkL
   d. Ld
7. The symbol for ______ is μg.
   a. nanogram
   b. kilogram
   c. microgram
   d. milligram
8. ______ is the distance between two points.
   a. Volume
   b. Length
   c. Mass
   d. Density
9. Which of the following is *not* a derived unit?
   a. liter
   b. meter
   c. cubic centimeter
   d. grams per milliliter
10. 1000 mL is equal to all of the following except ______.
    a. 1 L
    b. 100 cL
    c. 1 dm^3
    d. 1 cm^3

UNDERSTANDING CONCEPTS

Complete each sentence.

ALL

11. A(n) ______ is used to measure the volume of a liquid.
12. The ______ of a block can be found by multiplying its length × width × height.
13. To convert from milligrams to grams, ______ by 1000.
14. Water freezes at ______ kelvin.
15. The SI unit used to measure distance between two cities would be the ______.

THINK AND WRITE CRITICALLY

ANY 2

16. Why are SI measurements used in science classes?
17. Explain how to convert from one length measurement in the SI system to another. Can volume and mass measurements be converted in the same way? Why or why not?
18. Describe three different types of graphs and the types of data best displayed by each.
19. Suppose you set a glass of water in direct sunlight for two hours and measured its temperature every ten minutes. What type of graph would you use to display your data? What would the dependent variable be? the independent variable?
20. What are some advantages and disadvantages of adopting the SI system for use in the United States?

APPLY

21. Make the following conversions.
    a. 1500 mL to liters
    b. 2 km to centimeters
    c. 5.8 dg to milligrams
    d. 22° C to kelvin

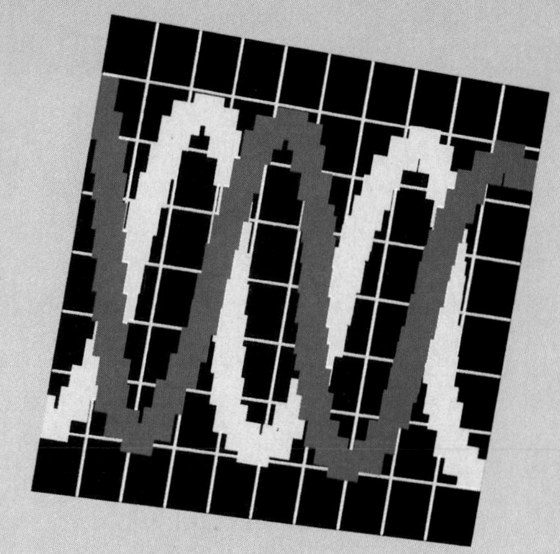

22. If you were able to travel back in time to the Middle Ages, you would find that different kingdoms had different standards of measurement, and that these standards were often based on such things as the length of the king's or queen's arm. What arguments would you use to convince people of the need for a true system of standard measurements?
23. List the SI units of length you would use to express the following. Refer to Table 2-1 on page 31.
    a. the diameter of an atom
    b. the width of your classroom
    c. the width of a pencil lead
    d. the length of a sheet of paper
    e. the distance to the moon
24. Determine the density of each of the following objects.
    a. mass = 15 g, volume = 2 cm^3
    b. mass = 200 g, volume = 80 mL
    c. mass = 1.8 kg, volume = 0.2 L
25. Suppose you want to study the motion of a go-cart for a period of one minute. To do this, you measure the distance it travels every five seconds for the 60-second period. What kind of graph would you use to display your data? What would the dependent and independent variables be?

MORE SKILL BUILDERS

If you need help, refer to the Skill Handbook.

1. **Comparing and Contrasting:** Compare and contrast the SI system of measurement and the system now used in the United States. Be sure to discuss the base units in each system and how conversions are made in each system.
2. **Hypothesizing:** A metal sphere is found to have a density of 5.2 g/cm^3 at 25°C and a density of 5.1 g/cm^3 at 50°C. Propose a hypothesis to explain this observation. How could you easily test your hypothesis?
3. **Measuring in SI:** Determine the mass, volume, and density of your textbook, a container of milk, and an air-filled balloon. Make your measurements in SI units using the appropriate measuring tool and the quickest, most accurate method possible.
4. **Making and Using Graphs:** Using the data in Table 2-3 on page 40, graph the densities of the following materials: water, sugar, salt, iron, copper, lead, and gold. Use the proper type of graph and let each unit on your graph represent 1 g/cm^3. Then, answer the following questions:
    a. Why did you choose this type of graph to display this data?
    b. What would be the mass of 5 cm^3 of sugar?
    c. If you had a 1-g sample of each material shown in the graph, which sample would have the greatest volume?
    d. How could your graph be made more accurate?

PROJECTS

1. Devise your own system of measurements. What will be the standard for each type of measurement in your system? How will conversions between units be made?
2. Find the metric equivalent of such things as your weight in pounds, a gallon of milk, and the distance to your school in miles.

UNIT 1

GLOBAL CONNECTIONS

Physical Science Basics

In this unit, you studied the nature of science and physical science methods. Now find out how the nature and methods of physical science are connected to other subjects and places around the world.

120° 60°

PHYSICS

ROBOT CLEANUP CREW
Cambridge, Massachusetts

Two robots small enough to crawl through a 15-centimeter duct have been designed. They can go into a nuclear generator to inspect machinery and pick up nuclear litter. What problem will these robots help solve in nuclear power plants?

GEOGRAPHY

THE SLIDING ROOF
Washington, D.C.

The National Cathedral was built to be like the cathedrals in England, including its lead roof. When the National Cathedral was only a few years old, it was discovered that the lead roof was flowing downward, a problem not encountered in England. What did the geographic location, particularly the latitude of Washington, have to do with the problem?

0°

CHEMISTRY

BURNING A DIAMOND
Paris, France

In 1772, Antoine Lavoisier placed a diamond in a closed vessel and focused sunlight on it with a magnifying glass. When it grew hot enough, the diamond disappeared and carbon dioxide appeared in the vessel. Lavoisier concluded that a diamond was made of carbon and was thus chemically related to coal. How did Lavoisier's experiment use the scientific method?

ART

ZAPPING ARTWORK CLEAN
Venice, Italy

How do you clean corrosion from ancient statues without destroying them? John Asmus zaps them with a laser. The laser quickly vaporizes the black crust of calcium sulfate caused by air pollution without harming the marble underneath. His lasers have also been used to clean tapestries and remove coffee stains from ancient parchment. Find out about other methods used to clean artwork.

HISTORY

HOW BIG IS EARTH?
Alexandria, Egypt

Around 240 B.C., Eratosthenes found a way to measure the circumference of Earth. He used the positions of the sun at summer solstice at Alexandria and Syrene and the distance between the two cities to calculate a circumference equal to 40 000 kilometers. Find out how accurate he was.

CAREERS

SURVEYOR

Before any construction project can begin, a *surveyor* must establish land boundaries, collect information from maps, charts, or plats, and measure or locate elevations and land contours.

Surveyors work in parties ranging from 3 to 6 people, consisting of a party chief and assistants. An instrument worker sets up the transit and takes gradings. A rod worker holds a graduated rod that measures elevations. The chain workers work in pairs to measure distances between surveying points.

If you're interested in becoming a surveyor, you should enjoy outdoor work, have good eyesight, and be in good physical condition. You should also enjoy teamwork. High school classes in science, mathematics, and drafting would be helpful.

Technical and community colleges offer 1-, 2-, or 3-year programs in surveying. All states require surveyors to be licensed or registered.

For Additional Information

Contact American Congress on Surveying and Mapping, 210 Little Falls Street, Falls Church, Virginia 22046.

QUALITY-CONTROL INSPECTOR

Quality-control inspectors oversee a production process to ensure that the quality of a given product meets certain minimum standards. The products they inspect include things as varied as automobiles, chemicals, clothing, pharmaceuticals, food products, computers, and electronics.

If you're interested in becoming a quality-control inspector, you should like the practical aspects of science and mathematics, especially laboratory work. You must pay close attention to details, and your work must be accurate.

Most quality-control inspectors have a college degree with an emphasis on science. An inspector in the food industry, for example, should have a degree in food science or biology, while an inspector in the chemical or pharmaceutical industry should have a degree in chemistry.

For Additional Information

Contact American Society for Quality Control, 310 West Wisconsin Avenue, Milwaukee, Wisconsin 53203.

UNIT READINGS

- Aaseng, Mathan. *Better Mousetraps: Product Improvements That Led to Success.* Minneapolis, MN: Lerner Publications Co., 1990.
- Holzinger, Philip R. *The House of Science.* New York, NY: John Wiley & Sons, 1990.

Asimov on Physics

by Isaac Asimov

The passage that follows is a brief history of the development of the common thermometer.

One applicable physical characteristic, which must have been casually observed by countless people, is the fact that substances expand when warmed and contract when cooled. The first of all those countless people, however, who tried to make use of this fact to measure temperature was the Italian physicist Galileo Galilei. In 1603 he inverted a tube of heated air into a bowl of water. As the air cooled to room temperature, it contracted and drew the water up into the tube. Now Galileo was ready. The water level kept on changing as room temperature changed, being pushed down when it warmed and expanded the trapped air, and being pulled up when it cooled and contracted the trapped air. Galileo had a thermometer (which, in Greek, means "heat measure"). The only trouble was that the basin of water was open to the air and air pressure kept changing. That also shoved the water level up and down, independently of temperature, and skewed the results.

By 1654, the Grand Duke of Tuscany, Ferdinand II, evolved a thermometer that was independent of air pressure. It contained a liquid sealed into a tube, and the contraction and expansion of the liquid itself was used as an indication of temperature change. The volume change in liquids is much smaller than in gases, but by using a sizable reservoir of liquid which was filled so that further expansion could only take place up a very narrow tube, the rise and fall within that tube, for even tiny volume changes, was considerable.

This was the first reasonably accurate thermometer, and was also one of the few occasions on which the nobility contributed to scientific advance.

In 1701, Isaac Newton suggested that the thermometer be thrust into melting ice and that the liquid level so obtained be marked as 0, while the level attained at body temperature be marked off as 12, and the interval divided into twelve equal parts.

In Your Own Words

▶ The measurement of temperature is a fairly recent idea—less than 400 years old. Write an essay on how your life might be different if thermometers had never been invented.

UNIT

2 ENERGY AND MOTION

What's Happening Here?

Would you like to have a car that never needs gas? If so, then the car in this picture—built by students competing in the National Collegiate Solar Car Race—is the car for you. It runs on sunshine, or solar energy. Do you run on solar energy? The vegetables and grains that give you energy couldn't grow without the sun. So, in a way, you run on sunshine, too. How is energy changed into motion? Is heat a form of energy? In Unit 2, you'll learn more about energy and motion.

UNIT CONTENTS

CHAPTER

3 Moving Objects

Every day people and things move around you—cars go by, your classmates mill about in the halls, leaves blow in the wind. You know these things are moving because you see the motion. Now think about motion that you don't see. A magician makes an object seem to disappear by distracting the people in the audience so that they don't see where the object goes. If you don't see motion, how can you tell something has moved?

FIND OUT!

Do the following activity to find out if you can detect movement without seeing motion.

Close your eyes while a classmate moves something in the classroom. Now open your eyes and see if you can tell what was moved. Be aware of the clues you're using. Are you using only your eyes, or are other senses helping? If you figure out what was moved, can you tell how far it moved? How do you know?

Gearing Up

Previewing the Chapter

Use this outline to help you focus on important ideas in this chapter.

Previewing Science Skills

- ▶ In the **Skill Builders**, you will make a concept map, graph, outline, and observe and infer.
- ▶ In the **Activities**, you will observe, collect and organize data, and infer.
- ▶ In the **MINI-Labs**, you will observe and infer and make and use graphs.

What's next?

You can tell that something has moved without actually seeing the motion. Now you will learn about how and why things move and how different forces affect motion.

3-1 Describing Motion

New Science Words

speed
instantaneous speed
constant speed
average speed

Objectives

- ▶ Describe speed as a rate.
- ▶ Perform calculations involving speed, time, and distance.
- ▶ Interpret distance-time graphs.

Figure 3-1. Although the tuning fork does not move from one place to another, the prongs of the fork are in motion.

EcoTip

When you have to go somewhere, move your muscles. Walk, bike, or skate to the store or to a friend's house instead of riding in a car or bus. It's good for you and for the environment.

Speed

When something moves, it changes position. It travels from one place to another, if only for an instant. Look at the tuning fork. Its prongs are vibrating—they are moving. You may not be able to see their motion, but the sound they produce tells you they are moving. If asked to describe the motion of a tuning fork, you would probably say something like "back-and-forth." How would you describe the motion of a rubber ball bouncing along a sidewalk?

You don't always have to see something move to know that motion has taken place. For example, suppose you look out a window and see a mail truck parked next to a mailbox. One minute later, you look out again and see the same truck parked down the street from the mailbox. Although you didn't observe the motion, you know the truck moved. How do you know? Its position relative to the mailbox has changed.

Motion can be described as a change in position. To know if the position of something has changed, you need a reference point. In the case of the mail truck, the mailbox was a reference point. You can also use the reference point to get a rough idea of how far the truck moved. But there's one thing you don't know. You don't know how *fast* the truck moved in reaching its new position.

Descriptions of motion often include speed—how "fast" something moves. If you think of motion as a change in position, then speed is an expression of how much time it takes for that change in position to occur. Any change over time is called a rate. **Speed,** then, is the rate of change in position. Speed can also be described as simply a rate of motion.

There are different "kinds" of speed. The speedometer in a car shows instantaneous speed. **Instantaneous**

speed is the rate of motion at any given instant. At the moment the picture in Figure 3-2 was taken, the car was traveling at a speed of 80 km/h. On a highway, a car may travel at the same speed for a fairly long period of time. A speed that does not vary is called a **constant speed.**

Much of the time, the speeds you deal with are not constant. Think about riding your bicycle for a distance of 5 kilometers. As you start out, your speed increases from 0 km/h to, say, 30 km/h. You slow down to 18 km/h as you pedal up a steep hill and speed up to 45 km/h going down the other side of the hill. You stop for a red light, speed up again, and move at a constant speed for a while. As you near the end of the trip, you slow down and then stop. Checking your watch, you find that the trip took 15 minutes, or one-quarter of an hour. How would you express your speed on such a trip? Would you use your fastest speed, your slowest speed, or some speed in-between the two?

In cases where rate of motion varies a great deal, such as this bicycle trip, the best way to describe speed is to use average speed. **Average speed** is total distance traveled divided by total time of travel. On the trip just described, your average speed was 5 kilometers divided by 1/4 hour, or 20 km/h.

Figure 3-2. The speedometer of a car shows how fast the car is moving at any given instant.

Did You Know?

In the finals of the 100-m dash of the 1988 Olympics, Ben Johnson and Carl Lewis each reached a peak speed of 43.37 km/h during one 10-m stretch.

Calculating Speed

How could you find out who is the fastest runner in your school? One way would be to get all the students together to run in a giant race. However, this isn't very practical. A better way would be to have each student run a certain distance and to time each runner. The runner with the shortest time is the fastest student. In other words, if you know the distance and time, you can calculate speed. Knowing these values, you can use this equation:

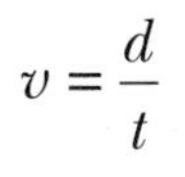

$$v = \frac{d}{t}$$

EXAMPLE PROBLEM: Calculating Speed

Problem Statement:

Your neighbor says she can skate at a speed of 1 m/s. To see if you can skate faster, you have her time you as you skate as fast as you can for 100 m. Your time is 67 s. Who skates faster?

Known Information:

Strategy Hint: Remember that speed is a rate.

distance, $d = 100$ m
time, $t = 67$ s

Unknown Information:

speed, v

Equation to Use:

$$v = \frac{d}{t}$$

Solution:

$$v = \frac{100 \text{ m}}{67 \text{ s}} = 1.5 \text{ m/s}$$

You skate faster than your neighbor.

PRACTICE PROBLEM

Strategy Hint: What units will your answer be given in?

1. Florence Griffith Joyner set a world record by running 200 m in 21.34 s. What was her speed?

EXAMPLE PROBLEM: Calculating Time from Speed

Problem Statement:

Sound travels at a speed of 330 m/s. If a firecracker explodes 3630 m away from you, how long does it take for the sound of the explosion to reach you?

Known Information:

Strategy Hint: Rearrange equation to solve for time.

velocity, $v = 330$ m/s
distance, $d = 3630$ m

Unknown Information:

time, t

Equation to Use:

$$v = \frac{d}{t}$$ Rearranged becomes: $$t = \frac{d}{v}$$

Solution:

$$t = \frac{d}{v} = \frac{3630 \text{ m}}{330 \text{ m/s}} = 11 \text{ s}$$

It takes 11 seconds for the sound of the explosion to reach you.

PRACTICE PROBLEM

Strategy Hint: Rearrange the equation.

1. The world's fastest passenger elevator operates at a speed of about 10 m/s. If the 60th floor is 219 m above the first floor, how long does it take the elevator to go from the first floor to the 60th floor?

Graphing Speed

A distance-time graph makes it possible to "see" the motion of an object over a period of time. For example, the graphs in Figure 3-3 show how two swimmers performed during a 30-minute workout. The smooth, red line represents the motion of a swimmer who swam at a constant speed during the entire workout. She swam 800 m during each 10-minute period. Her speed was constant at 80 m/min.

The blue line represents the motion of a second swimmer, who did not swim at a constant speed. She covered 400 m during the first 10 minutes of her workout. Then she rested for the next 10 minutes. During this time, her speed was 0 m/min. The steepness of the graph over the next 10 minutes shows that she swam faster than before. During this period she covered 800 m. How much distance did she cover during the workout? What was her average speed for the 30-minute period?

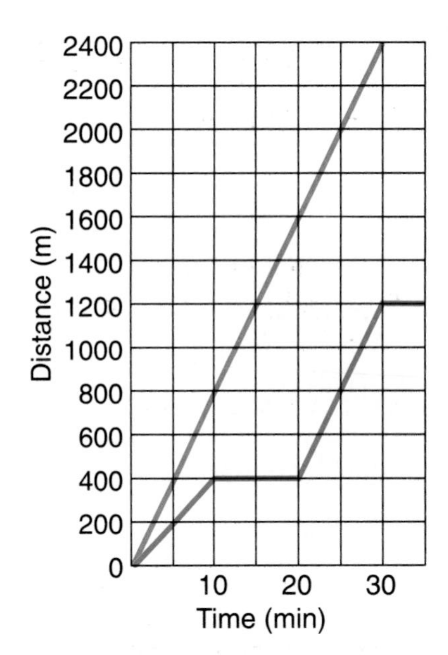

Figure 3-3. Distance-time graphs like the one shown here make it possible to visualize motion over a period of time.

SECTION REVIEW

1. What units would you use to describe the speed of a car? Would you use different units to give the speeds of runners in a neighborhood race? Explain your answer.
2. In a skateboarding marathon, the winner covered 435 km in 36.75 h. What was the winner's average speed?
3. **Apply:** Make a graph of distance versus time for a 2-hour car trip. During the first 30 minutes the car covered 50 km. During the next 30 minutes the car was stopped. An additional 50 km was covered during the final 60 minutes of the trip. Note the three graph segments. Which graph segment slopes the most? Which one does not slope? What was the car's average speed?

Concept Mapping

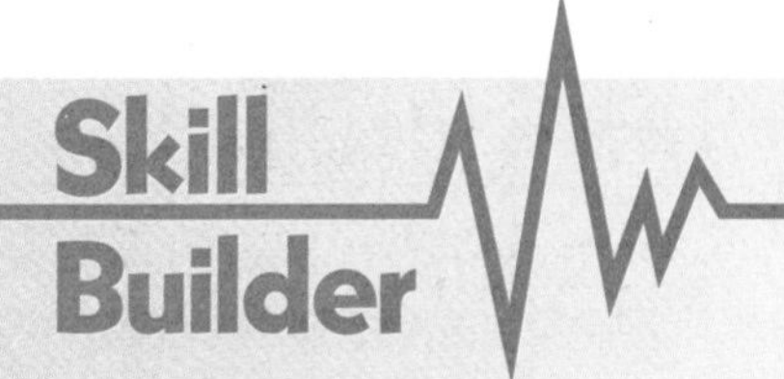

Make a network tree concept map that shows and defines the three kinds of speed described in this section. If you need help, refer to Concept Mapping in the **Skill Handbook** on pages 684 and 685.

ACTIVITY 3-1
Measuring Speed

Problem: *How slow can you make a glider fly?*

Materials
- stopwatch or timer with second hand
- metric tape measure or meterstick
- string
- paper sheets of various types, weights, and sizes
- transparent tape
- paper clips and stapler

Procedure
1. Design a paper glider. Construct your glider using the materials provided.
2. Test fly the glider following all rules that have been established by the class.
3. Measure the distance of flight in centimeters and time of flight in seconds. Record this data in a table like the one shown here.
4. Calculate the speed of the glider.
5. Make any adjustments in the glider to achieve the slowest possible speed. If necessary, redesign the glider.
6. Repeat Steps 2, 3, and 4.
7. When you are satisfied with your design, fly the glider, record the measurements, and calculate the speed. Compare your results with those of other teams.

Data and Observations

	Distance (cm)	Time (s)	Speed (cm/s)
Test 1			
Test 2			
Final			

Analyze
1. If your glider travels a curved path, which distance measurement will give the slowest speed calculation—along the curved path or along a straight line between the starting point and landing point? Explain your reasoning.
2. Which is more important in glider speed—how hard you throw the glider or the design of the glider?

Conclude and Apply
3. When calculating the speed of your glider, did you find its fastest speed, slowest speed, or average speed?
4. In designing a slow glider, which should you try for, long distance or long time?
5. What factors affected the flight of your glider? Which of these factors were you able to control or influence, and by what means?

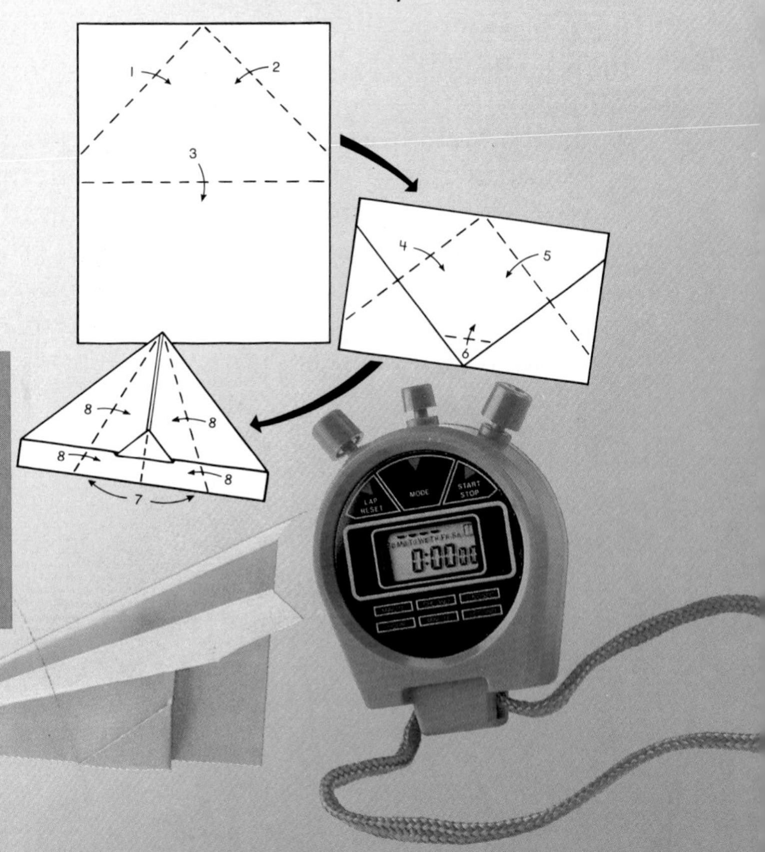

Velocity and Acceleration

3-2

Objectives

- ▶ Compare and contrast speed, velocity, and acceleration.
- ▶ Calculate acceleration.

New Science Words

velocity
acceleration

Velocity and Speed

You turn on the radio and hear the tail-end of a news story about a swarm of killer bees. The swarm, moving at a speed of 60 km/h, has just left a town 60 kilometers north of your location. Should you be worried? What should you do? Unfortunately, you don't have enough information. Knowing the speed of the swarm isn't much help. Speed only describes how fast something is moving. You also need to know the direction the swarm is moving. In other words, you need to know the velocity of the swarm. **Velocity** describes both speed and direction.

Picture a motorcycle racing down the highway at 100 km/h. It passes another motorcycle going 100 km/h in the opposite direction. The speeds of the motorcycles are the same, but their velocities are different because the motorcycles are not moving in the same direction.

You learned earlier that speed isn't always constant. Like speed, velocity may also change. Unlike speed, the velocity of an object can change, even if the speed of the object remains constant! How can this be? Read on and you'll find out.

Acceleration

At the starting line of a drag strip, a driver sits, idling the dragster's engine. With the starting signal, the driver presses the gas pedal to the floor. The car leaps forward and builds up speed, moving faster and faster until it crosses the finish line. Then the driver releases a drag chute, and the car rapidly slows down and comes to a stop. All the while the car gains speed, it is accelerating. Strange as it may seem, the car is also accelerating as it slows down! How is this possible?

Acceleration is the rate of change of velocity. Keep in mind that velocity includes both speed and direction. If the direction of motion stays the same, as with the dragster, then acceleration is just the rate of change in speed. Because "slowing down" is a change in speed, the dragster is accelerating as it slows down. If the acceleration is opposite in direction to the velocity, then the speed decreases.

MINI-Lab

Does greater velocity require greater acceleration?

Make a ramp by propping a board on a textbook. Let a marble roll down the ramp and across a hard, flat surface. Make two time measurements: travel time of the marble down the ramp and travel time of the marble across the flat surface for a distance of 1 m from the bottom of the ramp. Calculate the marble's velocity across the flat surface. Change the starting point of the marble on the ramp and repeat the procedure. Does acceleration change? Does velocity change?

Because velocity includes both speed and direction, if *either* value changes, velocity will change. For example, if a car goes around a curve, its direction changes. So even if its speed remains constant, the velocity of the car changes. In other words, acceleration occurs.

The size of an acceleration depends on both the change in velocity and the time interval. The *time interval* is the amount of time that passed while the change in velocity was taking place. If the change in velocity is large, the acceleration will be large. Acceleration will also be large if the change in velocity occurs in a small time interval.

To calculate acceleration, divide the change in velocity by the time interval. To find the *change in velocity,* subtract the initial velocity (starting velocity) from the final velocity.

$$a = \frac{v_f - v_i}{t} = \frac{\Delta v}{t}$$

The symbol Δ is the Greek letter *delta* and stands for "change in."

When an object is slowing down, its final velocity will be less than its initial velocity. Thus, the acceleration will have a negative value. When calculating acceleration, be sure to include all proper units and algebraic signs. The unit for velocity is meters/second (m/s) and the unit for time is seconds (s). Thus, the unit for acceleration is

$$\frac{\text{meters/second}}{\text{second}}.$$

This unit is usually written as m/s^2 and is read as "meters per second square" or "meters per second per second."

EXAMPLE PROBLEM: Calculating Acceleration

Problem Statement: The velocity of a dragster changes from 0 m/s at the starting line to 60 m/s when it crosses the finish line 10 seconds later. Calculate the car's average acceleration.

Known Information:
initial velocity, v_i, = 0 m/s
final velocity, v_f, = 60 m/s
time interval, t, = 10 s

Strategy Hint: Figure velocity change by subtracting initial velocity from final velocity.

Unknown Information: Acceleration, a

Equation to Use:

$$a = \frac{v_f - v_i}{t}$$

Solution:

$$a = \frac{v_f - v_i}{t} = \frac{60 \text{ m/s} - 0 \text{ m/s}}{10 \text{ s}} = 6 \text{ m/s}^2$$

PRACTICE PROBLEM

Strategy Hint: Find the change in velocity by subtracting initial velocity from final velocity.

1. At the top of its highest hill, a roller coaster's velocity is 10 m/s. Plunging downward, it gains speed, reaching a velocity of 32 m/s just before it gets to the bottom three seconds later. What is the roller coaster's acceleration?

SECTION REVIEW

1. A jet plane is flying east at 880 km/h. In the air above it, another plane is traveling north at 880 km/h. Do the two planes have the same velocity? Are their speeds the same? Explain your answer.
2. Near the end of a daily swim, a swimmer pushes himself to swim faster. His speed gradually increases from 1.1 m/s to 1.3 m/s during the last 20 s of his workout. What is his acceleration during this interval?
3. **Apply:** Describe three different ways to change your velocity when you're riding a bicycle.

Making and Using Graphs

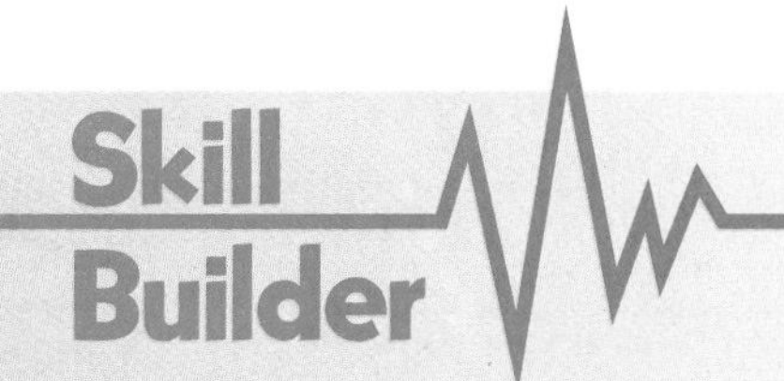

Decide which kind of graph—a line graph, a bar graph, or a pie graph—you should use to show how velocity changes over time. Explain your choice. Show how you would set up the graph. If you need help, refer to Making and Using Graphs in the **Skill Handbook** on page 687.

3-3 Crashing to Save Lives

Objectives

- **Evaluate the effects of wearing seat belts during a car crash.**
- **Form an opinion about whether laws should make people wear seat belts.**

Studying Crashes

How would you like to develop and perfect something that could save thousands of lives every year and keep hundreds of thousands of other people from being hurt? That's what scientists are trying to do with experiments called crash tests. In crash tests, researchers put lifelike dummies in cars, then crash the cars into each other or into concrete walls. Sometimes the dummies are placed on a sledlike device that runs on tracks. As cameras and other instruments record the process, the sled accelerates, then stops suddenly.

By studying the results of crash tests and real car collisions, scientists have learned what happens to people in accidents and how some injuries and deaths can be prevented.

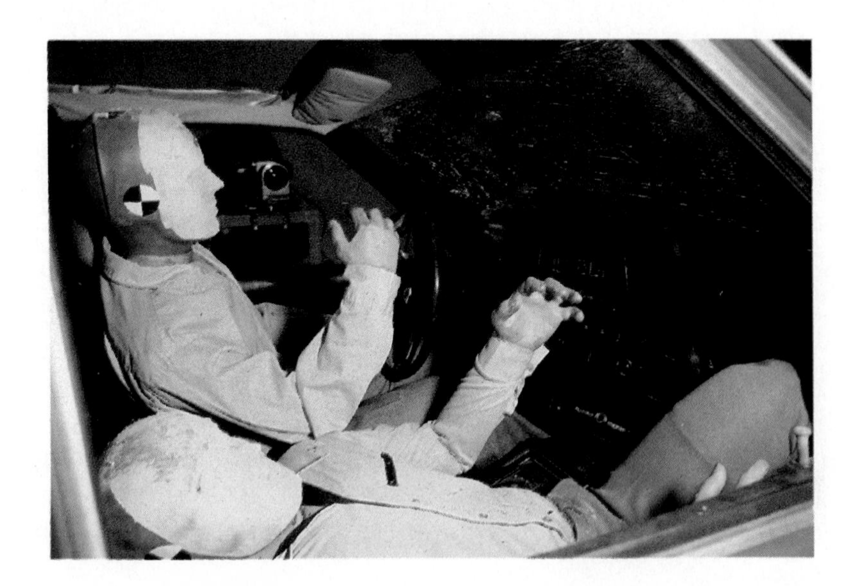

When a car traveling about 50 km/h collides head-on with something solid, the car begins to crumple and slow down. Within 0.1 second after the crash, the car stops. Any passenger not wearing a seat belt continues to move forward at the same speed the car was traveling.

Within 0.02 second (one-fiftieth of a second) after the car stops, the unbelted person slams into the windshield, dashboard, or steering wheel with great force. Back-seat passengers slam into the backs of the seats in front of them at a speed of 50 km/h. That's as much as the speed you would reach while falling from a three-story building.

A person wearing a seat belt becomes "part" of the car. When the car slows down, the person also slows down. The force needed to slow a person down from 50 km/h to zero in 0.1 seconds is equal to 14 times that person's weight. The belt not only holds the person in place, it also "gives", reducing the force and spreading out the force so that it's not all concentrated on one part of the body.

SECTION REVIEW

1. Describe what happens to a person who's not wearing a seat belt during a car crash.
2. Describe how seat belts protect passengers and drivers during accidents.

You Decide!

Safety experts say that about half the people who die in car crashes would survive if they wore seat belts. Most states have passed laws that require drivers and front-seat passengers to wear seat belts. But some people resent the laws. They think everyone should be free to decide whether or not to use seat belts. Some people feel the same way about laws that require motorcycle riders to wear helmets. Should laws require people to wear seat belts? What about motorcycle helmets?

3-4 Force and Motion

New Science Words

force
balanced forces
net force
inertia
friction

Objectives

- Recognize different kinds of forces.
- Identify cause and effect relationships between force and changes in velocity.
- Give examples of the effects of inertia.
- State Newton's first law of motion.

Figure 3-4. The force exerted by the bat sends the ball flying. How does the force exerted by the ball affect the motion of the bat?

What Is a Force?

Push a door open. Stretch a rubber band. Squeeze a piece of clay. Shove a book across a table. In each case, you are applying a force. A **force** is a push or a pull one body exerts on another. Sometimes the effects of a force are obvious, as when a moving car crashes into a stationary object, such as a tree. Other forces aren't as noticeable. Can you feel the force the floor exerts on your feet?

List all the forces you might exert or encounter in a typical day. Think about pushing, pulling, stretching, squeezing, bending, and falling.

Effects of Forces on Objects

In the examples you thought of, what happened to the objects that had forces exerted on them? If an object was moving, did the force change the object's velocity? Think of a speeding baseball meeting the force of a swinging bat. The ball's velocity certainly changes when the bat hits the ball.

Force does not always change velocity. Think about a game of tug-of-war with your dog. You plant your feet firmly and push against the ground. This force enables you to pull on one end of a rope. If your dog on the other end pulls just as hard as you do, the rope doesn't move. The forces acting on the rope balance each other. Forces that are equal in size and opposite in direction are called **balanced forces.**

Now what happens if your feet hit a slippery spot on the ground? Your feet slip and you can't exert as much force on the rope. The forces acting on the rope become unbalanced, and there is a net force. A **net force** on an object always changes the velocity of the object. So, when your dog on the other end exerts more force on the rope than you do, the rope (and you) will accelerate in the direction of greater force.

You should keep in mind that velocity involves both speed and direction. If a net force acts on an object, the object will change speed, change direction, or both. In the tug-of-war, the net force causes both speed and direction to change.

Inertia and Mass

Picture a hockey puck sliding across the ice. Its velocity hardly changes until it hits something, such as the wall, net, or another stick. The velocity of the puck is constant, and its acceleration is zero until it hits something that alters its speed or direction.

The sliding puck demonstrates the property of inertia. **Inertia** (ihn UR shuh) is the tendency of an object to resist any change in its motion. If an object is moving, it tends to keep moving at the same speed and in the same direction unless a force acts on it. In other words, the velocity of the object remains constant unless a force changes it. If an object is at rest, it tends to remain at rest. Its velocity remains equal to zero unless a force makes it move.

Would you expect that a bowling ball would have the same inertia as a table tennis ball? Why would there be a difference? The more mass an object has, the greater its inertia. Recall that mass is the amount of matter in an object, and a bowling ball certainly contains more matter than a table tennis ball. So the bowling ball would have greater inertia than the table tennis ball.

Science and READING

Before a runner is given credit for a record in track, officials carefully analyze the conditions under which the event was held. What are some of the factors they consider?

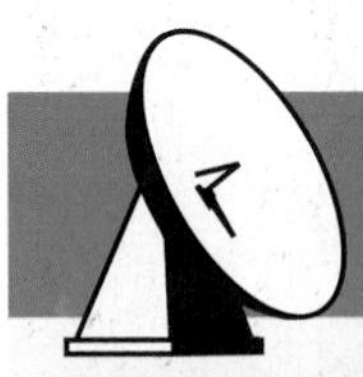

TECHNOLOGY

Inertia Sponges

Seat belts are designed to reduce the effect of inertia in a crash by holding the passengers in place. However, in a high-speed crash, belts provide limited protection to the head and upper body. These parts of the body can be protected by air bags, which provide an instantaneous cushion for the head and upper body at the time of impact.

Air bags are designed to be used in addition to seat belts. An air-bag system consists of one or more crash sensors, an ignitor and gas generator, and an inflatable nylon bag. The nylon bag for the driver is stored in the steering wheel, and the bag for the front-seat passenger is inside the dashboard. If a car hits something with sufficient force (speeds in excess of from 15 to 20 kilometers per hour), impact sensors trigger the flow of electric current to an ignitor. The ignitor causes a chemical reaction to occur, producing harmless nitrogen gas. The nitrogen gas pushes the air bag from its storage compartment just in time to absorb the inertia of the occupants. The bag then immediately deflates so that it will not interfere with the driver.

Think Critically: Under what crash conditions would an air bag offer little or no protection?

You wouldn't change the velocity of a bowling ball very much by swatting it with a paddle, but you could easily change the velocity of a table tennis ball. Because of its greater inertia, a much greater force would be needed to change the velocity of the bowling ball.

Newton's First Law

Forces change the motion of an object in very specific ways—so specific that Sir Isaac Newton (1642 - 1727) was able to state laws to describe the effects of forces.

Newton's first law of motion says that an object moving at a constant velocity keeps moving at that velocity unless a net force acts on it. If an object is at rest, it stays at rest unless a net force acts on it. Does this sound familiar? It

Figure 3-5. When the wheelbarrow strikes a rock, it stops suddenly. The rake keeps moving forward at its original speed because of its inertia.

is the same as the earlier discussion of inertia. Thus, you'll understand why this law is sometimes called the *law of inertia.* You've probably seen—and felt—this law at work without even knowing it.

Suppose you're pushing a wheelbarrow full of leaves across your yard. Your rake is resting on top of the load. The wheel hits a rock and the wheelbarrow stops suddenly. What would happen to the rake? The rake would probably continue forward and fly out of the wheelbarrow. Why would this happen? No one would have pushed the rake. No net forward force would have acted on it. But because of inertia, the rake would keep moving forward at the same speed. If it wasn't for the rake hitting the ground, it would have kept moving until some other force stopped it.

Friction

You've just learned that inertia causes an object that is moving at constant velocity to keep moving at that velocity unless a net force acts on it. But you know that if you shove a book across a long table, it seems to slow down and stop by itself. You don't see any force acting on the book. Why does it stop?

There is a force between the surfaces of the book and the table. The force is friction. **Friction** is the force that opposes motion between two surfaces that are touching each other. Would you expect more friction between an

MINI-Lab

Is friction a force?

Place a sheet of plain white paper on a flat surface. Set a 20-g mass on the paper about 7 cm from one end of the paper. Grip the edge of the other end of the paper and give it a quick, smooth yank. What happens to the 20-g mass? Replace the paper with a sheet of coarse sandpaper, rough side up, and repeat the procedure. What happens to the 20-g mass now? How do you account for the different results? Use Newton's first law to explain your observations.

Figure 3-6. How is friction helping this ballerina?

oily floor and a slick, leather shoe sole or between a rough sidewalk and the bottom of a tennis shoe? The amount of friction that exists between two surfaces depends on two factors—the kinds of surfaces and the force pressing the surfaces together.

If there were no friction, your life would be much different. You wouldn't be able to walk or hold things between your fingers. Your shoes would fall off. Friction between the soles of your shoes and the floor makes it possible for you to walk. You can hold with your fingers because of friction. Shoelaces remain tied because of friction, and friction keeps your shoes on your feet.

As you complete this section, you should be more aware of the importance of force and motion. They are part of everything you do and everything that happens around you. A force—gravity—keeps you on the ground. Muscles in your body exert forces that move your arms and legs and eyes. Friction makes it possible for you to walk and to turn the pages of this book. And these are but a few examples of how force and motion affect your life.

SECTION REVIEW

1. Before dancing on a smooth wooden floor, ballet dancers sometimes put a sticky powder called rosin on their shoe soles. Why? What force are they taking advantage of?
2. Explain which has greater inertia, a speeding car or a jet airplane sitting on a runway.
3. **Apply:** Think of and describe three examples from sports in which a force changes the velocity of an object or a person.

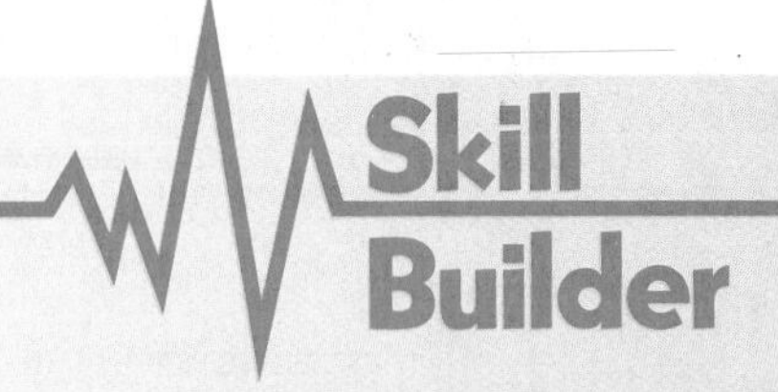

Outlining

In an outline, organize all of the information you have learned relating to inertia and Newton's first law of motion. If you need help, refer to Outlining in the **Skill Handbook** on page 677.

Effects of Gravity

3-5

Objectives

- Give examples of the effects of gravity.
- Examine how gravitational force is related to mass and distance.
- Distinguish between mass and weight.

New Science Words

gravity
weight

Gravitational Force

An Olympic diver is poised high above the water on a diving platform. The diver bounces up in the air and then hurtles toward the water. Did you ever wonder why the diver plunges downward instead of flying off into space? Probably not. Seeing objects "fall" is a very common experience. You may not have thought about it, but you've been watching the force of gravity at work.

Every object in the universe exerts a force on every other object, and that force is **gravity.** Often, the force is too slight to notice. For example, there's a gravitational force of attraction between your hand and your notebook, but when you let go of your notebook, it doesn't stay in your hand. The force is too small.

The amount of gravitational force between objects depends on two things: their masses and the distance between them. The masses of your hand and your notebook are quite small, so the force of attraction between them is weak. The mass of the Earth is very large, so its gravitational force is strong.

The amount of Earth's gravity acting on an orbiting satellite depends on its distance from Earth. The closer it is to Earth, the stronger the pull of gravity. The farther away it is, the less effect gravity has on it. How would this affect the satellite's velocity?

Weight

The measure of the force of gravity on an object is the object's weight. The term weight is most often used in reference to the gravitational force between Earth and a body

PROBLEM SOLVING

An Experiment for the Shuttle

NASA was having a competition to select several student experiments for scientists to conduct while the shuttle orbited Earth. Ellen decided to enter an experiment about how the time spent on a shuttle flight would affect the masses of the astronauts. The mass of each astronaut would be determined before and after the mission. During the flight, the astronauts would have to list the foods they ate and the liquids they drank and the masses of each. Ellen's experiment required that the masses of the food and liquid packets be measured and labeled to the nearest 0.01 gram.

How would the mass of any material on Earth compare with its mass during the shuttle mission?

Think Critically: What factors could cause changes in the astronauts' masses?

at Earth's surface. Weight isn't the same as mass, but the two are related. Recall from Chapter 2 that mass is the amount of matter in an object. The greater an object's mass, the stronger the gravitational force on it. In other words, the more mass an object has, the more it weighs.

Mass is measured in grams (g) and kilograms (kg). Weight, which is a force, is measured in units called newtons (N). A kilogram of mass on Earth's surface weighs 9.8 N. On Earth, a tape cassette weighs about 0.5 N, a backpack full of books weighs about 40 N, you probably weigh 450 to 500 N, and a wide-bodied jumbo jet weighs about 3.4 million N.

The gravitational force an object exerts on other objects is related to its mass. Earth exerts a stronger gravitational force than the moon, because Earth has more mass. Because of the moon's weaker gravitational force, a person weighing about 480 N on Earth would weigh only about 80 N on the moon. Does this mean that the person would have less mass on the moon than on Earth? No. Unlike weight, mass doesn't change with changes in gravity. Because mass remains constant, the person would have the same inertia on the moon as on Earth.

Measuring Forces

Scales use the principle of balanced forces to measure how much something weighs. To see how the principle works, hang a rubber band from a hook or a nail. Then attach something heavy to the lower end of the rubber band and see how much the band stretches. If you attach something even heavier, will the band stretch more? It will, because the length of the rubber band is a measure of the force on it. The band stretches until it is exerting an upward force equal to the weight of the object hung on it.

A scale works something like the rubber band. When you step on a bathroom scale, the force of your body stretches a spring inside the scale. The stretched spring pulls on levers, as shown in Figure 3-7, until the upward force of the scale equals the downward force of your weight.The dial on the scale, which is marked off in units of weight, moves as the spring stretches. When the spring stops moving, the number showing on the dial indicates your weight.

Gravity, like friction, is a force we tend to take for granted, even though it affects everything we do. Try to imagine living on a planet where the force of gravity was only half as great as Earth's. How would your life be different?

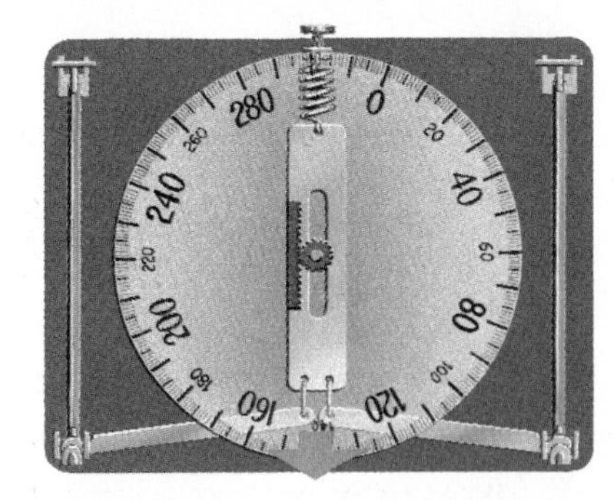

Figure 3-7. When you step on a bathroom scale, the downward force of gravity—your weight—is balanced by the upward force exerted by the spring.

SECTION REVIEW

1. Arriving on a newly discovered, Earth-sized planet, you find that you weigh one-third as much as on Earth. Is the planet's mass greater or less than Earth's?
2. Why don't you feel the gravitational force between your hand and a pencil?
3. **Apply:** Use Newton's first law and the concept of gravity to explain how a satellite orbits Earth.

Observing and Inferring

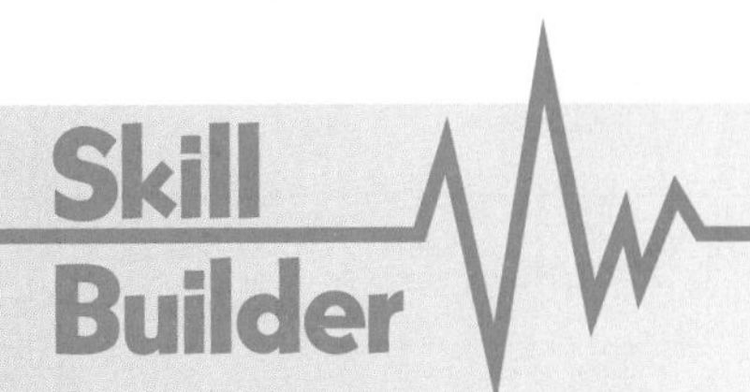

Select three objects in the room and, without touching them, try to guess which weighs the most. What clues help you to make your guesses? How can you tell if you guessed right? If you need help, refer to Observing and Inferring in the **Skill Handbook** on page 678.

ACTIVITY 3-2
Balancing Forces Against Gravity

Problem: *How can gravity be used to test the strength of a material?*

Materials
- selection of paper strips
- scissors
- masking tape
- plastic cup
- string
- sand, 250 mL
- beaker
- balance
- ring stand and ring

Procedure
1. Prepare a data table with the headings "sample," "mass of sand," and "weight of sand."
2. Place the ring stand as shown. Select a paper strip and record its identity in the data table. Cut the strip as shown. Tape one side of the strip to the ring and tape the other side to the handle of the cup as shown.
3. *Slowly* pour sand into the cup. When the paper strip *begins* to tear, stop pouring.
4. Use the balance to measure the combined mass of the cup and sand. Record this measurement and return the sand to its container.
5. Repeat Steps 3, 4, and 5 using different paper strips.
6. Using the formula below, calculate the weights of the cup and sand for each paper strip tested. Record these weights.

$$\text{Weight} = \frac{\text{mass of sample in g}}{1000\text{ g/kg}} \times 9.80\text{ N/kg}$$

Data and Observations

Sample	Mass of Sand (g)	Weight of Sand (N)
a		
b		
c		

Analyze
1. The ability of a material to resist tearing is called shear strength. What did this investigation show about the shear strengths of different types of paper?
2. Why would it be incorrect to refer to shear strength in grams or kilograms?

Conclude and Apply
3. This investigation tests the shear strength of each paper sample in one direction only. How could you find out if the shear strength of a type of paper depends on the direction in which the paper is torn?
4. Would this investigation work as well if water were used in place of sand?
5. Why is gravity a good choice of force to use for measuring the strength of different materials?

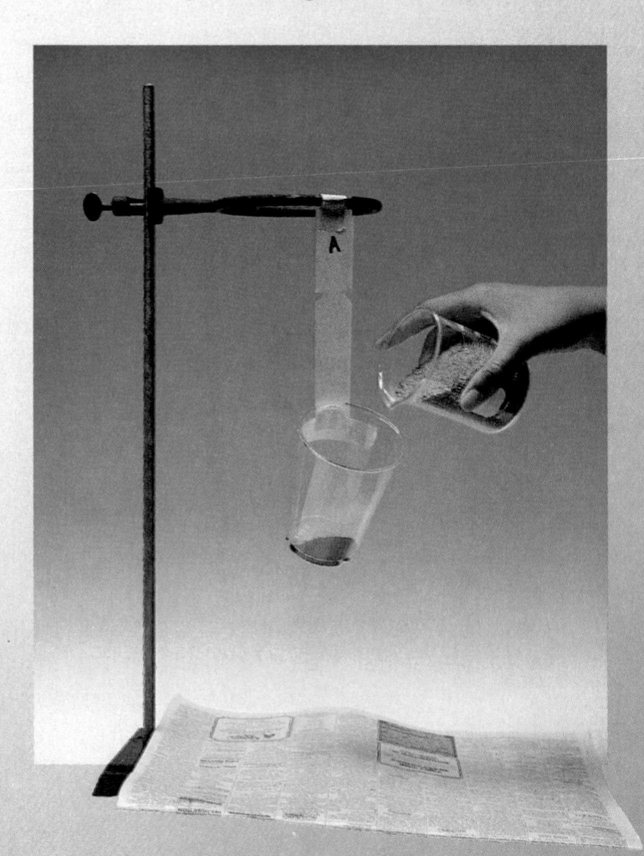

CHAPTER

REVIEW

SUMMARY

3-1: Describing Motion

1. Motion is a change in position of a body. Speed is the rate at which a body changes position.

2. Average speed, which is the ratio of distance traveled to travel time, describes the motion of a body, even if its speed is not constant.

3. A distance-time graph is a visual representation of the motion of an object throughout a travel period.

3-2: Velocity and Acceleration

1. Velocity describes the speed and direction of a moving body. A change in velocity may be a change in speed, direction, or both.

2. Acceleration is the rate of change in the velocity. It is calculated by dividing change in velocity by the time interval involved.

3-3: Science and Society: Crashing to Save Lives

1. Researchers conduct crash tests on automobiles. Crash test results are used to design safer vehicles and safety devices for occupants.

2. Some people believe that seat belts should be required by law, others don't. Seat belts have been proven to save lives.

3-4: Force and Motion

1. A force is a push or a pull one body exerts on another body. Balanced forces acting on a body do not change the motion of the body. Unbalanced forces result in a net force, which always changes the motion of a body.

2. Inertia is the tendency of a body to resist any change in its motion.

3. Friction is a force that opposes motion between two surfaces that are touching.

4. Newton's first law says that the motion of an object will not change unless a net force acts on the object.

3-5: Effects of Gravity

1. Gravity is the force of attraction that exists between any two bodies in the universe.

2. Weight is a measure of the force of gravity between two objects. The term *weight* is most often used in reference to the gravitational force between Earth and a body at Earth's surface.

3. A force can be measured by determining the change it produces in a material, such as a rubber band or a steel spring.

KEY SCIENCE WORDS

a. **acceleration**
b. **average speed**
c. **balanced forces**
d. **constant speed**
e. **force**
f. **friction**
g. **gravity**
h. **inertia**
i. **instantaneous speed**
j. **net force**
k. **speed**
l. **velocity**
m. **weight**

UNDERSTANDING VOCABULARY

Match each phrase with the correct term from the list of Key Science Words.

1. rate of change in position
2. speed that does not change
3. rate of change in velocity
4. a push or pull exerted on an object
5. type of force that changes the motion of an object
6. tendency of an object to resist change in motion
7. a force that opposes motion between surfaces
8. force exerted by every object in the universe on every other object
9. measure of the force of gravity on an object
10. rate of motion at a given point in time

CHAPTER

REVIEW

CHECKING CONCEPTS

Choose the word or phrase that completes the sentence or answers the question.

1. The best way to describe the rate of motion of an object that changes speed several times is to calculate the object's ______.
a. average speed **c.** instantaneous speed
b. constant speed **d.** variable speed

2. Which of the following is a force?
a. inertia **c.** acceleration
b. friction **d.** velocity

3. The unit for ______ is m/s^2.
a. weight **c.** inertia
b. acceleration **d.** gravity

4. Which of the following is not used in calculating acceleration?
a. initial velocity **c.** time interval
b. average speed **d.** final velocity

5. A body accelerates if it ______.
a. speeds up **c.** changes direction
b. slows down **d.** all of these

6. The gravitational force between two objects depends on their ______.
a. masses **c.** shapes
b. velocities **d.** volume

7. ______ opposes motion.
a. Inertia **c.** Gravity
b. Friction **d.** A net force

8. The weight of an object is directly related to its ______.
a. volume **c.** mass
b. velocity **d.** shape

9. Compared to an object of small mass, an object of large mass has ______.
a. less inertia **c.** less weight
b. more inertia **d.** greater acceleration

10. If the velocity of an object is constant, its acceleration is ______.
a. positive **c.** increasing
b. negative **d.** zero

UNDERSTANDING CONCEPTS

Complete each sentence.

11. The SI unit for ______ is the newton.

12. Your ______ on the moon would be less than it is on Earth.

13. The speedometer on a car indicates ______ speed.

14. Newton's first law is called the law of ______.

15. ______ forces acting on an object do not cause any change in its motion.

THINK AND WRITE CRITICALLY

16. How can you tell an object has moved if you do not see its motion? What information would you need to calculate the object's speed? Its velocity?

17. Explain how it is possible for an automobile traveling at constant speed to be accelerating.

18. Explain why friction is a net force.

19. How are mass and weight similar? How are they different?

20. Describe some common effects of inertia.

APPLY

21. Explain why an object can lose weight without losing mass, but it cannot lose mass without losing weight.

22. A cyclist must travel 800 kilometers. How many days will the trip take if the cyclist travels at an average speed of 16 km/h?

23. At 1:00 PM, a satellite's velocity is 30 000 m/s. At 1:01 PM, its velocity is 15 000 m/s. What is the satellite's acceleration during this time interval?

24. A cyclist leaves home and rides due east for a distance of 45 kilometers. She returns home on the same bike path. If the entire trip takes 4 hours, what is her average speed?

25. The return trip of the cyclist in Question 24 took 30 minutes longer than her trip east. What was her velocity in each direction?

MORE SKILL BUILDERS

If you need help, refer to the Skill Handbook.

1. **Measuring in SI:** Which of the following represents the greatest speed: 20 m/s, 200 cm/s, or 0.2 km/s? HINT: Express all three in meters/second and then compare them.
2. **Observing and Inferring:** A car sits motionless on a hill. What two major forces are acting on the car? Are the forces balanced or unbalanced? Explain how you inferred your answers.
3. **Making and Using Tables:** The four cars shown in the table were traveling at the same speed and the brakes were applied in all four cars at the same instant.

Car	Mass	Stopping Distance
A	1000 kg	80 m
B	1250 kg	100 m
C	1500 kg	120 m
D	2000 kg	160 m

From the data in the table, what is the relationship between the mass of a car and its stopping distance? How do you account for this relationship?

4. **Making and Using Graphs:** The following data were obtained for two runners.

SALLY		ALONZO	
Distance	Time	Distance	Time
2 m	1 s	1 m	1 s
4 m	2 s	2 m	2 s
6 m	3 s	2 m	3 s
8 m	4 s	4 m	4 s

Make a distance-time graph that shows the motion of both runners. What is the average speed of each runner? What is the instantaneous speed of each runner 1 second after they start? Which runner stops briefly? During what time interval do Sally and Alonzo run at the same speed?

5. **Making and Using Graphs:** Study this acceleration graph.

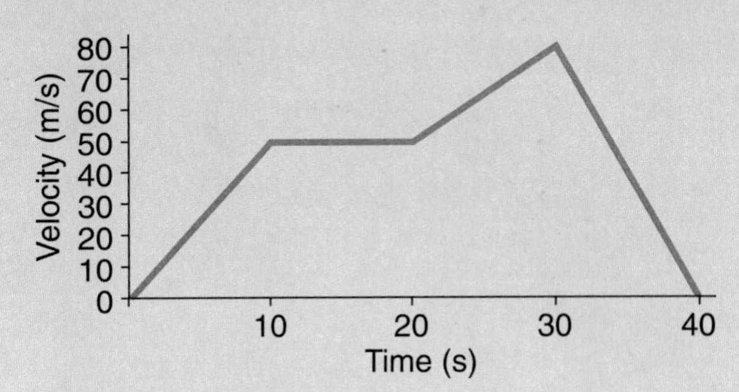

What is the acceleration of the object between 0 seconds and 10 seconds? Between 30 and 40 seconds? When is the object not accelerating? What is its speed during that interval? During what interval does the object have negative acceleration?

PROJECTS

1. Look up the mass of the sun, Earth's moon, and each planet in the solar system. Make a poster to share this information with your classmates. Include some information about conditions on each of the bodies. Speculate what your weight might be on each of the planets if they were the same size as Earth. Discuss how conditions might affect the motion of objects on and near the surface of each planet.
2. Write a letter to your state representative explaining your position on whether or not there should be a law requiring the use of safety belts in cars. Be sure to use scientific facts to support your position.

CHAPTER

4 Acceleration and Momentum

The force of gravity acts on this sky diver, causing him to accelerate toward Earth. A second force acting on the diver allows him to change speed and direction as he falls. What do you think this second force is?

FIND OUT!

Do this activity to find out what determines how a balloon moves.

Drop an uninflated balloon from shoulder level. What does it do? Now, blow up the balloon, but don't tie it closed. Again, hold the balloon at shoulder level and let it go. What happens to it? Does it fall to the ground right away?

Next, blow up the balloon, tie it closed, and drop it from shoulder level. How is its motion different from its motion in the first two trials? If you keep batting the balloon with your hand, can you keep it from touching the floor?

Gearing Up

Previewing the Chapter

Use this outline to help you focus on important ideas in this chapter.

Section 4-1 Accelerated Motion
- Newton's Second Law
- Falling Objects
- Terminal Velocity

Section 4-2 Projectile and Circular Motion
- Projectiles
- Moving in Circles
- Weightlessness in Orbit

Section 4-3 Science and Society
To Boldly—and Safely—Go
- Effects of Weightlessness

Section 4-4 Action and Reaction
- Newton's Third Law
- Rocket Propulsion
- Momentum

Previewing Science Skills

- In the **Skill Builders**, you will design an experiment, make and use tables, and make a concept map
- In the **Activities**, you will observe, collect and organize data, and analyze.
- In the **MINI-Lab**, you will construct models, observe and infer, and hypothesize.

What's next?

Now that you know that conditions can cause the motion of an object to vary, find out what some of those conditions are. You can also learn how outside forces can affect the motion of an object.

4-1 Accelerated Motion

New Science Words

Newton's second law of motion
air resistance
terminal velocity

Objectives

- ▶ **Explain how force, mass, and acceleration are related.**
- ▶ **Compare the rates at which different objects fall.**
- ▶ **Observe the effects of air resistance.**

Newton's Second Law

With Newton's first law, you learned how to describe the motion of a speeding sports car or a stationary hockey puck. You also learned that the motion of an object will not change unless a net force acts on it, such as the brakes of a car or a fast-moving hockey stick. As you read on in this chapter, you will find out some of the reasons why things move the ways they do.

Suppose you are a passenger in a car stalled on the tracks at a railroad crossing. It is threatening to rain at any minute, and you want to push the car off the tracks before you get soaked. Would you rather be riding in a compact car or a stretch limousine? Would you rather

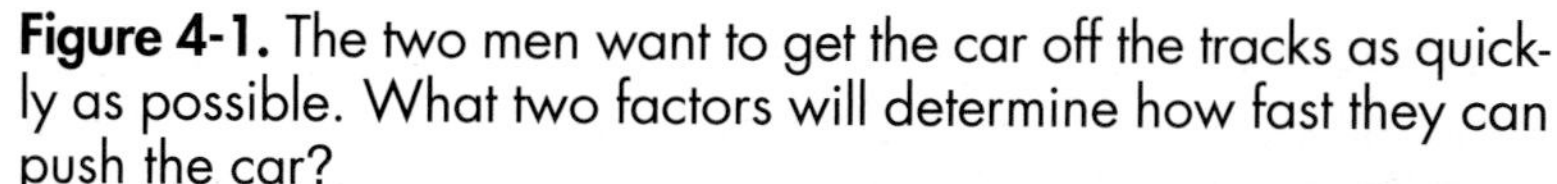

Figure 4-1. The two men want to get the car off the tracks as quickly as possible. What two factors will determine how fast they can push the car?

the driver be about as strong as you or a weightlifting champion?

From experience, you know that mass, force, and acceleration are somehow related. You may not realize it, but in arriving at your answers to the questions, you used Newton's second law of motion. **Newton's second law of motion** says that a net force acting on an object causes the object to accelerate in the direction of the force. The acceleration of the object is affected by two factors—the size of the force and the mass of the object. The larger the force acting on an object, the greater the acceleration of the object. The larger an object's mass, the greater the force needed to give it the same acceleration.

Think about the stalled car on the tracks. To get the greatest acceleration across the tracks, you'd want to push the smallest mass while exerting the greatest force. So, you'd want to push the compact car, and you'd want the weightlifter to help you exert the strongest force.

Newton's second law can be expressed in equation form as:

$$\textit{force} = \textit{mass} \times \textit{acceleration}$$
$$F = ma$$

Mass is expressed in kilograms and acceleration in m/s^2. Thus, force is expressed in $kg \cdot m/s^2$.

You learned in Chapter 3 that one newton is the standard unit for measuring force. The equation for force can be used to define a newton. A newton is the amount of force needed to give a sample of matter having a mass of 1 kg an acceleration of 1 m/s^2. In other words, $1\ N = 1\ kg \cdot m/s^2$.

EXAMPLE PROBLEM: Calculating Force

Problem Statement: How much force is needed to accelerate a 70-kg rider and the 200-kg motorcycle the rider is on at 4 m/s^2?

Known Information: mass, $m = 70\ kg + 200\ kg = 270\ kg$
acceleration, $a = 4\ m/s^2$

Strategy Hint: Remember to combine the masses of the rider and motorcycle.

Unknown Information: force (F)

Equation to Use: $F = m \times a$

Solution: $F = m \times a = 270\ kg \times 4\ m/s^2$
$= 1080\ kg \cdot m/s^2 = 1080\ N$

PRACTICE PROBLEMS

Strategy Hint: What units combine to make a newton?

1. It takes a force of 3000 N to accelerate an empty 1000-kg car at 3 m/s^2. If a 160-kg wrestler is inside the car, how much force will be needed to produce the same acceleration?

Strategy Hint: Rearrange the equation.

2. A 63-kg skater pushes off from a wall with a force of 300 N. What is the skater's acceleration?

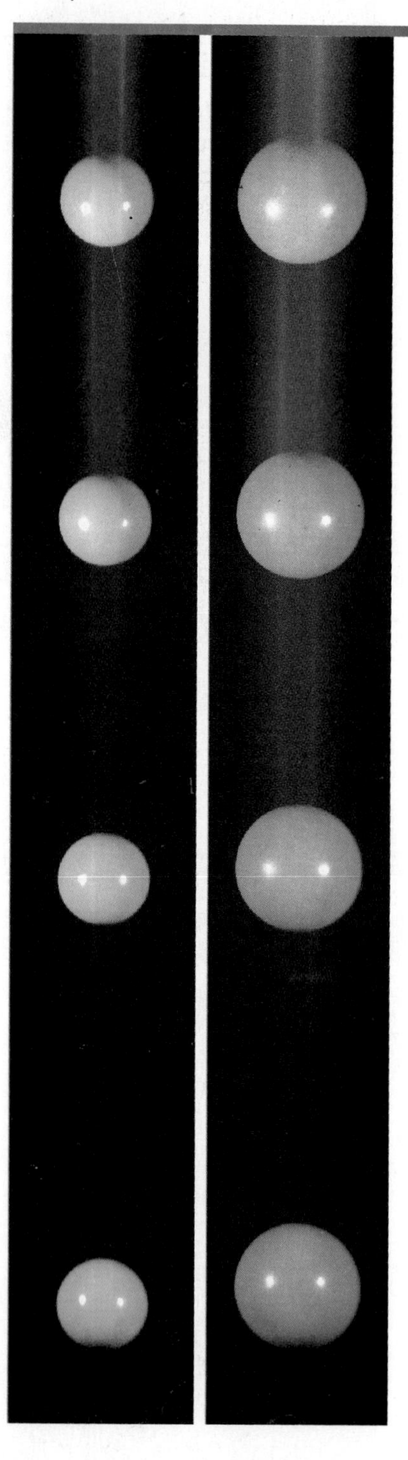

Falling Objects

You may find this hard to believe, but if you dropped a bowling ball and a marble from a bridge at the same time, they'd both splash into the water at almost the same instant. (As you read further, you'll find out why they don't hit the water at exactly the same instant.) As the two objects fall through the air, their accelerations would be just about the same. Would you have expected the bowling ball to hit the water sooner because it has more mass? Think about that. It's true that the force of gravity would be greater on the bowling ball because of its larger mass. But the larger mass also gives the bowling ball more inertia, so more force is needed to change its velocity. The marble has a much smaller mass than the bowling ball, but its inertia also is much less. Figure 4-2 shows the motion of two balls frozen by high-speed photography. The blue ball is more massive than the green one, but you can see that they fall at the same rate.

Near Earth's surface, gravity causes all falling objects to accelerate at a rate of 9.8 m/s^2. Does this number 9.8 seem familiar? When you studied the relationship between mass and weight, you learned that any sample of matter having a mass of one kilogram weighs 9.8 newtons on Earth. Now you'll find out why.

The weight of an object is the force of gravity acting on its mass. Any force can be calculated using the equation $F = m \times a$. Because weight is a force, we can substitute W for F and write $W = m \times a$. If acceleration due to gravity is 9.8 m/s^2, then $W = m \times 9.8\ m/s^2$. So a mass of 1 kg weighs 9.8 kg • m/s^2, or 9.8 newtons. You could calculate your weight in newtons if you knew your mass. For example, a person with a mass of 50 kg would have a weight of 490 newtons.

Figure 4-2. As the photograph shows, the rate of acceleration of a falling body is not affected by the mass of the body.

Acceleration due to gravity (g) is the same for all objects, regardless of mass. This means that if no force other than gravity is present, all samples of matter fall at the same rate—9.8 m/s^2. Think about that for a minute. Does a leaf fall as fast as an acorn? Does a feather fall as fast as a penny?

Suppose you took two identical sheets of paper, crumpled one into a tight ball, and dropped both sheets from a balcony at the same time? What would happen? If your answer is that the crumpled ball of paper would fall faster than the flat sheet of paper, you are correct. But this behavior does not agree with what you've just learned about falling objects near Earth's surface. How can this disagreement be explained?

MINI-Lab

How does mass affect acceleration due to gravity?

With a small toy truck, some masses, and two large rubber bands, you can make a model of the force of gravity. Attach one rubber band to the truck and pull the truck back until the rubber band is fully stretched. Release the truck and let the force of the rubber band accelerate the truck across the table top. Now place masses in the truck to double its mass. Stretch the rubber band the same distance as before and release the truck. What happens to the acceleration of the truck? Double the force by attaching a second rubber band beside the first one. Repeat the procedure. What do the rubber bands represent in this model? Why did you add a second rubber band?

Figure 4-3. Some force other than gravity must affect the flat sheet of paper, causing it to fall more slowly than the crumpled sheet of paper.

Figure 4-4. The Frisbee is designed to use air resistance to help it soar and maneuver as it moves through the air.

Gravity accelerates all samples of matter at the same rate. So, the only explanation for the behavior of the two sheets of paper is that some force is at work in addition to gravity. Anything that moves in Earth's atmosphere is affected by air resistance. **Air resistance** is the force air exerts on a moving object. This force acts in the opposite direction to that in which the object is moving. In the case of a falling object, air resistance pushes up as gravity pulls down.

The amount of air resistance on an object depends on the speed, size, and shape of the object. The larger the

Figure 4-5. The snowflakes (left) and the hailstones (right) are both solid forms of water. Yet, because of differences in shape and size, snowflakes tend to drift and blow through the air, while hailstones fall straight to the ground.

object, the greater the amount of air resistance on it. This is why feathers, leaves, and sheets of paper fall more slowly than acorns, pennies, and crumpled balls of paper. Now think back to the example of the bowling ball and marble dropped from a bridge. Recall that they don't fall at exactly the same rate. Which do you think hits the water first?

Terminal Velocity

As an object falls, air resistance gradually increases until it equals the pull of gravity. When this happens, the two forces are balanced. According to the law of inertia, when the forces acting on an object are balanced, the motion of the object will not change. So, the falling object will stop accelerating. It will continue to fall, but at a constant, final velocity. This **terminal velocity** is the highest velocity reached by a falling object.

Think about all of the things you now know about moving objects. You always knew that a leaf fell more slowly than an acorn. But now you know why. And you will learn more about moving things as you continue reading this chapter.

Figure 4-6. Air resistance acts on the parachute, allowing the parachutist to fall at a terminal velocity that is slow enough to allow a safe landing.

SECTION REVIEW

1. A weightlifter raises a 440-kg barbell with an acceleration of 2 m/s^2. How much force does the weightlifter exert on the barbell?
2. A flower pot falls from the balcony of a 12th-floor apartment. It smashes on the ground 2.5 s later. How fast is it moving just before it hits?
3. **Apply:** Use what you have learned about falling objects, air resistance, and terminal velocity to explain why a person can parachute safely to Earth from a high-flying airplane.

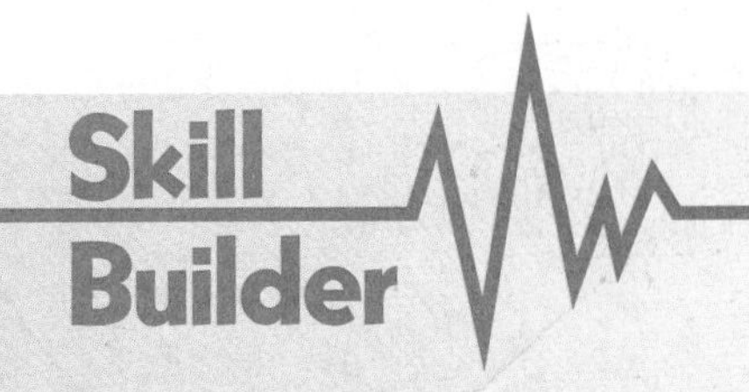

Comparing and Contrasting

Find the masses of an uninflated balloon and a balloon filled with air. Drop the two balloons from the same height at the same time and compare and contrast the rates at which they fall. If you need help, refer to Comparing and Contrasting in the **Skill Handbook** on page 679.

4-2 Projectile and Circular Motion

New Science Words

projectile
centripetal acceleration
centripetal force

Objectives

- Explain why things that are thrown or shot follow a curved path.
- Compare motion in a straight line with circular motion.
- Define weightlessness.

Figure 4-7. The fireworks in this photograph illustrate the curved path followed by a projectile.

Projectiles

Have you noticed anything about the moving objects described in this unit so far? Nearly all have been moving in a straight line. But that's not the only kind of motion you know about. Skateboarders wheel around in circles, cars go around hairpin curves, and rockets shoot into the air and curve back to Earth. How do the laws of motion account for these kinds of motion?

If you've ever played darts, thrown a ball, or shot an arrow from a bow, you have probably noticed that the dart, ball, or arrow didn't travel in a straight line. It started off straight, but then curved downward. That's why dart players and archers learn to aim above the targets they're trying to hit.

Anything that's thrown or shot through the air is called a **projectile.** Because of Earth's gravitational pull and their own inertia, projectiles follow a curved path.

Here's why. When you throw a ball, the force from your hand makes the ball move forward. Suppose that it gives the ball *horizontal motion,* that is, motion parallel to Earth's surface. Once you let go of the ball, no other force moves it forward, so it doesn't accelerate in the horizontal direction. Its horizontal velocity is constant.

When you let go of the ball, something else happens as well. Gravity starts pulling it downward, giving it *vertical motion,* or motion perpendicular to Earth's surface. Gravity makes the ball accelerate downward. Now the ball has constant horizontal velocity, but increasing vertical

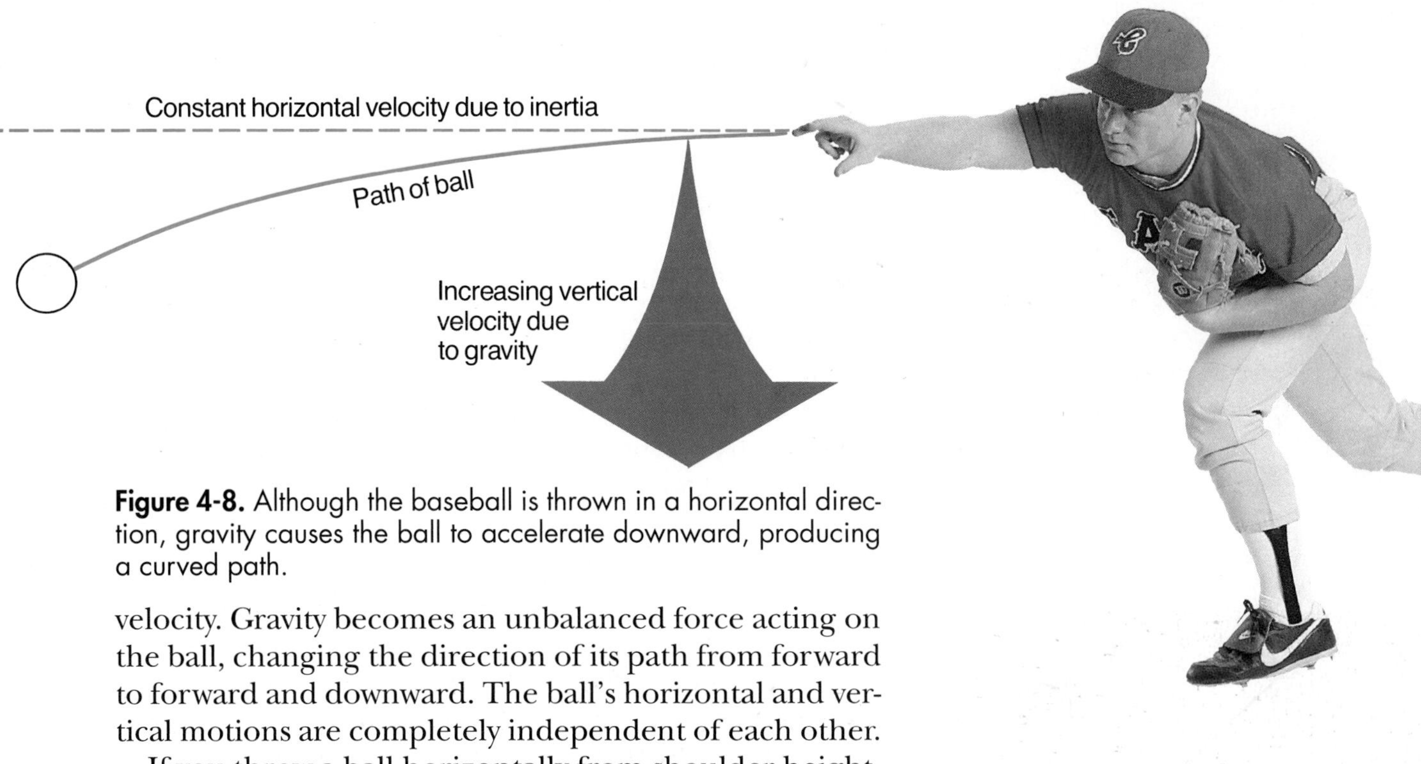

Figure 4-8. Although the baseball is thrown in a horizontal direction, gravity causes the ball to accelerate downward, producing a curved path.

velocity. Gravity becomes an unbalanced force acting on the ball, changing the direction of its path from forward to forward and downward. The ball's horizontal and vertical motions are completely independent of each other.

If you throw a ball horizontally from shoulder height, will it take longer to hit the ground than a ball you simply drop from the same height? Surprisingly, the answer is no. Both will hit the ground at the same time. If you have a hard time believing this, Figure 4-9 may help. The two balls have the same acceleration due to gravity, 9.8 m/s^2 downward.

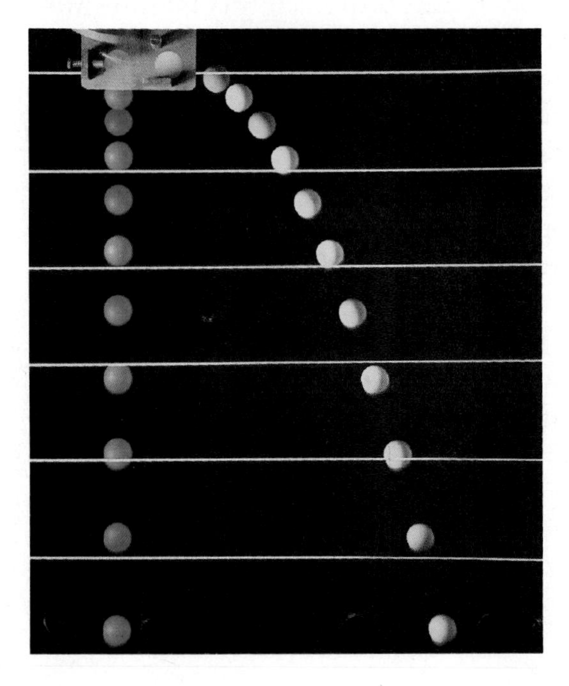

Figure 4-9. The two balls in the photograph were released at the same time. Although one ball has horizontal velocity, gravity causes both balls to accelerate downward at the same rate.

Moving in Circles

Recall that acceleration is a change in velocity. That change may be a change in speed, a change in direction, or both. Now picture a bicycle moving at a constant speed along the westbound straightaway of an oval track. Because its speed is constant in a straight line, the bicycle is not accelerating. However, when the bicycle enters a curve, even if its speed does not change it is accelerating, because its direction is changing.

While the bicycle was moving on the straightaway, its velocity was toward the west. As it entered the curve, it accelerated because the direction of its velocity changed. The change in the direction of the velocity was toward the center of the curve. Acceleration toward the center of a curved or circular path is called **centripetal** (sen TRIHP uh tuhl) **acceleration.** The word *centripetal* means "toward the center."

Figure 4-10. The chains exert centripetal force on the swings, causing the swings to accelerate toward the center of the ride.

In order for the bicycle to be accelerating, some unbalanced force must be acting on it in a direction toward the center of the curve. That force is a centripetal force. **Centripetal force** is a force that causes a moving object to move in a curved or circular path.

When a car rounds a sharp curve on a highway, the centripetal force is the friction between the tires and the road surface. But if the road is icy or wet, and the tires lose their grip, the centripetal force may not be enough to overcome the car's inertia. Then, the car would not follow the curve in the road, but would shoot off in a straight line in the direction it was traveling from the spot where it lost traction.

EcoTip

The faster a car goes, the faster it burns fuel. Every day in the United States, cars traveling over the speed limit waste hundreds of liters of gasoline. Encourage drivers you ride with to obey speed limits.

Weightlessness in Orbit

Maybe you've seen pictures of astronauts floating inside the space shuttle, with various pieces of equipment suspended in midair beside them. The astronauts and their belongings are experiencing weightlessness.

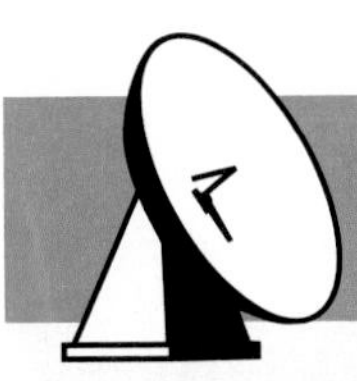

TECHNOLOGY

Scary Physics

A roller coaster applies the laws of motion in an effort to be the scariest ride in the park. A ride begins when a chain drags the cars to the top of the first hill. Once there, the cars have gravitational potential energy. Once the cars are released, acceleration increases until all of the cars are headed downward.

The debate on which seat is the scariest continues to rage, and the answer is, "that depends." As the cars descend, their speed increases. The rear car starts down the slope at a much greater speed than the front car, thus giving the passengers the sense of being hurled over the edge. At the bottom of the hill, it is a different story. When the change in direction from down to up occurs, the front car will be going fastest and its passengers will experience the greater forces. As the cars pop over the top of the hill, the passengers in the rear car may experience a considerable force, resulting in the sensation of being thrown free.

As ride technology improves, roller coasters get larger and faster. The Magnum XL 200 at Cedar Point in Sandusky, Ohio, has a first hill 201 feet high, reaches a speed of 112 km/h, and covers 5106 feet of track in two-and-one-half minutes.

Think Critically: Describe the roller coaster design that would result in the greatest sensations for the passengers.

But to be truly weightless, the astronauts would have to be free from the effects of gravity. Orbiting 400 km above Earth, the shuttle and everything inside it still respond to those effects. In fact, gravity keeps the shuttle in orbit.

So what does it really mean to say that something is weightless in orbit? Think about how the weight of an object is measured. When you place an object on a scale, gravity causes the object to push down on the scale. In turn, the scale "pushes back" on the object with the same force. The dial on the scale measures the amount of upward force needed to offset gravity.

Did You Know?

The pull of gravity differs from place to place on Earth. In the U.S., gravity is greatest in Minot, North Dakota, and smallest in Key West, Florida.

Figure 4-11. The space shuttle and everything in it are in free-fall around Earth, thus producing apparent weightlessness.

Now suppose that the scale is falling, being pulled downward by gravity at the same rate as the object being weighed. The scale couldn't push back on the object, so its dial would read zero. The object would seem to be weightless. This is what is happening in a space shuttle orbiting Earth. The shuttle and everything in it, including the astronauts, are all "falling" toward Earth at exactly the same rate of acceleration. When an object is influenced only by gravity, it is said to be falling freely, or in free-fall. An orbiting space shuttle and all its contents are in free-fall around Earth.

What is free-fall?

SECTION REVIEW

1. Use a diagram similar to Figure 4-8 to show why a dart player has to aim above the target to hit the bull's-eye. In your diagram, show the forces acting on the dart, the dart's path, and the two kinds of motion involved.
2. A child is swinging a yo-yo in a circle around her head. What provides the force to keep the yo-yo going in a circle? What is the force called? What happens if the string breaks?
3. **Apply:** Does the mass of an astronaut change when he or she becomes weightless in orbit?

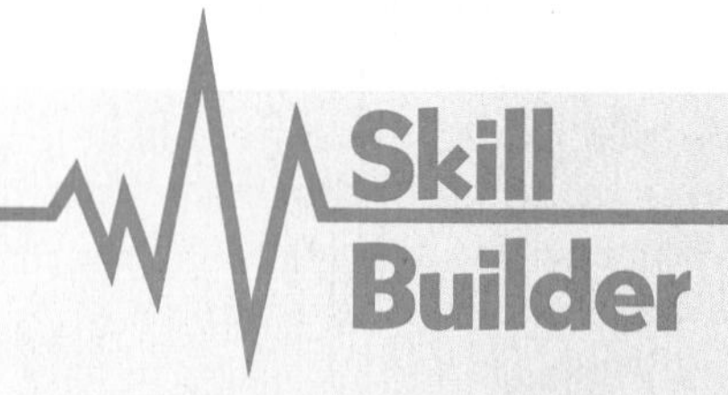

Making and Using Tables

Make a table showing important characteristics of three kinds of motion mentioned in this section: projectile motion, circular motion, and free-fall. Table headings should include: Kind of Motion, Shape of Path, and Laws or Forces Involved. You may add other headings. If you need help, refer to Making and Using Tables in the **Skill Handbook** on page 686.

ACTIVITY 4-1
Trajectories

Problem: *What pathway will a thrown object follow?*

Materials
- stick or dowel, slightly more than 2 m long
- meterstick
- string or thread
- corks (10)
- thumbtacks (10)
- felt-tip pen

Procedure
1. Using a felt-tip pen, place marks at 20-cm intervals along the length of the stick as shown. Number the marks 0 through 10.
2. Obtain 10 corks. Use thumbtacks to attach a length of string to each cork.
3. Tie one cork to each numbered position along the stick. For each position, adjust the length of the string to match the length shown on the drawing.
4. While the stick is held in a horizontal position, try to throw a small object, such as an eraser, exactly 2 meters along the length of the stick. Observe the path followed by the object.

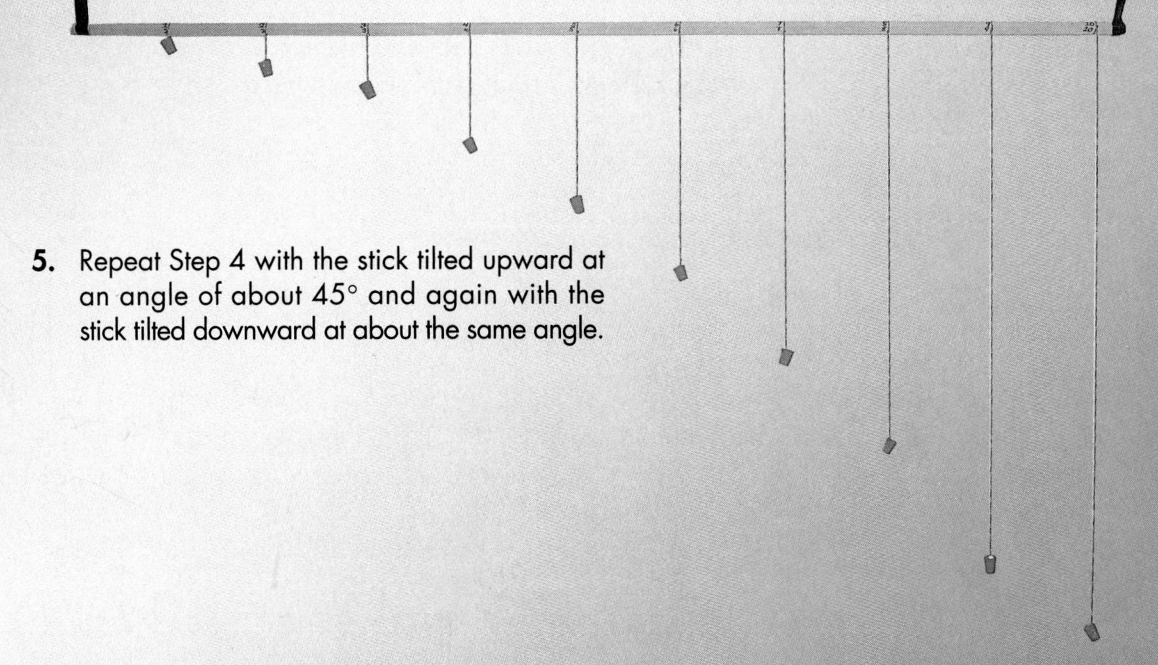

5. Repeat Step 4 with the stick tilted upward at an angle of about 45° and again with the stick tilted downward at about the same angle.

Analyze
1. Describe the path followed by the thrown object. What forces acted on the object to cause it to follow this path?
2. Describe the path followed by the object when it was thrown along the length of the stick when it was tilted upward and when it was tilted downward.
3. In this model, the distance between each string represents the speed of the moving object. What do the lengths of the strings represent?

Conclude and Apply
4. How could you use this model to determine the upward angle at which a thrown object would travel the greatest distance?
5. If you are aiming a rifle at a target, where would you aim in order to hit the bull's-eye? How would your aim at a distance of 100 meters be different from your aim at a distance of 50 meters? 200 meters?

4-3 To Boldly—and Safely—Go

New Science Words

isometric exercises

Objectives

- Analyze the advantages and disadvantages of exposing astronauts to weightlessness.
- Draw conclusions about the safety of space travel.

Effects of Weightlessness

If you could be the first person to set foot on Mars, would you go? What if you knew the trip might be bad for your health? It takes about nine months for a spacecraft to travel from Earth to Mars. No one is sure how astronauts' bodies might react to such long exposure to weightlessness.

When Russian cosmonauts experienced weightlessness for more than 200 consecutive days, they had health problems. Their experiences and other experiments show that long periods of weightlessness weaken the heart and bones. After being in space for nine months, an astronaut might be too weak to perform the delicate steps involved in landing a spacecraft on Mars.

Some space experts say the problems could be prevented by building artificial gravity into the spacecraft. A special exercise program might help, too. Some exercises, like jogging, wouldn't be as effective on Mars as on Earth. But **isometric exercises,** in which muscles push against other muscles, with or without gravity, could help astronauts stay in shape.

Other space experts argue that it's better not to send people to Mars at all. These experts claim that robots loaded with sensors, instruments, and arms for gathering samples could do the job just as well as humans, if not better.

What are isometric exercises?

But could robots explore the planet as thoroughly as humans? And should humans have to miss out on the adventure?

SECTION REVIEW

1. Why do you think scientists don't know as much as they'd like to know about the effects of prolonged weightlessness on astronauts?
2. Do space mission planners need to consider the effects of weightlessness on anything besides astronauts? Explain your answer.

You Decide!

You are a space agency official planning a mission to Mars. You can send instruments to be operated by astronauts or robots. What would be your choice, and how would you make the decision? Now suppose you're an astronaut. Would you volunteer for the Mars mission?

4-4 Action and Reaction

New Science Words

Newton's third law of motion
momentum
law of conservation of momentum

Objectives

- Analyze action and reaction forces.
- Calculate momentum.
- Explain conservation of momentum.

Newton's Third Law

A boy blows up a balloon for his sister. He lets the balloon go and it darts away on a zigzag course, making her giggle. A young soldier, firing a rifle for the first time, is startled by the backward "kick" of the rifle. A man leaping from a boat toward land falls in the water when the boat scoots away from the shore. As different as these examples of motion may seem, they all illustrate one point: forces always act in pairs, called action-reaction pairs.

State Newton's third law of motion.

Newton's third law of motion describes action-reaction pairs this way: When one object exerts a force on a second object, the second one exerts a force on the first that is equal in size and opposite in direction. A less formal way of saying the same thing is "to every action there is an equal and opposite reaction."

Let's look at the examples of action-reaction pairs described earlier. The balloon exerts force on the air inside, causing the air to rush out of the neck of the balloon. The air exerts an equal force on the balloon, but in the opposite direction. This reaction force causes the balloon to dart away from the escaping air.

When a soldier fires a rifle, the hot gases from the exploding gunpowder exert a force on the bullet, sending it speeding out of the barrel of the gun. The bullet exerts an equal and opposite force on the trapped gases, causing the rifle to "kick" backward.

In the third example, when the man leaps from the boat, the boat exerts a force on his feet, moving him forward. His feet exert an equal and opposite force on the boat, sending it backward.

St. Patrick School
840 N. Calumet Road
Chesterton, IN 46304

Figure 4-12. As the swimmer's hands and feet push against the water, the water pushes back, moving the swimmer forward.

Newton's third law can be used to explain how a swimmer moves through the water. With each stroke, the swimmer's arm exerts a force on the water. The water pushes back on the swimmer with an equal force in the opposite direction. But if the forces are equal, how can the swimmer move forward? It's possible because the forces are acting on different things. The "action" force acts on the water; the "reaction" force acts on the swimmer. The swimmer, having less mass than the pool full of water, accelerates more than the water.

A very important point to keep in mind when dealing with Newton's third law is that action-reaction forces always act on *different* objects. Thus, even though the forces may be equal, they are not balanced. In the case of the swimmer, one force acts on the swimmer. Thus, a net force, or unbalanced force, acts on the swimmer, and a change in motion can take place.

Compare the example of the swimmer with that of two teams in a tug-of-war contest. Both teams exert force on the ground with their feet. This force is transferred to the rope. Thus, all of the forces exerted in the contest act on the *same* object—the rope. So, if both teams exert equal forces in opposite directions, the forces *on the rope* will be balanced, and no change in motion will take place. Only when one team exerts a greater force than

Figure 4-13. The action of passing the basketball forward will propel the player backward.

the other will a change in motion occur. There will be an unbalanced force on the rope, and the rope (and the teams) will move in the direction of the greater force.

Rocket Propulsion

Rockets work on a similar principle to that which causes a balloon to move in one direction when gases escape from the balloon in the opposite direction. In the rocket, the burning of fuel produces hot gases. As these gases expand, they push against the inside of the rocket and escape out the bottom of the rocket. The force of the escaping gases causes a reaction force that moves the rocket in the opposite direction.

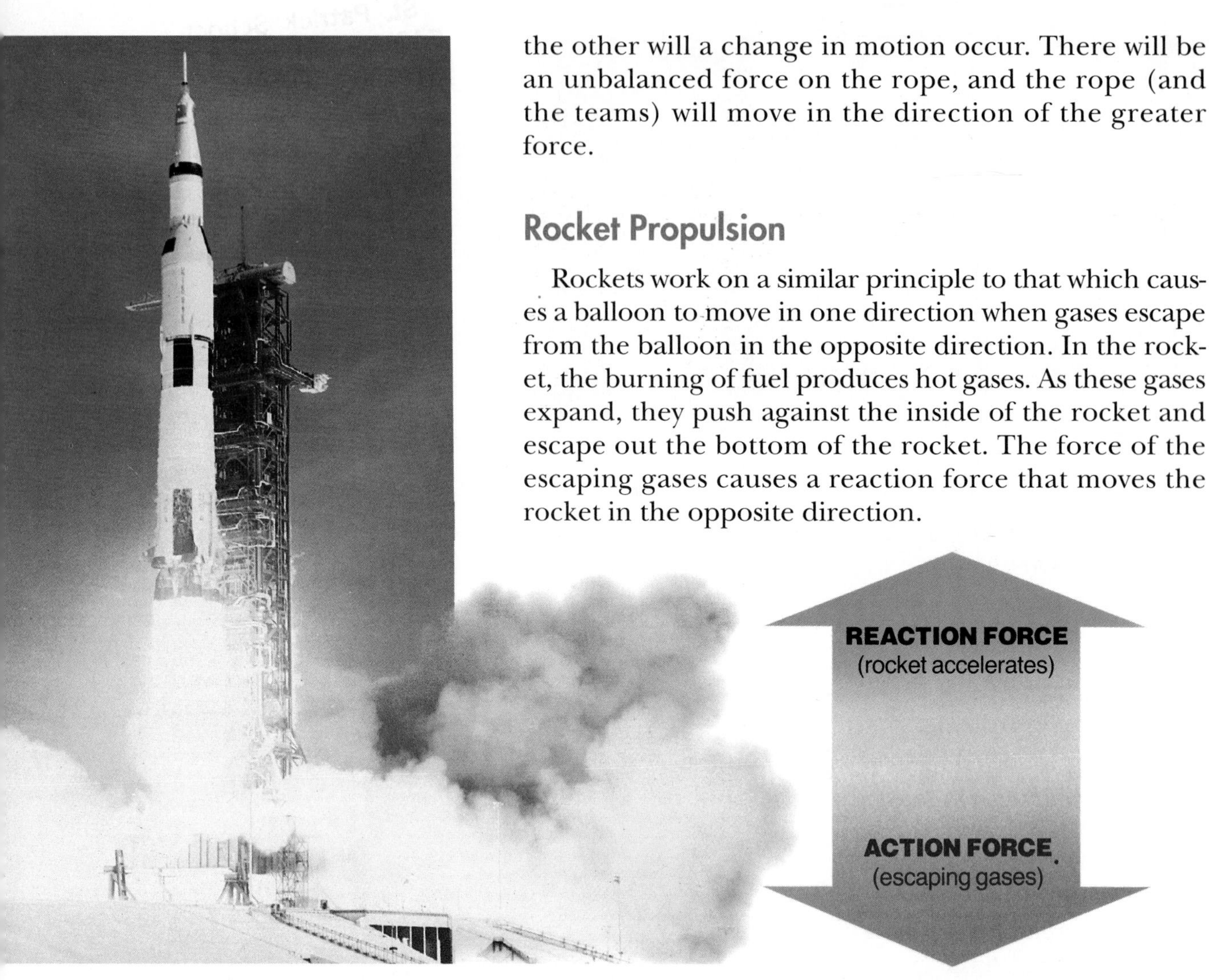

Figure 4-14. The "action force" of the expanding gases rushing out of the rocket results in a "reaction force" being exerted on the rocket, sending the rocket in the opposite direction.

Momentum

If a toy truck rolls toward you, you can easily stop it with your hand. However, such a tactic would not work with a full-sized truck, even if it were moving at the same speed as the toy truck. It takes more force to stop the full-sized truck because it has more momentum (moh MENT um) than the toy truck has. **Momentum** is a property a moving object has due to its mass and velocity. Momentum can be calculated with this equation, in which p represents momentum:

$$momentum = mass \times velocity$$
$$p = m \times v$$

The unit for momentum is kg • m/s. Notice that momentum has a direction, because velocity has a direction.

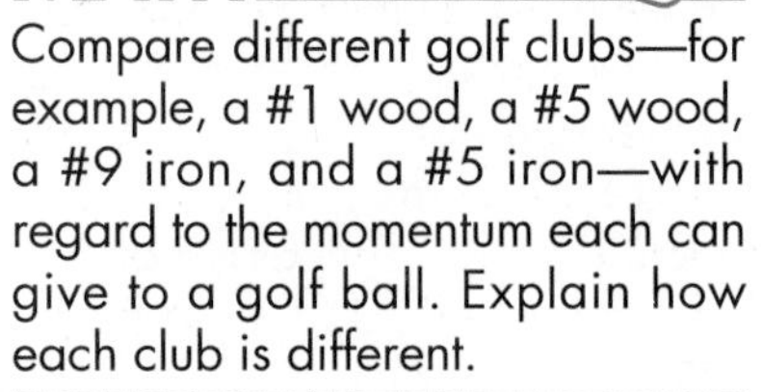

Science and MATH

Compare different golf clubs—for example, a #1 wood, a #5 wood, a #9 iron, and a #5 iron—with regard to the momentum each can give to a golf ball. Explain how each club is different.

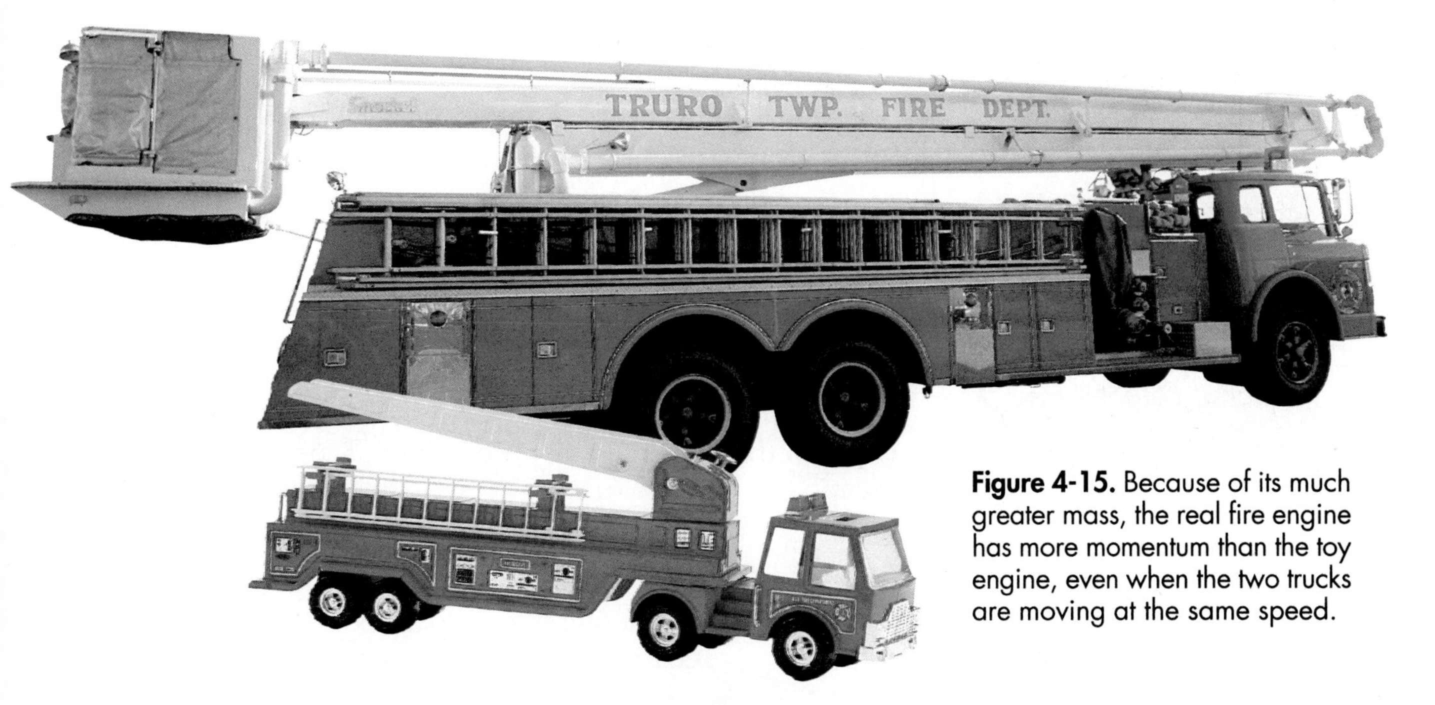

Figure 4-15. Because of its much greater mass, the real fire engine has more momentum than the toy engine, even when the two trucks are moving at the same speed.

The two trucks described on the previous page may have the same velocity, but the full-sized truck has more momentum because of its greater mass. A speeding bullet can have a large momentum because of its high velocity, even though its mass is small. A lumbering elephant may have a low velocity, but because of its large mass it has a large momentum.

The momentum of an object doesn't change unless its mass or velocity, or both, change. But momentum can be transferred from one object to another. Think about what happens when a ball rolling across a pool table hits another ball that is standing still. At first, the rolling ball has momentum, the motionless ball does not. When they collide, the ball that was at rest starts moving. It gains

Figure 4-16. Before the balls collide, the moving ball has all the momentum (left). After the balls collide, all of the balls have momentum (right). The total momentum of the balls is the same in both photographs.

PROBLEM SOLVING

The Icy Challenge

The winter had been very cold, and the ice on the local pond was thick and smooth—just right for ice hockey. One day Stewart and his friends were walking across the pond, carrying their skates and hockey equipment. A few meters from the edge of the pond, Stewart slipped and fell and landed on his back.

After making sure he wasn't hurt, Stewart's friends challenged him to make it to land without turning over or standing up. Stewart tried pushing against the ice with his hands and feet, but the ice was so slippery that he didn't move. Then he had a brainstorm. He took one of his skates and threw it as hard as he could toward the center of the pond. Stewart continued to throw pieces of his hockey equipment toward the center of the pond until he found himself at the pond's edge.

Think Critically: Describe the forces involved in the throwing of the equipment. Explain what motions took place and why they occurred.

EcoTip

Get in motion! Weed gardens by hand or by hoe instead of using harmful chemicals. You and your garden will benefit from the exercise.

momentum. The first ball slows down and loses momentum. If you were to measure the total momentum of the two balls before and after the collision, it would be the same. The momentum the second ball gains is equal to the momentum that the first ball loses. Total momentum is conserved—it doesn't change.

The **law of conservation of momentum** states that the total amount of momentum of a group of objects does not change unless outside forces act on the objects. After the collision, the balls on the pool table eventually slow down and stop rolling. What outside force makes that happen?

With Newton's third law and conservation of momentum, you can explain all sorts of motion that may seem complicated at first. Bouncing on a trampoline, knocking down bowling pins with a ball, and tackling a football player are a few examples. Think about how you would explain these and other examples of motion that you think of.

SECTION REVIEW

1. After rowing to within a few feet of shore, a boater stands up in the boat and tries to jump to land. Instead, he lands in the water. Explain why he took the unexpected dip.
2. Compare the momentum of a 50-kg dolphin swimming 16.4 m/s with the momentum of a 6300-kg elephant walking 0.11 m/s.
3. **Apply:** Some choreographers assign larger dancers to parts with slow, graceful movements, saving the parts that require quick starts and stops for smaller dancers. Does this plan make sense?

Concept Mapping

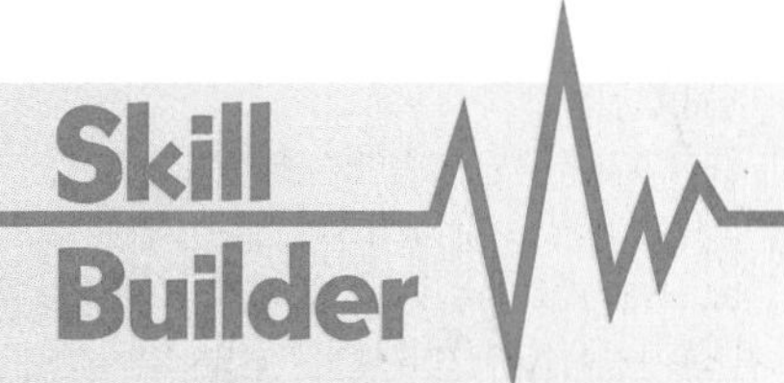

Use the words provided to make two events chains. The chains should show what happens to two pool balls when the rolling ball (Ball One) hits the resting ball (Ball Two). Phrases to use: *gains momentum; rests; rolls more slowly or stops; hits Ball Two; rolls; loses momentum; is hit by Ball One; starts rolling*. If you need help, refer to Concept Mapping in the **Skill Handbook** on pages 684 and 685.

ACTIVITY 4-2
Momentum

Problem: *How are mass and momentum related?*

Materials
- dynamics carts (2)
- long rubber band
- building bricks (2)
- meterstick
- masking tape

Procedure
1. Prepare a data table like the one shown.
2. Attach a long rubber band to the two dynamics carts. Move the carts apart until the rubber band is taut but not stretched.
3. Place a piece of tape on the table to mark the halfway point between the two carts. Lay the meterstick on the table with the 50-cm mark beside the piece of tape.
4. Pull the carts apart until the ends of the rubber band line up with the ends of the meterstick.
5. Release both carts at the same time so that they gain the same momentum. Observe and record the point along the meterstick where the carts collide. Also observe where the carts stop after the collision.
6. Place a brick on cart A and repeat Steps 4 and 5.
7. Add a second brick to cart A and repeat Steps 4 and 5.

Analyze
1. How can you tell from the data which cart was moving faster?
2. How can both carts have the same momentum if they are traveling at different speeds?
3. How does the addition of mass to one cart affect the location of the collision point? How does it affect what happens to the carts after the collision?

Conclude and Apply
4. If one cart were released slightly before the other, how would the momentum of the two carts be affected?
5. If one cart has more momentum than the other, what happens when the carts collide?
6. Suppose momentum is said to be negative (–) in one direction and positive in the opposite direction. If two carts having the same amount of momentum are traveling in opposite directions, what is the total momentum of the two-cart system?

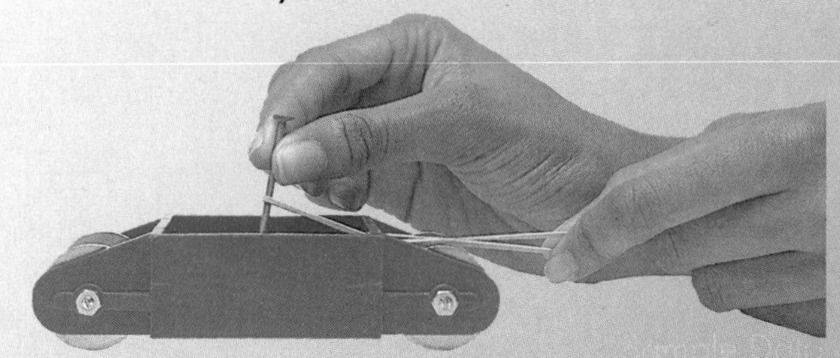

Data and Observations

	Collision Point	Distance Traveled		Location after Collision	
		Cart A	Cart B	Cart A	Cart B
Trial 1					
Trial 2					
Trial 3					

CHAPTER

REVIEW

SUMMARY

4-1: Accelerated Motion

1. According to Newton's second law, a net force acting on an object causes the object to accelerate in the direction of the force. The size of the acceleration depends on the strength of the force and the mass of the object.

2. Near Earth's surface, gravity causes falling objects to accelerate at a rate of 9.8 m/s^2. All objects accelerate at this rate, regardless of mass.

3. Air resistance acts in the opposite direction to that in which the object is moving.

4-2: Projectile and Circular Motion

1. Objects that are thrown or shot through the air are called projectiles. All projectiles have both horizontal and vertical velocities. The horizontal velocity is constant; the vertical velocity, which is affected by gravity, is accelerated.

2. When an object moves along a circular path, it is accelerated toward the center of the circle.

3. When an object is influenced only by gravity, it is said to be in free-fall. Objects in free-fall are weightless. To be truly weightless, an object would have to be free from gravity.

4-3: Science and Society: To Boldly—and Safely—Go

1. Health problems have resulted from long exposure to weightlessness. Experimentation has shown that some of the problems can be prevented.

2. Space experts argue whether or not robots could explore planets as well as humans without endangering astronauts.

4-4: Action and Reaction

1. Forces always act in pairs. The forces in an action-reaction pair are always equal in size and opposite in direction.

2. All moving objects have momentum. The momentum of an object is the product of its mass and velocity.

3. The total momentum of a set of objects is conserved unless a net force acts on the set.

KEY SCIENCE WORDS

a. **air resistance**
b. **centripetal acceleration**
c. **centripetal force**
d. **isometric exercises**
e. **law of conservation of momentum**
f. **momentum**
g. **Newton's second law of motion**
h. **Newton's third law of motion**
i. **projectile**
j. **terminal velocity**

UNDERSTANDING VOCABULARY

Match each phrase with the correct term from the list of Key Science Words.

1. deals with action-reaction forces
2. force that opposes the motion of a falling object near Earth's surface.
3. an object that is thrown through the air
4. acceleration toward the center of a circle
5. product of an object's mass and velocity
6. describes the effect of a net force on an object
7. exerting muscles against muscles
8. causes circular motion
9. achieved when acceleration due to gravity is balanced by air resistance
10. unchanging nature of the total momentum of a set of objects

CHAPTER REVIEW

CHECKING CONCEPTS

Choose the word or phrase that completes the sentence or answers the question.

1. A net force acting on a moving object causes the object to ______.
a. fall **c.** stop
b. accelerate **d.** curve

2. ______ is the effect of gravity on an object.
a. Mass **c.** Centripetal force
b. Momentum **d.** Weight

3. Which of these opposes acceleration due to gravity?
a. momentum **c.** reaction force
b. air resistance **d.** terminal velocity

4. According to Newton's second law, ______ equals mass times acceleration.
a. gravity **c.** force
b. momentum **d.** weight

5. What force causes a leaf to fall more slowly than a penny?
a. gravity **c.** inertia
b. momentum **d.** air resistance

6. Which illustrates Newton's third law?
a. projectile motion **c.** rocket propulsion
b. circular motion **d.** centripetal force

7. The ______ velocity of a projectile is considered to be constant.
a. horizontal **c.** accelerated
b. circular **d.** vertical

8. An object in free-fall is ______.
a. moving horizontally **c.** motionless
b. moving vertically **d.** weightless

9. ______ is reached when air resistance and acceleration due to gravity are equal.
a. Negative acceleration
b. Terminal velocity
c. Centripetal acceleration
d. Weightlessness

10. Which of the following does not affect the amount of air resistance that acts on an object?
a. mass **c.** shape
b. size **d.** speed

UNDERSTANDING CONCEPTS

Complete each sentence.

11. ______ force causes a moving object to move in a curved or circular path.

12. The vertical acceleration of a projectile is caused by ______.

13. The kick of a rifle illustrates Newton's ______ law.

14. ______ is a property a moving object has due to its mass and velocity.

15. In ______ exercises, muscles push against other muscles.

THINK AND WRITE CRITICALLY

16. On Earth, why does an object of large mass weigh more than an object of smaller mass?

17. Explain why gravity does not cause a falling object of large mass to accelerate at a faster rate than a falling object of smaller mass.

18. If the forces in an action-reaction pair are equal in size and opposite in direction, why aren't they balanced forces?

19. A spaceship orbiting Earth is held in its orbit by Earth's gravity. Yet, astronauts in the spaceship are said to be weightless. Explain.

20. Explain why a marble moves in a straight line as it rolls across the table, but follows a curved path once it rolls off the table.

APPLY

21. What force is exerted by a 1000-kg car accelerating at a rate of 50 m/s^2?
22. The motion of a 12-kg object is opposed by a 30-N force of friction. At what rate does friction slow the object down?
23. You are asked to design a winding mountain road. What force must you try to increase in designing this road? How might you do this?
24. A 5-kg object with a velocity of 6 m/s strikes the motionless 10-kg ball. The object stops moving as a result of the collision. What is the velocity of the ball after the collision?
25. The moon has no atmosphere and its gravity is about one-sixth as strong as that of Earth. Considering these factors, how would the motions of objects near the moon be different than the same motions near Earth?

MORE SKILL BUILDERS

If you need help, refer to the Skill Handbook.

1. **Interpreting Data:** The table contains data about four objects dropped to the ground from the same height at the same time.

Object	A	B	C	D
Mass	5.0 g	5.0 g	30.0 g	35.0 g
Time of Fall	2.0 s	1.0 s	0.5 s	1.5 s

   a. Which object falls fastest? slowest?
   b. On which object is the force of gravity greatest?
   c. Is air resistance stronger on A or B?
   d. Which object is probably largest? Explain your reasoning.

2. **Observing and Inferring:** A girl weighing 360 N gets on a motionless elevator at the ground floor. She steps onto a scale and remains on the scale while the elevator slowly accelerates up to the 120th floor. During that time, the readings on the scale range from a high of 365 N to a low of 355 N. Infer what the reading was on the ground floor, on the way up, stopping, and stopped on the 120th floor. Why do these readings change?
3. **Recognizing Cause and Effect:** When using a high-pressure hose, why is it necessary for firefighters to grip the hose strongly and plant their feet firmly?
4. **Making and Using Graphs:** Construct a time-distance graph of the following data for a ball thrown into the air at an angle to the ground.

Height	0	25	40	45	40	25	0
Time	0	1	2	3	4	5	6

   Use the graph to answer the following:
   a. Does the ball accelerate vertically? How do you know?
   b. When is the ball's vertical velocity zero?
   c. If the ball has a horizontal velocity of 40 m/s, how far will it travel before it hits the ground?

PROJECTS

1. Make a poster diagram of a rocket engine showing how it works. If possible, build a model rocket. Share the results of the project with your classmates. Use Newton's third law to explain why a rocket lifts off.
2. Research the positive and negative aspects of prolonged space flight. Write an essay stating your position on this topic. Read your essay aloud and have a class debate.

CHAPTER 5 Energy

How many ways do you use your own energy every day? Do some kinds of work take more effort than others? Is all exertion work?

FIND OUT!

Do this activity to get started thinking about energy and work.

Standing, hold your arms out in front of you at waist level, with your hands together, palms up. Have a classmate stack two books on your hands. Raise the books to about shoulder level, then lower them. Now try raising them overhead. Are you working harder than you did when you raised them to shoulder level? Lower the books again. Have your classmate put two more books on the pile, so you're holding four books. Try to raise them to shoulder level. Are you using more force than when you were holding only two books?

Hold the four books at shoulder level until your arms get tired. Are you exerting force? Do you think you're doing work?

Now fill a box of books and try pushing it along the floor. Can you push it farther if a classmate helps?

Gearing Up

Previewing the Chapter

Use this outline to help you focus on important ideas in this chapter.

Section 5-1 Energy and Work
- Kinetic and Potential Energy
- Work
- Conservation of Energy

Section 5-2 Temperature and Heat
- Temperature
- Thermal Energy
- Heat

Section 5-3 Science and Society
Energy from the Oceans and Earth
- Exploring New Energy Resources

Section 5-4 Measuring Thermal Energy
- Specific Heat
- Using Specific Heat

Previewing Science Skills

- In the **Skill Builders**, you will compare and contrast, make a concept map, and interpret data.
- In the **Activities**, you will measure in SI, observe and infer, collect and interpret data, and hypothesize.
- In the **MINI-Lab**, you will measure in SI, observe and infer, and hypothesize.

What's next?

You have seen that sometimes things move when you exert force, sometimes they don't. Now find out why this is so. As you move through this chapter, you will learn what energy is and how it's related to work. You will learn to recognize when work is done and when it isn't. And, finally, you will find out some things about heat and temperature that may surprise you, especially if you've always thought they meant the same thing.

5-1 Energy and Work

New Science Words

energy
kinetic energy
potential energy
work
mechanical energy
law of conservation of energy

Objectives

- Distinguish between kinetic and potential energy.
- Recognize that energy can change from one form to another with no loss of energy.
- Compare the scientific meaning of work with its everyday meaning.

Kinetic and Potential Energy

Have you seen any examples of energy in action today? Unless you stayed in bed all day with the covers over your head, the answer to the question is "yes." Just about everything you see or do involves energy.

Energy is a bit mysterious. You can't feel it or smell it. In most cases, you can't even see it. Light is one form of energy you can see. Light doesn't seem to do much, but without it, you wouldn't be able to see anything else. You can't see electricity, but you can see its effects in a glowing light bulb and you can feel its effects in the coils of a toaster. You can't see the energy in milk, but you can see and feel its effects when your muscles move.

Figure 5-1. A healthful diet, such as the well-balanced breakfast shown here, provides the body with "fuel." Energy stored in food is converted to energy that the body can use.

Scientists have a problem defining energy, because they don't know exactly what it is. However, they can measure it. The basic unit of energy is the joule (JEWL), named for British scientist James Prescott Joule. You'll learn more about this unit later in this chapter.

Traditionally, energy has been defined as the ability to do work—to cause something to move. But this definition doesn't go far enough. As all of the examples above show, energy involves change. This close association with change offers a more precise and useful definition: **Energy** is the ability to cause change. Any sample of matter has energy if it can produce a change in itself or in its surroundings. Energy comes in many forms. Some of these forms include radiant, electrical, chemical, thermal, and nuclear energy.

Usually when you think of energy, you think of action—of some motion taking place. Motion-related energy is called kinetic energy. **Kinetic energy** is energy in the form of motion. A spinning motorcycle wheel, a leaping ballet dancer, and a flying Frisbee all have kinetic energy. How much? That depends on the mass and velocity of the moving object.

The greater the mass of a moving object, the more kinetic energy it has. Similarly, the greater its velocity, the more kinetic energy it has. A truck traveling at 100 km/h has more kinetic energy than a motorcycle traveling at the same speed. However, the motorcycle has more kinetic energy than an identical motorcycle moving at 80 km/h.

Energy doesn't have to involve motion. Even motionless, any sample of matter may have stored energy that gives it the potential to cause change if certain conditions are met. **Potential energy** is stored energy. The amount of potential energy a sample of matter has depends on its position or condition.

A flowerpot sitting on a second-floor windowsill has potential energy due to its position. If something knocks it off the windowsill, gravity will cause it to fall toward the ground. As it falls, its potential energy will change to kinetic energy.

Figure 5-2. This motorcycle is converting energy stored in gasoline into kinetic energy.

Figure 5-3. The kinetic energy of each vehicle is different because kinetic energy depends on mass and velocity.

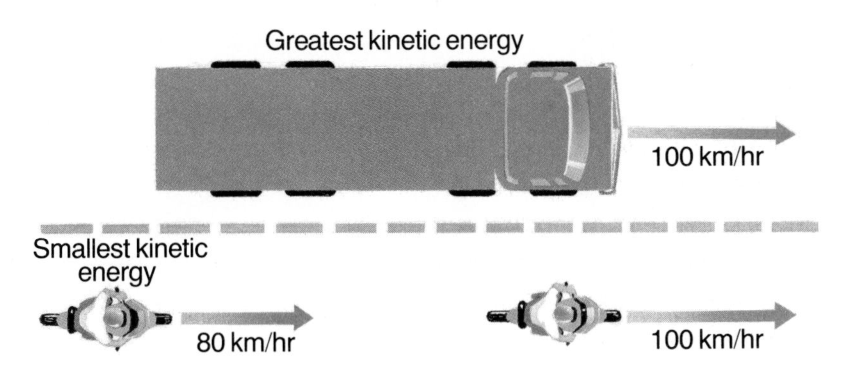

Potential energy due to height above Earth's surface is sometimes called gravitational potential energy. The greater the height, the greater the potential energy. A flowerpot sitting on a fifth-floor windowsill has more potential energy than one sitting on a lower windowsill.

Think of the spring in a wind-up toy. The tension in the spring is its condition. As the spring is wound, it gains potential energy. When the spring is released, the spring unwinds and makes the toy move. The potential energy of the spring is changed to kinetic energy of the toy.

The energy stored in foods, fuels, and dry cells are examples of chemical potential energy. These and other forms of potential energy will be discussed in later chapters of this book.

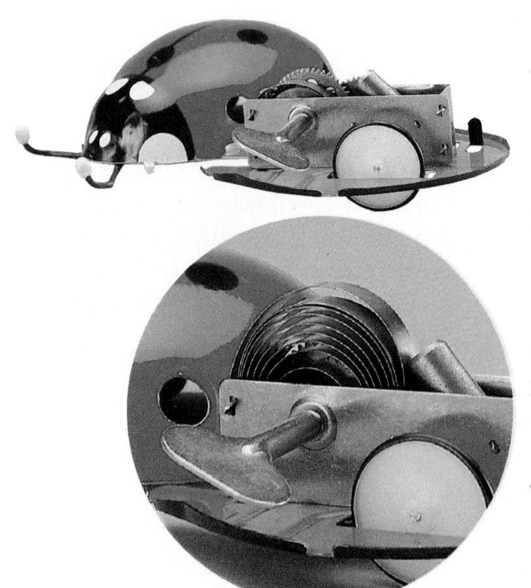

Figure 5-4. The spring in the wound condition has potential energy that can be used to make the toy move. In the enlarged view, the unwound spring has neither potential nor kinetic energy.

Work

To most people, the word *work* means something they do to earn money. Work can be anything from filling fast-food orders, loading trucks, or teaching, to lying around all day testing mattresses. The scientific meaning of work is more specific. **Work** is the transfer of energy through motion. In order for work to take place, a force must be exerted through a distance.

Figure 5-5. Work is done on the books when they are being lifted, but no work is done on them when they are being held or carried horizontally.

In which case would you do more work—lifting a pack of gum from the floor to waist level or lifting a pile of books through the same distance? Would more work be done if you lifted the books from the floor to your waist or if you raised them all the way over your head? Common sense tells you that the amount of work done depends on two things: the amount of force exerted and the distance over which the force is applied.

When a force acts over a distance, the work done can be calculated as

$$\text{Work} = \text{force} \times \text{distance}$$
$$W = F \times d$$

Work, like energy, is measured in joules. One joule is equal to a newton-meter (N • m), which is the amount of work done when a force of one newton acts through a distance of one meter.

Science and WRITING 

Spend a few minutes observing the different forms of energy around you. List all the different forms and describe events that result from one form of energy changing to another.

EXAMPLE PROBLEM: Calculating Work

Problem Statement: A student's full backpack weighs 10 N. She lifts it from the floor to a shelf 1.5 m high. How much work is done on the pack full of books?

Known Information: force, F = 10 N
distance, d = 1.5 m

Strategy Hint: Remember that weight is a measure of the force of gravity on an object.

Unknown Information: Work (W)

Equation to Use:
$W = F \times d$
$= 10 \text{ N} \times 1.5 \text{ m}$
$= 15 \text{ N} \bullet \text{m}$

Solution: $= 15 \text{ J}$

PRACTICE PROBLEMS

Strategy Hint: The joule is a derived unit. What other units make it up?

1. A carpenter lifts a 45-kg beam 1.2 m. How much work is done on the beam?

Strategy Hint: Work requires a force to be exerted over a distance.

2. A dancer lifts a 400-N ballerina overhead a distance of 1.4 m and holds her there for several seconds. How much work is done on the ballerina?

Name two factors to keep in mind when deciding when work is being done.

There are two factors to keep in mind when deciding when work is being done: something has to move, and the motion must be in the direction of the applied force. If you pick up a pile of books from the floor, work is done on the books. They move upward, in the direction of the applied force. If you hold the books in your arms, no work is done. Some upward force is still being applied (to keep the books from falling), but no movement is taking place. Even if you carry the books across the floor at a constant speed, no work is done on the books. The force being applied to the books is still upward, but your motion across the floor is sideward, or horizontal.

Conservation of Energy

Have you ever ridden on the swings in a playground? Try to remember what it was like swinging back and forth, high and low. Now think about the energy changes involved in such a ride.

The ride starts with a push to start you moving—to give you some kinetic energy. As the swing rises, kinetic energy changes to potential energy of position. At the top of each swing, potential energy is greatest. Then, as the swing moves downward, potential energy changes to kinetic energy. At the bottom of each swing, kinetic energy is greatest, and potential energy is at its minimum.

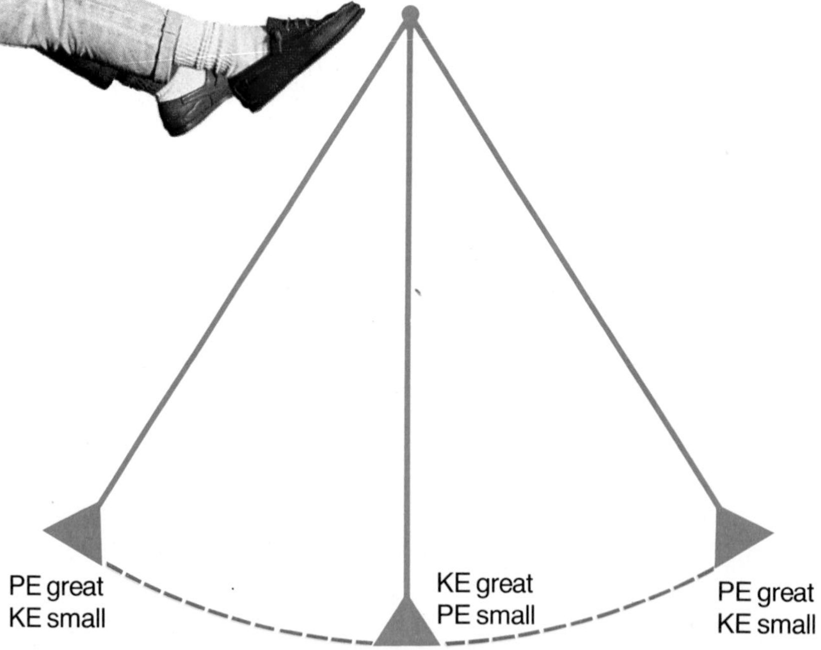

Figure 5-6. The diagram shows the energy conversions that take place in a moving swing.

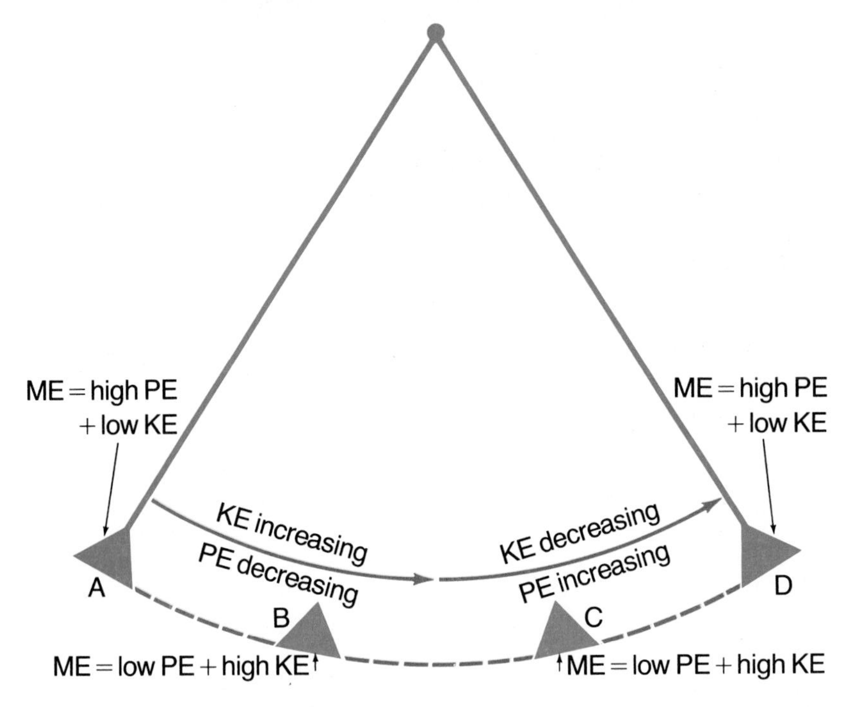

Figure 5-7. The mechanical energy (K.E. + P.E.) of a moving swing is always the same.

As the swing continues to move back and forth, energy is converted from kinetic to potential to kinetic, over and over again. At any point along its path, the swing will have both potential energy and kinetic energy. Taken together, potential and kinetic energy of the swing make up its mechanical energy. **Mechanical energy** is the total amount of kinetic and potential energy in a system.

Scientists have learned that in any given situation, energy may change from one form to another, but the total amount of energy remains constant. In other words, energy is conserved. This fact is recognized as a law of nature. According to the **law of conservation of energy,** energy may change form but it cannot be created or destroyed under ordinary conditions.

Suppose the law of conservation of energy is applied to the swing. Would you expect the swing to continue moving back and forth forever? You know this doesn't happen. The swing slows down and comes to a stop. Where does the energy go?

If you think about it, friction and air resistance are constantly acting on the swing and rider. These unbalanced forces cause some of the mechanical energy of the swing to change to thermal energy—heat. With every pass of the swing, the temperatures of the swing, the rider, and the air around them go up a little bit. So the mechanical energy of the swing isn't lost, it is converted to thermal energy. Thermal energy is discussed in the next section.

Did You Know?

A person on a bicycle converts chemical energy into kinetic energy ten times more efficiently than does a seagull in flight.

Figure 5-8. As the sled moves down the hill, what energy changes are taking place? Is any work being done on the sled?

The next time you hear someone talking about *energy* or *work,* think about the scientific meanings of those words. Ask yourself what kind of energy is being discussed and whether the work involves a force being applied over a distance.

SECTION REVIEW

1. Imagine you're standing on a stepladder and someone tosses a basketball up to you. When you drop the ball, it bounces several times. The first bounce will be highest, and each bounce after that will be lower and lower until the ball stops bouncing. Describe the energy changes that take place, starting with the ball being tossed to you.
2. To win a prize on a game show, a contestant pushed a bowling ball a distance of 20 m using just his nose. The amount of work done was 1470 J. How much force did the person exert on the ball?
3. **Apply:** In recent years a lot of discussion has focused on the need to save energy by driving more efficient cars and using less electricity. If the law of conservation of energy is true, and the total amount of energy always stays the same, why are people worried about energy conservation?

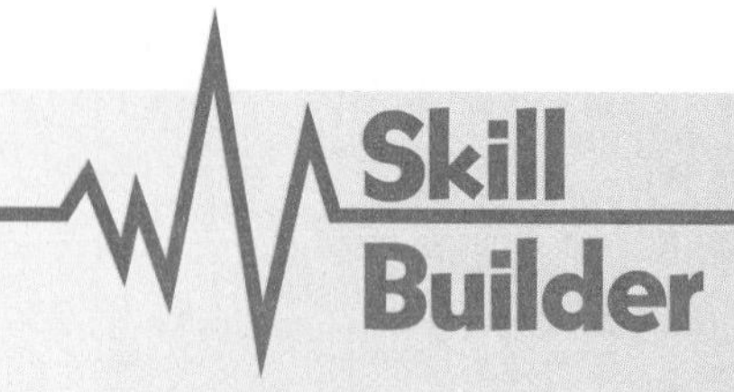

Comparing and Contrasting

Compare and contrast the everyday meaning of *work* with the scientific definition of that term. Give examples of work in the everyday sense that would not be considered work in the scientific sense. If you need help, refer to Comparing and Contrasting in the **Skill Handbook** on page 679.

ACTIVITY 5-1
Conversion of Energy

Problem: *What happens to the energy of a pendulum?*

Materials
- ring stand and ring
- support rod clamp, right angle
- support rod, 30 cm
- metersticks (2)
- rubber stopper, 2-hole, medium
- string (100 cm)
- masking tape

Procedure
1. Prepare a data table like the one shown.
2. Set up the apparatus as shown.
3. Use masking tape to mark the center of the stopper. Use this line to measure heights above the tabletop.
4. Move the stopper away from the cross arm. Measure the height of the stopper above the table. Record this measurement.
5. Release the stopper and let it swing. Observe carefully and measure the height the stopper reaches at the opposite end of its swing. Record this measurement.
6. Repeat Steps 4 and 5 several times, each time starting the stopper at a greater height.

Data and Observations

Trial	Starting Height	Ending Height
1		
2		

Analyze
1. For a single swing, is the ending height of the stopper exactly the same as its starting height? Explain why or why not.
2. What happens when the starting height is higher than the cross arm?
3. What is the highest ending point that the stopper will reach? What happens if the starting point is higher than that point?

Conclude and Apply
4. At what point along a single swing does the stopper have the greatest kinetic energy? the least kinetic energy?
5. At what point does the stopper have the greatest potential energy? the least potential energy?
6. Under what conditions can the cross arm prevent the stopper from returning to its maximum potential energy?
7. When are the potential energy and the kinetic energy of the stopper both zero at the same time?

5-2 Temperature and Heat

New Science Words

temperature
thermal energy
heat

Objectives

- **Recognize the difference between the motion of an object and the motion of the particles that make up the object.**
- **Contrast heat and temperature.**
- **Explain what determines the thermal energy of a sample of matter.**

Temperature

What do you know about temperature? When the air temperature outside is high, you probably describe the weather as "hot." Ice cream, which has a low temperature, feels "cold." The words *hot* and *cold* are commonly used to describe the temperature of a material. Although not very scientific, these terms can be useful. Just about everyone understands that "hot" indicates high temperature and "cold" indicates low temperature.

Most people, when they think of temperature, automatically think of heat also. This association makes sense, because heat and temperature are related. But, they are not the same. To understand the relationship between temperature and heat, you need to know about matter.

All matter is made up of particles so small that you can't see them, even with an ordinary microscope. The particles that make up any sample of matter are constantly moving, even if the sample itself is perfectly still. Everything you can think of—the book on your desk, the shoe on your foot, even the foot inside the shoe—is made up of moving particles.

You know that moving things have kinetic energy. Because they are in constant motion, the particles that make up matter have kinetic energy. The faster the particles move, the more kinetic energy they have. **Temperature** is a measure of the average kinetic energy of the particles in a sample of matter. The higher the temperature of a material, the faster its particles are

MINI-Lab

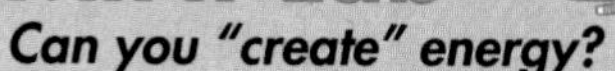

Can you "create" energy?

Pour sand into a plastic foam cup until the cup is about half full. Measure the temperature of the sand to the nearest tenth of a degree. Remove the thermometer and place a lid on the cup. While holding the lid firmly in place, shake the cup vigorously for several minutes. Stop shaking, remove the lid, and measure the temperature of the sand immediately. What effect did shaking have on the temperature of the sand? Was energy "created"? Explain.

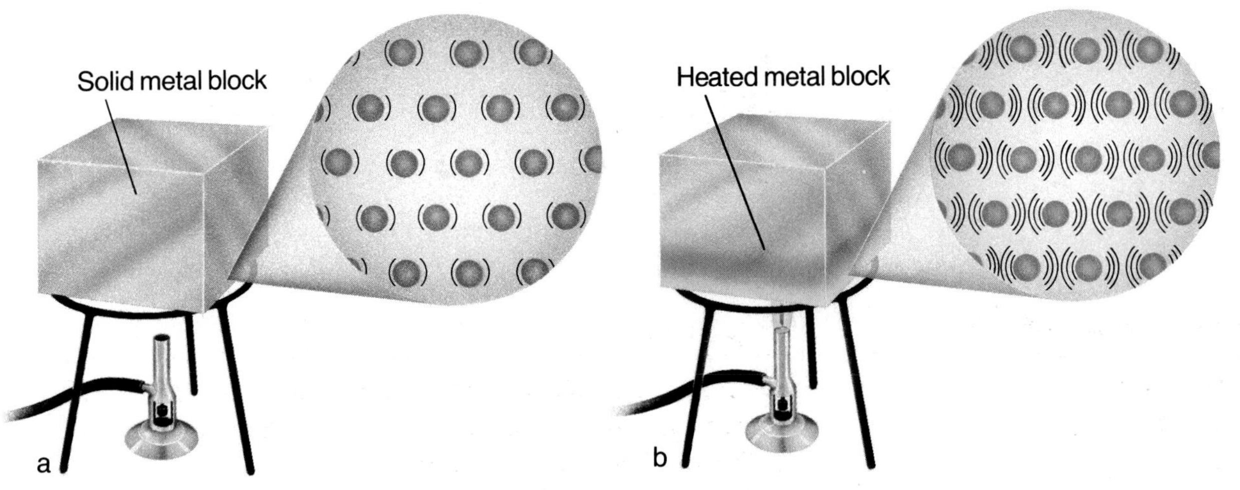

Figure 5-9. The drawing illustrates the motion of the particles of a material when it is cool (a) and when it is hot (b).

moving and the greater their average kinetic energy. Similarly, the lower the temperature of a material, the more slowly its particles are moving. Which particles are moving faster, those in a cup of hot tea or those in the same amount of iced tea?

Thermal Energy

If you place an ice-cold teaspoon on top of a scoop of ice cream, nothing will happen. But suppose you place a hot teaspoon on the ice cream. Now the ice cream under the spoon starts to melt. The hot spoon causes the ice cream to change because it transfers energy to the ice cream. Where does this energy come from? The spoon isn't moving, and its position is the same as that which the cold spoon had. So the energy is not due to motion or position of the spoon. It must be related to the temperature of the spoon.

The change in the ice cream is caused by thermal energy. Like temperature, thermal energy is related to the energy of the particles that make up matter. **Thermal energy** is the total energy of the particles that make up a material. This total includes both kinetic and potential energy.

Now suppose you stack two hot teaspoons and place them on a scoop of ice cream. What will happen? The two spoons will melt more ice cream than the single spoon did in the same amount of time. The stacked spoons have twice as much mass and, therefore, twice as many moving particles. The more mass a material has, the greater its thermal energy.

Figure 5-10. An ice-cold spoon (a) has no effect on ice cream. Two hot spoons (c) have more thermal energy than one hot spoon (b), so they melt more ice cream.

PROBLEM SOLVING

A Cold Cup of Tea and a Warm Soft Drink

Carol and Alicia were tired after playing a hard game of soccer. Shortly after arriving at Alicia's house and sitting down on the back porch, Alicia's grandmother peeked her head out the door.

"I am preparing myself a cup of herbal tea," she said. "Would you girls like some?"

"That sounds good," replied Carol. "I'm thirsty."

Alicia was thirsty too but didn't want hot tea. She told her grandmother, "No, I'll just have a cold soft drink."

They had just taken a sip of their drinks when Alicia suggested that they listen to a new cassette tape of her favorite group. The girls left their drinks and went to listen to the tape. When they finally returned to finish their drinks, Carol's tea was cold, and Alicia's soft drink was warm. How did the thermal energy of the two drinks compare when the girls first got the drinks?

Think Critically: Explain how heat was transferred in both drinks while the girls were listening to the tape.

Different kinds of matter have different thermal energies, even when mass and temperature are the same. For example, a 5-g sample of sand has a different thermal energy than a 5-g sample of pudding at the same temperature. This difference is due mainly to the ways in which the particles of the materials are arranged.

It is important to remember that the thermal energy of a material depends on the total energy of its particles. The energy of the material itself has no effect on its thermal energy. For example, at 20°C a golf ball has the same thermal energy whether it's sitting on the ground or speeding through the air.

EcoTip

Thermal energy must be used to heat water. Take a shower instead of a bath. A shower uses one-third the amount of hot water a bath does.

Heat

On a warm day, what would happen if you pressed your left hand against a cool tile wall? Your hand would feel cooler. Its temperature would have decreased. If you touched the same spot on the wall with your right hand, the spot wouldn't feel as cool as it did. The temperature of the spot would have increased when you touched it with your left hand. Energy flowed from your warm hand to the cool tile. **Heat** is the energy that flows from something with a higher temperature to something with a lower temperature. It is important to remember that heat always flows from warmer to cooler materials—never from cooler to warmer.

Like work, heat is measured in joules. That's not the only similarity between heat and work. Both involve transfers of energy. Heat is energy transferred between objects at different temperatures. Work is energy transferred when a force acts over a distance.

The next time you listen to a weather report, think about the difference between temperature and heat. And when you drop an ice cube into your drink, think about how the cooling occurs. Does the melting ice cause the liquid to cool? Or does heat flowing from the liquid to the ice, cool the drink and cause the ice to melt?

Figure 5-11. Heat flows from hot cocoa to your hand, making your hand feel hot. Heat flows from your hand to an ice cube, making your hand feel cold.

SECTION REVIEW

1. If temperature is not a direct measure of how much thermal energy something contains, why does a bottle of soda left in the sun have a higher temperature than one left in an ice chest?
2. Which has more thermal energy, a 5-kg bowling ball that has been resting on a hot driveway for 4 hours on a 35°C day, or the same bowling ball rolling down a lane in an air-conditioned bowling alley?
3. **Apply:** Using your understanding of temperature and heat, explain what happens when you heat a pan of soup on the stove, then put some leftover warm soup in the refrigerator.

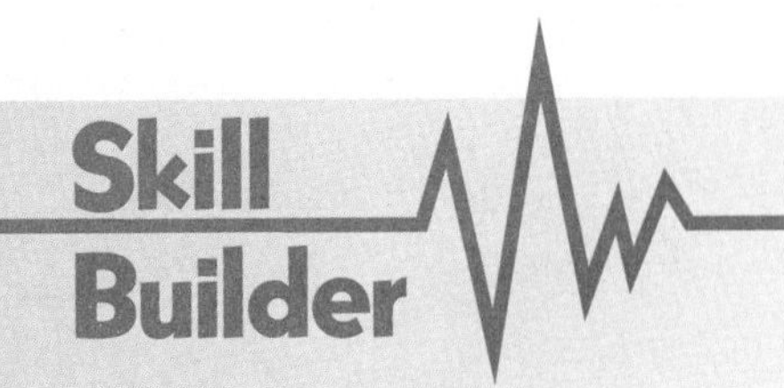

Concept Mapping

Create a network tree that shows how the following words and phrases are related: *energy, potential energy of particles, energy transfer (higher or lower temperature), heat, kinetic energy of particles,* and *thermal energy.* If you need help, refer to Concept Mapping in the **Skill Handbook** on pages 684 and 685.

5-3 Energy from the Oceans and Earth

New Science Words

magma

Objectives

- Explain why ocean waters and subsurface rock may represent possible new sources of thermal energy.
- Discuss the benefits and drawbacks of proceeding with research and development of these new energy sources.

Exploring New Energy Resources

Scientists are always searching for new sources of energy and improved methods of using our present energy sources. Two new possibilities being explored involve the harnessing of thermal energy present in oceans waters and in rocks beneath Earth's surface.

You have learned that heat flows from regions of higher temperature to regions of lower temperature. In some ocean areas the temperature difference between surface water and deeper water is as much as 15°C. Scientists believe that they can use some of the thermal energy that flows between such regions of different temperature to produce electricity.

Another possible source of energy is **magma** (MAG muh), the molten rock that lies several kilometers beneath Earth's surface. Scientists are working on the idea of drilling deep wells in order to use the thermal energy stored in the magma.

Both of these proposed projects are ambitious and, if successful, could be of tremendous benefit to all peoples of the world. However, possible drawbacks must be considered. Each of these projects will be very expensive and will take

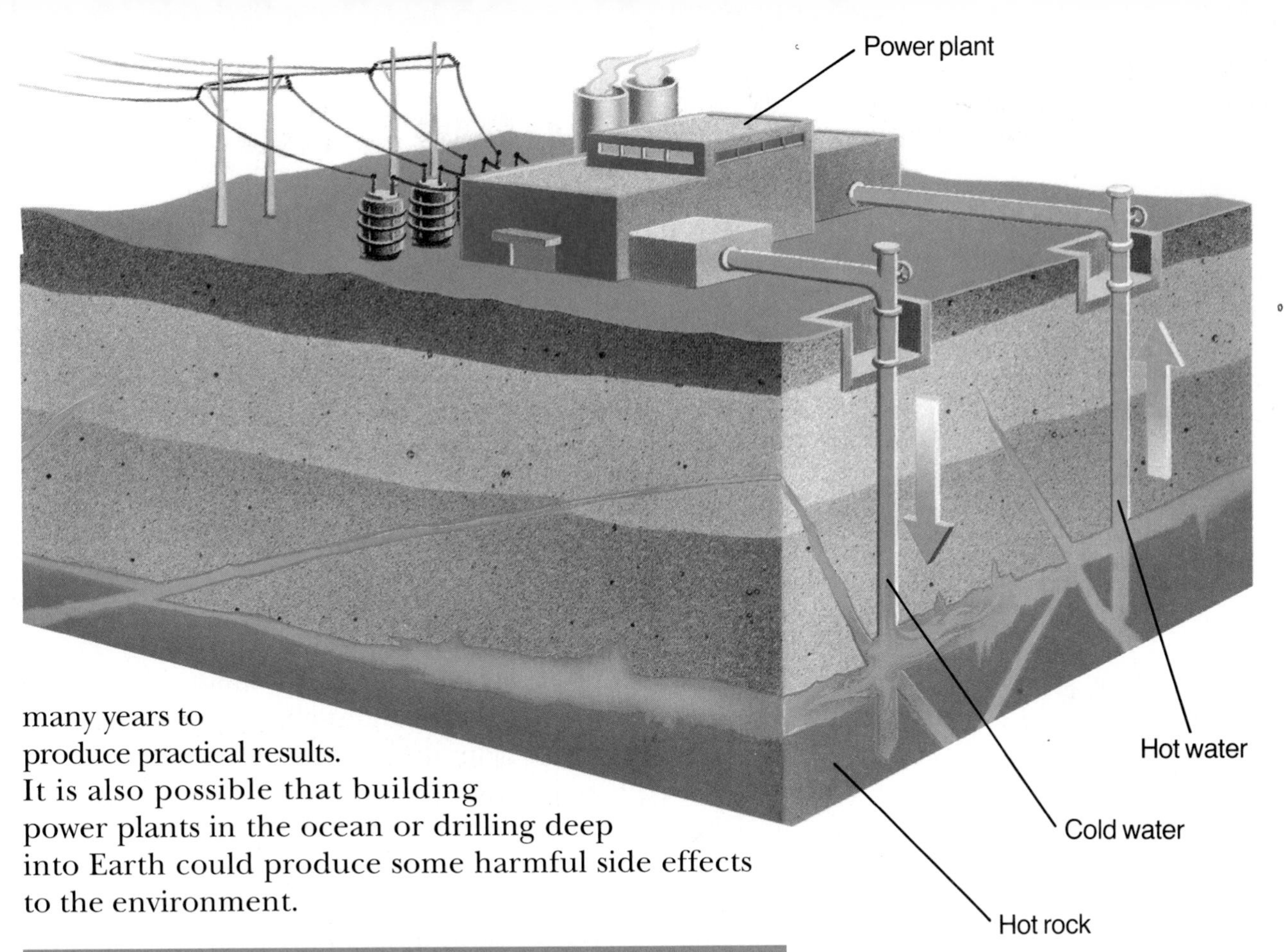

many years to produce practical results. It is also possible that building power plants in the ocean or drilling deep into Earth could produce some harmful side effects to the environment.

SECTION REVIEW

1. Explain how temperature differences at different depths of the ocean provide a possible energy source.
2. Why do you think projects like the ones mentioned in this section are so expensive and take so long to complete?

You Decide!

The growing demand for electricity combined with diminishing natural sources of fuel has made the need for new sources of energy used to produce electricity essential. All possible methods of developing new energy sources should be examined and evaluated carefully. It is equally important, however, to consider the negative aspects of proceeding with such projects as those described here. The most obvious negative aspects include possible harmful effects on the environment and the huge cost in time and money. Should tax dollars be used to support research and development of projects designed to provide new energy sources? If not, who should foot the bill?

5-4 Measuring Thermal Energy

New Science Words

specific heat

Objectives

- Define *specific heat.*
- Calculate changes in thermal energy.

Specific Heat

Have you ever jumped into a swimming pool or lake on a hot summer day and found the water surprisingly cold? Even though lots of radiant energy has been transferred to the water from the sun, the temperature of the water is still cooler than that of the surroundings.

Different materials need different amounts of heat to produce similar changes in their temperatures. The materials have different specific heats. The **specific heat** (C) of a material is the amount of energy it takes to raise the temperature of 1 kg of the material 1 degree Celsius. Specific heat is measured in joules per kilogram per degree Celsius (J/kg • °C). Table 5-1 shows the specific heats of some familiar materials. How does the specific heat of water compare with the specific heats of the other materials?

Now that you see how high the specific heat of water is compared to other materials, do you understand why jumping into the water took your breath away on that hot day? The materials around the water heat up much faster than the water itself. So the water seems cold in comparison with its surroundings. Even if the water is 20°C, it seems much colder than air at 20°C. The water can take heat away from your body more quickly, because its specific heat is much higher than that of air.

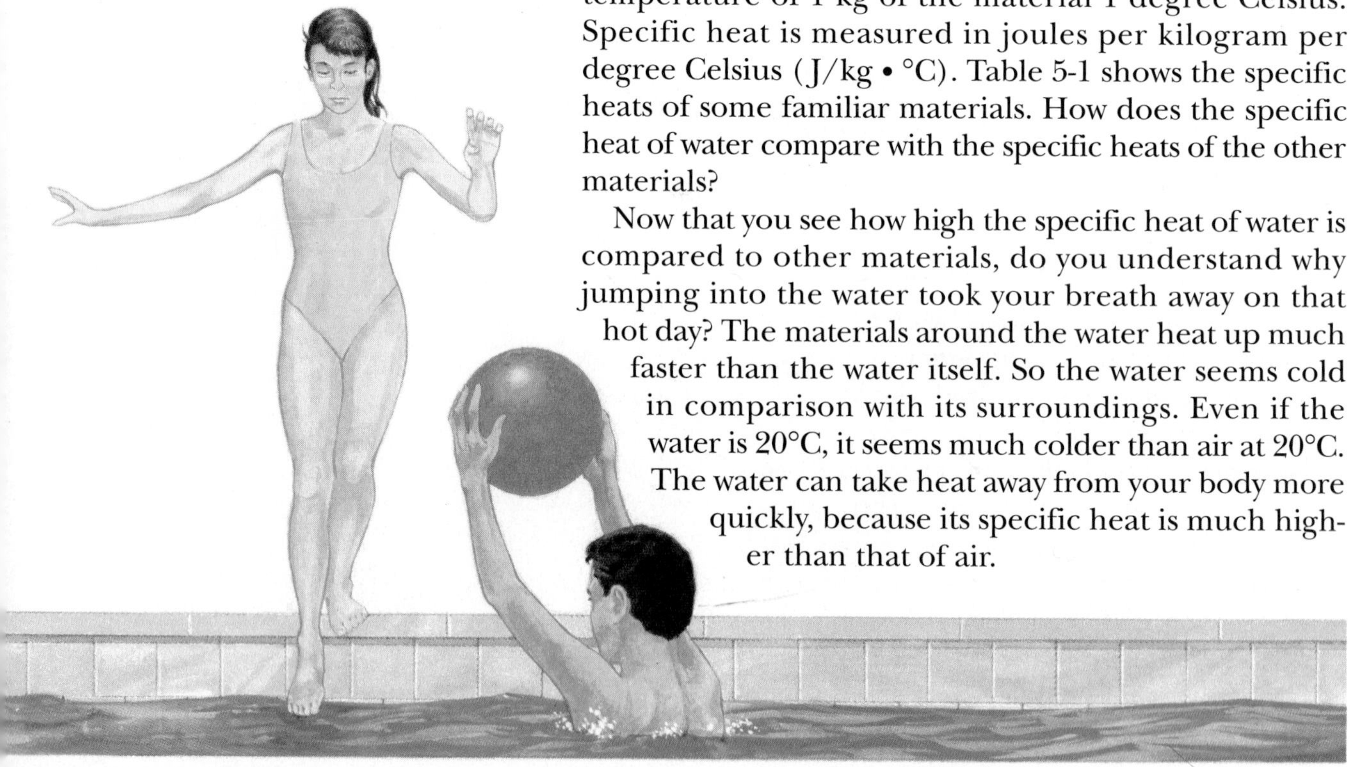

Figure 5-12. Because of its high specific heat, water warms up more slowly than its surroundings.

Table 5-1

SPECIFIC HEAT OF SOME COMMON MATERIALS*			
Water	4190	Iron	450
Alcohol	2450	Copper	380
Aluminum	920	Silver	235
Carbon (Graphite)	710	Clay	130
Sand	664		

*(J/kg • °C)

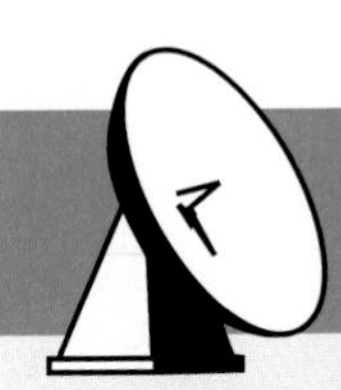

TECHNOLOGY

Infrared Weather Eyes

The satellite picture that you see on your TV weather show is usually an infrared image captured by a GOES satellite. GOES (**G**eostationary **O**perational **E**nvironmental **S**atellite) satellites remain directly above the same point on Earth's surface. Each satellite monitors a circular region of the surface 10 000 kilometers across. Within this circle, clouds appear white and the Earth's surface appears gray. A meteorologist can point out a line of clouds that indicates a weather front and run a sequence of images to demonstrate how that front is moving.

The satellite's sensors measure many bands of infrared radiation. One band detects moisture in the air. Dry air appears black and moist air appears in varying shades of gray. Because bad weather often breaks out when dry air intrudes into moist air, these water vapor images can be used to predict storms. Other bands of radiation reveal information about wind speed and direction, rainfall, fog, snow, and ice. Newer satellites, with a "sharper eye," may one day provide data for making accurate global weather forecasts 30 to 90 days in advance.

Think Critically: In addition to weather forecasting, what are some other uses for satellite data from infrared sources?

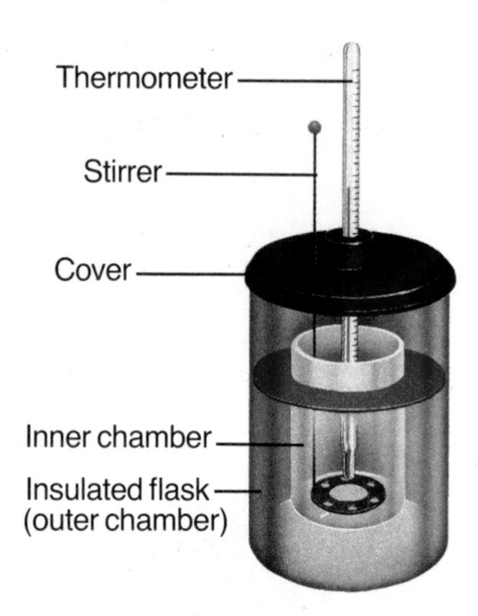

Figure 5-13. Devices like this simple calorimeter are used to measure thermal energy transfer.

Using Specific Heat

Changes in thermal energy cannot be measured directly. No instrument can make such measurements. However, specific heat can be used to measure changes in thermal energy. For example, suppose you take a 3.1-g ball of aluminum foil from a pot of water at a temperature of 30°C and allow it to cool to room temperature, which is 15°C. You now have enough information to find out the change in the thermal energy of the ball of foil using the following equation:

$$\text{Change in thermal energy} = \text{mass} \times \text{Change in temperature} \times \text{specific heat}$$

$$Q = m \times \Delta T \times C_p$$

The symbol Δ (delta) means change, so ΔT is the change in temperature. "Change" is included in Q, which is the variable for energy change.

$$\Delta T = T_{final} - T_{initial}$$

When ΔT is positive the object has increased in temperature and gained heat. When ΔT is negative the object has decreased in temperature and given off heat.

EXAMPLE PROBLEM: Calculating Changes in Thermal Energy

Problem Statement:

A 3.1-g ball of aluminum foil cools from 30°C to 15°C. What is the change in its thermal energy?

Known Information:

Strategy Hint: Make sure you're using the appropriate units.

Mass = m = 3.1 g = 0.0031 kg
T_{final} = 15.0°C
$T_{initial}$ = 30.0°C
Specific heat (C_p) = 920 J/kg • °C

Unknown Information:

Energy change (Q)

Equation to Use:

$Q = \Delta T \times m \times C_p$
$\Delta T = T_{final} - T_{initial}$

Solution:

$Q = (T_{final} - T_{initial}) \times m \times C_p$
$= (15.0°C - 30.0°C) \times 0.0031 \text{ kg} \times 920 \text{ J/kg} \cdot °C$
$= -43 \text{ J}$

The foil ball loses 43 J of thermal energy as it cools.

PRACTICE PROBLEMS

Strategy Hint: Will your answer be a positive or negative number?

Strategy Hint: What is the unknown information?

1. Calculate the change in thermal energy when 230 g of water warms from 12°C to 90°C.
2. A 45-kg brass sculpture gains 180 480 J of thermal energy as its temperature increases from 28°C to 40°C. What is the approximate specific heat of brass?

With your new knowledge of specific heat, think about temperature changes you've observed in objects around your home or in your neighborhood. Now you have an idea about why a kettle of water takes so long to boil. And why a sandy beach heats up quickly on a sunny day.

Figure 5-14. Computers will not work at high temperatures, so heat must be removed by an internal fan.

SECTION REVIEW

1. A bucket of sand and a bucket of water are side by side in direct sunlight. Which warms faster? Why?
2. Use Table 5-1 on page 125 to calculate the change in thermal energy when a 55-g iron nail cools from 90°C to 25°C.
3. **Apply:** If you wanted to quickly cool a piece of hot metal, would it be smarter to plunge it into a container of water or a container of sand at the same temperature?

Interpreting Data

Equal amounts of clay, iron, water, and sand, all at the same temperature, were placed in an oven and heated briefly. Use the data in Table 5-1 on page 125 to match each final temperature with the appropriate material: 31°C, 5°C, 160°C, and 46°C. If you need help, refer to Interpreting Data in the **Skill Handbook** on page 683.

ACTIVITY 5-2
Specific Heat

Problem: *How much heat will curl your hair?*

Materials

- set of electric hair curlers
- thermometers, Celsius (2)
- plastic foam cup
- graph paper
- balance
- graduated cylinder

Procedure
1. Prepare a data table like the one shown.
2. Measure the mass of the plastic foam cup. Fill the cup about halfway with cool water and measure its mass again. Determine the mass of the water in kilograms.
3. Carefully remove a heated curler from its heating unit. **CAUTION:** *Don't touch any hot metal parts.* Stand the curler, open end up, on the table and pour in 2 mL of cool water.
4. Using two thermometers, measure and record the temperature of the water in the cup and the temperature of the water in the curler.
5. Carefully lower the curler into the cup of water. Measure and record the water temperatures every minute for five minutes.
6. Prepare a time-temperature graph, with time along the *x*-axis and temperature along the *y*-axis. Plot both heating and cooling curves.

Analyze
1. What happened to the water in the cup? Explain in terms of heat.
2. What was the change in temperature of the water in the cup over the 5-minute interval?
3. Using the formula below, find the change in thermal energy (Q), in joules, of the water in the cup.

$$Q = m \times \Delta T \times C_p$$

Data and Observations

Time in Minutes	Water Temperature (°C)	
	in curler	in cup
0		
1		
2		
3		
4		
5		

Conclude and Apply
4. Does the curler still have thermal energy available to continue heating the water after five minutes? How do you know?
5. Compare your results with those of your classmates. Do some curlers provide more heat than others? Which curlers provide the most heat?
6. How do the starting temperatures of all the curlers compare?
7. Which statement is more accurate: "Some curlers are hotter than others," or "Some curlers contain more thermal energy than others?" Explain your answer.

CHAPTER REVIEW

SUMMARY

5-1: Energy and Work

1. Energy is the ability to cause change. Energy may be in the form of motion (kinetic energy) or it may be stored (potential energy).
2. Energy exists in many different forms, and it can change from one form to another with no loss of energy.
3. Work is the transfer of energy through motion. Work is done only when force produces motion in the direction of the force.

5-2: Temperature and Heat

1. All matter is made up of tiny particles that are in constant motion. This motion is not related to or dependent on the motion of the matter.
2. Heat and temperature are related, but they are not the same. The temperature of a material is a measure of the average kinetic energy of the particles that make up the material. Heat is the energy that flows from a warmer to a cooler material.
3. The thermal energy of a material is the total energy—both kinetic and potential—of the particles that make up the material.

5-3: Science and Society: Energy from the Oceans and Earth

1. Temperature differences between layers of ocean waters and the energy of magma beneath Earth's surface represent two possible new sources of thermal energy.
2. The benefits and drawbacks of projects to develop new energy sources should be thoroughly investigated and evaluated before the projects are allowed to proceed.

5-4: Measuring Thermal Energy

1. Different materials have different heat capacities, or specific heats. Thus, their thermal energies change at different rates.
2. The specific heat of a material can be used to calculate changes in the thermal energy of the material.

KEY SCIENCE WORDS

a. **energy**
b. **heat**
c. **kinetic energy**
d. **law of conservation of energy**
e. **magma**
f. **mechanical energy**
g. **potential energy**
h. **specific heat**
i. **temperature**
j. **thermal energy**
k. **work**

UNDERSTANDING VOCABULARY

Match each phrase with the correct term from the list of Key Science Words.

1. the ability to cause change
2. energy of motion
3. under normal conditions, energy cannot be created or destroyed
4. energy required to raise the temperature of 1 kg of a material 1 degree Celsius
5. total energy of the particles in a material
6. the transfer of energy through motion
7. flows from warmer to cooler materials
8. stored energy
9. measure of the average kinetic energy of the particles in a material
10. the total amount of kinetic and potential energy in a system

CHAPTER

REVIEW

CHECKING CONCEPTS

Choose the word or phrase that completes the sentence or answers the question.

1. The basic SI unit of energy is the ______.
   a. Calorie c. newton
   b. joule d. Kelvin
2. If the velocity of an object increases, the ______ of the object will also increase.
   a. kinetic energy c. specific heat
   b. mass d. potential energy
3. Which of these is not used to calculate change in thermal energy?
   a. volume c. specific heat
   b. temperature change d. mass
4. The ______ of a material is a measure of the average kinetic energy of its particles.
   a. potential energy c. temperature
   b. thermal energy d. specific heat
5. Which of these does not represent work done on a rock in the scientific sense?
   a. lifting a rock c. holding a rock
   b. throwing a rock d. moving a rock
6. The total amount of kinetic and potential energy in a closed system is called ______.
   a. specific heat c. stored energy
   b. mechanical energy d. temperature
7. As the temperature of a material increases, the average ______ of its particles increases.
   a. kinetic energy c. specific heat
   b. potential energy d. mass
8. Kinetic energy is directly related to ______.
   a. volume c. mass
   b. force d. position
9. The ______ of an object depends upon its position.
   a. kinetic energy c. potential energy
   b. thermal energy d. mechanical energy
10. The particles in a material all have ______.
    a. the same mass
    b. kinetic energy
    c. the same temperature
    d. the same velocity

UNDERSTANDING CONCEPTS

Complete each sentence.

11. Specific heat is the amount of energy needed to raise the temperature of a material ______.
12. ______ is molten rock below Earth's surface.
13. The kinetic energy of an object depends on the mass and ______ of the object.
14. Energy is the ability to cause ______.
15. Work is the transfer of ______ through motion.

THINK AND WRITE CRITICALLY

16. Describe two types of potential energy. How does this energy differ from kinetic energy?
17. Describe the energy changes that occur in a swinging pendulum. Explain how energy is conserved, even as a pendulum slows down and eventually stops swinging.
18. Compare and contrast heat, temperature, and thermal energy.
19. A copper bowl and a clay bowl of equal mass were heated from 27°C to 100°C. Which required more heat? Explain.
20. Describe some possible benefits and drawbacks of developing ways to convert thermal energy of the oceans and magma to useful purposes.

APPLY

21. While performing a chin-up, Carlos raises himself 0.8 m. How much work does Carlos, who weighs 600 N, accomplish doing a chin-up?
22. A football player picks up a football, runs with it, and then throws it to a teammate. Describe the work done on the ball.
23. Wind has more kinetic energy than does still air. Why does air feel cold on a windy winter day and hot on a calm summer day?
24. How much thermal energy does 420 g of liquid water gain when it is heated from its freezing point to its boiling point?
25. 50 g of water and 50 g of sand each absorb 200 J of solar energy. What will be the temperature change?

MORE SKILL BUILDERS

If you need help, refer to the Skill Handbook.

1. **Comparing and Contrasting:** Compare and contrast heat and work.
2. **Sequencing:** Equal amounts of the following materials listed in Table 5-1 (page 125) are sitting in the sun: carbon, silver, alcohol, copper, and aluminum. List the materials in order of the average kinetic energies of their particles, from highest to lowest, after they have been in the sun for several hours.
3. **Measuring in SI:** A non-SI unit often used to measure thermal energy is the calorie, which is equal to 4.18 J. The number of calories needed to raise the temperature of 1-kg samples of three different materials 1 degree Celsius are given below. Use the factor-label method to convert each value to joules.

Material	Calories
wood	420
glass	120
mercury	33

4. **Hypothesizing:** Propose a hypothesis to explain why a person with a fever often feels chills, even in a warm room.
5. **Concept Mapping:** Below is a blank concept map of the energy changes of a gymnast bouncing on a trampoline. Complete the map by indicating the type of energy—kinetic, potential, or both—the gymnast has at each of the following stages in his or her path: a. halfway up; b. the highest point; c. halfway down; d. the lowest point, just before hitting the trampoline.

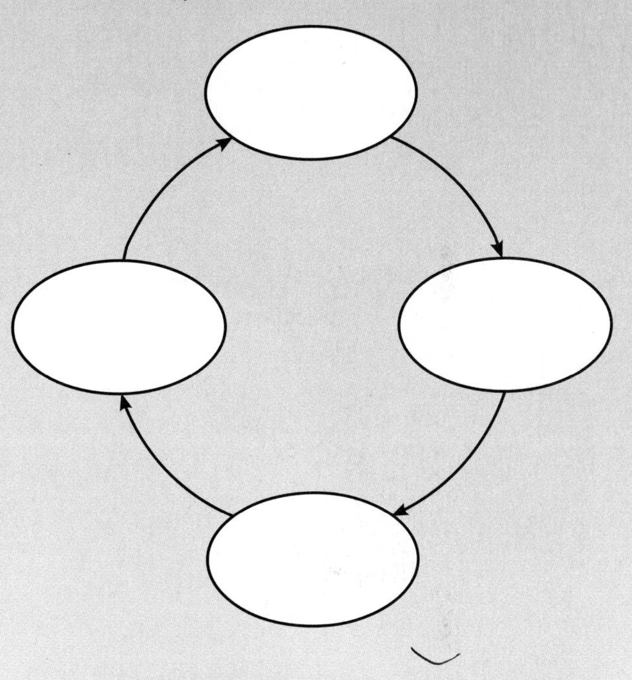

PROJECTS

1. Research and write a paper about the life of Albert Einstein. Describe how he explained the law of conservation of mass and energy.
2. Make a poster showing possible energy sources other than burning fossil fuels. Note the advantages and disadvantages of each and indicate which you think is the best resource to develop further and why.

CHAPTER

6 Using Thermal Energy

The clothes you wear can make you feel warmer or cooler. They affect the amount of thermal energy that reaches and leaves your body. How else can the movement of thermal energy be affected?

FIND OUT!

Do this simple activity to find out how you can affect the movement of thermal energy.

Turn on a lamp with a bare light bulb. *Being careful not to touch the bulb,* put your hand near it. Do you feel warmth from the bulb? How is thermal energy getting to your hand? What happens if you move your hand nearer to the bulb or farther away? What happens if you put a book between your hand and the lamp? Suppose you use only a piece of paper instead of a whole book. Find some other things that you can put between your hand and the light bulb. Do some seem to block heat better than others? Feel the objects after they've been near the light bulb. Do some feel warmer than others? How can you explain the differences?

Gearing Up

Previewing this Chapter

Use this outline to help you focus on important ideas in this chapter.

Previewing Science Skills

- In the **Skill Builders,** you will use variables, constants, and controls, make and use tables, and map concepts.
- In the **Activities,** you will observe, collect and organize data, sequence, analyze, and infer.
- In the **MINI-Lab,** you will observe and hypothesize.

What's next?

You have discovered that you can exert some control over the movement of thermal energy. Now you will learn about how thermal energy moves and how that movement can be put to useful purposes.

6-1 Moving Thermal Energy

New Science Words

conduction
fluid
convection
radiation
insulators

Objectives

- ▶ **Compare and contrast the transfer of thermal energy by conduction, convection, and radiation.**
- ▶ **Differentiate between conductors and insulators.**
- ▶ **Explain how insulation affects the transfer of energy.**

Conduction

You have learned that thermal energy travels as heat from a material at higher temperature to a material at lower temperature. You see examples of this energy transfer all the time. If you pick up an ice cube, heat from your hand is transferred to the ice, causing it to melt. If you pick up a hot spoon, the heat from the spoon moves to your hand, causing you to drop the spoon. The question is, how does the thermal energy move from place to place?

What is conduction?

One way thermal energy travels is by conduction. **Conduction** is the transfer of energy through matter by direct contact of particles. Recall that all matter is made up of tiny particles that are in constant motion. The temperature of a material is a measure of the average kinetic energy of its particles.

EcoTip

When cooking or baking, leave the tops on the pots and keep the oven door closed. This will prevent energy from escaping and being wasted.

Energy is transferred when particles moving at different speeds bump into each other, or collide. When faster-moving particles collide with slower-moving particles, some of the energy of the faster-moving particles is passed along, or transferred, to the slower-moving particles. The faster particles slow down and the slower particles speed up. Thus, energy is transferred by means of conduction.

Heat may be transferred by conduction through a given material or from one material to another. Think about what happens when one end of a metal spoon is placed in boiling water. Heat from the water is transferred to the spoon. The end of the spoon in the water becomes

Figure 6-1. Part of the spoon is heated by contact with the hot water (left). Heat is transferred through the metal spoon, particle by particle (center), until the entire spoon is hot (right).

hotter than the other end of the spoon. But eventually the entire spoon becomes hot. Figure 6-1 shows the energy transfer involved in this situation.

Conduction can take place in solids, liquids, and gases. Because their particles are packed closer together, solids usually conduct heat better than liquids or gases. However, some solids conduct heat better than others. Metals such as silver, copper, and aluminum are good heat conductors, while wood, plastic, glass, and fiberglass are poor conductors of heat. Why do you think cooking pots are made of metal? What are the handles usually made of?

Convection

You know that liquids and gases are different from solids. Liquids and gases can move about more readily—they can flow. Any material that can flow is a **fluid.** The most important way thermal energy is transferred in fluids is by convection. **Convection** is the transfer of energy by the movement of matter. How does this differ from conduction? In conduction, energy moves from particle to particle, but the particles themselves remain in place. In convection, the particles move from one location to another, "carrying" energy with them.

When heat is added to a fluid, the particles of the fluid begin to move faster, just as the particles of a solid do. However, the particles of a fluid have more freedom of movement. So they spread out—they move farther apart.

Figure 6-2. The motion of the sawdust shows that a convection current is present in the liquid.

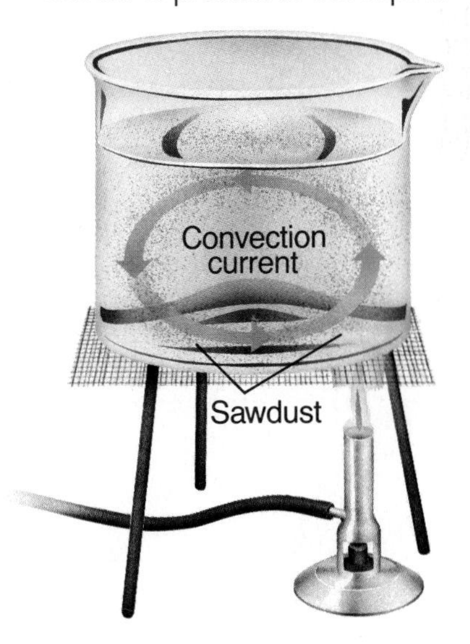

The fluid is said to expand. A hot-air balloon is a good example of the expansion of a fluid upon being heated. When the air in the balloon is heated, the particles move faster and farther apart. The air particles striking the sides of the balloon exert force, causing it to inflate.

Now think about what happens when a pot of water is heated. The stove burner heats the bottom of the pot by conduction. Water touching the bottom of the pot is also heated by conduction. As this water is heated, it expands and becomes less dense. Cooler, denser water at the top of the pot sinks and pushes the hot water upward. As the hot water rises, it cools, becomes more dense, and moves toward the bottom again, forcing warmer water to rise. This movement of particles within a fluid creates convection currents. These currents transfer thermal energy from warmer to cooler parts of the fluid. Wind and ocean currents are examples of convection currents.

Radiation

In order for conduction or convection to take place, matter must be present. There is a third type of heat transfer that does not require matter. **Radiation** is the transfer of energy in the form of invisible waves. Energy that travels by radiation is often called radiant energy. Radiant energy from the sun travels 150 million kilometers through mostly empty space to reach Earth. When this energy reaches Earth, some of it is reflected, or "bounced back," toward space, and some is absorbed. Only radiant energy that is absorbed is changed to thermal energy.

Different materials absorb radiant energy differently. Shiny materials reflect radiant energy; dull materials absorb it. Dark-colored materials absorb more radiant energy than light-colored materials do. This fact explains why summer clothing is usually made of lighter-colored materials than winter clothing.

If you hold your hand near a lighted electric bulb, your hand feels hot. This heat is produced when radiant energy from the bulb is absorbed by your hand and changed to thermal energy.

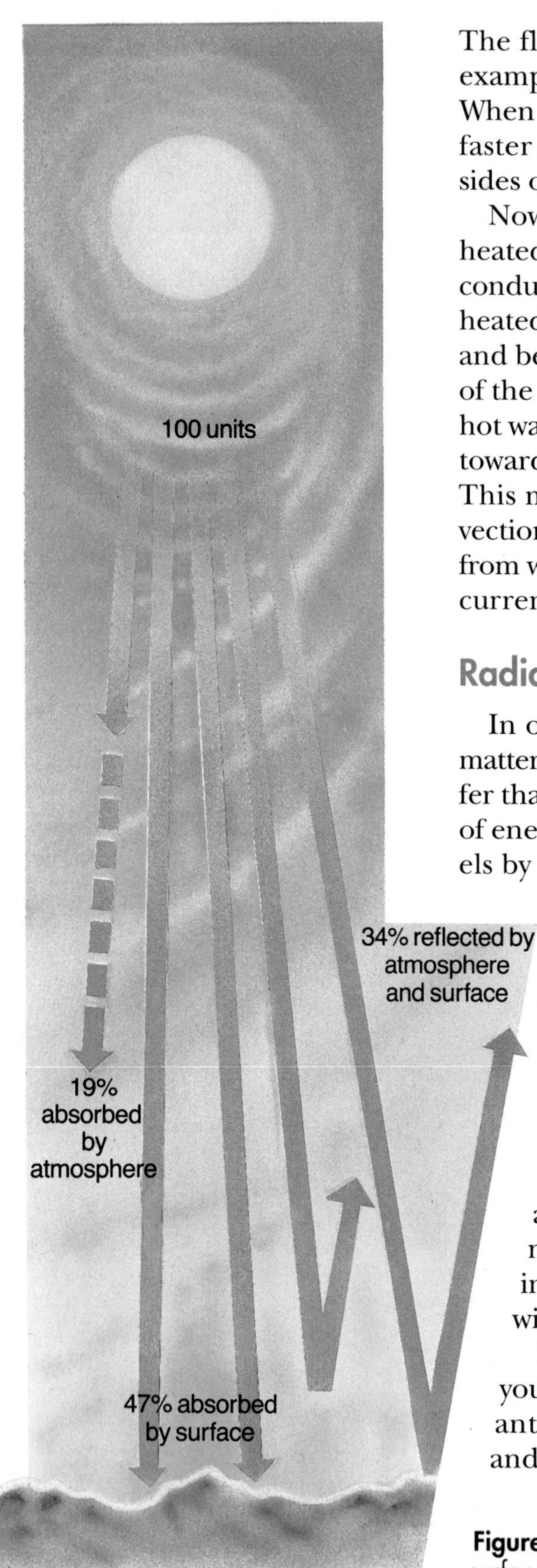

Figure 6-3. Only the radiant energy that is absorbed by Earth's surface is converted to thermal energy.

Reducing Movement of Thermal Energy

When the weather is really cold, doesn't it feel good to wrap yourself up in a thick sweater or curl up under a fluffy quilt? And in hot weather, wouldn't you rather have juice from a bottle that has been inside a picnic cooler than one that has been sitting out on a table?

What do these two situations have in common? In each case, some material is used to reduce the flow of heat by conduction, convection, or radiation. In the first case, the material of the sweater or quilt traps your body heat and keeps it from escaping to the open air. In the second case, the material of the picnic cooler keeps heat from flowing to the juice.

Earlier you learned that good conductors are materials that allow heat to move easily through them. Now you're finding out about good **insulators**—materials that do not allow heat to move easily through them. Some insulators, such as wood, plastic, glass, and fiberglass, have already been identified as being poor conductors.

Gases such as air are excellent insulators. Many types of insulation consist of materials that contain many tiny "pockets" of trapped air. These pockets are too small to allow convection currents to form, so the trapped air acts as an insulator. Plastic foam is a type of insulation commonly used in beverage cups and picnic coolers. This "foam" is mostly tiny pockets of trapped air. Down jackets and quilts are stuffed with tiny feathers or fibers that trap air.

Buildings are insulated to keep them warm in winter and cool in summer. In cold weather, a heated building is warmer than its surroundings. Heat tends to flow from the building to the outside. Insulation can help to reduce the amount of heat lost this way. In the United States, about 10 percent of all energy produced is used to heat buildings, so you can see why it is important to prevent as much heat loss as possible. In warm weather, air conditioners use a lot of energy to remove heat from building interiors. Insulation reduces the amount of heat that flows into a cool building from the outside, thus keeping the inside of the building cooler.

Building insulation is usually made of some fluffy material, such as fiberglass, cellulose, or treated paper. The insulation, which is packed into outer walls and under

Science and READING

Form a team to design and develop an energy-efficient home. Each member of the team should draw up a house plan, and the team should select the best one. Then each member researches one aspect of the new house for the best energy conservation ideas.

Figure 6-4. Air trapped in its shaggy coat keeps this polar bear warm.

PROBLEM SOLVING

The Warm House

Mary and her family lived in a small house near the Canadian border. Because their house had become too small for their needs, the family was having a larger house built nearby.

One day Mary went to the new house with her father to check on a few things. They wanted to make sure that the house was being properly constructed to withstand the cold winters in the area. Mary's father had her check all the exterior walls to see that they were insulated. Mary found that the workers had used foam insulation backed with aluminum foil. Next Mary's father went up to the attic to make sure that rolls of fiberglass insulation had been installed between the rafters. Meanwhile, Mary checked to see that all the windows had stickers indicating that they were double-paned thermal windows. Satisfied that their new house would be nice and warm, Mary and her father returned home.

Think Critically: What was the purpose of the aluminum backing on the exterior wall insulation? What do the foam insulation, the fiberglass insulation, and the thermal windows have in common that helps them to prevent the loss of heat?

roofs, is sometimes covered with shiny aluminum foil. By reflecting radiant energy back toward its source, the foil cuts down on energy transfer due to radiation.

Many materials are used in building construction. To help consumers understand the energy-transfer qualities of these different materials, a rating system has been established in which each material is given an R-value. The *R* indicates resistance to heat flow. Table 6-1 shows the R-values for some common building materials.

What does the *R* indicate in R-values?

In order to have a well-insulated house, materials with an R-value of at least 19 should be used in the outer walls and those with R-values of 30-44 in the roof or ceilings. Higher R-values are needed for roofs and ceilings because the warmest air inside the house is carried upward by convection currents.

Even though glass isn't a good conductor, energy transfer does occur through windows. A single pane of glass has an R-rating of only 1, but the use of double-pane windows can reduce heat loss considerably. Such windows have a thin "sandwich" made of air trapped between two panes of glass. The air is an excellent insulator, and the space is too narrow to allow convection currents to form in the air.

In some double-pane windows, air is replaced with a harmless, colorless gas. This gas is a better insulator than air, thus giving the windows a higher R-value. Keep in mind that high R-values help keep buildings cool during hot weather, too.

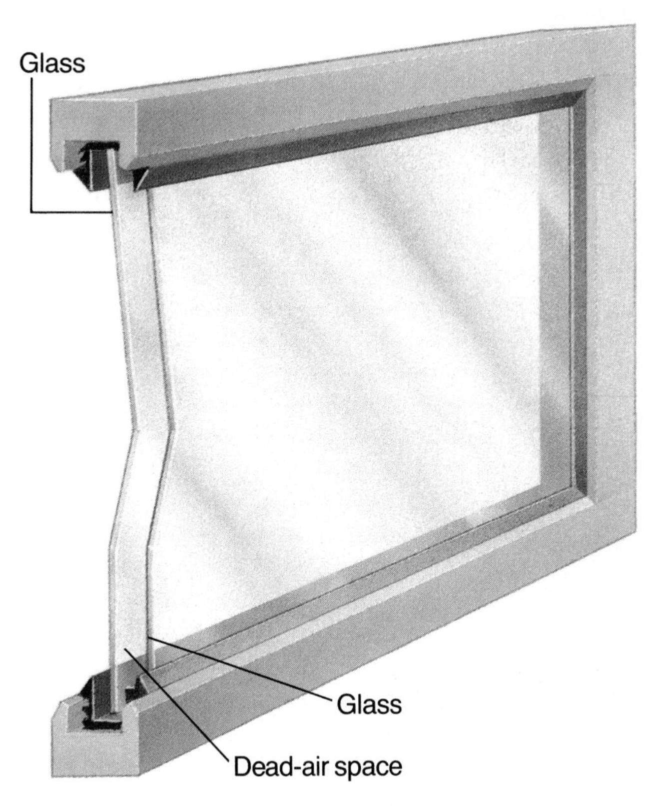

Figure 6-5. The air trapped in this double-pane window serves as a layer of insulation.

Table 6-1

R-VALUES OF VARIOUS MATERIALS

Material	R-Value
Brick	0.08/cm
Plasterboard (drywall)	0.35/cm
Stucco	0.08/cm
Wood siding	0.60/cm
Air space	1.82-3.56/cm
Fiberglass (bolts)	1.22/cm
Loose cellulose	1.46/cm
Aluminum siding	0.01/cm
Loose foam	1.89/cm
Loose vermiculite	1.09/cm

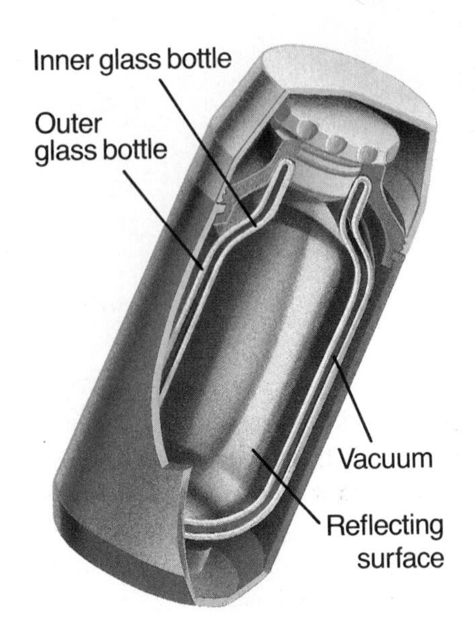

Figure 6-6 . This cutaway drawing of a vacuum bottle shows that its construction is similar to that of a double-pane window.

You may have used a vacuum bottle to carry cold or hot liquids for lunch. This bottle works much like a double-pane window; but instead, it has a double glass wall with a vacuum between the two glass layers. One side of each layer is coated with aluminum to reduce heat transfer by radiation.

Adding insulation and special windows are not the only ways to reduce heat loss from buildings. Many buildings, especially older ones, have cracks and gaps around windows and doors through which heat can escape. These "heat leaks" should be filled with caulking, putty, or weather stripping to reduce energy loss and fuel bills.

Now that you know more about how thermal energy is transferred, think about things you can do to influence the amount of energy that affects you. You can sit under a shady umbrella or put on a sweater. You can close a window or wear light-colored clothing. These are just a few examples of ways to cool off or warm up. What other ways can you think of?

SECTION REVIEW

1. Name and describe three methods by which thermal energy is transferred.
2. Explain why poor conductors of heat are good insulators of heat.
3. Why do many pots and pans used for cooking have wood or plastic handles?
4. **Apply:** Many fast-food restaurants serve their hot sandwiches in plastic foam containers. Why don't they just wrap the sandwiches in paper, which is much less expensive than plastic foam?

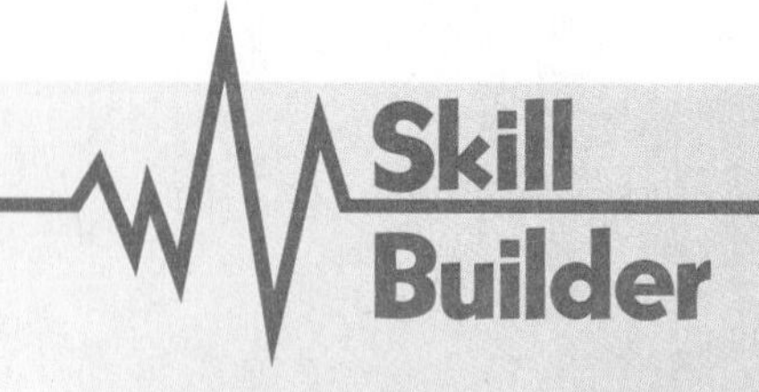

Using Variables, Constants, and Controls

Design an experiment to find out which material makes the best insulation: plastic foam pellets, shredded newspaper, or crumpled plastic bags. Remember to state your hypothesis and indicate what factors must be held constant. If you need help, refer to Using Variables, Constants, and Controls in the **Skill Handbook** on page 682.

ACTIVITY 6-1
Convection

Problem: *Where does ice go when it melts?*

Materials
- colored ice cubes
- tongs
- thermometer
- beaker, 250-mL
- salt
- stirring rod

Procedure
1. Prepare a data table like the one shown.
2. Fill the beaker with warm water.
3. Obtain an ice cube that has been strongly dyed with food coloring. Using tongs, *gently* place the ice cube in the warm water. Do not stir or mix. Keep the beaker and water as still as possible.
4. Observe the ice-water mixture for several minutes. Then measure the temperature at the surface and at the bottom of the mixture, and at three levels in between. Record the temperatures in your data table.
5. Empty the beaker and refill it with warm water. Add as much salt as will dissolve in the water, stirring vigorously as you pour.
6. Repeat Steps 3 and 4 with the salt water solution.

Data and Observations

Fresh Water		Salt Water	
Depth	**Temp (°C)**	**Depth**	**Temp (°C)**
surface		surface	
bottom		bottom	

Analyze
1. As the ice melts, what happens to the meltwater in the fresh water? In the salt water?
2. Does the meltwater blend readily with the warm water or does it tend to remain separate from it?
3. Describe the changes in temperature within the meltwater-warm water mixtures.

Conclude and Apply
4. If the three fluids involved in this activity—fresh water, salt water, and meltwater—which is the most dense? How do you know?
5. Why does convection occur between fresh water and meltwater but not between salt water and meltwater?
6. What would happen if you were to add warm water to the bottom of a beaker of cold water?

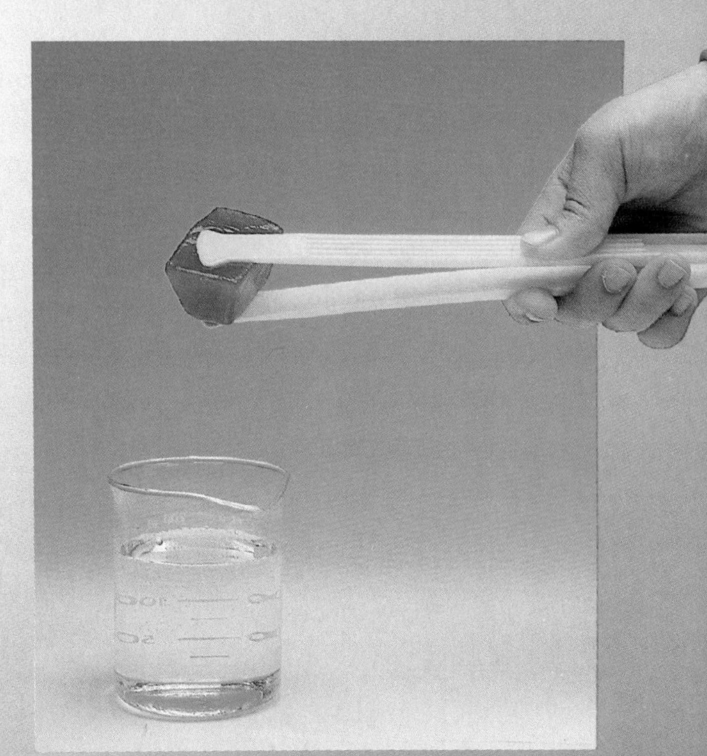

6-2 Heating Systems

New Science Words

radiator
solar energy
solar collectors

Objectives

- Describe three types of conventional heating systems.
- Explain how solar energy can be used to heat buildings.
- Explain the differences between passive and active solar heating systems.

Figure 6-7. The design of this radiator permits large quantities of air to be heated by contact with its surface.

Conventional Heating Systems

What is the weather like where you live? Is it cold part of the year or is it warm all year round? Even in warm climates, sometimes the weather is cold enough so that buildings need to be heated. For this reason, most buildings have some sort of heating system.

All heating systems must have a source of heat, such as fuel or electricity. The simplest type of heating system is one in which fuel is burned right in the area to be heated, such as in a stove or fireplace. The energy released by the burning fuel is transferred to the surrounding air by conduction, convection, and radiation.

Many heating systems use radiators to transfer energy. A **radiator** is a device with a large surface area designed to heat the air near it by conduction. Convection currents then circulate the heat to all parts of the room.

In some heating systems, radiators are heated by electricity. However, most systems are set up so that fuel is

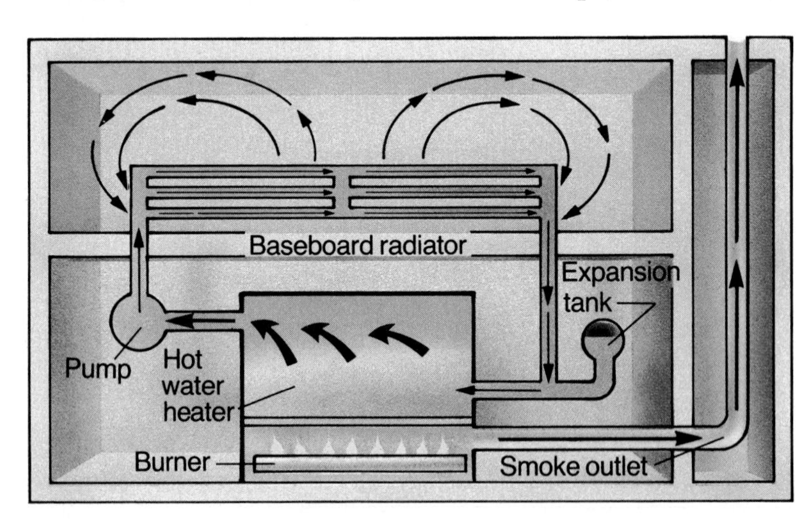

Figure 6-8. In this heating system, water is heated by the furnace and the hot water is pumped to the radiators to heat the rooms of the house.

burned in a furnace, and the heat is transported to radiators throughout the building. In one such system, the energy released in the furnace is used to heat water, which is then pumped through the pipes to the radiators in the system. After the water has given up some of its thermal energy, it is returned to the furnace to be heated again.

In a similar type of heating system, the furnace heats water to its boiling point, producing steam. The steam travels through insulated pipes to the radiators of the system. As it gives up its thermal energy, the steam condenses to water, which is returned to the furnace. Steam-heating systems need only about one-fiftieth as much water as hot-water systems, but the pipes and furnace in a steam-heating system need special insulation to keep the steam from condensing before it reaches the radiators.

Another type of heating system is the forced-air system, in which energy released in the furnace is used to heat air. A blower forces the heated air through a system of large pipes, called ducts, to openings, called vents, in each room. In the rooms the warm air circulates by convection. When the air has cooled, it passes through other vents and ducts and returns to the furnace to be heated again.

Some buildings are heated entirely by electricity. Heating coils are enclosed within floors or ceilings, and these are heated by electrical energy. Nearby air is heated by conduction, and people and materials in the room are also heated by radiation. Such systems, sometimes called radiant electric heating systems, provide even heating but are usually expensive to operate due to the high cost of electricity.

Did You Know?

For every degree you lower your thermostat, your heating costs are lowered by 2-3 percent.

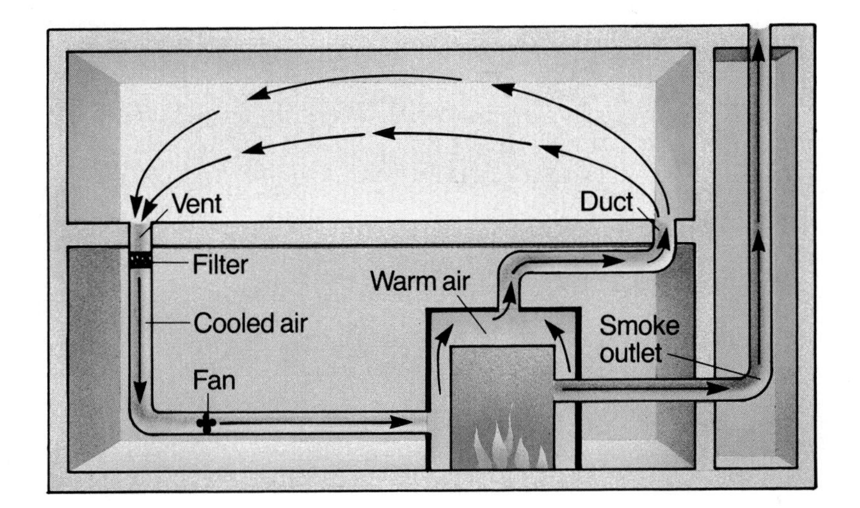

Figure 6-9. In a forced-air heating system, air heated by the furnace is used to heat the rooms of the house.

MINI-Lab

Can the sun be used to cook food?

Make a solar cooker by gluing aluminum foil to a large piece of poster board. Bend the board into an arc so that the ends of the board are nearly parallel to one another. Hold the board in this shape with string stretched between its corners. Use wire coat hangers to make a mount that will hold the board with its arc pointed directly at the sun. Using another coat hanger, fashion a device to hold a hot dog. Position the hot dog at the hottest region within the arc. Where is this region and why is it hot? The solar cooker is a passive system that converts radiant energy into thermal energy to heat the hot dog.

Solar Heating

If you have ever gotten into a car that has been sitting in direct sunlight for any length of time, you know that energy from the sun can be changed to thermal energy. Energy from the sun is known as **solar energy.** Because solar energy is free, the idea of using it to heat buildings is especially appealing.

Two basic types of systems have been designed to capture solar energy and convert it to thermal energy for use in heating buildings. The first type is passive solar heating. Passive systems use no fans or mechanical devices to transfer heat from one area to another. Some materials in the system absorb radiant energy during the day, convert it to thermal energy, and radiate the thermal energy after dark.

A house with a passive solar heating system usually has a wall of large windows on the south side to receive maximum sunlight. The other exterior walls are heavily insulated and have few windows. During the day, sunlight passes through the windows and is absorbed by some material, such as water or concrete. The radiant energy is converted to thermal energy, which is stored in the absorbing material. Later, when the house begins to cool, the stored energy radiates from the material, warming the rooms.

As you may have guessed, the second type of heating system using solar energy is called an active solar heating system. Most active solar heating systems include **solar collectors,** devices that absorb radiant energy from the sun. The collectors are usually installed on the roof or south side of a building.

Figure 6-10. The passive (left) and active (right) solar heating systems change the sun's energy to thermal energy.

Figure 6-11 shows one type of solar collector. The metal plate absorbs radiant energy from the sun. Why do you think it's painted black? The glass or plastic sheets reduce energy loss due to convection. Water-filled pipes are located just beneath the metal plate. When radiant energy is absorbed, it is converted to thermal energy, which heats the water in the pipes. A pump circulates the heated water to radiators in the system. When the water is cooled, it is returned to the collector to be reheated. Some systems also have large, insulated tanks for storing heated water to be used as needed.

Figure 6-11. In an active solar system, the liquid heated in the solar collector is circulated throughout the house.

What type of a heating system is in the building where you live? If you were asked to redesign your building, what type of heating system would you install? What would you use for insulation in your building, and where would you install it? What other steps would you take to keep the building comfortable in all kinds of weather?

SECTION REVIEW

1. What are the main differences between electrical heating systems and more conventional radiator and forced-air systems?
2. Compare and contrast active and passive solar heating systems.
3. **Apply:** Suppose you are an architect who has always designed buildings for cold climates. You're asked to design a building for Phoenix, Arizona, where the average temperature is 22°C, and temperatures can reach 50°C in summer. How would you use what you know about keeping buildings warm to design a building that will stay cool in hot weather?

Making and Using Tables

In a table, organize information about the kinds of heating systems discussed in this chapter. Include any type of information you think is important. If you need help, refer to Making and Using Tables in the **Skill Handbook** on page 686.

6-3 Thermal Pollution

New Science Words

thermal pollution
cooling towers

Objectives

- Identify problems associated with thermal pollution.
- Discuss solutions for thermal pollution problems.

Not So Hot!

Have you ever been in a city on a warm day, surrounded by cars, large buildings, and concrete? If so, you may have noticed that it seems to be hotter there than in the suburbs, where there's less traffic and less activity. Well you're right. It is hotter in the city. Much of the energy used in everyday life—electrical, chemical, mechanical, radiant, or nuclear energy—ends up as waste thermal energy that is given off into the surroundings. And the heat removed from buildings and vehicles by air conditioners is released to the outside air, just as heat is released into a kitchen by a refrigerator.

The release of waste thermal energy into the environment can reach unhealthy levels. **Thermal pollution** is a problem caused when waste thermal energy raises the temperature of the environment. Thermal pollution is a particular problem in areas where power plants and factories use water to cool their buildings and equipment, raising the temperature of the water in the process. When the warmed water is dumped into a nearby river, lake, or ocean, the added heat may cause problems for the plants and animals living there.

Fish are especially sensitive to increases in water temperature. Some species will die within hours in water warmer than 25°C.

Thermal pollution can be reduced by releasing small amounts of warm water at a time, mixed with plenty of cooler water. Some factories and power plants use **cooling towers,** devices in which water is cooled by fans or evaporation. After cooling, the water can be released into the environment without causing harm. Another solution is to put the extra thermal energy to use by heating greenhouses or other buildings.

SECTION REVIEW

1. Thermal pollution may encourage the growth of certain water plants. Why might this be a problem?
2. A company plans to build several greenhouses to get rid of waste heat from cooling water. Suggest reasons why this plan might not be sufficient. What might the company do to improve the plan?

You Decide!

A company wants to build a factory by a river that runs through your city. Many new jobs will be created, but the factory will generate waste thermal energy. What steps would you take to find out whether the environment will be damaged? Should the company be allowed to build its factory?

6-4 Using Heat to Do Work

New Science Words

heat engines
combustion
internal combustion engine
external combustion engine
heat mover
heat pump

Objectives

- Describe how internal combustion engines and external combustion engines work.
- Explain how a heat mover can transfer thermal energy in a direction opposite to that of its natural movement.

Heat Engines

Heat engines are devices that convert thermal energy into mechanical energy. These engines burn fuel in a process called combustion. **Combustion** means rapid burning. The two main types of heat engines are classified according to where combustion happens—inside the engine or outside the engine.

In an **internal combustion engine,** fuel burns inside the engine, in chambers called cylinders. Gasoline engines and diesel engines, such as the ones used in cars and trucks, are examples of internal combustion engines.

Figure 6-12 shows what the cylinders look like inside the gasoline engine of a car. Each cylinder has two openings that open or close with valves. A piston inside each cylinder moves up and down, turning a rod called a crankshaft. The motion of the crankshaft is transferred to the wheels of the car through a series of moving parts. The wheels exert a force on the road, through the tires. The equal and opposite force of the road on the tires accelerates the car forward.

Each movement of the piston up or down is called a stroke. A gasoline engine is called a four-stroke engine because the piston makes four strokes in each cycle. Follow the steps of the four-stroke cycle in Figure 6-12.

1. *Intake stroke.* In another part of the engine called the carburetor (CAR buh ray tur), gasoline is broken up into fine droplets and mixed with air. In the cylinder, the intake valve opens and the piston moves downward, drawing the fuel-air mixture into the cylinder

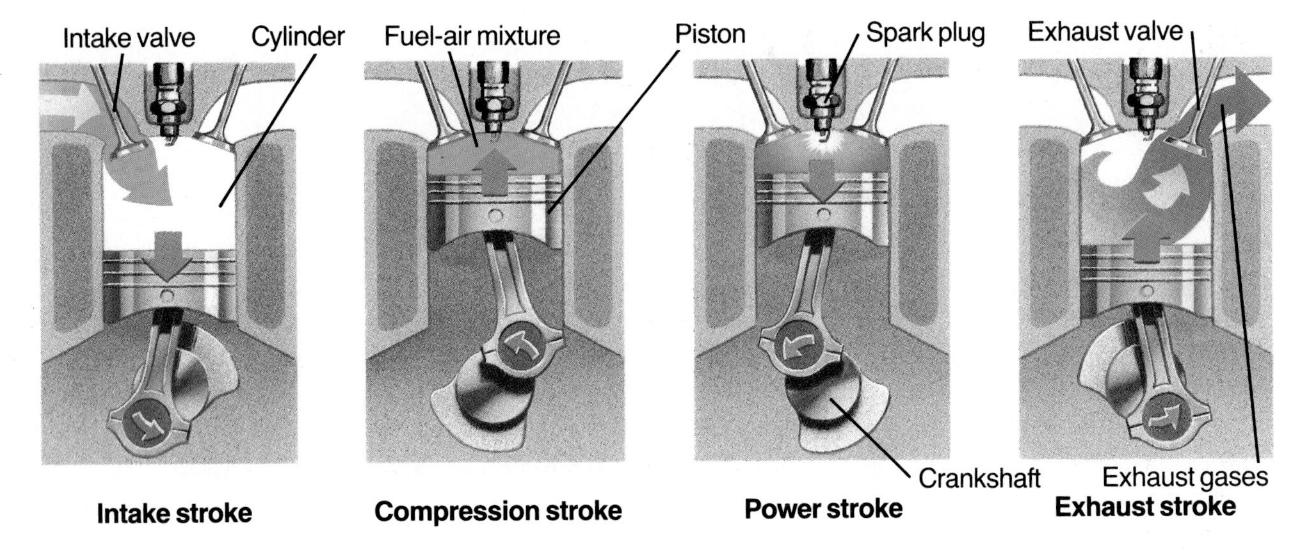

Figure 6-12. This drawing shows what takes place during each stroke of a four-stroke engine.

2. *Compression stroke.* The intake valve closes, and the piston moves up. The fuel-air mixture is squeezed, or compressed, into a smaller space.

3. *Power stroke.* When the piston is almost at the top of the cylinder, a spark plug produces a hot spark that ignites the fuel-air mixture. As the mixture burns, hot gases expand, forcing the piston down. Energy is transferred from the piston to the wheels of the car, through the crankshaft and other moving parts.

4. *Exhaust stroke.* The piston moves up again, compressing the waste products left over from burning the fuel-air mixture. The exhaust valve opens to let the waste products out.

Some engines have fuel injectors instead of carburetors. In fuel injector engines, only air enters the cylinder during the intake stroke. During the compression stroke, fine droplets of fuel are injected directly into the compressed air in the cylinder. The other steps are the same as in an engine with a carburetor.

How do fuel injectors operate?

In a diesel engine, fuel also is injected into compressed air in the cylinder. But the engine has no spark plugs. The fuel-air mixture is compressed so much that it becomes hot enough to ignite without a spark.

In an internal combustion engine, only part of the thermal energy produced by burning fuel is converted to mechanical energy. The rest is left over as waste thermal energy. Gasoline engines convert only about 12 percent of the chemical potential energy in the fuel to mechanical energy. Diesel engines convert about 25 percent of the potential energy to mechanical energy.

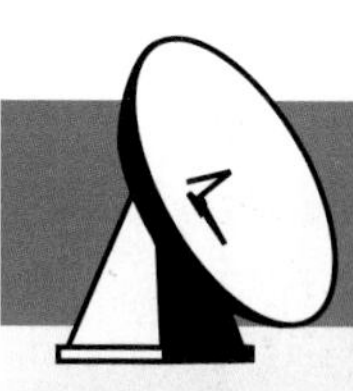

TECHNOLOGY

Cooling Crystals

A conventional refrigerator works on the principle that when a liquid is allowed to evaporate and expand, it absorbs heat from its surroundings. Scientists are now working on an entirely different approach to refrigeration. This new approach is based on the fact that certain crystals give off heat when they are magnetized and absorb heat when demagnetized.

One substance that shows this behavior is a clear crystal called gadolinium gallium garnet. To create a continuous cycle of heat exchange, scientists have mounted crystal wafers of this substance on the outside of the wheel. The wheel is then positioned so that the wafers rotate in and out of a magnetic field. As they rotate, they alternately absorb and give off heat. This magnetic refrigerator can attain temperatures colder than a conventional refrigerator, reaching temperatures close to absolute zero.

Possible applications for this refrigerator include the cooling of infrared sensors on satellites and spacecraft, cooling medical research equipment, and cooling the components of future super computers.

Think Critically: What factor would determine how cold a gas-cycle refrigerator could get?

In an **external combustion engine,** fuel is burned outside the engine. In old-fashioned steam engines, such as those used to power early locomotives, fuel was burned to boil water in a chamber outside the engine. The steam produced passed through a valve in the engine, where it pushed a piston. The motion of the piston was transferred to the wheels of the locomotive.

Modern steam engines, such as those used in electrical power stations, don't have pistons. Instead, steam is directed onto huge, fanlike devices called turbines. The steam pushes against the turbine blades, and the turbine rotates rapidly.

Figure 6-13. Turbines are used to convert thermal energy to mechanical energy.

Heat Movers

When you put warm food into the refrigerator, the food gets cooler. Where does the thermal energy in the food go? Feel the back of the refrigerator, and you'll notice that it's warm. But you know that heat always flows from warmer to cooler areas. So how can heat flow from the cool refrigerator to the warm room? It can't unless work is done. The energy to do the work comes from the electricity that powers the refrigerator.

A refrigerator is an example of a heat mover. A **heat mover** is a device that removes thermal energy from one location and transfers it to another location at a different temperature. Refrigerators use the process of evaporation to remove heat from the food inside. A liquid is pumped through coils inside the refrigerator. In most cooling systems, liquid Freon is used because it evaporates at low temperatures. As the liquid evaporates and becomes a gas, it absorbs heat, cooling the inside of the refrigerator. The Freon gas is then pumped to a compressor on the outside of the refrigerator. Compressing the Freon causes its temperature to rise above room temperature. So the Freon loses heat to the air around it and becomes liquid again. The excess heat is transferred into the room, sometimes with the help of fans.

An air conditioner is another kind of heat mover, removing thermal energy from a warm house and transferring it to the even warmer outdoor surroundings.

A **heat pump** is a two-way heat mover. In warm weather, it operates like an air conditioner. But in cold weather, it removes thermal energy from the cool outside air and transfers it to the inside of the house.

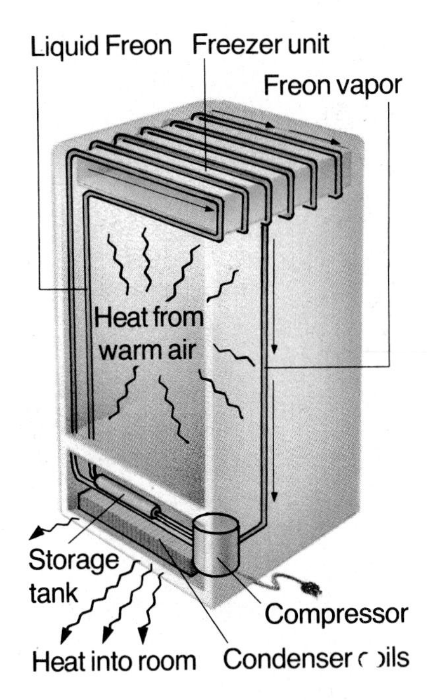

Figure 6-14. In a heat mover, such as a refrigerator, thermal energy is removed from one location and is released in another location.

SECTION REVIEW

1. What are the main differences between a diesel engine and a gasoline engine? How are they alike?
2. In a heat engine, chemical energy in the fuel is converted to thermal energy. What happens to the thermal energy?
3. **Apply:** On a hot day, a friend suggests you leave the refrigerator door open to make your house cooler. Is this a good idea? Explain your answer.

Concept Mapping

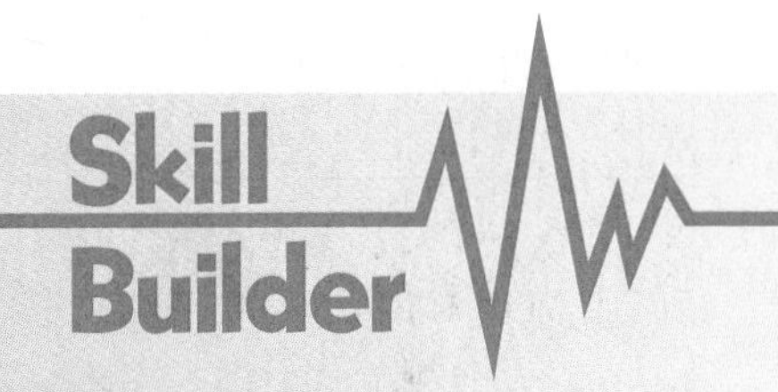

Make a cycle concept map to show the steps in one cycle of a four-stroke internal combustion engine. If you need help, refer to Concept Mapping in the **Skill Handbook** on pages 684 and 685.

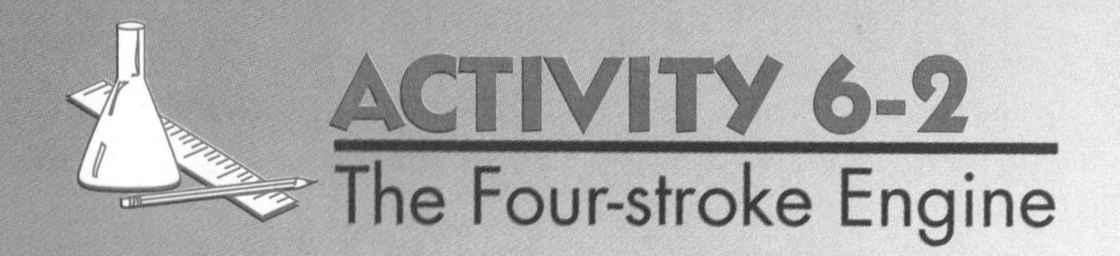

ACTIVITY 6-2
The Four-stroke Engine

Problem: *When does potential energy change to kinetic energy?*

Materials 

- matches
- flask, 250-mL
- glass or plastic "T"
- pinch clamps (2)
- large syringe, plastic
- rubber tubing (3 pieces)
- small piece of cloth or yarn
- rubber stopper, 2-hole, with glass tubing

Procedure

1. Set up a model four-stroke engine as shown.
2. Prepare a data table like the one shown. As you complete each step, identify the stroke and record your observations.
3. Ignite a small piece of cloth or yarn and drop it in the flask. **CAUTION:** *Exercise caution when using open flames.* Allow the flask, representing the carburetor, to fill with smoke.
4. With the piston inside the cylinder, open the intake valve and pull the piston down.
5. Close the intake valve and push the piston up into the cylinder.
6. Release the piston and observe what happens.
7. Open the exhaust valve and push the piston up into the cylinder.
8. Close the exhaust valve and repeat Steps 4-7.

Analyze

1. During which stroke are the smoke particles most widely separated?
2. What happens to the smoke particles when the intake valve is closed and the piston moves into the cyinder?
3. What happens when the piston is released?
4. What happens to the smoke particles when the exhaust valve is opened and the piston moves into the cylinder?
5. During what strokes are both valves closed?

Conclude and Apply

6. In this model, what does the smoke represent in Steps 4 and 5? In Step 7?
7. When would be the best instant to explode a fuel-air mixture?
8. In which stroke is kinetic energy changed to potential energy? potential to kinetic?

Data and Observations

Step	Stroke	Observations
4		
5		
6		
7		

CHAPTER

REVIEW

SUMMARY

6-1: Moving Thermal Energy

1. Thermal energy can be transferred by conduction, convection, and radiation. Conduction and convection can only occur when matter is present. Radiation does not require matter.
2. Materials that do not allow heat to move through them easily are insulators. Conductors allow heat to move through them easily.
3. Insulation slows down or prevents the movement of thermal energy.

6-2: Heating Systems

1. Heating systems are generally identified by the medium that transfers the thermal energy. The three most common types of heating systems are hot water, steam, and hot air.
2. A solar heating system converts radiant energy from the sun to thermal energy.
3. Passive solar systems have no devices to transfer heat from one part of the system to another. Active systems use fans or pumps to serve this purpose.

6-3: Science and Society: Thermal Pollution

1. Thermal pollution can adversely affect living things.
2. Specific practices have been identified that can greatly reduce thermal pollution at the source.

6-4: Using Heat to Do Work

1. Heat engines are devices that convert thermal energy produced by burning fuel into mechanical energy. In an internal combustion engine, fuel is burned inside the engine. In an external combustion engine, fuel is burned outside the engine.
2. Heat movers remove thermal energy from one place and release it in another place. In many cases, this transfer is from cooler to warmer regions.

KEY SCIENCE WORDS

a. **combustion**
b. **conduction**
c. **convection**
d. **cooling towers**
e. **external combustion engine**
f. **fluid**
g. **heat engines**
h. **heat mover**
i. **heat pump**
j. **insulators**
k. **internal combustion engine**
l. **radiation**
m. **radiator**
n. **solar collectors**
o. **solar energy**
p. **thermal pollution**

UNDERSTANDING VOCABULARY

Match each phrase with the correct term from the list of Key Science Words.

1. energy transfer by direct contact of particles
2. energy transfer by movement of particles from place to place
3. energy transfer by invisible waves
4. materials that resist the flow of heat
5. devices that absorb the sun's radiant energy
6. devices that convert thermal energy into mechanical energy
7. rapid burning
8. a device that transfers thermal energy from one place to another
9. devices in which warm water is cooled by fans or by evaporation
10. a device designed to heat the air that comes in contact with it

CHAPTER

REVIEW

CHECKING CONCEPTS

Choose the word or phrase that completes the sentence or answers the question.

1. Which is not a method of heat transfer?
   a. conduction **c.** radiation
   b. insulation **d.** convection
2. In ______, fuel is burned inside chambers called cylinders.
   a. internal combustion engines
   b. external combustion engines
   c. heat pumps
   d. steam engines
3. Waste gases are removed during the ______ of a four-stroke engine.
   a. power stroke **c.** compression engine
   b. intake stroke **d.** exhaust stroke
4. Which material is a poor insulator of heat?
   a. aluminum **c.** air
   b. feathers **d.** plastic
5. A ______ is an example of a heat mover.
   a. refrigerator **c.** radiator
   b. steam engine **d.** four-stroke engine
6. In which of these forms is water not a fluid?
   a. liquid water **c.** water vapor
   b. ice **d.** steam
7. Heat can move easily through a good ______.
   a. insulator **c.** conductor
   b. convector **d.** collector
8. Which of these does not require the presence of particles of matter?
   a. radiation **c.** convection
   b. conduction **d.** combustion
9. In order for radiant energy to change to thermal energy, it must be ______.
   a. reflected **c.** convected
   b. conducted **d.** absorbed
10. A(n) ______ is a two-way heat mover.
    a. refrigerator **c.** air conditioner
    b. steam engine **d.** heat pump

UNDERSTANDING CONCEPTS

Complete each sentence.

11. Double-pane windows have a thin layer of ______ trapped between two panes of glass.
12. ______ results when waste energy raises the temperature of the environment.
13. In an internal combustion engine, the flow of gases is controlled by ______ that open and close.
14. The ______ stroke of a four-stroke engine begins when the fuel-air mixture is ignited.
15. A radiator heats the air in a room by conduction and ______.

THINK AND WRITE CRITICALLY

16. Describe all of the ways in which energy is transferred while a bowl of soup is heated on an electric stove. Indicate how each type of energy transfer takes place.
17. Explain how convection currents are created. Describe two examples of convection currents that occur in nature.
18. Why is winter clothing generally darker in color than summer clothing? Explain why wearing two or three layers of clothing helps to keep you warmer than one thick layer in cold weather.
19. Compare and contrast passive and active solar heating. What basic principle are both systems based on?
20. Describe some causes and effects of thermal pollution. Suggest some solutions to this environmental problem.

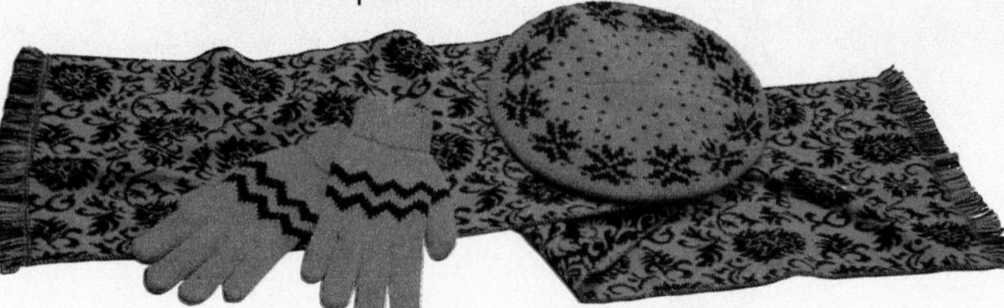

APPLY

21. The energy transfer shown in Figure 6-1 takes place at the particle level of matter. Thus, the transfer of energy cannot be observed directly. Think of an analogy or model using visible objects that you could use to demonstrate the process of conduction.
22. Explain why the inside of an automobile left sitting in direct sunlight for several hours becomes very warm.
23. Design a line of clothing to be used on an Arctic expedition. Describe the articles of clothing and explain why each will keep the wearer warm in extremely cold conditions.
24. The engines of many high-performance cars have four valves per cylinder rather than the usual two-valve arrangement. These engines also have fuel injectors at each cylinder rather than a single carburetor. How do these differences improve the performance of the engine?
25. Describe how an automobile air conditioner using Freon gas works. Explain why the engine must be running in order for the air conditioner to work.

MORE SKILL BUILDERS

If you need help, refer to the Skill Handbook.

1. **Interpreting Data:** Using the R-values given in Table 6-1, design an energy-efficient house. Indicate the type and thickness of the different materials to be used in constructing the walls and ceilings.
2. **Sequencing:** Order the events that occur in the removal of heat from an object by a refrigerator. Start with the placing of a warm object in the refrigerator and finish with the change in Freon from a gas to a liquid.
3. **Concept Mapping:** Complete the following events chain to show how an active solar heating system works.

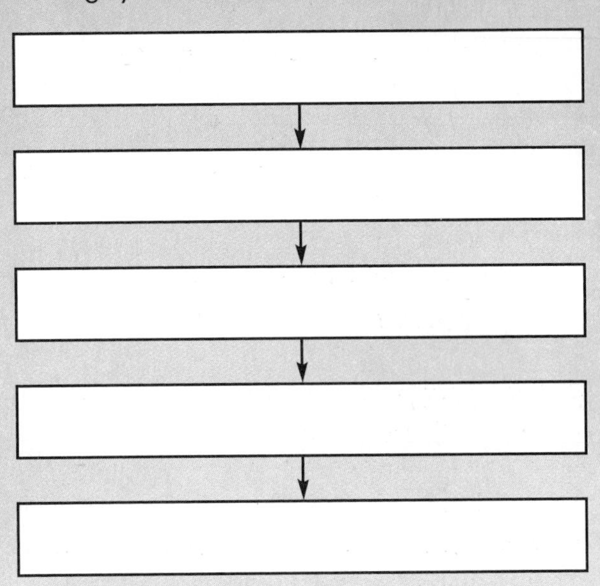

4. **Recognizing Cause and Effect:** Describe the probable effect of each of the following problems that might occur in a fuel-injected gasoline engine. Indicate the engine stroke that will be affected. (a) stuck exhaust valve; (b) clogged fuel injector; (c) bad spark plug; (d) intake valve will not close.
5. **Using Variables, Constants, and Controls:** Design an experiment to test the effects of surface area and length of a material on heat conduction. Indicate your hypothesis, controls, and constants. How will you organize and interpret your data?

PROJECTS

1. Design and construct an insulated container using household materials.
2. Research the development of the automobile engine. Construct a time line showing the most significant events.

CHAPTER

7 Machines

When you think of machines, you might think of gears. Not all machines have gears, though. Some have no moving parts at all. One way that people make jobs easier is by using machines. You might use a claw hammer to pull out a nail or a cart to help you carry a heavy load. How do devices such as these make work easier?

FIND OUT!

Do this activity to show how you can reduce effort needed to move an object.

Stack two books on a flat desk or table. Use one hand to push them along the surface. Observe the amount of effort you exert. Now put several round pencils under the bottom book and try again to push the books. Are they easier to push?

Remove the pencils and position the books so that they just hang over the edge of the desk. Place your fingertips under the bottom book and try to lift the books with your fingers. Set the books flat on the surface again and slide a ruler under the edge of the bottom book. Push up on the ruler to lift the books. (Make sure the books are not so heavy that the ruler will break.) Is it easier to lift the books using the ruler?

Gearing Up

Previewing the Chapter

Use this outline to help you focus on important ideas in this chapter.

Section 7-1 Why We Use Machines
- What Are Simple Machines?
- Advantages of Simple Machines

Section 7-2 The Simple Machines
- Levers
- Pulleys
- Wheel and Axle
- Inclined Plane
- Screw and Wedge

Section 7-3 Science and Society
Human-Powered Flying Machines
- Pedaling through the Sky

Section 7-4 Using Machines
- Compound Machines
- Efficiency
- Power

Previewing Science Skills

- In the **Skill Builders,** you will recognize cause and effect, make and use tables, and map concepts.
- In the **Activities,** you will observe, classify, measure in SI, and analyze.
- In the **MINI-Lab,** you will observe and measure in SI.

What's next?

You've shown that work can be made easier by reducing friction and using simple devices to reduce the amount of force you have to exert to move something. Now find out about some different devices used to make work easier, how they operate, and how much easier they make your work.

7-1 Why We Use Machines

New Science Words

machine
simple machine
effort force
resistance force
ideal machine
mechanical advantage

Objectives

- ▶ Explain how machines make work easier.
- ▶ Calculate mechanical advantage.

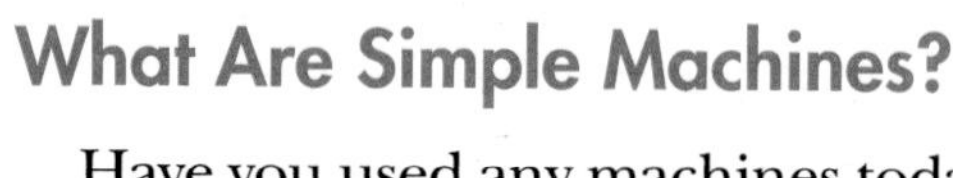

What Are Simple Machines?

Have you used any machines today? You probably know that a bicycle is a machine. Pencil sharpeners and can openers are also machines. Even if you haven't used any of these things, you have probably used at least one machine today. If you turned a doorknob or twisted off a bottle cap, you have used a machine. A **machine** is a device that makes work easier.

Some machines are powered by engines or electric motors; others are "people-powered." Some machines are very complex; others are quite simple. A **simple machine** is a device that does work with only one movement. There are six types of simple machines, examples of which are pictured below. You'll learn more about each type in a later section of this chapter.

Advantages of Simple Machines

Suppose you wanted to pry the lid off a paint can with a screwdriver. You'd slip the end of the screwdriver blade under the edge of the can lid and push down on the handle. You would do work on the screwdriver and the screwdriver would do work on the lid.

Recall from Chapter 5 that work is done when a force is exerted through a distance. A machine makes work easier by changing the size or direction of the force you exerted on it, or both. For example, when you use a screwdriver to lift a can lid, as shown in the photo on the right, both the size and direction of the force you exert on the screwdriver are changed. The force you exert on the screwdriver is less than the force exerted by the screwdriver on the lid. And when you push down, the lid moves up.

When you use a simple machine, you are trying to move something that resists being moved. You are trying to overcome some force of resistance, usually gravity (weight) or friction, or both. For example, when you use a crowbar to move a large rock, you are working against gravity—the weight of the rock. When you use a screwdriver to move a paint can lid, you are working against friction—the friction between the lid and the can.

What forces are always involved when a machine is used to do work?

Two forces are always involved when a machine is used to do work. The force applied *to* the machine is called the **effort force (F_e)**. The force applied *by* the machine to overcome resistance to gravity or friction is called **resistance force (F_r)**. In the screwdriver example, the effort force is the force you apply to the screwdriver handle. The resistance force is the force the screwdriver applies to the lid.

There are also two kinds of work to be considered when a machine is used—the work done *on* the machine and the work done *by* the machine. The work done on the machine is called work input (W_{in}); the work done by the machine is called work output (W_{out}). Recall that work is the product of force and distance: $W = F \times d$. Work input is the product of the effort force and the distance that force is exerted: $W_{in} = F_e \times d_e$. Work output is the product of the resistance force and the distance that force moves: $W_{out} = F_r \times d_r$.

It is important to remember that energy is always conserved. So, you can never get more work out of a machine than you put in. In other words, W_{out} can never be greater than W_{in}. In reality, whenever a machine is used, some

Figure 7-1. To lift the lid with the screwdriver, the effort distance (d_e) must be greater than the resistance distance (d_r).

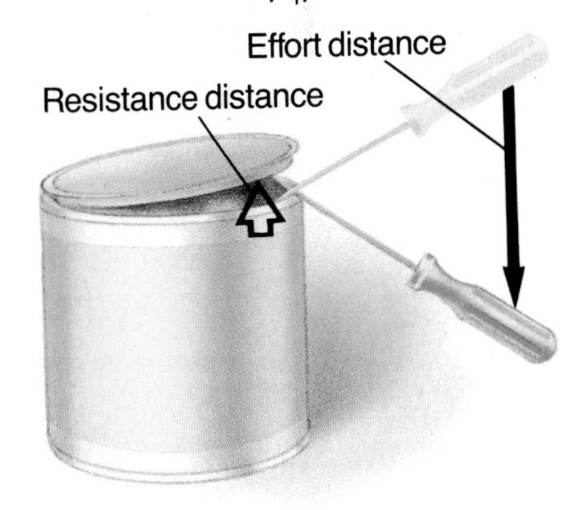

kinetic energy is changed to heat due to friction. So, W_{out} is always smaller than W_{in}.

To understand how machines work, it helps to imagine a frictionless machine, in which no energy is converted to heat. Such an **ideal machine** is one in which work input equals work output. For an ideal machine,

$$W_{in} = W_{out}$$

$$F_e \times d_e = F_r \times d_r$$

In most cases, a machine multiplies the force applied to it—F_r is greater than F_e. So, in order for work input to equal work output, the effort force must travel farther than the resistance force—d_e must be greater than d_r.

Think once again about the screwdriver and the can lid. The distance you move the screwdriver handle (d_e) is greater than the distance the screwdriver blade moves the lid (d_r). So, the blade must exert more force on the lid (F_r) than you exert on the handle (F_e). The machine multiplies your effort.

The number of times a machine multiplies the effort force is the **mechanical advantage (MA)** of the machine. To calculate mechanical advantage, you divide the resistance force by the effort force.

$$MA = \frac{\text{resistance force}}{\text{effort force}} = \frac{F_r}{F_e}$$

EcoTip

Use a simple machine and save energy resources. Use hand-operated tools to trim your lawn or remove snow from your sidewalk. You'll help to save natural resources and you'll get a little exercise, too.

EXAMPLE PROBLEM: Calculating Mechanical Advantage

Problem Statement:

A worker applies an effort force of 10 N to pry open a window that has a resistance of 500 N. What is the mechanical advantage of the crowbar?

Known Information:

Strategy Hint: Mechanical advantage has no units.

resistance force, F_r = 500 N
effort force, F_e = 10 N

Unknown Information:

mechanical advantage (MA)

Equation to Use:

$$MA = \frac{F_r}{F_e}$$

Solution:

$$MA = \frac{500 \text{ N}}{10 \text{ N}} = 50$$

PRACTICE PROBLEM

Strategy Hint: Rearrange the equation.

1. Find the effort force needed to lift a 2000-N rock, using a jack with a mechanical advantage of 10.

Some machines don't multiply force. Instead, they change the direction of the effort force. For example, when you pull down on the cord of window blinds, the blinds go up. Only the direction of the force changes; the effort force and resistance force are equal, so the mechanical advantage is 1.

Other machines have mechanical advantages less than 1. Such machines are used to increase the distance an object moves or the speed at which it moves.

Think again about all the machines you've seen in use today. What kind of work went into each machine, and what came out? Was the mechanical advantage greater than, less than, or equal to 1?

SECTION REVIEW

1. Explain how simple machines can make work easier without violating the law of conservation of energy.
2. A carpenter uses a claw hammer to pull a nail from a board. The nail has a resistance of 2500 N. The carpenter applies an effort force of 125 N. What is the mechanical advantage of the hammer?
3. **Apply:** Give an example of a simple machine you've used recently. How did you apply effort force? How did the machine apply resistance force?

Recognizing Cause and Effect

When you operate a machine, it's often easy to observe cause and effect. For example, when you turn a doorknob, the latch in the door moves. Give five examples of machines and describe one cause-and-effect pair in the action of each machine. If you need help, refer to Recognizing Cause and Effect in the **Skill Handbook** on page 679.

ACTIVITY 7-1
Using Machines

Problem: *Can you invent a machine?*

Materials
- brick
- book
- string
- dowel, pencil-sized (2)
- hard board
- pulley
- ring stand and ring

NOTE: While conducting this activity, follow these simple rules:

Do not touch the brick with your hands.

Only one person at a time may apply force on the brick.

Procedure
1. Place the brick and the book about 30 cm apart on the table top.
2. Use any of the materials or combinations of materials to move the brick until it rests on top of the book.
3. Make a written record of your attempts. Describe what you did and what happened. Explain any failures as best you can.
4. Try as many different ways as you can think of to accomplish the task.

Analyze
1. Prepare a set of instructions for one of the methods you devised for moving the brick.
2. Identify the kind(s) of machine(s) you used in each of the steps in your method.

Conclude and Apply
3. Of the different methods you tried, describe the one you like best and explain why you prefer it.
4. Of the machines you used, which provided the greatest mechanical advantage?
5. Give your set of instructions for moving the brick to another team. See if they can use your method successfully.

The Simple Machines 7-2

Objectives

- Describe the six types of simple machines.
- Calculate the mechanical advantage for different types of simple machines.

New Science Words

lever
fulcrum
effort arm
resistance arm
pulley
wheel and axle
inclined plane
screw
wedge

Levers

If you've ever ridden a seesaw, pried the cap from a bottle of soda pop, or swung a tennis racket, you have used a lever. A **lever** is a bar that is free to pivot, or turn, about a fixed point. The fixed point of a lever is called the **fulcrum** (FUL krum). The part of the lever on which the effort force is applied is called the **effort arm.** The part of the lever that exerts the resistance force is called the **resistance arm.**

Suppose you are using a crowbar to pry the lid from a crate. You can see in Figure 7-2 that the edge of the crate acts as the fulcrum. You push down on the effort arm of the crowbar. The bar pivots about the fulcrum, and the resistance arm exerts a force on the lid, lifting it upward.

Figure 7-2. The crowbar is being used as a lever. The edge of the crate acts as the fulcrum.

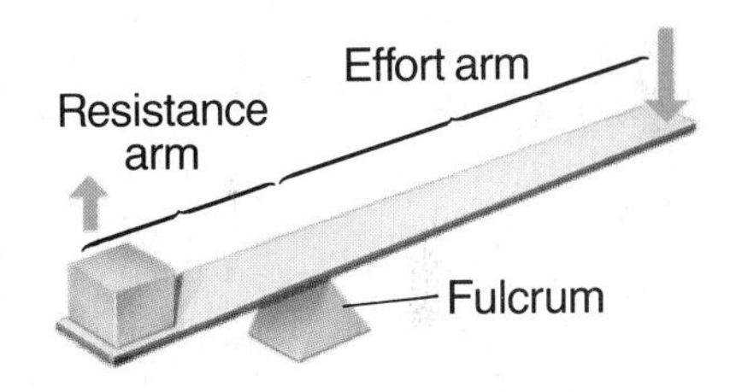

Science and WRITING

When you are playing baseball or softball, your coach may tell you to "choke up on the bat." The bat is a lever. Explain how changing the position of your hands on the bat affects the operation of this simple machine.

The type of lever shown in Figure 7-2 makes work easier by multiplying your effort force. Like all simple machines, this lever has a mechanical advantage. You've learned that the mechanical advantage of any machine can be calculated by dividing the resistance force by the effort force. You can also use the lengths of the arms of a lever to find the mechanical advantage of the lever. The length of the effort arm is the distance from the fulcrum to the point where effort force is applied. The length of the resistance arm is the distance from the fulcrum to the point where the resistance force is applied. The following equation can be used to find the mechanical advantage of any lever:

$$MA = \frac{\text{length of effort arm}}{\text{length of resistance arm}} = \frac{L_e}{L_r}$$

EXAMPLE PROBLEM: Mechanical Advantage of a Lever

Problem Statement:

A worker uses an iron bar to raise a manhole cover weighing 65 N. The effort arm of the lever is 60 cm long. The resistance arm is 25 cm long. What is the mechanical advantage of the bar?

Known Information:

Strategy Hint: Which equation for mechanical advantage will you use?

length of effort arm, L_e = 60 cm
length of resistance arm, L_r = 25 cm

Unknown Information:

mechanical advantage (MA)

Equation to Use:

$$MA = \frac{L_e}{L_r}$$

Solution:

$$MA = \frac{60 \text{ cm}}{25 \text{ cm}} = 2.4$$

PRACTICE PROBLEM

Strategy Hint: Find the lengths of the effort arm and the resistance arm.

1. You use a crowbar 160 cm long as a lever to lift a large rock. The rock is 20 cm from the fulcrum. You push down on the other end of the crowbar. What is the MA of the lever?

There are three different types, or classes, of levers. These classes are based on the positions of the effort force, resistance force, and fulcrum. Figure 7-3 shows the three classes of levers.

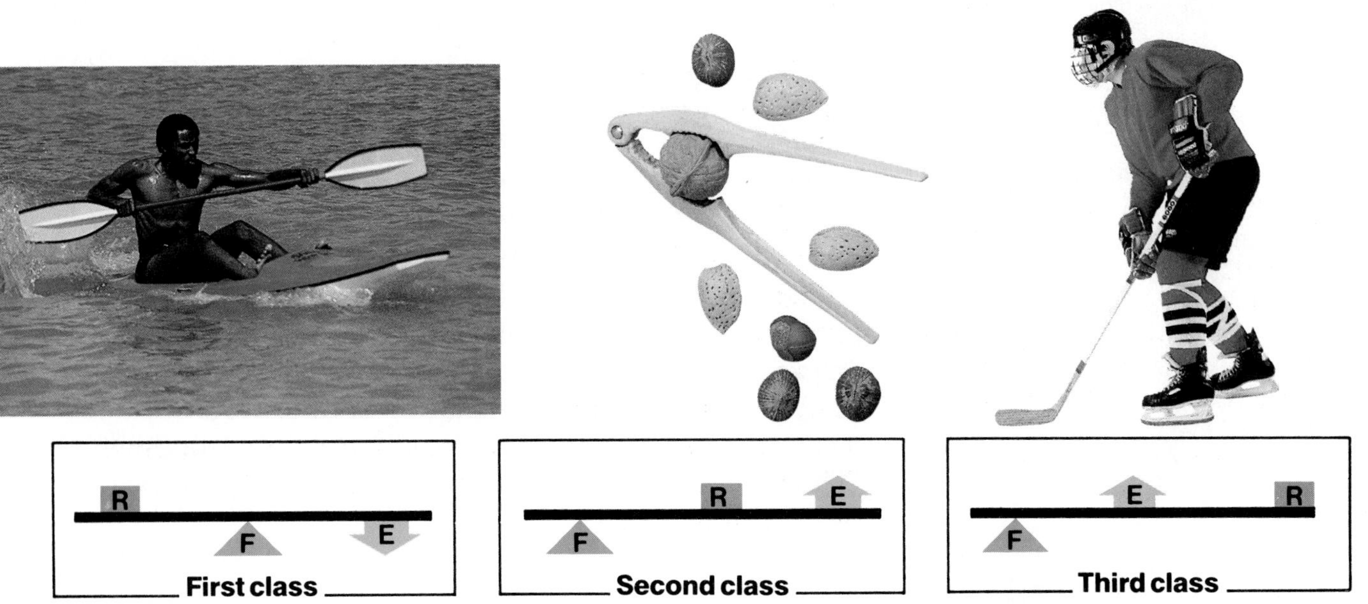

Figure 7-3. The classes of levers differ in the positions of the effort force, the resistance force, and the fulcrum.

If you look at the examples of third-class levers, you will see that the effort arm is always shorter than the resistance arm. So, the *MA* of a third-class lever is always less than 1. This means that a third-class lever does not multiply force. A third-class lever multiplies the distance the effort force travels.

PROBLEM SOLVING

How Do You Use Your Arm as a Lever?

The muscles and bones of your body work together as levers. Try contracting your biceps muscle to see how a simple body lever works.

The two bones in your forearm act as the bar of the lever. Because the elbow is the point where the arm lever pivots, it is the fulcrum. The bones in your forearm are attached to the upper arm bone by ligaments at the elbow. When you contract your biceps, this muscle exerts an effort force on the forearm bones to pull them upward. The entire forearm is the resistance force. What class of lever is being demonstrated when you raise your forearm?

Think Critically: Identify the fulcrum, effort force, and resistance force when you lower your arm, using the triceps muscle on the back of your upper arm.

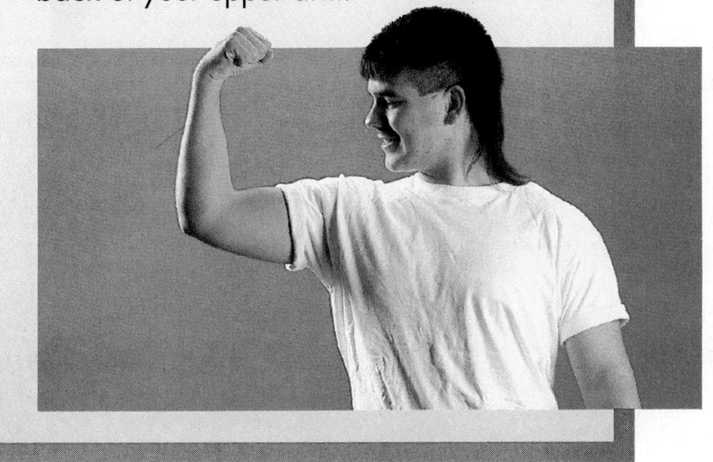

Figure 7-4. This single fixed pulley changes the direction of the effort force.

Pulleys

Have you ever seen someone raise a flag on a flagpole? A pulley is used to help get the flag to the top of the pole. A **pulley** is a grooved wheel with a rope or a chain running along the groove. Figure 7-4 shows a typical pulley.

A pulley works something like a first-class lever. Instead of a bar, a pulley has a rope. The two ends of the rope are the effort arm and the resistance arm. The wheel of the pulley acts like the fulcrum.

Pulleys can be fixed or movable. A fixed pulley is attached to something that doesn't move, such as a ceiling, wall, or tree. A fixed pulley can change the direction of an effort force. When you pull down on the effort arm of the rope, the pulley raises the object attached to the resistance arm. Because the resistance arm and effort arm are of equal length, the *MA* of a fixed pulley is 1. Thus, a fixed pulley does not multiply the effort force.

A movable pulley is attached to the object being moved, as shown in Figure 7-5. The difference between a fixed pulley and a movable pulley is shown in Figure 7-6. Unlike the fixed pulley, a movable pulley does multiply the effort force. Because a movable pulley multiplies force, its *MA* is greater than 1. In fact, the *MA* of a single movable pulley is 2. This means that an effort force of 1 N will lift a weight (resistance) of 2 N. In order to conserve energy, the effort distance must be twice as large as the resistance distance.

Fixed and movable pulleys can be combined to make a system of pulleys called a block and tackle. Depending on the number of pulleys used, a block and tackle can have a large mechanical advantage. The mechanical advantage of any ideal pulley or pulley system is equal to the number of ropes that support

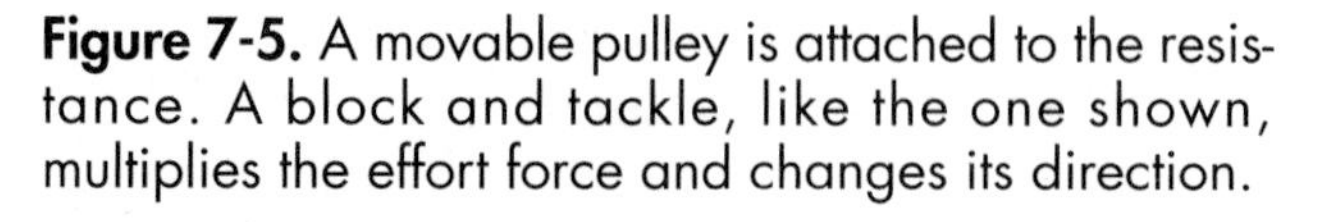

Figure 7-5. A movable pulley is attached to the resistance. A block and tackle, like the one shown, multiplies the effort force and changes its direction.

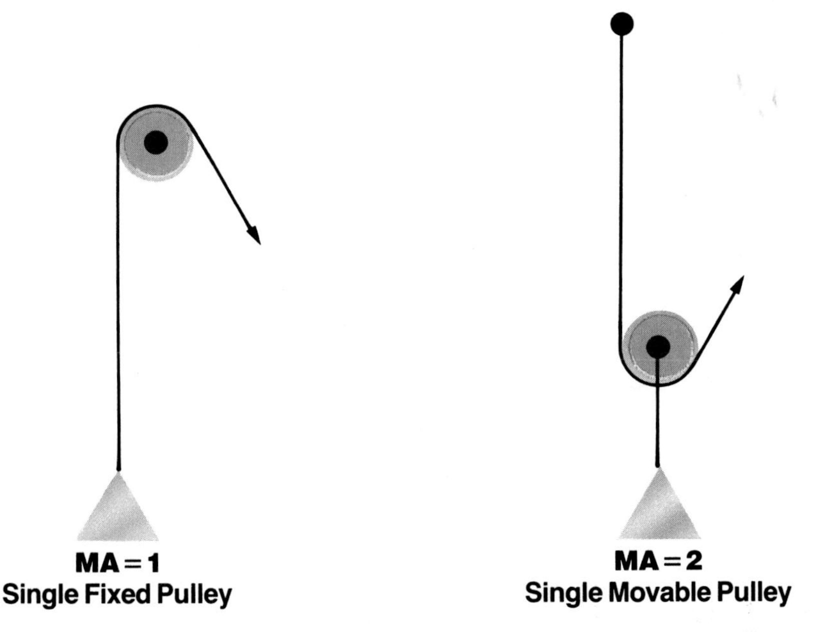
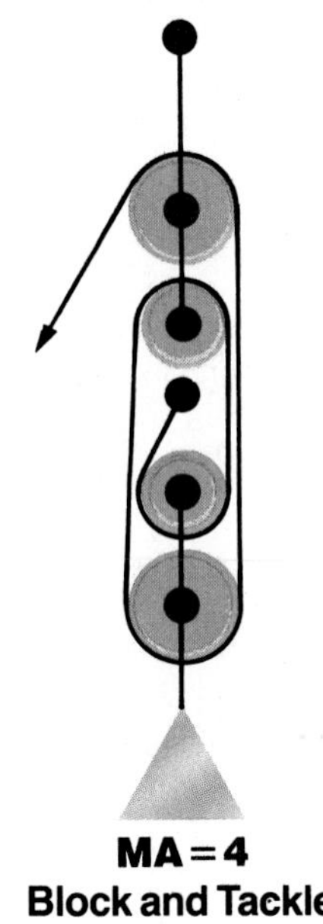

Figure 7-6. The mechanical advantage of each type of pulley can be found by counting every rope except the effort rope.

the resistance weight. As Figure 7-6 shows, the only rope that does not support the resistance weight is the rope leading from the pulley system to the effort force.

Wheel and Axle

Look closely at a doorknob or a water faucet. Do they look like simple machines to you? Do they help you make work easier? If you don't think so, remove the knob or handle from its narrow shaft. Now try opening the door or turning on the water by rotating that shaft with your fingers. After a few minutes, you'll appreciate the fact that the knob and handle, together with their shafts, do make work easier. They are machines.

Doorknobs and faucets are examples of a wheel and axle. A **wheel and axle** is a simple machine consisting of two wheels of different sizes that rotate together. An effort force is usually applied to the larger wheel. The smaller wheel, called the axle, exerts the resistance force. In many cases the larger wheel doesn't look like a typical circular wheel. It may be a crank handle, like that of an ice cream freezer or a meat grinder. But it always travels in a circle.

Figure 7-7. A water faucet is an example of a wheel and axle. Without the faucet handle (wheel), the shaft of the faucet (axle) is difficult to turn.

Figure 7-8. The length of the crank handle represents the radius of the wheel in this simple machine.

It might help to think of a wheel and axle as being a lever attached to a shaft. The radius of the wheel is the effort arm, and the radius of the axle is the resistance arm. The center of the axle is the fulcrum. As with the lever, the mechanical advantage of a wheel and axle can be calculated by dividing the radius of the wheel ("effort arm") by the radius of the axle ("resistance arm").

$$MA = \frac{\text{radius of wheel}}{\text{radius of axle}} = \frac{r_w}{r_a}$$

EXAMPLE PROBLEM: Calculating *MA* of a Wheel and Axle

Problem Statement:

In the ice-cream freezer shown in Figure 7-8, the wheel has a radius of 20 cm. The axle has a radius of 2 cm. What is the mechanical advantage of the wheel and axle?

Known Information:

Strategy Hint: What happens to the units when you divide?

radius of wheel, r_w = 20 cm
radius of axle, r_a = 2 cm

Unknown Information:

mechanical advantage (*MA*)

Equation to Use:

$$MA = \frac{r_w}{r_a}$$

Solution:

$$MA = \frac{20 \text{ cm}}{2 \text{ cm}} = 10$$

PRACTICE PROBLEM

Strategy Hint: Use the diameter to find the radius of circle.

1. An automobile steering wheel having a diameter of 48 cm is used to turn the steering column, which has a radius of 4 cm. What is the *MA* of this wheel and axle?

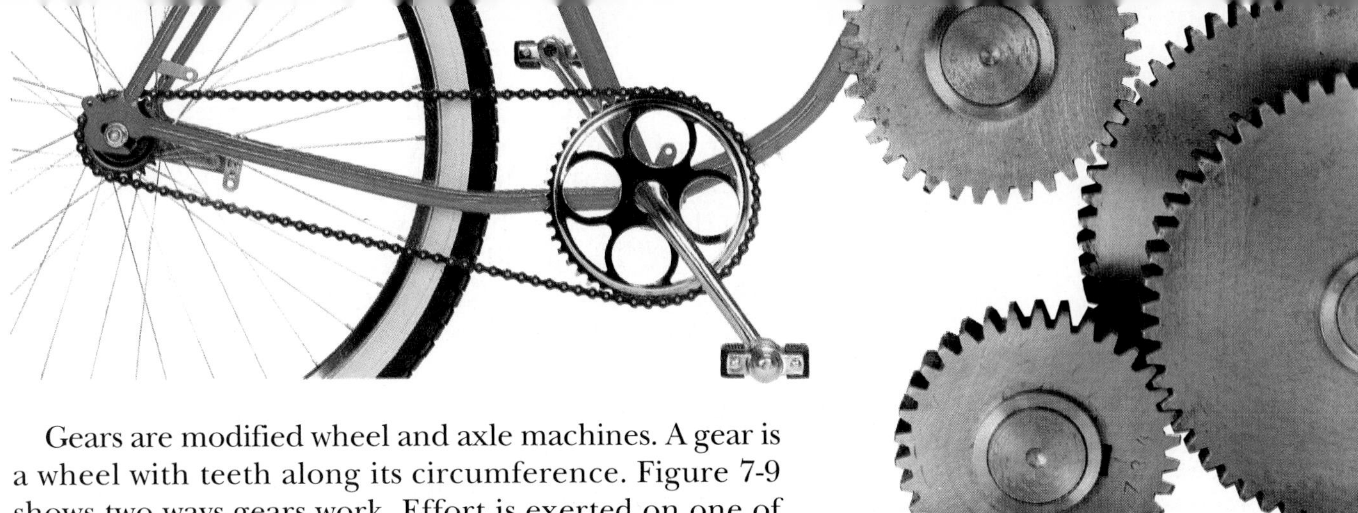

Gears are modified wheel and axle machines. A gear is a wheel with teeth along its circumference. Figure 7-9 shows two ways gears work. Effort is exerted on one of the gears, causing the other gear to turn. In most gears, the larger gear is the effort gear. The mechanical advantage of a pair of gears is found by dividing the radius of the effort gear by the radius of the resistance gear. This is known as the gear ratio of the pair.

Figure 7-9. In both cases, turning one gear causes the other gear to turn.

Inclined Plane

Suppose you had to move a heavy box from the ground up onto a porch. Would you rather lift the box straight up or slide it up a ramp? The ramp would make your job easier. A ramp is a type of **inclined plane,** a sloping surface used to raise objects.

The amount of work done on the box is the same whether you lift it straight up or slide it up the ramp. But remember that work has two parts, force and distance. When you lift the box straight onto the porch, the distance is small, but you must exert a large force. Using the ramp, you have to cover more distance, but you exert less force.

You can calculate mechanical advantage of an ideal inclined plane using distances, just as you did for a lever.

$$MA = \frac{\text{effort distance}}{\text{resistance distance}} = \frac{\text{length}}{\text{height}} = \frac{l}{h}$$

Figure 7-10. The ramp is an example of an inclined plane.

Screw and Wedge

The screw and the wedge are both examples of inclined planes that move. A **screw** is an inclined plane wrapped in a spiral around a cylindrical post. If you look closely

at the screw, you'll see that the threads form a tiny "ramp" that runs around the screw from its tip to near its top.

Imagine you're driving a screw into a board. As you turn the screw, the threads seem to "pull" the screw into the wood. The wood seems to "slide" up the inclined plane. Actually, the plane slides through the wood.

A **wedge** is an inclined plane with one or two sloping sides. Chisels, knives, and axe blades are examples of wedges. A typical inclined plane, such as a ramp, stays in one place while materials move along its surface. With a wedge, the material remains in one place while the wedge moves through it.

Figure 7-11. The blade of the axe and the threads of the screw are special types of inclined planes.

While reading about the six types of simple machines, perhaps you've noticed that they are all variations of two basic machines—the lever and the inclined plane. As you go about your daily activities, look for examples of each type of simple machine. See if you can tell how each makes work easier.

SECTION REVIEW

1. Give one example of each kind of simple machine. Use examples different from the ones in the text.
2. Explain why the six kinds of simple machines are really variations on just two basic machines.
3. **Apply:** When would the friction of an inclined plane be useful?

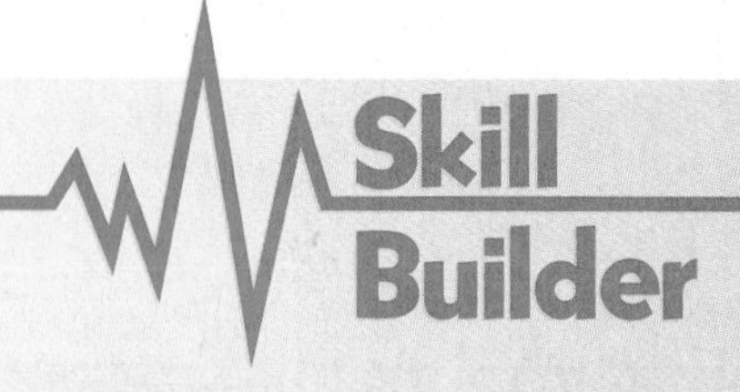

Making and Using Tables

Organize information about the six kinds of simple machines into a table. Include the type of machine, an example of each type, and a brief description of how it works. You may include other information if you wish. If you need help, refer to Making and Using Tables in the **Skill Handbook** on page 686.

ACTIVITY 7-2
Levers

Problem: *Can you measure mass with a lever?*

Materials
- sheet of paper, 20 cm × 28 cm ($8\frac{1}{2}$" × 11")
- coins, 3 (quarter, dime, nickel)
- balance
- metric ruler

Procedure
1. Make a lever by folding the paper into a strip 3 cm wide by 28 cm long.
2. Mark a line 2 cm from one end of the paper strip. Label this line "Resistance."
3. Slide the other end of the paper strip over the edge of a table until the strip begins to teeter on the edge. Mark a line across the paper at the table edge and label this line "Effort."
4. Measure the mass of the paper to the nearest 0.1 g. Write this mass on the "Effort" line.
5. Center a dime on the "Resistance" line.
6. Locate the fulcrum by sliding the paper strip until it begins to teeter on the edge. Mark the balance line. Label it "Fulcrum #1."
7. Measure the lengths of the resistance arm and the effort arm to the nearest 0.1 cm.
8. Calculate the *MA* of the lever.
9. Multiply the *MA* times the mass of the lever to find the mass of the coin.
10. Repeat Steps 5 through 9 with the nickel and then with the quarter. Mark the fulcrum line #2 for the nickel and #3 for the quarter.

Analyze
1. In this activity, is the effective total length of the lever a constant or a variable?
2. Are the lengths of the resistance and effort arms constants or variables?
3. What provides the effort force?
4. What does it mean if the MA is less than 1.0?

Conclude and Apply
5. Is it necessary to have the resistance line 2.0 cm from the end of the paper?
6. The calculations are done as if the entire weight of the paper is located at what point?
7. Why can mass units be used in place of force units in this kind of problem?

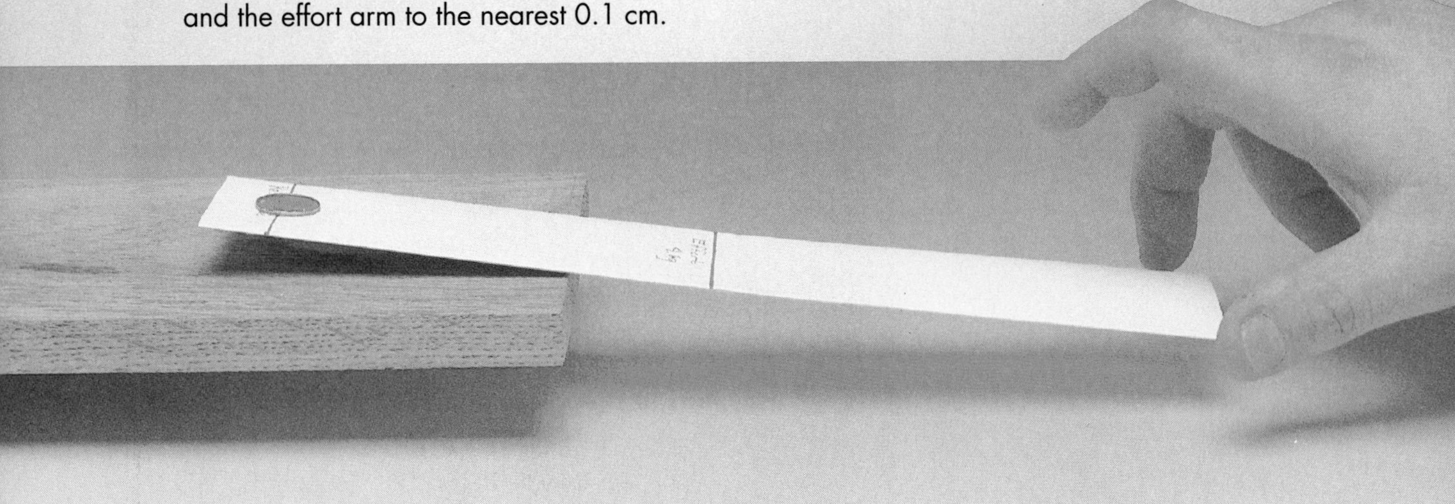

7-3: Human-Powered Flying Machines

Objectives

- **Analyze the simple machines in a human-powered aircraft.**
- **Consider the value of experiments with no obvious practical value.**

Pedaling through the Sky

Can you imagine how it would feel to pedal a bicycle through the air? That's probably how Greek cycling champion Kanellos Kanellopoulos felt in 1988, when he flew the Daedalus, a human-powered aircraft, 115 kilometers across the Aegean Sea.

Designed at the Massachusetts Institute of Technology, the Daedalus has pedals like a bicycle. The pilot applies an effort force to the pedals, and the force is transferred, through gears, to a propeller. The plane is human-powered because the pilot's legs are the only source of power.

In designing the plane, engineers did experiments to find out exactly how much power would be needed to fly it. One earlier model required about 1.5 watts of power for every pound the pilot weighed. That wasn't good enough—even a well-conditioned pilot would be able to provide enough power to fly the plane only 80 kilometers. By redesigning the aircraft, the engineers came up with a version that needed less power.

Kanellopoulos bicycled 800 kilometers a week to train for the flying feat. During the flight, he pedalled for nearly four hours, swigging a special high-energy drink until he complained that his stomach was full and "sloshing around."

As Kanellopoulos soared 12 meters above the sea, the director of the Daedalus project mused, "This is insane, but wonderful." Just 9 meters away from shore, a gust of wind snapped the tail off the Daedalus, and the plane fell, landing on an inflatable raft. Daedalus was a mess, but Kanellopoulos was safe, and the flight was declared a success.

SECTION REVIEW

1. Look at the simple diagram of the Daedalus. How many simple machines can you identify?
2. Would you feel differently about the value of the Daedalus project if Kanellopoulos had been hurt when the plane fell into the sea?

You Decide!

The researchers who worked on Daedalus often are asked if the project had any practical value. Can you think of any useful applications of their research? Do you think it is ever worthwhile to spend time and money on research that has no immediate practical applications? What would help you decide whether a research project is worth doing?

7-4 Using Machines

New Science Words

compound machine
efficiency
power
watt

Objectives

- Recognize the simple machines that make up a complex machine.
- Calculate efficiency of a machine.
- Describe the relationship between work, power, and time.

Compound Machines

Many machines that you use, such as a lawn mower or a pencil sharpener, are made up of several simple machines. A combination of two or more simple machines is a **compound machine.** Even a tool as simple as an axe is a compound machine made up of a wedge and a lever.

Often the simple machines that make up a compound machine are concealed. However, in one familiar compound machine—the bicycle—many of the simple machines are visible and easily recognized.

Look at the bicycle in Figure 7-12. The pedal mechanism is a wheel-and-axle system made up of two wheels

Figure 7-12. A bicycle is made up of many simple machines that work together.

attached to the same axle. Each pedal moves in a circle, like a wheel. The axle is a gear. The effort force exerted on the pedals by the rider turns this pedal gear. The bicycle chain transfers the force to a smaller gear attached to the rear wheel. This wheel gear is actually the effort wheel of the rear wheel-and-axle system. As the wheel gear turns, it causes the rear wheel to turn, and the wheel exerts the resistance force, through the tires, on the road. Because the wheel gear is smaller than the pedal gear that drives it, the rear wheel turns faster than the pedals do.

The overall mechanical advantage of a bicycle is the ratio of the resistance force exerted by the tires on the road to the effort force exerted by the rider on the pedals. The bicycle shown in Figure 7-12 has only two gears. Its gear ratio is fixed, so its mechanical advantage cannot be changed. This makes it a one-speed bike. A ten-speed bike has two pedal gears and five wheel gears. By shifting gears, the rider can change gear ratios, thus changing the mechanical advantage of the bicycle.

Figure 7-13. The rear wheel of a ten-speed bicycle has five different gears.

A bicycle has many other simple machines. Some of these machines are shown in Figure 7-12. See if you can tell what each does. Can you think of any others?

Efficiency

You learned earlier that some of the energy put into a machine is "lost" as thermal energy produced as a result of friction. So the work put out by a machine is always less than the work put into the machine.

Efficiency is a measure of how much of the work put into a machine is changed to useful work put out by a machine. The higher the efficiency of a machine, the greater the amount of work input is changed to useful work output. Efficiency is calculated by dividing work output by work input and is usually expressed as a percentage.

$$\text{efficiency} = \frac{W_{out}}{W_{in}} \times 100\% = \frac{F_r \times d_r}{F_e \times d_e} \times 100\%$$

Why must the efficiency of a machine always be less than 100 percent? Can you think of ways to increase the efficiency of a machine?

Did You Know?

Talk about a complex machine! The longest tandem bicycle is about 20 meters long and weighs about 1100 kilograms. With this vehicle you could take 34 of your friends along for a ride.

EXAMPLE PROBLEM: Calculating Efficiency

Problem Statement:

A piece of furniture weighing 1500 N is pushed up an inclined plane that is 4.0 m long and 1.0 m high. A worker pushing the furniture uses a force of 500 N. What is the efficiency of the inclined plane?

Known Information:

Strategy Hint: Can your answer be greater than 100 percent?

resistance force, $F_r = 1500$ N
resistance distance, $d_r = 1.0$ m
effort force, $F_e = 500$ N
effort distance, $d_e = 4.0$ m

Unknown Information:

efficiency

Equation to Use:

$$\text{efficiency} = \frac{F_r \times d_r}{F_e \times d_e} \times 100\%$$

Solution:

$$\text{efficiency} = \frac{1500 \text{ N} \times 1.0 \text{ m}}{500 \text{ N} \times 4.0 \text{ m}} \times 100\% = 75\%$$

PRACTICE PROBLEM

Strategy Hint: How is this problem different from the sample problem?

1. Using a fixed pulley, you exert a 72-N force to raise a 65-N object. What is the efficiency of the pulley?

Many machines can be made more efficient by reducing friction. This is usually done by adding a lubricant, such as oil or grease, to surfaces that rub together. After a time, dirt will build up on the grease or oil, and the lubricant will lose its effectiveness. The dirty lubricant should be wiped off and replaced with clean grease or oil. Can you think of any other ways to increase the efficiency of a machine?

Power

Suppose you and a friend are pushing boxes of books up a ramp to load them into a truck. The boxes weigh the same, but your friend is able to push a box a little faster than you can. Your friend moves a box up the ramp in 30 seconds. It takes you 45 seconds. Do you both do the same amount of work? Yes. This is true because the boxes weighed the same and were moved the same distance. The only difference is in the time it takes you and your friend to do the work.

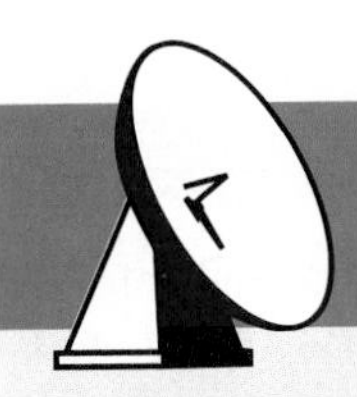

TECHNOLOGY

Micromachines

Imagine a robot the size of a flyspeck. Thousands of these robots could be injected into your bloodstream to clean out deposits or to identify and destroy bacteria, viruses, and cancer cells. This is the future predicted by a new group of engineers called micromechanical engineers.

These engineers use a sculpting process similar to that used in microelectronics to create mechanical devices a few microns thick. (A human hair is about 75 microns across.) The sculpting is done in silicon, which at this size demonstrates a strength similar to that of steel.

Micromechanical sensors are already widely used to detect pressure, acceleration, and temperature. However, these sensors are passive. Tiny robots will reduce micromachines that can make things move. Recently, scientists at the University of California at Berkeley constructed a rotary motor that is only about two-thirds the diameter of a human hair. The central motor is 0.002 inches across, and the rotor arm is about the size of a red blood cell. Although working on this very small scale still involves many unknowns, the possibilities are unlimited.

Think Critically: What are some of the problems encountered by mechanical engineers that may be quite different in machines constructed at the micron level?

Your friend has more power than you have. **Power** is the rate at which work is done. In other words, power is a measure of the amount of work done in a certain amount of time. To calculate power, divide the work done by the time required to do the work.

$$\text{power} = \frac{\text{work}}{\text{time}}$$

$$P = \frac{W}{t}$$

Power is measured in watts, named for James Watt, the inventor of the steam engine. A **watt (W)** is one joule per second. A watt is pretty small—about equal to the power used to raise a glass of water from your knees to your

MINI-Lab

Can you measure the power of a toy car?

Wind up a toy car and place it at the bottom of an inclined plane. Adjust the angle of the inclined plane so the car will reach the top at the *slowest* speed possible. Measure the time in seconds for the car to travel to the top. Measure the *weight* of the car in newtons. Measure the height of the inclined plane in meters. Use weight and height to calculate the work in joules. Divide work by time to get power in watts.

EXAMPLE PROBLEM: Calculating Power

Problem Statement: A figure skater lifts his partner, who weighs 450 N, 1 m in 3 s. How much power is required?

Known Information:

Strategy Hint: Remember that work = force × distance.

force, $F = 450$ N
distance, $d = 1$ m
time, $t = 3$ s

Unknown Information: power (P)

Equation to Use:

$$P = \frac{W}{t} = \frac{F \times d}{t}$$

Solution:

$$P = \frac{450 \text{ N} \times 1 \text{ m}}{3 \text{ s}} = 150 \text{ W}$$

PRACTICE PROBLEM

Strategy Hint: Should your answer be in watts or kilowatts?

1. A 500-N passenger is inside a 24 500-N elevator that rises 30.0 m in exactly 1 minute. How much power is needed for the elevator's trip?

mouth in one second. Because the watt is such a small unit, large amounts of power often are expressed in kilowatts. One kilowatt (kW) equals 1000 watts.

SECTION REVIEW

1. Give an example of a compound machine. What are the simple machines that make it up?
2. How are power, work, and time related?
3. **Apply:** You buy a secondhand lawn mower with an efficiency of 30 percent. By repairing and lubricating it, you increase its efficiency to 40 percent. How does this affect the work put out by the lawn mower for a given amount of work put in?

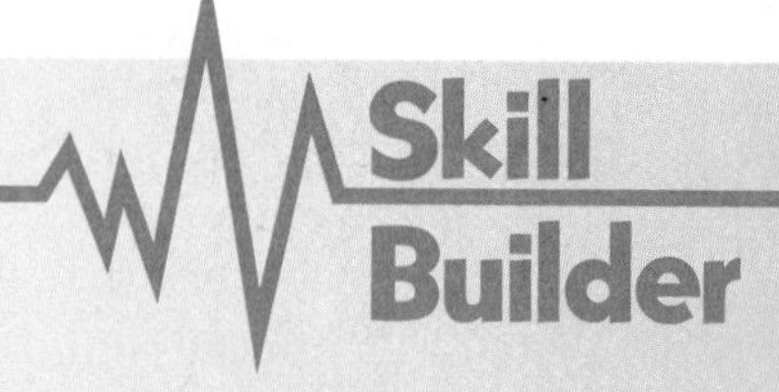

Concept Mapping

Make an events chain concept map to show how some of the simple machines in a bicycle work together to move the bicycle. Start with the feet applying force to the pedals. If you need help, refer to Concept Mapping in the **Skill Handbook** on pages 684 and 685.

CHAPTER

REVIEW

SUMMARY

7-1: Why We Use Machines

1. A machine makes work easier by changing the size of the force applied to it, the direction of that force, or both.

2. The number of times a machine multiplies the force applied to it is the mechanical advantage of the machine.

7-2: The Simple Machines

1. A lever is a bar that is free to pivot about a fixed point called a fulcrum. A pulley is a grooved wheel with a rope running along the groove. A wheel and axle consists of two different-sized wheels that rotate together. An inclined plane is a sloping surface used to raise objects. The screw and the wedge are special types of inclined planes.

2. Each type of simple machine has a specific equation for calculating its mechanical advantage. Each equation is related to the distance the effort force moves divided by the distance the resistance force moves.

7-3: Science and Society: Human-Powered Flying Machines

1. Simple machines can be combined to increase force and transfer that force from one place to another. Using a combination of simple machines, a human was able to propel a specially built airplane for a distance of more than 100 kilometers. The effort force for this flight was exerted by the pilot's legs.

2. Any experiment may have practical value that is not obvious at first.

7-4: Using Machines

1. A combination of two or more simple machines is called a compound machine.

2. The efficiency of any machine is a ratio of the work put into a machine to the useful work put out by the machine.

3. Power is a measure of the amount of work done in a certain amount of time. The SI unit of power is the watt, which is equivalent to one joule per second.

KEY SCIENCE WORDS

a. **compound machine**
b. **efficiency**
c. **effort arm**
d. **effort force**
e. **fulcrum**
f. **ideal machine**
g. **inclined plane**
h. **lever**
i. **machine**
j. **mechanical advantage**
k. **power**
l. **pulley**
m. **resistance arm**
n. **resistance force**
o. **screw**
p. **simple machine**
q. **watt**
r. **wedge**
s. **wheel and axle**

UNDERSTANDING VOCABULARY

Match each phrase with the correct term from the list of Key Science Words.

1. any device that accomplishes work with only one movement
2. force applied by a machine
3. a device in which work output equals work input
4. a bar that pivots about a fixed point
5. two different-sized wheels that rotate together
6. a combination of simple machines
7. the work output of a machine divided by the work input
8. the rate at which work is done
9. the fixed point of a lever
10. an inclined plane wrapped around a cylinder

CHAPTER REVIEW

CHECKING CONCEPTS

Choose the word or phrase that completes the sentence or answers the question.

1. There are ______ types of simple machines.
   a. 3 **c.** 8
   b. 6 **d.** 10
2. Which of these cannot be done by a machine?
   a. multiply force
   b. multiply energy
   c. change direction of a force
   d. all of these
3. In an ideal machine, the work input ______ work output.
   a. is equal to **c.** is less than
   b. is greater than **d.** none of these
4. The ______ of a machine is the number of times it multiplies the effort force.
   a. efficiency **c.** mechanical advantage
   b. power **d.** resistance
5. To raise a resistance 4 meters, the effort rope of a fixed pulley must move ______.
   a. 2 meters **c.** 1 meter
   b. 8 meters **d.** 4 meters
6. The mechanical advantage of a pulley system in which 5 ropes support an object is ______.
   a. 2.5 **c.** 10
   b. 5 **d.** 25
7. In a wheel and axle, the resistance force is usually exerted by the ______.
   a. axle **c.** gear ratio
   b. larger wheel **d.** pedals
8. The *MA* of an inclined plane 8 meters long and 2 meters high is ______.
   a. 2 **c.** 16
   b. 4 **d.** 8
9. As the efficiency of a machine increases, the ______ of the machine increases.
   a. work input **c.** friction
   b. work output **d.** *MA*
10. The *MA* of an inclined plane can be increased by ______.
    a. increasing the length
    b. increasing the height
    c. decreasing the length
    d. all of these

UNDERSTANDING CONCEPTS

Complete each sentence.

11. In an actual machine, the work output is almost always ______ than the work input.
12. In order to increase the *MA* of a first-class lever, move the fulcrum toward the ______.
13. In a wheel and axle, the ______ force is usually applied to the larger wheel.
14. ______ is measured in watts.
15. If the effort rope of a single movable pulley is pulled 4 meters, the resistance will be moved ______ meters.

THINK AND WRITE CRITICALLY

16. Describe three ways that a simple machine can make work easier. Give examples of each.
17. If machines make work easier, explain why most machines actually increase the amount of work you do in accomplishing a task.
18. Distinguish between a fixed pulley and a single movable pulley and describe the advantages of using each. Compare each type of pulley to its corresponding class of lever.
19. How can the mechanical advantage of an inclined plane be increased? Explain how sharpening a knife changes its *MA*.
20. The efficiency of an automobile is usually expressed in terms of gas mileage. How can changing the engine oil increase the gas mileage of the automobile?

APPLY

21. A cyclist applies a force of 8 N to the pedals of a bicycle. If the rear wheel applies a force of 52 N to the road surface, what is the *MA* of the bicycle?
22. An adult and a small child get on a seesaw that has a movable fulcrum. When the fulcrum is in the middle, the child can't lift the adult. How should the fulcrum be moved so that the two can seesaw? Explain your answer.
23. You have two screwdrivers. One is long with a thin handle, and the other is short with a fat handle. Which would you use to drive a screw into a board? Explain your choice.
24. Using a ramp 4 meters long, workers apply an effort force of 1250 N to move a 2000-N crate onto a platform 2 meters high. What is the efficiency of the ramp?
25. How much power does a person weighing 500 N need to climb a 3-meter ladder in 5 seconds?

MORE SKILL BUILDERS

If you need help, refer to the Skill Handbook.

1. **Outlining:** Make an outline describing the six types of simple machines. Be sure the outline indicates the two major types of simple machines and includes the following for each type of machine: (1) a description; (2) how it works; (3) a method for finding its *MA*; (4) an example.
2. **Making and Using Graphs:** A lever has a fixed effort arm length of 40 cm. Calculate effort force needed to raise a 10-N object with these resistance arm lengths: 80 cm, 40 cm, 20 cm, and 10 cm. Construct a line graph relating these resistance arm lengths to effort force. Describe the relationship between these two variables.
3. **Interpreting Scientific Illustrations:** Study the diagram of a garden hoe and answer the questions.
   a. What type of machine does the diagram represent? (Be specific.)
   b. What does the lower arrow represent?
   c. What does point A represent?
   d. What is represented by segment AC? segment AB?
   e. What is the *MA* of this machine?
   f. How does this machine make work easier?

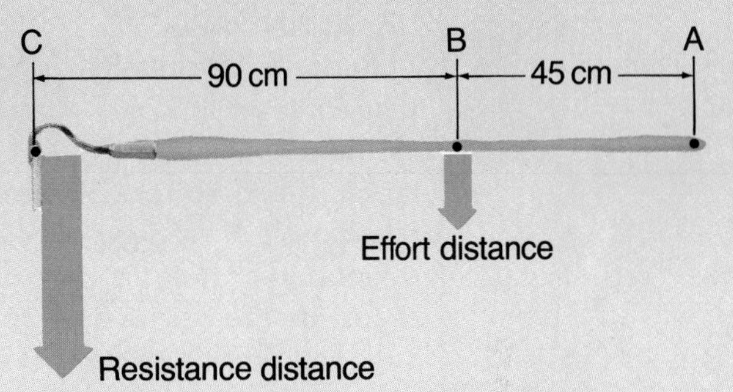

4. **Measuring in SI:** The SI unit of power, the watt, is a derived unit. Using the definition of power, develop the formula for calculating power and determine the fundamental SI units for expressing power.

PROJECTS

1. Divide the class into teams of 3 or 4 students each. Have the members of each team spend one week daily identifying, describing, and classifying as many simple machines as they can find at school and at home. At the end of the week, each team should report their findings. Members should be prepared to support their own classifications and to challenge classifications they feel are incorrect.
2. Design a human-powered machine of some kind. Describe the simple machines used in your design and tell what each of these machines does.

UNIT 2

GLOBAL CONNECTIONS

Energy and Motion

In this unit, you studied how objects move, how motion and energy are related, and how machines work. Now find out ways energy and motion are connected to other subjects and places around the world.

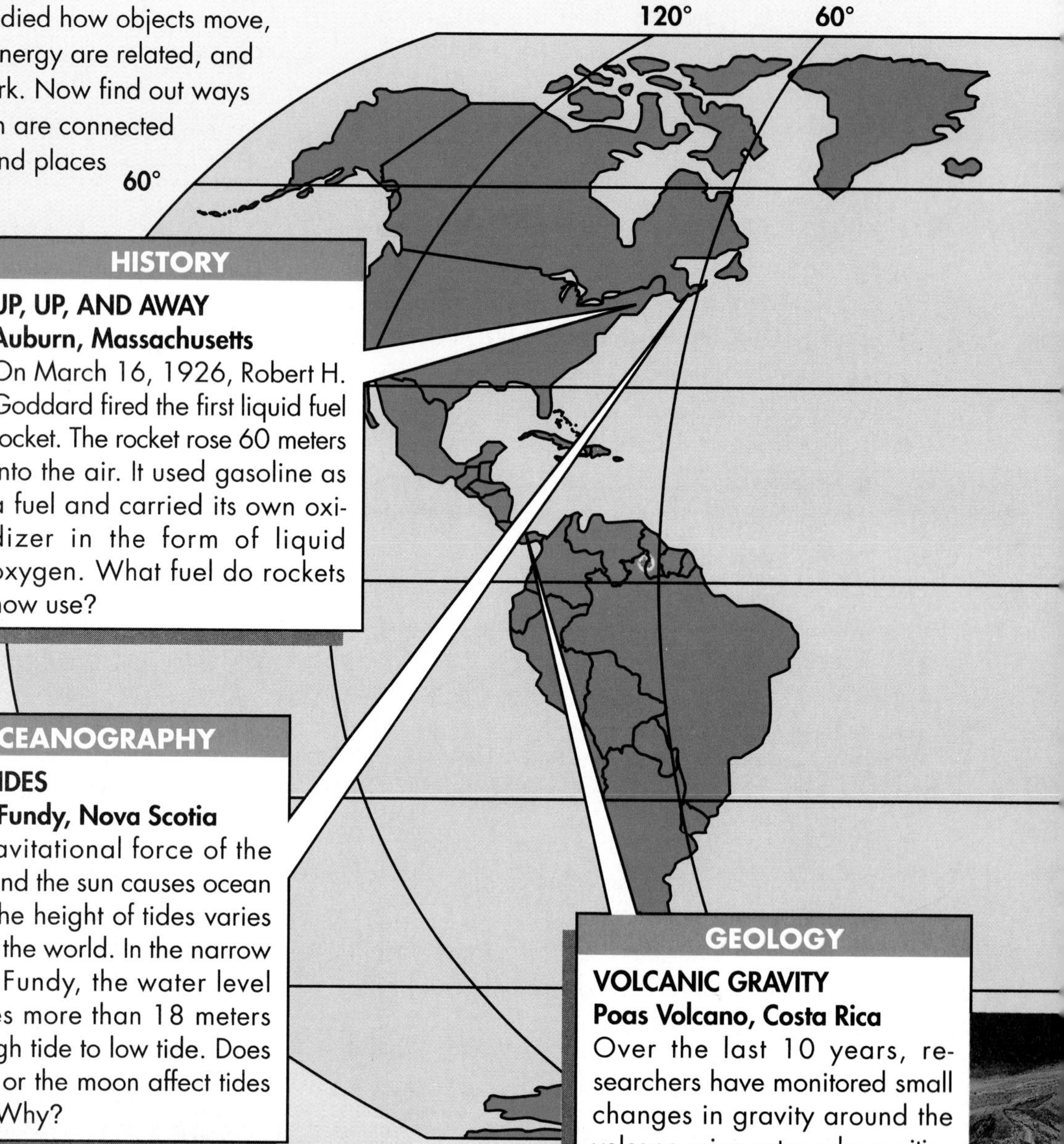

120° 60° 60°

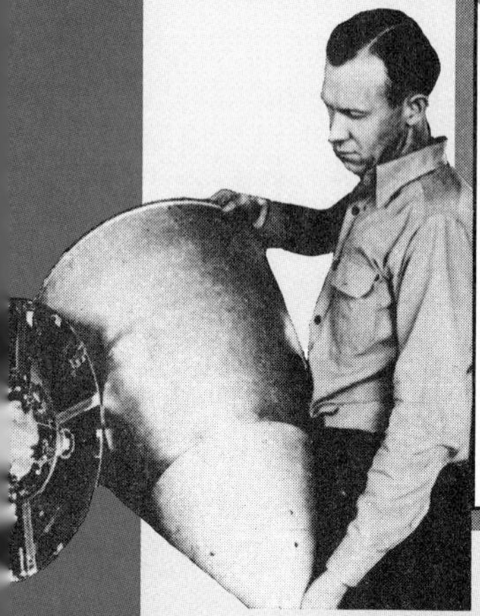

HISTORY

UP, UP, AND AWAY
Auburn, Massachusetts

On March 16, 1926, Robert H. Goddard fired the first liquid fuel rocket. The rocket rose 60 meters into the air. It used gasoline as a fuel and carried its own oxidizer in the form of liquid oxygen. What fuel do rockets now use?

OCEANOGRAPHY

HIGH TIDES
Bay of Fundy, Nova Scotia

The gravitational force of the moon and the sun causes ocean tides. The height of tides varies around the world. In the narrow Bay of Fundy, the water level changes more than 18 meters from high tide to low tide. Does the sun or the moon affect tides more? Why?

GEOLOGY

VOLCANIC GRAVITY
Poas Volcano, Costa Rica

Over the last 10 years, researchers have monitored small changes in gravity around the volcano using extremely sensitive instruments. They found a slight increase in gravity over a two-year period before a 1989 eruption. How could this information prove helpful?

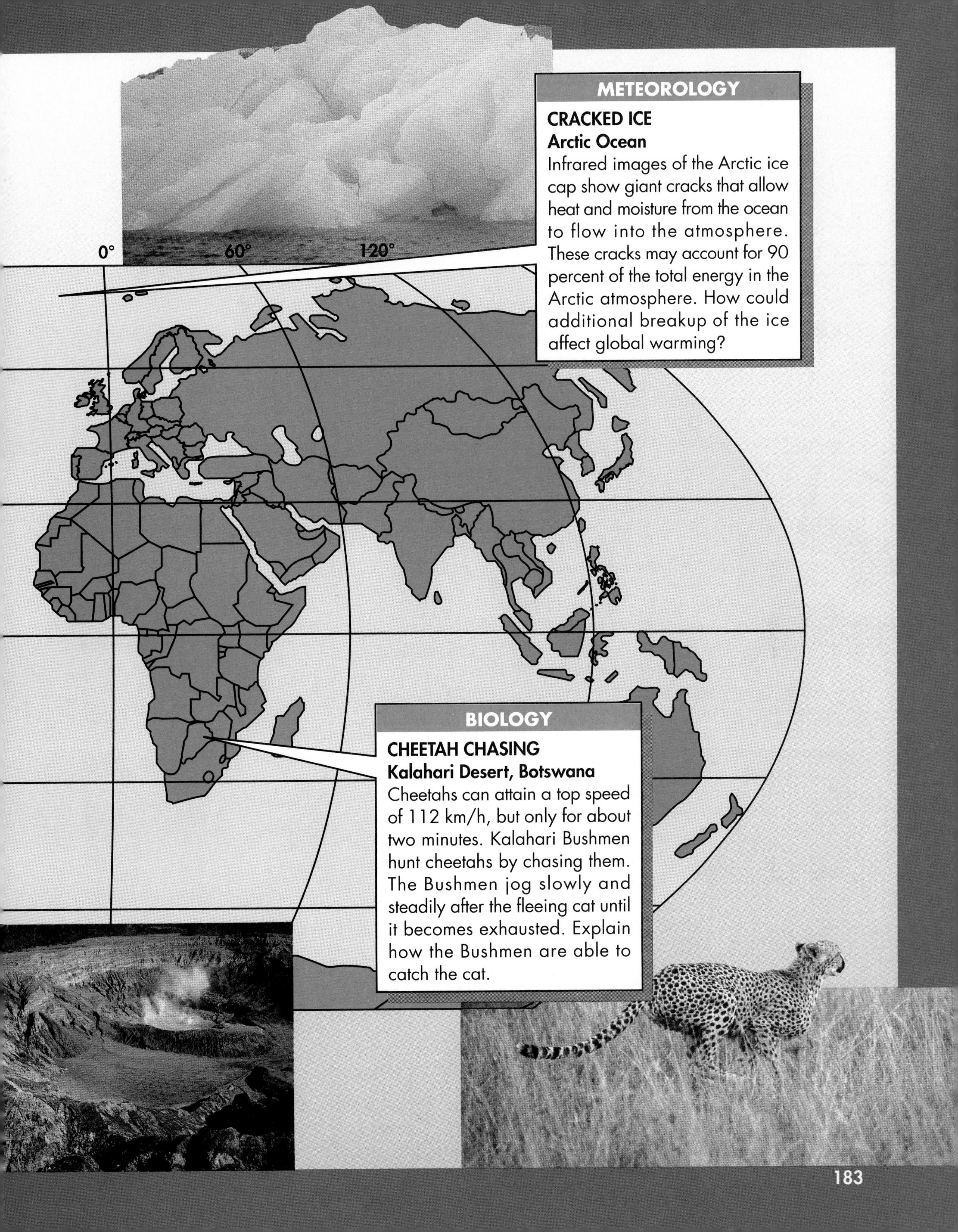

METEOROLOGY

CRACKED ICE
Arctic Ocean

Infrared images of the Arctic ice cap show giant cracks that allow heat and moisture from the ocean to flow into the atmosphere. These cracks may account for 90 percent of the total energy in the Arctic atmosphere. How could additional breakup of the ice affect global warming?

BIOLOGY

CHEETAH CHASING
Kalahari Desert, Botswana

Cheetahs can attain a top speed of 112 km/h, but only for about two minutes. Kalahari Bushmen hunt cheetahs by chasing them. The Bushmen jog slowly and steadily after the fleeing cat until it becomes exhausted. Explain how the Bushmen are able to catch the cat.

HVAC TECHNICIAN

Heating, ventilation, and air-conditioning (HVAC) technicians work on equipment that heats and cools homes, schools, offices, and other buildings. Some technicians specialize in one of these areas, while others are skilled in all of them. They install, maintain, and repair units from the size of a room air conditioner to a central heating and cooling system for a large building.

If you're interested in becoming an HVAC technician you should take high school classes in math and physics and have mechanical aptitude. Some technicians learn the trade by working for several years as helpers with experienced technicians. Others take a two- or three-year program at a vocational or technical school.

For Additional Information

Contact the American Association of Heating, Refrigeration, and Air-Conditioning Engineers, 345 E. 47th Street, New York, New York 10017.

AERONAUTICAL ENGINEER

Aeronautical engineers design airplanes. They usually begin with a drawing that uses mathematics and engineering principles. Often they use computers to help them in the study and design of airplanes. Aeronautical engineers also use computers to simulate how the airplane they are designing will perform in flight. When the engineer has completed a design, a small model is built based on the design.

If you're interested in becoming an aeronautical engineer you should take classes in mathematics and physics in high school. Aeronautical engineers must have a college degree in engineering and may have advanced degrees.

For Additional Information

Contact the American Institute of Aeronautics and Astronautics, 1290 Avenue of the Americas, New York, New York 10019.

UNIT READINGS

- Laithwaite, Eric. *Force: The Power Behind Movement.* Danbury, CT: Watts, 1986.
- Santray, Laurence. *Heat.* Mahwah, NJ: Troll, 1985.
- Zubrowski, Bernard. *Raceways: Having Fun With Balls and Tracks.* New York: Morrow, 1985.

SCIENCE & LITERATURE

Dolphins

by Jacques-Yves Cousteau and Philippe Diole

This passage that follows is a brief account of Jacques Cousteau's first encounter with dolphins.

The cruiser *Primauguet* cut through the water at full speed, its prow rising and falling among the waves and raising a great wave of its own as it pushed irresistibly through the liquid wall of the sea. It was an impressive sight. The cruiser, a ship of the French Navy, had just been released from dry dock and we were testing her in the waters of the Far East. At that moment, the *Primauguet's* engines were wide open, and we were moving at a speed of 33.5 knots.

I was standing on the bridge, enthralled by the performance of the mighty cruiser as it cut through the sea with incredible violence. Then, I glanced to starboard. A school of dolphins was alongside, their fins regularly appearing then disappearing beneath the surface, their dark backs moving with graceful power through the rough water. I watched. And suddenly I realized that the dolphins were moving faster than the *Primauguet.* Swimming some thirty or forty feet away from the cruiser and parallel to her, they were passing her! I could hardly believe my eyes.

Then, suddenly, the lead dolphin altered his course and cut toward our prow. When he reached the crest of the wave raised by the thrust of the *Primauguet's* engines, he hovered there until he was displaced by another dolphin, and then another. The dolphins had devised a game which they played in the midst of the waves: one by one, in turn, they rode the crest of the cruiser's wave, directly before our prow, for two or three minutes, then let themselves be carried to starboard or port so that the next dolphin could have his turn. It was an astonishing spectacle, but its importance to me at that time was practical rather than aesthetic. I realized that the school of dolphins, in catching up to and then passing the *Primauguet* as it moved at full power, must have been swimming at a speed of no less than fifty miles per hour!

That was forty years ago. Since then, I have had many encounters with dolphins, but I have never forgotten my first impression of those great mammals as they materialized in front of the *Primauguet's* stern—faster, and infinitely more maneuverable, than the best machines that human ingenuity had yet been able to devise.

In Your Own Words

- Write a brief, descriptive essay about energy and motion involved in an encounter you have had with an animal.

UNIT

3 THE NATURE OF MATTER

What's Happening Here?

The micrograph at the left shows a crystal of sodium thiosulfate ($Na_2S_2O_3$). Photographed in polarized light sodium thiosulfate, called *hypo,* is one of the chemicals used to develop photos. The atomic structure of sodium thiosulfate caused its crystals to form in this way. Atomic structure is one of the topics you'll study in Unit 3. Is matter made of other structures besides crystals? How is matter classified? What bonds hold it together? In Unit 3 you'll find the answers to these questions.

UNIT CONTENTS

CHAPTER

8 Solids, Liquids, and Gases

Perhaps you have seen bicycle tires or a soccer ball lose pressure and soften with a change of the seasons. Do objects lose pressure only if they leak air? Or does this mean a change in temperature affects pressure?

FIND OUT!

Do this activity to find out if the temperature and pressure of air are related.

Using a hand pump, pressure gauge, and an inflation needle, inflate a soccer ball until the gauge reads 20 lb/sq in. Drop the ball and have a partner measure the height of the first bounce. Next, submerge the ball in a bucket of ice water for 10 minutes and then use the needle and gauge to measure the pressure of the ball. Drop the cold ball from the same height as before and have your partner measure its first bounce. Then submerge the ball in warm water for 10 minutes (or longer) and repeat both measurements. Do the pressure and bounce heights vary with temperature?

Gearing Up

Previewing the Chapter

Use this outline to help you focus on important ideas in this chapter.

Previewing Science Skills

- In the **Skill Builders**, you will make and use a table, make a concept map, hypothesize, and measure in SI.
- In the **Activities**, you will observe, organize and collect data, infer, communicate, measure, and classify.
- In the **MINI-Labs**, you will observe and hypothesize.

What's next?

You have shown that temperature affects the pressure of air. You will learn more about the behavior of gases as you read the pages that follow.

8-1 Matter and Temperature

New Science Words

states of matter
kinetic theory of matter
crystals
plasma
thermal expansion

Objectives

- Describe the four states of matter.
- Use the kinetic theory of matter to explain the characteristics of solids, liquids, and gases.
- Explain the thermal expansion of matter.

States of Matter

When was the last time you poured solid water into a glass? It was probably just after you grabbed a handful of ice cubes from the freezer. If you let the solid cubes sit at room temperature, they melted into liquid water. If you heated the liquid water in a pan on the stove, the liquid water changed to a gas called water vapor, or steam. Ice, liquid water, and steam are examples of the three most familiar states of matter—solid, liquid, and gas.

All matter takes up space and has mass, yet matter can exist in different states. There are four **states of matter**—solid, liquid, gas, and plasma. The state of a sample of matter depends on its temperature. For example, water ordinarily exists as ice at low temperatures and as liquid water at moderate temperatures. At higher temperatures, water changes to the gas state as water vapor. At still higher temperatures, the matter in water would become plasma. Each state has characteristics that are used to identify it, as you'll see.

Figure 8-1. Water can exist in nature as a solid, a liquid, or a gas.

Solids

A metal spoon, a cube of sugar, and a piece of cement are classified as solids. Every solid has a definite shape and a definite volume. For example, a metal spoon stays spoon-shaped whether it's in your hand or in a glass of water. And because no ordinary amount of force can squeeze the spoon into a smaller space, it has a definite volume.

Figure 8-2. Although the particles in a solid, such as this crystal of salt, vibrate, they do not move out of position.

What accounts for the characteristics of solids? Tiny particles in constant motion make up all matter. This idea is called the **kinetic theory of matter**. The particles in solid matter are held very close together by forces between them. This is why a solid can't be squeezed into a smaller space. The particles can vibrate against their neighbors, but can't move out of position. Thus, they can't move over or around each other. This explains why a solid holds its shape.

Why does a solid hold its shape?

In solids, the particles are arranged in repeating geometric patterns. These arrangements form **crystals.** Different kinds of solids have crystals of different shapes. With a magnifier you can see that salt crystals are little cubes. A snowflake is a crystal of water that has the shape of a hexagon.

Some materials such as glass, many plastics, and some kinds of wax, appear to be solids but are not made of crystals. They are often called amorphous solids. The word *amorphous* means having no form. Many scientists think some of these noncrystalline materials should be classified as very thick liquids.

Liquids

When heated, most solids will change into liquids. A liquid does not have a definite shape, but it does have a definite volume. So a liquid flows and takes the shape of its container. However, like solids, liquids can't normally be squeezed to a smaller volume. If you push down on a liter of water with a moderate amount of force, its volume will remain a liter.

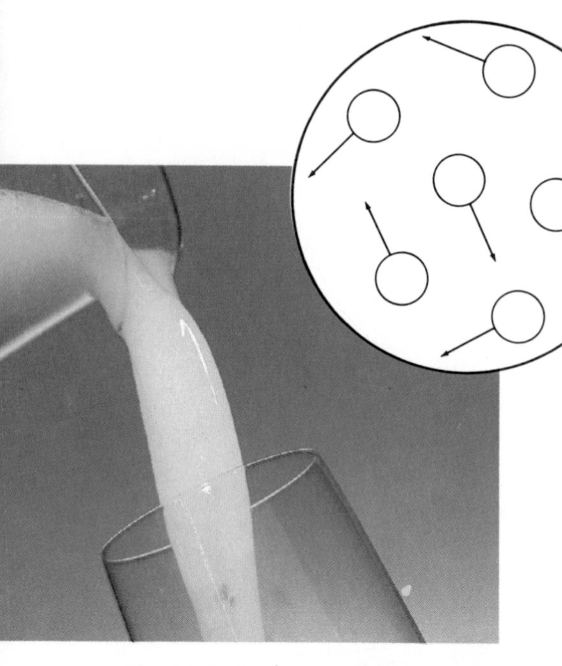

Figure 8-3. The particles in a liquid are close together, but have enough energy to vibrate over and around one another.

Just as the kinetic theory explains the properties of solids, it also explains the properties of liquids. Because a liquid can't be squeezed, its particles must also be very close together, like those of a solid. However, they have enough kinetic energy to vibrate over and around each other. This movement of particles lets a liquid flow and take the shape of its container. Thus, orange juice poured into a glass will take the shape of the glass.

Because its particles are held very close together, almost as close as those of a solid, liquid matter does have a definite volume. If you pour 1 liter of orange juice into a 2-liter bottle, it will not spread out to fill the bottle. Likewise, you couldn't force the liter of juice into a half-liter container. The two containers in Figure 8-4 contain the same volume of juice.

Figure 8-4. Although its volume does not change, the shape of a liquid depends on the shape of its container.

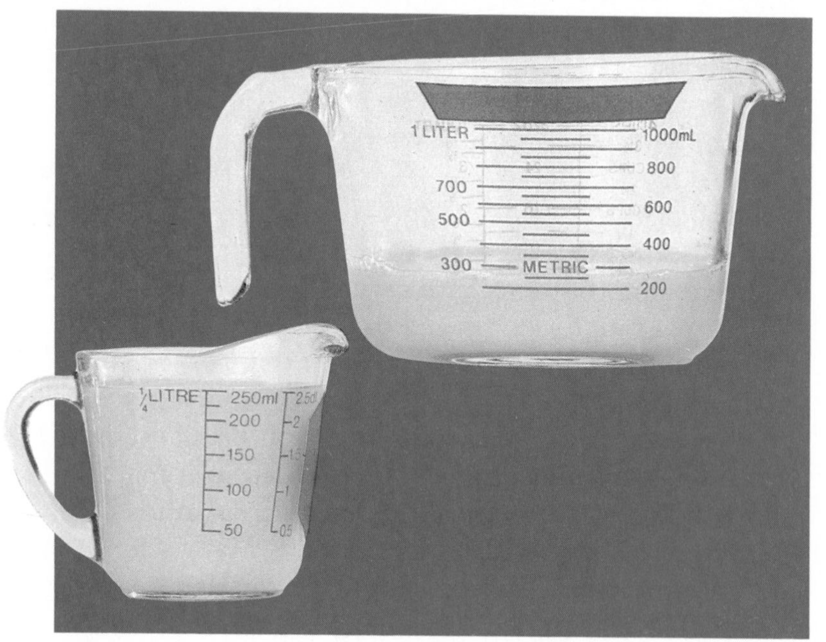

Gases

A gas has neither a definite shape nor a definite volume. You may have pumped air into a basketball, tire, or balloon and noticed that the air takes the shape of the object. Gases are springy—they expand or contract to fill the space available to them and can be squeezed into a smaller space.

According to the kinetic theory of matter, the particles of a gas have enough energy to separate completely from one another. Therefore, the particles are free to move in all directions until they have spread evenly throughout their container. Because the particles are not close together, they can also be squeezed into a smaller space. When you pump up a bicycle tire, you are forcing more and more air particles into the same space.

Compare the models of a solid, a liquid, and a gas shown in Figure 8-6. How are they different?

Figure 8-5. The particles in a gas have enough energy to spread widely apart from one another.

Plasma

So far you've learned about the three familiar states of matter. But none of these is the most common state of matter in the universe. For example, 99 percent of the

Figure 8-6. The diagrams below show the spacing and arrangements of the particles in the three familiar states of matter.

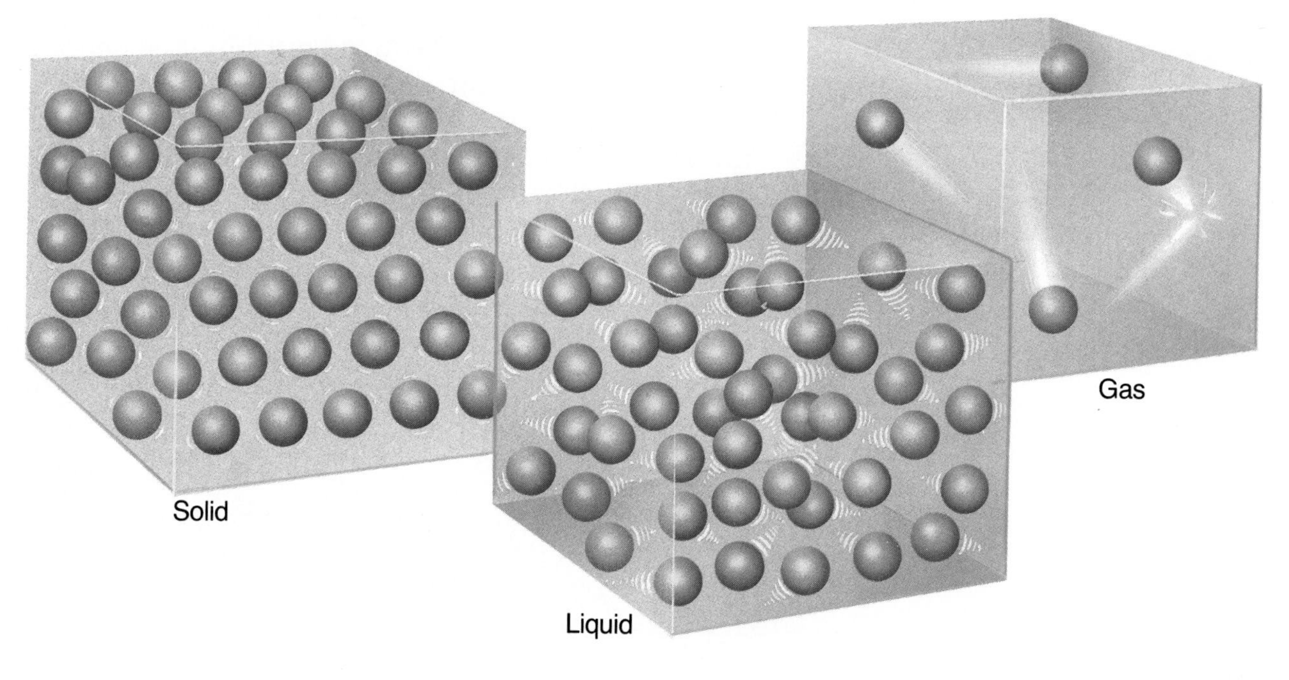

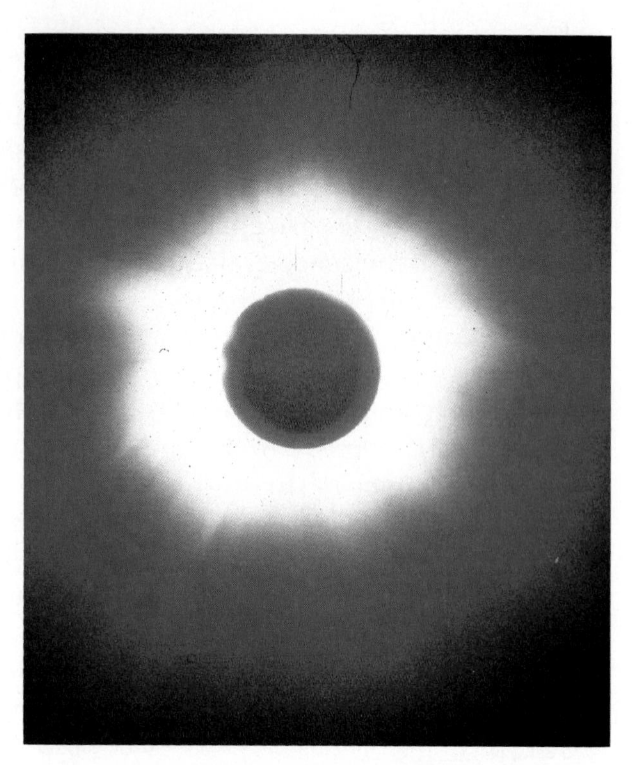

Figure 8-7. Most of the matter in the universe is in the plasma state. The stars at the center of this nebula and the sun contain plasma.

mass of our solar system is contained in the sun. The most common form of matter in the universe is the type found in stars like the sun. Such matter is called plasma.

Plasma is a gaslike mixture of positively and negatively charged particles. Besides light from the sun, you can observe the effects of plasma in your home or school. When a fluorescent light is switched on, electricity causes particles of mercury gas inside the tube to form plasma.

You know that particles of matter move faster as the matter is heated to higher temperatures. The faster they move, the greater the force with which they bump into other particles, or collide. As matter is heated to *very* high temperatures, the particles begin to collide violently. As a result, the particles break up into the smaller particles they are made of. These particles are electrically charged.

Did You Know?

The sun is getting smaller, losing over 400 km of radius in the past 50 years.

Thermal Expansion

You have learned how the kinetic theory accounts for characteristics of different states of matter you see and touch every day. The kinetic theory also explains other things you may have observed.

For example, have you ever noticed the strips of metal that run across the floors and up the walls in long hallways of concrete and steel buildings? Maybe you've seen these strips in your school. These strips usually cover gaps in the building structure called expansion joints. Expansion joints allow the building to expand in hot weather and shrink in cold weather without cracking the concrete. As you drive onto or off a bridge, you will usually pass over a large steel expansion joint as shown in Figure 8-8.

What is the purpose of expansion joints in buildings?

Almost all matter expands as it gets hotter and contracts when it cools. This characteristic of matter is called **thermal expansion.** How does the kinetic theory of matter explain thermal expansion? In a solid, forces between the particles hold them together. As the solid is heated, these particles move faster and faster and vibrate against each other with more force. As a result, the particles spread apart slightly in all directions and the solid expands. The same effect also occurs in liquids and gases.

EcoTip

Make your own air freshener. Put vinegar, a few spices, and a little cinnamon in a small glass jar. Heat the jar in the microwave oven for one minute and then place it where you need it most.

You can compare thermal expansion to a crowd of people. When the people are quiet and still, they are able to stand close together. As the people become restless, they jostle one another and the crowd spreads out.

Figure 8-8. Expansion joints in a bridge allow the structure to expand in warm weather without cracking.

PROBLEM SOLVING

Breakfast with Grandmother

Juan was visiting his grandmother for the weekend. On Saturday morning, he woke to the smell of muffins baking. The smell made him hungry, so he dressed quickly and ran down the stairs and into the kitchen.

Grandmother was taking the muffins out of the oven. After placing them on the table, she asked Juan to get a jar of jam from the cabinet and open it. Juan tried to remove the metal lid from the glass jar, but no matter how hard he tried, the lid would not budge. At his grandmother's suggestion, Juan ran hot water over the lid before trying again to remove the lid, and then it came off easily.

Think Critically: How did hot water affect the metal lid of the jar? Why was the lid easier to remove after running hot water over it?

SECTION REVIEW

1. Compare the characteristics of solids and liquids.
2. You pour 500 mL of a green material into a 1-liter flask and stopper it. The material completely fills the flask. What state of matter is the material? Explain how you know.
3. In terms of particle motion, explain why copper shrinks when it cools.
4. **Apply:** In very old houses, the window glass is thicker at the bottom of the panes than at the top. How can you account for this thickening?

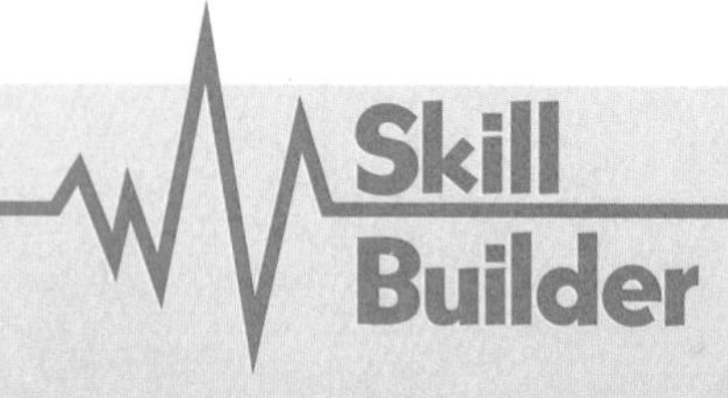

Making and Using Tables

Make a table to classify several materials as a solid, liquid, gas, or plasma. Include columns for properties and a description of particles for each state. If you need help, refer to Making and Using Tables in the **Skill Handbook** on page 686.

ACTIVITY 8-1
Properties of Liquids

Problem: *How can properties of a material be used to classify it?*

Materials    

- dropper
- food coloring
- wooden stick
- paper cup
- graduated cylinder
- 4% solution of powdered borax, in water
- 4% solution of polyvinyl alcohol (PVA)
- goggles
- apron

Procedure

1. Copy the data table and use it to record your observations of the new material.
2. Using a graduated cylinder, measure 30 mL (cm^3) of PVA solution into a paper cup. Add two drops of food coloring.
3. Using a dropper, add about 3 mL (cm^3) of borax solution to the PVA in the cup and begin to stir vigorously with a wooden stick.
4. After stirring for 2 minutes, what is the consistency of the material?
5. Transfer the material to your hand. **CAUTION:** *Do not taste or eat the material and be sure to wash your hands after the activity.* Rate the ease with which the material flows.
6. Form the material into a ball and then place it in the cup to test its ability to take the shape of its container.
7. Compare the volume of the new material with the volume of the original material before stirring.

Analyze

1. Is the new material more like a gas, a liquid, or a solid?
2. What other materials have you seen that have similar properties to this one?
3. Considering the slow flow of the new material, how would you rate the strength of the attraction among its particles?

Conclude and Apply

4. Using the kinetic theory of matter, how would you describe the closeness of the particles of matter in the new material?
5. How can properties of this material be used to classify it?

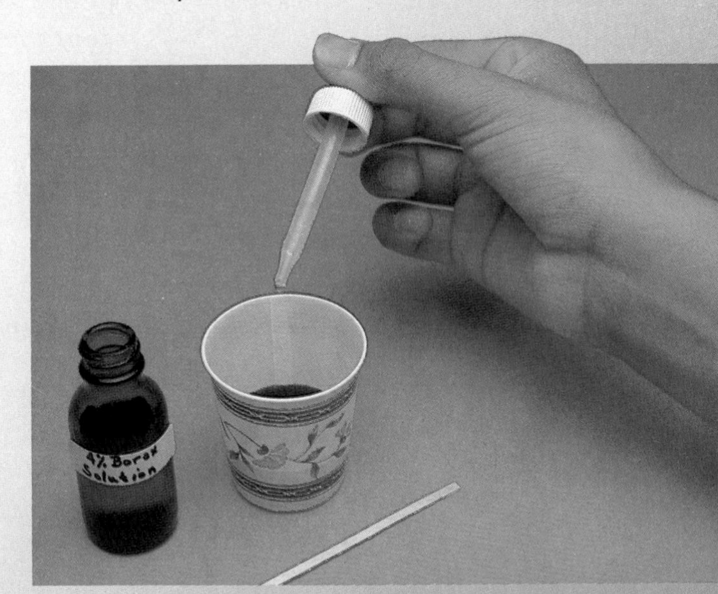

Data and Observations

Property	Observation	Interpretation
Ability to flow		
Shape changes		
Volume changes		

8-2 Water—Earth's Vital Liquid

New Science Words

polluted water

Objectives

- Describe how people use and pollute water.
- Discuss how people can save water and stop pollution.

Will There Be Enough Water?

For living things, like yourself, the most important liquid on Earth is fresh water. It is not as abundant as you might think. Fresh water, which is water that is not salty, makes up only 0.75 percent of the water available on Earth in the liquid state.

What percentage of the water on Earth is available fresh water?

How much water do you think you use in a day? Take a guess. Did you say 1700 gallons? For the average person in the United States, that's the correct answer! Each person uses about 200 gallons a day for cooking, bathing, toilet use, and heating and cooling homes. Add to this the 750 gallons per person a day used to produce materials and energy, and another 750 gallons per person a day used to water crops. Table 8-1 lists only a few ways you use water indirectly as well as directly.

Table 8-1

WAYS WATER IS USED

Gallons of Water Needed to	
5	Make 1 gallon of milk
5	Brush teeth with water running
5-7	Flush a toilet
5-7	Shower for 1 minute
6	Make enough steel for a table knife
5-10	Wash car at self-service car wash
10	Produce 1 gallon of gasoline
32-59	Do one load of laundry
80	Burn 100-watt light bulb for 10 hours
up to 150	Wash a car at home with a hose

Not only do people use huge amounts of fresh water, they also pollute their natural supplies of this liquid. **Polluted water** is water that is dirty and unfit for living things. Motor oil, paint thinner, bleach, and drain cleaners are a few examples of toxic materials that people dump down drains or on the ground. From there, the materials may move into water supplies.

Industry pollutes water by dumping raw sewage, toxic industrial chemicals, and radioactive materials into it. The farming industry pollutes water with chemical fertilizers, herbicides, and pesticides. Another form of pollution is the heating of rivers and lakes called thermal pollution. Hot water produced by electric power plants flows into and heats bodies of water where organisms live. This heating often kills the organisms.

Many toxic materials that pollute water stay in their original form for many years. Scientists are trying to develop products that are safe for the environment. For example, they are trying to make materials that are biodegradable. Organisms can break down biodegradable materials, changing them into harmless forms.

Many people seem to think fresh, clean water will always be plentiful. But, for reasons you have read about, some environmental scientists disagree.

SECTION REVIEW

1. What are two main reasons that there could be a shortage of clean water?
2. List five sources of water pollution.

You Decide!

The amount of water used by each person can be reduced 15 to 25 percent without any noticeable change in lifestyle. What are five things you could do to use less water or reduce water pollution?

8-3 Changes in State

New Science Words

evaporation
condensation
heat of fusion
heat of vaporization

Objectives

- ▶ **Interpret state changes in terms of the kinetic theory of matter.**
- ▶ **Account for the energy of the heats of fusion and vaporization in state changes.**

Kinds of State Changes

If you've ever seen ice cream melt before you could eat it, you have seen matter change state. Solid ice crystals in the ice cream melt when they change from the solid state to the liquid state. In melting, a solid changes into a liquid. You put water in the freezer to make ice cubes. In freezing, matter changes from the liquid state to the solid state.

When you boil water, you observe another change of state, called vaporization. In boiling, you add heat to a liquid until it reaches a temperature at which it changes to bubbles of gas below its surface. Many liquids don't need to boil to change to a gas. In **evaporation,** a liquid changes to a gas gradually at temperatures below the boiling point. When you come out of a pool into warm air,

Figure 8-9. When water boils, bubbles of gas particles form below the surface, rise to the top, and escape (a). When a liquid evaporates, individual gas particles escape from the surface (b).

water on your skin soon evaporates. You'll see later how this drying helps cool you.

Have you noticed that ice cubes seem to shrink when they've been in the freezer a long time? This shrinkage happens because of another change of state called sublimation. In sublimation, a solid changes directly to a gas without going through the liquid state.

You see another change of state when your glass of ice-cold soft drink "sweats." The drops of water on your glass appear when gaseous water condenses on the cold surface. **Condensation** takes place when a gas changes to a liquid. Generally, a gas will condense when cooled to or below its boiling point.

Figure 8-10. Gaseous water in the air often condenses on cool surfaces.

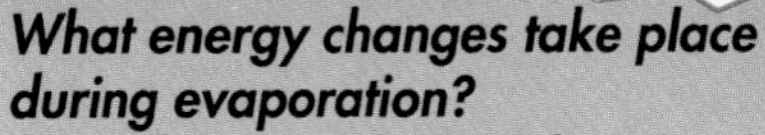

What energy changes take place during evaporation?

Use a dropper to place five drops of rubbing alcohol on the back of your hand. Wait for two minutes. What sensations did you feel? What change of state did you observe? Is energy entering or leaving your hand? Where does the energy for this process come from?

Heat and State Changes

The kinetic theory of matter explains changes of state. Suppose you take some ice cubes from your freezer, put them in a beaker, and heat them. Then, you measure the temperature of the cubes every 30 seconds. You will find that the temperature rises steadily as the cubes absorb thermal energy. Figure 8-11 on the next page plots these temperature changes.

After 5 minutes, the cubes warm up to 0°C and begin to melt. But the temperature stops rising and stays at 0°C while the cubes melt. What is happening to the energy? The particles of the solid water are absorbing energy. This energy enables them to overcome forces that hold them in place. Then the particles are free to tumble over one another. In other words, they have become particles of water in the liquid state.

The amount of energy needed to change a material from the solid state to the liquid state is the **heat of fusion** of that material. For water, the heat of fusion is 334 kJ/kg. This means that it takes 334 kJ of energy to melt 1 kg of ice without changing its temperature from 0°C.

What is the heat of fusion of a material?

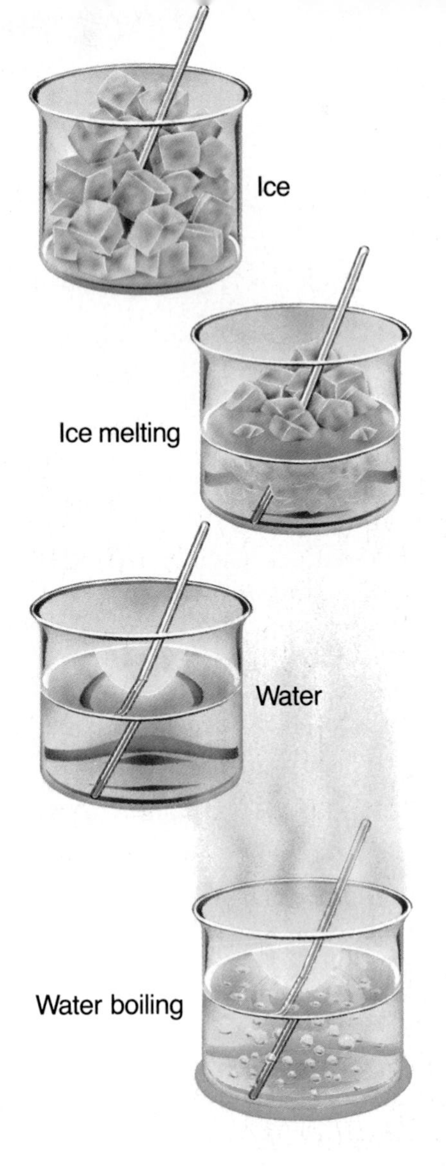

Suppose it takes 5 minutes for all the cubes to melt, and you continue to heat the liquid water. You observe that the temperature rises once again. After another 10 minutes the water begins to boil. The temperature has reached 100°C and rises no further. Again, the water particles are absorbing energy, which enables them to overcome attractive forces holding them together in the liquid state. After absorbing energy, the particles can separate to great distances from one another. They are becoming particles of gaseous water, steam. The amount of energy needed to change a material from a liquid to a gas is the **heat of vaporization** of that material. For water, the heat of vaporization is 2260 kJ/kg.

After some time, the water has boiled away, and the temperature of the remaining steam rises rapidly. Suppose you could condense the steam back into liquid water and then freeze the liquid into ice. You would remove all the energy you added before. And the temperature would stay at 100°C while the steam condensed and at 0°C while the ice froze.

You can also use the kinetic theory to explain how water evaporates from your skin and how it cools you. When a liquid evaporates, the particles do not all have the same kinetic energy. Some move faster than others. Many of these are moving fast enough to break away from the liquid and become a gas. As these fast-moving water particles leave, the average kinetic energy of the remain-

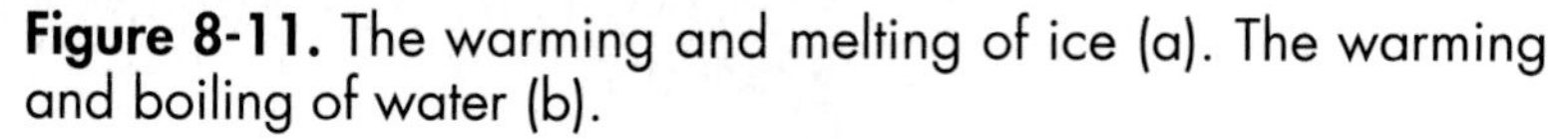
Figure 8-11. The warming and melting of ice (a). The warming and boiling of water (b).

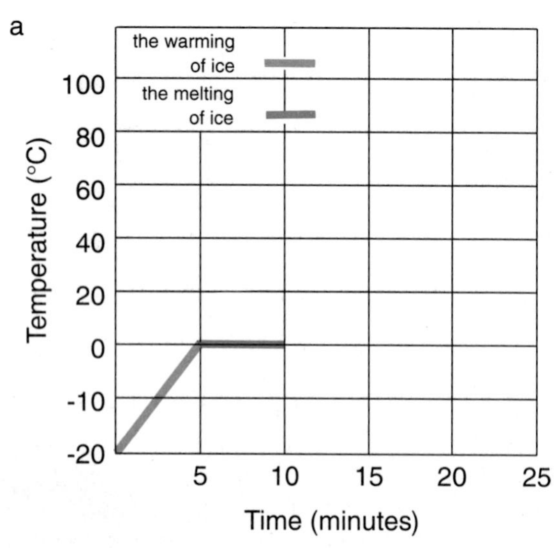

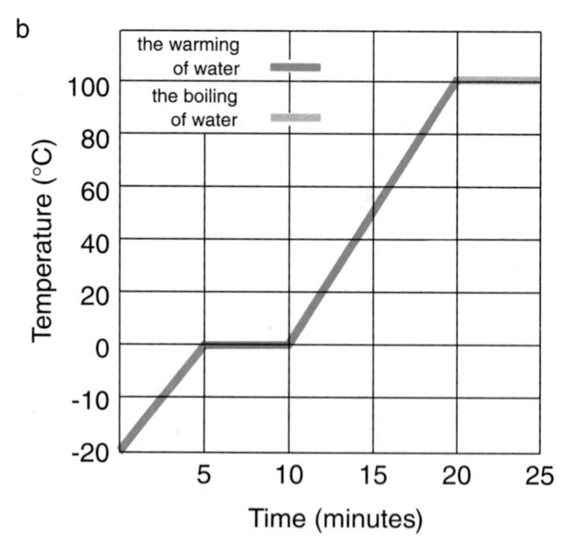

Figure 8-12. In warm air, water soon evaporates from wet skin and hair.

ing particles becomes less. As a result the temperature of the remaining water goes down. Because the water is now cooler than your skin, it takes heat from your skin and cools you.

SECTION REVIEW

1. Name and describe the state changes in which another state changes to a gas.
2. Use the kinetic theory to explain melting.
3. What happens to the energy put into a liquid during boiling?
4. **Apply:** Steam must lose its heat of vaporization in order to condense. How does this fact help explain why steam causes more severe skin burns than water at its boiling point?

Concept Mapping

Use a cycle map to show the changes in particles as cool water boils, changes to steam, and then changes back to cool water. If you need help, refer to Concept Mapping in the **Skill Handbook** on pages 684 and 685.

8-4 Behavior of Gases

New Science Words

pressure
pascal
Boyle's law
Charles's law

Objectives

- Explain how a gas exerts pressure on its container.
- State and explain how the pressure of a container of gas is affected when the volume is changed.
- Explain the relationship between the temperature and volume of a gas.

Pressure

Every time you feel the wind on your face, you observe the behavior of a gas—rather, the mixture of gases that is Earth's air, or atmosphere. Even when the wind is calm, the air exerts a force called pressure.

What causes the pressure of a gas? Particles of matter are very small—many billions of particles of air fill an inflated toy balloon. When riding on a bike, you're riding on pockets of colliding air particles inside your tires. You have learned that the particles of air, like those in all gases, are constantly moving. They're free to fly about and collide with anything in their way. The collisions with the inside walls keep the balloons or tires inflated and cause the force that you feel when you squeeze them.

Figure 8-13. The force of particles of air in constant motion colliding with the inside walls of the tire keeps a tire inflated.

The total amount of force exerted by a gas depends on the size of its container. **Pressure** is the amount of force exerted per unit of area.

$$P = F/A$$

The **pascal** (Pa) is the SI unit of pressure. One pascal of pressure is a force of one newton per square meter. This is a very small pressure unit, so most pressures are given in kilopascals (kPa).

Earth's atmosphere exerts a pressure on everything within it. At sea level, atmospheric pressure is 101.3 kPa. This means that at Earth's surface, the atmosphere exerts a force of about 100 000 newtons on every square meter. This amount of force is equal to a weight of 100 000 newtons—about the weight of a large truck.

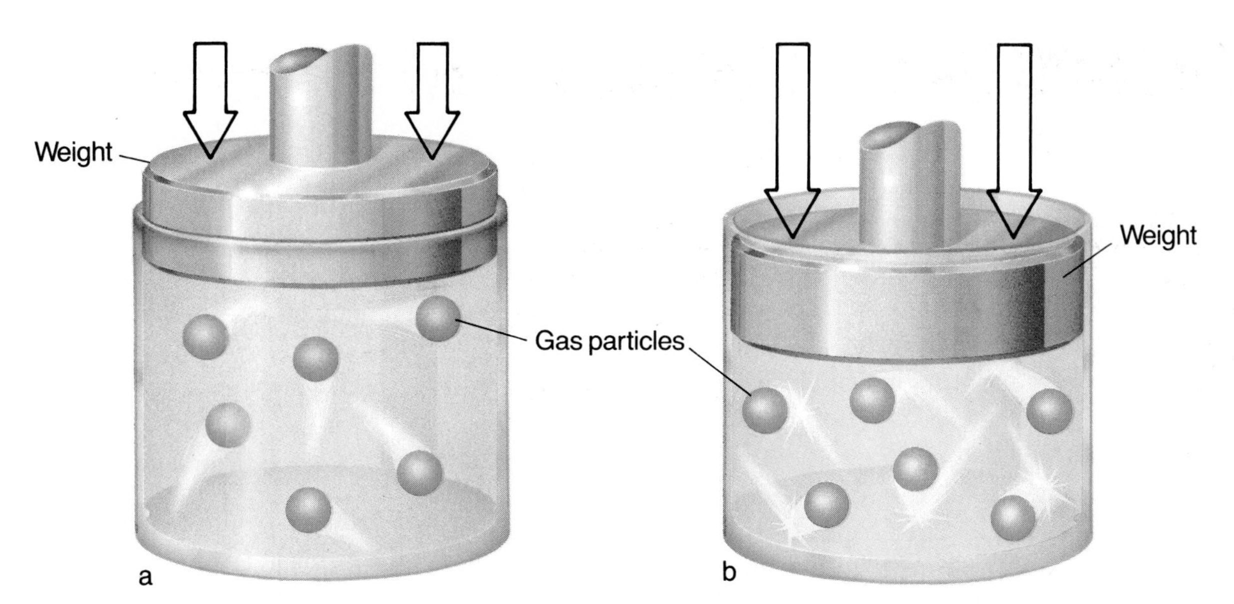

Figure 8-14. If you increase the pressure on air in an enclosed space (a), the volume of the air in the enclosed space decreases, (b).

Boyle's Law

Suppose you have some gas in a sealed flexible container, such as a balloon. You can squeeze or stretch the container without changing the amount of gas trapped inside.

The pressure of a gas depends on how often its particles strike the walls of the container. If you squeeze some gas into a smaller space, its particles will strike the walls more often, giving an increased pressure. This behavior explains why when you squeeze a balloon into a smaller space, it causes the balloon to push back with more force. The reverse happens too. If you give the gas particles more space, they will hit the walls less often and the gas pressure will be reduced. Robert Boyle (1627-1691), a British scientist, described this property of gases. According to **Boyle's law,** if you decrease the volume of a container of gas, the pressure of the gas will increase, provided the temperature does not change. Increasing the volume causes pressure to drop. As you'll see, it is important that the temperature remain constant.

Science and WRITING

Memorizing principles and laws
Can be full of errors and flaws.
But writing a poem or limerick
Can make learning fun and quick,
And may earn teachers' applause.
Pick a principle or law and try it!

Charles's Law

If you've seen a hot-air balloon being inflated, you know gases expand when heated. Jacques Charles (1742-1823) was a French scientist who studied gases. According to **Charles's law,** the volume of a gas increases with increasing temperature, provided the pressure does not change. As with Boyle's law, the reverse is true, also. A

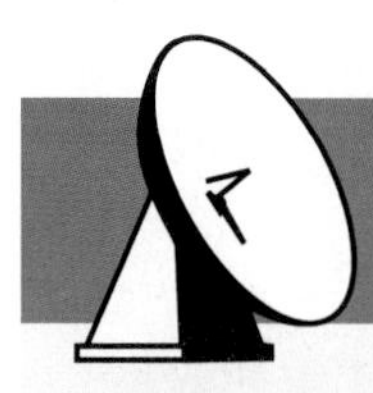

TECHNOLOGY

Gaseous Research Giants

Imagine a balloon so immense that, when fully inflated, it will hold a volume of gas equivalent to 168 Goodyear blimps! Scientists are sending such balloons into the stratosphere, the layer of the atmosphere that is above 99 percent of Earth's air. These giant balloons are filled with helium gas, which gives them their lift. One of these balloons may hoist a load higher than a cruising jumbo jet, but lower than an orbiting satellite in space. The initial volume of helium required to lift the load might be the size of a small house. In the stratosphere, the volume may reach the size of 283 of the houses!

Scientists use the balloons for research. For example, a load of equipment may gather data on how ozone gas is formed in the upper atmosphere. Ozone helps protect life by absorbing a dangerous form of energy given off by the sun. Because the sky is clear in the stratosphere, another load may be a telescope for studying the energy given off by the sun and other stars. Such studies help scientists understand the makeup and behavior of matter.

Think Critically: For some kinds of research, why do scientists launch giant balloons into the stratosphere instead of launching satellites into outer space where there is no air?

gas shrinks with decreasing temperature. Figure 8-15 shows a demonstration of Charles's law.

Using his law, Charles was able to calculate the temperature at which a gas would have a volume of zero. The kinetic theory would say that this is the temperature at which all particle motion of matter should stop. Charles found this temperature to be $-273°C$, or 0 K, also called absolute zero. In reality, gases cannot be cooled to zero volume. Instead, they condense to liquids when cooled to their boiling points.

You can explain Charles's law by using the kinetic theory of matter. As a gas is heated, its particles move faster and faster, and its temperature increases. Because the gas particles move faster, they begin to strike the walls of their container more often and with more force. If the walls are free to move, the gas pushes the walls out and expands.

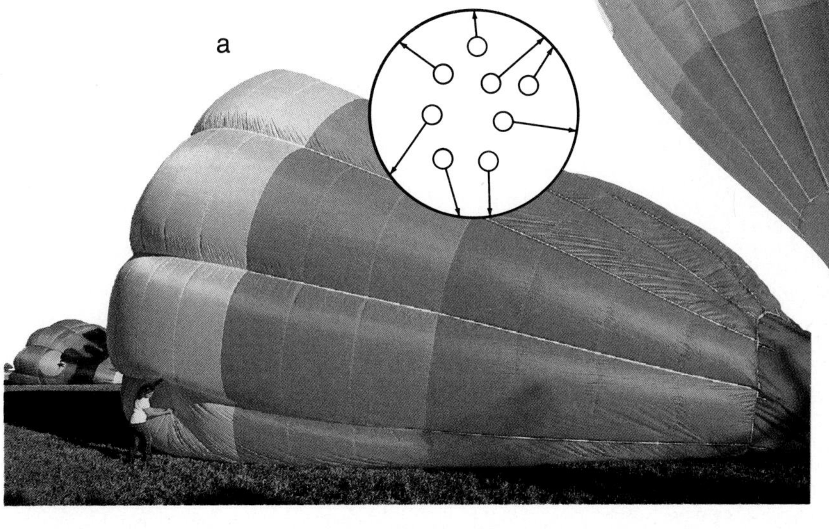

Figure 8-15. If you increase the temperature of the air in a balloon (a), the volume of the air in the balloon also increases (b).

SECTION REVIEW

1. When you bounce a basketball on the floor, the air pressure inside the ball increases for a moment. Explain why this increase occurs.
2. Why does a closed, empty 2-liter plastic soft-drink bottle "cave in" when placed in a freezer?
3. **Apply:** Labels on cylinders of compressed gases state the highest temperature to which the cylinder may be exposed. Give a reason for this warning.

Hypothesizing

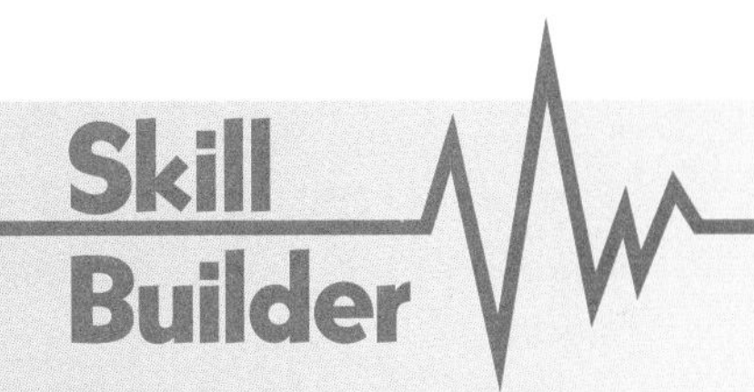

A bottle of ammonia begins to leak in an empty room. An hour later you walk into the room and can smell ammonia almost everywhere. The smell is stronger near the leaking bottle. State a hypothesis to explain your observations. If you need help, refer to Hypothesizing in the **Skill Handbook** on page 682.

ACTIVITY 8-2
Temperature and Volume Relations

Problem: *How is volume of air affected by changing temperature?*

Materials  

- string
- marking pen
- meterstick
- container of ice water
- tongs
- heat-proof glove or tongs
- beaker of boiling water
- thermometer
- goggles
- 2 medium, round balloons

Procedure

1. Copy the data table. Measure and record the room temperature.
2. Inflate two balloons to about the same size and tie them closed.
3. Use string to measure the circumference of each balloon at room temperature. For later use, place an ink dot where the string went around each balloon. Then use a meterstick to measure the length of the string.
4. Cube the circumference and then divide by 59 to find volume: $V = c^3/59$.
5. Place one balloon in ice water for 5 minutes. Measure and record the temperature of the ice water.
6. Remove the balloon and quickly use the string to measure the new circumference, using the ink dot as a guide, as shown in the drawings.
7. Using a heat-proof glove, place the second balloon in the steam above boiling water for 5 minutes. **CAUTION:** *Steam causes burns.* Measure and record the temperature of the steam.
8. Repeat Step 6 for this balloon.

Data and Observations

State	Circumference	Volume	Temperature
Room			
Cold			
Hot			

Analyze

1. Using the temperatures and volumes in your data table, make a line graph. What is the relationship between the temperature and volume of a gas?
2. Your graph should suggest a straight line. If you extended the line to zero volume, to what temperature would it correspond?

Conclude and Apply

3. Using the kinetic theory, explain how the movements of air particles inside each balloon are causing the volume to change.
4. Aerosol cans often bear the warning "Do not incinerate, contents under pressure." How can you apply what you have seen in this activity to explain this caution?

Uses of Fluids 8-5

Objectives

- State Archimedes' principle and predict whether an object will sink or float in water.
- State Pascal's principle and describe the operation of a machine that uses Pascal's principle.
- State Bernoulli's principle and describe a way that Bernoulli's principle is applied.

New Science Words

buoyant force
Archimedes' principle
Pascal's principle
Bernoulli's principle

Archimedes' Principle

Have you ever relaxed by floating quietly on your back in a swimming pool? You seem weightless as the water supports you. If you climb slowly out of the pool you feel as if you gain weight. The farther out you climb, the more you have to use your muscles to support yourself. When you were in the pool, you experienced buoyancy. Buoyancy is the ability of a fluid—a liquid or a gas—to exert an upward force on an object immersed in it. This force is called **buoyant force.**

The amount of buoyant force determines whether an object will sink or float in a fluid. If the buoyant force is

Figure 8-16. Forces acting on person lying on the floor beside a pool (a) and in water (b).

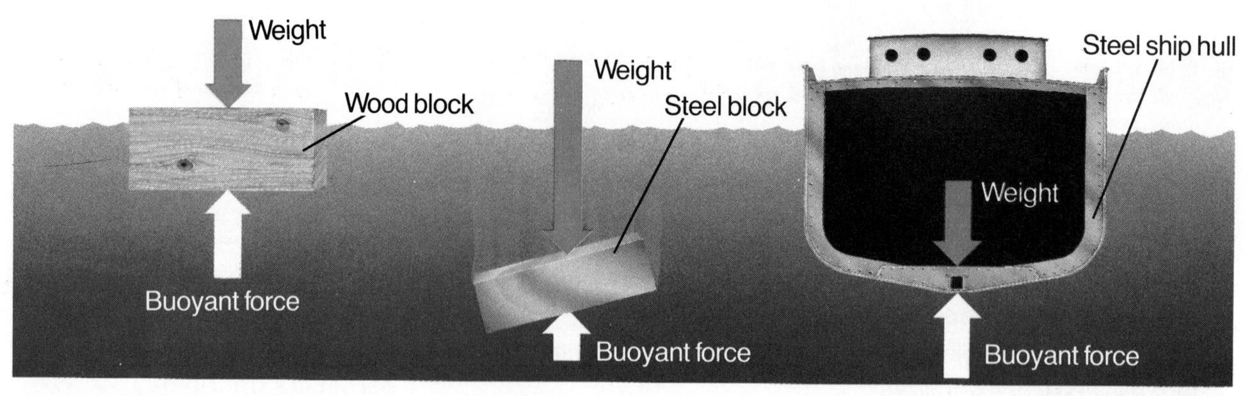

Figure 8-17. Forces acting on a wood block, a steel block, and a steel ship hull in water.

less than the object's weight, the object will sink. If the buoyant force equals the object's weight, the object floats. Sometimes the buoyant force on an object is greater than its weight. This force is what seems to pull a helium-filled balloon upward in the air. When the balloon is released, the unbalanced buoyant force causes the balloon to accelerate upward.

Archimedes, a Greek mathematician who lived in the third century B.C. made a discovery about buoyancy. According to **Archimedes' principle**, the buoyant force on an object in a fluid is equal to the weight of the fluid displaced by the object. If you place a block of pine wood in water, it will push water out of the way as it begins to sink—but only until the weight of the water it displaces equals the block's weight. The block floats at this level, as shown in Figure 8-17.

Suppose you drop a solid steel block the same size as the wood block into water. When the steel block is placed into the water, the steel block begins to push aside water as it sinks. Buoyant force begins to push up on the block. However, the density of steel is much greater than that of wood. So the buoyant force never becomes great enough to equal the weight of the steel block, and it sinks to the bottom.

How, then, does a steel ship float? Suppose you formed the steel block into a large hollowed-out bowl shape. As this shape sinks into water, it displaces much more water than the solid block. Soon, it displaces enough water to equal the weight of the steel, and it floats.

Pascal's Principle

If you dive underwater, you can feel the pressure of the water all around you. You live at the bottom of Earth's atmosphere, which also is a fluid that exerts a pressure.

MINI-Lab

How does applied pressure affect different areas of a fluid?

Draw water into a dropper and place it into a water-filled 2-L soft drink bottle. Suck in or squeeze out water from the dropper until it just barely floats. How does increasing the amount of water inside the dropper affect its density? Put the cap back on the bottle. Squeeze the bottle. What is the effect of applied pressure on the dropper?

This pressure is also all around you, even though you don't feel it. Blaise Pascal (1623-1662), a French scientist, discovered a useful property of fluids. **Pascal's principle** states that pressure applied to a fluid is transmitted unchanged throughout the fluid. For example, when you squeeze one end of a balloon, the balloon pops out on the other end. When you squeeze one end of a toothpaste tube, toothpaste emerges from the other end.

State Pascal's principle.

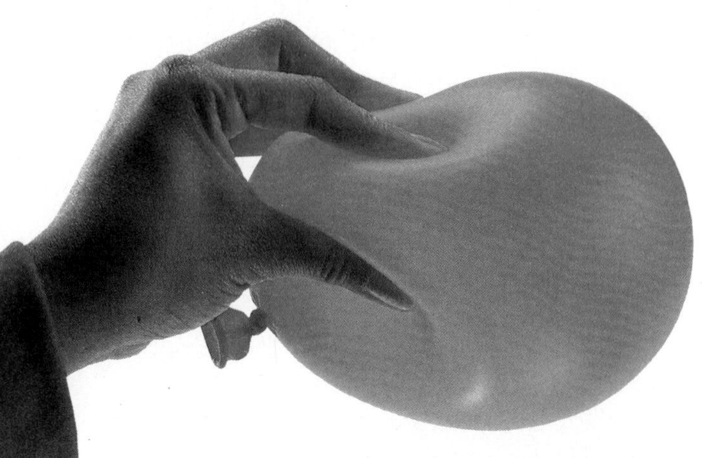

Figure 8-18. When you apply pressure on one end of an inflated balloon, the pressure is transmitted throughout the fluid—that is, the air—in the balloon.

Hydraulic machines that move very heavy loads use Pascal's principle. Maybe you've a seen car raised using a hydraulic lift. Look at Figure 8-19 to see how a machine of this type works. A small cylinder and a large cylinder are connected by a pipe. The cross section of the small cylinder has an area of 5 cm^2. The cross section of the large cylinder is 50 cm^2. Each cylinder is filled with a hydraulic fluid, usually oil, and has a piston that rests on the oil's surface.

Suppose you apply 500 N of force to the small piston. Therefore the pressure on the small piston is:

$$P = F/A = 500\ N/5\ cm^2 = 100\ N/cm^2.$$

Pascal's principle says that this pressure is transferred unchanged throughout the liquid. Therefore, the large piston will also have a pressure of 100 N/cm^2 applied to it. But the area of the large piston is 50 cm^2. So, the total force on the large piston is $100\ N/cm^2 \times 50\ cm^2 = 5000$ N. With this hydraulic machine, you could use your weight to lift something ten times as heavy as yourself. What action must be increased when using this machine?

Figure 8-19. A hydraulic lift is a machine that makes use of Pascal's principle.

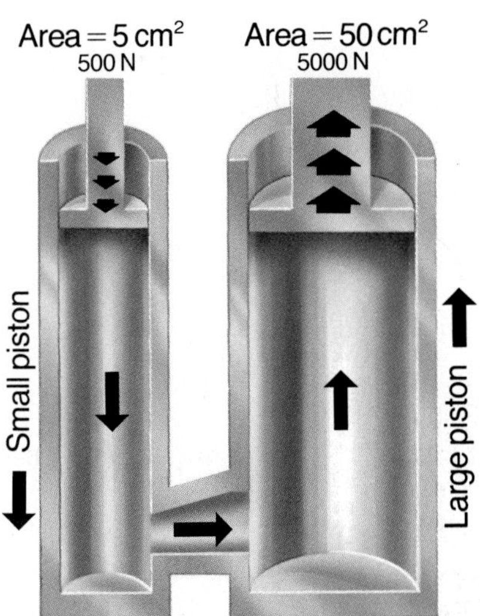

Bernoulli's Principle

It took humans thousands of years to learn to do what birds do naturally—fly, glide, and soar. Obviously it was no simple task to build a machine that could lift itself off the ground and fly with people aboard. The ability of an airplane to rise into the air is an example of another property of fluids called Bernoulli's principle. Daniel Bernoulli (1700-1782) was a Swiss scientist who studied the properties of moving fluids such as water and air. He published his discovery in 1738. According to **Bernoulli's principle**, as the velocity of a fluid increases, the pressure exerted by the fluid decreases.

Figure 8-20. If you hang a piece of paper and then blow across its surface, the paper rises.

To demonstrate Bernoulli's principle, blow across the surface of a sheet of paper, as in Figure 8-20. The paper will rise. The velocity of the air you blew over the top surface of the paper is greater than that of the quiet air below it. As a result, the downward air pressure above the paper decreases. The higher air pressure below the paper exerts a net force that pushes the paper upward.

Figure 8-21. The design of airplane wings is an application of Bernoulli's principle.

Now look at the curvature of the airplane wing in Figure 8-21. As the wing moves forward, the air passing over the wing must travel farther than air passing below it. Yet all the air takes the same time to get to the rear of the wing. Therefore, air must travel faster over the top of the wing than below it. Consequently, the pressure above the wing is less than the pressure below it. The result is a net upward force on the wing. This upward force makes up most of the force that lifts an airplane in flight.

How does a difference in air pressure help an airplane to fly?

Baseball pitchers also take advantage of Bernoulli's principle. If the pitcher puts a spin on the ball, air moves faster along the side of the ball that is spinning away from the direction of the throw. Look at Figure 8-22 on the next page. The ball's spin results in a net force that pushes the ball toward the low-pressure direction. The force gives the ball an unexpected curve that the pitcher hopes the batter won't be able to predict.

Fluids flow faster when forced to flow through narrow spaces. As a result of this speed increase, the pressure of the fluid drops. This reduction in pressure in these spaces is a special case of Bernoulli's principle called the Venturi effect. A dramatic demonstration of the Venturi effect

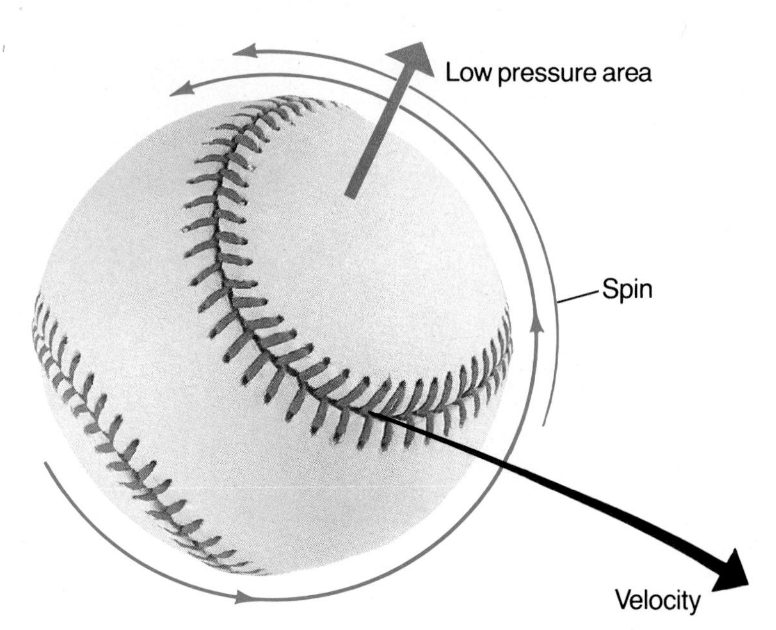

Figure 8-22. Air moves faster along the side of a spinning ball that is moving away from the direction of the throw.

has occurred in cities where the wind is forced to blow between rows of skyscrapers. The reduced air pressure outside of buildings during strong winds has caused windows to be forced out by the higher air pressure inside the buildings.

SECTION REVIEW

1. How is it possible that a boat made of concrete can float?
2. If you wanted to lift an object weighing 20 000 N, how much force would you have to apply to the small piston in Figure 8-19?
3. State Bernoulli's principle and tell how it helps produce lift on an airplane.
4. **Apply:** If you blow up a balloon with air and release it, it will fall to the floor. Why does it fall instead of floating?

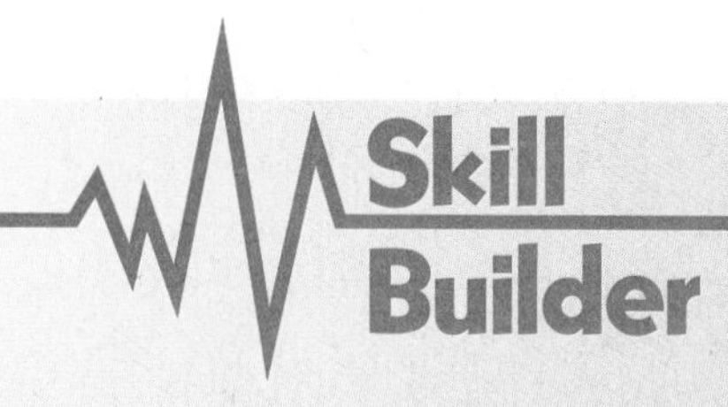

Measuring in SI

The density of water is 1.0 g/cm^3. How many kilograms of water does a submerged 120-cm^3 block displace? One kilogram weighs 9.8 N. What is the buoyant force on the block? If you need help, refer to Chapter 2 and to Measuring in SI in the **Skill Handbook** on page 680.

CHAPTER REVIEW

SUMMARY

8-1: Matter and Temperature

1. There are four states of matter: solid, liquid, gas, and plasma.

2. According to the kinetic theory, all matter is made of constantly moving particles.

3. Most matter expands when heated and contracts when cooled.

8-2: Science and Society: Water—Earth's Vital Liquid

1. Fresh water on Earth is scarce, and this water is often wasted or polluted.

2. There are many ways in which people can save water and stop its pollution.

8-3: Changes in State

1. Changes of state can be interpreted in terms of the kinetic theory of matter.

2. The energy of the heat of fusion and vaporization overcomes attractive forces between particles of matter.

8-4: Behavior of Gases

1. The pressure of a gas is caused by collisions of its moving particles.

2. Boyle's law states that the volume of a gas decreases when the pressure increases, at constant temperature.

3. Charles's law states that the volume of a gas increases when the temperature increases, at constant pressure.

8-5: Uses of Fluids

1. Archimedes' principle states that the buoyant force on an object in a fluid is equal to the weight of the fluid displaced.

2. Pascal's principle states that pressure applied to a fluid is transmitted unchanged throughout the fluid.

3. Bernoulli's principle states that the pressure exerted by a fluid decreases as its velocity increases.

KEY SCIENCE WORDS

a. **Archimedes' principle**
b. **Bernoulli's principle**
c. **Boyle's law**
d. **buoyant force**
e. **Charles's law**
f. **condensation**
g. **crystals**
h. **evaporation**
i. **heat of fusion**
j. **heat of vaporization**
k. **kinetic theory of matter**
l. **pascal**
m. **Pascal's principle**
n. **plasma**
o. **polluted water**
p. **pressure**
q. **states of matter**
r. **thermal expansion**

UNDERSTANDING VOCABULARY

Match each phrase with the correct term from the list of Key Science Words.

1. the volume of a gas is reduced when the temperature is decreased
2. water that is dirty and unfit for living things
3. liquid changes to gas below the boiling point
4. amount of force exerted per unit of area
5. the buoyant force on an object in a fluid equals the weight of the displaced fluid
6. the SI unit of pressure
7. particles are arranged in regular patterns
8. a gaslike mixture of charged particles
9. matter is made of tiny, moving particles
10. energy needed for a liquid to boil

CHAPTER

REVIEW

CHECKING CONCEPTS

Choose the word or phrase that completes the sentence.

1. The temperature at which all particle motion of matter would stop is ______.
   - **a.** absolute zero
   - **b.** its melting point
   - **c.** 0°C
   - **d.** 273°C
2. The state of matter that has a definite volume and a definite shape is ______.
   - **a.** gas
   - **b.** liquid
   - **c.** plasma
   - **d.** solid
3. The most common state of matter is ______.
   - **a.** gas
   - **b.** liquid
   - **c.** plasma
   - **d.** solid
4. Most pressure is measured in ______.
   - **a.** grams
   - **b.** kilopascals
   - **c.** newtons
   - **d.** pascals
5. Pascal's principle is the basis for ______.
   - **a.** aerodynamics
   - **b.** buoyancy
   - **c.** hydraulics
   - **d.** changes of state
6. Bernoulli's principle explains why ______.
   - **a.** airplanes fly
   - **b.** boats float
   - **c.** pistons work
   - **d.** ice melts
7. Particles separate completely from each other in a(n) ______.
   - **a.** gas
   - **b.** liquid
   - **c.** solid
   - **d.** amorphous material
8. The state of the matter in the sun and other stars is primarily ______.
   - **a.** amorphous
   - **b.** plasma
   - **c.** liquid
   - **d.** gas
9. In general, as a solid is heated, it ______.
   - **a.** becomes a gas
   - **b.** condenses
   - **c.** contracts
   - **d.** expands
10. A material's heat of fusion gives the amount of energy needed to ______.
    - **a.** condense a gas
    - **b.** boil a liquid
    - **c.** melt a solid
    - **d.** evaporate a liquid

UNDERSTANDING CONCEPTS

Complete each sentence.

11. Materials that appear to be solid but are not made of crystals are ______.
12. ______ is the process by which a gas changes to a liquid.
13. The fact that pressure applied to a fluid is transmitted unchanged throughout the fluid is ______ principle.
14. The state of a sample of matter depends on its ______.
15. When a balloon is placed in warmer air, its volume increases. This is an example of ______ law.

THINK AND WRITE CRITICALLY

16. How might waste water in the home be recycled instead of being poured into the sewer system?
17. Why would it be incorrect to say, "This room is full of air"?
18. What energy changes occur when hot tea is poured over ice?
19. Use the kinetic theory to explain why liquid water forms on the outside of a glass of cold lemonade.
20. Why might rocks in a creek hurt your feet more than the same rocks would in deeper water?

APPLY

21. Use Charles's and Boyle's laws to explain why you should check your tire pressure when the temperature changes.
22. Explain how food might get "freezer burn." How might you prevent it?
23. Alcohol evaporates more quickly than does water. What can you tell about the forces between the alcohol particles?
24. Why do aerosol cans have a "do not incinerate" warning?
25. Applying pressure lowers the melting point of ice. Why might an icy road at −1°C be more dangerous than an icy road at −10°C?

MORE SKILL BUILDERS

If you need help, refer to the Skill Handbook.

1. **Observing and Inferring:** Infer the effect related to air pressure that a large truck passing a small car would have on the car.
2. **Making and Using Graphs:** A group of students heated ice until it melted and then turned to steam. They measured the temperature each minute and graphed the results. Their graph is provided below. In terms of the energy involved, explain what is happening at each letter (a, b, c, d) in the graph.

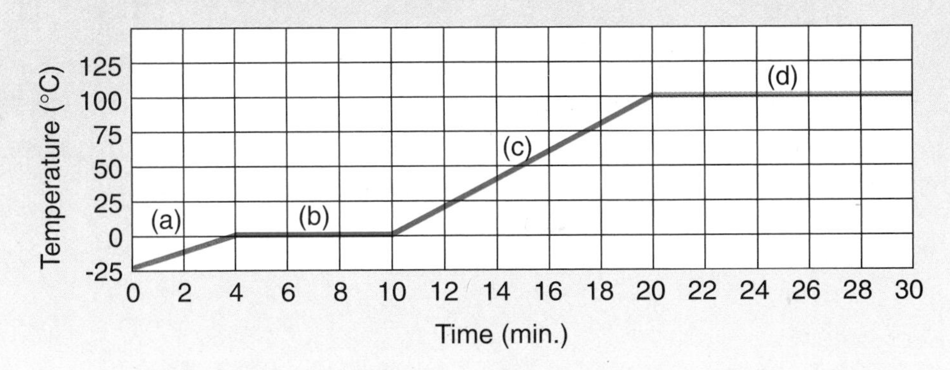

3. **Sequencing:** Sequence the processes that occur when ice is heated until it becomes steam and then the steam is cooled until it is ice again.
4. **Interpreting Data:** As elevation increases, boiling point decreases. List each of the following locations as at sea level, above sea level, or below sea level. (Boiling point of water in °C is given.)
   Death Valley (100.3), Denver (94), Madison (99), Mt. Everest (76.5), Mt. McKinley (79), New York City (100), Salt Lake City (95.6), San Francisco (100)
5. **Recognizing Cause and Effect:** List possible effects for each of the following causes.
   a. Perspiration evaporates.
   b. Pressure on a balloon decreases.
   c. Your buoyant force equals your weight.

PROJECTS

1. What would happen to an unprotected person at the bottom of the ocean or in outer space? Research the effects of pressure changes on the human body and write a report.
2. Research crystal growing and what conditions are needed to grow a perfect crystal. Grow crystals of several different materials and display them.

CHAPTER 9 Classification of Matter

Did you ever watch a construction crew pour concrete for a building? What is this material? Actually, you can't classify fresh concrete as one of the states of matter. Rather, it is a mixture of solids—portland cement, sand, rocks—and a liquid, water.

FIND OUT!

Do this activity to make some classroom concrete and observe its properties.

Mix together 10 g of crushed calcium carbonate tablets; 20 g of sand; 30 g of small, clean rocks; and 5 g of water. Mix thoroughly in a paper cup. Describe the appearance and state of the mixture. Allow to dry overnight and observe again.

Gearing Up

Previewing the Chapter

Use this outline to help you focus on important ideas in this chapter.

Section 9-1 Composition of Matter
- Substances
- Mixtures
- Solutions
- Colloids and Suspensions

Section 9-2 Science and Society
Smog, a Mixture in the Environment
- Visible Air Pollution

Section 9-3 Describing Matter
- Physical Properties
- Physical Changes
- Chemical Changes
- Chemical Properties
- The Conservation of Mass

Previewing Science Skills

- In the **Skill Builders,** you will make a concept map and observe and infer.
- In the **Activities,** you will classify, model, observe, and hypothesize.

What's next?

You have made a model of concrete, a useful mixture. Study Chapter 9 for a better understanding of mixtures and the physical and chemical properties of matter.

9-1 Composition of Matter

New Science Words

element
compounds
substance
heterogeneous mixture
homogeneous mixture
solution
colloid
suspension

Objectives

- Distinguish between substances and mixtures.
- Compare and contrast solutions, colloids, and suspensions.

Substances

You can easily tell whether a line is drawn in ink or pencil. The lines look different because they are made of different materials. Look at the parts of a pencil. Notice that it's made of several kinds of materials. You could classify the materials of the pencil according to the four states of matter. Another way to classify materials is by the particles they are made of.

The particles that make up all matter are called atoms. If all the atoms in a sample of matter are alike, that kind of matter is an **element.** The carbon in a pencil point, the oxygen in the air, and the copper in a penny are all examples of elements. Altogether, there are 109 elements. The names of all the elements are in the periodic table on pages 258-259. You will learn more about the other information in the table in later chapters.

Materials called **compounds** are made from atoms of two or more elements that are combined. The ratio of the different atoms in a compound is always the same. For example, the elements hydrogen and oxygen can combine to form the compound water. The atoms of elements in water are present in the ratio of two hydrogen atoms to one oxygen atom.

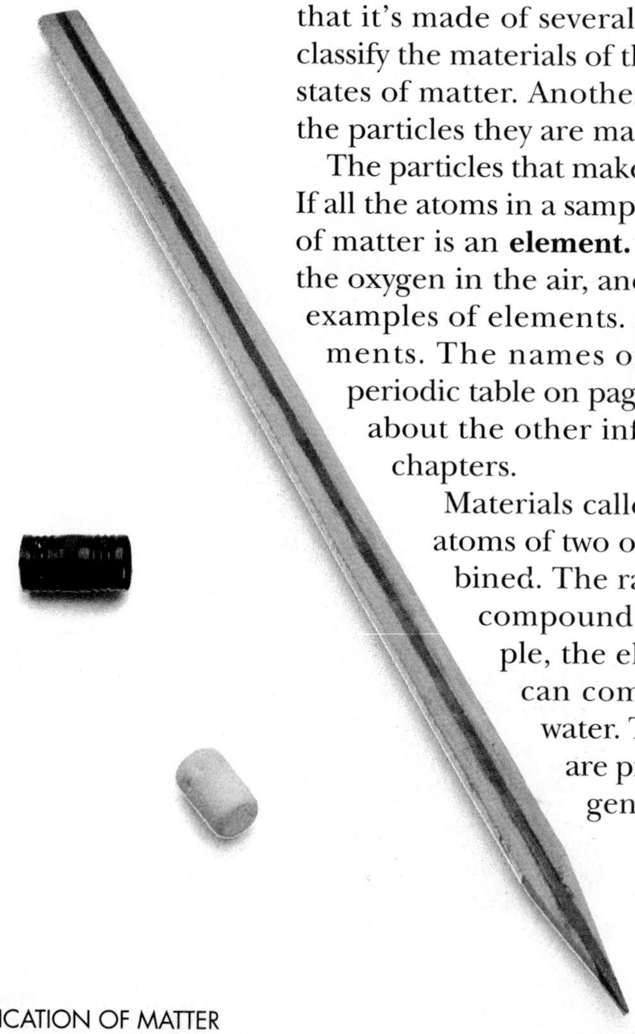

Figure 9-1. A pencil is made up of several different materials.

Figure 9-2. Sugar is a compound of carbon, oxygen, and hydrogen.

When was the last time you ate a compound whose elements are a black solid and two invisible gases? One compound that fits this description is sugar. You can recognize sugar by its white crystals and sweet taste. But the elements in sugar—carbon, hydrogen, and oxygen—are neither white nor sweet, Figure 9-2. Like sugar, compounds are usually very different from the elements that make them up.

Oxygen, carbon, water, sugar, and salt are examples of materials classified as substances. A **substance** is either an element or a compound.

Mixtures

When you have a sore throat, do you gargle with salt water? Salt water is classified as a mixture. A mixture is a material made up of two or more substances, and salt and water are different substances.

Unlike compounds, mixtures do not always contain the same amounts of different substances. You may be wearing clothing made of permanent-press fabric. This fabric is woven from fibers of two compounds—polyester and cotton. The fabric may contain 45 percent polyester and 55 percent cotton, or 65 percent polyester and 35 percent cotton, as shown Figure 9-3. Fabric with more polyester is more resistant to wrinkling than fabric with less polyester.

Figure 9-3. Permanent-press fabrics are mixtures that have variable composition.

A mixture in which different materials are spread out unevenly is called a **heterogeneous mixture.** Permanent-press fabrics are heterogeneous mixtures because you can detect the different materials by sight or with a microscope. Gravel, concrete, and dry soup mixes are examples of other heterogeneous mixtures.

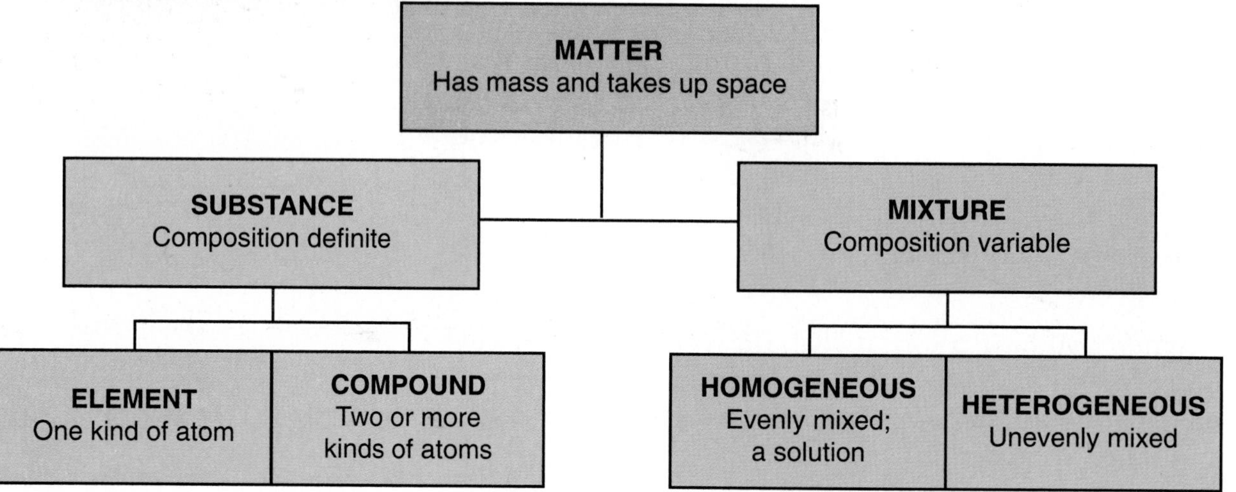

Figure 9-4. Every sample of matter is an element, a compound, or a mixture.

Solutions

The salt water you gargle with looks like water and tastes salty. Like a polyester-cotton fabric, salt water is in some ways similar to both of the substances it contains. But you can't see the particles in salt water even with a microscope. A material in which the substances are uniformly spread out is classified as a **homogeneous mixture.**

Have you ever looked closely at a bottle of white vinegar? Vinegar is a liquid solution made mostly of acetic acid and water. It appears clear, even though it is made up of particles of acetic acid in water. A **solution** is another name for a homogeneous mixture. Particles in solutions are so small that they cannot be seen even with a microscope. The particles have diameters of about 0.000 000 001 m (1 nm). The particles will also never settle to the bottom of their container. Solutions remain constantly and uniformly mixed.

Figure 9-5. Vinegar is a liquid solution containing acetic acid and water.

PROBLEM SOLVING

Jason Makes a Colloid

Jason makes a colloid to use on sandwiches. His friends think that his colloid tastes better than store-bought mayonnaise, although it is similar.

To make the colloid, Jason pours 60 cm^3 vinegar into a blender. He then adds 30 cm^3 sugar and blends until dissolved. Next, he adds 5 cm^3 dry mustard, one clove of fresh garlic, a pinch of salt, and one egg. He blends these ingredients until they are well mixed. While the blender is still on, he slowly adds 180 cm^3 vegetable oil in a steady stream. He continues blending until the colloid is thick.

At what stages in the preparation of his recipe does Jason have homogeneous and heterogeneous mixtures?

Think Critically: How can mayonnaise be distinguished from a solution?

Colloids and Suspensions

When you drink a glass of whole or low-fat milk, you are drinking a mixture of water, fats, proteins, and other substances. Milk is a colloid. A **colloid** is a heterogeneous mixture that, like a solution, never settles. Unlike the particles in a solution, the particles in a colloid are large enough to scatter light. Milk appears white because its particles scatter light. Gelatin is a colloid that may seem to be clear until you shine a light on it. Then you see that its particles also scatter light.

In what way is a colloid like a solution?

Figure 9-6. A beam of light goes straight through a solution (left) but is scattered by a colloid (right).

Table 9-1

COMPARING SOLUTIONS, COLLOIDS, AND SUSPENSIONS

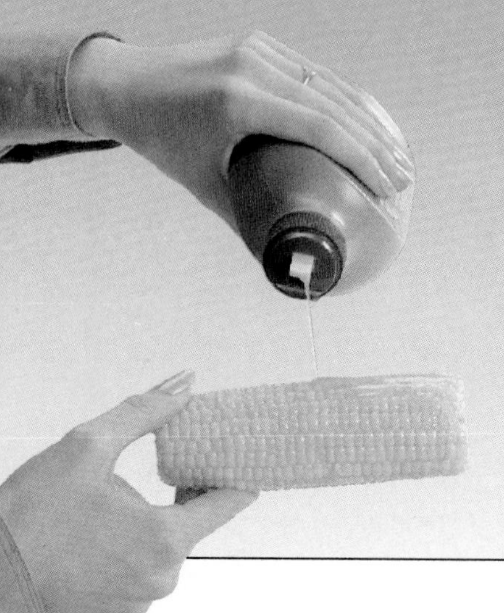

Description	Solutions	Colloids	Suspensions
Settle upon standing	No	No	Yes
Can be separated using filter paper	No	No	Yes
Sizes of particles	0.1-1 nm	1-100 nm	Greater than 100 nm
Scatter light	No	Yes	Yes

Have you ever been playing on a wet field and kicked a ball into a puddle of muddy water? Some mixtures, such as muddy water, are neither solutions nor colloids. If you fill a glass with tap water after a heavy rainstorm, the water may be slightly muddy. If you let it stand long enough, the silt will fall to the bottom of the glass and the water will clear. Muddy water is an example of a suspension. A **suspension** is a heterogeneous mixture containing a liquid in which visible particles settle.

You can use the information in Table 9-1 to classify different kinds of mixtures.

SECTION REVIEW

1. How is a container of hydrogen and oxygen different from a container of water vapor?
2. Distinguish between a substance and a mixture.
3. **Apply:** Why do the words "Shake well before using" on a bottle of fruit juice indicate that the juice is a suspension?

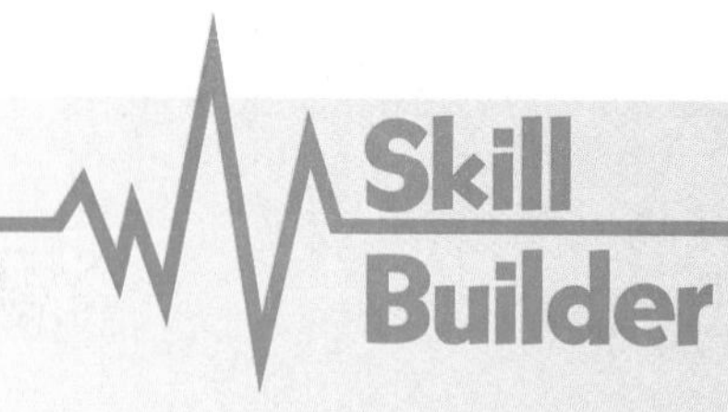

Concept Mapping

Make a network tree to show types of liquid mixtures. Include these terms: *homogeneous mixtures, heterogeneous mixtures, solutions, colloids,* and *suspensions*. If you need help, refer to Concept Mapping in the **Skill Handbook** on pages 684 and 685.

ACTIVITY 9-1
Elements, Compounds, and Mixtures

Problem: *What are the differences among elements, compounds, and mixtures?*

Materials
- plastic freezer bag containing tagged items
- copper foil
- small package of salt
- piece of solder
- aluminum foil
- baking soda or chalk (calcium carbonate)
- piece of granite
- sugar water in a vial

Procedure
1. Copy the data table and use it to record your observations.
2. Obtain a prepared bag of numbered objects.
3. Use the list above to identify each object.
4. The names of all the elements appear in the periodic table on pages 258-259. Use the table to classify any of the objects as elements.
5. Any of the objects that are compounds have been named as examples in Section 9-1.

Data and Observations

Object	Identity	Classification
1		
2		
3		
4		
5		
6		
7		

Analyze
1. If you know the name of a substance, how can you find out if it is an element?
2. How is a compound different from a mixture?
3. Were the mixtures you identified homogeneous or heterogeneous?

Conclude and Apply
4. Examine the contents of your refrigerator at home. Classify what you find as elements, compounds, or mixtures.
5. All materials can be classified with some descriptions. What are the differences among elements, compounds, and mixtures?

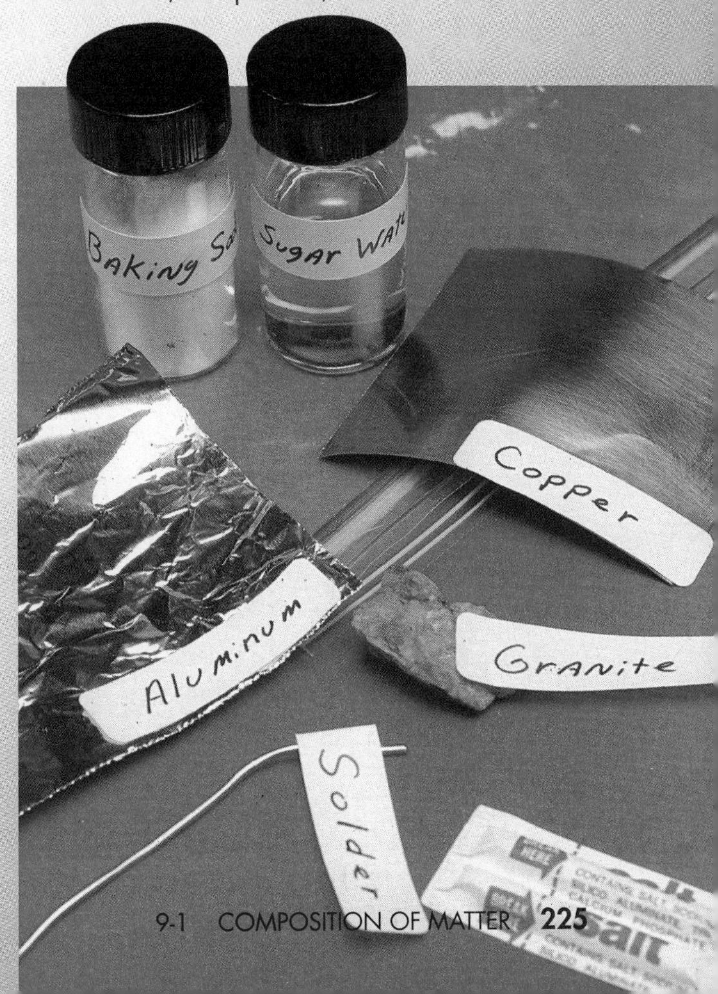

9-2 Smog, a Mixture in the Environment

New Science Words

Tyndall effect
smog

Objectives

- Identify smog as a harmful colloid by its properties.
- Describe how smog is formed and suggest several ways to eliminate it.

Visible Air Pollution

Have you ever watched the beam of a searchlight zoom across the night sky? The beam forms when light from the searchlight is scattered by invisible bits of dust and droplets of water in the air. The scattering of light by particles in a mixture is called the **Tyndall effect.** You can see the Tyndall effect in all colloids. As you recall, a colloid is a mixture in which the particles are invisible and never settle. However, the particles in the mixture are large enough to scatter light. Fog is a mixture of water droplets in air. The water droplets scatter light, causing the fog to appear cloudy or hazy. The air above large cities sometimes appears hazy. The haze is often smog.

Smog is a form of air pollution. It is a colloid of small, invisible pieces of solid materials mixed with the gases that make up air. Some of the solid material in smog is dust. The dust can occur naturally. It may come from

Did You Know?

One out of three Americans lives in an area where the air standards of the Clean Air Act are violated.

loose soil blown upward by the wind or from ash from volcanic eruptions and forest fires. However, smog also contains solid materials that are not produced naturally. In the early 1900s, ash and soot from burning coal produced most of the dust in smog. Today, unburned compounds in automobile exhaust account for most of the particles of solids in smog. Other sources of solid materials in the air are gasoline stations, industrial plants, hair sprays, and spray paints.

Normally, warm air will rise in the atmosphere. However, sometimes a layer of warm air will be trapped beneath a layer of colder air. Smog forms in this layer of warm, trapped air. The constant motion of the warm air mixes the dust and other solid particles in the air, producing the colloid. Within the smog, new compounds that are harmful to humans begin to form. These compounds cause eye irritation and can cause lung damage. Sometimes smog becomes so severe that city governments must declare smog alerts. These alerts advise elderly people and people with respiratory problems to remain indoors. Industries are asked to cut back their use of fuels, and nonessential traffic is restricted. Winds eventually blow smog away from the cities over which it forms.

SECTION REVIEW

1. Why does smog appear hazy?
2. How does smog form?

You Decide!

One way to reduce air pollution is to reduce the consumption of gasoline. Suppose there was a bill in Congress to raise gasoline taxes and use the proceeds to help clean up the environment. Would you want your representatives to vote for the higher taxes? Why or why not?

9-3 Describing Matter

New Science Words

physical property
physical change
chemical change
chemical property
law of conservation of mass

Objectives

- ▶ Give examples of physical properties.
- ▶ Distinguish between physical and chemical changes.
- ▶ Distinguish between chemical and physical properties.
- ▶ State and explain the law of conservation of mass.

Physical Properties

You can bend an empty aluminum can. But you can't bend a piece of chalk. Chalk doesn't bend—it breaks. Brittleness is a characteristic that describes a piece of chalk. Its color and shape also describe the chalk. A **physical property** is any characteristic of a material that you can observe easily without changing the substances that make up the material. You can describe matter using physical properties. Does all matter have properties?

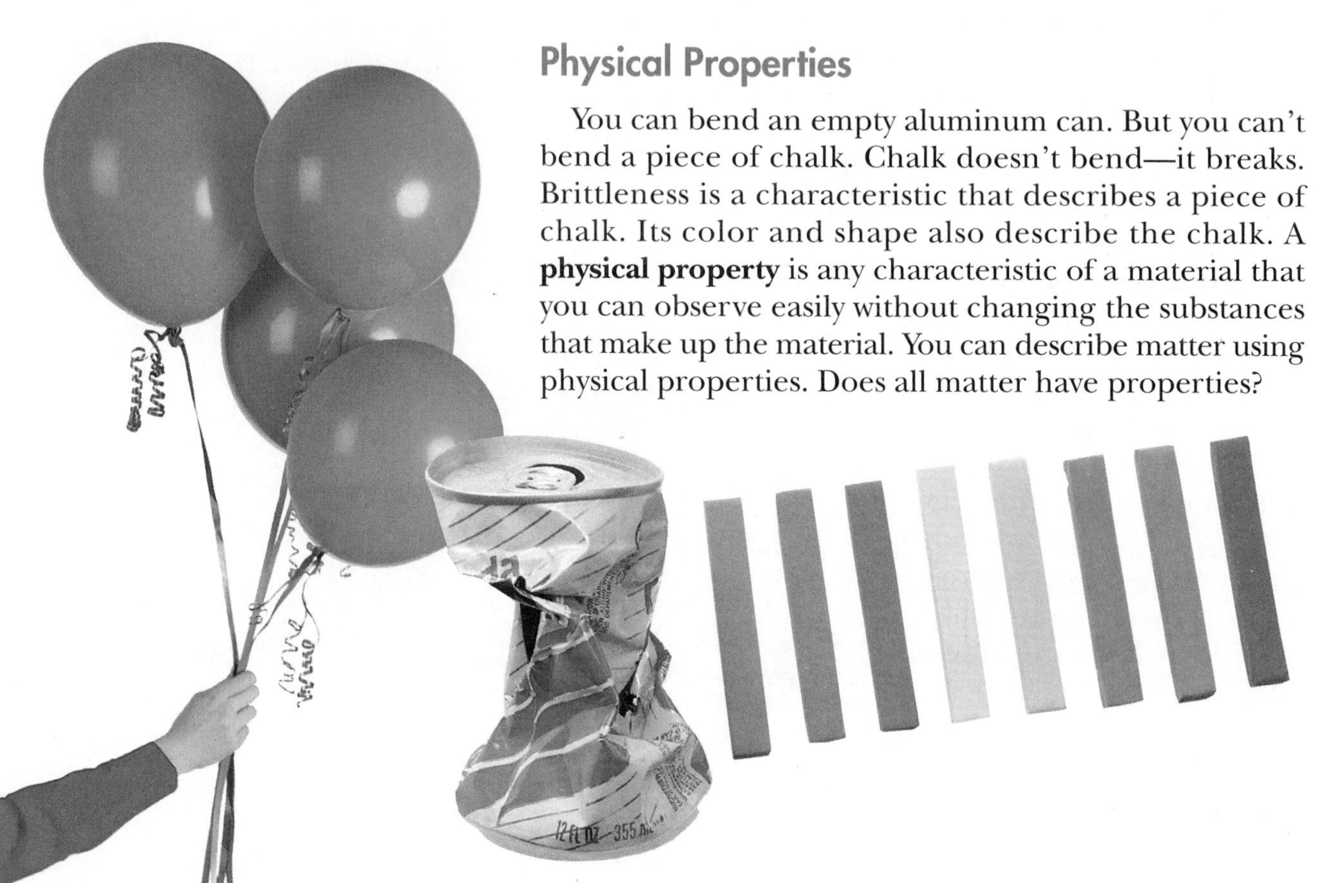

Figure 9-7. What are the physical properties of the balloons and the gas inside them?

Some physical properties describe a particular object. For example, you might describe an iron nail as a pointy-ended cylinder made of dull, gray-colored solid. By describing the shape, color, and state of the nail, you have listed several of its physical properties. Some physical properties can be measured. For instance, you could use a metric ruler to measure another property of the nail—its length. What physical property of the nail is measured with a balance?

If you had some water in a test tube, you might measure its volume and temperature and describe its odor. Each characteristic is a physical property. Some physical properties describe a material or a substance. As you may know, all objects made of iron are attracted by a magnet. Attraction by a magnet is a property of the substance iron. Every substance has physical properties that distinguish it from other substances. Examples of physical properties you have learned about are color, shape, size, density, melting point, and boiling point.

Figure 9-8. This mixture of pebbles and sand could be separated with a sifter.

Do you pick out the grapes in a fruit salad and eat them first, last, or maybe not at all? If you do, you are using physical properties to identify the grapes and separate them from the other fruits in the mixture. Figure 9-8 shows a mixture of pebbles and sand. You can identify the pebbles and grains of sand by differences in color, shape, and size. By sifting the mixture, you can quickly separate the pebbles from the grains of sand because they have different sizes.

Look at the mixture of iron filings and sand shown in Figure 9-9. It would be impossible to separate this mixture with a sieve because the filings and grains of sand are the same size. A more efficient way is to pass a magnet through the mixture. When you pass a magnet through the mixture, the magnet attracts the iron filings and pulls them from the sand. In this way, the difference in a physical property, such as attraction to a magnet, can be used to separate substances in a mixture.

Figure 9-9. A mixture of sand and iron filings can be separated with a magnet. The iron filings are magnetic. The sand is not.

Physical Changes

If you break a piece of chalk, it loses its original size and shape. You have caused a change in some of its physical properties. But you have not changed the substances that make up the chalk.

The changes of state that you studied in Chapter 8 are all examples of physical changes. When water—or any substance—freezes, boils, evaporates, sublimates, or condenses, it undergoes physical changes. There are energy changes during these changes in state, but the kind of substance—the identity of the element or compound—does not change.

List five examples of physical changes in water.

As shown in the picture above, iron, like water, will change states if it absorbs enough energy. In each state it will have physical properties that can be used to identify it as the substance iron. A change in size, shape, color, or state of matter is called a **physical change.** Physical changes do not change the substances in a material.

Just as physical properties can be used to separate mixtures, so can physical changes. For example, if you let salt water stand, you'll find at a later time that

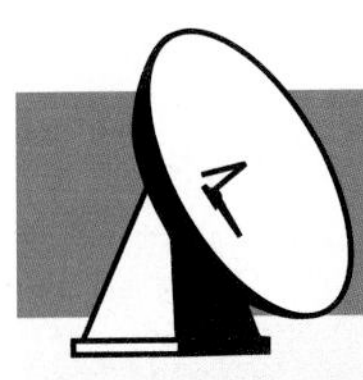

TECHNOLOGY

Aerogels—Next to Nothing at All

Imagine a block of gelatin dessert in which all of the liquid has been replaced with air. It might look like a frozen cloud and would be called an aerogel.

Light passing through the tiny pores and microscopic framework of an aerogel is bent, giving the aerogel a bluish color against a dark background and a yellowish color in the light. Unlike a solid, the framework is so weakly connected that the aerogel is a poor conductor of heat. Therefore, an aerogel is an excellent insulator. The insulating property of aerogels has caught the interest of industry. Thus, you may soon see aerogels used as insulation in everything from refrigerators to double pane windows.

Think Critically: What property of aerogels might limit their use as an insulator in double pane windows?

the water has evaporated, leaving salt crystals inside the glass. The process of evaporating water from salty seawater is used to produce drinking water.

Chemical Changes

In any physical change of a material, the substances in the material do not change their identities. But you know that substances do change their identities. Fireworks explode, matches burn, eggs rot, and bikes and car bodies rust. What do changes in these materials have in common?

Burned toast, burned soup, and burned steak all smell burned. The smell is different from the smell of bread, soup, or steak. The odor is a clue that a new substance

has been produced. A change of one substance in a material to a different substance is a **chemical change.** There are many signs that can tell you when a chemical change has taken place. For example, the foaming of an antacid tablet in a glass of water and the smell in the air after a thunderstorm indicate that new substances have been produced. In some chemical changes a rapid production of energy, such as the light and sound of an exploding firecracker, is a clue.

When iron is exposed to the oxygen and water in the air, the iron and oxygen slowly form a new substance, rust. When hydrogen gas is burned in a rocket engine, the elements hydrogen and oxygen combine to form water. Burning and rusting are chemical changes because different substances are produced.

Chemical Properties

Look at Figure 9-10. You have probably seen this warning on cans of paint thinners and lighter fluids for charcoal grills. The warning indicates that they burn quickly. The tendency of a substance to burn is an example of a chemical property. A **chemical property** is a characteristic of a substance that indicates if it can undergo a certain chemical change. Many substances are flammable. Knowing which materials contain substances that have this chemical property allows you to use them safely.

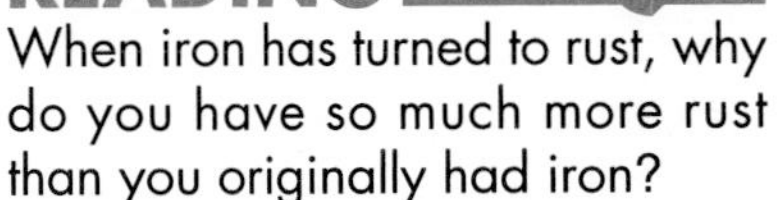

Science and READING

When iron has turned to rust, why do you have so much more rust than you originally had iron?

Figure 9-10. Flammability is a chemical property of some materials used in the home.

If you look around a drugstore, you might notice that many medicines are stored in dark bottles. These medicines contain compounds with a similar chemical property. Chemical changes will take place in the compounds if they are exposed to light. What physical property do these bottles have in common?

Even though there are thousands of substances and billions of mixtures, they do share a few common physical and chemical properties. You can use these properties to study matter further.

EcoTip

Cleaners with the words *warning, caution,* or *poison* on them can be dangerous to you and to the environment. Call the local EPA to find out how to dispose of them when they are no longer needed.

The Conservation of Mass

What are some signs of a chemical change when a log burns?

Suppose you burn a large log on a campfire until nothing is left but a small pile of ashes. During the burning, smoke, heat, and light are given off. It's easy to see that a chemical change occurs. At first, you might also think that matter was lost during this change, because the pile of ashes looks much smaller than the log. In fact, if you could measure both the mass of the log and the mass of the ashes, the mass of the ashes would be less than that of the log. But suppose that during the burning, you could collect all the oxygen in the air that was combined with the log during the burning. And suppose you could also collect all the smoke and gases that escape from the burning log and measure their masses, too. Then you would find that there is no loss of mass during the burning.

Not only is there no loss of mass during burning; there is no loss or gain of mass during any chemical change. In other words, matter is neither created nor destroyed during a chemical change. This statement is known as the **law of conservation of mass.** According to this law, the mass of all substances present before a chemical change equals the mass of all the substances remaining

Figure 9-11. Although you can't see the gases used or formed when a log burns, there is no loss or gain of mass.

Figure 9-12. A chemical change between two compounds illustrates the law of conservation of mass.

after the change. Figure 9-12 shows a chemical change inside a flask. What evidence is there that a chemical change has occurred? How do the pictures demonstrate the law of conservation of mass?

SECTION REVIEW

1. What physical properties could you use to distinguish between iron and aluminum?
2. In terms of substances, explain why evaporation of water is a physical change and not a chemical change.
3. Give an example of a chemical change that occurs when you prepare a meal.
4. Why is being flammable a chemical property rather than a physical property?
5. **Apply:** The law of conservation of mass applies to physical changes as well as to chemical changes. How might you demonstrate this law for melting ice?

Observing and Inferring

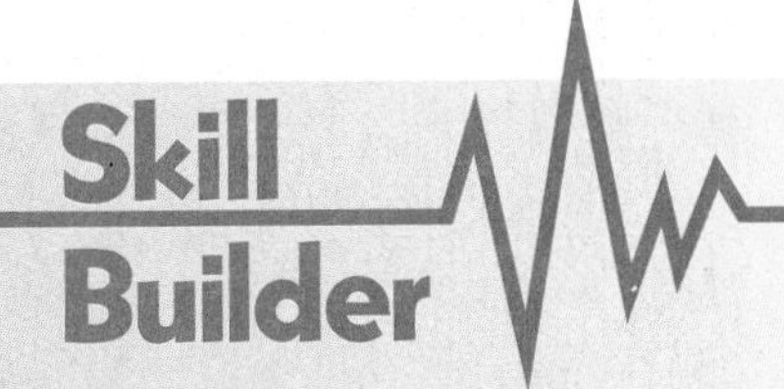

Observe a burning candle. What evidence do you have that there are chemical and physical changes in the candle as it burns? If you need help, refer to Observing and Inferring in the **Skill Handbook** on page 678.

ACTIVITY 9-2
A Chemical Change

Problem: *What is considered evidence for a chemical change?*

Materials   

- safety goggles
- 0.5 g baking soda
- small evaporating dish
- hand lens
- 3 cm^3 of dilute hydrochloric acid
- 10 cm^3 graduated cylinder
- electric hot plate

Procedure

1. Make a chart like the one shown to record your data. Place 0.5 g of baking soda in an evaporating dish. Examine the substance with a hand lens and record your observations.
2. Slowly add 1 cm^3 of dilute hydrochloric acid to the 0.5 g of baking soda in the dish. **CAUTION:** *Hydrochloric acid is corrosive and can burn the skin.* Record your observations of any changes.
3. Slowly add 1 cm^3 more hydrochloric acid to the dish. Heat the dish until the contents become dry, and let it cool. Examine the contents of the dish with the hand lens and record your observations.
4. Add another 1 cm^3 of acid to the material in the dish. Record your observations.

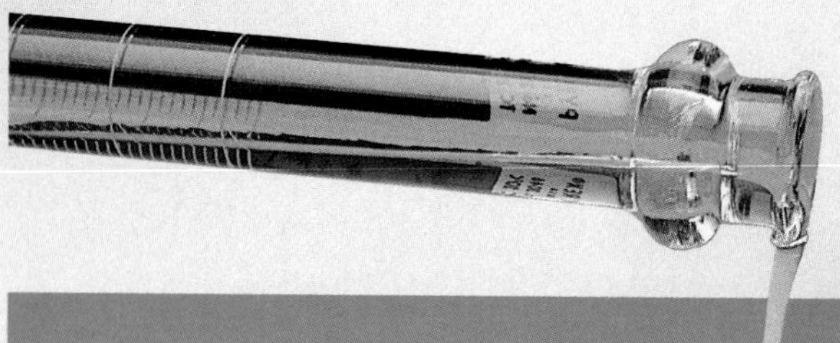

Data and Observations

Appearance of baking soda	
Effect of adding acid	
Appearance after adding acid	
Effect of adding final acid	

Analyze

1. What differences do you notice in the appearances of the materials under the magnifying lens?
2. How did adding the final 1 cm^3 of acid help you know a chemical change took place with the earlier additions of acid?

Conclude and Apply

3. What is the evidence that a chemical change took place between the substances you mixed? In general, what evidence must be present to conclude that a chemical change has taken place?
4. Baking soda can neutralize acids. In what type of consumer products might you find baking soda?

CHAPTER

REVIEW

SUMMARY

9-1: Composition of Matter

1. Elements and compounds are substances; a mixture is composed of two or more substances.
2. A liquid solution is a homogeneous mixture. Colloids and suspensions are two kinds of heterogeneous mixtures.

9-2: Science and Society: Smog, a Mixture in the Environment

1. Smog is a form of air pollution that can be identified as a colloid by the Tyndall effect.
2. Ways to eliminate smog include reducing the use of materials responsible for air pollution.

9-3: Describing Matter

1. Physical properties are characteristics of materials that you can observe without changing substances.
2. In physical changes, substances in materials do not change. In chemical changes, substances in materials change to different substances.
3. Physical properties can be observed without changing substances; chemical properties indicate chemical changes substances can undergo.
4. The law of conservation of mass states that during any chemical change, matter is neither created nor destroyed.

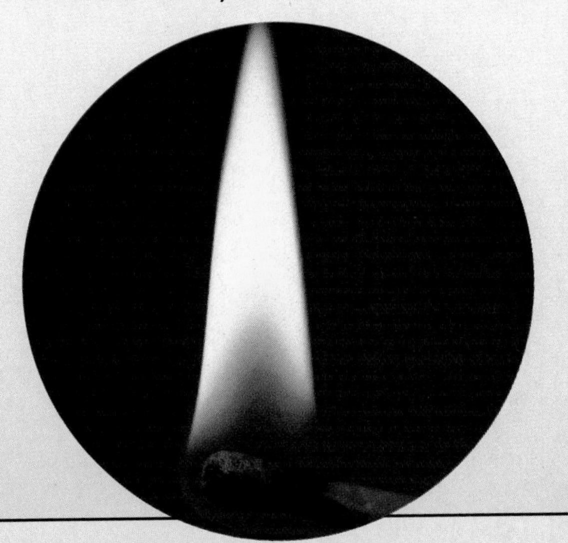

KEY SCIENCE WORDS

a. **chemical change**
b. **chemical property**
c. **colloid**
d. **compounds**
e. **element**
f. **heterogeneous mixture**
g. **homogeneous mixture**
h. **law of conservation of mass**
i. **physical change**
j. **physical property**
k. **smog**
l. **solution**
m. **substance**
n. **suspension**
o. **Tyndall effect**

UNDERSTANDING VOCABULARY

Match each phrase with the correct term from the list of Key Science Words.

1. a colloidal form of air pollution
2. mixture in which different materials are spread out unevenly
3. all atoms in a sample are alike
4. change in color, size, shape, or state
5. change of substance to a different substance
6. combined atoms of two or more elements
7. either an element or a compound
8. mixture that scatters light and never settles
9. an indication of whether a chemical change can occur in a substance
10. In a chemical change, matter is neither created nor destroyed.

CHAPTER REVIEW

CHECKING CONCEPTS

Choose the word or phrase that completes the sentence or answers the question.

1. A copper wire will bend. This is an example of ______.
   a. a chemical property **c.** conservation
   b. a physical property **d.** an element
2. Which of the following is *not* an element?
   a. water **c.** oxygen
   b. carbon **d.** hydrogen
3. An example of a chemical change is ______.
   a. boiling **c.** evaporation
   b. burning **d.** melting
4. Whipped cream is an example of a ______.
   a. colloid **c.** substance
   b. solution **d.** suspension
5. A sunbeam is an example of ______.
   a. an element **c.** a suspension
   b. a solution **d.** the Tyndall effect
6. Most smog is now caused by ______.
   a. automobile exhaust **c.** dust
   b. burning coal **d.** factories
7. The red color of a rose is a ______.
   a. chemical change **c.** physical change
   b. chemical property **d.** physical property
8. The process of evaporating water from seawater for drinking is a ______.
   a. chemical change **c.** physical change
   b. chemical property **d.** physical property
9. Which warning label indicates a chemical property of the material being labeled?
   a. "Fragile" **c.** "Handle with Care"
   b. "Flammable" **d.** "Shake Well"
10. Which of the following is a substance?
    a. colloid **c.** mixture
    b. element **d.** solution

UNDERSTANDING CONCEPTS

Complete each sentence.

11. The scattering of light by particles in a mixture is called the ______ effect.
12. When substances that make up a material are uniformly spread out, the material is said to be ______.
13. A heterogeneous mixture in which visible particles will settle is a(n) ______.
14. When different materials are spread out unevenly, the mixture is ______.
15. Another name for a homogeneous mixture is a(n) ______.

THINK AND WRITE CRITICALLY

16. Describe a carton of milk using its physical properties.
17. The soft metal sodium and the greenish gas chlorine change to form table salt, sodium chloride. How do you know table salt is a compound?
18. The word *colloid* means "gluelike." Why was colloid chosen for these mixtures?
19. Use a nail rusting in air to explain the law of conservation of mass.
20. Mai says that ocean water is a solution. Ed says that ocean water is a suspension. Are they both correct?

APPLY

21. Rust is formed from oxygen and iron. How might you keep an iron pipe from rusting?
22. By mistake, sugar was put into some dry rice. How might you separate the mixture?
23. Not all solutions are liquid. Why is a metal alloy, such as brass, considered a solution?
24. Use what you know about suspensions to explain why deltas form at the mouths of large rivers.
25. Why do many medications have instructions to "shake well before using"?

MORE SKILL BUILDERS

If you need help, refer to the Skill Handbook.

1. **Recognizing Cause and Effect:** List at least two causes of smog and two effects of smog.
2. **Making and Using Tables:** Different colloids may involve different states. For example, gelatin is formed from solid particles in a liquid. Complete the following table, using these common colloids: smoke, marshmallow, fog, paint.

Colloid	Example
Gas in solid	
Solid in liquid	
Solid in gas	
Liquid in gas	

3. **Comparing and Contrasting:** In terms of suspensions and colloids, compare and contrast a glass of milk and a glass of grapefruit juice.
4. **Interpreting Data:** From a 25-cm^3 sample of pond water, Joe poured 5 cm^3 through filter paper. He repeated this four more times. He dried each piece of filter paper and measured the mass of the sediment. Why did the last sample have a higher mass than did the first sample?
5. **Using Variables, Constants, and Controls:** Marcos took a 100-cm^3 sample of a suspension, shook it well, and divided it equally into four different test tubes. He placed one test tube in a rack, one in very hot water, one in warm water, and the fourth in ice water. He then observed the time it took for each suspension to settle. What was the variable in the experiment? What were the constants?

PROJECTS

1. Research the smog problem in Los Angeles. Report on what causes the problem, what health and other problems are caused by the smog, and possible solutions to the problem.
2. Make a display of an example of a solution, a heterogeneous mixture, a colloid, and a suspension. Label each and explain their differences.

CHAPTER

10 Atomic Structure and the Periodic Table

Did you ever go stargazing at a planetarium? If so, you may have seen a globular cluster like the one in the picture. The appearance of this collection of stars resembles one model of the structure of the atom. What are some other models of the atom?

FIND OUT!

In this activity, you will make another kind of model of an atom.

Your teacher will give you a certain number of bolts, nuts, and/or washers. Each group in the class will get different numbers of the pieces of hardware. Bury your hardware in a piece of modeling clay. Form the clay into a ball so that you can't see the hardware. Trade clay balls with another group that started with different kinds and/or numbers of hardware pieces. You have made a kind of model of an atom. Using toothpicks that you stick into the ball, try to find out how many of each hardware piece are hidden in the clay without pulling it apart. Now you have used indirect evidence, as scientists do, to identify and count the hidden parts of your model atom.

Gearing Up

Previewing the Chapter

Use this outline to help you focus on important ideas in this chapter.

Previewing Science Skills

- In the **Skill Builders**, you will make a concept map, make and use a table, and make and use a graph.
- In the **Activities**, you will build models, infer, predict, and control variables.
- In the **MINI-Lab**, you will observe and infer.

What's next?

You have investigated one simple model of an atom. In the pages that follow, you will learn about scientists' models of atoms.

10-1 Structure of the Atom

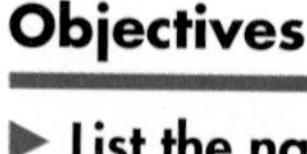

New Science Words

chemical symbol
nucleus
electrons
protons
neutrons
atomic number
electron cloud

Objectives

- List the names and symbols of common elements.
- Describe the present model of the atom.
- Describe how electrons are arranged in an atom.

Chemical Symbols

Do the letters C, Al, He, and Ag mean anything to you? Each letter or pair of letters is a **chemical symbol,** which is a shorthand way to write the name of an element. The black material on a burned match is carbon—C. You may wrap food in foil made of aluminum—Al. Did you ever lose a balloon filled with helium—He? You often use coins that contain copper—Cu.

Most chemical symbols consist of one capital letter or a capital letter plus a small letter. For some elements, the symbol is the first letter of the element's name. For other elements, the symbol is the first letter of the name plus another letter from its name. Some symbols, such as Ag, are derived from Latin. *Argentum* is Latin for silver. Which symbols in Table 10-1 might come from Latin?

Table 10-1

SYMBOLS OF SOME ELEMENTS

Element	Symbol	Element	Symbol	Element	Symbol
Aluminum	Al	Gold	Au	Mercury	Hg
Calcium	Ca	Hydrogen	H	Nitrogen	N
Carbon	C	Helium	He	Oxygen	O
Chlorine	Cl	Iodine	I	Potassium	K
Copper	Cu	Iron	Fe	Silver	Ag
Fluorine	F	Magnesium	Mg	Sodium	Na

Matter and Atoms

The idea of atoms began more than 2400 years ago with Greek thinkers, who defined atoms as the smallest parts of matter. Today scientists consider atoms to be the basic building blocks of matter. The atom consists of a positively charged center, or **nucleus.** Moving around the nucleus are negatively charged particles called **electrons.** The two major kinds of particles in the nucleus are **protons** and **neutrons.** The mass of a proton is about the same as that of a neutron. The mass of an electron is about 1/2000 the mass of a proton. The electron's mass is so small that it is considered negligible when finding the mass of an atom. The nucleus contains most of the mass of the atom.

Science and READING

The element platinum has an interesting history. Find out why it was called fool's silver.

A neutron is neutral, which means it has no charge. A proton has a positive charge. As a result, the net charge on the nucleus is positive. The amount of positive charge on a proton is equal to the amount of negative charge on an electron. Table 10-2 summarizes this information about the three particles in an atom.

Table 10-2

COMPARISON OF PARTICLES IN AN ATOM

	Relative Mass	Charge	Location in the Atom
Proton	1	1+	Part of nucleus
Neutron	1	none	Part of nucleus
Electron	0	1−	Moves around nucleus

The **atomic number** of an atom is the number of protons in its nucleus. Every atom of the same element has the same number of protons. Atoms of different elements have different numbers of protons. For example, every carbon atom has 6 protons. Therefore, it has the atomic number 6.

The number of electrons in a neutral atom is equal to the number of protons. A neutral carbon atom, then, has 6 electrons because it has 6 protons. Because the numbers of positively charged protons and negatively charged electrons in an atom are equal, the atom as a whole is electrically neutral.

How is the number of electrons in an atom related to the number of protons?

Table 10-3

ATOMIC NUMBER OF SOME ELEMENTS

Atom	Number of Protons	Number of Electrons	Atomic Number
Carbon	12	12	12
Aluminum	13	13	13
Helium	2	2	2
Silver	47	47	47

Figure 10-1. A globe is a physical model, unlike a scientific model, which is a mental picture.

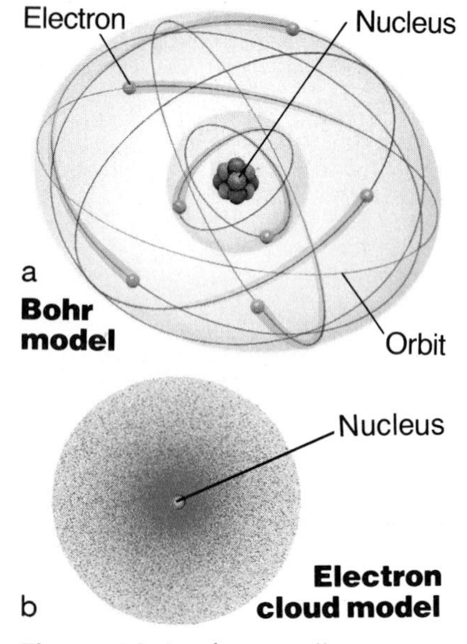

Figure 10-2. The top illustration is an early model of an atom with defined paths for electrons. The lower illustration is a later model showing a region where electrons are likely to be.

Models of the Atom

As scientists continued to study matter and atoms, they tried to form a mental picture or model of what an atom might look like. A model helps us understand something we cannot see directly. A good model of the atom must explain all the information about matter and atoms. As more information was collected, scientists changed their models. Therefore, the model of the atom we use today is the result of the work of many scientists.

One of the earliest models of an atom looked like the one in Figure 10-2a. It was developed by Niels Bohr in 1913. Bohr pictured the atom as having a central nucleus with electrons moving around it in well-defined paths, or orbits. Can you explain why Bohr's model is also called the planetary model of the atom?

In 1926, scientists developed a better model of the atom. In this model, the electrons moved about in a region called an **electron cloud** (Figure 10-2b). This cloud surrounds the nucleus of the atom. It describes the region where an electron is likely to be, at any time. The diameter of the nucleus is about 1/100 000 the diameter of the electron cloud. Suppose you built a model of an atom with an electron cloud as wide as a football field. The atom's nucleus would be about the thickness of the wire in a paper clip!

Because the electron's mass is so small, it is impossible for you—or anyone—to describe exactly where it is as it moves in the atom. All anyone can give

Figure 10-3. In an atom as wide as a football field, the nucleus would be as wide as a paper clip wire.

Figure 10-4. You can compare the spray of water from a lawn sprinkler to an electron cloud.

is its probable location. Describing the electron's location around a nucleus is like trying to describe your location in your science class at any given moment. Your most probable location during the class is at your desk. Other possible, though less probable, locations are at the pencil sharpener, in the supply closet, and at the teacher's desk.

The electron cloud represents the probable locations of electrons within an atom. You can compare the electron cloud to the spray of water drops from a lawn sprinkler. Each drop represents a probable location of an electron in the cloud. As you can see in Figure 10-4, most of the drops are concentrated near the center of the spray. In an atom, the most probable location of electrons is in the electron cloud, distributed about the nucleus.

What does the electron cloud represent?

Energy Levels of Electrons

All the electrons in an atom are contained in the electron cloud. Within the electron cloud, electrons are at various distances from the nucleus. Electrons near the nucleus have low energy. Electrons farther away have higher energy. You can represent the energy differences of the electrons by picturing the atom as having energy levels.

These energy levels are like the shelves of a refrigerator door. A carton on the lowest shelf represents an electron in the lowest energy level. The difference in spacing of the shelves indicates differences in the amount of energy the electrons in that level can have. Shelves of a refrigerator door can usually hold the same number of cartons. Unlike these shelves, each energy level of an atom has a maximum number of electrons it can hold.

Did You Know?

One ounce of gold can be made into a wire 50 miles long.

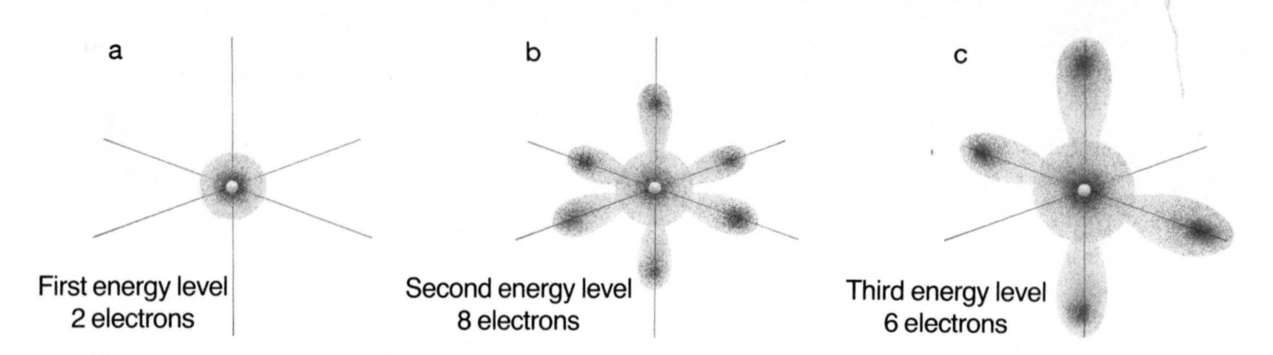

Figure 10-5. A sulfur atom has 16 electrons in three energy levels. Each of the colored regions at each level can hold two electrons. To get a complete picture, place (b) and (c) on top of (a).

The lowest energy level can hold just two electrons. The second energy level can hold eight electrons, and the third energy level can hold 18 electrons.

Sulfur's atomic number is 16. It has 16 protons and 16 electrons. Two of these electrons are in the first energy level, eight are in the second energy level, and six are in the third energy level. The electron arrangement of sulfur is shown in Figure 10-5.

Table 10-4

ELECTRONS IN ENERGY LEVELS	
Energy Level in Atom	**Maximum Number of Electrons**
1	2
2	8
3	18
4	32

SECTION REVIEW

1. Write the chemical symbols for the elements carbon, aluminum, hydrogen, oxygen, and sodium.
2. List the names, charges, and locations of three kinds of particles in an atom.
3. What does an electron cloud represent?
4. **Apply:** How might an electric fan that is turned on be a model of an atom? How is the fan unlike an atom?

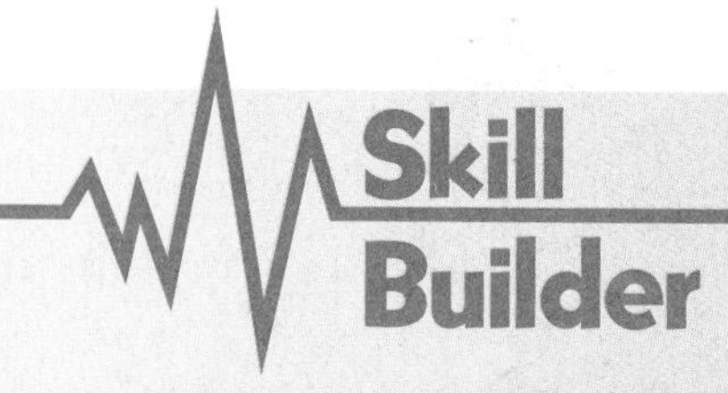

Concept Mapping

Make a concept map for the parts of an atom. Include the following terms: *electron cloud, nucleus, electrons, protons,* and *neutrons.* Also provide the charge of each part. If you need help, refer to Concept Mapping in the **Skill Handbook** on pages 684 and 685.

ACTIVITY 10-1
Models of Atomic Structure

Problem: *How can using a model allow you to predict similarities in atomic structure?*

Materials
- magnetic board about 20 cm × 27 cm
- one 0.5-cm piece and 20 1-cm rubber magnetic strips
- circles of white paper 4 cm wide
- circles of red paper 1 cm wide
- marker

Procedure
1. Choose an element with an atomic number of 1 through 20. Determine the number of each kind of particle needed to make up an atom of that element.
2. Use a marker to write the number of protons and neutrons on a paper circle. This represents the nucleus of the atom.
3. Use a 0.5-cm magnetic strip to attach the model nucleus to one side of a magnetic board.
4. Attach the red paper circles to the 1-cm magnetic strips. Arrange the model electrons in energy levels around the nucleus.
5. Remove either the model nucleus or the model electrons from the magnetic board and ask classmates to identify the element.
6. Repeat Steps 1 through 5 for another element.

Analyze
1. In a neutral atom, which particles will always be present in equal numbers?
2. What do you think would happen to the charge of an atom if one of the electrons were removed from the atom?
3. Except for hydrogen, how many first level electrons did each selected atom contain?

Conclude and Apply
4. How is this model of an atom similar to an actual atom?
5. Name two differences, other than size, between your model and an actual atom.
6. What happens to the atom if one proton is removed from the nucleus and one electron is also removed?

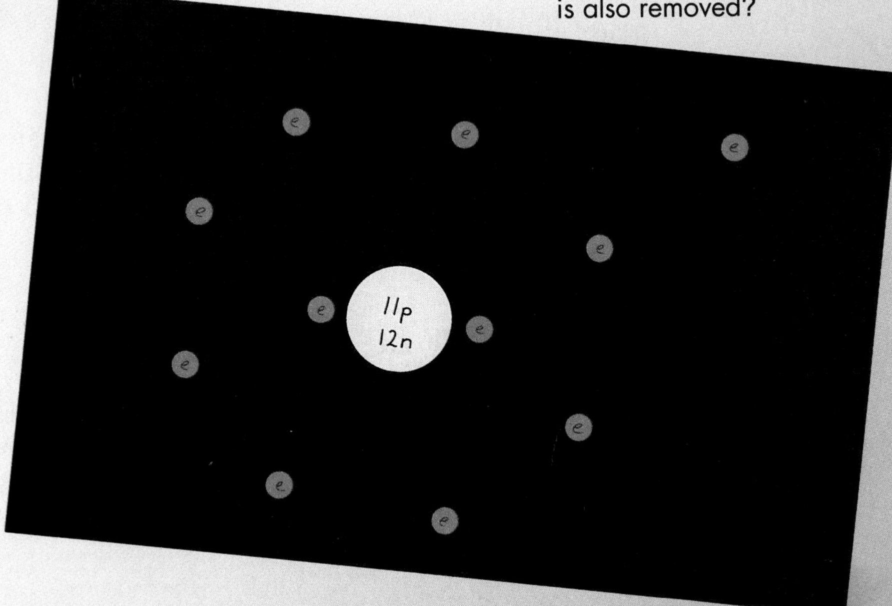

10-2 Smaller Particles of Matter

New Science Words

quarks

Objectives

- ▶ Identify quarks as particles of matter that make up protons and neutrons.
- ▶ Explain how protons can be broken apart.

Looking for Quarks

You know that protons and neutrons form the nucleus of atoms. What forms protons and neutrons? Many scientists agree that protons and neutrons are made of even smaller particles of matter called **quarks.** So far five different types of quarks have been postulated and there is evidence of a sixth type. Scientists hope someday to observe this type of quark by breaking apart protons with enough energy to release quarks.

The strong nuclear force holding quarks together gets stronger and stronger as quarks are pulled apart, just like a spring. So far, no collision has had enough energy to actually isolate individual quarks. Scientists will break protons apart by crashing them into other protons. How can scientists make protons crash into each other?

One way will be with a gigantic supercollider. The supercollider is expected to be completed at a cost of more than eight billion dollars early in the next cen-

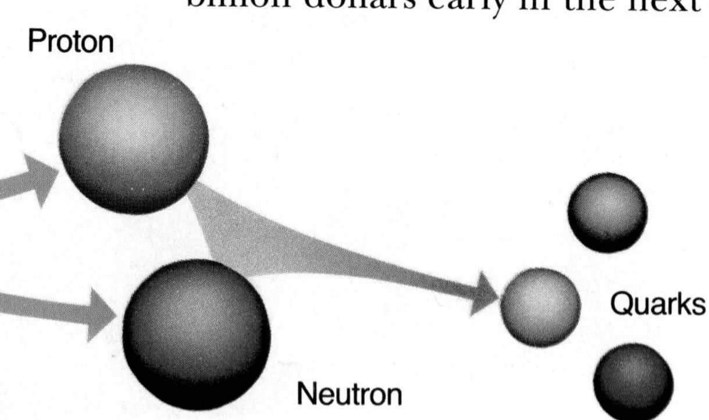

ORIGIN OF QUARKS

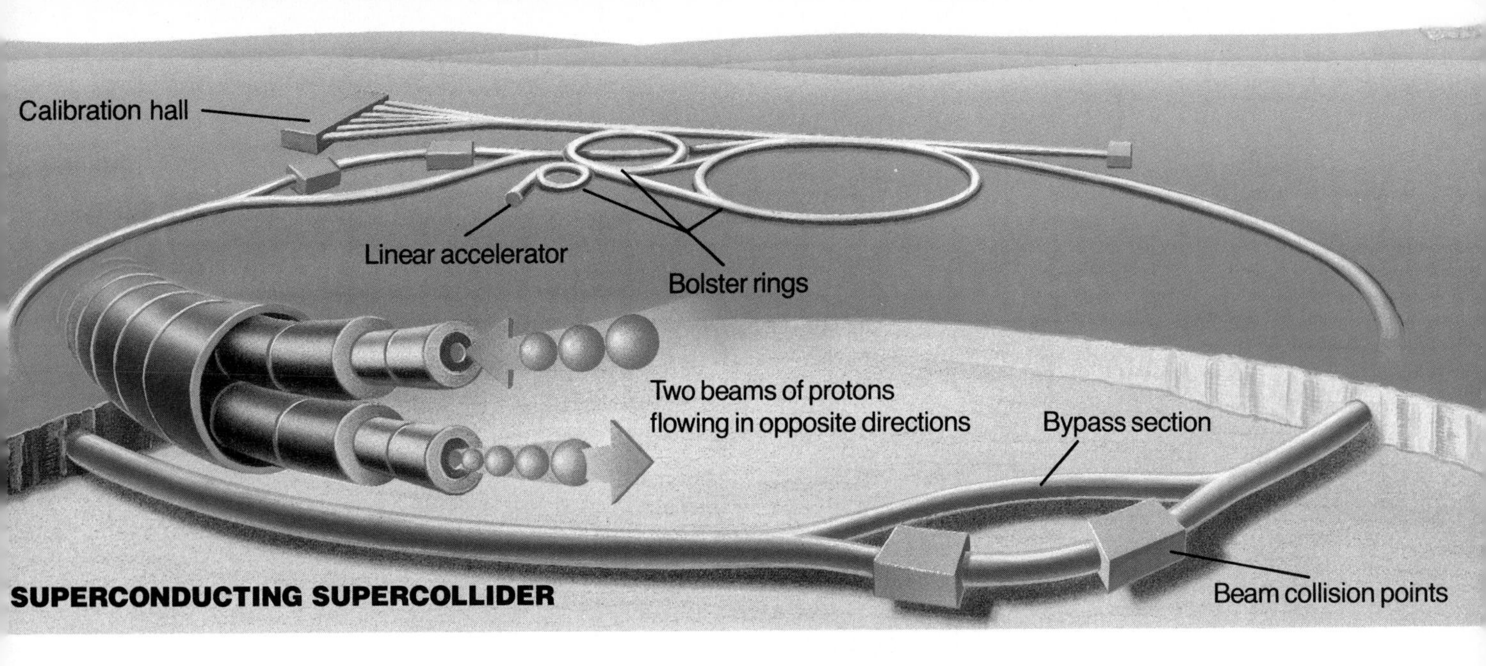

tury near the town of Waxahachie, Texas. The supercollider will include a 80-km track surrounded by more than 8500 magnets. These powerful magnets will force protons into two beams whirling in opposite directions inside the supercollider track. Accelerated by magnetic forces, the protons in each beam will move faster and faster. When the protons are moving at almost 300 000 000 m/s, the two beams will meet in a head-on collision. Large detectors and computers will record the particles produced by the destruction of the protons.

SECTION REVIEW

1. What are quarks?
2. Describe the supercollider and its research use.

You Decide!

Supporters of the supercollider say that it will help scientists to better understand what matter is made of and how matter behaves. They point out that the money spent will create thousands of new jobs. It will also create new technology just as the space program did. However, critics argue that important, smaller research projects may be cancelled because of lack of funds due to the supercollider's high costs. What factors do you think are important in evaluating scientific research like the supercollider? Why?

10-3 Masses of Atoms

New Science Words

mass number
isotopes
average atomic mass

Objectives

- Compute the atomic mass and mass number of an atom.
- Identify and describe isotopes of common elements.
- Interpret the average atomic mass of an element.

Atomic Mass

You may have guessed that the mass of an atom is *very* small. Yet, scientists are able to measure that mass with great accuracy. They can even measure the masses of protons and neutrons. The unit of measurement of those particles is the atomic mass unit (u). In fact, the mass of a proton or a neutron is almost equal to 1 u. This is not a coincidence—the unit was defined that way.The atomic mass unit is defined as one-twelfth the mass of a carbon atom containing six protons and six neutrons. Remember that the mass of a carbon atom is in its nucleus because the atom's six electrons have a negligible mass. Therefore, each of the 12 particles in the nucleus must have a mass nearly equal to one-twelfth the mass of the carbon atom. Thus, a proton or a neutron has a mass of about 1 u.

What is the atom mass unit?

To help you understand this, suppose you have a egg carton containing six brown eggs and six white eggs, as shown in Figure 10-6. You could define a mass unit as one-twelfth the mass of the entire dozen. Because the carton itself has very little mass, the mass of each egg, brown or white, would be equal to your defined unit.

Figure 10-6. You can compare a carton of eggs to a carbon atom.

Mass Number

The **mass number** of an atom is the sum of the number of protons and the number of neutrons in an atom. Put another way, the mass number is the number of particles in the nucleus of an atom. As you can see in Table 10-5, the mass number of an atom is almost equal to its mass expressed in atomic mass units.

If you know the mass number and the atomic number of an atom, you can then calculate the number of neutrons. The number of neutrons is equal to the atomic number subtracted from the mass number:

number of neutrons = mass number − atomic number

Table 10-5

MASS NUMBERS OF SOME ATOMS					
Element	**Symbol**	**Protons**	**Neutrons**	**Mass Number**	**Atomic Mass***
Boron	B	5	6	11	10.81
Carbon	C	6	6	12	12.01
Oxygen	O	8	8	16	16.00
Sodium	Na	11	12	23	22.99
Copper	Cu	29	34	63	63.55

* to two decimal places

Isotopes

Not all the atoms of an element have the same number of neutrons. Atoms of the same element that have different numbers of neutrons are called **isotopes.**

Suppose you have a sample of the element boron, which is a dark gray powder. Naturally occurring atoms of boron have mass numbers of 10 or 11. How many neutrons are there in a boron atom? It depends upon which boron atom you are referring to. Look at Table 10-5 and use the formula above to calculate that a boron atom may contain five or six neutrons. Use the example on the left to help you.

B
Boron

11 mass number
−5 number of protons
6 number of neutrons

10 mass number
−5 number of protons
5 number of neutrons

Figure 10-7. Boron has two naturally occurring isotopes.

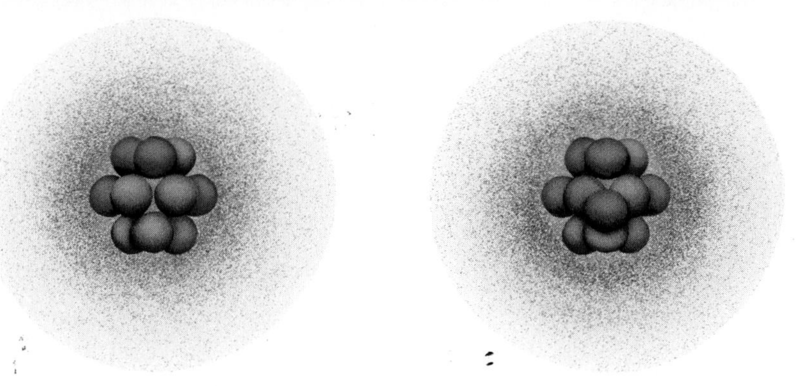

Figure 10-8. The two isotopes of boron have different numbers of neutrons and different mass numbers.

Figure 10-8 shows the two isotopes of boron. Because the numbers of neutrons in the isotopes are different, the mass numbers are also different. You use the name of the element followed by the mass number of the isotope to identify each isotope: boron-10 and boron-11. Because most elements have more than one isotope, each element is given an average atomic mass. The **average atomic mass** of an element is the average mass of the mixture of its isotopes.

PROBLEM SOLVING

Ivan's Isotopes

After carrying out many medical tests, the doctor found a tumor in Ivan's thyroid gland. The doctor decided to treat the tumor with iodine-131, an isotope of iodine. Ivan asked her how the treatment would work. She explained that atoms of some isotopes, like iodine-131, are unstable. One of these atoms has too many neutrons for the number of protons. The nucleus in an unstable isotope rearranges itself spontaneously, resulting in the release of energy called radiation.

The thyroid gland absorbs iodine because the gland needs iodine to function properly. The doctor told Ivan the tumor cells in his thyroid are more sensitive to radiation than the healthy thyroid cells. A controlled dose of radiation from the iodine-131 would kill the tumor cells but would not affect the healthy cells.

Think Critically: Why is iodine-131 unstable? Why is the number of neutrons in an atom important in the field of medicine?

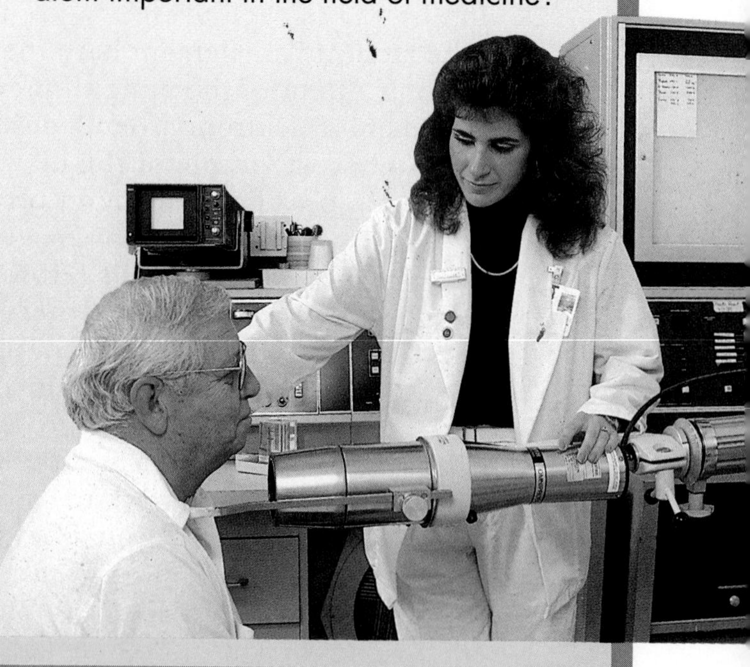

For example, four out of five atoms of boron are boron-11, and one out of five is boron-10, as shown in Figure 10-8. Thus, in an average sample of five atoms of boron, four atoms are likely to have a mass of 11 u. One atom will have a mass of 10 u. If you measured the mass of the five atoms, you would find it to be 54 u. The average atomic mass of the boron mixture is 54 u divided by five, or 10.8 u. That is, the average atomic mass of the element boron is 10.8 u. Note that the average atomic mass of boron is close to the mass of its most abundant isotope, boron-11.

For another example, hydrogen has three isotopes—H-1, H-2, and H-3. Each has one proton. How many neutrons does each have? The most abundant isotope is H-1, and the element's average atomic mass is 1.008.

The average atomic mass of each element can be found in the periodic table of elements. As you will see later, the periodic table also holds much more information about the elements.

EcoTip

Many batteries contain the elements mercury and cadmium. These are hazardous materials that contaminate landfills when the batteries break apart. Reduce waste. Use rechargeable batteries.

SECTION REVIEW

1. A chlorine atom has 17 protons and 18 neutrons. What is its mass number? What is its atomic number?
2. How are the isotopes of an element alike and how are they different?
3. The atomic number of magnesium is 12. The three naturally occurring isotopes of magnesium are Mg-24, Mg-25, and Mg-26. The average atomic mass of magnesium is 24.3 u. Why does this indicate that most magnesium atoms contain 12 neutrons?
4. **Apply:** An isotope of phosphorus used to treat bone cancer is P-30. Another isotope of phosphorus is P-31. What are two reasons why most of the phosphorus in your food must be P-31 and not P-30?

Making and Using Tables

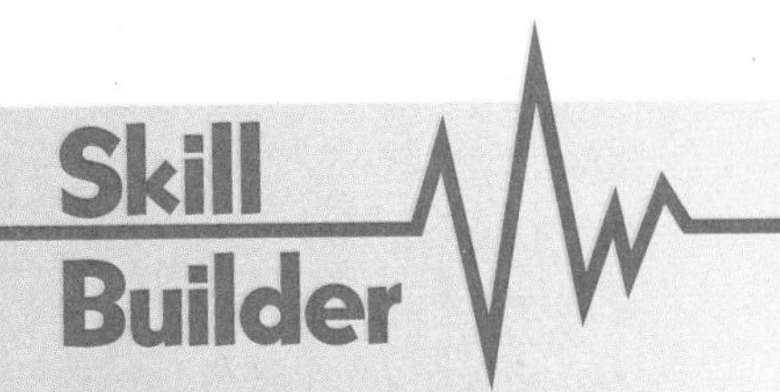

Construct a table organizing information about the atomic numbers, atomic mass numbers, and the number of protons, neutrons, and electrons in atoms of oxygen-16 and oxygen-17. If you need help, refer to Making and Using Tables in the **Skill Handbook** on page 686.

ACTIVITY 10-2
Isotopes and Atomic Mass

Problem: *How do isotopes affect average atomic mass?*

Materials
- 4 red and 3 green candy-coated peanuts
- 2 red and 3 green candy-coated chocolates

Procedure
1. Copy the data table and use it to record your observations.
2. Make a pile of four red candy-coated peanuts and two red candy-coated chocolates. The two different kinds of candy represent isotopes of the same element.
3. Assume that a red peanut has a mass of two candy units and a red chocolate has a mass of one candy unit.
4. To calculate the average mass of the element, multiply the number of red peanuts by its mass expressed in candy units. Do the same for the red chocolates. Combine the two values and divide this total mass by the total number of candies. Record your calculations.
5. Repeat Steps 2 through 4, but use three green peanuts and three green chocolates. Assume a green peanut has a mass of four units and a green chocolate has a mass of three units.

Analyze
1. There were six red and six green candies. Why were their average masses not the same?
2. If a sample of element X contains 100 atoms of X-12 and ten atoms of X-14, what is the average mass of X?

Conclude and Apply
3. An element needed for most nuclear reactors is uranium. Its two major isotopes are U-235 and U-238. Look at the mass of uranium on the periodic table. Which isotope is the most common? Explain.
4. How do the masses of isotopes affect the average atomic mass of an element so that it is often not a whole number?

Data and Observations

	Peanut	Chocolate	Average
	candy × mass	candy × mass	total mass / total candies
Red			
Green			

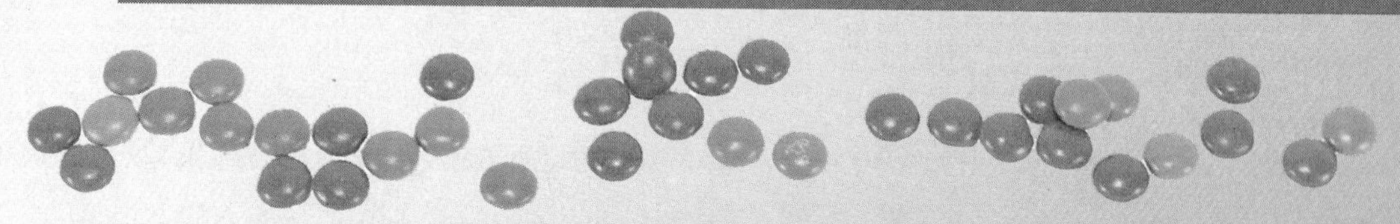

The Periodic Table 10-4

Objectives

- ▶ **Describe the periodic table of elements and use it to find information about an element.**
- ▶ **Distinguish between a group and a period.**
- ▶ **Use the periodic table to classify an element as a metal, nonmetal, or metalloid.**

New Science Words

periodic table
groups
dot diagram
periods
metals
nonmetals
metalloids

Structure of the Periodic Table

Remember the last time you sat on a swing and moved back and forth, over and over? Your movement was periodic. *Periodic* means "repeated in a pattern." Look at a calendar. The days of the week are periodic because they repeat themselves every seven days. The calendar is a periodic table of days. You use calendars to organize your time.

In the late 1800s, Dimitri Mendeleev, a Russian chemist, searched for a way to organize the elements. He arranged all the elements known at that time in order of increasing atomic masses. He discovered that there was a pattern to the properties of the elements. This pattern was periodic. The arrangement of elements according to repeated changes in properties is called a **periodic table** of elements. Look at the early periodic table at the right.

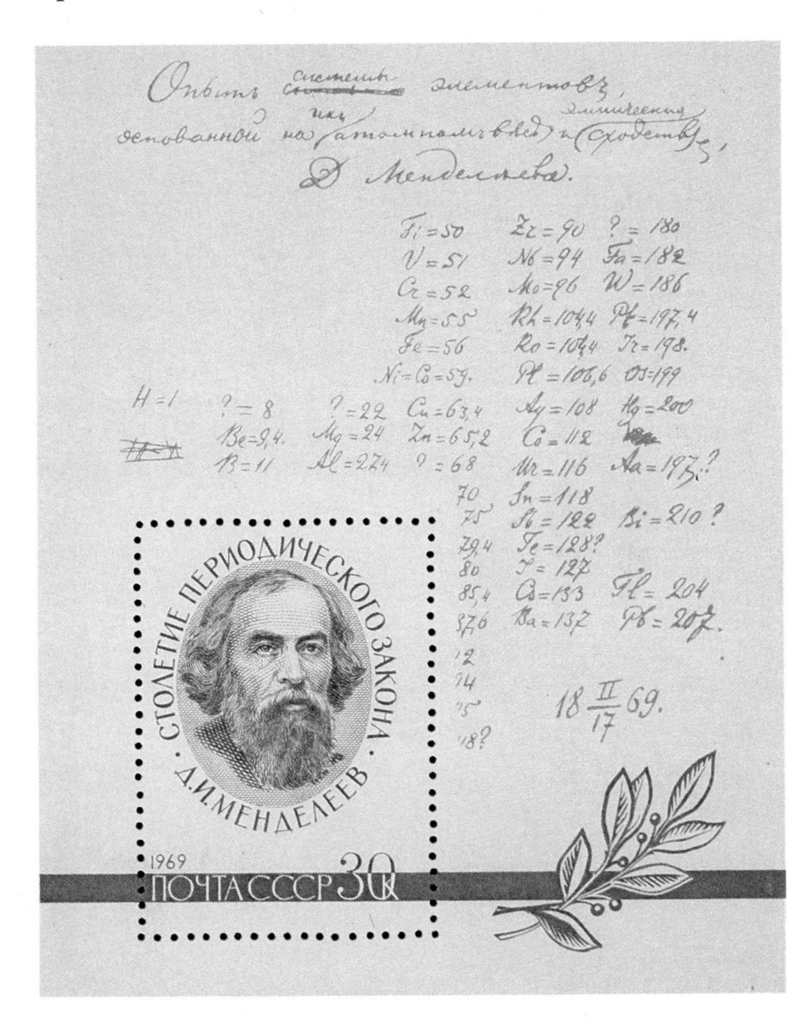

Figure 10-9. In his first periodic table, Mendeleev wrote question marks in spaces for elements not yet discovered.

Mendeleev's periodic table had blank spaces. He looked at the properties and atomic masses of the elements surrounding these blank spaces. From this information he predicted the properties and the mass numbers of new elements that had not yet been discovered. Sometimes you make predictions like this. Suppose someone crossed out a date on a calendar, as shown. You could predict the missing date by looking at the surrounding dates. Mendeleev's predictions proved to be quite accurate. Scientists later discovered elements, such as germanium, having the properties that he had predicted (Table 10-6).

The periodic table of the elements is shown on pages 258 and 259. It's not as complex as it may seem to be. Each box in the table contains information about the elements that you studied earlier in this chapter. Look at Figure 10-10. This box represents the element boron. The atomic number, chemical symbol, name, and average atomic mass are included in this box. The boxes for all of the elements are arranged in order of their atomic numbers.

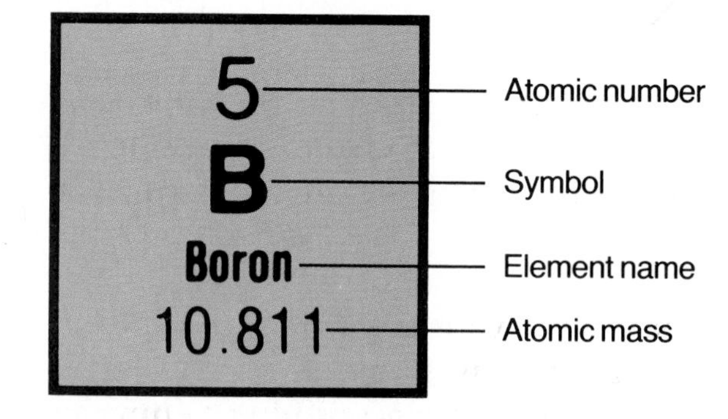

Figure 10-10. The periodic table shows the symbol, name, atomic number, and atomic mass of each element.

Table 10-6

"EKASILICON" (GERMANIUM)

Properties	Predicted	Actual
Atomic mass	72	72.6
Density	5.5 g/cm^3	5.35 g/cm^3
Color	dark gray	gray-white
Effect of water	none	none
Effect of acid	slight	HCl: no effect
Effect of base	slight	KOH: no effect

Groups of Elements

The vertical columns in the periodic table are called **groups.** The groups are numbered 1 through 18. The elements in each group have similar properties. For example, Figure 10-11 shows rings made of three elements in Group 11, copper—Cu, silver—Ag, and gold—Au. These elements have similar properties. Each is a shiny metal and a good conductor of electricity and heat.

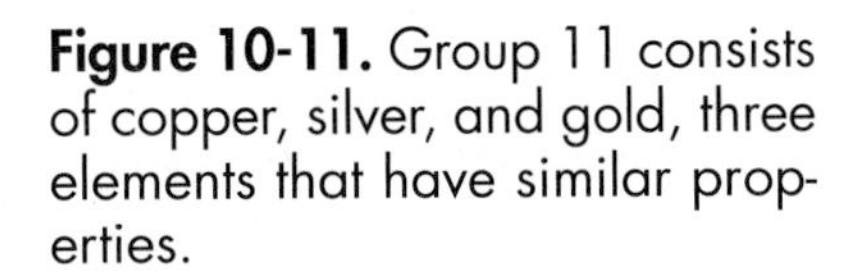

Figure 10-11. Group 11 consists of copper, silver, and gold, three elements that have similar properties.

MINI-Lab

What are the advantages of a periodic table?

Observe the mass and other properties of your pen or pencil, such as color and composition. With your class, develop a "periodic table" of pens and pencils. Arrange similar pens and pencils in columns and in order of mass. What can you say about (a) the properties of the elements and (b) the masses of the elements in a column, or group, of the periodic table?

Why do elements in a group have similar properties? It is because they have similar electron arrangements. Think about how the properties of different kinds of balls are related to their shape. You expect a soccer ball and a basketball to bounce in similar ways because they have similar shapes. But a football will bounce differently, because it has a different shape.

Atoms of different elements have different numbers of electrons. However, atoms of different elements may have the same number of electrons in their outer energy levels. It is the number of electrons in the outer energy level that determines the properties of the element. Different elements with the same number of electrons in their outer energy level have similar properties. These outer electrons are so important that a special way to represent them has been developed. A **dot diagram** uses the symbol of the element and dots to represent the electrons in the outer energy level.

Table 10-7.

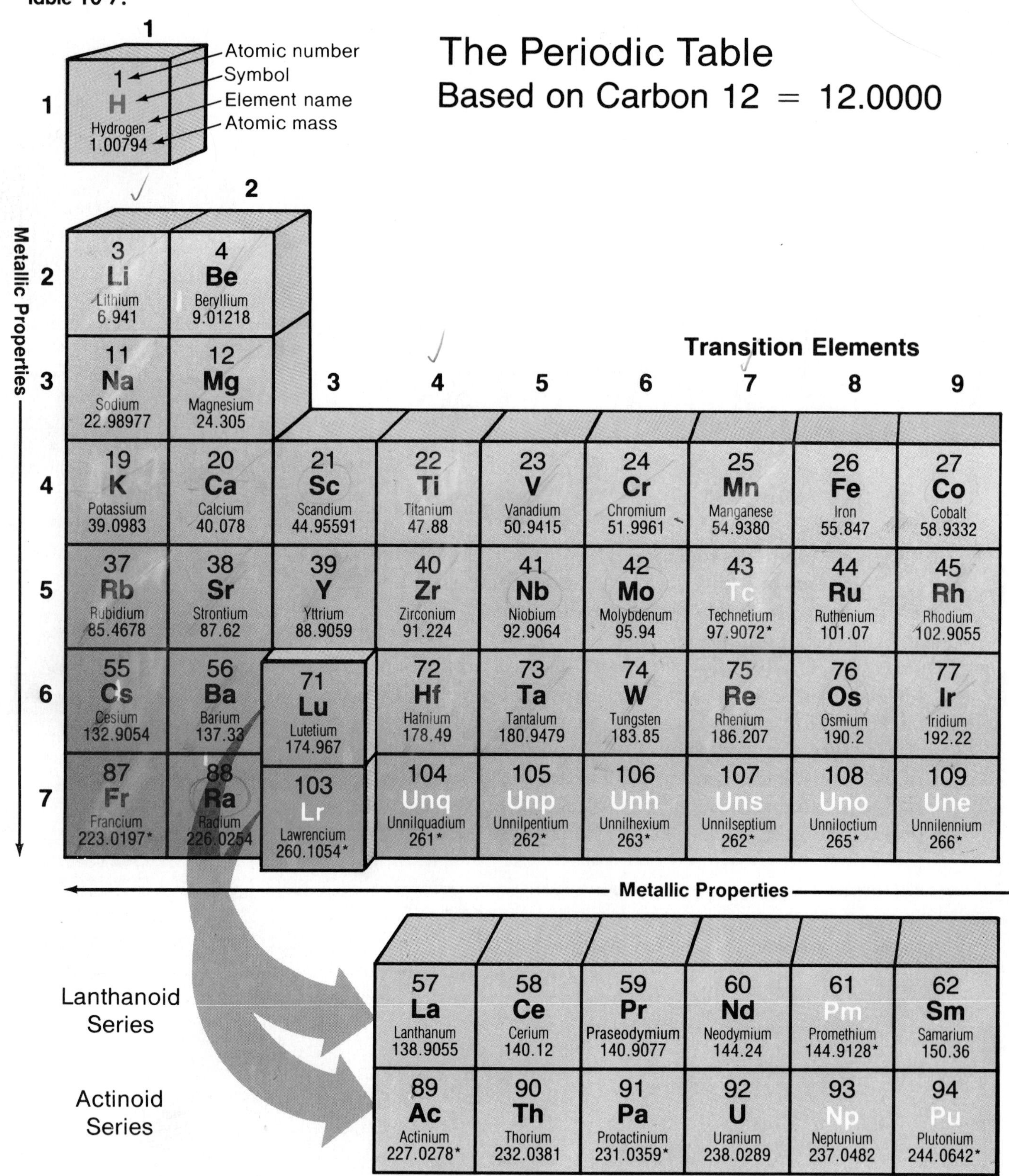

*Mass of isotope with longest half-life, that is, the most stable isotope of the element

Noble Gases

10	11	12	13	14	15	16	17	18
								2 He Helium 4.002602
			5 B Boron 10.811	6 C Carbon 12.011	7 N Nitrogen 14.0067	8 O Oxygen 15.9994	9 F Fluorine 18.998403	10 Ne Neon 20.179
			13 Al Aluminum 26.98154	14 Si Silicon 28.0855	15 P Phosphorus 30.97376	16 S Sulfur 32.06	17 Cl Chlorine 35.453	18 Ar Argon 39.948
28 Ni Nickel 58.69	29 Cu Copper 63.546	30 Zn Zinc 65.39	31 Ga Gallium 69.723	32 Ge Germanium 72.59	33 As Arsenic 74.9216	34 Se Selenium 78.96	35 Br Bromine 79.904	36 Kr Krypton 83.80
46 Pd Palladium 106.42	47 Ag Silver 107.8682	48 Cd Cadmium 112.41	49 In Indium 114.82	50 Sn Tin 118.710	51 Sb Antimony 121.75	52 Te Tellurium 127.60	53 I Iodine 126.9045	54 Xe Xenon 131.29
78 Pt Platinum 195.08	79 Au Gold 196.9665	80 Hg Mercury 200.59	81 Tl Thallium 204.383	82 Pb Lead 207.2	83 Bi Bismuth 208.9804	84 Po Polonium 208.9824*	85 At Astatine 209.98712*	86 Rn Radon 222.017*

Nonmetallic Properties

Metallic Properties
Nonmetallic Properties
Metalloids
Synthetic Elements

State at Room Temperature: and Solid   Liquid   Gas

63 Eu Europium 151.96	64 Gd Gadolinium 157.25	65 Tb Terbium 158.9254	66 Dy Dysprosium 162.50	67 Ho Holmium 164.9304	68 Er Erbium 167.26	69 Tm Thulium 168.9342	70 Yb Ytterbium 173.04
95 Am Americium 243.0614*	96 Cm Curium 247.0703*	97 Bk Berkelium 247.0703*	98 Cf Californium 251.0796*	99 Es Einsteinium 252.0828*	100 Fm Fermium 257.0951*	101 Md Mendelevium 258.986*	102 No Nobelium 259.1009*

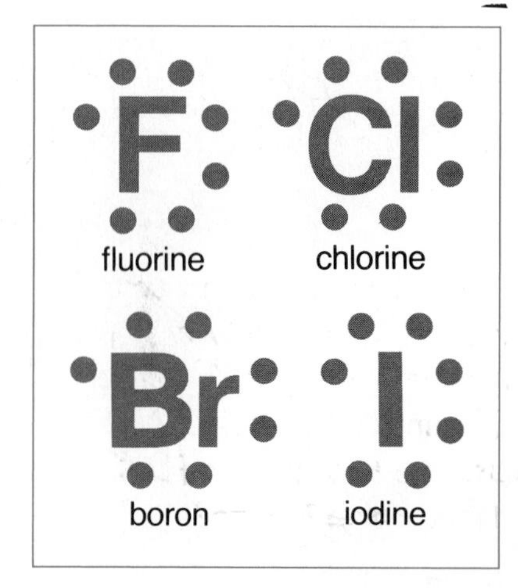

Figure 10-12. In each of these dot diagrams, the seven dots represent seven outer electrons.

For example, the dot diagrams of the atoms of the elements in Group 17, called the halogens, are shown in Figure 10-12. They all have seven electrons in their outer energy levels. One similar property of the halogens is the ability to form compounds with elements in Group 1. The elements in Group 18 are known as noble gases. Noble gases do not usually form compounds. We say they are stable. The atoms of all the noble gases except helium have outer energy levels that contain eight electrons, as shown in Figure 10-13. You will learn more about the significance of electron arrangement of halogens, noble gases, and other elements in later chapters.

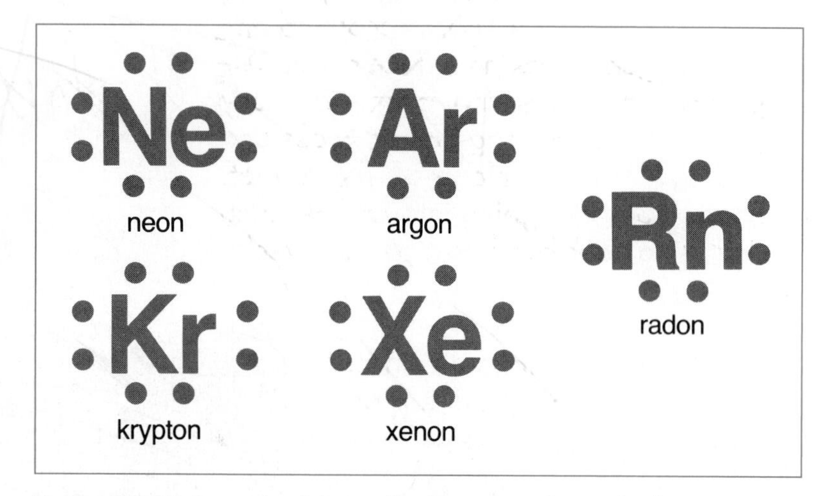

Figure 10-13. In each of these dot diagrams, the eight dots represent eight outer electrons.

Periods of Elements

The horizontal rows of elements in the periodic table are called **periods.** Notice the stair-step line on the right side of the periodic table. All the elements to the left of this line, except hydrogen, are metals. **Metals** are elements that have several properties in common. Iron, zinc, and copper are examples of metals. Most metals are solids at room temperature. They are shiny and good conductors of heat and electricity.

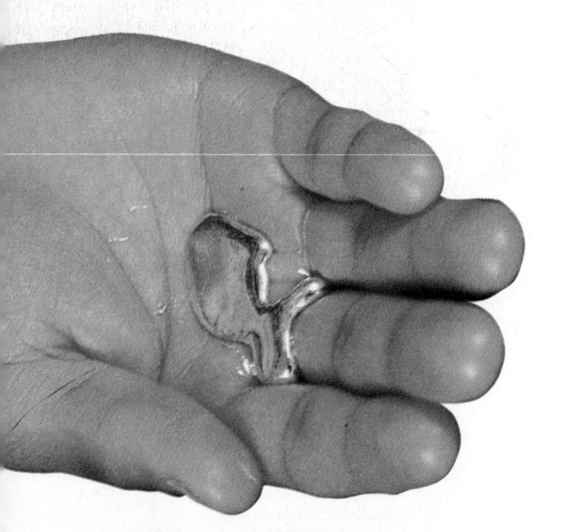

Figure 10-14. Gallium is a metal that has a low melting point.

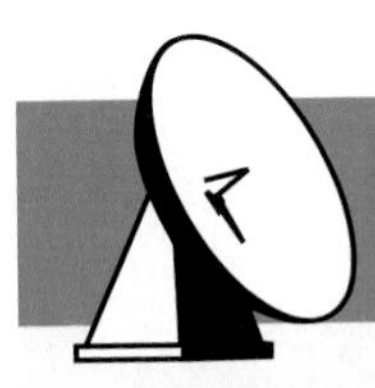

TECHNOLOGY

Seeing Atoms

For more than 50 years, scientists have been able to see extremely tiny things with electron microscopes. But it was less than ten years ago that scientists first saw atoms with scanning probe microscopes. These microscopes are the result of a new approach to how we see objects. Instead of shining light or a beam of electrons on an object, these new microscopes drag a probe across the surface of an object. The position of the probe is then changed and it is dragged across the surface again. This process, called scanning, is repeated many times to build an image of the peaks and valleys on the surface of the object. Scanning is like going into a dark room and using your hand as a probe to feel a chair to determine its shape, instead of shining a light on it.

The key development in the invention of the scanning probe microscope was a system that moves the probe in precise steps smaller than the width of an atom. In addition to seeing atoms, these probes enable scientists to move single atoms. Scientists at IBM used xenon atoms to spell out "IBM" in letters only five atoms tall! This ability to handle materials on an atom-by-atom basis could lead to ways of developing new materials that, up until now, were just not possible.

Think Critically: Scientists are using scanning probe microscopes to view atoms. Atoms range in radius from 0.053 nm for hydrogen to 0.27 nm for francium. What everyday objects, like two kinds of balls, would represent this range in size?

Those elements to the right of the stair-step line on the periodic table are classified as **nonmetals.** Oxygen, nitrogen, and carbon are examples of nonmetals. At

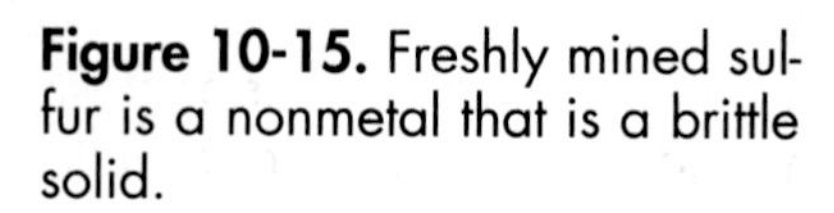

Figure 10-15. Freshly mined sulfur is a nonmetal that is a brittle solid.

room temperature, most nonmetals are gases and some are brittle solids. Most nonmetals do not conduct heat and electricity well.

Where are the metalloids located in the periodic table?

The elements next to the stair-step line are classified as **metalloids,** because they have properties of both metals and nonmetals. Boron and silicon are examples of metalloids.

Elements in Groups 3 through 12 are called the transition elements. They are metals but have properties not found in elements of other groups. Copper and iron are examples of common transition elements. Others, such as platinum, are much more rare.

SECTION REVIEW

1. Use the periodic table to find the name, atomic number, and average atomic mass of the following elements: N, Ca, Kr, and W.
2. Give the period and group in which each of these elements is found: nitrogen, sodium, iodine, and mercury.
3. Write the name of each of these elements and classify it as a metal, a nonmetal, or a metalloid: K, Si, Ba, and S.
4. **Apply:** What property of mercury makes it different from other metals and also makes it useful in thermometers and "silent" light switches?

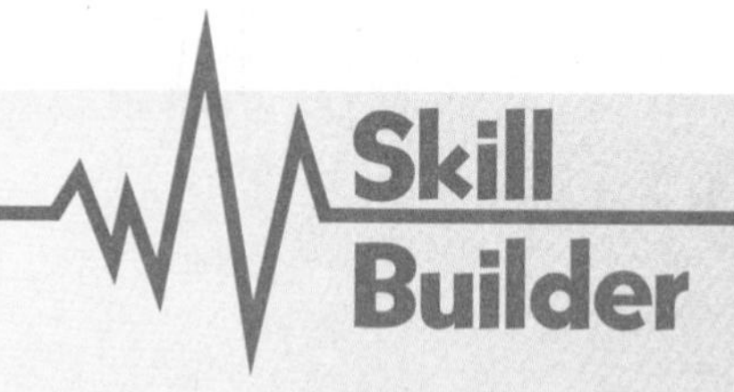

Making and Using Graphs

Construct a pie graph showing the elements classified as metals, metalloids, and nonmetals. If you need help, refer to Making and Using Graphs in the **Skill Handbook** on page 687.

CHAPTER

REVIEW

SUMMARY

10-1: Structure of the Atom

1. A chemical symbol is a shorthand way of writing the name of an element.
2. An atom consists of a nucleus made of protons and neutrons surrounded by an electron cloud.
3. The electrons in an atom are arranged in several energy levels, each of which is able to hold a certain number of electrons.

10-2: Science and Society: Smaller Particles of Matter

1. Quarks are particles of matter that make up protons and neutrons.
2. Protons can be broken into quarks by having them collide while traveling at the speed of light.

10-3: Masses of Atoms

1. The number of neutrons in an atom can be computed by subtracting the atomic number from the mass number.
2. The isotopes of an element are atoms of that same element that have different numbers of neutrons.
3. The average atomic mass of an element is the average mass of the mixture of its isotopes.

10-4: The Periodic Table

1. The periodic table of elements is an arrangement of elements according to repeated changes in properties.
2. In the periodic table, the 109 elements are arranged in 18 vertical columns, or groups, and seven horizontal rows, or periods.
3. Metals are found at the left of the periodic table, nonmetals at the right, and metalloids along the line that separates the metals from the nonmetals.

KEY SCIENCE WORDS

a. **atomic number**
b. **average atomic mass**
c. **chemical symbol**
d. **dot diagram**
e. **electron cloud**
f. **electrons**
g. **groups**
h. **isotopes**
i. **mass number**
j. **metalloids**
k. **metals**
l. **neutrons**
m. **nonmetals**
n. **nucleus**
o. **periodic table**
p. **periods**
q. **protons**
r. **quarks**

UNDERSTANDING VOCABULARY

Match each phrase with the correct term from the list of Key Science Words.

1. a shorthand way to write the name of an element
2. atomic particles with no charge
3. atoms of the same element with different numbers of neutrons
4. average mass of the mixture of isotopes
5. positively charged center of an atom
6. particles that make up protons and neutrons
7. the region occupied by electrons
8. the number of protons in the nucleus
9. total number of particles in the nucleus
10. horizontal rows in the periodic table

CHAPTER

REVIEW

CHECKING CONCEPTS

Choose the word or phrase that completes the sentence or answers the question.

1. The state of matter of most of the elements to the left of the stair-step line in the periodic table is ______.
a. gas **c.** plasma
b. liquid **d.** solid

2. If a pattern repeats itself, it is ______.
a. isotopic **c.** periodic
b. metallic **d.** transition

3. ______ is an element that would have similar properties to those of neon.
a. Aluminum **c.** Arsenic
b. Argon **d.** Silver

4. Boron is a ______.
a. metal **c.** noble gas
b. metalloid **d.** nonmetal

5. The element potassium is a ______.
a. metal **c.** nonmetal
b. metalloid **d.** transition element

6. The element bromine is a ______.
a. metal **c.** nonmetal
b. metalloid **d.** transition element

7. The halogens are those elements in Group ______.
a. 1 **c.** 15
b. 11 **d.** 17

8. In its group, nitrogen is the only element that is a ______.
a. gas **c.** metal
b. metalloid **d.** liquid

9. ______ is a shiny element that conducts electricity and heat well.
a. Chlorine **c.** Hydrogen
b. Sulfur **d.** Magnesium

10. The atomic number of Re is 75. The atomic mass of one of its isotopes is 186. How many neutrons are in an atom of this isotope?
a. 75 **c.** 186
b. 111 **d.** 261

UNDERSTANDING CONCEPTS

Complete each sentence.

11. Negatively charged particles called ______ move around the nucleus.

12. Elements are arranged in the periodic table according to repeated changes in their ______.

13. Vertical columns of elements in the periodic table are called ______.

14. Hafnium-178 and hafnium-179 are examples of ______.

15. Cadmium's atomic number is 48. The number of protons in a cadmium atom is ______.

THINK AND WRITE CRITICALLY

16. Why do electrons keep moving around the nucleus and not away from the atom?

17. Why do some chemical symbols have one letter and some have two letters?

18. A silver sample contains 52 atoms, each having 60 neutrons, and 48 atoms, each having 62 neutrons. What is the sample's average atomic mass?

19. Using Table 10-2 on page 243, what might be the masses and charges of quarks that make up protons?

20. Why are protons and neutrons also known as "nucleons"?

APPLY

21. We know that properties of elements are periodic. List at least two other things in nature that are periodic.
22. Lead and mercury are two pollutants in the environment. From information about them in the periodic table, why are they called "heavy metals"?
23. Ge and Si are used in making semiconductors. Are these two elements in the same group or the same period?
24. U and Pu are named for objects in nature. What are these objects, and what other element is named after a similar object?
25. Ca is used by the body to make bones and teeth. Radioactive Sr is in nuclear waste. Why is this Sr hazardous to people?

MORE SKILL BUILDERS

If you need help, refer to the Skill Handbook.

1. **Making and Using Tables:** Use the periodic table to list a metal, a metalloid, and a nonmetal with 5 outer-level electrons.
2. **Comparing and Contrasting:** From the information found in the periodic table and reference books, compare and contrast the properties of chlorine and bromine.
3. **Interpreting Data:** If scientists have determined that a neutral atom of rubidium has an atomic number of 37 and a mass number of 85, how many protons, neutrons, and electrons does the atom have?
4. **Sequencing:** What changes in the periodic table would occur in Periods 1 through 4 if the elements are arranged according to increasing average atomic mass instead of atomic number? How do we know that arrangement by atomic number is correct?
5. **Concept Mapping:** As a star dies, it becomes more dense. Its temperature rises to a point where He nuclei are combined with other nuclei. The atomic numbers of the other nuclei are increased by 2 because each gains the two protons contained in the He nucleus. For example, Cr fused with He becomes Fe. Complete the concept map below showing the first four steps in He fusion.

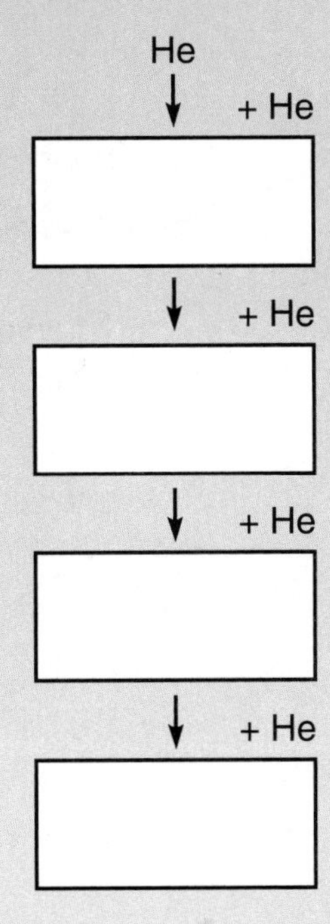

PROJECTS

1. Do research on the attempts made by Johann Dobereiner and John Newlands to classify the elements. Write a report on your findings.
2. Make a display of samples or pictures of several elements. List the name, symbol, atomic number, average atomic mass, and several uses for each element.
3. Research and report on models of the atom from the time of the ancient Greeks until the present.

CHAPTER 11 Chemical Bonds

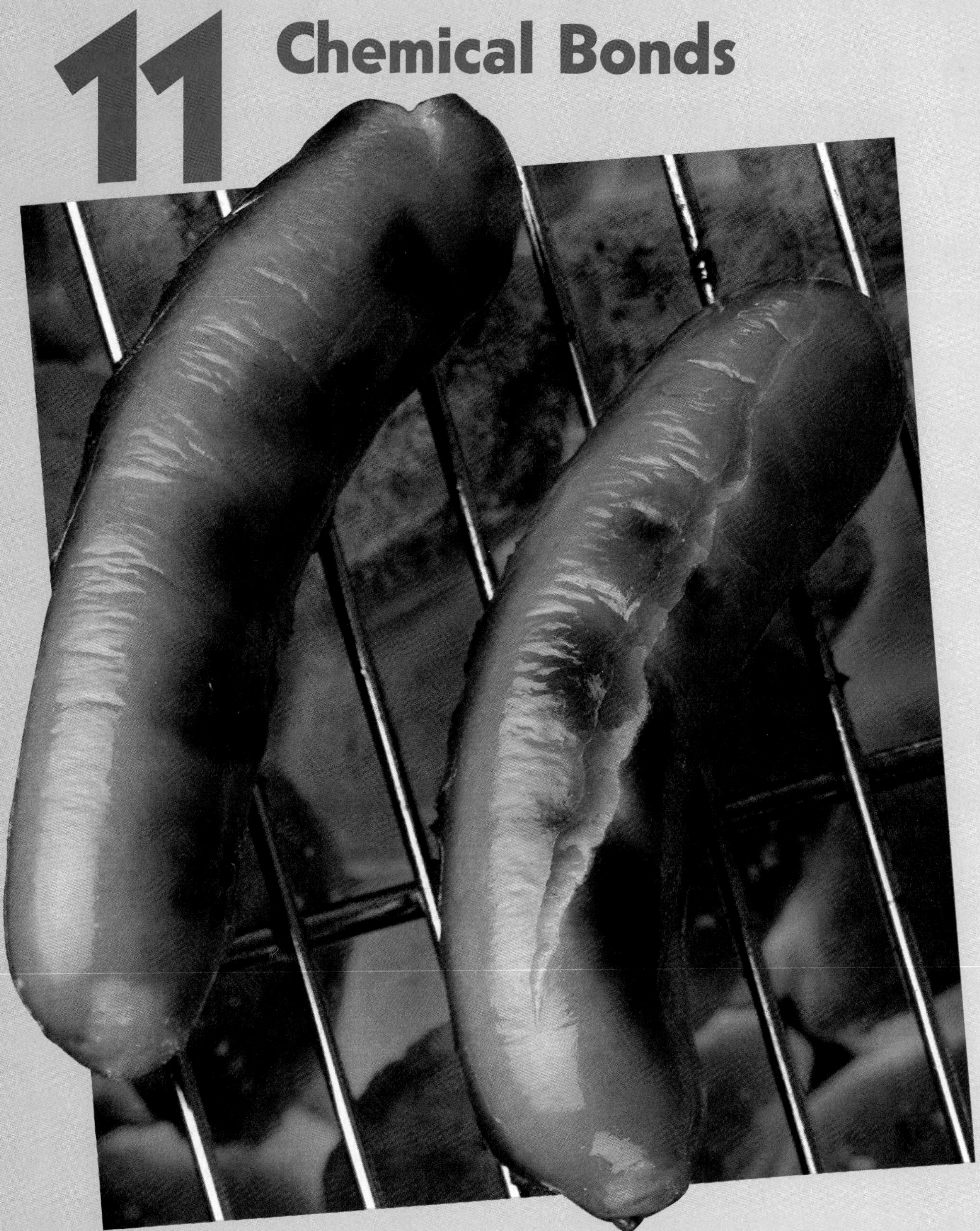

Whenever you watch charcoal burning, you observe a change in which chemical bonds form. These bonds form between the carbon in the charcoal and oxygen in the air. What is another chemical change in which oxygen bonds with another element?

FIND OUT!

Do this simple activity to find out how oxygen can bond with another element.

Stuff some wet steel wool into the bottom of a test tube. Invert the test tube in a beaker of water. Invert a tube containing only air beside the first one. Adjust the water levels in both tubes so that they are equal, with the water rising about 1 cm above the openings of the test tubes. Let the tubes stand a few days. What evidence of chemical change do you observe?

Gearing Up

Previewing the Chapter

Use this outline to help you focus on important ideas in this chapter.

Section 11-1 Why Atoms Combine
- Compounds
- Formulas
- Chemically Stable Atoms

Section 11-2 Science and Society Hazardous Compounds at Home
- Corrosive, Flammable, and Toxic Compounds

Section 11-3 Kinds of Chemical Bonds
- Ions and Ionic Bonds
- Molecules and Covalent Bonds
- Polar and Nonpolar Molecules

Section 11-4 Formulas and Names of Compounds
- Oxidation Numbers
- Formulas for Binary Compounds
- Naming Binary Compounds
- Compounds with Polyatomic Ions
- Hydrates

Previewing Science Skills

- In the **Skill Builders,** you will make and use a table, make a concept map, and use variables, constants, and controls.
- In the **Activities,** you will observe, compare, classify, and hypothesize.
- In the **MINI-Lab,** you will observe and infer.

What's next?

You have shown that moist iron rusts as it combines with the oxygen in a test tube of air. You will learn more about how elements combine as you read the pages that follow.

11-1 Why Atoms Combine

New Science Words

chemical formula
chemically stable
chemical bond

Objectives

- Describe how a compound differs from the elements it is composed of.
- Explain what a chemical formula represents.
- State a reason why chemical bonding occurs.

Did You Know?

In the last two centuries, industrialization has greatly increased the amounts of the compound carbon dioxide in Earth's atmosphere. This increase is, in part, responsible for recent trends in global warming.

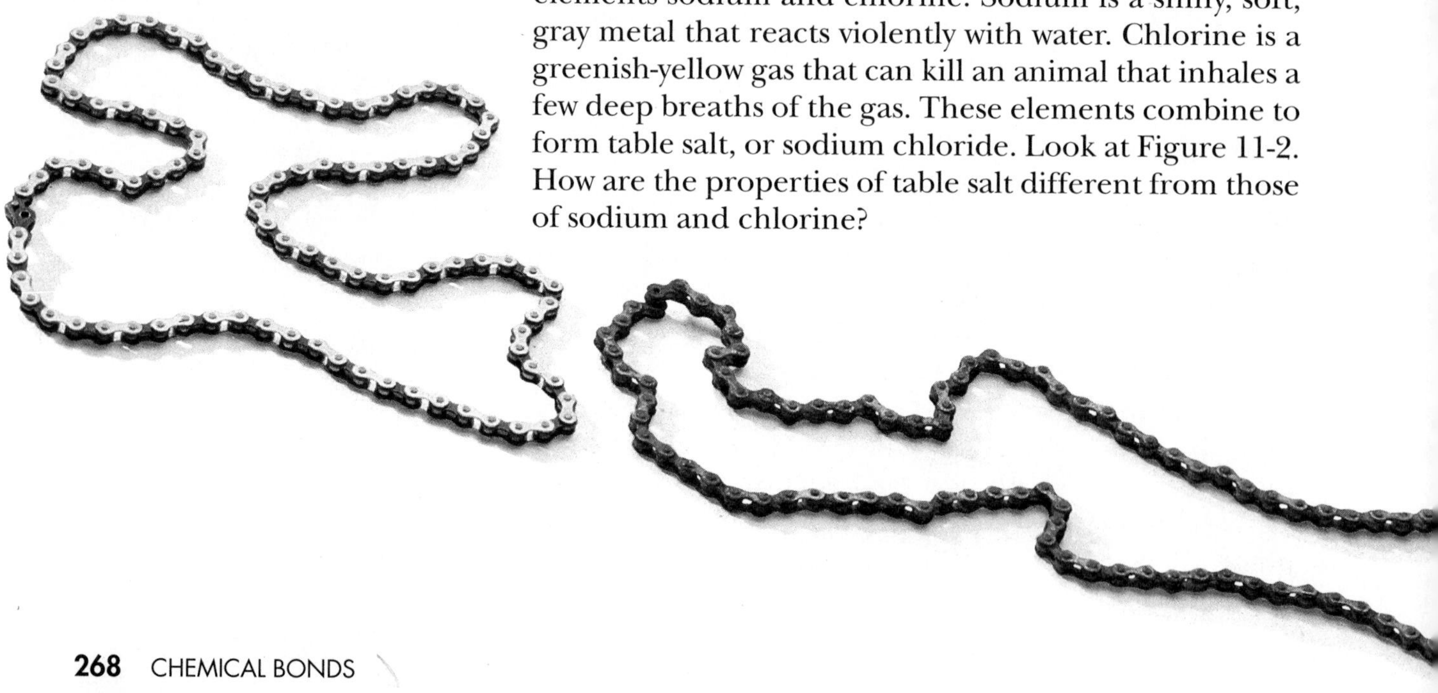

Figure 11-1. When iron rusts, iron and oxygen combine to form a new substance.

Compounds

Most of the matter around you is in the form of compounds or mixtures of compounds. The water you drink, the carbon dioxide you exhale, and the salt you put on food are examples of compounds.

Some of the matter around you is in the form of elements, such as iron and oxygen. But, like many other pairs of elements, iron and oxygen tend to unite chemically to form a compound when the conditions are right. You know how iron in moist steel wool exposed to oxygen forms rust, a compound. Rusting is a chemical change because a new substance, rust, is produced.

Compounds have properties unlike those of their elements. Table salt, for example, is composed of the elements sodium and chlorine. Sodium is a shiny, soft, gray metal that reacts violently with water. Chlorine is a greenish-yellow gas that can kill an animal that inhales a few deep breaths of the gas. These elements combine to form table salt, or sodium chloride. Look at Figure 11-2. How are the properties of table salt different from those of sodium and chlorine?

Figure 11-2. Sodium, a soft, gray metal, combines with chlorine, a greenish-yellow gas, to form sodium chloride, a white crystalline solid.

Formulas

Do you recall that the chemical symbols Na and Cl represent sodium and chlorine? When written as NaCl, the symbols make up a formula, or chemical shorthand for the compound sodium chloride. Another formula you may recognize is H_2O, for water. The formula is a combination of the symbols H and O and the subscript number 2. *Subscript* means "written below." A subscript number written after a symbol tells how many atoms there are of that element in a unit of the compound. If a symbol has no subscript, there's one atom of that element. The formula H_2O, then, shows there are two atoms of hydrogen for one atom of oxygen in one unit of the compound water. Put another way, the ratio of hydrogen atoms to oxygen atoms in water is 2 to 1.

Look at the formula for rust: Fe_2O_3. The symbol for iron, Fe, is followed by the subscript 2, and the symbol for oxygen, O, is followed by the subscript 3. For two atoms of iron there are three atoms of oxygen in the compound. That is, the ratio of iron atoms to oxygen atoms in rust is 2 to 3.

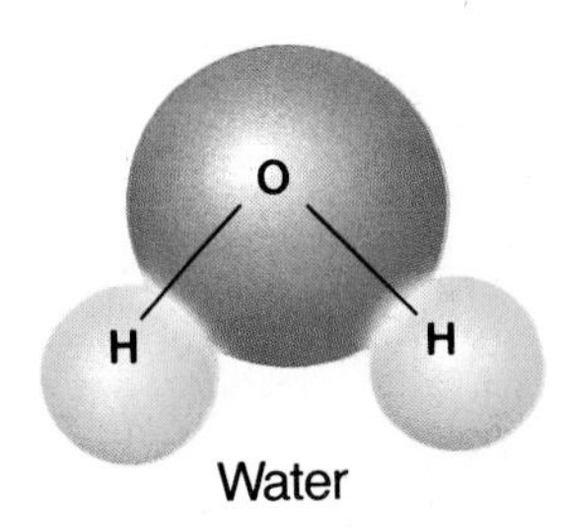

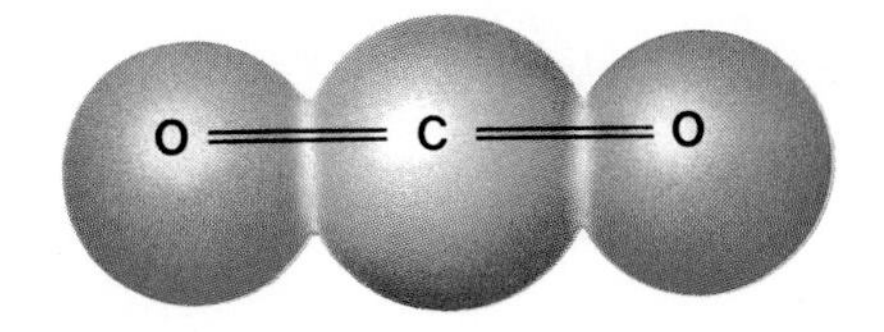

Figure 11-3. These models show the ratios and the arrangements of atoms in water and carbon dioxide.

Table 11-1

SOME FAMILIAR COMPOUNDS

Familiar Name	Chemical Name	Formula
Lye	Sodium hydroxide	$NaOH$
Vinegar	Acetic acid	$HC_2H_3O_2$
Ammonia	Ammonia	NH_3
Grain alcohol	Ethanol	C_2H_5OH
Sand	Silicon dioxide	SiO_2
Battery acid	Sulfuric acid	H_2SO_4
Stomach acid	Hydrochloric acid	HCl
Milk of magnesia	Magnesium hydroxide	$Mg(OH)_2$
Cane sugar	Sucrose	$C_{12}H_{22}O_{11}$

The **chemical formula** for any compound tells what elements it contains and the ratio of the atoms of those elements. What elements are in each compound listed in Table 11-1? What is the ratio of atoms in each compound?

Chemically Stable Atoms

What causes elements to form compounds? Look again at the periodic table on pages 258 and 259. It lists 109 elements, most of which can, and often do, combine with other elements. But the six noble gases in Group 18 seldom combine with other elements. Why do the noble gases almost never form compounds? The reason is that the arrangement of electrons in their atoms makes them chemically stable, or resistant to change.

What electron arrangements make atoms stable? An atom is **chemically stable** if its outer energy level is completely filled with electrons. For the atoms of most elements, the outer energy level is filled when it contains eight electrons. Atoms of the noble gases neon, argon, krypton, xenon, and radon all contain eight electrons in the outermost energy level. For atoms of helium, the outermost energy level is filled when it has two electrons.

Figure 11-4 shows dot diagrams of some of the noble gases. Remember that a dot diagram of an atom shows

Science and READING

Check the labels on the products you find in such places in your home as the medicine cabinet, the refrigerator, and the cupboard under the sink. Match the name of the active ingredient with a formula, and vice versa, for as many products as you can.

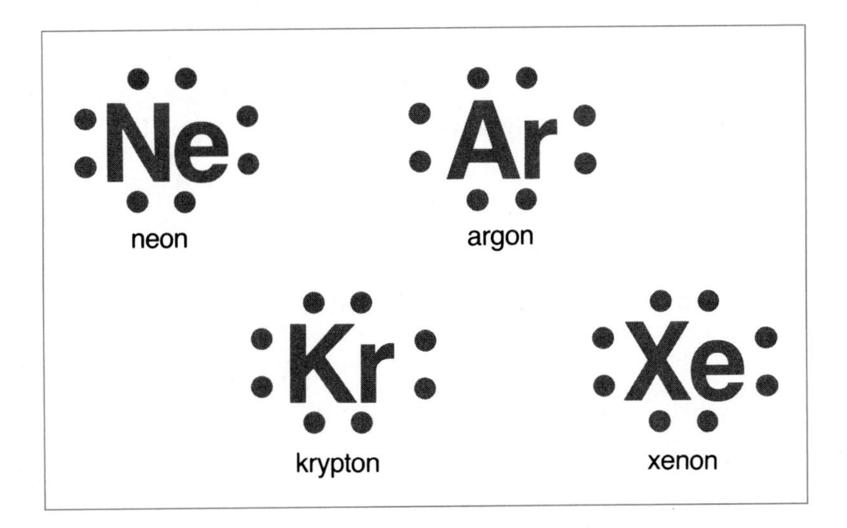

Figure 11-4. Dot diagrams of neon—Ne, krypton—Kr, argon—Ar, and xenon—Xe

the number of electrons in its outer energy level. Notice that each of these elements has eight outer electrons. Because each noble gas has an outer level that is filled to capacity with electrons, each of these elements is chemically stable. Thus, the noble gases don't form compounds naturally. A few compounds of xenon and radon do exist, but these have been prepared in the laboratory under special conditions. Each atom of all the elements *except* the noble gases has from one to seven electrons in its outer energy level. These atoms tend to lose, gain, or share electrons with other atoms. It is the gaining, losing, or sharing of electrons that causes chemical changes to happen. In one of these ways, an atom may have its outer energy level filled, like a noble gas.

Losing, gaining, and sharing electrons are the means by which atoms form chemical bonds. A **chemical bond** is a force that holds together the atoms in a compound. When a chemical bond forms between sodium and chlorine, each sodium atom loses one electron and each chlorine atom gains one. As a result, each atom in sodium chloride, NaCl, has eight electrons in its newly formed outer energy level, as shown in Figure 11-5. Why is the compound sodium chloride stable?

What is a chemical bond?

Figure 11-5. When sodium combines with chlorine, each sodium atom loses an electron and each chlorine atom gains an electron.

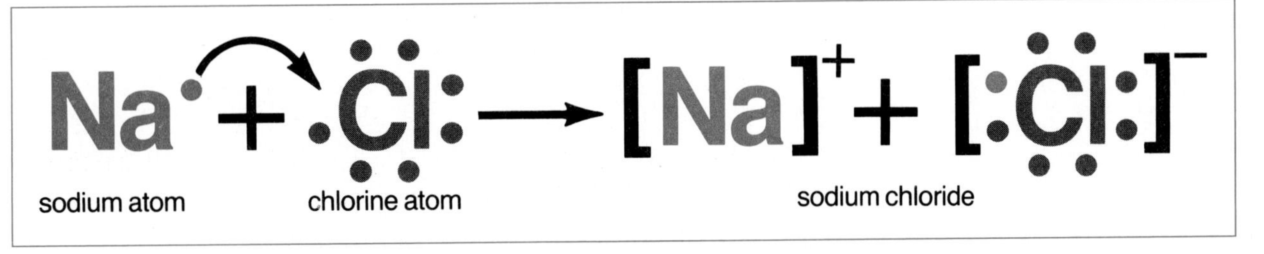

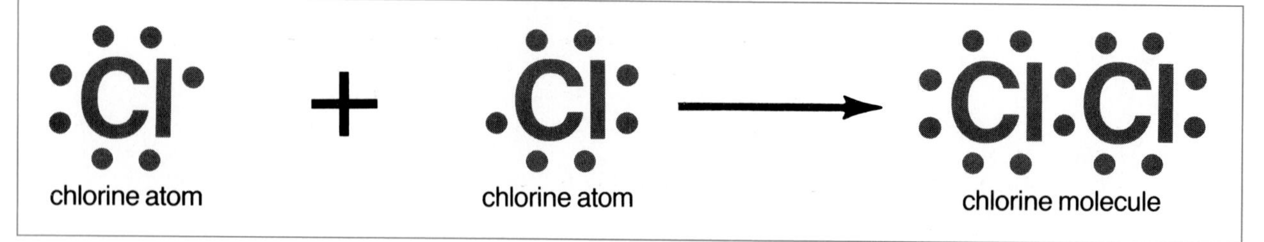

Figure 11-6. Dot diagram for the formation of chlorine gas, Cl_2, from two atoms of chlorine

What makes most atoms chemically unstable?

Chlorine is a gas made up of particles in which two chlorine atoms share electrons. In its formula, Cl_2, the subscript 2 shows that there are two atoms bonded together. Look at Figure 11-6. How is the bond in Cl_2 different from the bond in NaCl?

As you read at the start of this section, compounds, rather than elements, make up most of the matter around you. Why is this so? The answer is that the arrangements of electrons in most atoms make them chemically unstable. Thus, atoms combine with other atoms by sharing or transferring electrons. By doing so, the atoms achieve more stable arrangements of electrons.

SECTION REVIEW

1. What happens to the properties of elements when they form compounds?
2. Write formulas for (a) a compound with one atom of calcium and two atoms of fluorine and (b) a compound with two atoms of aluminum and three atoms of sulfur.
3. Why do most elements tend to form compounds?
4. **Apply:** The label on a box of washing soda states that it contains Na_2CO_3. Name the elements in this compound. In what ratio are they present?

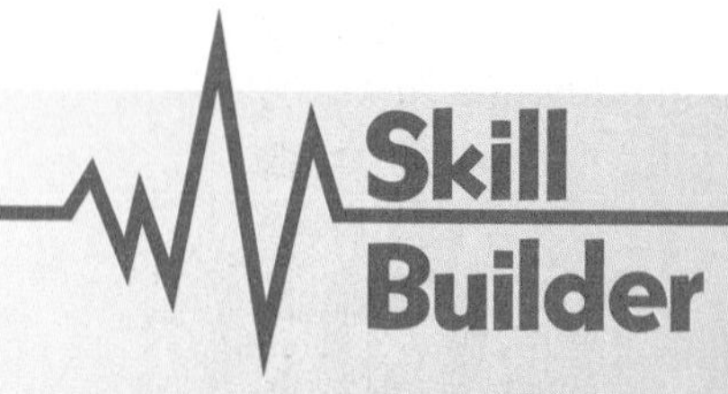

Making and Using Tables

The compounds in Table 11-1 on page 270 that contain carbon are classified as organic, and the others are classified as inorganic. Reorganize the contents of the table using these groups. If you need help, refer to Making and Using Tables in the **Skill Handbook** on page 686.

ACTIVITY 11-1
Models of Combining Atoms

Problem: *How can a model show the way atoms lose, gain, or share electrons?*

Materials
- modified egg carton
- marbles

Procedure
1. Obtain a modified egg carton and marbles from your teacher. The carton will represent the first and second energy levels of an atom, and the marbles will represent electrons.
2. Place one marble in each receptacle of the carton. Start with the pair of receptacles representing the first energy level of the atom.
3. Place the remaining marbles in receptacles representing the second energy level. In which column would your element appear on the periodic chart?
4. Compare your model with those of your classmates. Find one or more other cartons that, when combined with yours, will make it possible for each of the two cartons to have eight marbles in its second energy level.
5. Make a list of the combinations you were able to make with your classmates' models.

Analyze
1. Generally, do groups of metals on the periodic table have more or fewer electrons in their outer energy levels than nonmetals?
2. The combinations you found could represent chemical formulas. Why did some formulas require more than one atom of an element?

Conclude and Apply
3. Would your model be more likely to represent a metal or a nonmetal atom? Explain.
4. What group of elements would your model be in if you received eight marbles? Explain.

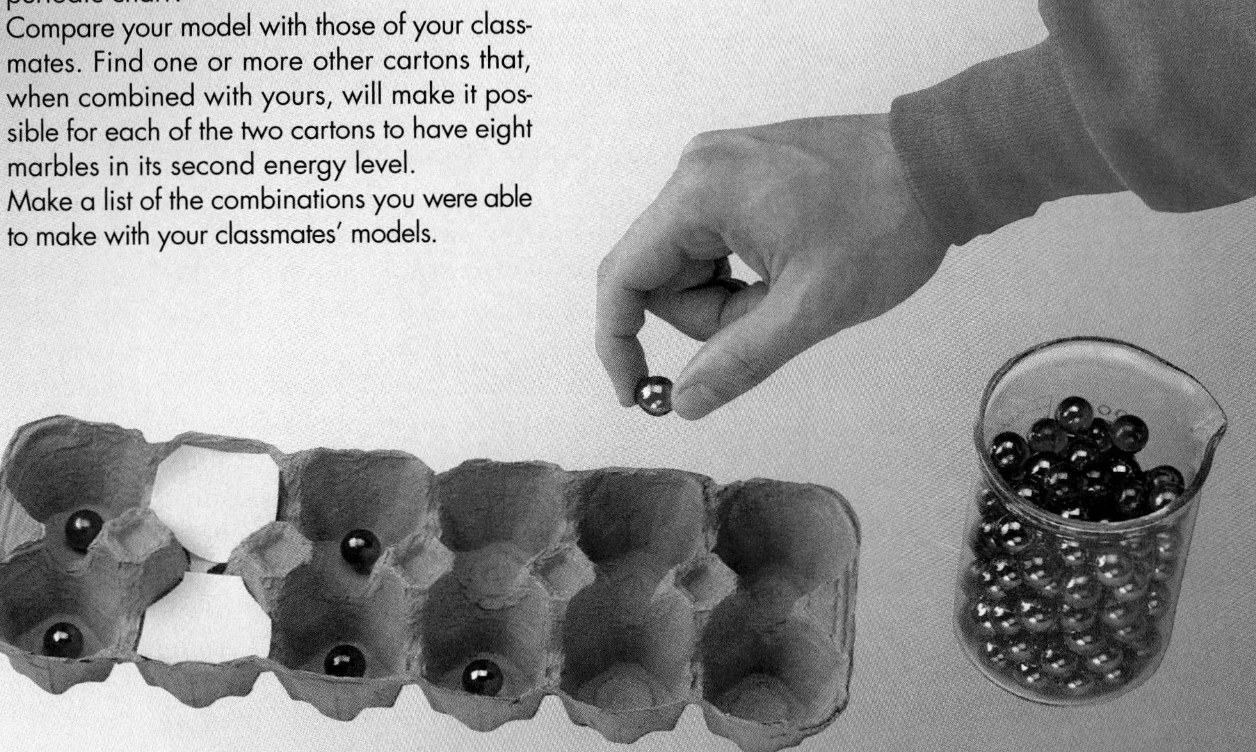

11-2 Hazardous Compounds at Home

New Science Words

toxic
corrosive

Objectives

- ▶ Describe the dangers posed by hazardous compounds in the home.
- ▶ Demonstrate an understanding of ways to avoid hazardous compounds or ways to use them safely.

Corrosive, Flammable, and Toxic Compounds

In 1989, the oil tanker *Exxon Valdez* spilled 11 million gallons of oil. This was one of the worst oil spills in history. People were shocked and outraged. But think about this. Every year do-it-yourself oil changers improperly dispose of 176 million gallons of oil. This is equal to 16 *Exxon Valdez* spills! One quart of oil can contaminate 250 000 gallons of drinking water. Many common household products are hazardous. This means that they contain compounds that can affect the health and safety of people.

Hazardous household chemicals can be toxic, corrosive, or flammable. Compounds that are **toxic** are poisonous. Toxic compounds are in products such as disinfectants, insect sprays, medicine, antifreeze, and nail polish remover. Compounds that are **corrosive** attack and destroy metals, human tissues, and other materials. Corrosive compounds are found in battery acid, drain cleaners, oven cleaners, bleach, and toilet cleaners. Compounds that are flammable burn readily. Flammable compounds include ingredients of gasoline, paint thinner, oil-based paint, and some aerosols.

Toxic, corrosive, and flammable compounds threaten the health and safety of people in their homes. These materials can poison children and pets and pose fire hazards. They may cause cancer and other diseases. When people handle or dispose of hazardous chemicals improperly, they can pollute air, soil, and water. Many times people dump these materials into sewer systems. Hazardous compounds can pass unchanged through septic systems and water treatment plants and into clean

Table 11-2

ALTERNATIVES TO HAZARDOUS HOME CHEMICALS

Product	Safe Alternatives
Aerosols	Use gels, lotions, and nonaerosol sprays.
Chlorine bleach	Use dry bleach or borax.
Moth balls	Use cedar chips.
Toilet bowl cleaners	Use nonphosphate detergents and baking soda.
Drain cleaners	Use a plumbing snake or a plunger to unplug drains.
Window cleaner	Use 2 teaspoons of vinegar in a quart of water and wipe dry with newspaper.
Insecticides	Provide houses and the proper environment in your yard to attract birds, bats, toads, and snakes to eat insects.

water supplies. Hazardous chemicals dumped on soil and in landfills seep into and pollute groundwater supplies. Freon from refrigerators and air conditioners and evaporated gasoline and paint products are examples of chemicals that pollute the air and destory the ozone layer.

How can you and your family remain healthy and safe and prevent pollution? Some suggestions are: (1) Use safe alternatives to hazardous materials, as suggested in Table 11-2. (2) Do not pour automotive fluids into the sewer or on the ground. (3) Recycle oil, antifreeze, and used batteries. (4) If you must purchase a hazardous product, buy only the amount you need and give the excess to someone who will use it. (5) Store hazardous materials in their original containers, away from children. (6) Keep hazardous materials that easily evaporate in tightly closed containers, to prevent the escape of vapors. (7) Share your knowledge of the problem of hazardous household compounds with others.

EcoTip

Instead of using poisonous chemical sprays, chase away insect pests by planting chrysanthemums near your doorways or in your garden.

SECTION REVIEW

1. What are three dangerous properties of hazardous compounds in many household products?
2. What are five ways you can protect yourself and the environment from hazardous materials?

You Decide!

Your neighbor changes his own automobile oil. Several times you have seen him dump the used liquids at the edge of his property and yours. What should you do?

11-3 Kinds of Chemical Bonds

New Science Words

ion
ionic bond
covalent bond
polar molecule
nonpolar molecule

Objectives

- Describe ionic bonds and covalent bonds.
- Identify the particles produced by ionic bonding and by covalent bonding.
- Distinguish between a nonpolar covalent bond and a polar covalent bond.

Ions and Ionic Bonds

Figure 11-7. Dot diagrams for sodium atom becoming a sodium ion (top), and chlorine atom becoming a chloride ion (bottom)

The brilliant flash in the photograph shows what happens when sodium is put in a flask of chlorine gas. (**CAUTION:** *It is very dangerous to handle or mix sodium and chlorine—do not try it.*) Recall how the atoms of these elements—sodium and chlorine—bond chemically when mixed. An atom of sodium has one electron in its outer energy level, as shown in Figure 11-7. When the atom loses that electron, its second energy level is then outermost and complete, because it contains eight electrons. But the atom now has 11 protons, with a total charge of 11+, and 10 electrons, with a total charge of 10–. Because (11+) + (10–) = 1+, the atom has a net positive charge of 1+. Atoms that have charges are called ions. Thus, the sodium atom, Na, that has lost an electron is now a sodium ion, Na^+. You write the symbol for the ion with a superscript plus sign to indicate its charge. *Superscript* means "written above."

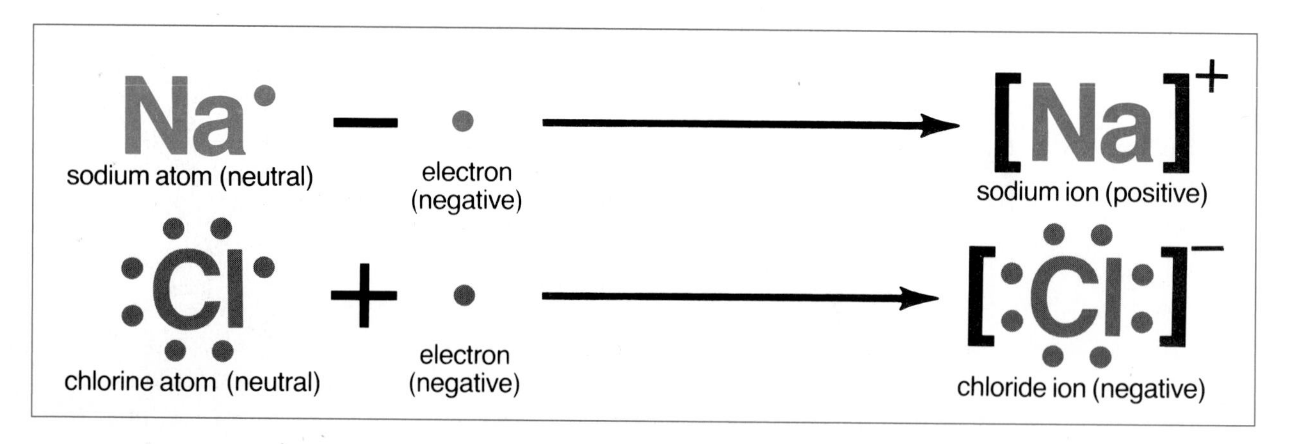

A chlorine atom has seven electrons in its outer energy level, as shown in Figure 11-7. When the atom gains an electron, its outermost energy level contains eight electrons. But the atom now has 17 protons, with a total charge of 17+, and 18 electrons, with a total charge of 18–. Because (17+) + (18–) = 1–, the atom has a net negative charge of 1–. In other words, it is now a chloride ion, which you write with a superscript minus sign, Cl^-, to indicate its charge. The compound NaCl as a whole, however, is neutral, because the total net positive charge equals the total net negative charge.

Figure 11-8. Dot diagram for sodium chloride, NaCl

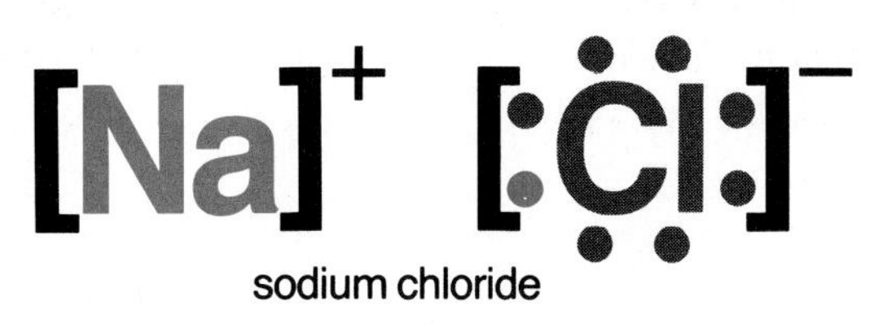

An **ion** is an atom that is either positively or negatively charged. Compounds made up of ions are ionic compounds, and the bonds that hold them together are ionic bonds. An **ionic bond** is the force of attraction between the opposite charges of the ions in an ionic compound.

Figure 11-9 shows another example of ionic bonding—the formation of magnesium fluoride, MgF_2. When magnesium reacts with fluorine, a magnesium atom loses two electrons and becomes a positively charged ion, Mg^{2+}. Notice that you write 2+ on the symbol for magnesium to indicate the ion's net charge. At the same time, each of the two fluorine atoms gains one electron each and becomes a negatively charged fluoride ion, F^-. The compound as a whole is neutral. Why? Because the sum of the net charges on all three ions is zero.

Why is the charge on a magnesium ion positive?

Molecules and Covalent Bonds

Most atoms become more chemically stable by sharing electrons, rather than by losing or gaining electrons. In Figure 11-6 on page 272, you saw how two chlorine atoms share electrons. Notice that the chlorine parti-

Figure 11-9. Dot diagram for magnesium fluoride, MgF_2

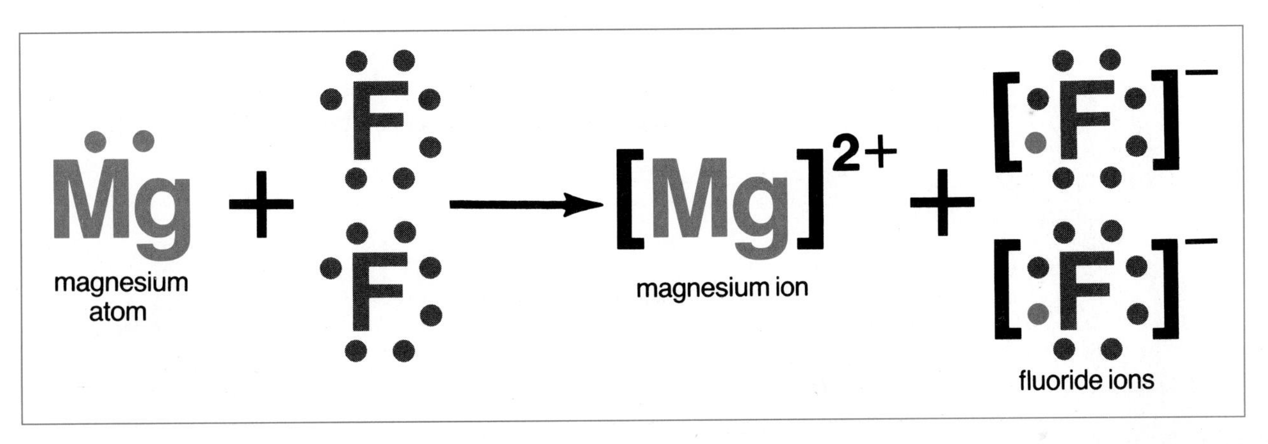

Why is a chlorine molecule neutral?

cle, Cl_2, is not charged—it is neutral. The chlorine is not in the form of ions, but molecules. Neutral particles formed as a result of electron sharing are called molecules.

A bond that forms between atoms when they share electrons is known as a **covalent bond.** In the case of chlorine, a covalent bond is formed between two atoms of the same element. Covalent bonds also form between atoms of nitrogen, the gas that makes up most of the air. As you can see in Figure 11-10, two atoms of nitrogen in N_2 share six electrons, forming three covalent bonds between the atoms.

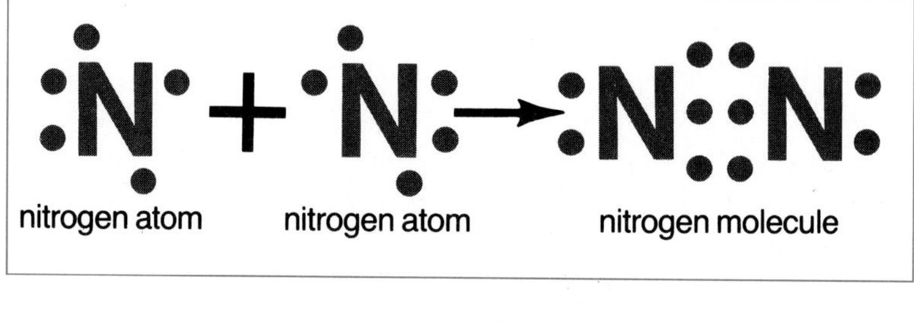

Figure 11-10. Dot diagrams for the formation of nitrogen gas, N_2, from two atoms of nitrogen

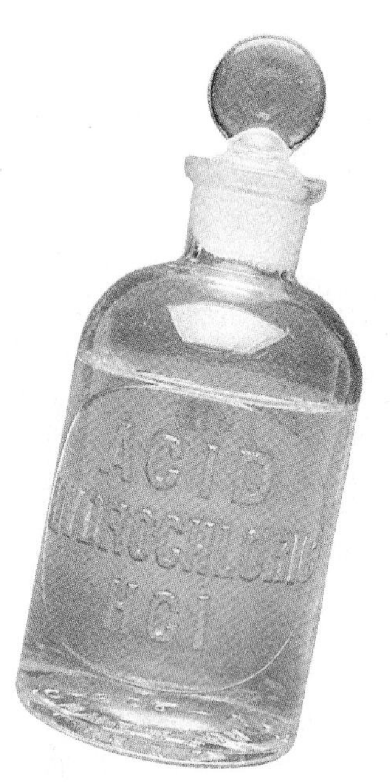

Polar and Nonpolar Molecules

Atoms in molecules do not always share electrons equally. An example is a molecule of hydrogen chloride, HCl. A water solution of HCl is hydrochloric acid, which is used in laboratories, to clean metal, and in your stomach to digest food. The chlorine atom has a stronger attraction for electrons than does the hydrogen atom. As a result, the electrons they share in hydrogen chloride will spend more time near the chlorine atom than near the hydrogen atom. This type of molecule is called polar. *Polar* means "having two opposite ends." A **polar molecule** is one that has a positive end and a negative end.

Water is another example of a compound with polar molecules, as shown in Figure 11-12. A water molecule contains two polar covalent bonds, one between each hydrogen atom and the oxygen atom. The oxygen atom

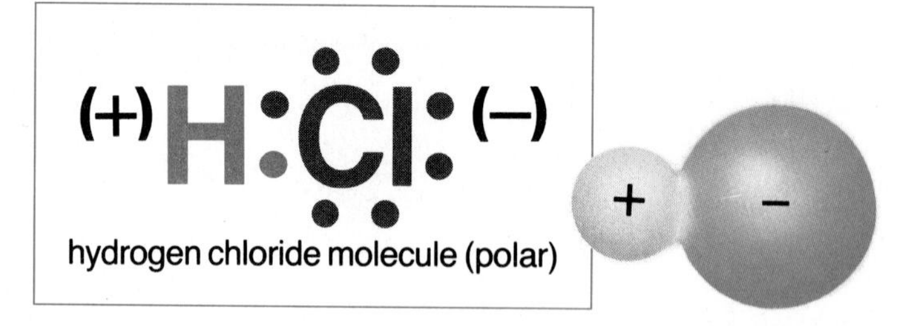

Figure 11-11. Dot diagram and model for a molecule of hydrogen chloride

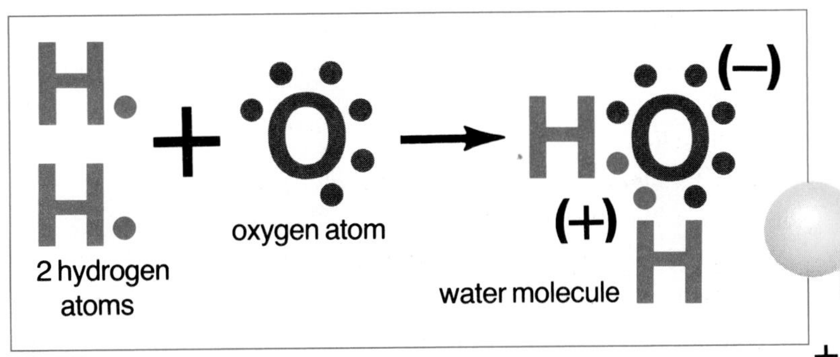

Figure 11-12. Dot diagram and model for a molecule of water

has a stronger attraction for electrons than the hydrogen atoms do. As a result, the oxygen end of the water molecule is negative and the hydrogen end of the molecule is positive.

TECHNOLOGY

Bond Busters

Toxic compounds with names such as vinyl chloride, benzene, and pentachlorophenol are among the pollutants that human activities generate in huge amounts and that damage the environment. One way to get rid of toxic compounds is to change them chemically into other, harmless compounds. That is, the chemical bonds holding together the atoms in molecules of toxic compounds must be broken. Then the atoms are bonded into different molecules of harmless substances.

Scientists are now enlisting new strains of microbes as bond busters to change toxic compounds into nontoxic ones. The microbes eat the compounds, which change chemically as they are digested. To create a strain of pollutant-eating microbes, scientists first add a pollutant to a population of microbes. Most of the microbes die, leaving only the hardiest ones to reproduce. Scientists then seed polluted soil with these microbes and add fertilizer and oxygen to promote their growth. The microbes break down the toxic compounds and then, with the food source gone, the microbes die.

At least 1000 different strains of bacteria and fungi are now helping to get rid of pollutants. The biggest advantage of the microbial approach is that instead of relocating the pollutants—by moving toxic substances to other places—the microbes destroy them.

Think Critically: What would be the disadvantages of using microbes compared to removing or burning contaminated soil?

Figure 11-13. Sugar is an example of a covalent compound that has polar molecules.

Some molecules, such as those of nitrogen, are nonpolar. Because the two nitrogen atoms share their electrons equally, the molecule's ends are neither positive or negative. A **nonpolar molecule** is one that does not have oppositely charged ends. Look again at the diagram of a nitrogen molecule in Figure 11-10 on page 278.

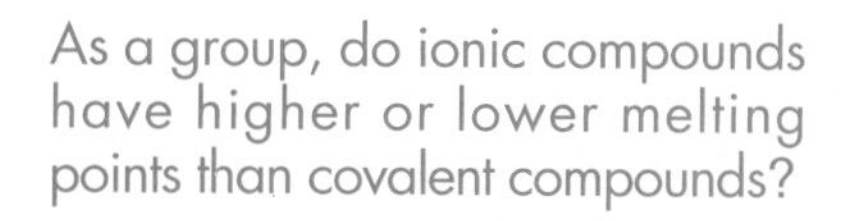

As a group, do ionic compounds have higher or lower melting points than covalent compounds?

You have read about two main ways chemical bonding takes place, producing two kinds of compounds—ionic and covalent. These groups of compounds have contrasting properties. For example, like sodium chloride, most ionic compounds are crystalline solids with high melting points. Like water, most covalent compounds are liquids or gases at room temperature. But some covalent compounds, such as sugar, are solids. In later chapters, you will learn more about compounds of each type.

SECTION REVIEW

1. Compare ionic and covalent bonds.
2. What type of particle is formed by the following bonds: (a) ionic (b) polar covalent (c) nonpolar covalent?
3. **Apply:** The label on a tube of toothpaste states that it contains the decay preventative sodium fluoride, NaF. Draw a dot diagram of sodium fluoride, which is an ionic compound.

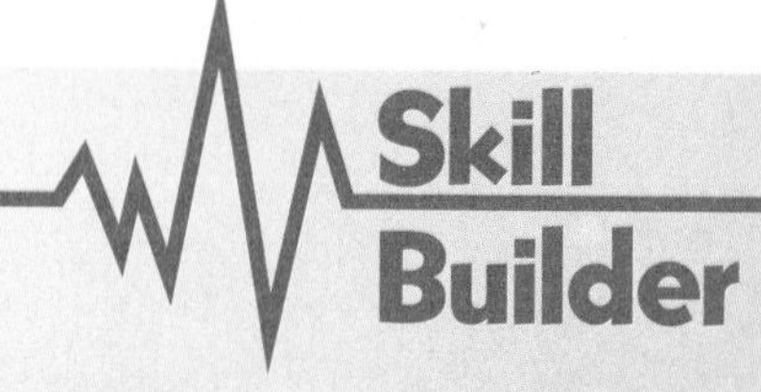

Concept Mapping

Using the following terms, make a network tree concept map of chemical bonding: *ionic, covalent, ions, positive ions, negative ions, molecules, polar, nonpolar.* If you need help, refer to Concept Mapping in the **Skill Handbook** on pages 684 and 685

ACTIVITY 11-2
Covalent and Ionic Bonds

Problem: *How can melting point be used to compare covalent and ionic substances?*

Materials  

- 1 tablespoon each of crushed ice, sugar, and salt
- wire test-tube holder
- 3 test tubes
- goggles
- laboratory burner

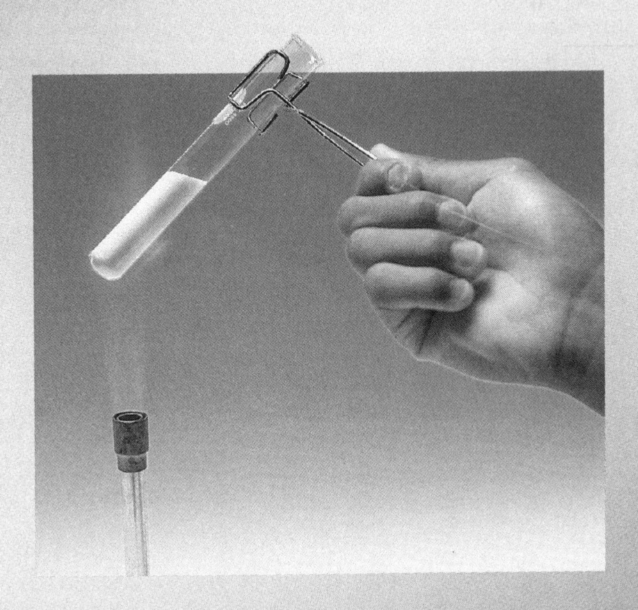

Procedure

1. Copy the data table below and use it to record your observations.
2. Place a tablespoon each of crushed ice, sugar, and salt in separate test tubes.
3. Wearing goggles and using a wire test-tube holder, heat each test tube with a laboratory burner for no longer than five minutes.
4. Observe and record the appearance of each substance at one-minute intervals.
5. Rank the three materials from the easiest to the most difficult to melt.

Analyze

1. Which one of the three compounds do you believe to be ionic?
2. What is the role of energy during a change of state, such as melting?

Conclude and Apply

3. Butter is a common material that is easy to melt. Would you conclude that butter is composed of mainly covalent compounds or of ionic compounds?
4. In general, how do the melting points of covalent compounds and ionic compounds compare?

Data and Observations

	Appearance after Heating				
Substance	**1 min**	**2 min**	**3 min**	**4 min**	**5 min**
Salt					
Sugar					
Ice					

11-4 Formulas and Names of Compounds

New Science Words

oxidation number
binary compound
polyatomic ion
hydrate

Objectives

- Explain how to determine oxidation numbers.
- Write formulas for compounds from their names.
- Name compounds from their formulas.
- Describe hydrates and their formulas.

Oxidation Numbers

What two elements are present in tarnish?

The two people in these pictures seem to have little in common. Yet, in a sense, the medieval alchemist is the ancestor of the modern chemist. Both are shown at work investigating matter. Notice how each would write symbols for the elements silver and sulfur. Tarnish is silver sulfide, a compound of silver and sulfur. If the alchemist knew the composition of tarnish, how might he write its formula? The modern chemist does know its composition; she would write it Ag_2S. When you get to the end of this section, you, too, will know how to write such formulas.

You can figure out formulas with the help of oxidation numbers. What are these numbers? An **oxidation number** is a positive or negative number assigned to an element to show its combining ability in a compound. In other words, an oxidation number indicates how many electrons an atom has gained, lost, or shared when bonding with other atoms. For example, when sodium forms an ion, it loses an electron and has a charge of 1+. So the oxidation number of sodium is 1+. And when chlorine forms an ion, it gains an electron and has a charge of 1–. So the oxidation number of chlorine is 1–.

What does an oxidation number indicate?

Oxidation numbers are often a periodic property of elements. The red numbers printed on the periodic table shown in Figure 11-14 are the oxidation numbers for many elements in binary compounds. *Bi-* means "two," and a **binary compound** is one that is composed of two elements. Sodium chloride is an example of a binary compound.

Like sodium, each metal in Group 1 loses its one outer electron in bonding, so each of these elements has an oxidation number of 1+. Remember, losing electrons produces a positive oxidation number in an element. Each metal in Group 2 loses both its outer electrons in bonding, so each has an oxidation number of 2+.

Like chlorine, each of the nonmetals in Group 17 gains one electron in bonding, so each of these elements has an oxidation number of 1–. Remember, gaining electrons

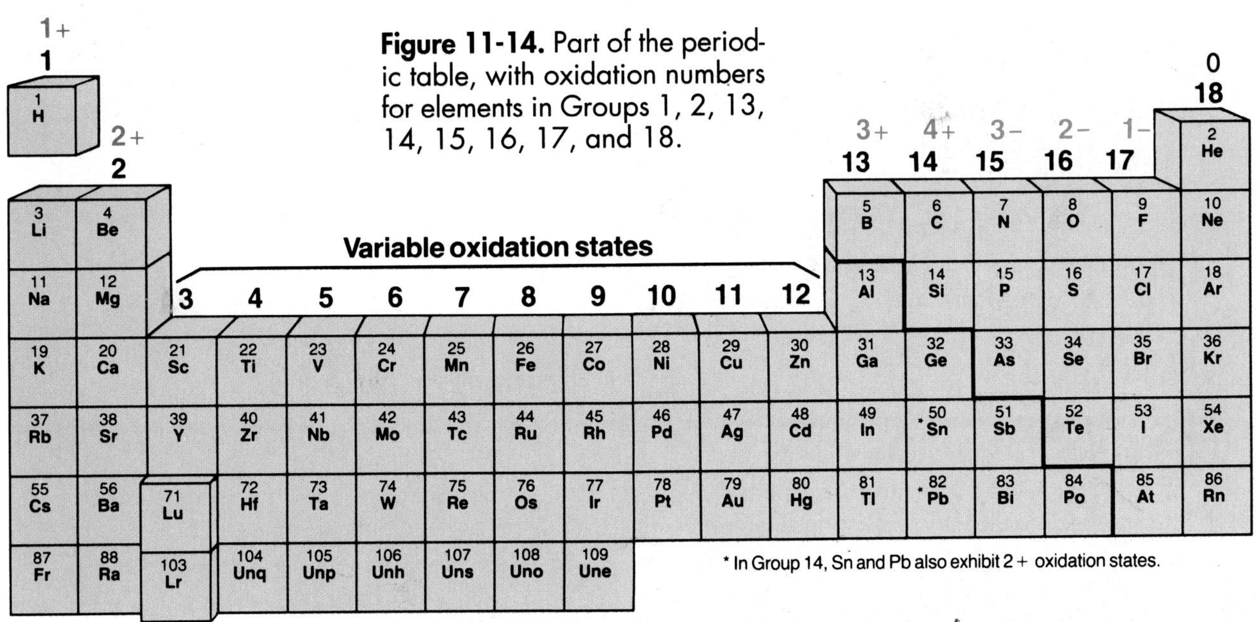

Figure 11-14. Part of the periodic table, with oxidation numbers for elements in Groups 1, 2, 13, 14, 15, 16, 17, and 18.

The lanthanoid and actinoid elements are not shown in this table.

copper(I)	Cu^{+}
copper(II)	Cu^{2+}
iron(II)	Fe^{2+}
iron(III)	Fe^{3+}
chromium(II)	Cr^{2+}
chromium(III)	Cr^{3+}
lead(II)	Pb^{2+}
lead(IV)	Pb^{4+}

Figure 11-15. Here are some elements that have variable oxidation numbers.

produces a negative oxidation number in an element. Each nonmetal in Group 16 gains two electrons in bonding, so each has an oxidation number of 2–.

Some elements have more than one oxidation number. Copper, as you can see in Figure 11-15, can be both Cu^{+} and Cu^{2+}. In the name of a compound of copper, the Roman numeral equals the oxidation number of copper in that compound. Thus, the oxidation number of copper in copper(II) oxide is 2+. Iron may be Fe^{2+} or Fe^{3+}. Thus, the oxidation number of iron in iron(III) oxide is 3+.

Formulas for Binary Compounds

Once you know how to find the oxidation numbers of elements in binary compounds, you can write formulas by using these rules: (1) Write first the symbol of the element with the positive oxidation number. Hydrogen and all metals have positive oxidation numbers. (2) Then write the symbol of the element with the negative oxidation number. (3) Add subscripts so that the sum of the oxidation numbers of all the atoms in the formula is zero.

EXAMPLE PROBLEM: Writing Formulas for Binary Compounds

Problem Statement : What is the formula of a compound composed of sulfur and aluminum?

Problem-Solving Steps:

1. Write the symbol of the positive element followed by the symbol of the negative element. — Al S
2. Look up oxidation numbers for each element. Write oxidation numbers above the symbols. — $\overset{3+}{Al}$ $\overset{2-}{S}$
3. Write in subscripts so that the sum of the oxidation numbers is zero. — $\overset{3+}{Al_2}$ $\overset{2-}{S_3}$
4. Check to see if the sum of the oxidation numbers is zero. — $2(3+) + 3(2-) = (6+) + (6-) = 0$

Solution: Final Formula: Al_2S_3

PRACTICE PROBLEMS

Strategy Hint: Be sure to use the smallest possible subscript numbers to make the sum zero.

Strategy Hint: The Roman numeral II tells you the oxidation number of copper.

1. Write the formula for a compound of calcium and oxygen.
2. Write the formula of a compound of copper(II) and sulfur.

Figure 11-16. Many binary compounds of transition elements are brightly colored.

Naming Binary Compounds

You can name a binary compound from its formula by using these rules: (1) Write the name of the first element. (2) Write the root of the name of the second element. (3) Add the ending *-ide* to the root. Table 11-3 lists several elements and their *-ide* counterparts. For example, $CaCl_2$ is named calcium chloride.

To name compounds of elements having two oxidation numbers you must first figure out the oxidation numbers of the elements. Study the next example problem and do the practice problems.

EXAMPLE PROBLEM: Naming Some Binary Compounds

Problem Statement: What is the name of CrO?

Problem-Solving Steps:

1. Look up the oxidation number of the negative element.

   $\overset{}{Cr}\ \overset{2-}{O}$

2. Figure out the oxidation number of the positive element.

   $\underset{Cr}{?} + \underset{O}{(2-)} = 0;\ ? = 2+$

3. Write the name of the compound, using a Roman numeral for the positive oxidation number if necessary.

   $\underset{Cr}{(2+)} + \underset{O}{(2-)} = 0$

Solution: chromium(II) oxide

PRACTICE PROBLEM

Strategy Hint: For names of elements with more than one oxidation number, remember to include the Roman numeral. For names of nonmetals in binary compounds use Table 11-3.

1. Name the following compounds: Li_2S, MgF_2, FeO, CuCl

Table 11-3

ELEMENTS IN BINARY COMPOUNDS	
Element	***-ide* Naming**
Chlorine	Chloride
Fluorine	Fluoride
Nitrogen	Nitride
Oxygen	Oxide
Phosphorus	Phosphide
Sulfur	Sulfide

Compounds with Polyatomic Ions

Table 11-4

POLYATOMIC IONS		
Charge	Name	Formula
1+	Ammonium	NH_4^+
1–	Acetate	$C_2H_3O_2^-$
	Chlorate	ClO_3^-
	Hydroxide	OH^-
	Nitrate	NO_3^-
2–	Carbonate	CO_3^{2-}
	Sulfate	SO_4^{2-}
3–	Phosphate	PO_4^{3-}

Not all compounds are binary. Have you ever used baking soda in cooking, as a medicine, or to brush your teeth? Baking soda, which has the formula $NaHCO_3$, is an example of a compound that is not binary. What four elements does it contain? Some compounds, including baking soda, are composed of more than two elements because they contain polyatomic ions. The prefix *poly-* means "many," so *polyatomic* means "having many atoms." A **polyatomic ion** is a positively or negatively charged group of atoms. So the compound as a whole contains three or more elements.

Table 11-4 lists several polyatomic ions. To name a compound that contains one of these ions, write first the name of the positive element. For a compound of the ammonium ion, NH_4^+, write ammonium first. Then use Table 11-4 to find the name of the polyatomic ion. For example, K_2SO_4 is potassium sulfate. What is the name of $Sr(OH)_2$?

To write formulas for compounds containing polyatomic ions, follow the rules for writing formulas for binary compounds, with one addition. Write parentheses around the group representing the polyatomic ion when more than one of that ion is needed.

EXAMPLE PROBLEM: Writing Formulas with Polyatomic Ions

Problem Statement: What is the formula for calcium nitrate?

Problem-Solving Steps:

1. Write symbols and oxidation numbers for calcium and the nitrate ion.

   $\overset{2+}{Ca}\ \overset{1-}{NO_3}$

2. Write in subscripts so that the sum of the oxidation numbers is zero. Enclose the NO_3 in parentheses.

   $\overset{2+}{Ca}\ \overset{1-}{(NO_3)_2}$

Solution: Final formula: $Ca(NO_3)_2$

PRACTICE PROBLEMS

Strategy Hint: When only one polyatomic ion is needed in a formula, do not enclose the ion in parentheses.

Strategy Hint: Because the subscript *3* in ClO_3 is part of the ion, it should not be changed when written as part of a formula.

1. What is the formula for sodium sulfate?
2. What is the formula for magnesium chlorate?

Hydrates

Some ionic compounds may have water molecules as part of their structure and written into their formulas. These compounds are called hydrates. A **hydrate** is a compound that has water chemically attached to its ions. *Hydrate* comes from a word that means water. For example, when a water solution of cobalt chloride evaporates, pink crystals that contain six water molecules for each unit of cobalt chloride are formed. The formula for this compound is $CoCl_2 \cdot 6H_2O$ and its name is cobalt chloride hexahydrate. *Hexa-* means "six." You can remove water from these crystals by heating them. The resulting blue compound is called anhydrous, which means without water. The blue paper in Figure 11-17 has been soaked in cobalt chloride solution and heated.

Figure 11-17. The paper strips have been soaked in a solution of $CoCl_2$. The blue strips have been heated to drive water molecules out of the crystals.

Like many anhydrous compounds, cobalt chloride gains water molecules easily. You may have seen "weather predictors" made from blue paper that turns pink in humid air. The paper contains cobalt chloride. How does it detect water vapor?

Have you ever made a mold or cast with plaster of paris? If so, you have made a hydrate. Plaster of paris is the anhydrous form of calcium sulfate dihydrate, $CaSO_4 \cdot 2H_2O$. When you mix plaster of paris with water, it absorbs water and changes chemically into the hydrate.

Water in a hydrate has lost its properties because it is chemically attached. Not all crystals are hydrates. The only way to detect the presence of water in crystals is to heat the solid material and see if it gives off steam and changes to powder. For example, if you heat hardened plaster of paris, it will give off steam, crumble, and become powdery. How would you write the formula for this powder?

MINI-Lab

How does heat affect a hydrate?
Using a light pink solution of $CoCl_2 \cdot 6H_2O$ as ink and a glass rod as a pen, write your name on white paper. After you have allowed the writing to air dry, it should be nearly invisible. Next, *carefully* wave the paper above a flame until the writing starts to appear blue. What part of the $CoCl_2 \cdot 6H_2O$ was changed? How does heat affect a hydrate? What term is applied to the remainder of the hydrate?

You have learned how to write formulas of binary ionic compounds and of compounds containing polyatomic ions. Using oxidation numbers to write formulas, you can predict the ratio in which atoms of elements may combine to form compounds. You have also seen how hydrates have water molecules as part of their structure and formulas. As you study the chapters that follow, you will see many uses of formulas.

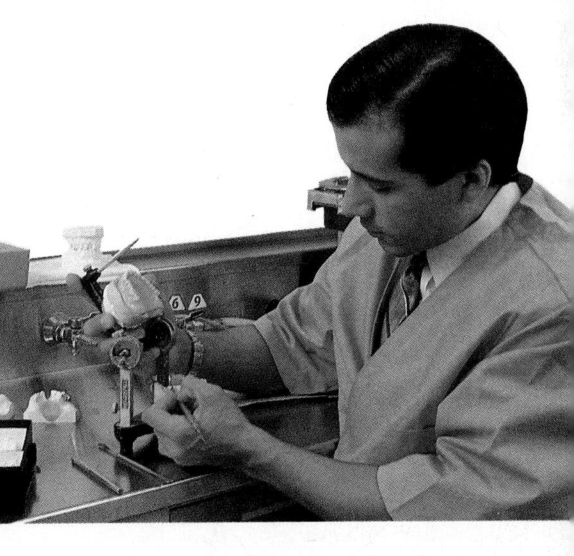

PROBLEM SOLVING

The Packet of Mystery Crystals

When a new video cassette recorder (VCR) was delivered to Peter's home, he was eager to start using it to tape programs. So he asked for and got the job of unpacking the VCR. When he lifted the instrument from the carton, a small flat packet fell out. A label on the packet read "Contains silica gel. Do not eat."

Peter was curious about the contents of the packet, so he looked up "silica gel" in a reference book. There he read that silica gel is the anhydrous form of silica, a mineral that consists mainly of silicon(IV) oxide, SiO_2.

Think Critically: What would silica gel do if water molecules were in the air? Why was the packet of silica gel placed in the carton with the VCR?

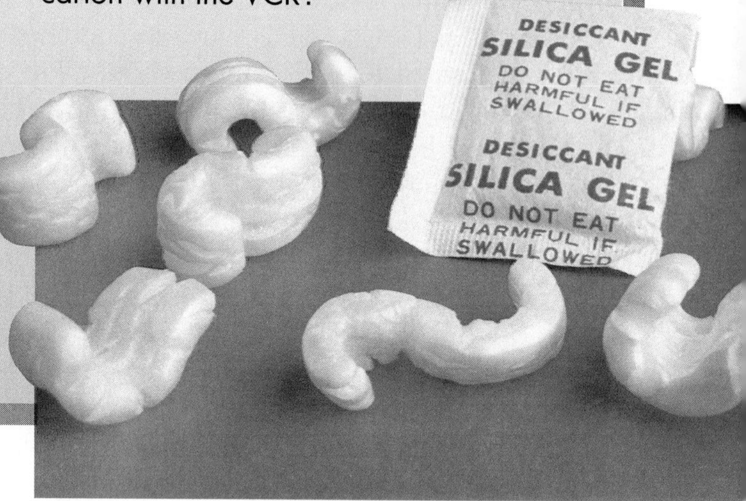

SECTION REVIEW

1. Name the following: NaI, FeI_3, K_2SO_4, NH_4Br.
2. Write formulas for compounds composed of (a) lithium and sulfur, (b) calcium and the acetate ion, and (c) barium and oxygen.
3. Write formulas for the following: (a) the anhydrous form of $CoCl_2 \cdot 6H_2O$ and (b) calcium sulfate dihydrate.
4. **Apply:** The label on a package of plant food lists potassium nitrate as one ingredient. What is the formula for this compound?

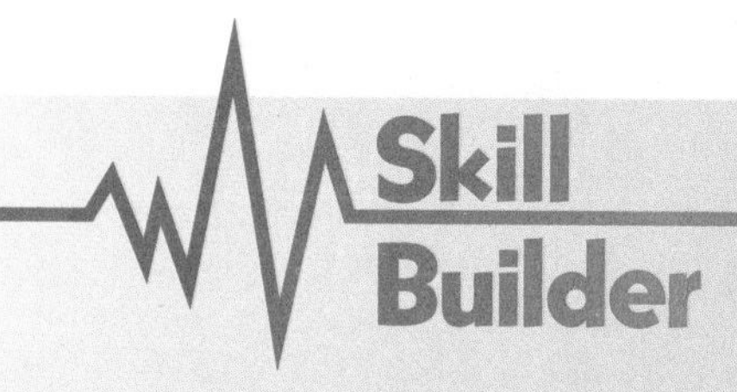

Using Variables, Constants, and Controls

Design an experiment to distinguish between crystals that are hydrates and those that are not. Include crystals of iron(II) chloride, copper(I) nitrate, and crystals of sucrose. If you need help, refer to Using Variables, Constants, and Controls in the **Skill Handbook** on page 682.

CHAPTER

REVIEW

SUMMARY

11-1: Why Atoms Combine

1. The properties of compounds are generally different from those of the elements they are composed of.

2. The symbols and subscripts in a chemical formula for a compound indicate the composition of a unit of the compound.

3. Chemical bonding occurs when atoms of most elements become more stable by gaining, losing, or sharing electrons.

11-2: Science and Society: Hazardous Compounds at Home

1. Compounds that are toxic, corrosive, or flammable are hazardous.

2. There are many ways in which people can protect their health and the environment from hazardous compounds in the home.

11-3: Kinds of Chemical Bonds

1. Ionic bonds between atoms are formed by the transfer of electrons, and covalent bonds are formed by the sharing of electrons.

2. Ionic bonding produces charged particles called ions. Covalent bonding produces particles called molecules.

3. The unequal sharing of electrons produces polar compounds, and the equal sharing of electrons produces nonpolar compounds.

11-4: Formulas and Names of Compounds

1. An oxidation number indicates how many electrons an atom has gained, lost, or shared when bonding with other atoms.

2. In the formula of an ionic compound, the element or ion with the positive oxidation number is written first, followed by the one with the negative oxidation number.

3. The name of a binary compound is derived from the names of the two elements it is composed of.

4. A hydrate is a compound that has water chemically attached to its ions and written into its formula.

KEY SCIENCE WORDS

a. **binary compound**
b. **chemical bond**
c. **chemical formula**
d. **chemically stable**
e. **corrosive**
f. **covalent bond**
g. **hydrate**
h. **ion**
i. **ionic bond**
j. **nonpolar molecule**
k. **oxidation number**
l. **polyatomic ion**
m. **polar molecule**
n. **toxic**

UNDERSTANDING VOCABULARY

Match each phrase with the correct term from the list of Key Science Words.

1. a charged group of atoms
2. a compound composed of two elements
3. a molecule with a charge on each end
4. a positively or negatively charged atom
5. bond formed by transfer of electrons
6. bond formed from shared electrons
7. crystalline substance that contains water molecules
8. outer energy level is filled with electrons
9. shows an element's combining ability
10. tells what elements are in a compound and their ratios

CHAPTER

REVIEW

CHECKING CONCEPTS

Choose the word or phrase that completes the sentence or answers the question.

1. The elements that are least likely to react with other elements are the ______.
   a. metals c. nonmetals
   b. noble gases d. transition elements
2. The oxidation number of Fe in Fe_2S_3 is ______.
   a. 1+ c. 3+
   b. 2+ d. 4+
3. The name of CuO is ______.
   a. copper oxide c. copper(II) oxide
   b. copper(I) oxide d. copper(III) oxide
4. The formula for iron(III) chlorate is ______.
   a. $FeClO_3$ c. $Fe(ClO_3)_3$
   b. FeCl d. $FeCl_3$
5. Which of the following is a nonpolar molecule? ______
   a. N_2 c. NaCl
   b. H_2O d. HCl
6. The number of electrons in the outer energy level of Group 17 elements is ______.
   a. 1 c. 17
   b. 2 d. 7
7. An example of a binary compound is ______.
   a. O_2 c. H_2SO_4
   b. NaF d. $Cu(NO_3)_2$
8. An example of an anhydrous compound is ______.
   a. H_2O c. $CuSO_4{\cdot}5H_2O$
   b. $CaSO_4$ d. $CaSO_4{\cdot}2H_2O$
9. An atom that has gained an electron is a ______.
   a. negative ion c. polar molecule
   b. positive ion d. nonpolar molecule
10. An example of a covalent compound is ______.
   a. sodium chloride c. calcium chloride
   b. calcium fluoride d. water

UNDERSTANDING CONCEPTS

Complete each sentence.

11. An uncharged group of covalently bonded atoms is a(n) ______.
12. An iodine atom can form an ionic compound by accepting ______ electron(s) from a metal.
13. A molecule that has no charge on either end is said to be ______.
14. In a formula, a(n) ______ written after a symbol tells how many atoms of that element are in that compound.
15. Household products that are ______ may be toxic, flammable, or corrosive.

THINK AND WRITE CRITICALLY

16. What does the formula CO_2 tell you about a molecule of carbon dioxide?
17. By what three ways can atoms become chemically stable?
18. How can chromium form two different compounds with oxygen?

19. Why is the formula for milk of magnesia written $Mg(OH)_2$ instead of MgO_2H_2?
20. What compounds can be formed from element X, with oxidation numbers 3+ and 5+, and element Z, with oxidation numbers 2– and 3–? Write their formulas.

APPLY

21. Anhydrous calcium chloride attracts water and is used on dusty roads. Draw a dot diagram of calcium chloride.
22. Write the formula for a compound that is safe to use for cleaning. For help in answering, see Table 11-2 on page 275 and Table 11-4, page 286.
23. Artificial diamonds are made using thallium carbonate. If thallium has an oxidation number of 1+, what is the formula for the compound?
24. Ammonium sulfate is used as a fertilizer. What is its chemical formula?
25. The formula for a compound that can cause kidney stones is $Ca_3(PO_4)_2$. What is the chemical name of this compound?

MORE SKILL BUILDERS

If you need help, refer to the Skill Handbook.

1. **Comparing and Contrasting:** Compare and contrast polar and nonpolar molecules.
2. **Interpreting Scientific Illustrations:** Write the name and formula for the compound illustrated below.

H:S:
H

3. **Hypothesizing:** Several uses of HCl were given to you in Section 11-3. HF is another acid and is used to etch glass. If HCl is hydrochloric acid, what would be the name of HF?
4. **Observing and Inferring:** Ammonia gas and water react to form household ammonia, NH_4OH. If the formula for water is H_2O, what is the formula for ammonia gas?
5. **Concept Mapping:** In photosynthesis, green plants, in sunlight, convert carbon dioxide and water to glucose, $C_6H_{12}O_6$, and oxygen, O_2. In respiration, glucose and oxygen react to produce carbon dioxide and water and release energy. In the following map, write in the formulas of the molecules and the names of the processes.

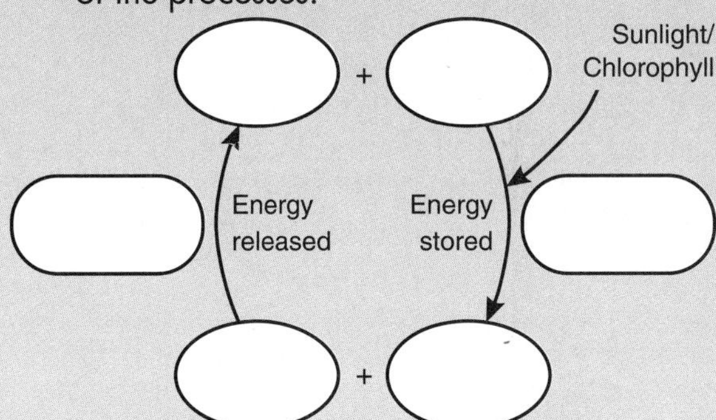

PROJECTS

1. One common form of phosphorus, white phosphorus, has the formula P_4 and is formed by four covalently bonded phosphorus atoms. Make a model of this molecule, showing that all four atoms are now chemically stable.
2. More sulfuric acid, H_2SO_4, is made in the United States than is any other chemical. Research the production and uses of sulfuric acid and write a report on your findings.

UNIT 3

GLOBAL CONNECTIONS

The Nature of Matter

In this unit, you studied what matter is, how it is classified, and how it is put together. Now find out how matter is connected to other subjects and places around the world.

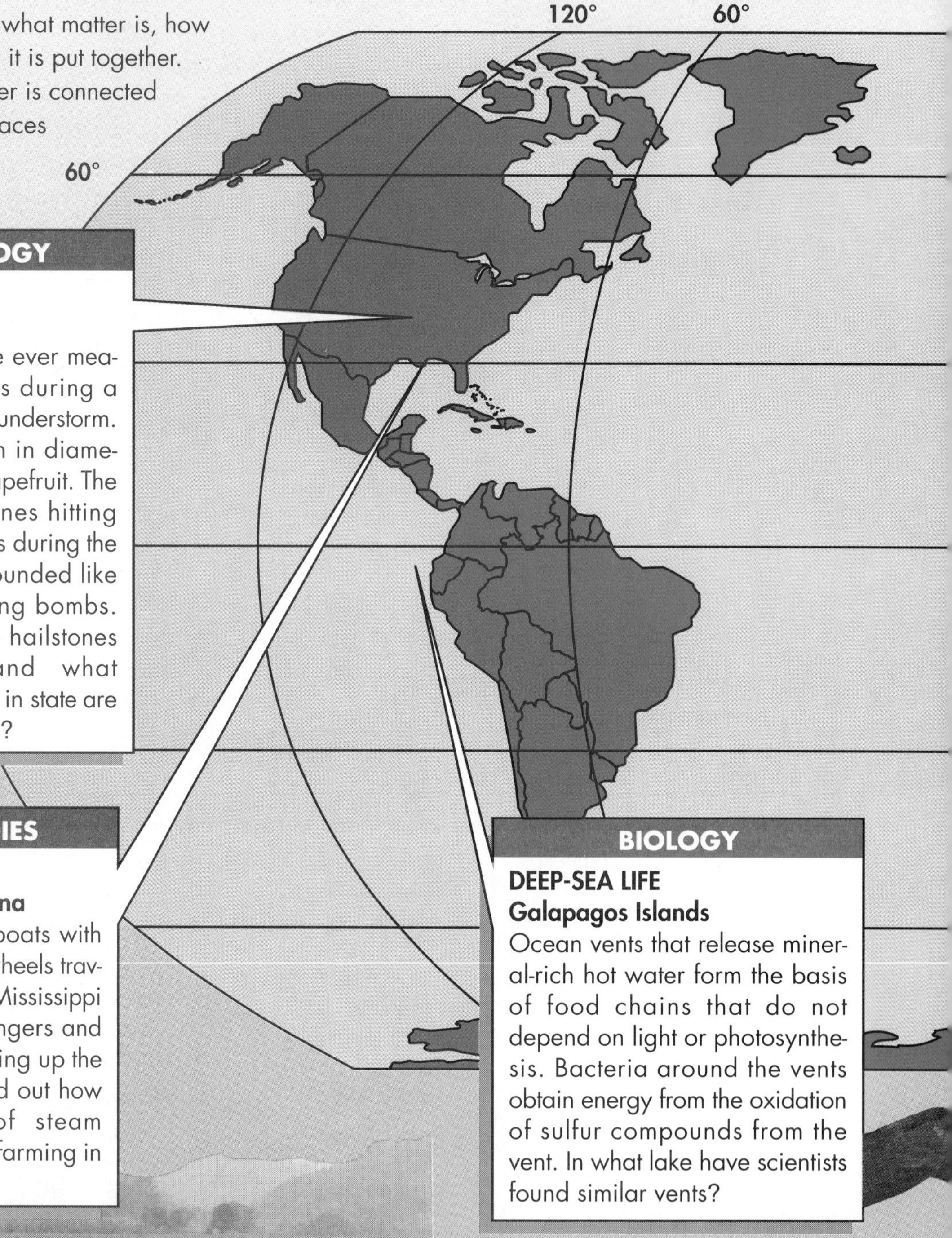

120° 60° 60°

METEOROLOGY

THE SKY IS FALLING
Central Kansas

The largest hailstone ever measured fell in Kansas during a September, 1970, thunderstorm. It was almost 14 cm in diameter—the size of a grapefruit. The noise of the hailstones hitting buildings during the storm sounded like exploding bombs. How do hailstones form and what changes in state are involved?

SOCIAL STUDIES

STEAM POWER
New Orleans, Louisiana

By the early 1900s, boats with steam-driven paddle wheels traveled the length of the Mississippi River, carrying passengers and farm goods and opening up the frontier to settlers. Find out how the development of steam engines also affected farming in the Midwest.

BIOLOGY

DEEP-SEA LIFE
Galapagos Islands

Ocean vents that release mineral-rich hot water form the basis of food chains that do not depend on light or photosynthesis. Bacteria around the vents obtain energy from the oxidation of sulfur compounds from the vent. In what lake have scientists found similar vents?

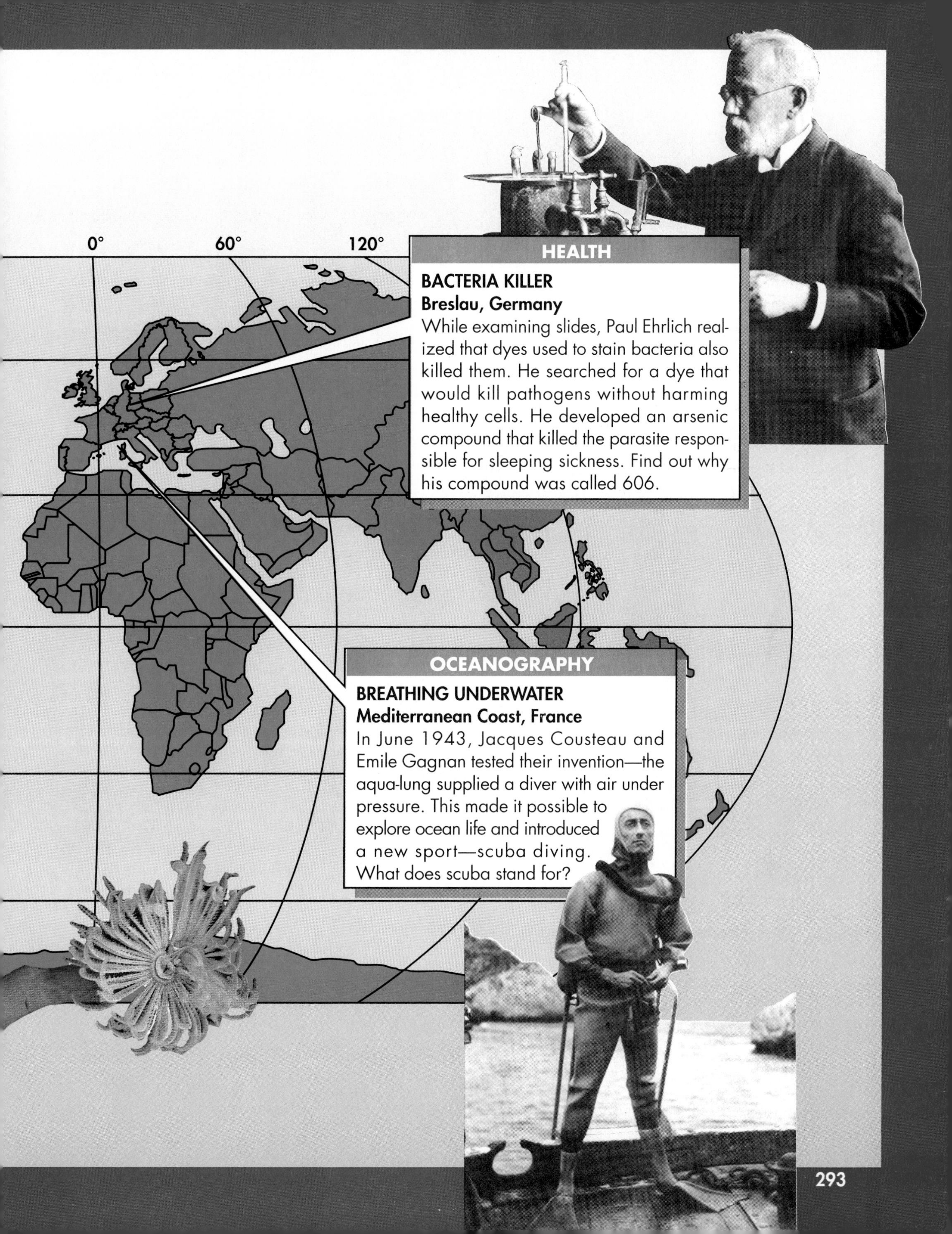

HEALTH

BACTERIA KILLER
Breslau, Germany

While examining slides, Paul Ehrlich realized that dyes used to stain bacteria also killed them. He searched for a dye that would kill pathogens without harming healthy cells. He developed an arsenic compound that killed the parasite responsible for sleeping sickness. Find out why his compound was called 606.

OCEANOGRAPHY

BREATHING UNDERWATER
Mediterranean Coast, France

In June 1943, Jacques Cousteau and Emile Gagnan tested their invention—the aqua-lung supplied a diver with air under pressure. This made it possible to explore ocean life and introduced a new sport—scuba diving. What does scuba stand for?

CAREERS

HYDRAULIC ENGINEER

Hydraulic engineers use a knowledge of fluids to design bridges and dams. They must study bodies of water to find out about drainage and water supplies. They also need to know how a bridge or dam will be affected by the normal water pressure, as well as extra pressure exerted by water from heavy storms. Hydraulic engineers must be sure that the structures they design will not collapse after a storm.

If you're interested in becoming a hydraulic engineer you should like working with measurements, formulas, statistics, and graphs. In high school, you should take math, physics, and chemistry classes. Hydraulic engineers have at least a bachelor's degree, and many have advanced degrees.

For Additional Information

Contact the American Society of Civil Engineers, 345 E. 47th Street, New York, New York 10017.

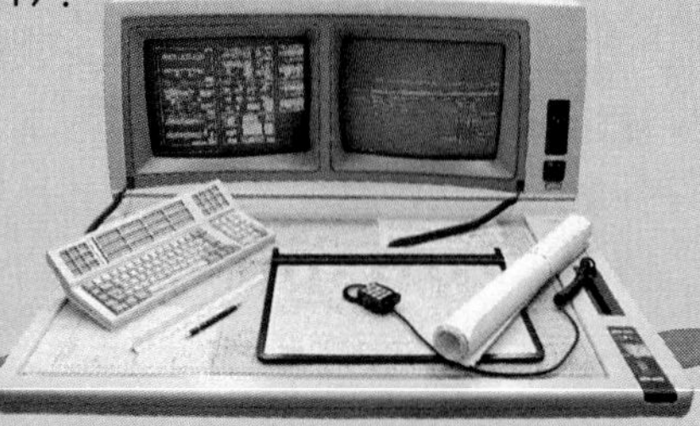

CHEMISTRY TEACHER

A *chemistry teacher* works with students to help them learn about chemistry and how it is a part of their everyday lives. Chemistry teachers must make daily lesson plans, set up laboratory activities, demonstrate experiments, and work with students having different backgrounds and interests.

If you're interested in becoming a chemistry teacher, you should enjoy math and science classes, and should like working with young people. Many colleges and universities offer programs for bachelor's and master's degrees in chemical education.

For Additional Information

Contact the National Science Teachers Association, 1742 Connecticut Avenue, NW, Washington, DC 10009-1171.

UNIT READINGS

- Hamilton, J.H. and Maruhn, J.A. "Exotic Atomic Nuclei." *Scientific American,* July, 1986, pp. 80-89.
- Maxwell, James C. *Maxwell on Molecules and Gases.* Cambridge, MA: MIT Press, 1986.
- Sprackling, Michael. *Liquids and Solids.* New York: Methuen, 1985.

SCIENCE & LITERATURE

Connections

by James Burke

The passage that follows describes the invention of the barometer.

In June 1644, Torricelli wrote to a colleague and friend in Rome, Michelangelo Ricci, to explain an experiment carried out by his own assistant Vincenzo Viviani, to which he added drawings in the margin. Viviani had filled a 6-foot long tube with mercury and upended it in a dish full of the same metal, with the open end of the tube beneath the surface of the mercury in the dish. When he took his finger away from the open end of the tube, the mercury in it ran out into the dish, but stopped when the mercury column left in the tube was still about 30 inches above the dish. Torricelli reasoned that the weight of the air pressing on the mercury in the dish had to be exactly equal to the weight of the mercury left in the tube. If there were no weight of air, all the mercury in the tube would have run out into the dish. If this were so, he wrote, "we live submerged at the bottom of an ocean of air." What was more, in the space at the top of the tube left by the mercury was the thing thought to be impossible: a vacuum. Torricelli wrote that if he was right, the pressure of the air in our atmospheric ocean must vary according to how far up or down in the ocean we are.

Ricci, realizing that current church opinion in Rome would not take kindly to these arguments (since if they were true several things followed, such as the existence of interplanetary vacuum, with sun-orbiting planets), made a copy of Torricelli's letter and sent it to a priest in Paris, Father Marin Mersenne. . . . the first thing he did was send another copy of it to a friend who was interested in the same problem, the son of a Paris tax inspector, Blaise Pascal. Two years after receiving the letter (he had been busy meanwhile in the Paris gambling halls working on laws-of-chance mathematics) Pascal found himself in Rouen. It was here that he repeated Torricelli's experiment, to check it; only he did it full-scale, with water. Unfortunately he was in no position to check the second part of the argument—there were no mountains around Rouen. However, Pascal had a brother-in-law called Francois Perier who lived in central France, in Clermont Ferrand, which is surrounded by mountains. So Pascal wrote to Perier, asking him to take things to the next stage.

In Your Own Words

1. Pascal asked his brother-in-law, Perier, to take things to the next stage. If you had been Perier, what would you have done next?
2. How might Pascal's knowledge of Torricelli's barometer influenced him in his discovery of Pascal's principle?

UNIT

4 KINDS OF SUBSTANCES

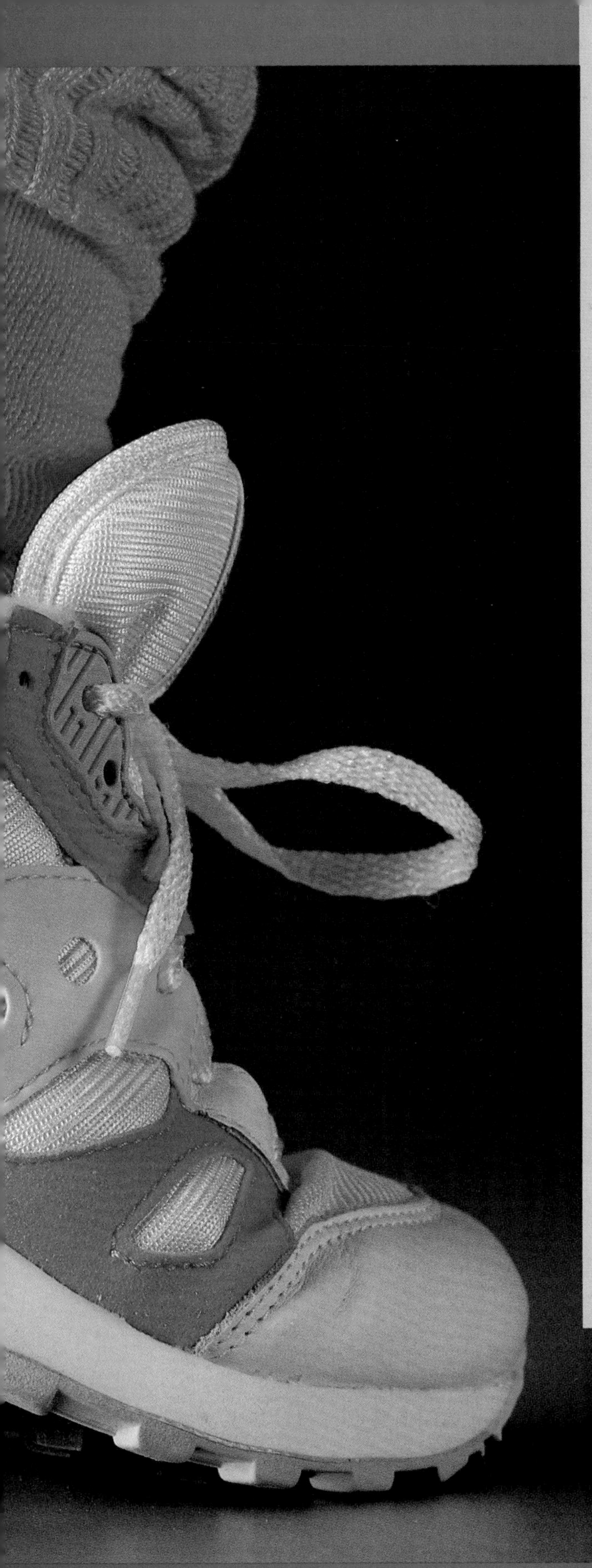

What's Happening Here?

Even after you think *you're* done with a piece of chewing gum, look again—it still has plenty of stretch and give for the shoe of the next passerby. Chewing gum gets its stretch from its structure—a special arrangement of atoms called a polymer. A gum drop model of the chewing gum polymer is shown below. In this unit you'll learn about polymers and many other kinds of substances—metal, nonmetal, organic, biological—and the special properties of each. But hey, next time put your gum in the trash.

UNIT CONTENTS

CHAPTER

12 Elements and Their Properties

Did you know that the Chinese invented fireworks hundreds of years ago? They used certain substances mixed with gunpowder —which they also invented—to produce colorful explosions.

FIND OUT!

In this activity, observe the colors some compounds give to a flame.

Using tongs, hold a clean paper clip in a flame until no color is added to the flame. Dip the paper clip in a solution of sodium chloride and hold it in the flame again. Observe and record the color produced. Repeat the procedure using strontium chloride, and again using copper(II) sulfate. How might you find out which element in each compound causes the color? Test your hypothesis. Besides fireworks, what do you think is another use for brightly colored flames?

Gearing Up

Previewing the Chapter

Use this outline to help you focus on important ideas in this chapter.

Previewing Science Skills

- In the **Skill Builders,** you will interpret scientific illustrations, make and use a graph, and make a concept map.
- In the **Activities,** you will observe, classify, predict, infer, and build a model.
- In the **MINI-Lab,** you will observe and draw a conclusion.

What's next?

Read Chapter 12 to learn more about elements that give colors to flames. You will also study other properties of elements.

12-1 Metals

New Science Words

malleable
ductile
metallic bonding
radioactive element
transition elements

Objectives

- Describe the properties of a typical metal.
- Identify the alkali and alkaline earth metals.
- Differentiate among three groups of transition elements.

Properties of Metals

Have you ever seen very old jewelry or statues made of gold and copper? These were the two first metals that people discovered, thousands of years ago. The use of silver and tin soon followed. Then came iron. But aluminum—the metal used in your soft drink cans—wasn't discovered until a little more than 100 years ago.

Gold, copper, silver, tin, iron, and aluminum are typical metals. What do these and other metals have in common? Most metals are hard, shiny solids. Metals are also good conductors of both heat and electricity. These properties make metals suitable for uses ranging from kitchen pots and pans to wires for electric appliances. Because metals reflect light well, they are used in mirrors. Metals are **malleable,** which means they can be hammered or rolled into sheets. Metals are also **ductile,** which means they can be drawn into a wire.

Figure 12-1. Gold is so malleable it can be rolled into thin sheets. Very thin gold sheets, called gold leaf, can be used to plate domes.

Figure 12-2. Metals are ductile, which means they can be drawn into a wire.

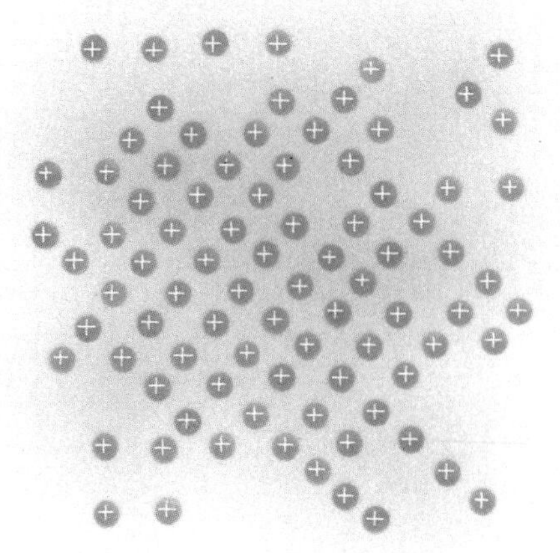

Figure 12-3. In metallic bonding, an electron cloud surrounds positively charged ions.

The atoms of metals generally have from one to three electrons in their outer energy levels. Metals tend to give up electrons easily. Remember from Chapter 11 what happens when metals combine with nonmetals. The atoms of the metals tend to lose electrons to the atoms of nonmetals, forming ionic bonds. The other type of bond you have studied is the covalent bond, which generally forms between atoms of nonmetals.

A third type of bonding, neither ionic nor covalent, occurs among the atoms in a metal. In **metallic bonding,** positively charged metallic ions are surrounded by a "sea of electrons." Outer level electrons are not held tightly to their particular nucleus. Rather, the electrons move freely among many positively charged ions. The electrons form a cloud around the ions of the metal as shown in Figure 12-3.

Metallic bonding explains many of the properties of metals. For example, when a metal is hammered or drawn into a wire, it does not break because the ions are in layers that slide past one another. And because the outer level electrons are free to move, metals are good conductors of electricity.

Look at the periodic table on pages 258-259. How many of the elements in the table are classified as metals? Except for hydrogen, all the elements in Groups 1 through 12 are metals. You will read about metals in some of these groups in this section. Some other metals are discussed in later sections.

MINI-Lab

How is metallic bonding related to the flexibility of a metal?

Carefully, using tongs, hold two pieces of thin wire in a flame until they are red hot. Drop one wire into a beaker of cold water. Let the other wire slowly cool. Be sure both wires cool to room temperature. Try to quickly bend both pieces of wire. What do you observe about the flexibility of the wires? How can metallic bonding be used to explain what you observe?

1
3 **Li** Lithium 6.941
11 **Na** Sodium 22.98977
19 **K** Potassium 39.0983
37 **Rb** Rubidium 85.4678
55 **Cs** Cesium 132.9054
87 **Fr** Francium 223.0197*

The Alkali Metals

The elements in Group 1 of the periodic table are the alkali metals. Like metals generally, these metals are shiny, malleable, and ductile. They are good conductors of both heat and electricity. The alkali metals are the most highly reactive of all metals. For this reason, they are found in nature only in the combined state.

Each atom of an alkali metal has one electron in its outer energy level. This electron is given up when an alkali metal combines. The result is a positively charged ion in a compound such as sodium chloride, NaCl, or potassium bromide, KBr. As shown in Figure 12-4, you can use flame tests to identify compounds of alkali metals.

Alkali metals and their compounds have many and varied uses. You and other living things need potassium and sodium compounds—such as table salt, NaCl—to stay healthy. Doctors use lithium compounds to treat manic-depressive disease. The operation of some photocells depends upon rubidium or cesium compounds.

Francium, the last element in Group 1, is radioactive. The nucleus of a **radioactive element** breaks down and gives off particles, radiation, and large amounts of energy. You will study radioactive elements later.

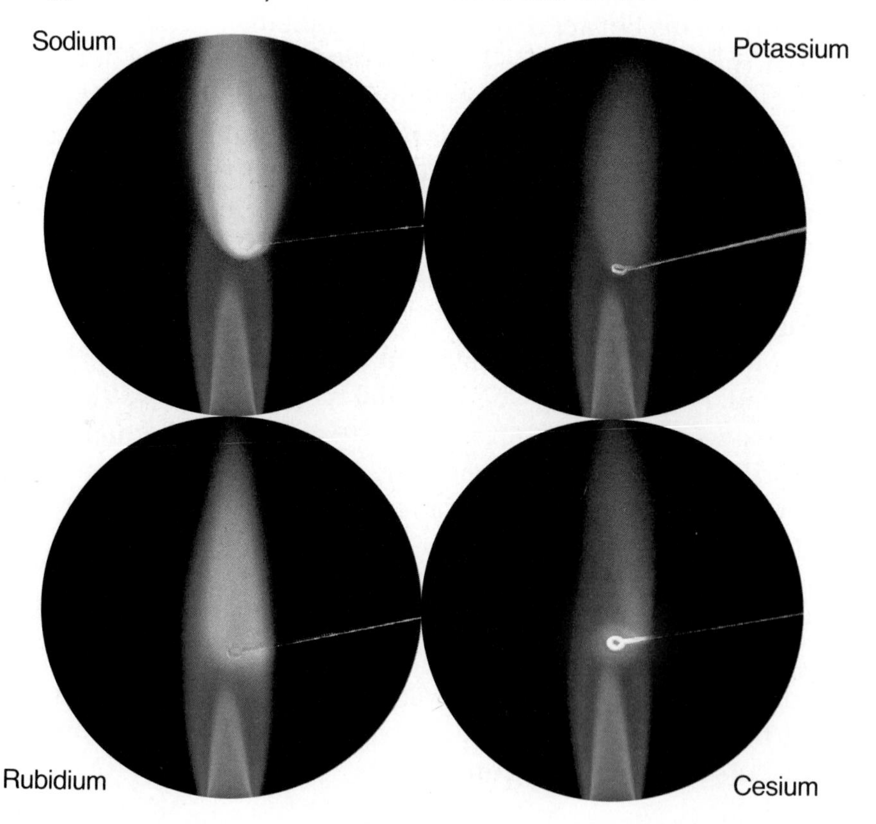

Figure 12-4. Alkali metals and their compounds give distinctive colors to flames.

The Alkaline Earth Metals

2
4 **Be** Beryllium 9.01218
12 **Mg** Magnesium 24.305
20 **Ca** Calcium 40.078
38 **Sr** Strontium 87.62
56 **Ba** Barium 137.33
88 **Ra** Radium 226.0254

The alkaline earth metals make up Group 2 of the periodic table. Like the alkali metals, these metals are shiny, malleable, ductile, and so reactive that they are not found free in nature. Each atom of an alkaline earth metal has two electrons in its outer energy level. These electrons are given up when an alkaline earth metal combines. The result is a positively charged ion in a compound such as calcium fluoride, CaF_2, or barium chloride, $BaCl_2$.

Emeralds and aquamarines are gemstone forms of beryl, a mineral that contains beryllium. Do you watch fireworks on the Fourth of July? The brilliant red in fireworks is produced by compounds of strontium.

Magnesium can be made into a ribbon that burns so brightly that it is used in some photographic flashbulbs. Magnesium metal is also used in fireworks to produce brilliant white. Magnesium's lightness and strength account for its use in cars, planes, and spacecraft. Magnesium is also used to make such things as household ladders and baseball and softball bats.

Calcium is almost never used as a free metal, but its compounds are needed for life. Calcium carbonate in your bones helps make them strong. Marble and lime-

Figure 12-5. Bones contain calcium carbonate (a); magnesium burns easily (b); and magnesium is used in bats (c).

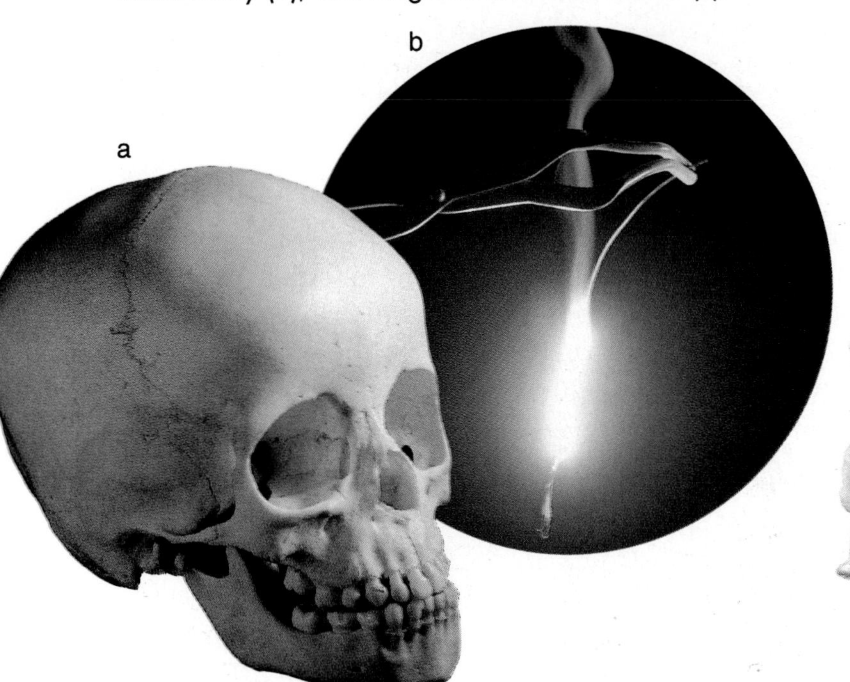

What metal is part of the compound chlorophyll?

stone are calcium carbonate. Most life on Earth depends upon chlorophyll, a magnesium compound that enables plants to make food.

Some barium compounds are used to diagnose digestive disorders. The patient swallows a barium compound, which absorbs X rays. As the barium compound goes through the digestive tract, a doctor can study the X rays. Radium, the last element in Group 2, is radioactive. It was once used to treat cancers. Today, other radioactive substances are replacing radium in cancer therapy.

Transition Elements

An iron nail, a copper wire, and a silver dime are examples of objects made from transition elements. The **transition elements** are those elements in Groups 3 through 12 of the periodic table. Typical transition elements are metals and have one or two electrons in the outer energy level. These metals are less active than those in Groups 1 and 2.

Many gems contain brightly colored compounds of transition elements. Brilliant cadmium yellow and cobalt blue paints are made from compounds of transition elements. But cadmium and cobalt paints are so toxic that their use is now limited.

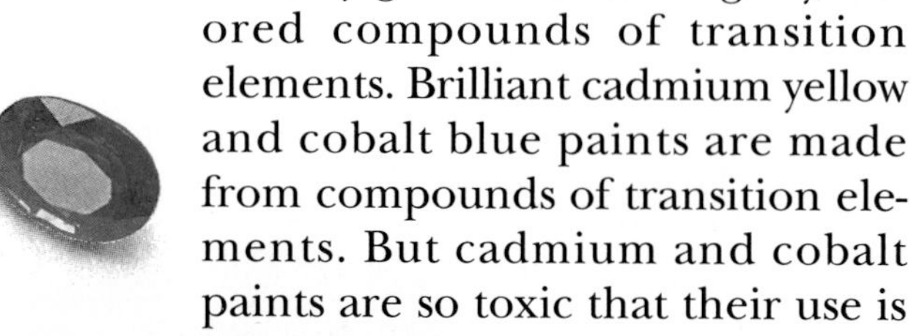

Figure 12-6. The colors of these gems are due to compounds of transition elements.

Iron, Cobalt, and Nickel

Which elements are able to create a magnetic field?

Iron, cobalt, and nickel form an unusual cluster of transition elements. The first elements in Groups 8, 9, and 10, respectively, these three metals are known as the iron triad. The iron triad elements are the only substances known to create a magnetic field.

25 Mn Manganese 54.9380	26 Fe Iron 55.847	27 Co Cobalt 58.9332	28 Ni Nickel 58.69	29 Cu Copper 63.546
43 Tc Technetium 97.9072*	44 Ru Ruthenium 101.07	45 Rh Rhodium 102.9055	46 Pd Pallidium 106.42	47 Ag Silver 107.8682

Iron is second only to aluminum among the metals in abundance in Earth's crust. As the main component of steel, iron is the most widely used of all metals. Some steels also contain cobalt. Nickel is added to other metals to give them strength. Nickel is also often used to give a shiny, protective coating to other metals, as shown in the picture above.

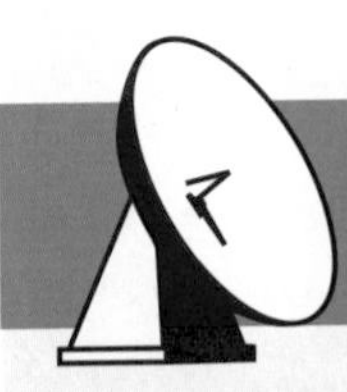

TECHNOLOGY

Metallic Moments

A large radio antenna was folded into a compact shape and launched into space. Once in orbit it absorbed heat from the sun and unfolded as a working antenna! This antenna was made of Nitinol, a mixture of nickel and titanium.

Nitinol is one of a class of metal mixtures, or alloys, that is able to remember an earlier shape. About 20 of the transition elements can form shape memory alloys (SMAs). If you bend and then heat an object made from an SMA, it returns to its original shape. Products made from SMAs include eyeglass frames, orthodontic wires, and electrical connectors.

Because SMAs absorb heat and convert it to mechanical energy, they are used in heat engines. A device that delivers small doses of medication into veins uses SMA power.

Think Critically: Elements that can form SMAs are found in Groups 3 through 12 of the periodic table. What are some other common properties of these elements?

Copper, Silver, and Gold

11

29
Cu
Copper
63.546

47
Ag
Silver
107.8682

79
Au
Gold
196.9665

Can you name the main metals in the coins in the photograph below? They are copper, silver, and gold, the three elements in Group 11. They are so unreactive that they are found as elements in nature. For centuries, these metals have been widely used as coins. For this reason, they are known as the coinage metals.

Copper is often used in electric wiring, because of its superior ability to conduct electricity and its low cost. Can you imagine a world without photographs and movies? Because silver iodide and silver bromide break down when exposed to light, these compounds are used to make photographic film and paper. Much silver is also used in jewelry. The yellow color, relative softness, and rarity of gold account for its use in jewelry.

Zinc, Cadmium, and Mercury

12

30
Zn
Zinc
65.39

48
Cd
Cadmium
112.41

80
Hg
Mercury
200.59

Zinc, cadmium, and mercury make up Group 12 of the periodic table. Zinc combines with oxygen in the air to form a thin protective coating of zinc oxide on the surface of the metal. Zinc is often used to coat, or plate, other metals, such as iron. Cadmium is also used in plating and in rechargeable batteries.

Mercury is a silvery, liquid metal used in thermometers, thermostats, switches, and batteries. Mercury is poisonous, and mercury compounds may accumulate in the body. People have died of mercury poisoning that resulted from eating fish from mercury-contaminated water.

Figure 12-7. Mercury is liquid at room temperature (left). Metallic copper is found in nature (right).

Look again at the periodic table on pages 258-259. Which elements do you think of when you think of typical metals? Probably transition elements, such as iron or copper. The reason is that Group 1 and Group 2 metals are not found in nature except in compounds. But many transition elements occur in nature as elements, and thus are the most familiar metals.

Why are transition metals more familiar than Group 1 and Group 2 metals?

SECTION REVIEW

1. You are given a piece of the element palladium. How would you test it to see if it is a metal?
2. On the periodic table, how does the arrangement of the iron triad differ from the arrangements of the coinage metals and of the zinc group?
3. **Apply:** If X stands for a metal, how can you tell from the formulas XCl and XCl_2 which compound contains an alkali metal and which contains an alkaline earth metal?

Interpreting Scientific Illustrations

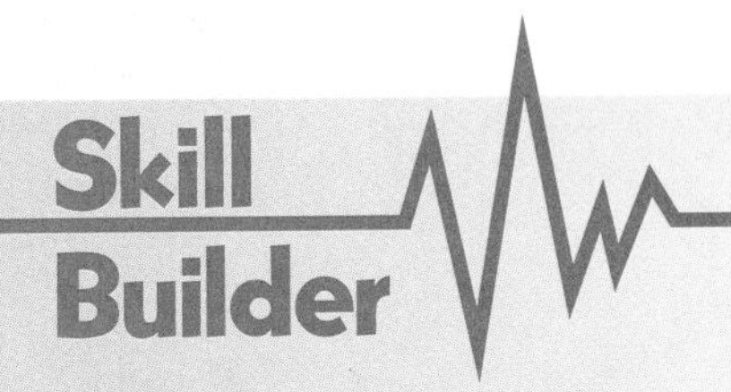

Draw dot diagrams to show the similarity among chlorides of three alkali metals: lithium chloride, sodium chloride, and potassium chloride. If you need help, refer to Interpreting Scientific Illustrations in the **Skill Handbook** on page 689.

12-2 Synthetic Elements

New Science Words

transuranium element

Objectives

- **Distinguish among elements classified as lanthanoids, actinoids, and transuranium elements.**
- **Compare the pros and cons of making synthetic elements.**

Why Make Synthetic Elements?

What synthetic element is used in smoke alarms?

Did you know that the smoke alarm in your home may contain americium? This element does not form naturally. Because it can be made only in a laboratory, americium is called a synthetic element. There are 19 synthetic elements. One of these, technetium, is a period-5 transition metal. The other synthetic elements are found in periods 6 and 7.

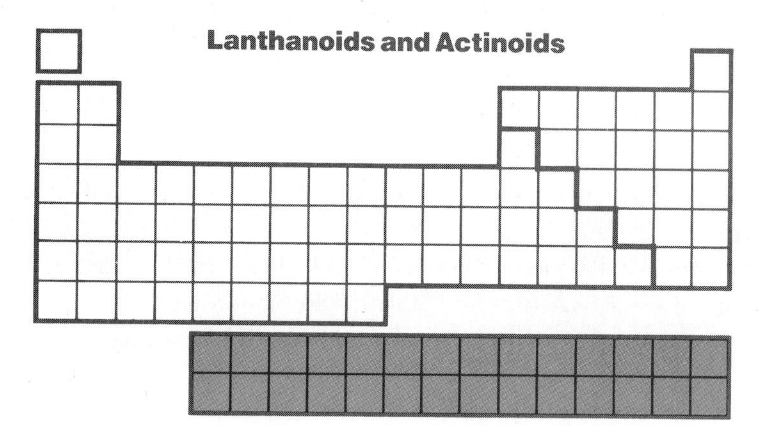

If you look at the periodic table on pages 258-259, you will see breaks in periods 6 and 7. The first break includes a series of 14 elements with atomic numbers of 57 through 70. The second break include those elements with atomic numbers ranging from 89 to 102. The two series include elements that have similar electron structures and similar properties. They also include many synthetic elements.

The picture tube in your color TV contains pigments that glow bright red when struck by electrons. These pigments are oxides of europium and ytterbium, two lanthanoids. A lanthanoid is an element with an atomic number of 57-70. The lanthanoid series contains one synthetic element, promethium, used to power pacemakers and artificial hearts.

Americium is one of the ten synthetic elements in the actinoid series. An actinoid is an element with an atomic number of 89-102. One important actinoid you may have heard of is uranium.

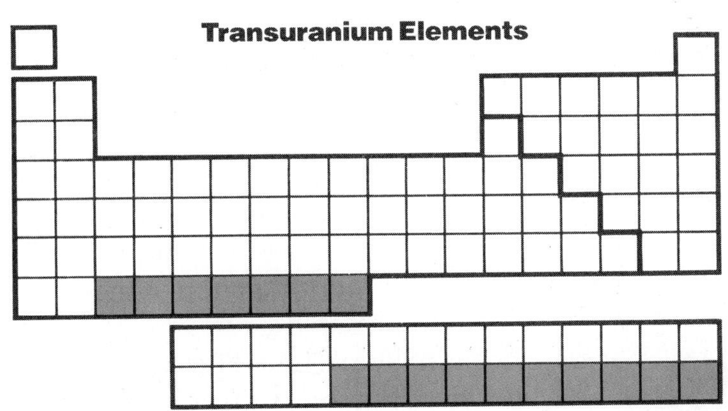

All elements with atomic numbers higher than that of uranium are synthetic elements called transuranium elements. A **transuranium element** has an atomic number greater than 92. One of these is plutonium.

Plutonium has been used in nuclear reactors and in nuclear warheads. Because it is the most poisonous substance known, its production has been banned. Other transuranium elements in the actinoid series are used as nuclear energy sources for generating electric power and in nuclear weapons. However, like all synthetic elements, they are radioactive and some can be very harmful.

The other transuranium elements are presently being used to research the structure of matter. Perhaps these elements will provide future sources of energy.

SECTION REVIEW

1. Compare the lanthanoid and actinoid series.
2. What are the transuranium elements?

EcoTip

The amount of hazardous waste produced each year in the United States is equal to the weight of a car for each U.S. citizen.

You Decide!

Plutonium was banned after much debate. Suppose you had to vote on a petition to ban the production of another synthetic element. What information would you want to help you decide how to vote?

12-3 Nonmetals

New Science Words

diatomic molecule
sublimation

Objectives

- **Recognize hydrogen as a typical nonmetal.**
- **Compare and contrast properties of the halogens.**
- **Describe properties and uses of the noble gases.**

Properties of Nonmetals

Figure 12-8 shows that you're mostly made of oxygen, carbon, hydrogen, and nitrogen. Calcium, a metal, and other elements make up the remaining four percent of your body's weight. Phosphorus, sulfur, and chlorine are among other elements found in your body. These elements are among those classified as nonmetals.

Look at the periodic table on pages 258 and 259. How many elements are nonmetals? Notice that most nonmetals are gases at room temperature. Several nonmetals are solids, and one nonmetal is a liquid.

In contrast to metals, solid nonmetals are dull. Because they are brittle and powdery, they are neither malleable nor ductile. The electrons in nonmetals are tightly held and are not free to move as in metals. So nonmetals are poor conductors of heat and electricity.

Most nonmetals form both ionic and covalent compounds. When nonmetals gain electrons from metals, the nonmetals become negative ions in ionic compounds. An example is potassium

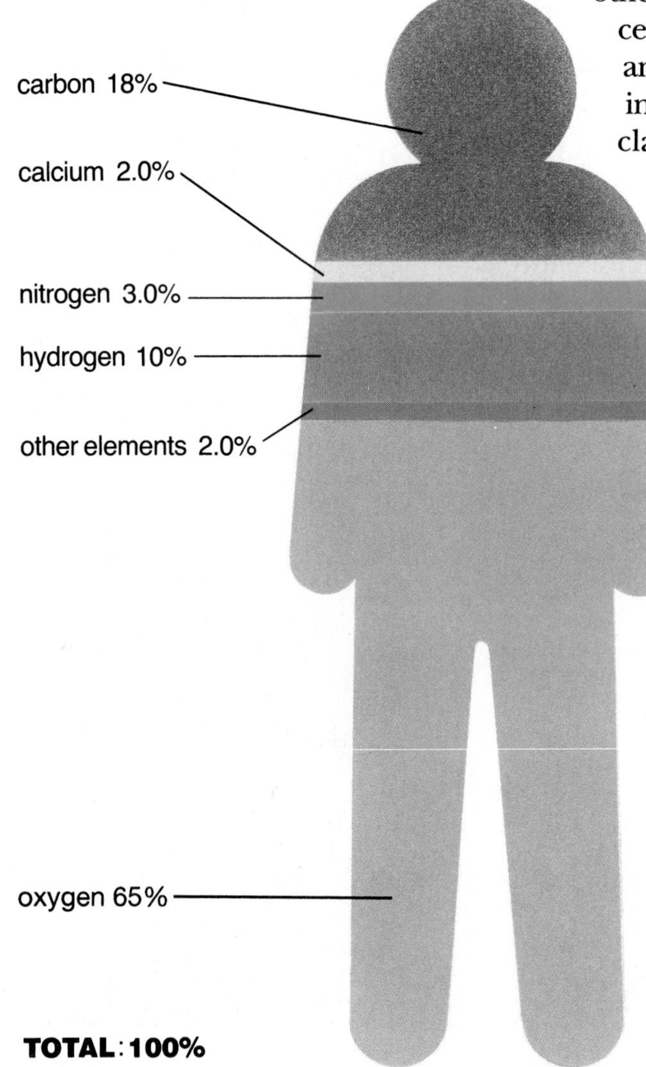

Figure 12-8. Most of your body weight consists of compounds of nonmetals.

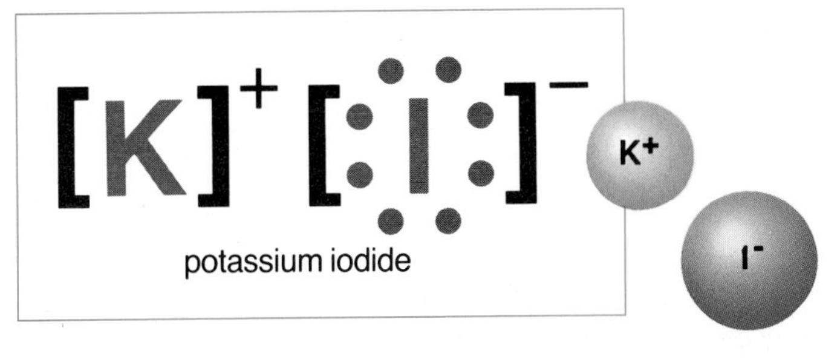

Figure 12-9. Nonmetals form both ionic and covalent compounds.

iodide, KI, which is found in iodized table salt. KI is formed from the nonmetal iodine and the metal potassium. On the other hand, when bonded with other nonmetals, atoms of nonmetals usually share electrons and form covalent compounds. An example is ammonia, NH_3, the gas you may smell when you open a bottle of household ammonia.

The noble gases, Group 18, make up the only group of elements that are all nonmetals. Group 17 elements, except for astatine, are also nonmetals. Several other nonmetals, found in Groups 13 through 16, will be discussed later. Except for hydrogen, all of the nonmetals are located on the right side of the periodic table.

Figure 12-10. Hydrogen gas, which consists of diatomic molecules, combines with oxygen in an oxyhydrogen torch.

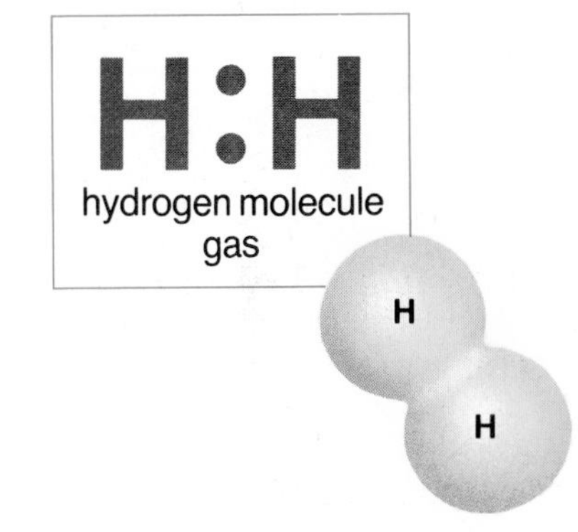

Hydrogen

Do you know that 90 percent of all the atoms in the universe are hydrogen? Most hydrogen on Earth is found in the compound water. When water is broken down into its elements, hydrogen forms as a gas made up of diatomic molecules. A **diatomic molecule** consists of two atoms of the same element. Thus, the formula for hydrogen gas is H_2.

Hydrogen is highly reactive. A hydrogen atom has a single electron, which the atom shares when it combines with other nonmetals. Hydrogen burns in oxygen to form water, H_2O. In forming water, hydrogen shares electrons with oxygen. Hydrogen also shares electrons with chlorine to produce hydrogen chloride, HCl.

Hydrogen may gain an electron when it combines with alkali and alkaline earth metals. The compounds formed are hydrides, such as sodium hydride, NaH.

17
9 **F** Fluorine 18.998403
17 **Cl** Chlorine 35.453
35 **Br** Bromine 79.904
53 **I** Iodine 126.9045
85 **At** Astatine 209.98712*

The Halogens

Look how bright these high-tech lamps are in Figure 12-11. Their light and that of the headlights of some cars is supplied by halogen light bulbs. You may have seen these bulbs. They contain small amounts of bromine or iodine. These elements, as well as fluorine and chlorine, are called halogens and are found in Group 17.

Figure 12-11. The halogens bromine and iodine are used in the bulbs of halogen lamps such as these.

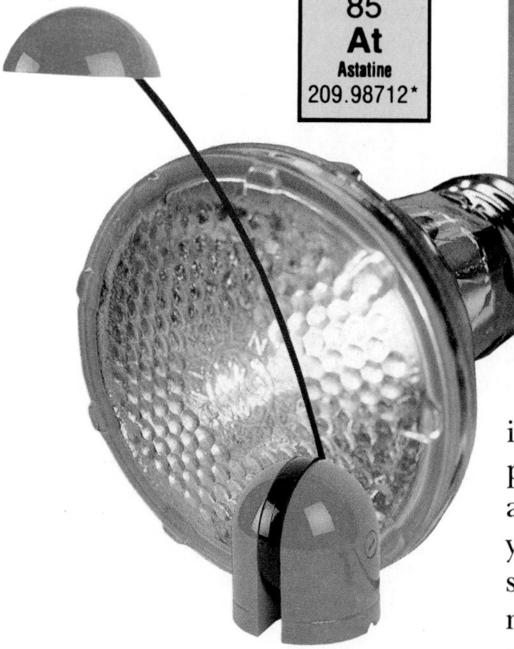

Because an atom of a halogen has seven electrons in its outer energy level, only one electron is needed to complete this energy level. If a halogen gains an electron from a metal, an ionic compound, called a salt, is formed. As you recall, sodium chloride, or table salt, is formed from sodium and chlorine. The word *halogen* means "salt former." In the gaseous state, the halogens form diatomic covalent molecules and can be identified by their distinctive colors.

Fluorine is the most chemically active of all the elements. Hydrofluoric acid, a mixture of hydrogen fluoride and water, is used to etch glass and to "frost" the inner surfaces of light bulbs. Other fluorides are added to toothpastes and to city water systems to prevent tooth decay. Does your community add fluorides to its water?

Figure 12-12. In the gaseous state, the halogens chlorine, bromine, and iodine have distinctive colors.

Are you familiar with the harsh odor near swimming pools? It's the odor of chlorine. Chlorine compounds are used to disinfect the water in these pools. Chlorine, the most abundant halogen, is obtained from seawater. Household bleach and industrial bleaches used to whiten flour and paper contain chlorine compounds.

Bromine, the only nonmetal that is liquid at room temperature, is extracted from compounds in seawater. Other bromine compounds are used as dyes in cosmetics.

Iodine, a shiny gray solid, is obtained from brine. When heated, iodine changes directly to a purple vapor. The process of a solid changing directly to a vapor without forming a liquid is called **sublimation.** Recall that sublimation accounts for ice cubes shrinking in freezers. Iodine is essential in your diet to prevent goiter, an enlarging of the thyroid gland in the neck.

As you have read, both silver iodide and silver bromide are also used to produce photographic paper and film.

Astatine, the last member of Group 17, is radioactive and very rare. But it has many properties similar to those of the other halogens.

Figure 12-13. Dyes in some cosmetics contain bromine compounds.

18
2 **He** Helium 4.002602
10 **Ne** Neon 20.179
18 **Ar** Argon 39.948
36 **Kr** Krypton 83.80
54 **Xe** Xenon 131.29
86 **Rn** Radon 222.017*

The Noble Gases

Why are the noble gases called "noble"? It was known that these gases did not naturally form compounds. Thus, they were thought of as the nobility of elements, because nobles did not mix with common folk. Scientists were later able to prepare some compounds of noble gases.

Figure 12-14. "Neon" signs contain several noble gases.

Figure 12-15. Noble gases are used in laser light shows.

As you recall, each element in Group 18 is stable because its outer energy level has eight electrons, except helium, which has two electrons. The stability of the noble gases plays an important role in their uses, such as those shown in Figures 12-14 and 12-15.

What are some uses of the noble gases?

Both the halogens and the noble gases illustrate the family relationships in vertical columns of the periodic table. Each element in a group, or family, has some similar properties. But each element also has unique properties and uses.

SECTION REVIEW

1. What are two ways in which hydrogen combines with other elements?
2. Compare bromine to the other halogens.
3. What property of noble gases makes them useful?
4. **Apply:** Why must hydrofluoric acid always be stored in plastic bottles?

Making and Using Graphs

Prepare a bar graph comparing nonmetals and metals as solids, liquids, and gases at room temperature. If you need help, refer to Making and Using Graphs in the **Skill Handbook** on page 687.

ACTIVITY 12-1
Nonmetal Reaction

Problem: *How can oxygen be produced from a common substance?*

Materials   

- large test tube
- large wooden match
- 20 mL liquid laundry bleach (5% sodium hypochlorite)
- 0.5 g cobalt chloride
- goggles

Procedure

1. Put on safety goggles.
2. Carefully pour about 20 mL of liquid laundry bleach into a large test tube.
3. Add about 0.5 g of cobalt chloride to the bleach.
4. A gas will start to form in the liquid. Place your thumb loosely over the opening of the tube until you feel some slight pressure, but do not attempt to prevent the escape of the gas from the tube.
5. Have a classmate carefully bring a lighted match near the opening of the tube.
6. Blow out the flame of the match and insert the glowing end of the match into the upper half of the tube.

Analyze

1. An increase in the amount of oxygen in a container can cause a glowing match to burst into flame. Were the bubbles given off in your tube oxygen? Explain your answer.
2. Look at the formula for sodium hypochlorite present in bleach, NaClO. What two nonmetals does this compound contain?

Conclude and Apply

3. Liquid bleach is sometimes used as a disinfectant in kitchens. As the sodium hypochlorite in bleach decomposes, or breaks down, what product do you predict might appear?
4. Sunlight can also decompose hypochlorite. Examine the materials used to make containers of different sizes and brands of bleach. In what way are the containers all alike? Suggest a reason for this similarity.

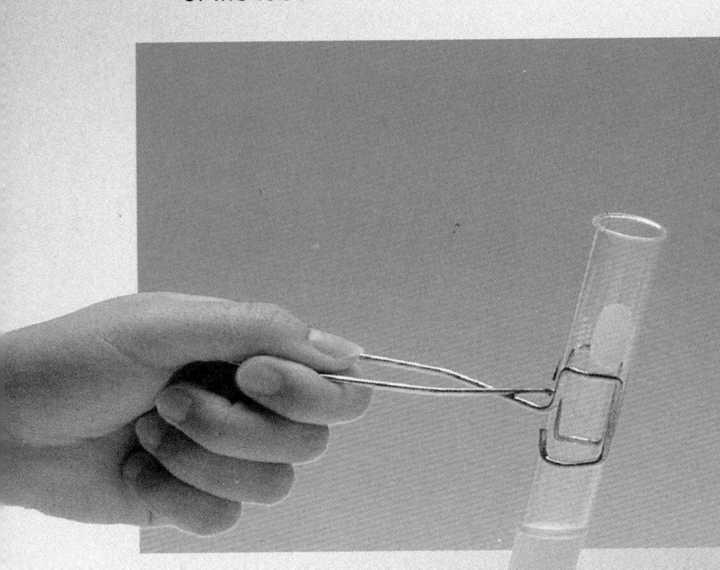

12-4 Mixed Groups

New Science Words

semiconductors
allotropes

Objectives

- Distinguish among metals, nonmetals, and metalloids in Groups 13 through 16 of the periodic table.
- Describe the nature of allotropes.
- Recognize the significance of differences in crystal structure in carbon.

Locating the Mixed Groups

What kind of properties do metalloids have?

Can an element be both a metal and a nonmetal? In a sense, some elements are. They are the metalloids, which have both metallic and nonmetallic properties. A metalloid may conduct electricity better than a nonmetal but not as well as a metal. In the periodic table on pages 258-259 the metalloids are the elements located along the stair-step line. The mixed groups—13, 14, 15, and 16—contain some metals, some nonmetals, and some metalloids.

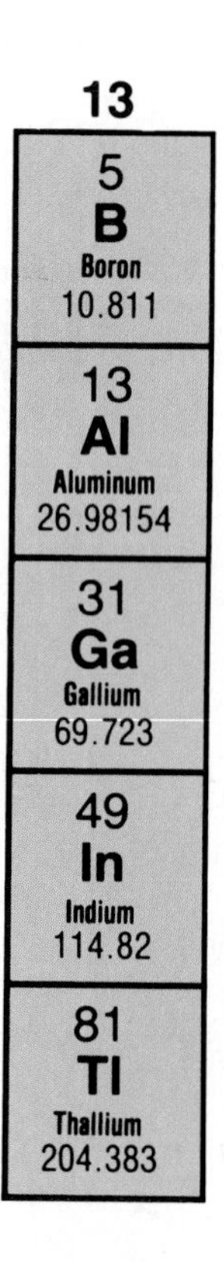

The Boron Group

Boron, a metalloid, is the first element in Group 13. If you look around your home, you may find two compounds of boron. One of these is boric acid, a mild antiseptic. The other is borax, used in laundry products to soften water. Less familiar are the boranes, compounds of boron used in fuels for rockets and jet planes.

Aluminum, a metal, is also in Group 13. Aluminum is the most abundant metal in Earth's crust. You use aluminum in soft drink cans, foil wrap, and cooking pans. You may also see aluminum on the sides of buildings, where it's used because it doesn't rust. And because aluminum is both strong and light, it is used to build airplanes.

When you operate electronic equipment, such as calculators and computers, you may be using one of the other metals in Group 13. These metals are gallium, indium, and thallium, used in the electronics industry to

produce semiconductors. **Semiconductors** are substances that conduct an electric current under certain conditions. You will learn more about semiconductors in Chapter 23.

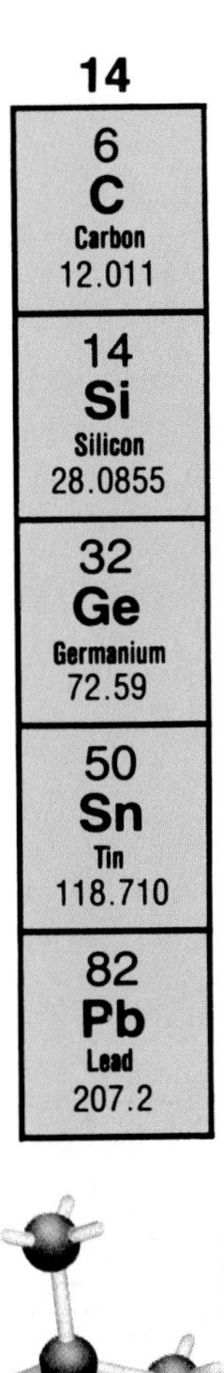

The Carbon Group

Each element in Group 14, the carbon family, has four electrons in its outer energy level. But here much of the similarity ends. Carbon is a nonmetal; silicon and germanium are metalloids; tin and lead are metals.

What do the diamond in a diamond ring and the graphite in your pencil lead have in common? It may surprise you to learn that they are both pure carbon. How can this be? Diamond and graphite are examples of allotropes. **Allotropes** are different forms of the same element having different molecular structures. Look at the diagrams below. Graphite is a black powder that consists of hexagonal layers of carbon atoms. In the hexagons,

Graphite

Diamond

PROBLEM SOLVING

The "Lead" in a Pencil

In a pencil factory, ground graphite crystals are mixed with clay to make the pencil "lead." The graphite-clay mixture is then shaped into long thin rods.

The rods are cut, dried, and heated. Grooves shaped to fit the rods are cut into half blocks of wood. The grooves are coated with glue, and then the rods are placed into the grooves. The other half of the block of wood is placed on the first half. After the glue has dried, the block is cut into individual pencils. After the pencils are painted, metal bands and erasers are added to make finished pencils.

Think Critically: What makes up the lead of a pencil? How do the amounts of graphite in hard (No. 3), medium (No. 2), and soft (No. 1) pencils compare? Explain your answer.

each carbon atom is bonded to three other carbon atoms. The fourth electron of each atom is bonded weakly to the layer below. This structure allows the layers to slide easily past one another, making graphite an excellent lubricant.

A diamond is clear and extremely hard. In a diamond, each carbon atom is bonded to four other carbon atoms at the vertices, or corner points, of a tetrahedron. In turn, many tetrahedrons join together to form a giant molecule in which the atoms are held tightly in a strong crystal structure. This structure accounts for the hardness of diamond. Look at the drawings of the structures of graphite and diamond on page 317. How are the structure and properties of diamond unlike those of graphite?

Carbon occurs as an element in coal and as compounds in oil, natural gas, and foods. Carbon in these materials may combine with oxygen to produce carbon dioxide, CO_2. Plants combine CO_2 with water to make food. In Chapter 13, you will study other carbon compounds—many essential to life.

Silicon is second only to oxygen in abundance in Earth's crust. Most silicon is found in sand, silicon dioxide, SiO_2,

Did You Know?

Synthetic diamonds, used extensively in industry, are made by subjecting graphite to extremely high pressure and temperature.

and in almost all rocks and soil. The crystal structure of silicon dioxide is similar to the tetrahedrons found in diamond. Silicon, too, occurs as two allotropes. One of these is a hard, gray substance, and the other is a brown powder.

What compound has a structure similar to that of diamond?

Figure 12-16. Most gasolines are no longer leaded (left). Pewter contains tin and other metals (right).

Both silicon and germanium, the other metalloid in the carbon group, are used in making semiconductors, which you'll learn about in Chapter 23. Tin and lead are typical metals. Tin is used to coat other metals to prevent corrosion. Tin is also combined with other metals to produce bronze and pewter. Lead was once used widely in paints and antiknock gasoline. But lead is poisonous, so it has been largely replaced in these materials.

The Nitrogen Group

The nitrogen family makes up Group 15. Each element has five electrons in its outer energy level. These elements tend to share electrons and to form covalent compounds with other elements.

Each breath you take is about 80 percent gaseous nitrogen, as diatomic molecules, N_2. If you look again at Figure 12-8 on page 310, you'll see that nitrogen is the element fourth in abundance in your body. Yet you and other animals and plants can't use nitrogen as N_2. The nitrogen must be combined into compounds, such as nitrates—compounds that contain the nitrate ion, (NO_3^-). Much nitrogen is used to make nitrates and ammonia, NH_3, both of which are used in fertilizers.

15
7 **N** Nitrogen 14.0067
15 **P** Phosphorus 30.97376
33 **As** Arsenic 74.9216
51 **Sb** Antimony 121.75
83 **Bi** Bismuth 208.9804

Phosphorus is a nonmetal. Uses of phosphorus compounds range from water softeners to fertilizers to match heads. Antimony is a metalloid, and bismuth is a metal. Both elements are used with other metals to lower their melting points. It is because of this property that the metal in automatic fire sprinkler heads contains bismuth.

16
8 **O** Oxygen 15.9994
16 **S** Sulfur 32.06
34 **Se** Selenium 78.96
52 **Te** Tellurium 127.60
84 **Po** Polonium 208.9824*

The Oxygen Group

The oxygen group makes up Group 16 on the periodic table. You can't live for more than a short time without the nonmetal oxygen, which makes up about 20 percent of the air. Oxygen exists in the air as diatomic molecules, O_2. During electric storms some oxygen molecules, O_2, change into ozone molecules, O_3. Do you see that O_2 and O_3 are allotropes?

Nearly all living things on Earth need free oxygen, as O_2, for respiration. Living things also depend on a layer of ozone, O_3, around Earth for protection from some of the sun's radiation, as you will learn in later chapters.

Sulfur is a nonmetal that can exist in several allotropes—as different-shaped crystals, as a noncrystalline solid, and in a liquid form. Sulfur combines with metals to form sulfides of such distinctive colors that they are used as pigments in paints.

Figure 12-17 Eight-sided and needlelike crystals are two of the allotropes of sulfur.

Figure 12-18. Selenium is one of several elements needed by the body in trace amounts.

The nonmetal selenium and two metalloids, tellurium and polonium, are the other Group 16 elements. Selenium is the most common of these. This element is one of several that you need in trace amounts in your diet. Larger amounts of selenium are toxic, however.

One thing is certain—your life would be impossible without the elements in the mixed groups. From oxygen, present in a large amount in your body, to selenium, present in a very minute amount, you are these elements.

Science and WRITING

Fluorescent lamps have been described as a major advantage in the energy conservation movement. Explain how they work and why they are so much better than the incandescent bulb.

SECTION REVIEW

1. Why are Groups 14 and 15 better representatives of mixed groups than Group 13 or Group 16?
2. How do the allotropes of sulfur differ?
3. Why is graphite a lubricant while a diamond is the hardest gem known?
4. **Apply:** Today aluminum is one of the most plentiful and least expensive of metals. Yet Napoleon III set the table for his most important guests with knives, forks, and spoons made of aluminum instead of silver or gold. Why?

Concept Mapping

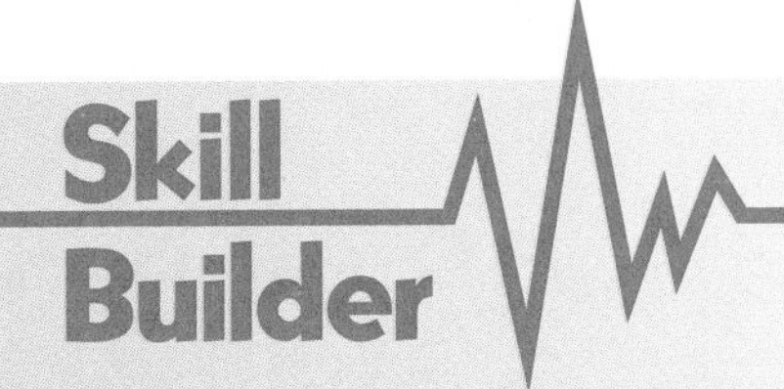

Make a concept map for allotropes of carbon, using the terms *graphite, diamond, hexagon,* and *tetrahedron.* If you need help, see Concept Mapping in the **Skill Handbook** on pages 684 and 685.

ACTIVITY 12-2
Carbon and Graphite

Problem: *Why can graphite be used as a lubricant?*

Materials
- nut and bolt
- powdered graphite
- 6 pieces of thin spaghetti
- polystyrene sheet
- marking pen

Procedure
1. Put together and then take apart a nut and bolt.
2. Coat the threads of the nut with powdered graphite, and then repeat Step 1.
3. Construct a model of graphite as follows. Cut out two polystyrene hexagons with sides about 10 cm long. Use a marking pen to label the intersections of sides with the letter *C*.
4. Insert six 10-cm pieces of thin spaghetti between the hexagons so that they pierce the letter *C* on each hexagon.
5. Set your finished two-layer model on your desk. Gently press down on the top layer and push the model forward.

Analyze
1. Compare your observations in Step 1 and Step 2. How do you account for any difference you noticed?
2. When you applied pressure to your model of graphite, what were the weakest parts of the structure?

Conclude and Apply
3. Your model represents the bonding of carbon in graphite. How is the way the spaghetti breaks related to the bond structure in graphite?
4. Why do the bonding and structure of graphite make it a good lubricant?

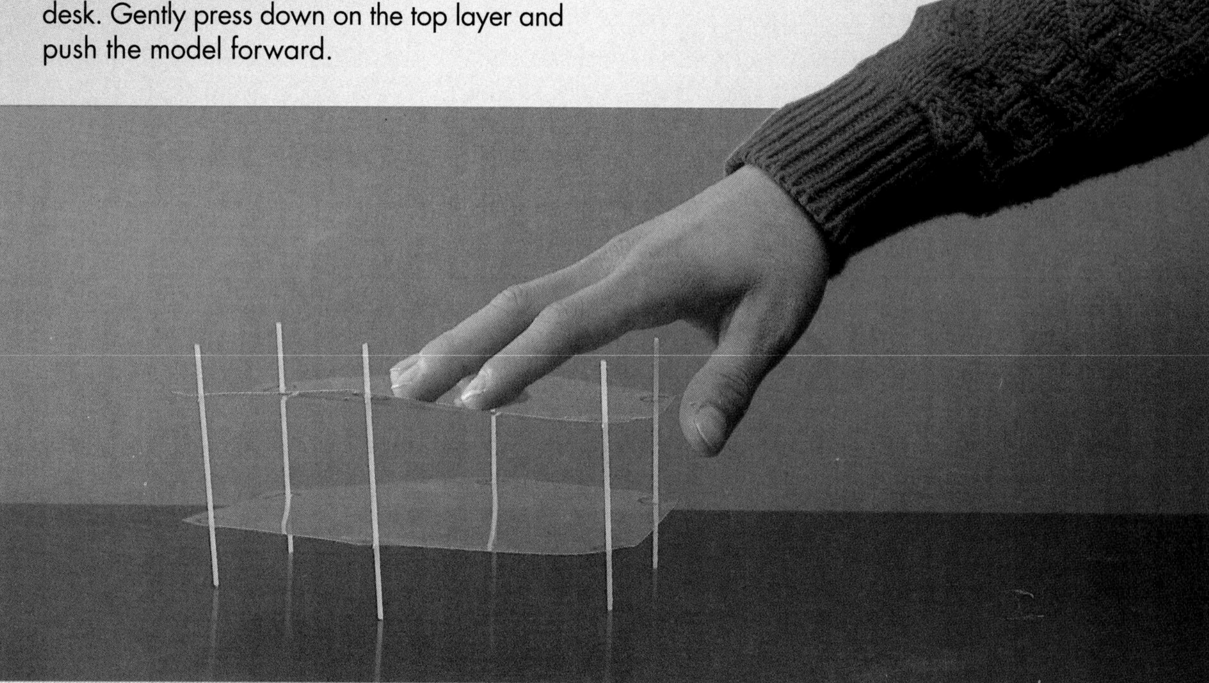

CHAPTER REVIEW

SUMMARY

12-1: Metals

1. A typical metal is a hard, shiny, solid that—due to metallic bonding—is malleable, ductile, and a good conductor of heat and electricity.
2. Groups 1 and 2 on the periodic table are the alkali and alkaline earth metals, which have some similar and some contrasting properties.
3. The iron triad, the coinage metals, and the zinc, cadmium, mercury group are among the transition elements, which make up Groups 3 through 12 on the periodic table.

12-2: Science and Society: Synthetic Elements

1. The lanthanoids and actinoids have atomic numbers 57-70 and 89-102, respectively, whereas transuranium elements have atomic numbers greater than 92.
2. The making of synthetic elements is a controversial issue.

12-3: Nonmetals

1. As a typical nonmetal, hydrogen is a gas that forms compounds by sharing electrons with other nonmetals and also with metals.
2. All the halogens, Group 17, have seven outer electrons and form both covalent and ionic compounds, but each halogen has some properties unlike the others.
3. The noble gases, Group 18, are elements whose properties and uses are related to their chemical stability.

12-4: Mixed Groups

1. Groups 13 through 16 of the periodic table include metals, nonmetals, and metalloids.
2. Allotropes are different forms of the same element having different molecular structures.
3. The properties of two forms of carbon, graphite and diamond, depend upon the differences in their crystal structure.

KEY SCIENCE WORDS

a. **allotropes**
b. **diatomic molecule**
c. **ductile**
d. **malleable**
e. **metallic bonding**
f. **radioactive element**
g. **semiconductors**
h. **sublimation**
i. **transuranium element**
j. **transition elements**

UNDERSTANDING VOCABULARY

Match each phrase with the correct term from the list of Key Science Words.

1. can be drawn out into a wire
2. appears after uranium on the periodic table
3. can be hammered into a thin sheet
4. change directly from a solid to a gas
5. will conduct an electric current under certain conditions
6. different structural forms of the same element
7. composed of two atoms of the same element
8. breaks down and gives off particles, radiation, and energy
9. Groups 3 through 12 on the periodic table
10. Positively charged ions are surrounded by freely moving electrons.

CHAPTER

REVIEW

CHECKING CONCEPTS

Choose the word or phrase that completes the sentence or answers the question.

1. When magnesium and fluorine react, what type of bond is formed?
a. metallic **c.** covalent
b. ionic **d.** diatomic

2. What type of bond is found in a piece of pure gold?
a. metallic **c.** covalent
b. ionic **d.** diatomic

3. Because electrons move freely in metals, metals are ______.
a. brittle **c.** dull
b. hard **d.** conductors

4. The ______ make up the most reactive group of all metals.
a. iron triad **c.** alkalis
b. coinage metals **d.** alkaline earths

5. The most reactive of all elements is ______.
a. fluorine **c.** hydrogen
b. uranium **d.** oxygen

6. The element ______ is always found in nature combined with other elements.
a. copper **c.** magnesium
b. gold **d.** silver

7. The least magnetic of these metals is ______.
a. cobalt **c.** nickel
b. iron **d.** titanium

8. The synthetic element ______ was banned after much controversy.
a. ytterbium **c.** americium
b. promethium **d.** plutonium

9. An example of a radioactive element is _____.
a. astatine **c.** chlorine
b. bromine **d.** fluorine

10. The only group that is completely nonmetallic is Group ______.
a. 1 **c.** 17
b. 2 **d.** 18

UNDERSTANDING CONCEPTS

Complete each sentence.

11. The crystal structure of the form of carbon called ______ makes it useful as a lubricant.

12. A group of elements named for their reactions in which salts are formed are the ______.

13. Red and white fireworks may be produced by two metals in the ______ group.

14. The class of elements that generally have from one to three outer electrons is the ______.

15. Many uses of the noble gases are related to their property of ______.

THINK AND WRITE CRITICALLY

16. Reading from top to bottom on the periodic table, metallic properties of elements *increase*, reading from left to right, metallic properties *decrease.* Which element is the most metallic of all? Explain your answer.

17. The most abundant elements in Earth's crust are a nonmetal, a metalloid, and two metals. List the four elements.

18. Why do oxygen and nitrogen occur in the air as diatomic molecules, but argon, neon, krypton, and xenon occur as monatomic molecules?

19. Explain why hydrogen, a nonmetal, is on the metal side of the periodic table.

20. Name three metals used to coat other metals. Why is one metal used to coat another?

APPLY

21. Why was mercury used in clinical thermometers, and why is it no longer used for that purpose?
22. The density of hydrogen is so low that it can be used to fill balloons to make them lighter than air. Why is helium used more frequently?
23. Why is aluminum used instead of steel in building airplanes?
24. Why are silver compounds used in photography? Name two nonmetals extracted from brine that are also part of these compounds.
25. Like selenium, chromium is poisonous but is needed in trace amounts in your diet. How does this information apply to the safe use of vitamin-mineral pills?

MORE SKILL BUILDERS

If you need help, refer to the Skill Handbook.

1. **Making and Using Tables:** Use the periodic table to classify each of the following as a lanthanoid or actinoid: californium, europium, cerium, nobelium.
2. **Comparing and Contrasting:** Aluminum is close to carbon on the periodic table. Explain why aluminum is a metal and carbon is not.
3. **Observing and Inferring:** You are shown two samples of phosphorus. One is white and burns if exposed to air. The other is red and burns if lit. Infer why the properties of two samples of the same element differ.
4. **Recognizing Cause and Effect:** Plants need nitrogen compounds. Nitrogen-fixing changes free nitrogen into nitrates. Lightning and legumes are both nitrogen-fixing. What are the cause and effect of nitrogen fixing?
5. **Concept Mapping:** Complete the concept map located to the right for some common metals. You may use symbols for the elements.

PROJECTS

1. Research the pros and cons of using nuclear energy to produce electricity. Prepare a report which includes data as well as your informed opinion on the subject. If several class members do research, conduct a debate on the issue.
2. Research the source, composition, and properties of asbestos. What properties made it suitable for use in construction in the past? How did these same properties cause asbestos to become a health hazard, and what is being done now to eliminate the hazard?

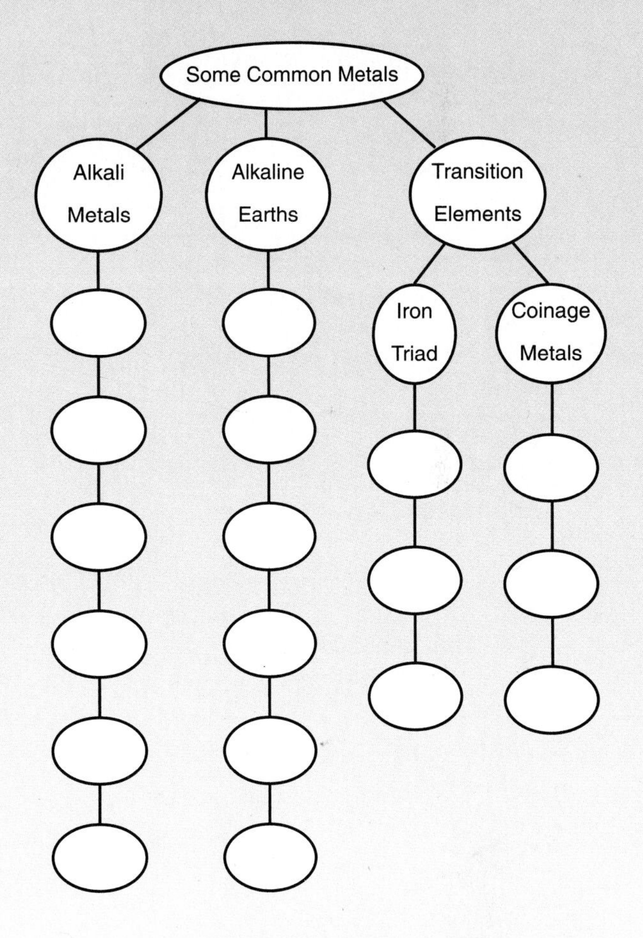

CHAPTER

13 Organic and Biological Compounds

FANCY CARROTS 59¢ lb.

ARTICHOKES 89¢ ea

SALAD SAVOY LETTUCE 149¢ lb.

Have you heard the saying "You are what you eat"? Actually, many of the same compounds in foods are found in your body. And one special element is basic to these compounds and to other substances made by living things.

FIND OUT!

Do this activity to observe the element that forms from the breakdown of some kinds of materials when they are heated.

Place a small piece of bread in a test tube. Hold the test tube over the flame of a laboratory burner. What do you observe? Using a clean test tube and a small amount of paper instead of bread, repeat the procedure. What do you observe this time?

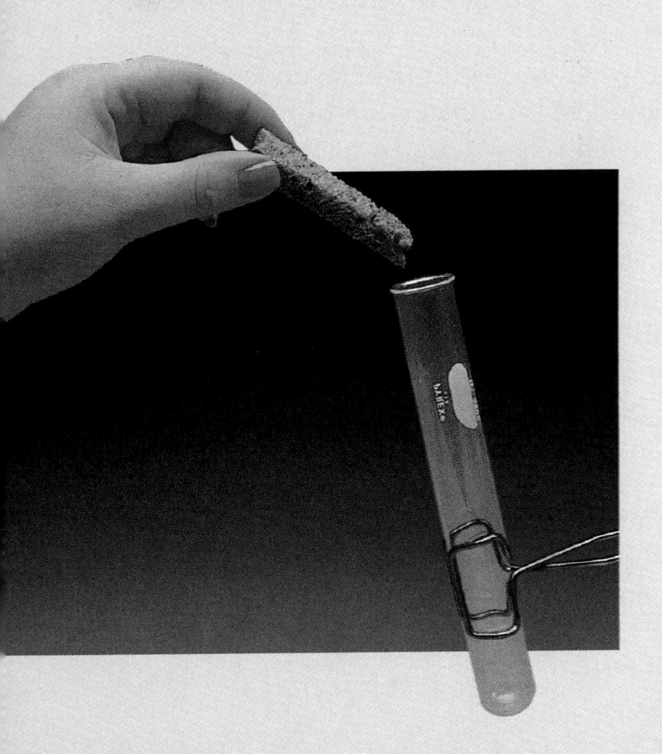

Gearing Up

Previewing the Chapter

Use this outline to help you focus on important ideas in this chapter.

Previewing Science Skills

- In the **Skill Builders,** you will make and use a graph, interpret scientific illustrations, and make a concept map.
- In the **Activities,** you will observe, predict, and build models.
- In the **MINI-Lab,** you will build a model, compare, and contrast.

What's next?

You have observed evidence of the presence of carbon in bread and paper, which contain organic compounds. As you study this chapter, you will find out more about organic compounds.

13-1 Simple Organic Compounds

New Science Words

organic compounds
hydrocarbon
saturated hydrocarbons
unsaturated hydrocarbons
isomers

Objectives

- Describe structures of organic compounds and explain why carbon forms so many compounds.
- Distinguish between saturated and unsaturated hydrocarbons.
- Identify isomers of organic compounds.

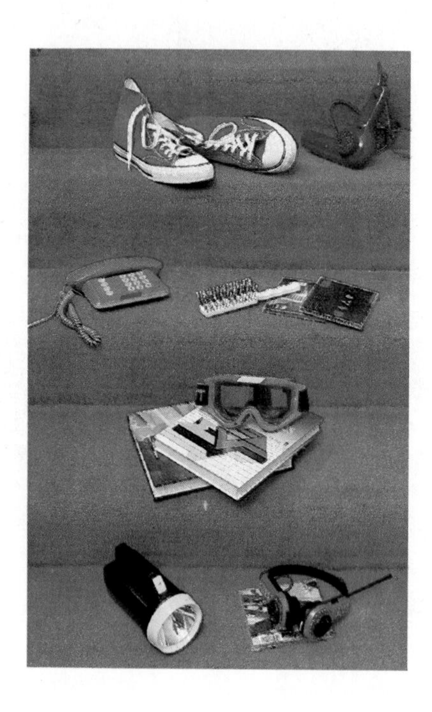

How many covalent bonds can a carbon atom form?

Organic Compounds

What do cassette tapes and CDs, you, and your athletic shoes have in common? Each is made up mostly of substances called organic compounds. Most compounds that contain the element carbon are **organic compounds**. There are several exceptions, such as carbon monoxide, carbon dioxide, and carbonates. More than 90 percent of all compounds are organic compounds.

You probably recognize that the word *organic* is related to *organism.* At one time, scientists assumed that only living organisms could produce organic compounds. However, by 1830 scientists were making organic compounds artificially in laboratories. But scientists didn't change the name of these carbon-containing compounds. Today, most of the millions of different organic compounds that exist are synthetic. The manufacturing of organic compounds is one of the world's largest industries. A chemical plant is shown in Figure 13-1 on the next page.

You may be wondering why there are so many organic compounds. There are several reasons, each related to the element carbon. First, a carbon atom has four electrons in its outer energy level. Recall that this electron arrangement means that each atom can form four covalent bonds with atoms of carbon or other elements. Four is a large number of bonds compared to the number of bonds that atoms of other elements can form. When carbon atoms bond to form the molecules of some organic compounds, they form long chains. These chains may

Figure 13-1. Many useful organic compounds are made in petrochemical plants like this one.

be continuous or branched. In other compounds the carbon atoms form closed rings. Molecules of organic compounds may contain from one to several thousand carbon atoms.

Second, a carbon atom can form a single, double, or triple bond with another carbon atom. There also can be many different arrangements of single, double, and triple bonds between carbon atoms. Each arrangement forms a molecule of a different organic compound. Finally, a carbon atom can bond with atoms of many other elements, such as hydrogen, oxygen, nitrogen, and chlorine. Carbon forms an enormous number of compounds with hydrogen alone. A compound made up of only carbon and hydrogen atoms is called a **hydrocarbon.** You can learn a lot about other organic compounds by studying hydrocarbons.

Figure 13-2. Natural pigments like the color of this flamingo are organic compounds.

Hydrocarbons

Does the furnace, stove, or water heater in your home burn natural gas? Almost all the natural gas people use for these purposes is the hydrocarbon methane. The chemical formula of methane is CH_4. There are two other ways to represent methane. The structural formula in Figure 13-3 shows how the atoms are arranged in a molecule.

Figure 13-3. Natural gas is mostly methane, CH_4.

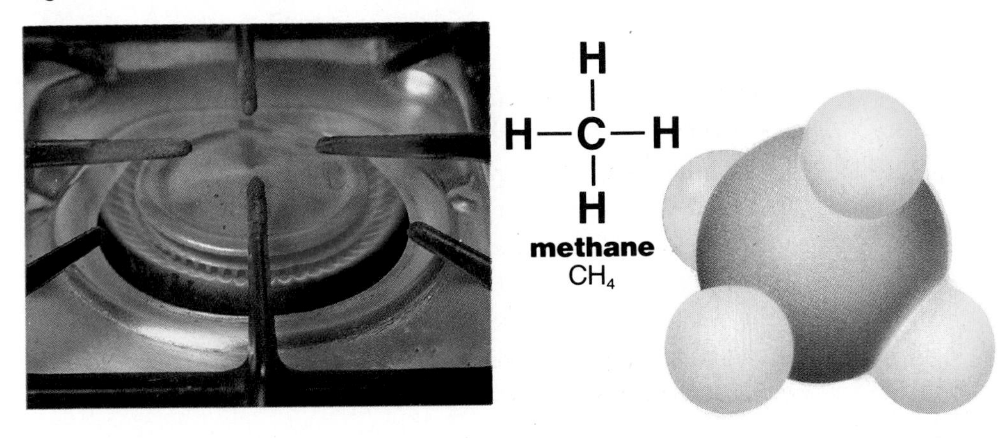

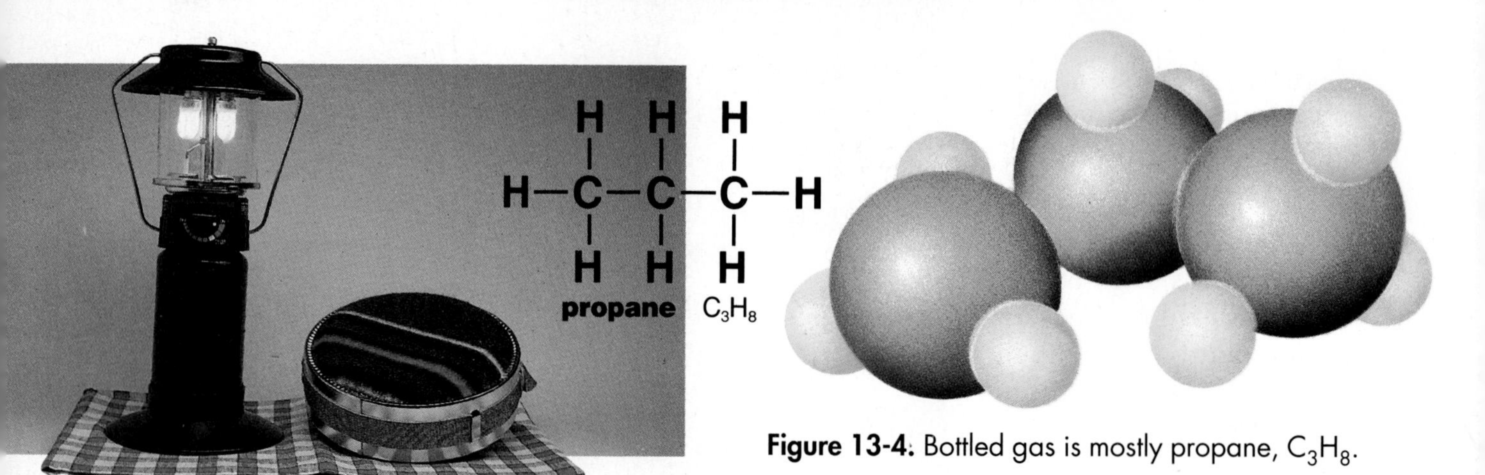

Figure 13-4. Bottled gas is mostly propane, C_3H_8.

MINI-Lab

What structures can octane have?

Octane, C_8H_{18}, is a hydrocarbon in gasoline. Using gum drops for carbon atoms, raisins for hydrogen atoms, and toothpicks for bonds that join the "atoms," make a model of one possible structure of octane. Each carbon atom can have four bonds and each hydrogen atom one bond. Compare the structure of your model to those of your classmates.

Each line between atoms represents a single covalent bond. As you recall, a covalent bond is formed when two atoms share a pair of electrons. The space-filling model in Figure 13-3 shows the relative volumes of the electron clouds in the molecule.

Methane and other hydrocarbons account for more than 90 percent of the energy sources used in homes, schools, industry, and transportation. Hydrocarbons are also important in manufacturing almost all the organic compounds used in products ranging from fertilizers to skateboards.

Some stoves, most outdoor grills, and hot-air balloons burn the bottled gas propane, another hydrocarbon. Its chemical formula is C_3H_8. Look at Figure 13-4. How many

Table 13-1

SOME HYDROCARBONS		
Name	**Chemical Formula**	**Structural Formula**
Methane	CH_4	H H-C-H H
Ethane	C_2H_6	H H H-C-C-H H H
Propane	C_3H_8	H H H H-C-C-C-H H H H
Butane	C_4H_{10}	H H H H H-C-C-C-C-H H H H H
Pentane	C_5H_{12}	H H H H H H-C-C-C-C-C-H H H H H H

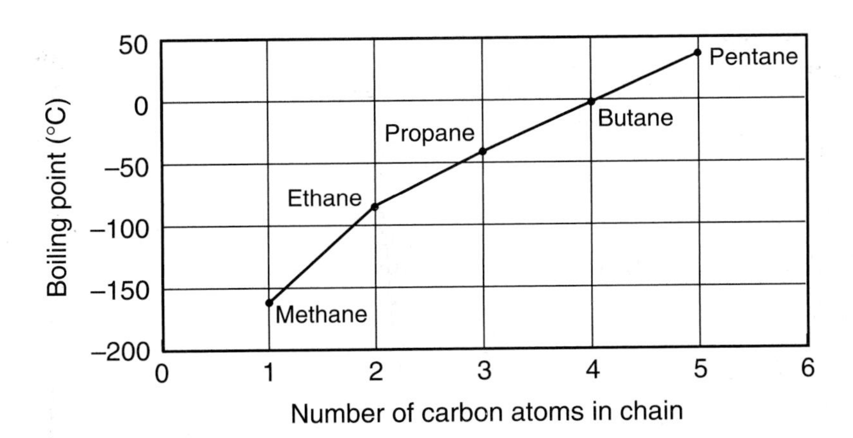

Figure 13-5. Boiling Points of Hydrocarbons in Natural Gas

atoms of each element are in a molecule of propane? How many covalent bonds are in each molecule?

In some hydrocarbons, the carbon atoms are joined by single covalent bonds. Hydrocarbons containing single-bonded carbon atoms are called **saturated hydrocarbons.** The carbon atoms in a molecule of propane are bonded by single covalent bonds. Propane is a saturated hydrocarbon. As you can see, the carbon atoms in propane seem to form a short chain. Propane is a member of a group of saturated hydrocarbons in which the carbon atoms form chains. Table 13-1 lists methane, propane, and three other similar hydrocarbons. Notice how each carbon atom appears to be a link in the chain within the molecule. Figure 13-5 shows a graph of the boiling points of these hydrocarbons. What happens to the boiling point as the number of carbon atoms in the chain increases?

Do you like bananas? They are among the many fruits and vegetables that are often ripened with the help of ethylene. Ethylene is the common name of the hydrocarbon ethene, C_2H_4. Did you ever watch a welder using an acetylene torch? Acetylene is the common name of the hydrocarbon ethyne, C_2H_2. Look at the structural formulas for ethene and ethyne. The double lines between the carbon atoms in ethene represent a double covalent bond. A double covalent bond is the sharing of two pairs of electrons—in other words, four electrons. The three lines in ethyne represent a triple covalent bond. How many pairs of electrons are shared in a triple covalent bond?

Hydrocarbons such as ethene and ethyne that contain double or triple bonds between carbon atoms are called **unsaturated hydrocarbons.** Remember that *saturated*

PROBLEM SOLVING

The Case of the Overripe Tomatoes

Maria helped out at home by preparing dinner on Mondays and Thursdays. She was also responsible for buying any groceries needed to prepare the meals. One Monday Maria bought an overripe avocado to use for guacamole sauce that evening and some green tomatoes to use for a salad on Thursday. She thought the tomatoes would be juicy but still firm by Thursday evening. The grocery clerk put the avocado and tomatoes in a brown paper bag.

When Maria arrived at home, her father decided to take the family out to dinner. So she didn't have to prepare dinner that evening.

On Thursday, Maria opened the paper bag. The avocado was rotten, and the tomatoes were overripe—not firm as she had expected. Maria knew that fruits give off ethylene gas as they ripen. But the tomatoes ripened more quickly than they should have.

Think Critically: Why did the avocado rot? What caused the tomatoes to ripen more rapidly than expected?

hydrocarbons contain only single bonds. As you will read in a later section, fats and oils can also be classified as unsaturated or saturated because parts of their molecules are similar to hydrocarbon molecules.

Isomers

Perhaps you have seen or know about butane, a gas sometimes burned in camping stoves and lighters. The chemical formula of butane is C_4H_{10}. Another hydrocarbon also has the same chemical formula as butane. How can this be? The answer lies in the arrangement of the four carbon atoms. Look at Figure 13-6. In a molecule of butane, the carbon atoms form a continuous chain. The carbon chain of isobutane is branched. The arrangement of carbon atoms in each compound changes the shape of the molecule. Isobutane and butane are isomers.

Table 13-2

PROPERTIES OF BUTANE ISOMERS		
	Butane	**Isobutane**
Description	Colorless gas	Colorless gas
Density	0.6 kg/L	0.6 kg/L
Melting point	−138°C	−160°C
Boiling point	−0.5°C	−12°C

Isomers are compounds that have identical chemical formulas but different molecular structures and shapes. There are thousands of isomers among the hydrocarbons. Table 13-2 summarizes several properties of the two isomers of butane. As you can see, the structure of an isomer does affect some of the compound's properties.

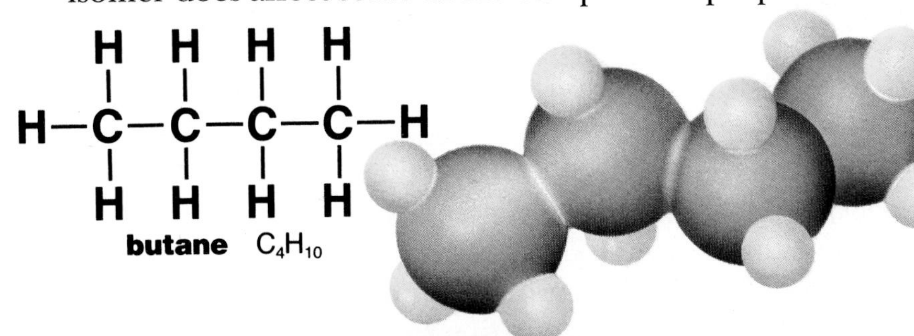

Figure 13-6. Isomers of Butane

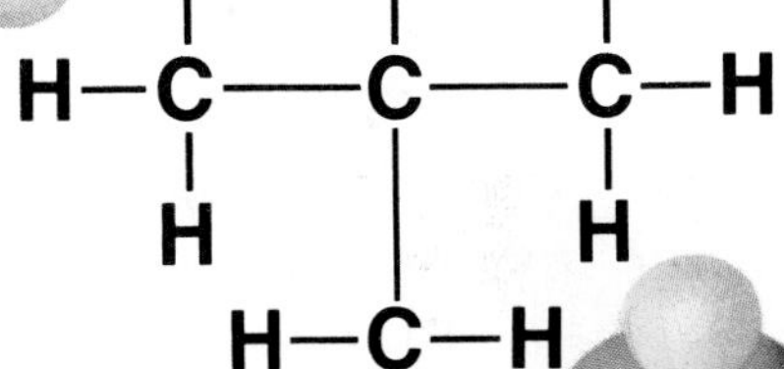

SECTION REVIEW

1. Why can carbon form so many organic compounds?
2. Compare and contrast ethane, ethene, and ethyne.
3. How is an unsaturated hydrocarbon different from a saturated hydrocarbon?
4. **Apply:** Cyclopropane is a saturated hydrocarbon containing three carbon atoms. In this compound, each carbon atom is bonded to two other carbon atoms. Draw its structural formula. Are cyclopropane and propane isomers? Explain.

Making and Using Graphs

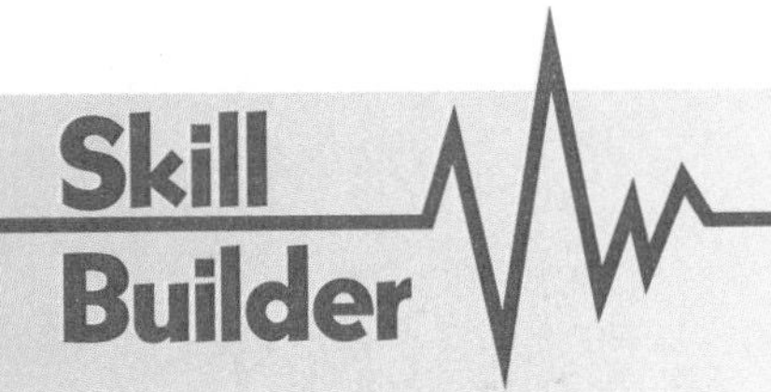

Make a graph of Table 13-1. For each compound, plot the number of carbon atoms on one axis and the number of hydrogen atoms on the other axis. Use the graph to predict the formula of hexane, which has six carbon atoms. If you need help, refer to Making and Using Graphs in the **Skill Handbook** on page 686.

13-2 Other Organic Compounds

New Science Words

aromatic compound
substituted hydrocarbon
alcohol

Objectives

- Describe characteristics of aromatic compounds.
- Classify groups of organic compounds as substituted hydrocarbons.

Figure 13-7. Vanilla extract comes from the dried pod of the vanilla orchid, shown above.

Aromatic Compounds

Do you like vanilla ice cream or vanilla yogurt? Perhaps you know that vanilla flavor, like many flavors, is due largely to smell. What you taste is actually the smell of vanillin, the compound in vanilla extract that produces the vanilla flavor. Another word for smell is aroma. So you might guess that aromatic compounds are smelly—and indeed most of them are. An **aromatic compound** is a compound that contains the benzene ring structure. Look at a model of benzene, C_6H_6, and its structural formula, Figure 13-8. As you can see, the benzene molecule has six carbon atoms bonded into a ring. The electrons in the three double bonds and three single bonds that form the ring are actually shared by all six carbon atoms in the ring. The sharing of these electrons causes the benzene molecule to be very stable. Because many compounds contain this stable ring structure, it is given a special symbol, as shown in (c).

Knowing the structure of benzene can help you to picture hundreds of different aromatic organic compounds.

a

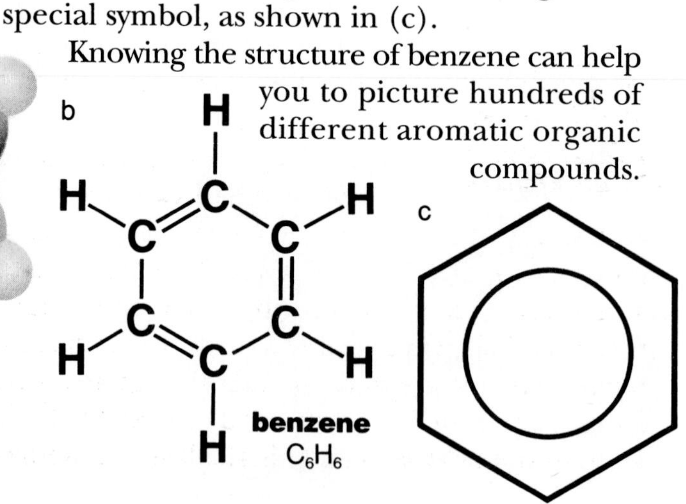

Figure 13-8. Benzene, C_6H_6, can be represented by (a) a space-filling model, (b) a structural formula, or (c) the benzene ring symbol.

Figure 13-9. Moth crystals are naphthalene.

naphthalene
$C_{10}H_8$

One example is naphthalene. Can you recognize the odor of moth crystals? Moth crystals are naphthalene, as shown in Figure 13-9. Notice that naphthalene is made up of two ring structures.

Substituted Hydrocarbons

Usually, a cheeseburger is a hamburger covered with melted American cheese and served on a bun. However, you can make a cheeseburger with Swiss cheese and serve it on slices of bread. If you ate this cheeseburger, you would notice how the substitutions affect the taste.

Chemists make similar changes to hydrocarbons. These changes produce compounds called substituted hydrocarbons. A **substituted hydrocarbon** has one or more of its hydrogen atoms replaced by atoms of other elements.

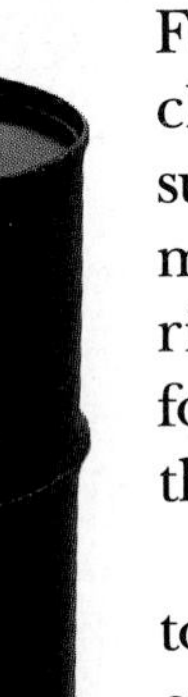

For example, a compound used in dry cleaning, tetrachloroethene, C_2Cl_4, is a substituted hydrocarbon. The prefix *tetra-* means "four," and *chloro-* refers to chlorine. Figure 13-10 shows how C_2Cl_4 is formed when four chlorine atoms replace the hydrogen atoms in ethene, C_2H_4.

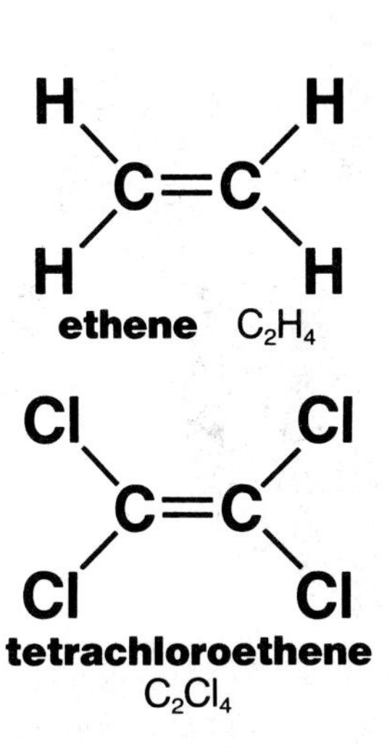

Figure 13-10. Tetrachloroethene is a substituted hydrocarbon.

Have you ever used rubbing alcohol to soothe aching muscles after too much exercise? Did you know you were using a substituted hydrocarbon? Alcohols are an important group of organic compounds. An **alcohol** is formed when –OH groups replace one or more hydrogen atoms in a hydrocarbon, as shown in Figure 13-11. Ethanol, C_2H_5OH, is an alcohol produced by the fermentation of sugar in corn and other grains, and in many fruits. Alcoholic beverages contain ethanol. As you will learn in the next section, this alcohol is sometimes added

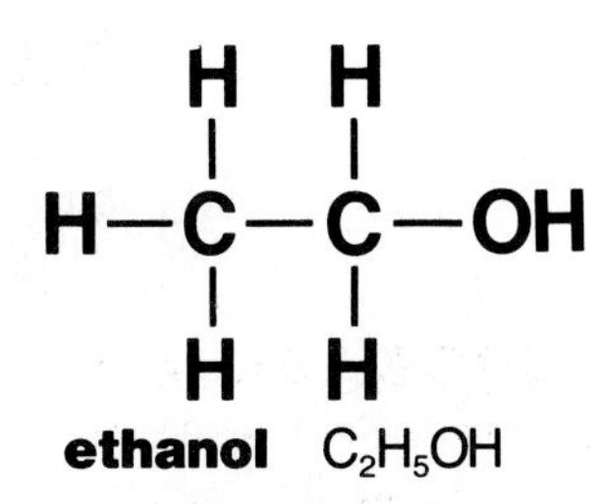

Figure 13-11. Ethanol is one of many alcohols.

Table 13-3

COMMON ALCOHOLS		Methanol	Ethanol	Isopropyl alcohol (rubbing alcohol)	Phenol
		H H-C-OH H	H H H-C-C-OH H H	H OH H H-C-C—C-H H H H	(benzene ring)—OH
Uses	Fuel	✓	✓		
	Cleaner	✓	✓	✓	
	Disinfectant		✓	✓	✓
	Manufacturing chemicals	✓		✓	✓

H H
H—C—C—H
H H
ethane C_2H_6

H H
H—C—C—OH
H H
ethanol C_2H_5OH

H O
H—C—C—OH
H
acetic acid CH_3COOH

Figure 13-12. The structures of these compounds are similar.

to gasoline. Ethanol is also a good cleaning fluid because it can dissolve substances that don't dissolve in water. Denatured alcohol is a mixture of ethanol and a poisonous substance such as methanol. It is used as a solvent. Several alcohols are listed in Table 13-3.

You may recall that vinegar contains acetic acid. Acetic acid is an example of a compound called an organic acid. Many fruit juices contain similar organic acids. Look at Figure 13-12. The structures of ethane, ethanol, and acetic acid are very similar. Do you see how this similarity indicates that acetic acid is a substituted hydrocarbon? Substituted hydrocarbons account for millions of organic compounds.

SECTION REVIEW

1. What do all aromatic compounds have in common?
2. How is each of the following a substituted hydrocarbon: (a) tetrachloroethene, (b) ethanol, (c) acetic acid?
3. **Apply:** Why is ethanol intended for use as a solvent denatured by the addition of a poisonous substance?

Skill Builder — Interpreting Scientific Illustrations

Formic acid, HCOOH, is the simplest organic acid. Draw its structural formula by referring to Figure 13-12. If you need help, refer to Interpreting Scientific Illustrations in the **Skill Handbook** on page 683.

ACTIVITY 13-1
Alcohols and Organic Acids

Problem: *What new compound can be formed from an alcohol?*

Materials    

- test tube and stopper
- 1 mL 0.01 *M* potassium permanganate solution
- 1 mL 6 *M* sodium hydroxide solution
- 3 drops of ethanol
- goggles
- apron

Procedure

1. Pour 1 mL of 0.01 *M* potassium permanganate solution and 1 mL of 6 *M* sodium hydroxide solution into a test tube. **CAUTION:** *Handle both of these chemicals with care; immediately flush any spill with water.*
2. Add three drops of ethanol to the test tube.
3. Stopper the test tube and gently shake it for one minute. Observe and record any changes you notice in the tube for the next five minutes.

Data and Observations

Changes in Mixture

Analyze

1. What is the structural formula for ethanol?
2. What part of a molecule identifies a compound as an alcohol?
3. What part of a molecule identifies a compound as an organic acid?

Conclude and Apply

4. What evidence did you observe of a chemical change taking place in the test tube?
5. In the presence of potassium permanganate, an alcohol may undergo a chemical change into an acid. If the alcohol used is ethanol, what would you predict to be the formula of the acid produced?
6. The acid from ethanol is found in a common household product. What is the acid's name? In what common household product is the acid found?

13-3 Alternative Sources of Energy

New Science Words

biomass
biogas
energy farming
gasohol

Objectives

- Describe the role of biomass as a source of two fuels for increasing our energy supply.
- Analyze the positive and negative effects of the widespread use of ethanol and gasohol.

Why Not New Fuels?

What fuels have you used today? Probably the main sources of energy you use are natural gas, coal, or petroleum. But did you know that most people in the world rely on biomass for their energy supply? **Biomass** refers to all animal and plant material, both dead and alive. Wood, leaves, animal and human wastes, and food waste are all biomass.

What is the composition of biomass?

If plant and animal wastes are allowed to rot in the absence of air, bacteria break down the wastes to produce biogas. **Biogas** is mainly methane, just like natural gas. People in rural areas in Third World countries cook, heat their homes, and generate electricity with biogas. China has some four million factories that produce biogas. This fuel is such a promising source of additional energy supplies that proposals have been made for energy farming. **Energy farming** involves growing plants for use as fuel. One proposal is to use the troublesome water hyacinth that clogs waterways.

Did you ever see a sign like the one to the right? **Gasohol** is a combination of ethanol and gasoline. If you have ridden in a car fueled with gasohol, you have used a product of biomass. Recall that fermentation produces the ethanol found in alcoholic beverages. The same process of fermentation is also used with a variety of grains and fruits to produce ethanol for use as a fuel. Pure ethanol can be used in cars if the engines are modified slightly. Car engines do not have to be modified to burn gasohol. When gasoline is in short supply because of a lack of petroleum, gasohol finds wider use. Is gasohol the answer to our periodic shortages of petroleum?

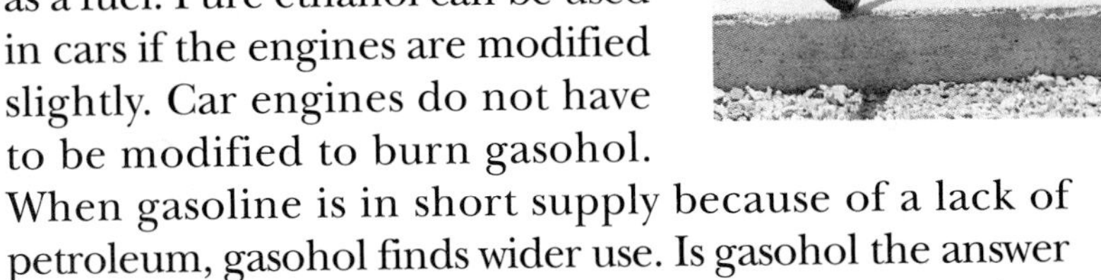

At first, biogas and gasohol seem like ideal energy sources. Yet producing them commercially results in numerous environmental problems. Among these are disturbing the ecosystem, fertilizer runoff, erosion, and air pollution. The decision for or against large-scale production of biogas and gasohol may not be an easy one.

Clearly the conversion of biomass to easily handled fuels such as methane and ethanol is an interesting possibility for supplying part of our energy needs. But, large-scale tests of energy production from biomass have not yet been carried out in the United States, and energy farming may have as yet unknown effects on our environment.

EcoTip

If you have a garden, grow beans or peas between other plants. The peas and beans supply the soil with nitrogen which is needed by other plants.

SECTION REVIEW

1. In what two major ways is biomass used as a source of fuels?
2. What are the main pros, cons, and concerns related to the use of ethanol in gasohol?

You Decide!

Increasing the production and use of both biogas and gasohol may help the United States to cope with petroleum shortages. Should government agencies encourage the production of these fuels? Why or why not?

13-4 Biological Compounds

New Science Words

polymers
proteins
nucleic acids
carbohydrates
lipids

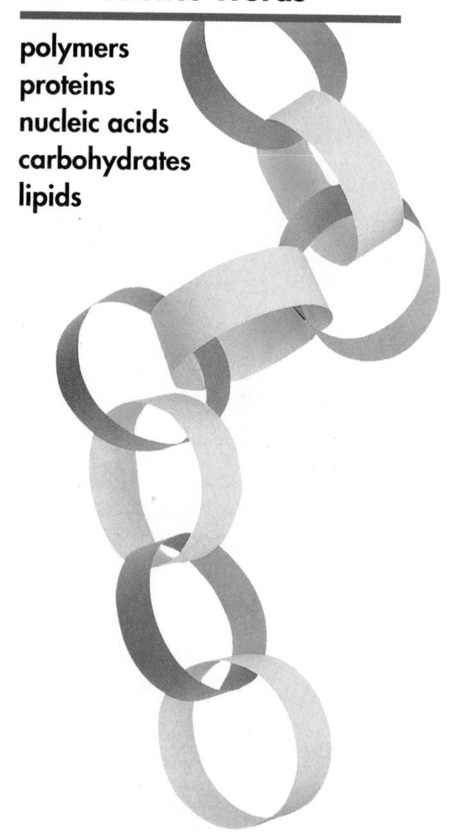

Objectives

- Describe the formation of polymers and discuss their importance as biological compounds.
- Compare and contrast proteins, nucleic acids, carbohydrates, and lipids.

Proteins

Did you ever loop together strips of paper to make paper chains for decorations? Have you ever strung paper clips together as a prank? Both a paper chain and a string of paper clips are very much like polymers. **Polymers** are huge molecules made of many smaller organic molecules that have formed new bonds and linked together. The smaller molecules are called monomers. Monomers are usually very similar in size and structure. You can picture a monomer as an individual loop of paper or an individual paper clip. The photograph on the left shows this model of a polymer. As you will see in Chapter 14, plastics are polymers. Many of the important biological compounds in your body also are polymers. Among them are the proteins.

Proteins make up many of the tissues in your body, such as muscles and tendons, as well as your hair and fingernails. A protein in your blood called hemoglobin carries oxygen, Figure 13-13. The enzymes that control chemical reactions in your body are proteins. In fact, proteins account for 15 percent of your weight. That's about half the weight of all materials other than water in your body.

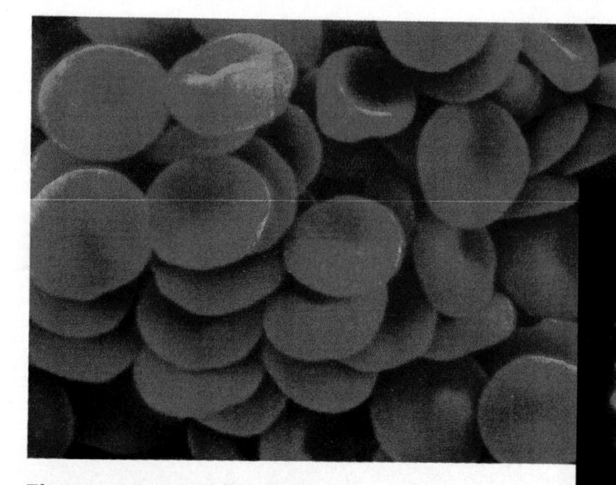

Figure 13-13. Blood contains a complex protein called hemoglobin.

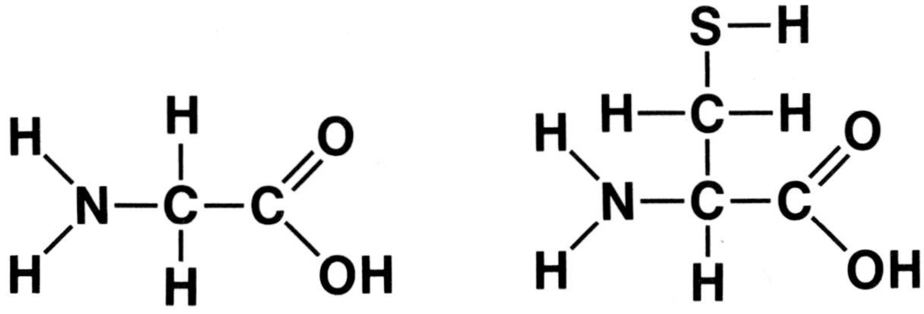

glycine

cysteine

Figure 13-14. Two Amino Acids

Proteins are polymers formed from organic compounds called amino acids. Even though there are millions of different proteins, there are only 20 common amino acids. Two amino acids are shown in Figure 13-14.

Notice that each molecule of an amino acid contains a –COOH group and a $-NH_2$ group. The –COOH group is called the carboxylic acid group. If you look again at Figure 13-12 on page 336, you'll see that the structure of this group appears also in acetic acid. The $-NH_2$ group is called the amine group. Both groups appear in every amino acid.

Figure 13-15. Some High-Protein Foods

In a protein polymer, peptide bonds link together molecules of amino acids. Peptide bonds form when the amine group of one amino acid combines with the organic acid group of another amino acid. Look at Figure 13-16. You might think of the 20 amino acids as letters of an alphabet. Each protein is a word spelled with these letters. However, unlike English words, words in this alphabet may contain hundreds of letters. Actually, some proteins may contain thousands of amino acids.

Your body makes proteins from amino acids. The amino acids come from eating and digesting foods that contain proteins. Digestion breaks the protein polymers into monomers of amino acids, which your body uses to make new proteins.

Figure 13-16. The protein molecule contains many peptide bonds.

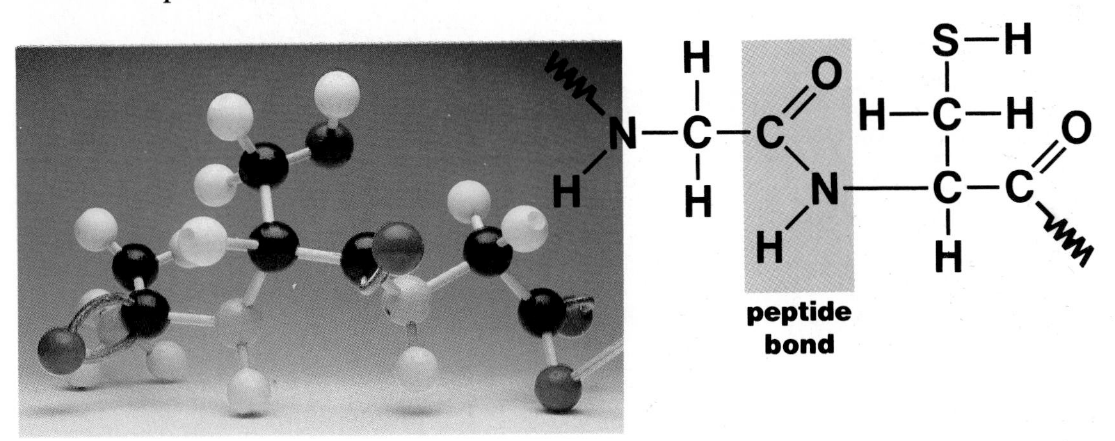

Nucleic Acids

The nucleic acids are another important group of organic compounds that are necessary for life. **Nucleic acids** are polymers that control the activities and reproduction of cells. One kind of nucleic acid, deoxyribonucleic acid (DNA), is found in the nuclei of cells. DNA codes and stores genetic information. Figure 13-17 shows a model and the formula for a portion of the DNA polymer. It resembles a twisted ladder. Like other polymers, DNA is made up of monomers. With the genetic code, DNA controls the production of ribonucleic acid (RNA), another kind of nucleic acid. RNA, in turn, controls the production of proteins that will make new cells.

Did You Know?

Rubber is an organic substance that was named because it could be used to rub out pencil marks.

What are nucleotides?

The monomers that make up DNA are called nucleotides. Each nucleotide looks like one-half of a ladder rung with an attached side piece. As you can see, each pair of nucleotides forms a rung on the ladder, while the side pieces give the ladder a little twist. Because the nucleotides may be made up of four different organic compounds, all the ladder rungs are not the same. Unless you're an identical twin, your DNA differs from that of every other person because the nucleotides and their locations are not the same in any two polymers.

Figure 13-17. DNA Models

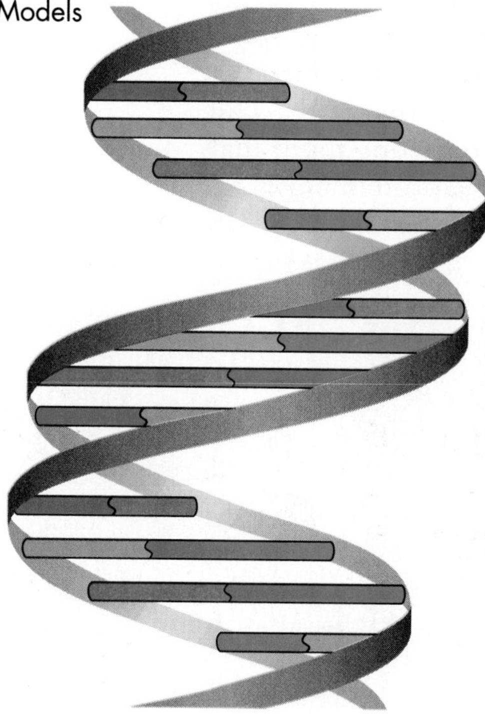

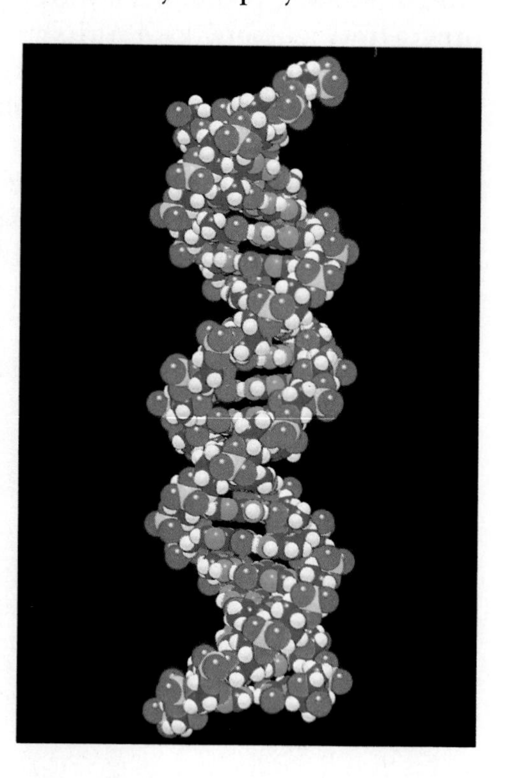

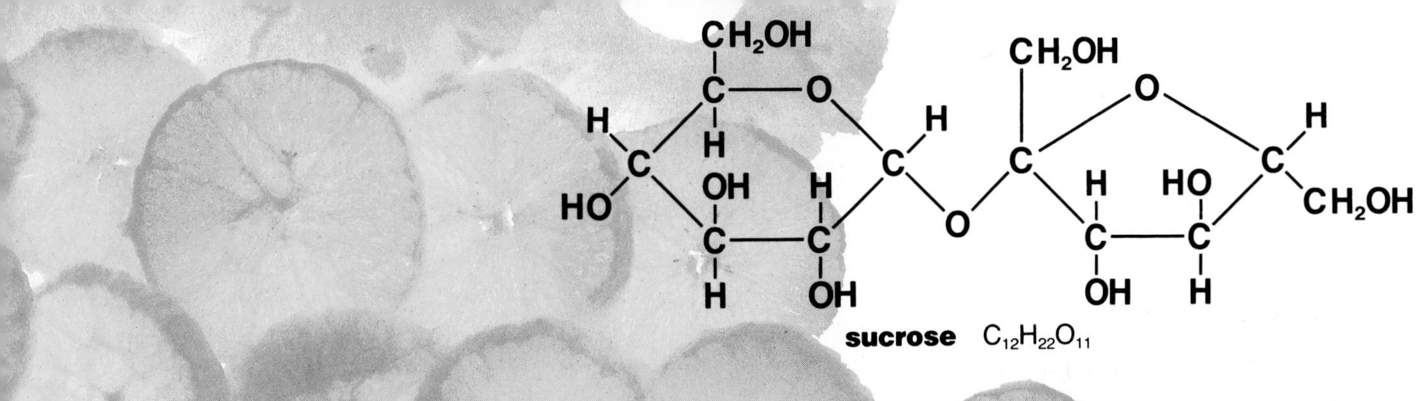

sucrose $C_{12}H_{22}O_{11}$

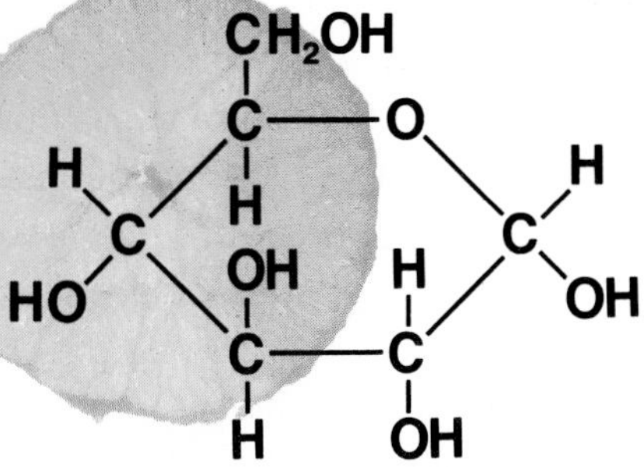

glucose $C_6H_{12}O_6$

Figure 13-18. Sucrose and glucose are sugars found in foods. Fruits contain glucose.

Carbohydrates

If you hear the word *carbohydrate*, you may think of a sweet fruit or sugary treat. Do you also think of carbohydrate loading by athletes? Runners, for example, often prepare for a long-distance race by eating, or "loading," carbohydrates in starchy foods such as vegetables and pasta. Starches provide high-energy, clean-burning fuel for the body.

Carbohydrates are organic compounds in which there are twice as many hydrogen atoms as oxygen atoms. One group of carbohydrates is the sugars, as shown in Figure 13-18. The sugar, glucose, is found in your blood and also in many sweet foods such as grapes and honey. The sugar, sucrose, is common table sugar. By counting the hydrogen and oxygen atoms in each formula, you will see that these sugars are carbohydrates.

What is the formula for the sugar found in your blood?

Figure 13-19 shows a part of a starch molecule. Starch is a carbohydrate that is also a polymer. During digestion, sucrose and starch are broken down into monomers of glucose and similar sugars.

Figure 13-19. Starch is the major component of pasta.

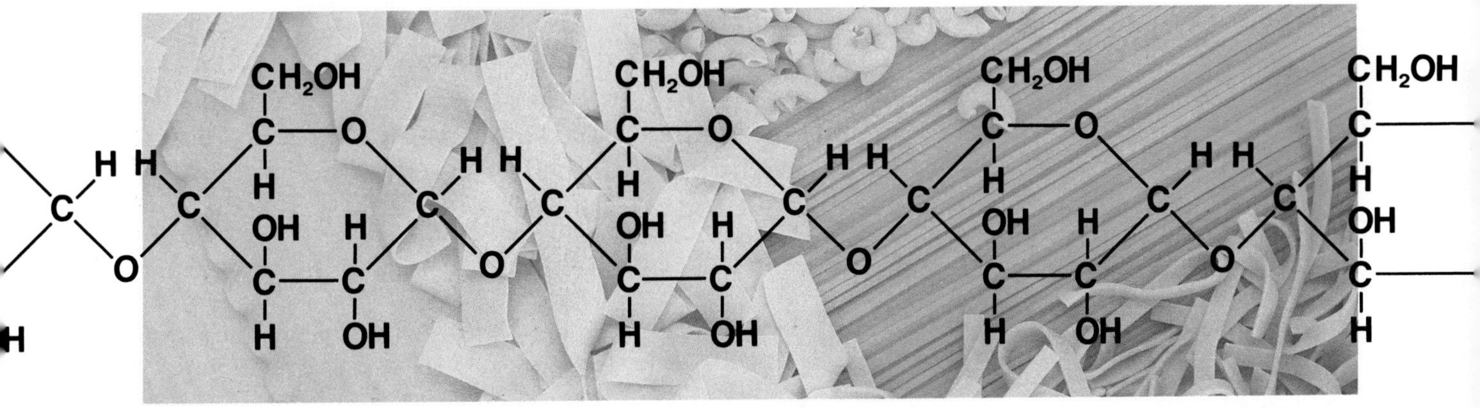

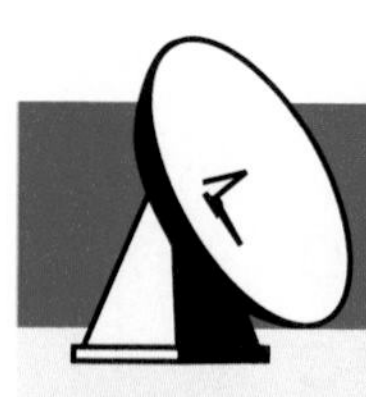

TECHNOLOGY

Fake Fats

Scientists at a company that produces processed foods have synthesized a molecule that promises the look and "mouth feel" of fats, but with no cholesterol and fewer calories. In a process involving heat and pressure, soybean or some other oil is combined with sugar. The result is a very large, complex molecule called a sucrose polyester. The enzyme responsible for breaking down fats during digestion has no effect on the sucrose polyester. So this "fake fat" passes through the body mostly unchanged.

A second fat substitute has been announced by another company. Because this product is made by combining water with egg or milk protein, its makers maintain that it is all natural. Special techniques shape the proteins into spheres to give the substance the smooth feel of fats. This compound substitutes protein and water for fat, so it is much lower in calories than fat. But because the product forms a gel when it is heated, it is limited to use in uncooked foods.

Think Critically: Both the sugar and oils used in one "fake fat" occur naturally. Why is this fat substitute considered synthetic?

Lipids

Fats, oils, and related compounds make up a group of organic compounds known as **lipids.** Lipids include animal fats, such as butter, and vegetable oils, such as corn oil. Lipids contain the same elements as carbohydrates, but in different proportions.

Have you heard that eating too much saturated fat can be unhealthy? You may also have heard that you should include unsaturated fat in your diet. Fats and oils are similar in structure to hydrocarbons, so they can be classified as saturated and unsaturated, according to the types of

Figure 13-20. At room temperature, fats are normally solids and oils are usually liquids.

Figure 13-21. Fats can be classified by the types of bonds in their carbon chains.

bonds in their carbon chains. Saturated fats contain only single bonds between carbon atoms and unsaturated fats contain at least one double bond. Most animal fats contain a great deal of saturated fats, whereas oils from most plants are mainly unsaturated.

Which fats, animal or plant, are mainly unsaturated?

Another lipid found in animal foods is cholesterol. Do you know that even if you never eat foods containing cholesterol, your body would make its own supply? The reason is simple. Cholesterol is used by the body to build cell membranes. Cholesterol is also found in bile, a digestive fluid. There is evidence that too much saturated fat and cholesterol in the diet contributes to heart disease. There is also evidence that unsaturated fats in the diet may help to prevent heart disease. A properly balanced diet includes some fats, just as it includes some proteins and carbohydrates.

Science and MATH

Molecular mass is the sum of the masses of the atoms in a molecule. Which substance has the greatest molecular mass: ethanol, propane, or formic acid?

SECTION REVIEW

1. What is a polymer? Why are polymers important organic compounds?
2. Compare and contrast proteins and nucleic acids.
3. **Apply:** Is ethanol a carbohydrate? Explain.

Concept Mapping

Skill Builder

Use a network tree to describe types of fats using the terms *saturated fats, unsaturated fats, single bonds,* and *double bonds.* If you need help, refer to Concept Mapping in the **Skill Handbook** on pages 684 and 685.

ACTIVITY 13-2
Biological Polymers

Problem: *What is the structure of some biological polymers?*

Materials
- index cards
- 4 paper clips

Procedure
1. Draw the structure of glucose, as shown on page 343, on an index card. Make the drawing large enough to fill the card.
2. Insert a paper clip where the OH appears at the left edge of the card and another paper clip where the H appears at the right edge of the card.
3. With your classmates, use the paper clips to join the glucose molecules on all your cards.
4. Your teacher will give you the structural formula of an amino acid. Draw its structure on another index card so that it fills the card. Place the acid group next to the right edge of the card and the amine group next to the bottom edge of the card.
5. Insert a paper clip through the card between the OH of the acid group and an H of the NH_2 (amine group).
6. With your classmates, use the paper clips on your cards to join together all the cards in the class.

Analyze
1. Starches and proteins are polymers. What are the monomers that make up each of these kinds of polymers?
2. For a bond to form between two glucose molecules or between two amino acid molecules, what small molecule has to be eliminated in each case?

Conclude and Apply
3. If you chew a starchy cracker and hold it in your mouth as it begins to digest, you may detect a sweet taste. What process can you suggest that would explain the change from starch into sugar?
4. The body builds its own proteins by forming peptide bonds between amino acids. Why, then, is it necesary for you to eat foods that contain protein?

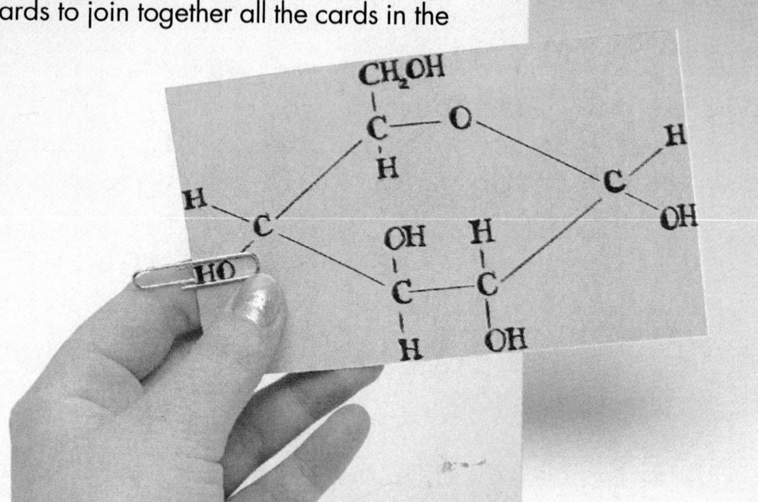

CHAPTER

REVIEW

SUMMARY

13-1: Simple Organic Compounds

1. Carbon is an element with a structure that enables it to form a very large number of compounds, known as organic compounds.
2. Saturated hydrocarbons contain only single bonds between carbon atoms, and unsaturated hydrocarbons contain double or triple bonds.
3. Isomers of organic compounds have identical formulas but different molecular shapes.

13-2: Other Organic Compounds

1. Aromatic compounds, many of which have odors, contain the benzene ring structure.
2. A substituted hydrocarbon contains one or more atoms of other elements that have replaced hydrogen atoms.

13-3: Science and Society: Alternative Sources of Energy

1. Biomass is the source of biogas and gasohol, two fuels that can be used to increase our energy supply.
2. Ethanol and gasohol are useful as substitutes for gasoline, but their production may damage the environment.

13-4: Biological Compounds

1. Many important biological compounds are polymers—huge organic molecules made of many smaller units, or monomers.
2. Proteins, nucleic acids, carbohydrates, and lipids are major groups of biological compounds found in organisms.

KEY SCIENCE WORDS

a. **alcohol**
b. **aromatic compound**
c. **biogas**
d. **biomass**
e. **carbohydrates**
f. **energy farming**
g. **gasohol**
h. **hydrocarbon**
i. **isomers**
j. **lipids**
k. **nucleic acids**
l. **organic compounds**
m. **polymers**
n. **proteins**
o. **saturated hydrocarbons**
p. **substituted hydrocarbon**
q. **unsaturated hydrocarbons**

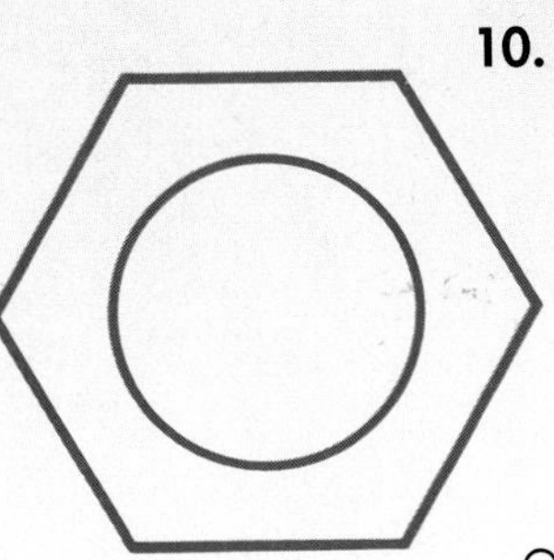

UNDERSTANDING VOCABULARY

Match each phrase with the correct term from the list of Key Science Terms.

1. a combination of ethanol and gasoline
2. hydrocarbons containing only single bonds
3. all animal and plant material
4. an –OH group replaces one or more hydrogen atoms in a hydrocarbon
5. compounds with identical chemical formulas but different molecular structures
6. hydrocarbons containing double or triple bonds between carbons
7. contains the benzene ring structure
8. fats, oils, and related compounds
9. formed from plant and animal waste
10. growing plants for use as fuel

CHAPTER REVIEW

CHECKING CONCEPTS

Choose the word or phrase that completes the sentence or answers the question.

1. A benzene ring is very ______.
   a. rare c. unstable
   b. stable d. saturated
2. Alcohols and organic acids are both ______ hydrocarbons.
   a. aromatic c. substituted
   b. saturated d. unsaturated
3. Two examples of ______ are a dog and a tree.
   a. biogas c. energy farming
   b. biomass d. hydrocarbons
4. Polymers are made from ______.
   a. monomers c. plastics
   b. isomers d. carbohydrates
5. Some examples of ______ are enzymes and hemoglobin.
   a. carbohydrates c. nucleic acids
   b. lipids d. proteins
6. DNA codes and stores ______.
   a. genetic information c. proteins
   b. nucleic acids d. lipids
7. DNA is made up of ______.
   a. amino acids c. polymers
   b. nucleotides d. carbohydrates
8. Glucose and fructose, both $C_6H_{12}O_6$, are ______.
   a. amino acids c. isomers
   b. alcohols d. polymers
9. If a carbohydrate has 16 oxygen atoms, how many hydrogen atoms does it have?
   a. 4 c. 16
   b. 8 d. 32
10. Cholesterol is a type of ______.
    a. sugar c. protein
    b. starch d. lipid

UNDERSTANDING CONCEPTS

Complete each sentence.

11. A ______ hydrocarbon has at least one of its hydrogen atoms replaced by atoms of another element.
12. Huge organic molecules made from many smaller ones are ______.
13. The organic compounds that make up muscle tissues in the body are ______.
14. Organic compounds called ______ have twice as many hydrogen atoms as oxygen atoms.
15. Polymers that control cell reproduction are ______.

THINK AND WRITE CRITICALLY

16. Why are more than 90 percent of all compounds organic compounds?
17. Use a diagram to explain single, double, and triple bonds in hydrocarbons. Draw a chain of carbon atoms that shows each type of bond.
18. Explain why a marsh provides an environment that produces biogas.
19. Show how the structure of an amino acid explains the term *amino acid*.
20. Some fats are polyunsaturated. Draw a chain of carbon atoms that would be polyunsaturated.

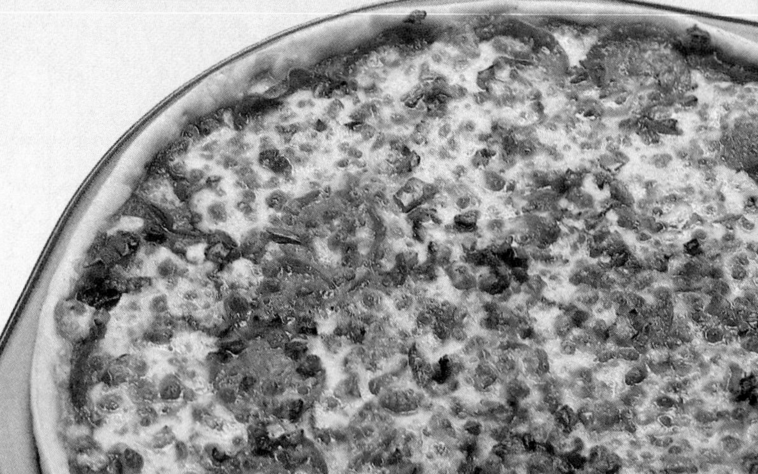

APPLY

21. Too much saturated fat in the diet is unhealthful. What is the difference in the composition of saturated fat and unsaturated fat?
22. Rubbing alcohol is isopropyl alcohol. How does this differ from propyl alcohol?
23. Carbon tetrachloride, a former dry cleaning fluid, is formed when all the hydrogen in methane is replaced by chlorine. Write the formula for carbon tetrachloride.
24. Explain how biomass has been used as an energy source throughout history.
25. Some vitamins are lipids and won't dissolve in water but will dissolve in other lipids. What is one reason we need fat in our diet?

MORE SKILL BUILDERS

If you need help, refer to the Skill Handbook.

1. **Making and Using Graphs:** Using the following table, plot the number of carbon atoms on one axis and the boiling point on the other axis. Use the graph to predict the boiling points of butane, octane, and dodecane ($C_{12}H_{26}$).

GRAPH DATA		
Name	**Formula**	**Boiling Point (°C)**
Methane	CH_4	–162
Ethane	C_2H_6	–89
Propane	C_3H_8	–42

2. **Interpreting Scientific Illustrations:** Which of the following terms apply to the illustration below? Terms: alcohol, aromatic, carbohydrate, hydrocarbon, lipid, organic compound, polymer, saturated, substituted hydrocarbon, unsaturated

```
H         H   H
 \        |   |
  C ═ C — C — H
 /            |
H             H
```

3. **Comparing and Contrasting:** In terms of DNA, compare and contrast identical twins and two people who are not identical twins.
4. **Recognizing Cause and Effect:** Our society has a definite need for more energy farming. List several causes and several effects of this need.
5. **Hypothesizing:** Sarah decided to go on a weight reduction diet. She is eating only lettuce and fruit. What do you predict will happen to Sarah as a result?

PROJECTS

1. Research hydrocarbons containing five carbon atoms. Draw diagrams of their structures, name them, and tell their uses.
2. Survey local gasoline stations and find out if they sell gasohol or sell gasoline. Find out how much of each fuel is sold per month. Display results in a table or graph.
3. Research ways crops are used as energy resources. Report your findings. Suggest how these ways could be implemented locally.

CHAPTER 14 Useful Materials

The Oscar is an award given for motion-picture excellence. It is a statue 25 centimeters high having a mass of 3.18 kilograms. The Oscar is made of a mixture of copper and tin that is covered with a very thin coating of pure gold. The total value of these materials is less than a few hundred dollars. If the Oscar were made of solid gold, it would be worth more than $40 000. Like Oscar, your body is made up of a combination of elements. How much do you think those elements are worth?

FIND OUT!

Do this activity to examine the elements that make up the human body.

Scientists have found that six elements—oxygen, carbon, hydrogen, nitrogen, calcium, and phosphorus—make up about 99 percent of a human body by weight. The remaining 1 percent of the body's weight is made up of other elements, including very tiny trace amounts of gold.

Just how much are all these elements worth? If you weigh 34 kilograms, the total value of all the elements in your body is about $3.88 at today's prices. Sorry about that!

Now try to guess what elements make up most of the following parts of the human body: muscles, bones, teeth, blood, fats, and water.

Gearing Up

Previewing the Chapter

Use this outline to help you focus on important ideas in the chapter.

Previewing Science Skills

- ▶ In the **Skill Builders,** you will map concepts and observe and infer.
- ▶ In the **Activities,** you will observe and infer and hypothesize.

What's next?

You have learned that the value or importance of an object often cannot be judged by the value of the materials of which it is composed. Now find out about the composition and properties of some very useful materials.

14-1 Materials with a Past

New Science Words

alloy
amalgam
ores
ceramic
glass
cermets

Objectives

- ▶ Identify common alloys and ceramics.
- ▶ Compare and contrast alloys and ceramics.

EcoTip

In the United States, 70 percent of all metals used are discarded after a single use.

Alloys

Imagine interstate highways without steel bridges, cities without brick buildings, and rooms without glass windows. It's almost impossible because such materials as steel, brick, and glass are part of your everyday life. As you will see, these and many more familiar materials are rooted in discoveries made thousands of years ago.

What is an alloy?

When a marching band goes by, you can easily recognize the brass section. The instruments are brilliant in both sound and color. Trumpets, trombones, and tubas are made of an alloy called brass. An **alloy** is a mixture of a metal and one or more other elements. Brass is a mixture of copper and zinc. The brass used in musical instruments and in some hardware is composed of about 80 percent copper and 20 percent zinc. These percentages indicate that a 10-gram brass key contains 8 grams of copper and 2 grams of zinc. Brass of this quality is a solid solution of the two metals. As you recall from Chapter 9, a solution is a homogeneous mixture. Any brass that contains more than 40 percent zinc is a heterogeneous mixture. This means that the mixture of molecules of the two metals is not completely uniform.

Have you ever been awarded a plaque or trophy? Chances are it is made of bronze, an alloy similar to brass. About 5000 years ago, people discovered that a new material could be made by mixing melted copper and tin. The new material—bronze—was stronger and

Figure 14-1. This bronze helmet is centuries old.

more durable than either copper or tin. This first known alloy became so popular and so widely used that a 2000-year span of history is known as the Bronze Age. The Bronze Age ended with the discovery of iron.

Bronze is more expensive than brass, because tin is more expensive than zinc. However, bronze is especially useful in plumbing fixtures and hardware that will be exposed to salt water. Brass is not suitable for such items as boat propellers, because the zinc reacts with minerals in salt water, leaving porous copper behind. The tin in bronze does not react with saltwater minerals.

Metals can be combined with other elements in different amounts to produce many different mixtures. Table 14-1 lists some common alloys. Thousands of alloys have been created since the time bronze was first made.

Table 14-1

COMMON ALLOYS		
Name	**Composition**	**Use**
Bronze	copper, tin	jewelry, marine hardware
Brass	copper, zinc	hardware
Sterling silver	silver, copper	tableware
Pewter	tin, copper	tableware
Solder	lead, tin	plumbing
Wrought iron	lead, copper, magnesium	porch railings, fences

An alloy has properties that are different from and more useful than the properties of the elements in it. Look at the bracelet shown in Figure 14-2. It appears to be made of gold. It is actually made of an alloy. As you know, gold is a very bright, very expensive element. It is

Figure 14-2. Like this bracelet, most gold jewelry is made of a gold-copper alloy.

also a soft metal that bends very easily. Copper, on the other hand, is a somewhat dull, inexpensive, hard metal. When melted gold and copper are mixed and then allowed to cool, an alloy is formed. It has most of the brilliance of gold and most of the sturdiness of copper. By varying the amounts of gold and copper, alloys with properties designed for different purposes can be produced. Figure 14-3 shows several gold alloys.

The alloys shown in Figure 14-3 contain only two metals. All alloys are not that simple. Do you or someone you know wear dental braces? The wire used in the braces is an alloy of gold, silver, platinum, palladium, zinc, and copper.

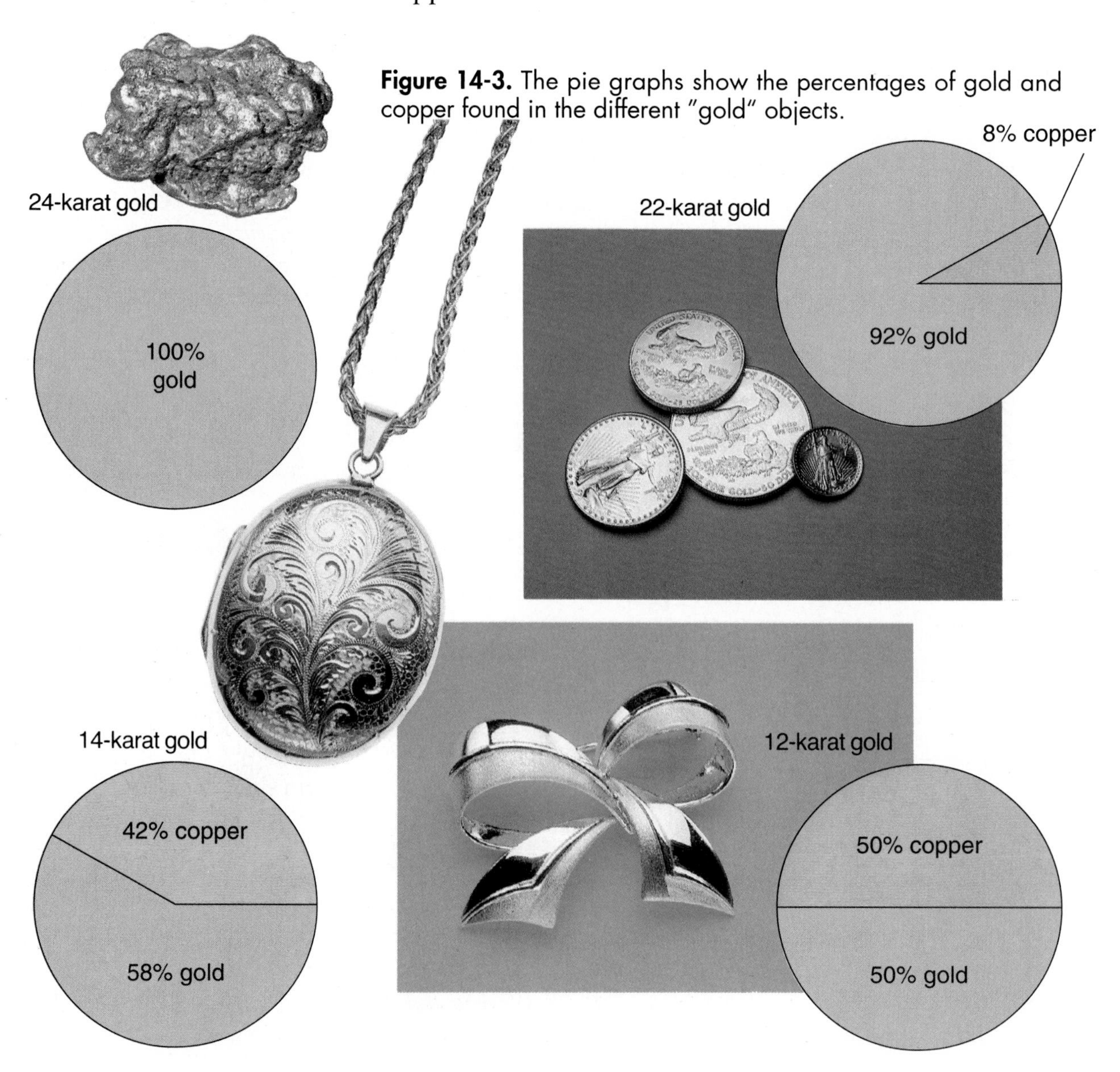

Figure 14-3. The pie graphs show the percentages of gold and copper found in the different "gold" objects.

PROBLEM SOLVING

Plastics Around You

Your writing pen, the cover of your notebook, a sandwich bag, and the covering on school desks are all plastics.

Plastics are stronger and more flexible than many natural products. They resist chemical change and wear. They are easy to clean and can be made in a variety of colors.

Many plastics are thermoplastics, which are plastics that soften or fuse when heated and harden again when cooled. The molecules in thermoplastics are linked together to form unbranched chains. Polyethylene, polystyrene, polyvinyl chloride, and nylon are some common thermoplastics.

Thermosets make up another group of plastics. Thermosets become permanently rigid when heated and will not melt again and reharden. The molecules in thermosets are linked in set chains. Common thermosets are Formica and Bakelite. What is one advantage of thermoplastics over thermosets?

Think Critically: Classify the materials in the first paragraph as thermoplastics or thermosets.

Some other alloys used by dentists are called amalgams. An **amalgam** is an alloy that contains mercury. Dental amalgams consist of mercury, silver, and zinc. You may have one in your mouth right now. They are used as fillings for cavities.

As you may have guessed by now, most metallic objects are manufactured from alloys. Various types of steel make up an important group of alloys. Steel production is greater than that of any other alloy. All types of steel are alloys of iron and carbon. You may have seen advertisements for carving knives with blades made of high-carbon steel. The carbon content of this alloy ranges from 1.0 percent to 1.7 percent. Because this steel

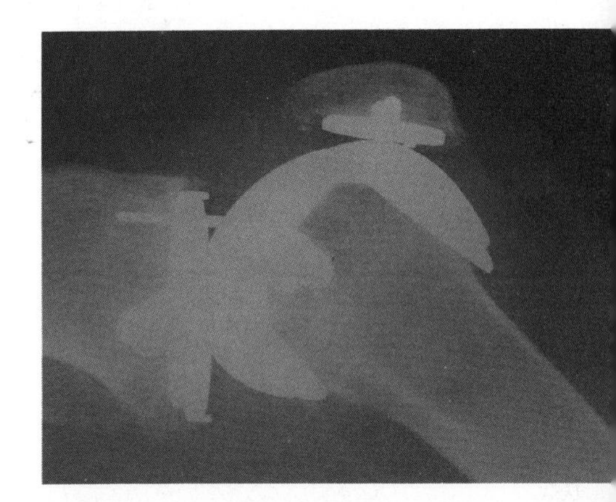

Figure 14-4. Surgical steel is used to join bones together

Table 14-2

SOME STEEL ALLOYS			
Name	**Composition**	**Properties**	**Uses**
Manganese	10–18% Mn	very hard	railroads, armor plate, conveyors
Duriron	12–15% Si	acid resistant	pipes, condensers, containers
Nickel	2–5% Ni	elastic, corrosion resistant	gears, drive shafts, cables
Invar	36% Ni	does not expand or contract	measuring tapes, pendulums
Permalloy	78% Ni	magnetic	cables
Stainless	14–19% Cr 7–9% Ni	strong, corrosion resistant	surgical instruments, knives, flatware
High speed	14–20% W, 4% Cr or 6–12% Mo, 4% Cr	keeps hardness at high temperatures	cutting tools, drill bits, saw blades

EcoTip

During a three-month period, Americans throw away enough aluminum to totally rebuild our entire commercial airline fleet.

is very hard, the knife blades will stay very sharp. As you can see from Table 14-2, steels of different compositions are made for different uses.

Aluminum alloys are the second largest group of alloys produced. Aluminum alloys are used to manufacture products ranging from foils used in food wraps to automobile bodies.

In the last decade, aluminum-lithium alloys have become very important. Because lithium is the lightest metal, these alloys are lightweight, yet exceedingly strong. Unlike other alloys, aluminum-lithium alloys maintain their strength at very high temperatures. In the future these alloys may be used to make the bodies of aircraft that will travel near the outer limits of Earth's atmosphere.

Most of the elements needed to make alloys are obtained from ores. **Ores** are materials in Earth from which metals can be economically obtained. If you look closely at the photo to the left, you can see the silver in the ore. Earth also contains clay. As you will see, clay is used in the manufacturing of another important group of useful materials.

Ceramics

Have you ever watched a potter making a bowl? If you have, you know that the potter spins wet clay on a wheel while shaping it into a bowl by hand. The bowl is then heated in a very hot oven to dry it. The bowl is removed from the oven and hardens as it cools. The bowl is made of a material called ceramic. A **ceramic** is a material made from dried clay or claylike mixtures. People began making ceramic containers thousands of years ago to store food and carry water.

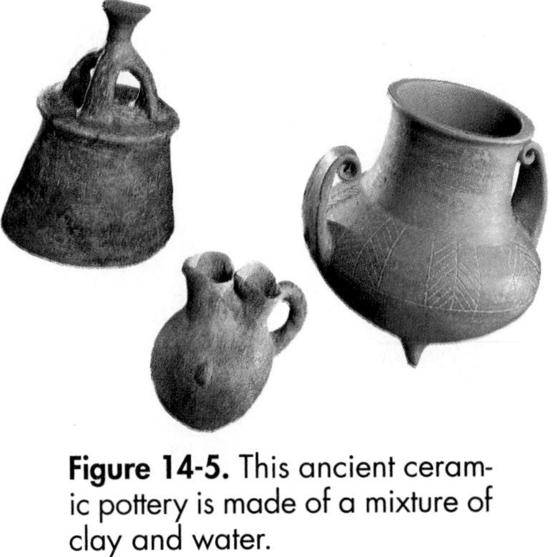

Figure 14-5. This ancient ceramic pottery is made of a mixture of clay and water.

As with alloys, there are thousands of different ceramics. Is your school building made of bricks? Does it have tiled hallways? Bricks and tiles are examples of a group of ceramics called structural ceramics. Structural ceramics are used by the construction industry because of their rigidity and strength. These ceramics contain silicon or aluminum. Recall that these elements can form many covalent bonds. These bonds make the ceramics strong and chemically stable. The porcelain ceramics used on sinks and bathtubs are called whitewares. Figure 14-6 shows examples of several important types of ceramics.

Look at some bricks or bathroom tiles, or at the porcelain enamel around the burner plates of a stove. You'll probably see small breaks in their surfaces. These breaks are evidence of one disadvantage of some ceramics: they are so rigid that they crack. If you've ever picked up the

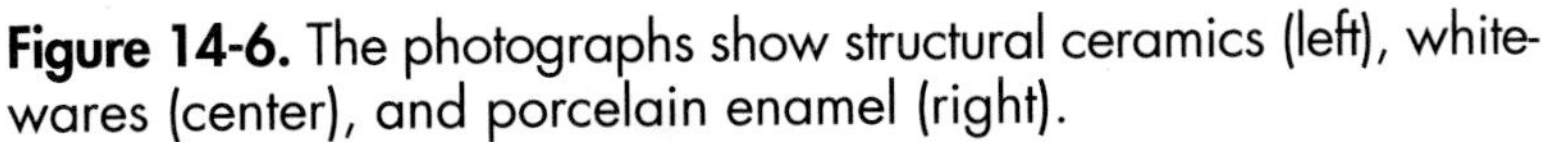

Figure 14-6. The photographs show structural ceramics (left), whitewares (center), and porcelain enamel (right).

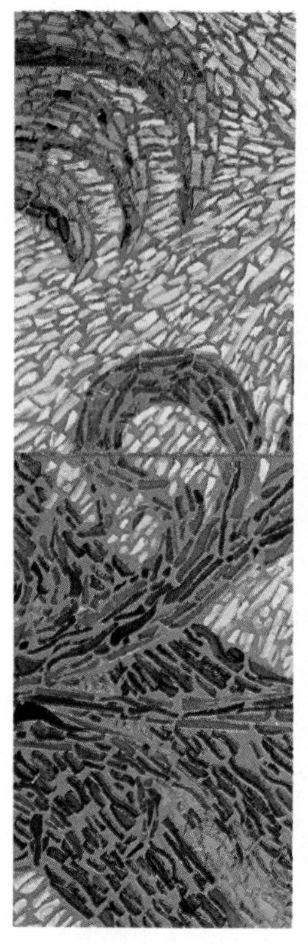
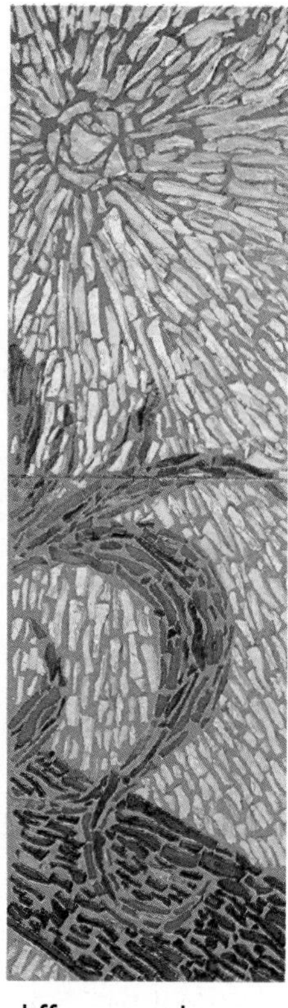

Figure 14-7. The different colors of the glass in this window are produced by pigments added to the glass. Such pigments include cadmium sulfide (red), cerium oxide (yellow), and cobalt oxide (blue).

pieces of a dinner plate you accidentally dropped, you are well aware of this.

Almost half of the ceramics produced today are classified as glasses. A **glass** is a ceramic without a regular crystal structure. Like all mixtures, glasses come in thousands of varieties. You are probably most familiar with the type of glass that you see in windows and drinking tumblers. This glass contains mostly oxygen and silicon, with smaller amounts of sodium and calcium, and a trace of aluminum. The major ingredient that is used to make glass is silicon dioxide—sand.

As with other ceramics, glasses can be made to have desired properties by changing the kinds and proportions of elements that make them up. Crystal pendants, vases, and chandeliers are made from glass that contains lead as well as silicon and oxygen. Food storage dishes that you can pull from a freezer and place in an oven to heat are also made of glass. These modern glasses contain boron and magnesium or lithium. As you can see in Figure 14-7, the addition of pigments to a glass alters its appearance.

Do you have magnets stuck to your refrigerator door? If so, chances are they are ceramic magnets. These magnets are examples of cermets. **Cermets,** or ceramic-metals, are materials designed and made to have properties of both ceramics and alloys. They are new materials with ancient pasts.

SECTION REVIEW

1. What is an alloy? List names and uses of several alloys.
2. Why are alloys produced?
3. What is a ceramic? List names and uses of several ceramics.
4. Why are ceramics very strong materials?
5. **Apply:** Ceramic magnets demonstrate properties of alloys of what element?

Concept Mapping

Make a network tree to describe the composition of common alloys using the alloys and elements mentioned in this section. If you need help, refer to Concept Mapping in the **Skill Handbook** on pages 684 and 685.

ACTIVITY 14-1
Preparing an Alloy

Problem: *How can two metals be combined to form an alloy?*

Materials

- copper penny
- zinc, 30-mesh
- hot plate
- nitric acid, HNO_3, dilute
- sodium hydroxide solution, NaOH, dilute
- evaporating dishes (2)
- tongs

CAUTION: *Acids and bases can cause burns. Rinse spills immediately.*

Procedure

1. CAREFULLY pour enough dilute HNO_3 into one evaporating dish to half fill the dish. Using tongs, grasp the penny and hold it in the acid for about 20 seconds.
2. Still using tongs, remove the penny from the acid and rinse it with cold tap water.
3. Place one teaspoon of 30-mesh zinc in the second evaporating dish. CAREFULLY add dilute NaOH to the dish to a depth of about 2 cm above the zinc.
4. Using tongs, carefully place the penny on top of the zinc. GENTLY heat the contents of the dish until the penny turns a silver color.
5. Set the control of the hot plate on medium high. Using tongs, carefully remove the penny from the dish and rinse it in cold tap water. Dry the penny and place it directly on the preheated hot plate until the penny has a golden color.

Analyze

1. Describe the appearance of the penny after it was immersed in the nitric acid. Why did its appearance change?
2. In Step 3, the penny turned a silver color. Was it actually becoming silver? Was it, at this point, an alloy?

Conclude and Apply

3. Do alloys require specific amounts of ingredients to form?
4. What alloy has this procedure produced?
5. Why is heat usually necessary for two metals to combine to form an alloy?

SCIENCE & SOCIETY

14-2 Recycling

New Science Words

recycling

Objectives

- Explain the importance of recycling solid wastes.
- Discuss ways in which state and local governments encourage recycling of solid waste materials.

Science and MATH

Choose an item that you could recycle, such as aluminum cans or newspapers. Save that item for one week, weigh the collected items, and find out how much money they are worth. Calculate how much you could make by recycling for a year.

Why Recycle?

Think about all the different things that get discarded every day. Paper products, bottles and cans, bicycles and automobiles—the list is endless. In the past few years, major efforts have been made in this country toward recycling some of our solid wastes. **Recycling** is the recovering and processing of waste materials to regain them for human use.

The reasons for recycling materials can be summed up in two words—*preservation* and *conservation*. We need to preserve and conserve natural resources.

Preserving the environment doesn't just mean picking up litter in our parks and along highways. Solid waste must be reduced. Most solid waste is deposited in landfills. Although today's landfills are a great improvement over the old municipal dumps, they are still smelly, unpleasant environmental eyesores. But perhaps more important, many of America's more populous areas are running out of space. For example, some states, such as New Jersey, are forced to transport much of their solid waste to landfills in other states, at considerable costs in money and energy. There's just no room for any more landfills. So, we have to find new ways to deal with solid waste. Recycling is one important way to reduce the amount of solid waste material.

When you think of conservation, you should think of these two things: conserving the raw materials and conserving

Figure 14-8. Most solid wastes are still buried in sanitary landfills like the one shown here.

energy. Consider the three most commonly recycled materials—aluminum, glass, and paper. When an aluminum can or a newspaper is recycled, some aluminum ore is conserved or a tree is saved. But of equal importance, much less energy is needed to process the recycled can or paper. For example, to produce one aluminum can from ore takes 12 times as much electricity as is needed to produce the same can from recycled aluminum.

Thus, recycling helps to conserve our fossil fuels and reduces air and water pollution. In the case of glass, the raw materials—mostly sand—are not in short supply. However, the amount of energy saved by recycling glass is significant.

If recycling is so beneficial, why don't we recycle more materials? There are several reasons. For one thing, most factory machines are designed to use raw materials. And in many cases, it is actually less expensive to make something from scratch than it is to use recycled materials. The entire process of recovering and reusing materials is a very complex one.

In some states the recycling of certain materials is required by law. People must separate recyclable materials and place them by the curb for pickup. Many states have deposit laws that require people to pay a deposit on all canned and bottled beverages. The deposit is refunded when the bottle or can is returned to the store. As space and raw materials become scarcer, more and more states will turn to recycling. Recycling is definitely the wave of the future.

SECTION REVIEW

1. What are the main reasons for recycling solid wastes?
2. In what two major ways is recycling encouraged in some states?

You Decide!

Assume you are a member of the city council of a town of 200 000 people. Your town is running out of space for storing solid wastes, but the city department responsible for collecting the 400 metric tons of solid waste produced daily is currently spending its total budget. Would you vote for or against a tax increase to develop a program of collecting recyclable materials? Why?

14-3 New Materials

New Science Words

plastic
synthetic fiber
composite

Objectives

- ▶ Compare and contrast plastics and synthetic fibers.
- ▶ Describe a composite.

Plastics

Think how often you and your family use the telephone. How often have you accidentally dropped the receiver or knocked a telephone over? Did the phone still work? A telephone never seems to wear out. It lasts because it is made mostly of plastics. The first plastic was made only about a century ago. You may be thinking that one hundred years is a long time. However, if you remember that alloys and ceramics have been around for thousands of years, you'll realize that plastics are really modern materials.

Recall from the last chapter that a polymer is a gigantic molecule formed from thousands of smaller organic molecules, such as hydrocarbons. Molecules that form polymers are called monomers. You are made of natural polymers, such as proteins and nucleic acids. Polymers that do not form naturally can be manufactured from organic compounds. These polymers are called synthetic polymers. A **plastic** is a material made from synthetic polymers.

You are probably familiar with the rolls of plastic bags that you find in the produce section of supermarkets. These bags are made of polyethylene (pahl ee ETH uh leen), one of the world's most widely produced and used plastics. Polyethylene is used to make, among other things, food storage containers, bottles, and the bands used around beverage six-packs. This synthetic polymer

Figure 14-9. The versatility and ruggedness of plastics make them ideal for use in objects that receive a lot of rough handling.

is made of monomers of ethene, an unsaturated hydrocarbon. The structural formula of ethene is shown to the right.

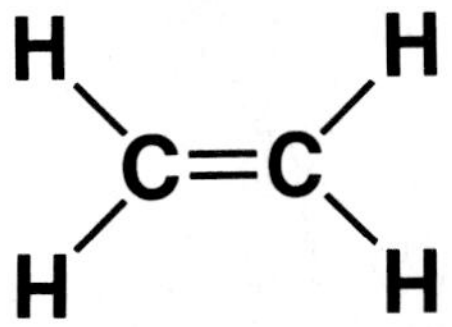

$$\begin{matrix} H & & H \\ & C=C & \\ H & & H \end{matrix}$$

Basically, polyethylene is formed by breaking the double bonds of many ethene molecules and allowing the molecules to reform as a polymer. Part of the polymer of polyethylene is shown below.

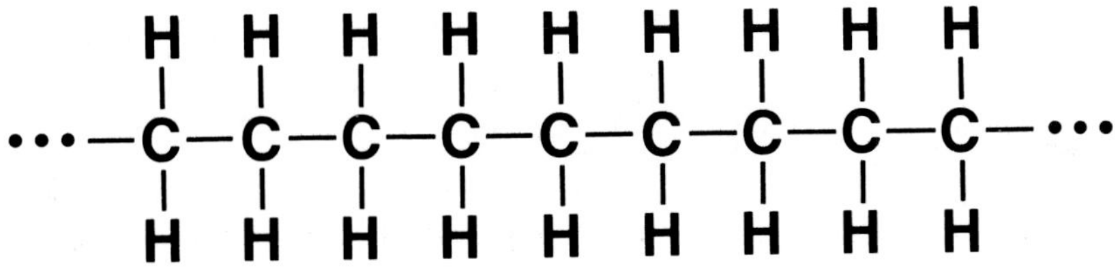

$$\cdots-\underset{H}{\overset{H}{C}}-\underset{H}{\overset{H}{C}}-\underset{H}{\overset{H}{C}}-\underset{H}{\overset{H}{C}}-\underset{H}{\overset{H}{C}}-\underset{H}{\overset{H}{C}}-\underset{H}{\overset{H}{C}}-\underset{H}{\overset{H}{C}}-\underset{H}{\overset{H}{C}}-\cdots$$

Because so many different organic compounds can be used as monomers, there are many different plastics, as shown in Table 14-3.

Table 14-3

COMMON PLASTICS		
Name	**Polymer Structure**	**Uses**
Polypropylene	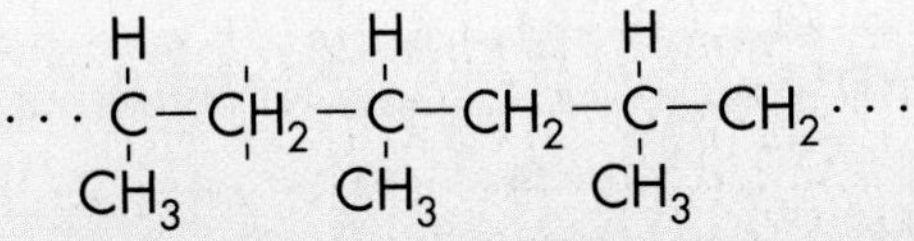 $\cdots\underset{CH_3}{\overset{H}{C}}-CH_2-\underset{CH_3}{\overset{H}{C}}-CH_2-\underset{CH_3}{\overset{H}{C}}-CH_2\cdots$	Rope, protective clothing, textiles, carpet
Polystyrene	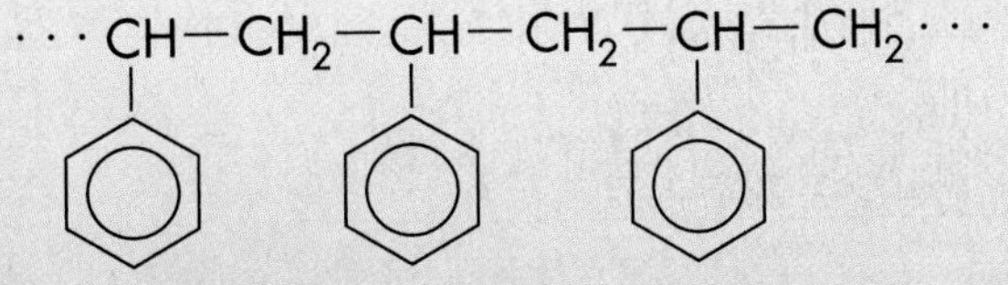 $\cdots CH-CH_2-CH-CH_2-CH-CH_2\cdots$ (each CH bearing a benzene ring)	Containers, boats, coolers, insulation, furniture, models
Polyvinyl chloride (PVC)	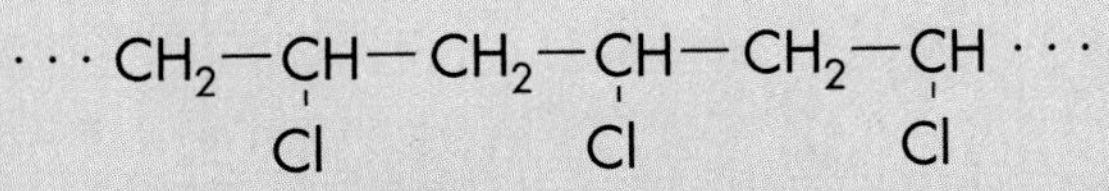 $\cdots CH_2-\underset{Cl}{CH}-CH_2-\underset{Cl}{CH}-CH_2-\underset{Cl}{CH}\cdots$	Rubber substitute, cable covering, tubing, rainwear, gaskets
Teflon (polytetrafluorethane)	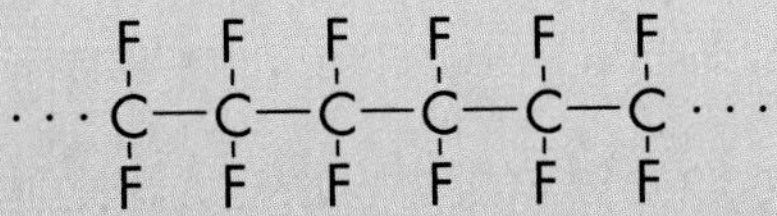 $\cdots\underset{F}{\overset{F}{C}}-\underset{F}{\overset{F}{C}}-\underset{F}{\overset{F}{C}}-\underset{F}{\overset{F}{C}}-\underset{F}{\overset{F}{C}}-\underset{F}{\overset{F}{C}}\cdots$	Nonstick cookware surfaces
Saran (polyvinylidene chloride)	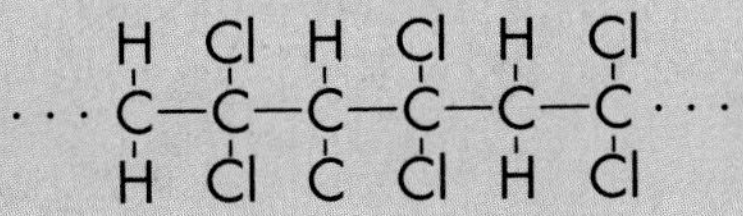 $\cdots\underset{H}{\overset{H}{C}}-\underset{Cl}{\overset{Cl}{C}}-\underset{C}{\overset{H}{C}}-\underset{Cl}{\overset{Cl}{C}}-\underset{H}{\overset{H}{C}}-\underset{Cl}{\overset{Cl}{C}}\cdots$	Clinging food wraps

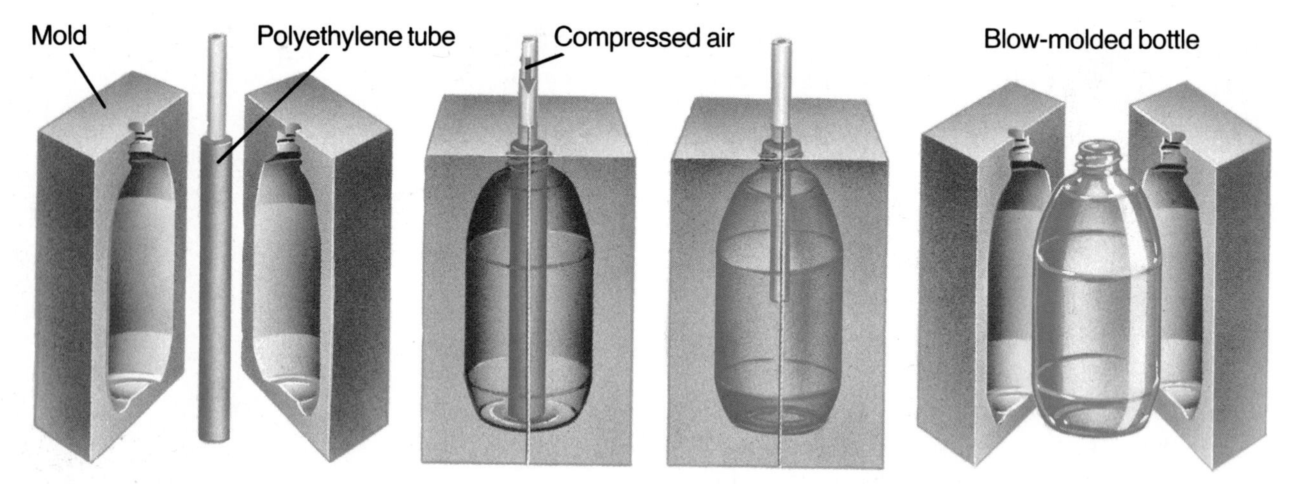

Figure 14-10. The major use of high-density polyethylene (HDPE) is to make blow-molded products, such as bottles for milk and other consumer products.

Do you know that making plastic soft drink bottles is similar to blowing up a balloon? Refer to Figure 14-10 as you read how polyethylene bottles are manufactured. First, a tube of warm polyethylene is placed inside a bottle-shaped mold. Then the mold is closed, sealing the bottom of the tube. Next, compressed air is blown into the polyethylene tube; the tube expands and takes the shape of the mold. The mold is then opened and the bottle is removed.

Table 14-4

COMMON POLYMERS		
Name	**Structural**	**Uses**
Dacron (a polyester)	$\cdots\underset{\underset{O}{\Vert}}{C}-C_6H_4-\underset{\underset{O}{\Vert}}{C}-OCH_2CH_2O-\underset{\underset{O}{\Vert}}{C}-C_6H_4-\underset{\underset{O}{\Vert}}{C}-OCH_2CH_2O\cdots$	Textiles, arterial grafts
Nylon 66	$\cdots\underset{\underset{O}{\Vert}}{C}(CH_2)_4-\underset{\underset{O}{\Vert}}{C}\overset{H}{N}(CH_2)_6\overset{H}{N}-\underset{\underset{O}{\Vert}}{C}(CH_2)_4\underset{\underset{O}{\Vert}}{C}-\overset{H}{N}(CH_2)_6\overset{H}{N}\cdots$	Tire cord, textiles, brush bristles, netting, carpet, athletic turf, sutures
Polyethylene	$\cdots CH_2-CH_2-CH_2-CH_2-CH_2-CH_2\cdots$	Tubing, prosthetic devices, packaging materials, kitchen utensils, paper coating
Orlon (polyacrylonitrile)	$\cdots\underset{H}{\overset{H}{C}}-\underset{CN}{\overset{H}{C}}-\underset{H}{\overset{H}{C}}-\underset{CN}{\overset{H}{C}}-\underset{H}{\overset{H}{C}}-\underset{CN}{\overset{H}{C}}\cdots$	Textiles

TECHNOLOGY

Plastic Parts Instantly

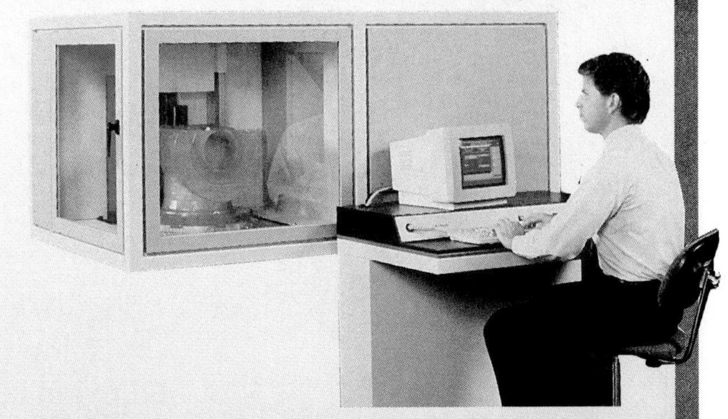

All over the world, powerful computer systems are being used to create electronic, three-dimensional models of the products of tomorrow. These systems, called CAD systems, have greatly reduced the amount of time needed to determine the size and shape of new products. Once a new product is designed, the next step is the construction of a model that can be held in your hand. This model is called a prototype, and it is tested to be sure that it works as the designer intended.

Now a process invented by Charles W. Hull permits engineers to grow a prototype from liquid plastic, using the information from the CAD electronic model. Software slices the electronic model into a series of horizontal layers. A laser under computer control is directed at the surface of a vat of photosensitive plastic. Each pass of the laser causes the plastic to harden. The hardened part sinks to the bottom of the vat, and the next laser pass adds another layer of hardened plastic. In this way the prototype actually grows from the bottom up. This technique, called stereolithography, should drastically reduce the time and expense required to bring many new products to market.

Think Critically: What properties make a material useful for building prototypes or models?

The clothing you are wearing may be made of fabrics that have been woven from synthetic fibers. A **synthetic fiber** is a strand of a synthetic polymer. Some synthetic fibers have amazing properties. For example, a strand of a synthetic fiber called Kevlar is five times stronger than a similar strand of steel. It is so strong it is used to make bulletproof vests. Synthetic fibers are used to weave both indoor and indoor-outdoor carpeting, upholstery coverings, and other textiles. Today, the use of synthetic fibers is greater than that of natural fibers. Table 14-4 lists the names and polymer structures of several familiar synthetic fibers. Fabrics with new properties are made by weaving natural fibers, such as cotton and silk, with synthetic fibers. If you look at the label of a permanent-press shirt, you will see that the fabric is a mixture of natural and synthetic fibers.

Figure 14-11. Wrinkle-resistant materials can be produced by combining synthetic fibers and natural fibers.

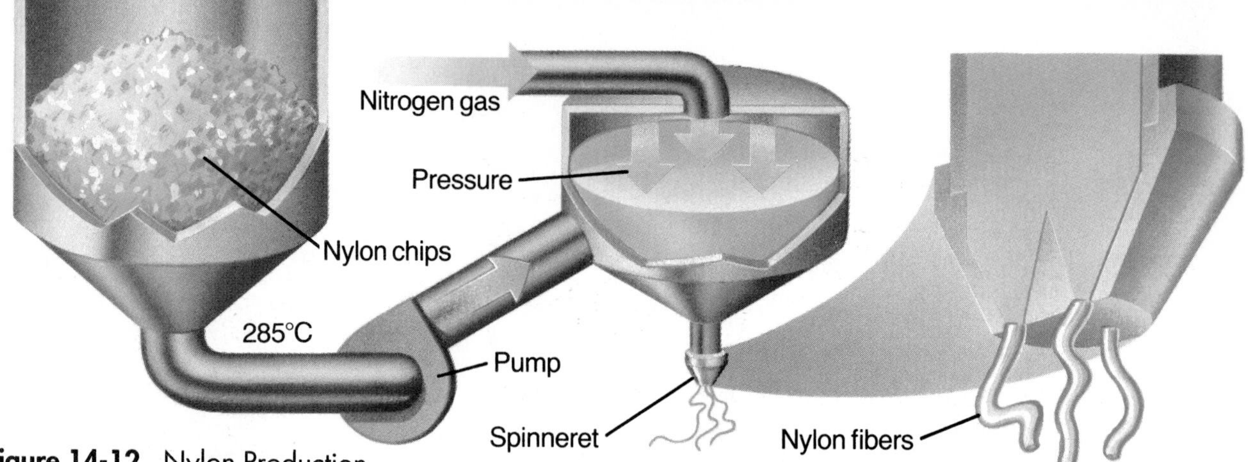

Figure 14-12. Nylon Production

Figure 14-12 shows how nylon fibers are manufactured. (a) Nylon chips are heated until they melt. (b) The melted nylon is pumped into a high-pressure chamber. (c) It is then forced through tiny openings of a nozzle called a spinneret. As it cools, the nylon forms long strands.

You may wonder where the raw materials—the hydrocarbons and organic compounds—used to produce plastics and synthetic fibers come from. Most of them are found in petroleum—crude oil—and in natural gas. Can you explain why plastics and synthetic fibers are sometimes called petrochemical products? As the production of plastics and synthetic fibers continues to increase, so will the demand for crude oil.

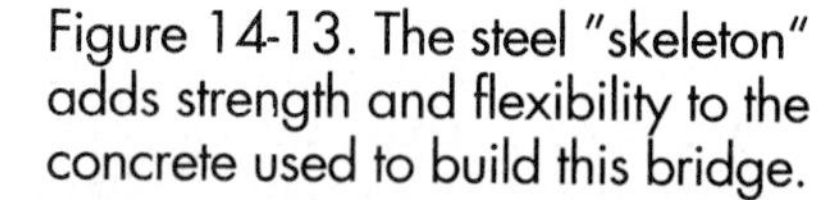

Figure 14-13. The steel "skeleton" adds strength and flexibility to the concrete used to build this bridge.

Composites

Have you ever seen a picture of a face made from cut-up photographs of famous people? These pictures are called composite pictures. The word *composite* means "made of two or more parts." Some materials are also composites.

Figure 14-13 shows a bridge being built of reinforced concrete. As you can see, the concrete has long steel rods

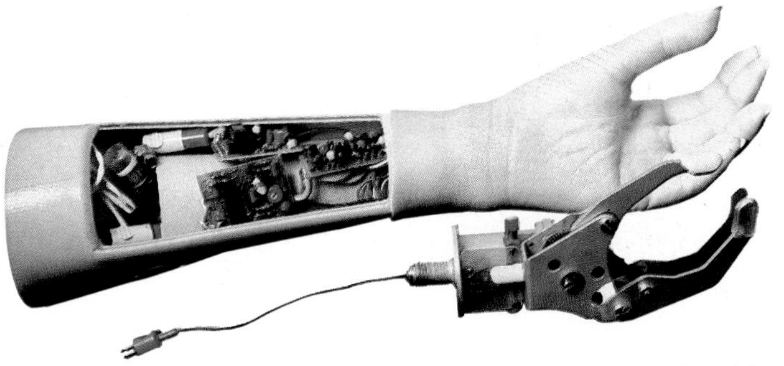

Figure 14-14. The composite material used in this artificial limb makes it strong, yet light in weight.

Figure 14-15. This familiar figure is a composite of the "potato" and whatever facial features are added to it.

running through it. These rods reinforce the concrete, giving it additional strength and support. Reinforced concrete is an example of a composite. A **composite** is a mixture of two materials, one embedded in the other.

Have you ever heard of cars with fiberglass bodies or boats with fiberglass hulls? These bodies and hulls are made of a glass-fiber composite. This composite is a mixture of small threads, or fibers, of glass, imbedded in a plastic. The structures of the fiberglass reinforce the plastic, making a strong, lightweight composite. A glass-fiber composite is an example of a ceramic imbedded in a plastic. How would you describe reinforced concrete? Many different composites can be made using various metals, plastics, and ceramics. Figure 14-14 shows an example. New composites are being produced every year. In the future you may be driving a car, working in a building, and living in a house that are made almost entirely of composites.

Did You Know?

The organs a spider uses to spin the fibers for its web are called spinnerets. The manufacture of nylon fibers mimics this natural process.

SECTION REVIEW

1. Name several plastics and synthetic fibers.
2. Compare and contrast plastics and synthetic fibers.
3. Describe a composite.
4. **Apply:** What advantages would an automobile engine made of a metal-ceramic composite have compared to one made of an alloy?

Observing and Inferring

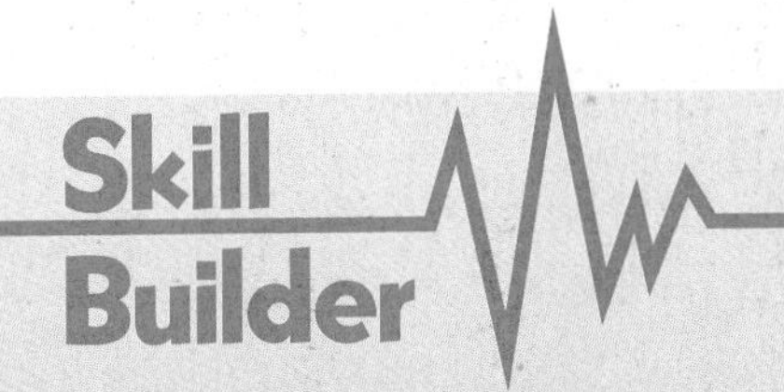

Look at the figures in this section. Describe a way to manufacture a roll of polyethylene bags. If you need help, refer to Observing and Inferring in the **Skill Handbook** on page 678.

ACTIVITY 14-2
Composite Model

Problem: *What new properties can result from combining materials?*

Materials 

- plaster of Paris
- paper clips
- water
- aluminum foil, heavy-duty
- measuring cup
- beaker
- hammer
- paper towels

Procedure

1. Shape the aluminum foil into a rectangle with a dividing ridge down the center. The approximate dimensions should be 20 cm long by 20 cm long, with sides about 3 cm high.
2. Measure 2/3 cup of water and 1 cup of plaster of Paris. Add the plaster of Paris slowly to the water.
3. Gently mix the two ingredients and let stand for five minutes.
4. Stir the mixture and pour approximately 1/4 of it into each side of the dividing ridge. Next, carefully place several paper clips on the surface of the plaster of Paris on one side of the divider.
5. After waiting five minutes, pour the rest of the mixture equally into the two compartments, covering the paper clips that are in one of the compartments. Let this set for 24 hours or more.
6. After 24 hours, remove the aluminum foil from the blocks and examine the outward appearance of both blocks.
7. Wrap each block in a towel. Using the hammer, firmly strike each block. (**CAUTION:** *Wear goggles. Do not strike too sharply.*) If nothing happens, strike the blocks again.

Analyze

1. Before striking the blocks with the hammer, was there any noticeable difference between the two blocks? If so, describe the difference.
2. How did the hammer blow affect each block?
3. If you had made the composite with pipe cleaners instead of paper clips, what differences might you have noticed?

Conclude and Apply

4. What can you conclude about the properties of the composite material made of plaster of Paris and paper clips?
5. In what way is the structure that you made similar to some concrete structures?

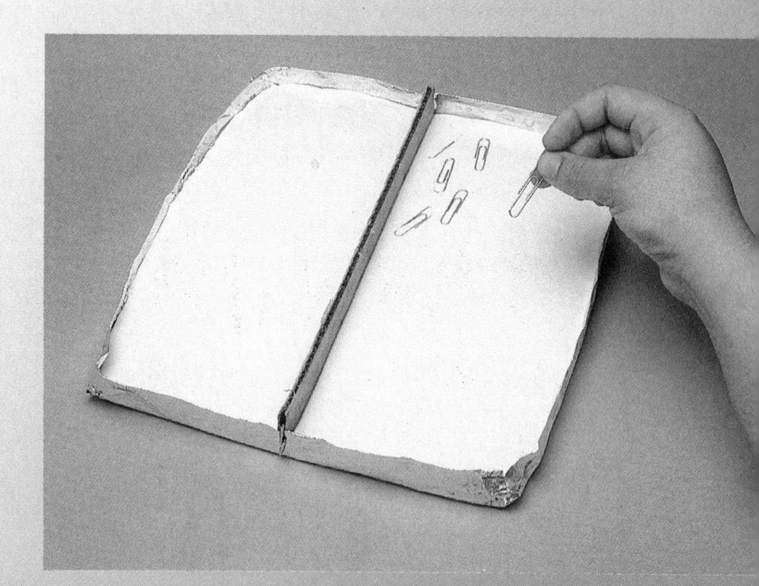

CHAPTER

REVIEW

SUMMARY

14-1: Materials with a Past

1. People have been making and using alloys and ceramics for thousands of years. Some common alloys include bronze, brass, amalgams, and various alloys of iron. Some common ceramics include structural ceramics, such as brick and tile, and various kinds of glass.

2. An alloy is a mixture of a metal with one or more other elements. Alloys exhibit metallic properties. Ceramics are composed of clay or claylike mixtures. Except for cermets—ceramic metals—ceramics generally have nonmetallic properties.

14-2: Science and Society: Recycling

1. There are two important reasons for recycling materials: preservation of the environment and conservation of natural resources.

2. State and local governments encourage recycling through educational programs and by passing laws requiring that certain materials be recycled.

14-3: New Materials

1. Plastics and synthetic fibers are materials made from synthetic polymers. Plastics can be produced in many forms, ranging from very thin films to thick slabs or blocks. Synthetic fibers are produced in thin strands that can be woven into fabrics.

2. A composite is a mixture of two materials, one embedded in the other. Reinforced concrete is an example of a composite.

KEY SCIENCE WORDS

a. **alloy**
b. **amalgam**
c. **ceramic**
d. **cermets**
e. **composite**
f. **glass**
g. **ores**
h. **plastic**
i. **recycling**
j. **synthetic fiber**

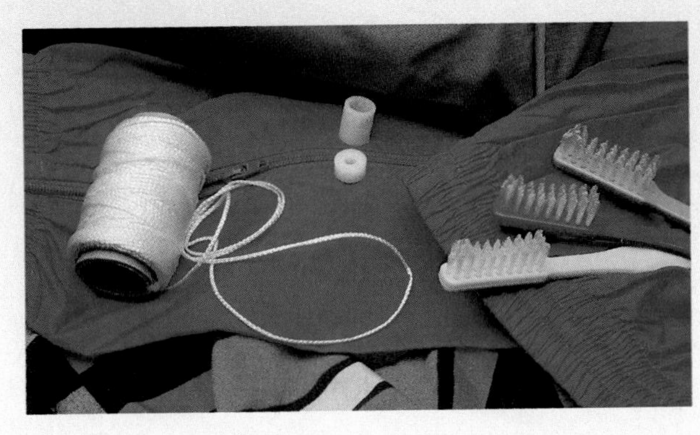

UNDERSTANDING VOCABULARY

Match each phrase with the correct term from the list of Key Science Words.

1. a strand of a synthetic polymer
2. ceramic with no regular crystal structure
3. mixture consisting of a metal and one or more other elements
4. made from dried clay or claylike mixtures
5. material made from synthetic polymers
6. mined sources of metals
7. mixture of one material embedded in another
8. recovering waste materials and reprocessing them for reuse
9. have properties of ceramics and alloys
10. alloy containing mercury

CHAPTER REVIEW

CHECKING CONCEPTS

Choose the word or phrase that completes the sentence.

1. The production of ______ is greater than that of any other alloy.
   a. amalgam **c.** bronze
   b. brass **d.** steel
2. Steel is an alloy of iron and ______.
   a. carbon **c.** tin
   b. mercury **d.** zinc
3. Structural ceramics contain silicon or ______.
   a. aluminum **c.** copper
   b. carbon **d.** lithium
4. The source of the materials used to make plastics is ______.
   a. clay **c.** petroleum
   b. ore **d.** synthetic fiber
5. The most commonly recycled metal is ______.
   a. aluminum **c.** iron
   b. glass **d.** paper
6. Brass and bronze both contain _____.
   a. mercury **c.** tin
   b. copper **d.** zinc
7. ______ alloys are very lightweight and strong.
   a. Aluminum-lithium **c.** Copper-tin
   b. Copper-zinc **d.** Iron-carbon
8. Most elements needed to make alloys are obtained from ______.
   a. amalgams **c.** ores
   b. ceramics **d.** recycling
9. Clay is used to make ______.
   a. alloys **c.** ores
   b. ceramics **d.** plastics
10. Most solid waste is ______.
    a. recycled
    b. in usable form
    c. deposited in landfills
    d. burned

UNDERSTANDING CONCEPTS

Complete each sentence.

11. Many magnets are made of ceramic-metals, known as ______.
12. ______ is formed by breaking the double bonds of many ethene molecules and allowing the molecules to reform as a polymer.
13. The Bronze Age ended when ______ was discovered.
14. Recycling helps to ______ fossil fuels.
15. Reinforced concrete is an example of a(n) ______.

THINK AND WRITE CRITICALLY

16. Explain why most glass products are relatively inexpensive.
17. Explain the difference between preservation and conservation.
18. Explain why it is important to recycle glass when the raw materials for making it are so plentiful.
19. Iron bonds more readily with other elements than does copper. Why do you think copper was discovered so much earlier than iron was?
20. In what way is steel different from such alloys as brass, bronze, and most aluminum alloys?

APPLY

21. Describe three ways you can conserve energy in your home.
22. List two reasons why you would choose to use recycled materials, even though other materials may cost less.
23. A lower carat gold has less gold in it than a higher carat gold. Why might you prefer a ring that is 10 carat gold over a ring that is 20 carat gold?
24. Explain how we contribute to air and water pollution when we don't recycle.
25. A synthetic fiber might be preferred over a natural fiber for use outdoors because it will not rot. Why might this property become a negative feature in the environment?

MORE SKILL BUILDERS

If you need help, refer to the Skill Handbook.

1. **Comparing and Contrasting:** Compare and contrast alloys and ceramics.
2. **Measuring in SI:** A bronze trophy has a mass of 952 grams. If the bronze is 85 percent copper, how many grams of tin are contained in the trophy?
3. **Interpreting Data:** Aluminum recycling saves 95 percent of the energy it takes to produce an aluminum product from ore. On the average, each American uses 320 aluminum beverage cans per year. If all 320 cans are recycled into other cans, how many new cans could be produced from ore for the same amount of energy used?
4. **Recognizing Cause and Effect:** Americans use 215 million aluminum cans per day. Compare the effects of recycling these cans to the effects of throwing them away.
5. **Concept Mapping:** Draw a network tree classifying matter, moving from the most general term to the most specific. Use the terms *compounds, elements, heterogeneous, heterogeneous mixtures, homogeneous, homogeneous mixtures, materials, solutions, substances*. Check (✔) the most specific term that describes an alloy and underline the most specific term that describes a composite.

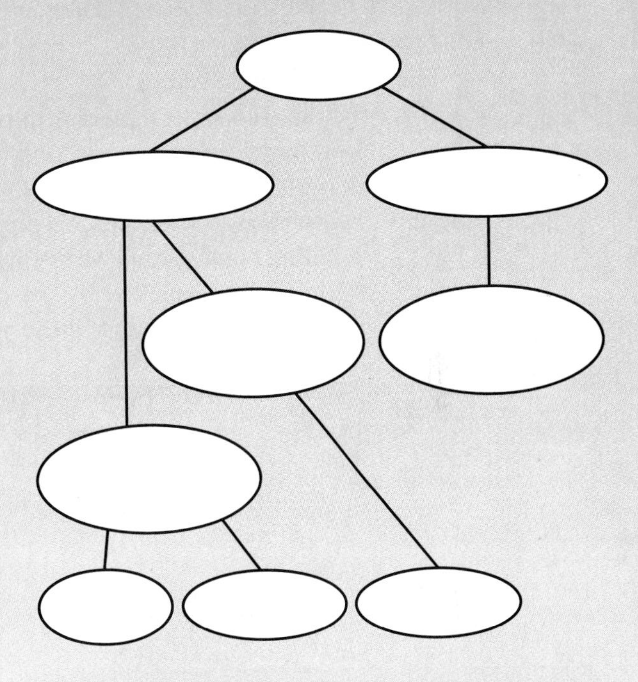

PROJECTS

1. Research gold, its alloys, and "carats." Find out several uses for gold and its alloys and what carat gold is used for each.
2. Make a poster of the floor plan of your school or an area of the school. On the floor plan, list locations where ceramics are used and the types of ceramics used there.
3. Research the production of silk fabric and compare it to production of synthetic fabrics such as nylon. Display samples of each.

UNIT 4

GLOBAL CONNECTIONS

Kinds of Substances

In this unit, you studied about elements, compounds, and other useful substances. Now find out how these different kinds of substances are connected to other subjects and places around the world.

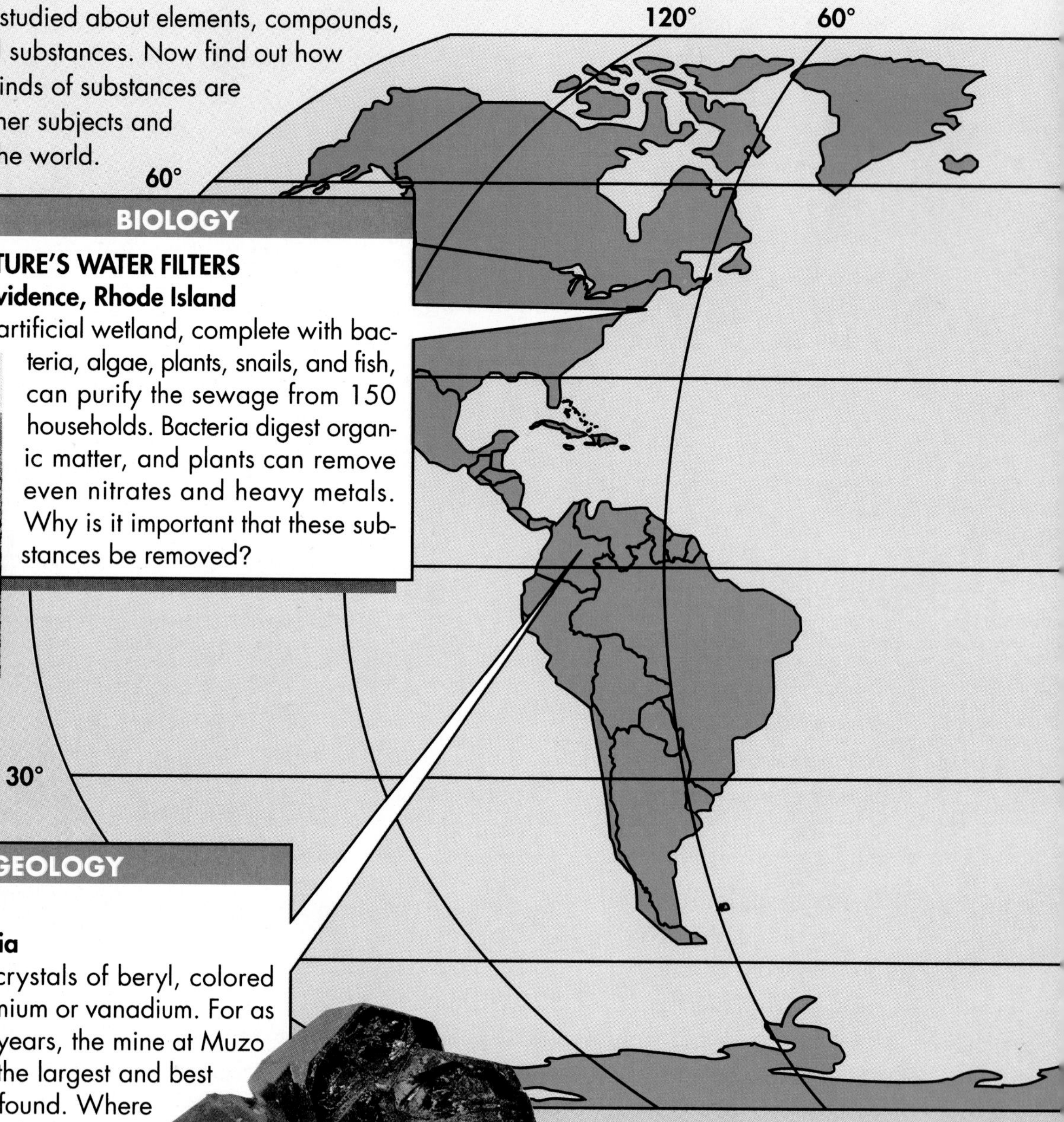

120° 60° 60° 30°

BIOLOGY

NATURE'S WATER FILTERS
Providence, Rhode Island

An artificial wetland, complete with bacteria, algae, plants, snails, and fish, can purify the sewage from 150 households. Bacteria digest organic matter, and plants can remove even nitrates and heavy metals. Why is it important that these substances be removed?

GEOLOGY

GREEN GEMS
Muzo, Columbia

Emeralds are crystals of beryl, colored green by chromium or vanadium. For as long as 1000 years, the mine at Muzo has produced the largest and best emeralds ever found. Where are some other places in the world where emeralds are mined?

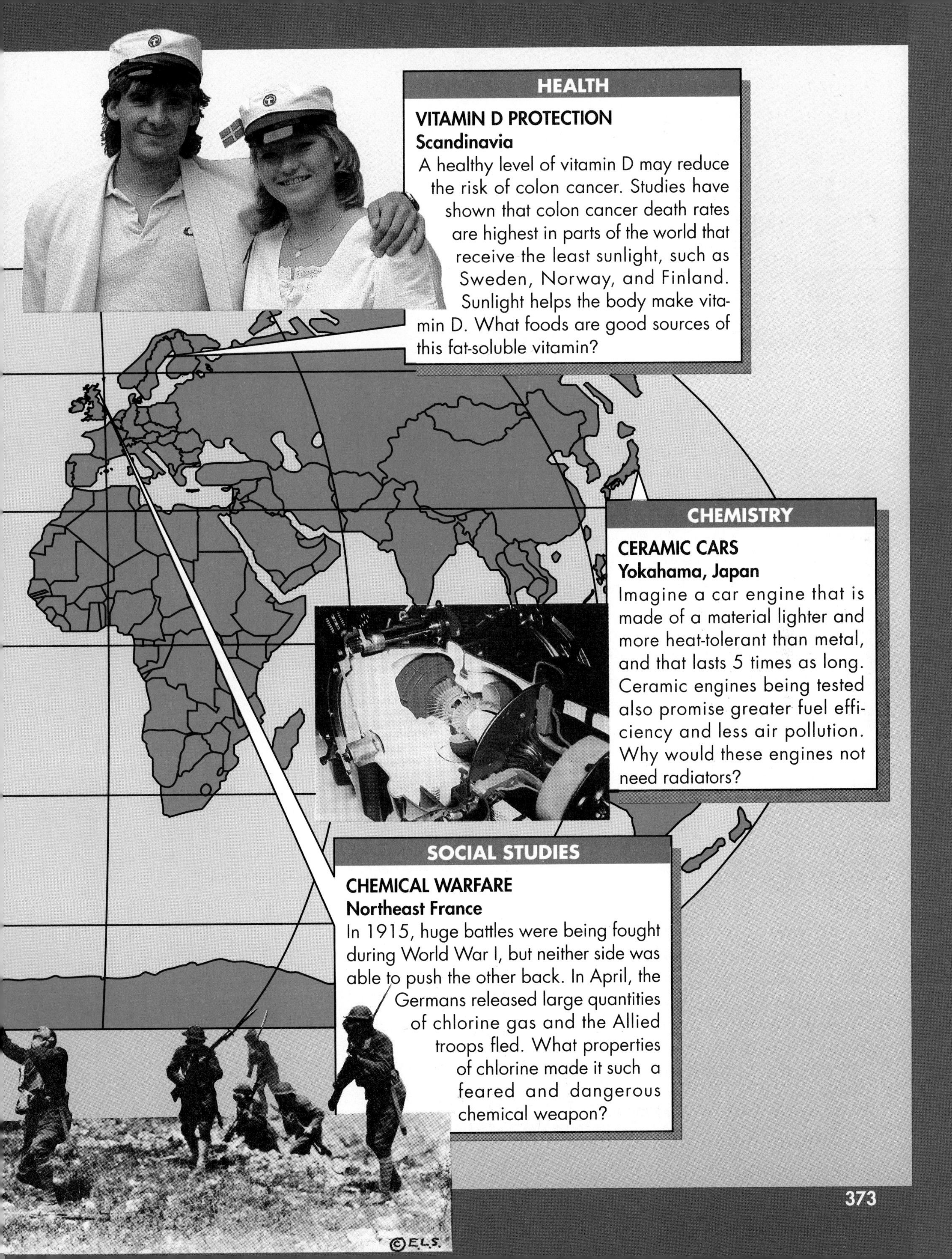

HEALTH

VITAMIN D PROTECTION
Scandinavia

A healthy level of vitamin D may reduce the risk of colon cancer. Studies have shown that colon cancer death rates are highest in parts of the world that receive the least sunlight, such as Sweden, Norway, and Finland. Sunlight helps the body make vitamin D. What foods are good sources of this fat-soluble vitamin?

CHEMISTRY

CERAMIC CARS
Yokahama, Japan

Imagine a car engine that is made of a material lighter and more heat-tolerant than metal, and that lasts 5 times as long. Ceramic engines being tested also promise greater fuel efficiency and less air pollution. Why would these engines not need radiators?

SOCIAL STUDIES

CHEMICAL WARFARE
Northeast France

In 1915, huge battles were being fought during World War I, but neither side was able to push the other back. In April, the Germans released large quantities of chlorine gas and the Allied troops fled. What properties of chlorine made it such a feared and dangerous chemical weapon?

©E.L.S.

CAREERS

PHARMACIST

A *pharmacist* dispenses drugs and medicines prescribed by physicians and dentists. He or she also advises consumers on the uses and possible side effects of medicines—both prescription and nonprescription. A pharmacist must know about the chemical properties of drugs and their effects on the body.

If you're interested in becoming a pharmacist, you should take high school classes in biology, chemistry, and mathematics. Pharmacists attend college for four to six years. All states require a pharmacist to pass a licensing examination.

For Additional Information

Contact the American Pharmaceutical Association, 2215 Constitution Avenue NW, Washington, DC 20037.

FARMER

Because modern farming is so complex, a *farmer* needs business skills, as well as an understanding of and experience in methods and problems of farming. Different kinds of farming include dairy production, livestock production, crop production, orchards, and vineyards.

To be a farmer, you should be in good physical condition, enjoy working outdoors, and be interested in working with plants and animals. You also need a good background in biology, chemistry, mathematics, and good mechanical ability.

Many farmers receive on-the-job training while working with relatives or as hired hands. Some farmers take vocational classes to expand and update their knowledge. Others take 2- or 4-year college courses in agriculture.

For Additional Information

Contact the American Farm Bureau Federation, 225 Touhy Avenue, Park Ridge, Illinois 60668.

UNIT READINGS

- Corrick, James A. *Recent Revolutions in Chemistry.* Danbury, CT: Watts, 1986.
- "Elements Show They're Metal." *New Scientist,* April 9, 1987, pp. 32-35.
- Ponte, Lowell. "Dawn of the New Stone Age." *Reader's Digest,* July, 1987, pp. 128-133.

The Art of Pottery

The passage that follows discusses an ancient technique for making pottery and a woman, Margaret Tafoya, who uses the technique to create highly prized pieces.

How and where pottery originated remains unknown, but early pottery can be traced back for about 9000 years. At some point, it was discovered that when dried clay bowls were placed in a fire and heated, they became hard and retained their shape—they became pottery, the first ceramics. Pottery could hold liquids, such as oil or water, which baskets could not.

In the areas of North America where pottery making flourished, three basic techniques were used—coiling, molding, and coiling and molding. Most pots were made by coiling or by a combination of coiling and molding. Coiling is done by forming a clay ball into a flat disk to serve as a base. Additional clay balls are rolled out to form coils and placed on top of one another to form the walls of the pot. Coiled pots are usually covered with slips to make the surface smooth for polishing, carving, or painting. Slip is made by mixing fine clay with water until it has the consistency of heavy cream. The pots are then polished with smooth, round polishing stones. The completed pots are fired in shallow pits or directly on the ground in fires of cedar wood. Potters can tell by the color of the fire when the pots are done.

Margaret Tafoya, a Pueblo potter from Santa Clara, New Mexico, uses the same methods to create her pottery that were used 1500 years ago by her Anasazi ancestors. She and other members of her family have dug clay from the same area for generations. She then shapes the clay, coil by coil, into a pot. The decorations she carves into her pots are symbols of the Santa Clara people. Her deeply carved redware and blackware are highly prized. She says the secret to the brilliant shine on her pottery is the polishing. She spends hours carefully rubbing her pots before firing them. The polishing stones she uses have been passed down from mother to daughter for generations.

In 1984, Margaret Tafoya was named a National Heritage Fellow by the National Endowment for the Arts. Since 1982 the Endowment has recognized, through its Folk Art Program, exceptional artists who have preserved their cultural and artistic traditions.

In Your Own Words

- Does a person have to be a painter or sculptor to be considered an artist? Write an essay supporting your position.

UNIT

5 INTERACTIONS OF MATTER

What's Happening Here?

What puts the fire in a fire ant's sting—and what in an aspirin takes the fire out? Acids are responsible in both cases. The itching and burning from the ant's bite are caused by formic acid. The easing of pain, fever, and swelling that an aspirin provides is caused by acetylsalicylic acid. How do acid solutions react with other substances to cause such different effects? You'll learn more about solutions and chemical reactions in this unit.

UNIT CONTENTS

CHAPTER 15 Solutions

Did you know that people in the United States consume about 1.5 trillion liters of water daily from sources such as the Colorado River? Almost all of this water is put through filtration.

FIND OUT!

Do this activity to find out what things are removed from water in the filtering process.

Use a sharp pencil to poke ten holes in the bottom of a foam cup. Place 1 cm of fine gravel in the cup. Then add 3 cm of clean sand. Place 1 cm of powdered charcoal on top of the sand. Finally, place another layer of fine gravel on top of the charcoal. Now your model filtration system is ready.

Slowly pour about 100 mL of dirty water through the cup. Catch the water that passes through the filtration system in a clear plastic cup. How does the filtered water compare to the original water? **CAUTION:** *This water is not suitable to drink.*

Gearing Up

Previewing the Chapter

Use this outline to help you focus on important ideas in this chapter.

Previewing Science Skills

- In the Skill Builders, you will compare and contrast, make and use a graph, and use a concept map.
- In the Activities, you will observe, organize, and collect data, and hypothesize.
- In the MINI-Lab, you will observe and infer.

What's next?

You have shown that filtering dirty water removes some contaminants. You will learn why all of them can't be removed by filtration alone when you read the pages that follow.

15-1 How Solutions Form

New Science Words

solute
solvent

Objectives

- Classify solutions into three types and identify their solutes and solvents.
- Explain the dissolving process.
- Describe the factors that affect the rates at which solids and gases dissolve in liquids.

Types of Solutions

To you the word *solution* may mean a kind of liquid mixture, like salt water or soda. Both these liquids are examples of solutions. But did you know that you also breathe a solution? Yes, air is a solution—and so is the sterling silver used to make fine jewelry. Solutions, then, can be gaseous or solid as well as liquid, as the examples show in Figure 15-1 and Figure 15-2. What makes all these mixtures solutions? Recall that a solution is a homogeneous mixture, in which the particles of the mixing substances are evenly distributed throughout.

There are three types of solutions, as shown in Table 15-1: gaseous solutions, liquid solutions, and solid solutions. A gaseous solution is a mixture of two or more gases. A liquid solution results when a gas, liquid, or solid is dissolved in a liquid solvent. A solid solution forms when a liquid and a solid or two or more solid substances

Figure 15-1. Examples of Gaseous and Liquid Solutions

Table 15-1

COMPOSITION OF SOLUTIONS		
	Types of Solutions	**Examples**
Gaseous Solutions	gas + gas	air
Liquid Solutions	liquid + gas liquid + liquid liquid + solid	club soda vinegar sugar water
Solid Solutions	solid + liquid solid + solid	dental amalgam steel, brass

Figure 15-2. These objects are made of solid solutions called alloys.

are melted, mixed, and cooled. Solid solutions containing metals are usually called alloys.

To describe a solution, you may say that one substance is dissolved in another. The substance being dissolved is the **solute.** The substance that dissolves the solute is the **solvent.** When a solid dissolves in a liquid, the solid is the solute and the liquid is the solvent. Thus, in salt water, sodium chloride is the solute, and water is the solvent. In a liquid-gas solution, the gas is the solute. In soda, carbon dioxide is the solute and water is the solvent.

In some solutions, either substance could be the solute or solvent. Generally, the substance present in the largest amount is considered to be the solvent. Air is 78 percent nitrogen, 21 percent oxygen, and 1 percent argon. Thus, nitrogen is the solvent. In the alloy sterling silver, made of 92.5 percent silver and 7.5 percent copper, silver is the solvent and copper is the solute.

In air—a gaseous solution—which substance is the solvent?

The Dissolving Process

A good way to make lemonade is to prepare a solution of sugar in water before you add the lemon juice and ice. By what process do a solid and a liquid, such as sugar and water, form a solution? The dissolving of a solid in a liquid occurs at the surface of the solid. For water solutions, keep in mind two things you have learned about water. Like the particles of any liquid, water molecules are constantly moving. You also know that a water molecule is polar, which means it has a positive end and negative end. Molecules of sugar are also polar.

Figure 15-3. To prepare a glass of lemonade, it helps to first dissolve the sugar in water.

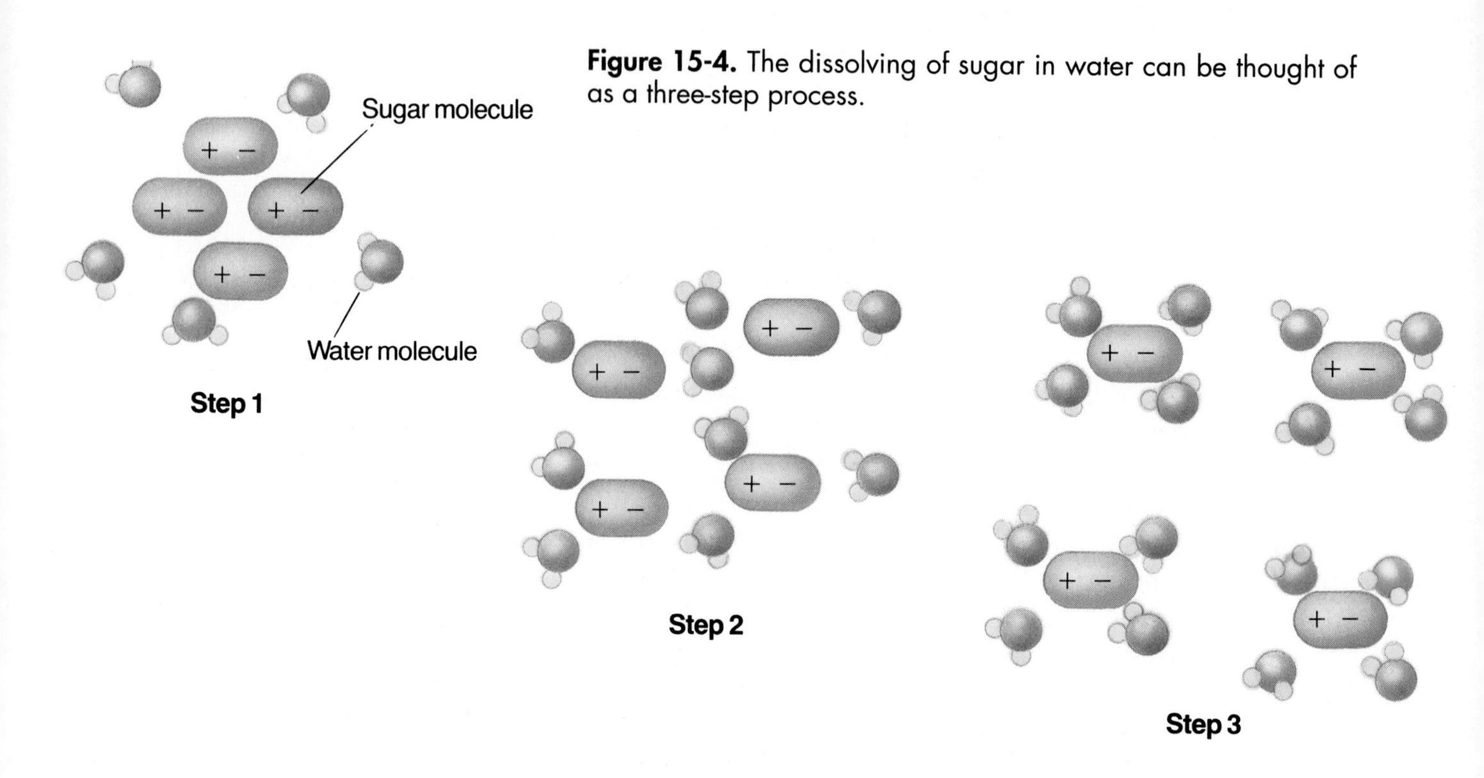

Figure 15-4. The dissolving of sugar in water can be thought of as a three-step process.

Study Figure 15-4 and the following steps to see how a sugar crystal dissolves in water.

Step 1: The moving water molecules cluster around the sugar molecules. The negative ends of the water molecules are attracted to the positive ends of the sugar molecules.
Step 2: The water molecules pull the sugar molecules into solution.
Step 3: The moving water molecules spread the sugar molecules out equally throughout the solution.

When sugar dissolves in water, why are the water molecules attracted to the sugar molecules?

The process repeats itself as layer after layer of sugar molecules move away from the crystal until all the molecules are evenly spread out. The same three steps occur when any polar or ionic compound dissolves in a polar liquid. A similar process also occurs when a gas dissolves in a liquid.

You know from your study of fluids in Chapter 8 that particles of liquids and gases move much more freely than the particles of solids. When gases dissolve in gases, or when liquids dissolve in liquids, this movement results in uniform distribution. Alloys are made by first melting and then mixing the components. What causes the particles in an alloy to be evenly spread out?

Rate of Dissolving

Think again about making a sugar solution for lemonade. When you add the sugar to the water, you stir it. Stirring a solution speeds up dissolving because it brings more fresh solvent in contact with more solute. The rapid movement of liquid solvent particles causes the solid solute to move into solution faster.

A second way to speed the dissolving of a solid in a liquid is to grind large crystals into smaller ones. Suppose you had to use a 5-g crystal of rock candy, which is made of sugar, to sweeten your lemonade. If you put the crystal into a glassful of water, it might take two minutes to dissolve even with stirring. However, 5 g of powdered rock candy would dissolve in the same amount of water in a few seconds with stirring.

Why does powdering a crystal cause it to dissolve faster? Breaking the crystal into smaller pieces greatly increases its surface area, as you can see in Figure 15-5. Because dissolving takes place at the surface of the solid, increasing the surface area allows more solvent to come in contact with more solid solute. Thus, the speed of the solution process increases.

A third way to increase the rate at which most solids dissolve is to increase the temperature of a solvent. Think of making a sugar solution for lemonade. You can make the sugar dissolve faster by putting it in hot water instead of cold water. Increasing the temperature of a solvent speeds up the movement of its particles. This causes more solvent particles to bump into the solute. As a result, solute particles break loose from the surface faster.

MINI-Lab

How does solute surface area affect dissolving?

Grind up two sugar cubes into granules. Compare the area covered by the granules to the area covered by the 12 sides of two sugar cubes. Place the granules and the cubes into separate 100-mL beakers of water, stir both evenly, and compare the times required to dissolve both. What do you conclude about dissolving rate and surface area?

Figure 15-5. As a crystal is broken down into smaller pieces, the total surface area of the crystal increases.

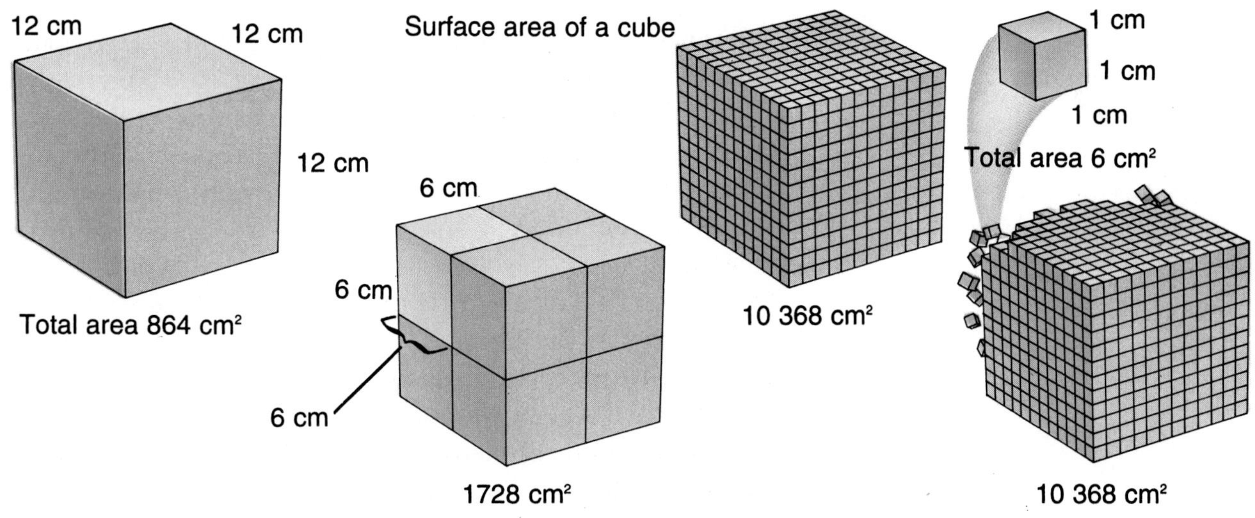

PROBLEM SOLVING

Derrick's Dilemma

Derrick's teacher asked the students to think about the dissolving process. She asked them to think of ways to speed up the rate of dissolving a solid in a liquid.

Derrick knew that granulated sugar dissolves faster than sugar cubes. He hypothesized that powdered sugar would dissolve even faster than granulated sugar.

Derrick tested his hypothesis at home. He placed one level spoonful of powdered sugar in one cup and the same amount of granulated sugar in an identical cup. He added 250 mL of water at the same temperature to each cup. To his surprise, all the powdered sugar didn't dissolve. His mother suggested he read the ingredients on the powdered sugar package.

Think Critically: What four factors did Derrick keep constant in his experiment? How can you explain why all the powdered sugar did not dissolve?

How do you think these same factors will affect a gas-liquid solution? When you shake or stir an opened bottle of soda, it bubbles up and usually spills over—or squirts out. Did you ever wonder why? Stirring or shaking a solution of a gas in a liquid causes the gas to come out of solution faster. This happens because as you shake or stir the solution, more gas molecules are exposed to the surface. These molecules escape more freely. Shaking and stirring also increase the temperature of the solution slightly.

Why does soda in an opened bottle bubble up when shaken?

How might you do the opposite—cause the gas to dissolve faster in the liquid? The answer is simple: cool the liquid solvent and increase the pressure of the gas. In a soda bottling plant, both of these things are done. The machinery cools the solution and keeps it under pressure.

Figure 15-6. When bottles of soda are opened, more gas comes out of solution in the warm bottle than in the cold one.

Maybe you have noticed the difference between opening a bottle of cold soda and a bottle of warm soda, Figure 15-6. Carbon dioxide gas is more soluble in cold water than in warm water. All gases are more soluble in cooler solvents. As shown in Figure 15-7, an unopened bottle of soda has no bubbles of carbon dioxide on its sides. In the sealed bottle, increased pressure keeps all of the gas dissolved. When the bottle is opened, the pressure of the carbon dioxide is greatly reduced. Then the carbon dioxide comes out of solution quickly.

Figure 15-7. Reduced pressure inside an opened bottle of soda causes the gas to come out of solution.

SECTION REVIEW

1. What are the three types of solutions? Give an example of each type.
2. What are three ways to increase the rate of dissolving a solid in a liquid?
3. **Apply:** Amalgams, sometimes used in tooth fillings, are alloys of mercury with other metals. Is an amalgam a solution? Explain.

Comparing and Contrasting

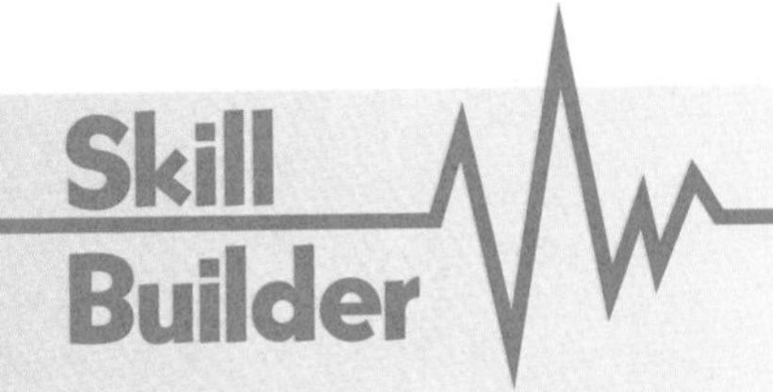

Compare and contrast the effects on the rate of dissolving (1) a solid in a liquid and (2) a gas in a liquid, when (a) the solution is cooled, (b) it is stirred, and (c) the pressure on it is lowered. If you need help, refer to Comparing and Contrasting in the **Skill Handbook** on page 679.

15-2 Oceans—The World's Largest Solution

New Science Words

desalination
distillation

Objectives

- ▶ Explain why an ocean is considered a solution.
- ▶ Compare and contrast methods of desalination.

Can Oceans Be Used as Fresh Water Sources?

About 97 percent of the water on Earth is in our salty oceans. Although the most abundant salt in the oceans is sodium chloride, the oceans also contain many other dissolved salts. Thus, the oceans make up the world's largest solution. Do we need this solution as a source of fresh water?

Science and WRITING

Prepare a report for the class explaining how minerals are mined from the ocean.

The need for fresh water in the world is greater today then ever before. Several reasons contributing to an increased need for fresh water are:

1. Increase in the world's population,
2. High concentration of people living in selected areas,
3. Increase in the uses of fresh water,
4. Increase in the pollution of existing sources of fresh water, and
5. Development of areas where water has always been scarce.

To meet this need, scientists are turning to desalination. Any method that removes dissolved salts from ocean water to produce fresh water is called **desalination.**

In 1989, two billion gallons of fresh water were produced per day by more than 1500 desalination plants throughout the world. The most common desalination methods used by these plants are distillation and freezing.

In **distillation,** water is evaporated from a solution. The water vapor is cooled, condensed, and collected as fresh water. The simplest and cheapest type of distillation uses a solar still. Heat from the sun evaporates the water. The water vapor condenses on the reservoir's transparent cover and runs into collecting trays.

Another type of distillation is flash distillation. Flash distillation makes use of the fact that water boils at a much lower temperature in a vacuum or reduced-pressure chamber. In flash distillation, ocean water is pumped into a vacuum chamber where it starts to boil. The salt-free water vapor is collected and condensed to form fresh water.

The freeze method also is being used to desalinate water. When salt water is cooled sufficiently, the ice that forms is salt-free. In the freeze method, ocean water enters a vacuum freezing chamber. The vapor produced is condensed directly to fresh water. The water that freezes is rinsed and then melted to form fresh water.

Many people are looking to our oceans as a vast resource of fresh water. But removing the solute from this solution is not a simple process.

Scraper
Water vapor
Wash water
Vacuum freezing chamber
Ice
Brine
Melter
Outgoing salt water
Outgoing fresh water
Incoming salt water
Heat exchanger

Figure 15-8. In the freeze process ocean water is frozen. This ice is rinsed and then melted to produce salt-free water.

SECTION REVIEW

1. Why are the oceans a solution?
2. Describe how distillation and freezing ocean water can be used to produce fresh water.

You Decide!

Suppose that you were in charge of building a desalination plant in a desert area. Large amounts of ocean water could be brought to the area. Which desalination method would you use and why?

15-3 Solubility and Concentration

New Science Words

solubility
saturated solution
unsaturated solution
supersaturated solution

Objectives

- Discuss how solubility varies among different solutes and for the same solute at different temperatures.
- Demonstrate an understanding of solution concentrations.
- Compare and contrast a saturated, unsaturated, and supersaturated solution.

Solubility

Sugar, you know, dissolves easily in water. Suppose you want to make super sweet lemonade. You stir two, three, four—or more—teaspoons of sugar into a cup of water, and it all dissolves. But eventually you add another teaspoon of sugar and it no longer dissolves, Figure 15-9.

Change the scene from your kitchen to a laboratory. Suppose now you measure out 1.3 g of lithium carbonate and add it to 100 g of water at 20°C. You observe that all of the lithium carbonate dissolves. But if you add more lithium carbonate to the same solution, none of it dissolves. However, you could add 34 g of potassium chloride to 100 g of water before no more will dissolve. You would have shown that the amount of these two substances that dissolves in 100 g of water at 20°C varies greatly.

Generally, the **solubility** of a substance is the maximum number of grams of the substance that will dissolve in 100 g of solvent at a certain temperature. Table 15-2 shows how the solubility of several substances varies at 20°C. For solutes that are gases, the pressure must also be given, for a reason you will learn soon.

Figure 15-9. The amount of sugar that can dissolve in a glass of water is limited.

Table 15-2

SOLUBILITY OF SUBSTANCES IN WATER AT 20°C	
Solid Substances	**Solubility in g/100 g of Water**
Barium sulfate	0.00025
Lithium carbonate	1.3
Potassium chloride	34.0
Sodium nitrate	87.6
Lithium bromide	166.0
Sucrose (sugar)	203.9
Gaseous Substances*	
Hydrogen	0.00017
Oxygen	0.005
Carbon dioxide	0.16

*when pressure = 1 atmosphere

Concentration

Suppose you added one spoonful of lemon juice to a glass of water to make lemonade. Your friend decided to add four spoonfuls of lemon juice to a glass. You could say that your glass of lemonade is dilute. Your friend's glass of lemonade is concentrated. It would have more lemon flavor than yours. A concentrated solution is one in which there is a large amount of solute in the solvent. A dilute solution is one in which there is a small amount of solute in the solvent.

Concentrated and *dilute* are not precise terms. But there are ways to describe solution concentrations precisely. One of these ways is to state the percentage by volume of the solute. Do you ever have a fruit juice drink in a box with your lunch or for a snack? Next time you do, read the label to see how much actual juice you are getting. The percentage by volume of the cherry juice in the drink shown in Figure 15-11 is 10 percent cherry juice and about 90 percent water. Ten mL of cherry juice plus 90 mL of water makes 100 mL of cherry drink. Generally, if two or more liquids are being mixed, the concentration is often given in percentage

Figure 15-10. The concentrated solution of lemonade contains more solute (lemon juice) than does the dilute solution.

Figure 15-11. The concentrations of fruit juices are often given in percent by volume.

Did You Know?

Floods have diluted the Great Salt Lake so much that you can sink in it now. In the past it was so salty that sinking in it wasn't possible.

by volume, stated in number of milliliters of solute plus enough solvent to make 100 mL of solution.

You can express concentration of a solid dissolved in a liquid as percentage by mass. This is the mass in grams of solute plus enough solvent to make 100 g of solution. Because 1 mL of water has a mass of 1 g, you would mix 10 g of sodium chloride with 90 mL of water to make a 10 percent solution of sodium chloride.

You can also express concentration as mass of solute in a liter of solution. When a certain volume of solution is measured out, the number of grams of solute it contains can easily be calculated.

EXAMPLE PROBLEM: Calculating the Mass of Solute/Liter of Solution

Problem Statement:

A potassium chloride solution contains 88 g of KCl in 1.0 L of solution. How many grams of solute are in 50 mL of solution?

Problem-Solving Steps:

1. Change 1.0 L to mL
   1.0 L = 1000 mL
2. Figure out the number of g of solute in 1 mL of solution.
   88 g/1000 mL = 0.088 g/mL
3. Use equation:
   Mass of solute = concentration of 1 mL solution × volume of solution

Solution:

Mass = 0.088 g/mL × 50 mL = 4.4 g

PRACTICE PROBLEM

Strategy Hint: Move decimal in 40.0 g three places to the left to find the mass of solute in 1 mL of solution.

1. Forty grams of lye (NaOH) was dissolved in enough water to make 1.0 L of solution. How many grams of lye would be in 20 mL of the solution?

Limits of Solubility

What is a saturated solution?

If you add 30.0 g of potassium chloride, KCl, to 100 g of water at 0°C, only 28 g will dissolve. You have a saturated solution because no more KCl can dissolve. A **saturated solution** is a solution that has dissolved all the solute it can hold at a given temperature. But if you heat the mixture to a higher temperature, more KCl can dissolve. As the temperature of the liquid solvent increases, the amount of solid that can dissolve also increases. Table 15-3 gives the amounts of a few solutes that can dissolve in water at different temperatures, forming saturated solutions.

Table 15-3

SOLUBILITY OF COMPOUNDS IN WATER AT VARIOUS TEMPERATURES					
		Solubility in g/100 g Water at the Temperature Indicated			
Compound	**Formula**	**0°C**	**20°C**	**60°C**	**100°C**
Ammonium chloride	NH_4Cl	29.4	37.2	55.3	77.3
Barium hydroxide	$Ba(OH)_2$	1.67	3.89	20.94	101.40
Copper(II) sulfate	$CuSO_4$	23.1	32.0	61.8	114
Lead(II) chloride	$PbCl_2$	0.67	1.00	1.94	3.20
Potassium bromide	KBr	53.6	65.3	85.5	104
Potassium chloride	KCl	28.0	34.0	45.8	56.3
Potassium nitrate	KNO_3	13.9	31.6	109	245
Sodium acetate	$NaC_2H_3O_2$	36.2	46.4	139	170.15
Sodium chlorate	$NaClO_3$	79.6	95.9	137	204
Sodium chloride	NaCl	35.7	35.9	37.1	39.2
Sodium nitrate	$NaNO_3$	73.0	87.6	122	180
Sucrose (sugar)	$C_{12}H_{22}O_{11}$	179.2	203.9	287.3	487.2

Another way to picture the effect of higher temperatures on solubility is with line graphs, like those in Figure 15-12. The lines are called solubility curves. You can use the curves to figure out the amount of solute that will dissolve at any temperature given on the graph. For example, at 47°C, about 82 g of both KBr and KNO_3 form saturated solutions with 100 g of water. About how much NaCl will form a saturated solution with 100 g of water at the same temperature?

An **unsaturated solution** is any solution that can dissolve more solute at a given temperature. Each time a saturated solution is heated to a higher temperature, it may becomes unsaturated. The term *unsaturated* isn't precise. At 20°C, 37.2 g of NH_4Cl dissolved in 100 g water is a saturated solution. However, an unsaturated solution of NH_4Cl could be any amount less than 37.2 g in 100 g of water at 20°C.

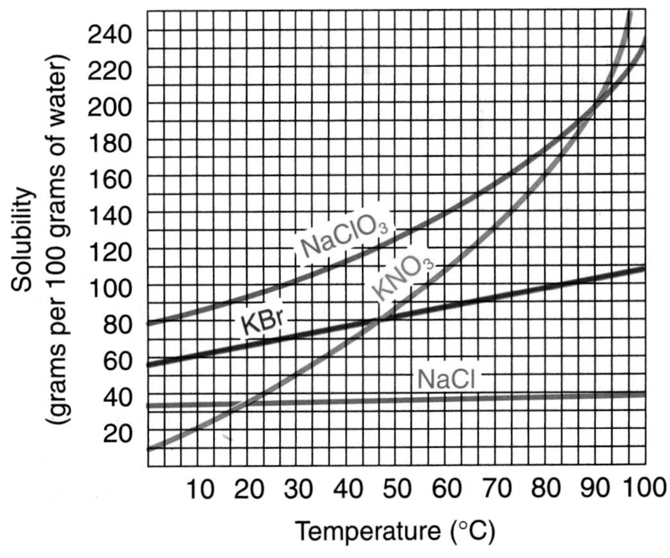

Figure 15-12. The solubilities of substances in water change with temperature.

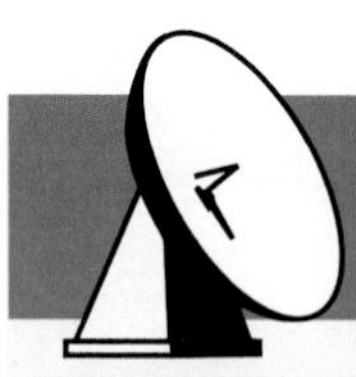

TECHNOLOGY

Replacing a Super Solvent

Scientists the world over are involved in a struggle to replace chlorofluorocarbons, often called CFCs. One of these compounds, named CFC-113, has been described as a super solvent. This compound doesn't bead up like water, so it is a better wetting agent. This means, for example, that CFC-113 can flow into all the tiny spaces on a printed circuit board to clean it up. This CFC has been used to clean sensitive equipment on the space shuttle and the electronic chips responsible for emission control in cars.

If this solvent is so fantastic, why are scientists trying to replace it? This super solvent has a serious drawback. Like other CFCs, it is damaging Earth's protective ozone layer, high in the atmosphere. As you will read in the next chapter, radiation from the sun splits off chlorine atoms from CFCs, and these chlorine atoms destroy ozone.

Thus, scientists need to develop solvents that can do the same jobs as CFCs but contain no chlorine. Recently, two new compounds called hydrochlorofluorocarbons, or HCFCs, have been tested. HCFCs work almost as well as the CFCs as solvents and cleaning agents, but they contain less chlorine and so cause less damage to the ozone layer. The HCFCs may be the new super solvents. They can be used until solvents containing no chlorine at all are available for use.

Think Critically: The inability of one substance to wet another is important in the development of many products. Provide some examples.

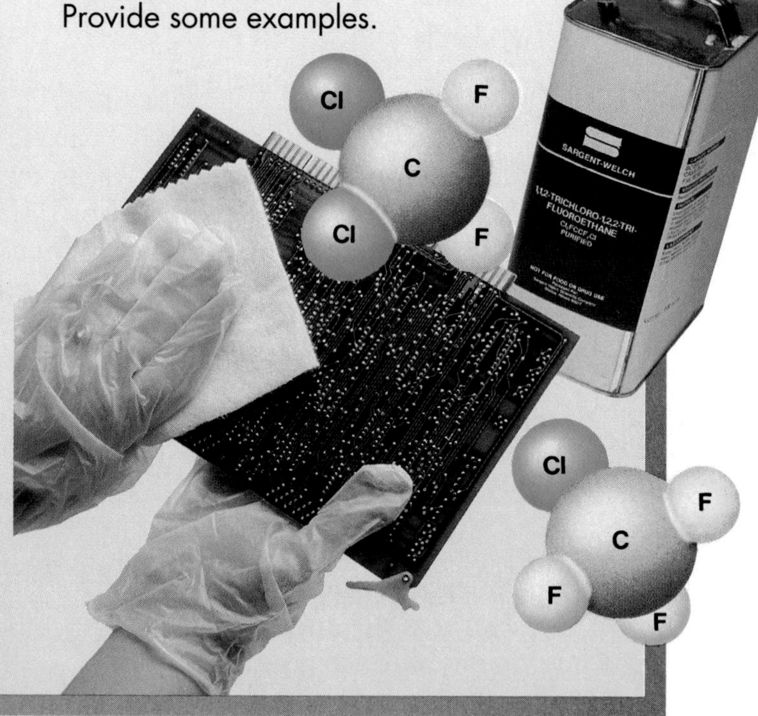

If you make a saturated solution of potassium nitrate 100°C and then let it cool to 20°C, part of the solute comes out of solution. You can see why—at the lower temperature, a saturated solution is formed with less solute. Most other saturated solutions behave in a similar way when cooled. But if you cool a saturated solution of sodium acetate from 100°C to 20°C, no solute comes out. This solution is supersaturated. A **supersaturated solution** contains more solute than a saturated one has at that temperature. This kind of solution is unstable.

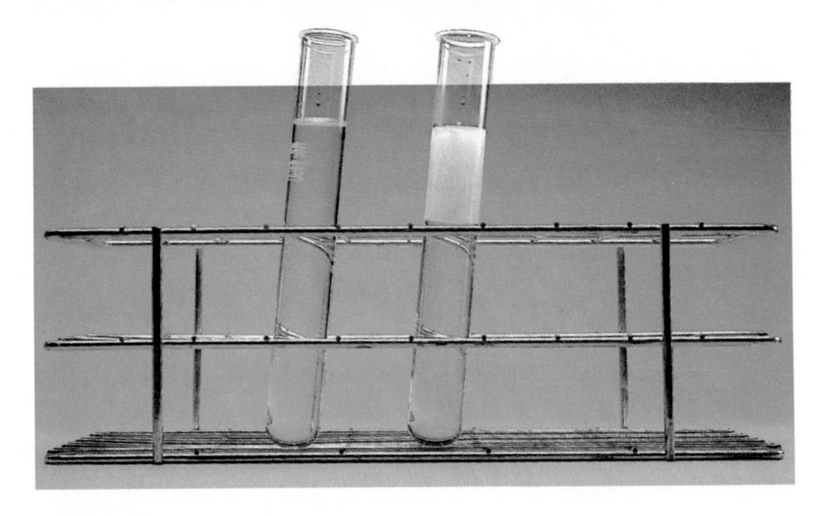

Figure 15-13. A supersaturated solution of sodium acetate (left) crystallizes out when a crystal of sodium acetate is added (right).

When a small crystal of the solute is added to a supersaturated solution, the excess solute quickly crystallizes out. Figure 15-13 shows this behavior in a supersaturated solution of sodium acetate.

Suppose you add a solute crystal to a solution. If the crystal dissolves, the solution is unsaturated. If the crystal does not dissolve, the solution is saturated. And if excess solute comes out, the solution is supersaturated. How would you explain each of these possible results?

SECTION REVIEW

1. Do all solutes dissolve to the same extent in the same solvent? How do you know?
2. Using Table 15-3 on page 391, state the following: the mass of $NaNO_3$ that would have to be dissolved in 100 g of water to form a saturated, an unsaturated, and a supersaturated solution of $NaNO_3$ at 20°C.
3. **Apply:** By volume, orange drink is 10 percent orange juice and 10 percent corn syrup. A 1500-mL can of the drink costs $0.95. A 1500-mL can of orange juice is $1.49, and 1500 mL of corn syrup is $1.69. How could you make orange drink? Is it cheaper to make or to buy?

Making and Using Graphs

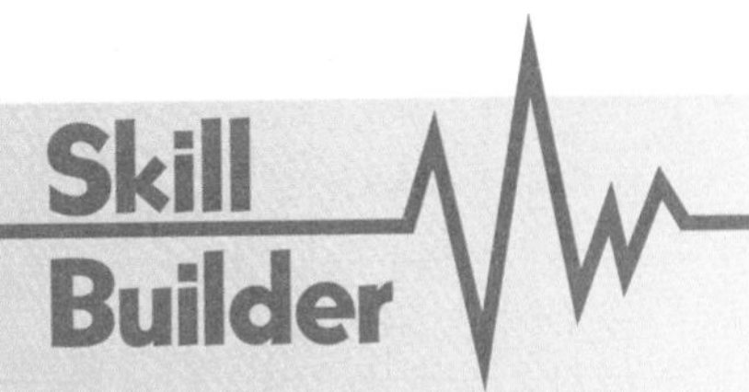

Using Table 15-3 on page 391, make a graph showing the solubility curves for $CuSO_4$ and $NaNO_3$. How would you make a saturated water solution of each substance at 80°C? If you need help, refer to Making and Using Graphs in the **Skill Handbook** on page 687.

ACTIVITY 15-1
A Saturated Solution

Problem: *How does temperature affect the solubility of a salt?*

Materials   

- 9.0 g potassium bromide, KBr
- distilled water
- copper wire stirrer
- laboratory burner
- large test tube
- test tube holder
- thermometer inserted in one hole of a 2-hole stopper

Procedure

1. Copy the data table and use it to record your observations.
2. Place 10 mL distilled water and 9.0 g potassium bromide in a large test tube.
3. Obtain a 2-hole stopper with a thermometer inserted in one hole. Place a copper wire stirrer through the second hole. Place the stopper in the test tube, as shown.
4. Using the wire stirrer, stir the contents of the tube while slowly heating it over a burner to 80°C. Remove the heat when all the KBr has dissolved.
5. Observe the solution as it cools. As soon as you see crystals begin to form, record the temperature. This is the saturation temperature.
6. Add 2 more mL of water to the tube and then repeat Steps 4 and 5.
7. Repeat Step 6.

Data and Observations

g KBr	mL H_2O	Saturation Temperature	g KBr per 100 g H_2O
9.0	10		
9.0	12		
9.0	14		

Analyze

1. Use your data to calculate the mass of KBr that would dissolve in 100 mL of water at the three different saturation temperatures you measured. Do this by setting up mathematical proportions. Write these masses in the right column of your data table.
2. How did the saturation temperature change as more water was added?
3. How does the mass of KBr that would dissolve in 100 mL of water change as temperature changes?

Conclude and Apply

4. Using your data and calculations, write a statement about how temperature affects the solubility of KBr in water.
5. In making hard candy, a solution of sugar in water is heated until a thick syrup forms. When the syrup is cooled and flavored, hard candy forms. Using what you have learned in this activity, explain what happens in this process.

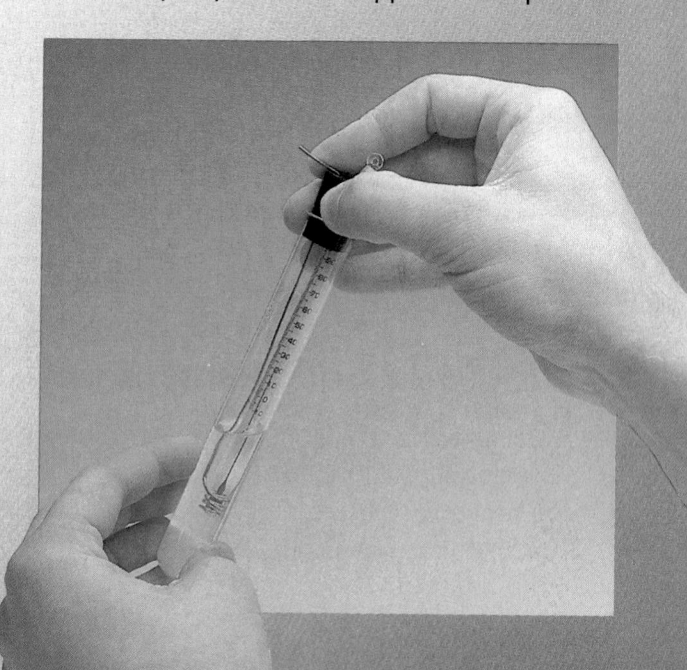

Particles in Solution 15-4

Objectives

- Compare and contrast the behavior of polar and nonpolar substances in forming solutions.
- Relate the processes of dissociation and ionization to solutions that conduct electricity.
- Explain how the addition of solutes to solvents affects the freezing and boiling points of solutions.

New Science Words

dissociation
ionization
electrolyte
nonelectrolyte

Solvents and Solutes

Why do you have to shake an oil and vinegar salad dressing, Figure 15-14, immediately before you use it? Oil and vinegar do not form a solution. Oil does not dissolve in vinegar.

Figure 15-14. Vinegar and oil don't form a solution. You can see oil drops in vinegar even when the mixture is shaken.

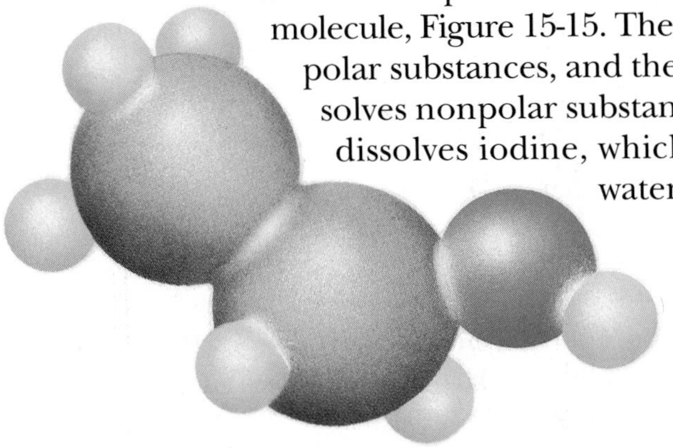

Why does a substance dissolve in one solvent but not in another? Solvents with nonpolar molecules dissolve solutes with nonpolar molecules. Benzene dissolves grease because both substances have nonpolar molecules. Similarly, polar solvents dissolve polar solutes. Water is a polar solvent, and it dissolves sucrose, a polar solute. Polar solvents also dissolve ionic solutes, such as sodium chloride. A polar solvent won't normally dissolve a nonpolar solute. That's why oil, which is nonpolar, won't dissolve in vinegar, which is polar. In general, when predicting which solutes will dissolve in which solvents, remember the phrase, "like dissolves like."

Some substances form solutions with both polar and nonpolar solutes, because their molecules have a polar and a nonpolar end. Ethanol is such a molecule, Figure 15-15. The polar end dissolves polar substances, and the nonpolar end dissolves nonpolar substances. Thus, ethanol dissolves iodine, which is nonpolar, and water, which is polar.

Figure 15-15. Ethanol has a polar –OH group at one end and a nonpolar $–CH_3$ group at the other end.

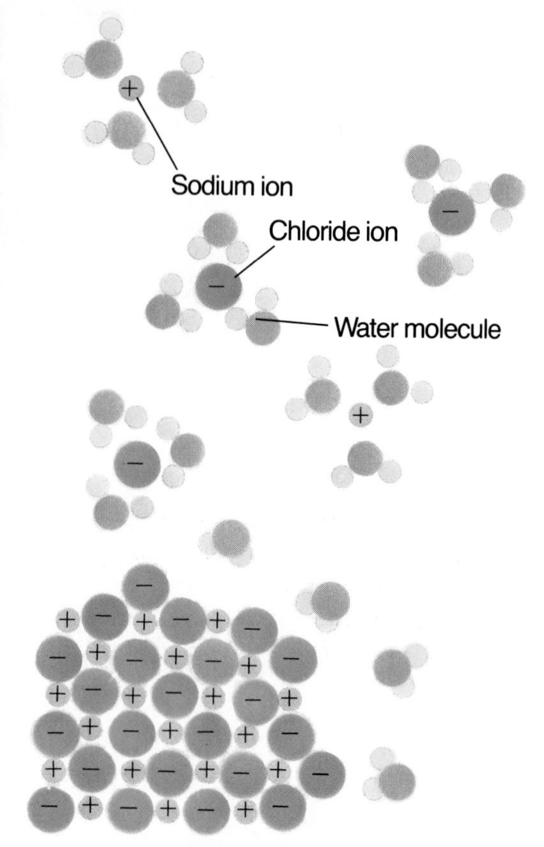

Figure 15-16. When sodium chloride dissolves in water, H_2O molecules surround, pull apart, and separate the Na^+ and Cl^- ions.

Solutions as Conductors

Why should you never use a hair dryer when standing on a wet bathroom floor? You take such precautions because, as you may have discovered in a safer situation, you are an excellent conductor of electricity. Your body is about 70 percent water with many ionic compounds dissolved in it. Like the metals used to wire lamps and appliances, water solutions of ionic compounds and of some polar compounds conduct electricity.

When an ionic solid dissolves in water, the positive and negative ions separate from one another. This separation process is called **dissociation.** For example, sodium chloride dissociates when it dissolves in water, as shown in Figure 15-16. When certain polar substances dissolve in water, the water pulls their molecules apart. This process is called **ionization.** Hydrogen chloride ionizes in water, as shown in Figure 15-17 below. A substance that separates into ions or forms ions in a water solution is called an **electrolyte.** Thus, both NaCl, which dissociates, and HCl, which ionizes, are examples of electrolytes.

Pure water does not conduct electricity. If a water solution is a conductor, the solute must be an electrolyte. But many polar substances, such as sugar and alcohol, do not ionize when they dissolve in water. These solutions do not conduct electricity. A substance whose water solutions are nonconducting is a **nonelectrolyte.**

Figure 15-17. When hydrogen chloride dissolves in water, H_2O molecules surround and pull apart HCl molecules, forming the ions H_3O^+ and Cl^-.

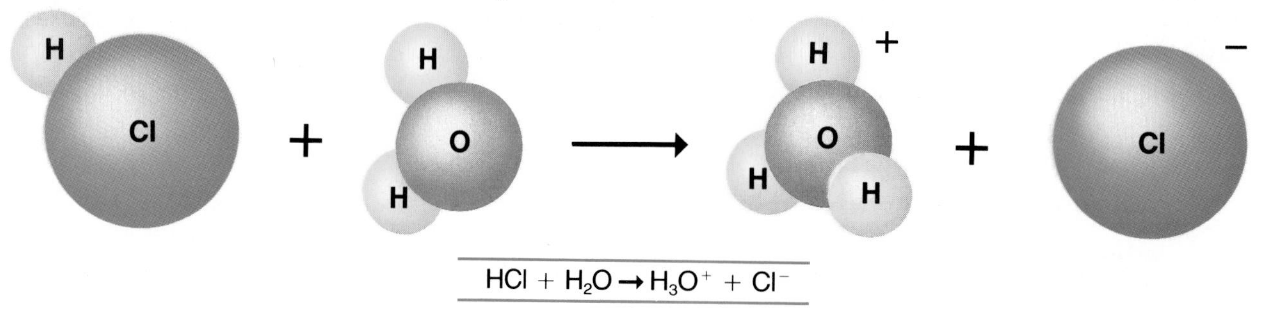

Effects of Solute Particles

Antifreeze that you may add to water in a car radiator prevents freezing. Adding a solute to a solvent lowers the freezing point of the solvent. How much the freezing point goes down depends upon how many solute particles you add.

How does antifreeze work? As a substance freezes, its particles organize themselves into an orderly pattern. The solute particles interfere with the formation of this orderly pattern. This prevents the solvent from freezing at its normal freezing point. To overcome this interference, a lower temperature is required to freeze the solvent.

Why do particles of solute lower the freezing point of water?

You may also know that antifreeze raises the boiling point of the water in a car radiator. As a result, the radiator does a better job of removing the heat from the engine in hot weather. The amount that the boiling point is raised depends upon the number of solute particles present. Generally, the more solute present, the higher the boiling point becomes. What causes this effect? Solute particles interfere with the evaporation of solvent particles. Thus, more energy is needed to allow the solvent particles to evaporate. And the solution boils at a higher temperature.

EcoTip

Antifreeze has a sweet odor and taste, but is deadly to pets. If antifreeze leaks onto the driveway, wash it away immediately. Never pour antifreeze into street gutters.

Why do particles of solute raise the boiling point of water?

Whatever the weather, solutions of antifreeze in water are part of your life every time you ride in a car or bus. And, as you read earlier, solutions such as lemonade and ocean water are also part of your everyday life.

SECTION REVIEW

1. Explain why (a) water dissolves sugar, (b) water does not dissolve oil, and (c) benzene does dissolve oil.
2. What kinds of solute particles are present in water solutions of (a) electrolytes and (b) nonelectrolytes?
3. **Apply:** In very cold weather, people often put salt on ice that forms on sidewalks and driveways. The salt helps melt the ice forming a saltwater solution. Explain why this solution may not refreeze.

Concept Mapping

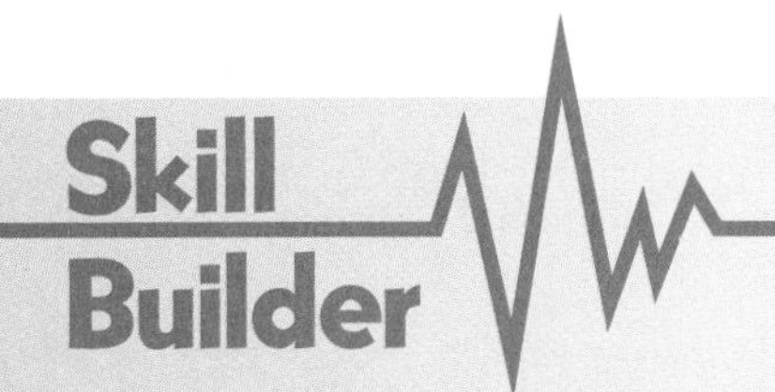

Draw a concept map to show the relationship among the following terms: *electrolytes, nonelectrolytes, dissociation, ionization, ionic compounds, certain polar compounds, other polar compounds*. If you need help, refer to Concept Mapping in the **Skill Handbook** on pages 684 and 685.

ACTIVITY 15-2
Boiling Points of Solutions

Problem: *How is boiling point affected by the addition of a solute?*

Materials   

- 400 mL distilled water
- thermometer
- ring stand
- 12 g table salt, NaCl
- laboratory burner
- 250-mL beaker

Procedure

1. Copy the data table and use it to record your observations.
2. Bring 100 mL of distilled water in a 250-mL beaker to a gentle boil. Record the temperature.
3. Dissolve 12 g of NaCl in 100 mL of distilled water. Bring this solution to a gentle boil and record its boiling point. **CAUTION:** *Always keep the thermometer away from the flame.*
4. Repeat Step 2, using 24 g of NaCl.
5. Repeat Step 2 again, using 36 g of NaCl.
6. Plot your results on a graph that shows boiling point on the vertical axis and g of NaCl on the horizontal axis.

Data and Observations

Grams of NaCl Solute	Boiling Point (°C)
0	
12	
24	
36	

Analyze

1. What difference is there between the boiling point of a pure solvent and a solution?
2. Instead of doubling the amount of NaCl in Step 4, what would have been the effect of doubling the amount of water?
3. What would be the result of using tap water instead of distilled water?

Conclude and Apply

4. In cooking, why would adding salt to water cause some foods to cook faster?
5. If you continued to add more salt, would you predict that your graph would continue in the same pattern or level off? Explain your prediction.

CHAPTER REVIEW

SUMMARY

15-1: How Solutions Form

1. Solutions are classified into three types according to their final state: gaseous, liquid, and solid.

2. Dissolving occurs when constantly moving solvent molecules attract particles of solute and surround them with solvent.

3. Stirring, surface area, temperature, and pressure may affect the rate of dissolving.

15-2: Science and Society: Oceans—The World's Largest Solution

1. The oceans form the world's largest solution because they contain, in addition to dissolved sodium chloride, many other dissolved salts.

2. Methods being used to desalinate ocean water include distillation, flash distillation, and freezing followed by melting.

15-3: Solubility and Concentration

1. Solubility of substances varies among different solutes and for the same solute at different temperatures.

2. Two precise ways to express solution concentrations are (1) percentage by volume and (2) percentage by mass.

3. A solution may be saturated, unsaturated, or supersaturated.

15-4: Particles in Solution

1. Usually, among polar and nonpolar solvents and solutes, "like dissolves like."

2. Ionic compounds dissociate when dissolved in water, and some polar compounds ionize when dissolved in water.

3. Adding a solute to a solvent lowers its freezing point and raises its boiling point.

KEY SCIENCE WORDS

a. **desalination**
b. **dissociation**
c. **distillation**
d. **electrolyte**
e. **ionization**
f. **nonelectrolyte**
g. **saturated solution**
h. **solubility**
i. **solute**
j. **solvent**
k. **supersaturated solution**
l. **unsaturated solution**

UNDERSTANDING VOCABULARY

Match each phrase with the correct term from the list of Key Science Words.

1. a solution that can dissolve more solute at a given temperature
2. the substance being dissolved
3. has more solute than a saturated solution has at that temperature
4. is ionized in a water solution
5. molecules are pulled apart into ions in solution
6. separation of negative and positive ions
7. the most solute in grams, that will dissolve in 100 g of solvent at a certain temperature
8. a solution that has dissolved all the solute it can hold at a given temperature
9. the substance that dissolves a solute
10. the general term for any method that removes salt from ocean water

CHAPTER REVIEW

CHECKING CONCEPTS

Choose the word or phrase that completes the sentence or answers the question.

1. Which of the following is not a solution?
   a. a glass of soda **c.** bronze (an alloy)
   b. air in a SCUBA tank **d.** muddy water
2. Solutions may not be ______.
   a. colloidal **c.** liquid
   b. gaseous **d.** solid
3. When iodine is dissolved in alcohol, the alcohol is the ______.
   a. alloy **c.** solution
   b. solvent **d.** solute
4. If a bronze alloy is 85 percent copper and 15 percent tin, tin is the ______.
   a. alloy **b.** solution
   b. solvent **d.** solute
5. Forty-nine mL of water has a mass of ____.
   a. 49 g **c.** 100 g
   b. 51 g **d.** 4900 g
6. A polar solvent will dissolve ______.
   a. any solute **c.** a nonpolar solute
   b. a polar solute **d.** no solute
7. If a water solution conducts electricity, the solute must be a(n) ______.
   a. gas **c.** liquid
   b. electrolyte **d.** nonelectrolyte
8. In a water solution, an ionic compound undergoes ______.
   a. dissociation **c.** ionization
   b. electrolysis **d.** no change
9. A gas becomes more soluble in a liquid when you increase ______.
   a. particle size **c.** stirring
   b. pressure **d.** temperature
10. Solute may come out of a solution that is ____.
    a. unsaturated **c.** supersaturated
    b. saturated **d.** all of these

UNDERSTANDING CONCEPTS

Complete each sentence.

11. A solution that contains a large amount of solute is said to be ______.
12. If a water solution of a compound does not conduct electricity, the compound is a(n) ____.
13. A(n) ______ solution contains less than the maximum amount of solute at a given temperature.
14. In the ocean, salt is a(n) ______.
15. In a solution, the substance present in the greatest amount is the ______.

THINK AND WRITE CRITICALLY

16. As the first step of distillation, salt water is boiled and the water vaporizes. Why doesn't the salt also vaporize?
17. Explain what happens when copper(II) sulfate, $CuSO_4$, an ionic compound, dissolves in water.
18. Why are *concentrated* and *dilute* not exact terms?
19. Explain how you would make a 25 percent solution of apple juice.
20. Why is the statement "Water is the solvent in a solution" not always true?

APPLY

21. Explain why tetrachloroethene, a dry cleaning fluid, will dissolve grease and water will not.
22. Why might a tropical lake have more minerals dissolved in it than a lake in Minnesota?
23. Explain why salt will melt ice on a sidewalk.
24. Why might potatoes cook quicker in salt water than in unsalted water?
25. Explain why an unrefrigerated glass of soda will go "flat" quicker in hot weather.

MORE SKILL BUILDERS

If you need help, refer to the Skill Handbook.

1. **Comparing and Contrasting**: Compare and contrast the processes of ionization and dissociation.
2. **Hypothesizing:** You are stocking a pond in a tropical climate and a pond in a temperate climate with fish. Both ponds contain about the same amount of water. Based on the amount of oxygen dissolved in the water, to which pond would you be able to add more fish? Explain why.
3. **Interpreting Data:** The label on a bottle of rubbing alcohol might read "70% isopropanol by volume." Assuming the rest of the solution is water, what does this label tell you about the contents and preparation of the solution in the bottle?
4. **Measuring in SI:** 153 g of potassium nitrate have been dissolved in enough water to make 1.00 L of solution. You use a graduated cylinder to measure 80.0 mL of solution. What mass of potassium nitrate do you have in the 80.0-mL sample?
5. **Making and Using Tables:** Using the data in Table 15-3 on page 391, fill in the following table. Use the words *saturated, unsaturated,* and *supersaturated.*

Compound	g Dissolved in 100 g Water at 20°C	Type of Solution
$Ba(OH)_2$	2.96	
$CuSO_4$	32.0	
KCl	45.8	
KNO_3	31.6	
$NaClO_3$	79.6	

PROJECTS

1. Research crystal growing using saturated and supersaturated solutions. Grow several crystals and display them. Accompany the display with a report explaining what you did.
2. Do research on a titanium alloy. Report on its production, composition, and uses.
3. Visit a SCUBA shop. Find out about the composition of the gas used in the tanks. In terms of solution, report your findings.

CHAPTER

16 Chemical Reactions

You may not realize it, but the Statue of Liberty is made of copper. Why is it green? Brand new pennies are bright and shiny. Older pennies are black and quite dull. Some very old pennies often have a green layer on them. What causes pennies and copper statues to lose their shiny surfaces and turn green?

FIND OUT!

Do this activity to find out why copper surfaces often turn green.

Obtain two dark copper pennies. Sprinkle some table salt on them. Drop about five or six drops of vinegar on the salt-covered pennies. Observe the pennies for about 20 minutes and then rinse them with water. How do the pennies look now?

Place one of the pennies in a piece of plastic wrap. Wrap the penny so that no air can get to it. Set this penny aside. Place the other penny on a saucer. Add just enough water to the saucer so that the penny is not completely covered. Let this coin remain in the water overnight. Observe the pennies the next day. How do they compare? What caused the changes that you observed?

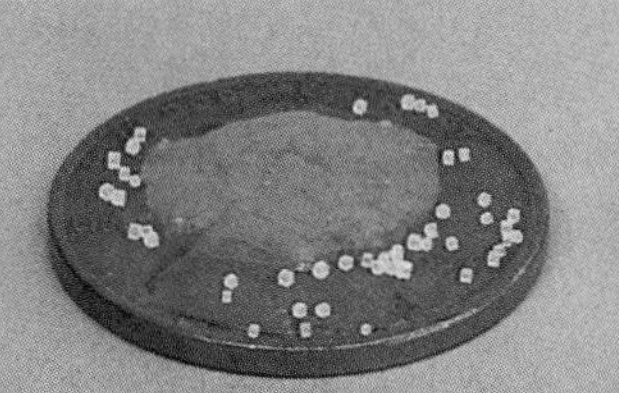

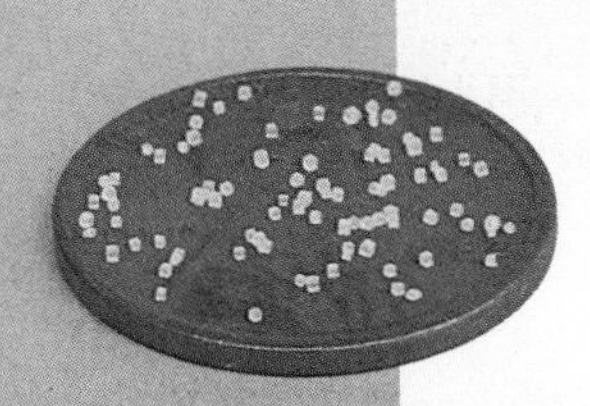

Gearing Up

Previewing the Chapter

Use this outline to help you focus on important ideas in this chapter.

Previewing Science Skills

- In the **Skill Builders,** you will recognize cause and effect, observe and infer, hypothesize, and make a concept map.
- In the **Activities,** you will observe, infer, and classify.
- In the **MINI-Labs,** you will observe and infer.

What's next?

You have seen what happens to a penny when it is exposed to air. You will learn more about this chemical change and others as you read the pages that follow.

16-1 Chemical Changes in Matter

New Science Words

chemical reaction
reactants
products
coefficients

Objectives

- Identify reactants and products in a chemical reaction.
- Explain how a chemical reaction satisfies the law of conservation of mass.
- Interpret chemical equations.

Reactants and Products

In Chapter 9 you learned about chemical changes. These changes are taking place all around you and even inside your body. One of the most important chemical changes on Earth is photosynthesis. During photosynthesis plants use sunlight, carbon dioxide, and water to make sugar and oxygen. Another important chemical change takes place in the cells in your body. This change combines sugar and oxygen to produce energy, carbon dioxide, and water.

A **chemical reaction** is a well-defined example of a chemical change. In a chemical reaction, one or more substances are changed to new substances. The substances you start with are called **reactants.** The new substances formed are called **products.** This relationship can be written as follows:

$$\text{reactants} \xrightarrow{\text{produce}} \text{products}$$

What are the reactants and products in the photosynthesis reaction described above?

Figure 16-1. Antoine Lavoisier used precise balances to perform experiments that led to the law of conversation of mass.

Conservation of Mass

In the early 1700s, scientists wondered what happened to the masses of the reactants and products in a chemical reaction. The French chemist Antoine Lavoisier performed many experiments to find out. In one experiment, Lavoisier placed a carefully measured amount of solid mercury(II) oxide into a sealed flask. When he heated this flask, oxygen gas and liquid mercury were produced:

solid mercury(II) oxide plus heat produces
oxygen gas plus liquid mercury

Lavoisier found that the mass of the oxygen gas and the mercury produced was equal to the mass of the mercury(II) oxide that he started with:

mercury(II) oxide	produces	oxygen	plus	mercury
10.0 g	=	0.7 g	+	9.3 g

This and many other experiments allowed Lavoisier to state the law of conservation of mass: in a chemical reaction matter cannot be created or destroyed; therefore, mass is conserved. In Chapter 9, you read how this law applies generally to chemical changes. For a chemical reaction, this law means that the mass of the reactants must equal the mass of the products. As you will see, the law of conservation of mass must be satisfied when describing a chemical reaction.

MINI-Lab

Does mass change in a reaction?

From your teacher, obtain solutions of the two reactants, $FeCl_3$ and NaOH—the $FeCl_3$ in a dropper plugged with soap and screwed into a bottle of NaOH. Determine the mass of the assembly. Then squeeze the dropper so that the plug is forced out. What do you observe as the reactants mix? Again determine the mass of the assembly, which now contains the products of the reaction—$Fe(OH)_3$ and NaCl. Was there a change in mass? What law does this procedure illustrate?

Describing Chemical Reactions

If you wanted to describe the chemical reaction shown in Figure 16-2, it might look something like this:

solid lead(II) nitrate, dissolved in water plus
solid potassium iodide, dissolved in water produce
solid lead(II) iodide plus potassium nitrate,
dissolved in water

This series of words is rather long and cumbersome. But, all information in this expression is important. The

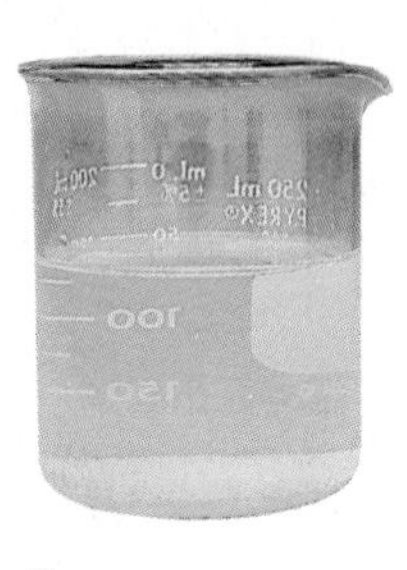

Figure 16-2. The beakers contain solutions of lead(II) nitrate and potassium iodide (a). When these solutions are mixed, a bright yellow solid forms (b). The yellow solid, lead(II) iodide, settles to the bottom of the beaker. The solution in the beaker is potassium nitrate (c).

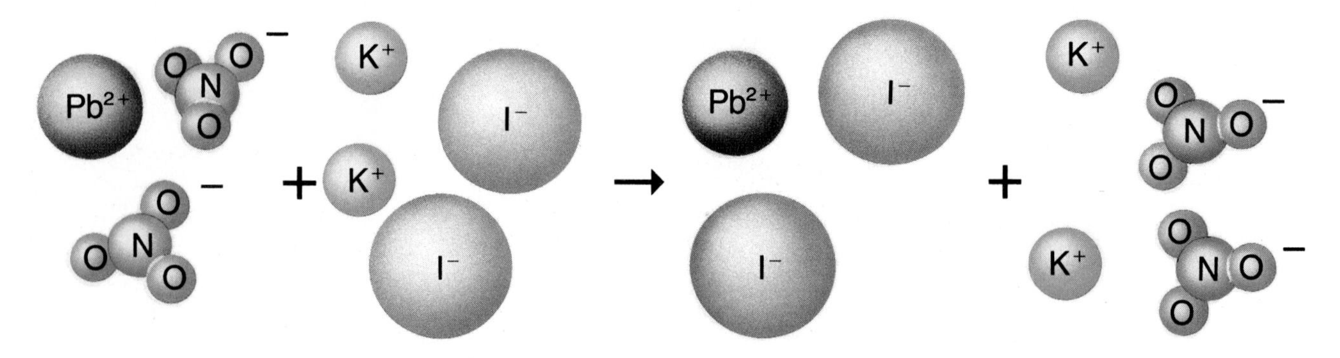

Figure 16-3. One unit of $Pb(NO_3)_2$ reacts with two units of KI to produce one unit of PbI_2 plus two units of KNO_3.

same is true of descriptions of most chemical reactions—many words are needed to state all the important information. So scientists have developed a shorthand method to describe chemical reactions. A chemical equation is an expression that decribes a chemical reaction using chemical formulas and other symbols. In Chapter 11, you learned how to use chemical symbols and formulas. Some of the other symbols used in chemical equations are listed in Table 16-1.

What is a chemical equation?

What would the chemical equation for the reaction in Figure 16-2 look like?

$$Pb(NO_3)_2(aq) + 2KI(aq) \rightarrow PbI_2(cr) + 2KNO_3(aq)$$

The symbols to the right of the formulas are (*cr*) for solid and (*aq*) for aqueous, which means dissolved in water.

What do the numbers to the left of the formulas for reactants and products mean? Remember that the law of conservation of mass states that matter cannot be created or destroyed. Atoms can be rearranged during chemical reactions, but never lost or destroyed. These numbers, called **coefficients,** represent the relative amounts of atoms taking part in a reaction. They show you what is really happening inside the reaction flask. For example, in the above reaction one unit of $Pb(NO_3)_2$ reacts with two units of KI to produce one unit of PbI_2 and two units of KNO_3. Figure 16-3 will help you visualize this reaction.

You don't always have to analyze the reaction mixture to find out what the coefficients in a chemical reaction are. In the next section you will find out how to choose coefficients for a chemical equation.

Table 16-1

SYMBOLS USED IN CHEMICAL EQUATIONS

Symbol	Meaning
→	produces or forms
+	plus
(cr)	solid
(l)	liquid
(g)	gas
(aq)	aqueous, a solid is dissolved in water
heat →	the reactants are heated
light →	the reactants are exposed to light
elect. →	an electric current is applied to the reactants

PROBLEM SOLVING

Metals and the Atmosphere

When metals are exposed to air, they often corrode. Rusting is one type of corrosion. Rust is iron(III) oxide.

Aluminum also reacts with oxygen in the air to form the white solid aluminum oxide. Unlike rust, which crumbles and exposes more iron to the air, aluminum oxide adheres to the aluminum surface on which it forms. This coating protects the aluminum underneath from further corrosion.

Copper is another metal that corrodes when exposed to air. When copper corrodes, a green coating called basic copper sulfate is formed. You may have seen this type of corrosion on the Statue of Liberty.

Think Critically: Identify the reactants and products in the corrosion of iron and aluminum. When the Statue of Liberty was restored, the green coating was not removed. Why?

SECTION REVIEW

1. Identify the reactants and the products in the following chemical equation

$$2B(cr) + 3I_2(g) \rightarrow 2BI_3(cr)$$

2. What is the name and state of matter of each substance in the following reaction?

$$4Al(cr) + 3O_2(g) \rightarrow 2Al_2O_3(cr)$$

3. **Apply:** Soap (sodium stearate) is made as follows:

   fat plus sodium hydroxide produce soap plus glycerin

   When 890 g of fat reacts totally with 120 g of sodium hydroxide, 92 g of glycerin is formed. How many grams of soap must be formed to satisfy the law of conservation of mass?

Recognizing Cause and Effect

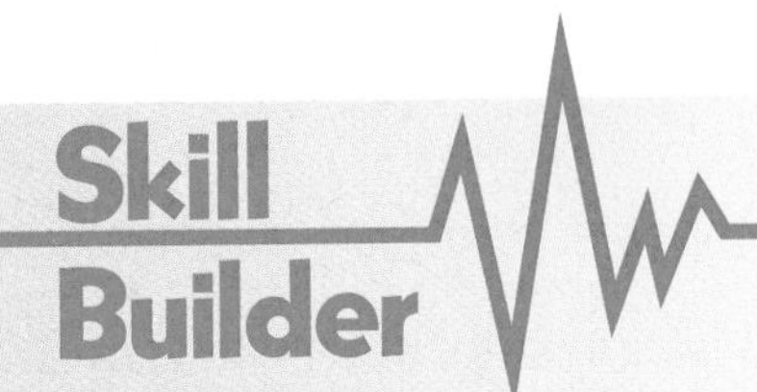

Lavoisier heated mercury(II) oxide in a sealed flask. Explain the effect on the mass of the products of the reaction if he had used an open flask. If you need help, refer to Recognizing Cause and Effect in the **Skill Handbook** on page 679.

16-2 The Hole in the Ozone Layer

New Science Words

chlorofluorocarbons (CFCs)

Objectives

- Describe the role of the ozone layer in protecting life on Earth.
- Explain the role of CFCs in the threat to the ozone layer.

How Do CFCs Affect Ozone?

Have you heard that a decrease of ozone in Earth's atmosphere has led to an increase in skin cancer? That is probably so, but it is only the beginning. Far more serious might be widespread damage to crops or total destruction of life in the ocean. Normally, the ozone layer absorbs much of the ultraviolet (UV) radiation from the sun. UV radiation is invisible, high-energy waves that can harm living things.

Ozone, remember, consists of O_3 molecules. Ozone can form from ordinary oxygen, O_2, under certain conditions. Near the ground, ozone is a major pollutant in smog produced from automobile exhausts. Even in minute amounts, the ozone in smog irritates the eyes and makes breathing difficult.

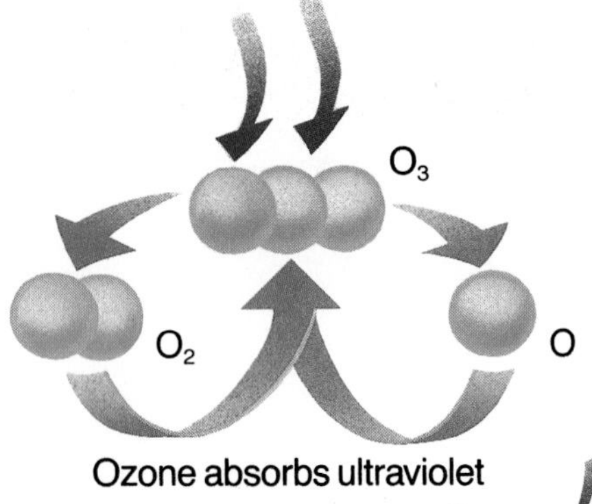

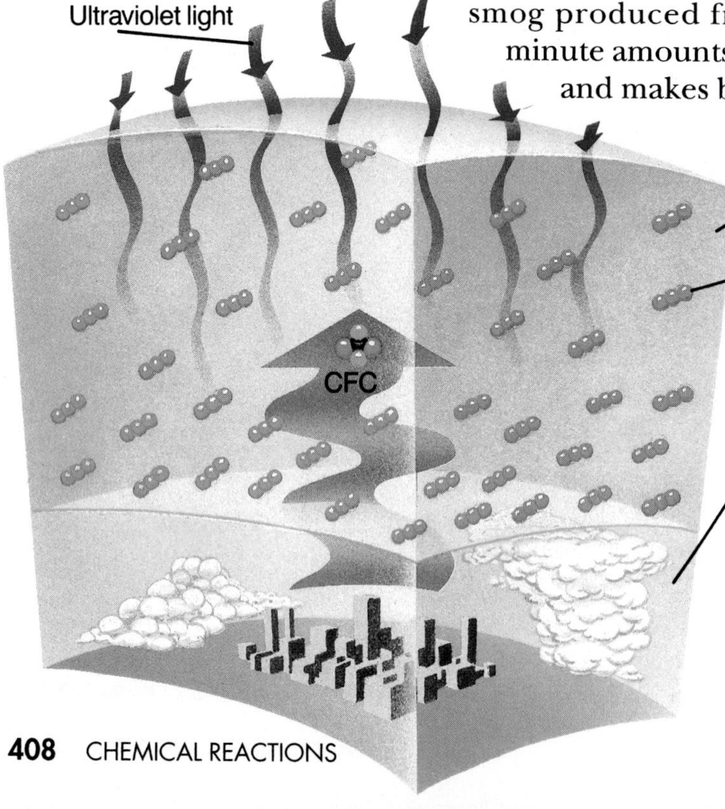

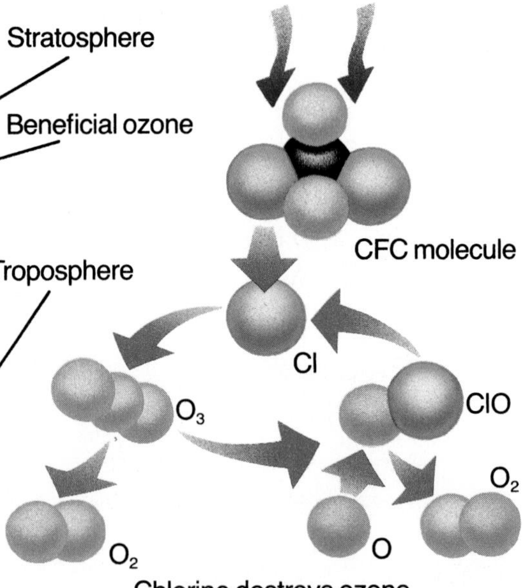

However, scientists have become concerned about a far more important ozone problem—the loss of more than three percent of the ozone high in Earth's atmosphere. Satellite photos of Antarctica, like the one to the right, show that every year the hole in the ozone layer, which is the size of the United States, gets bigger. And as the hole gets bigger, more and more life-damaging UV radiation can reach Earth.

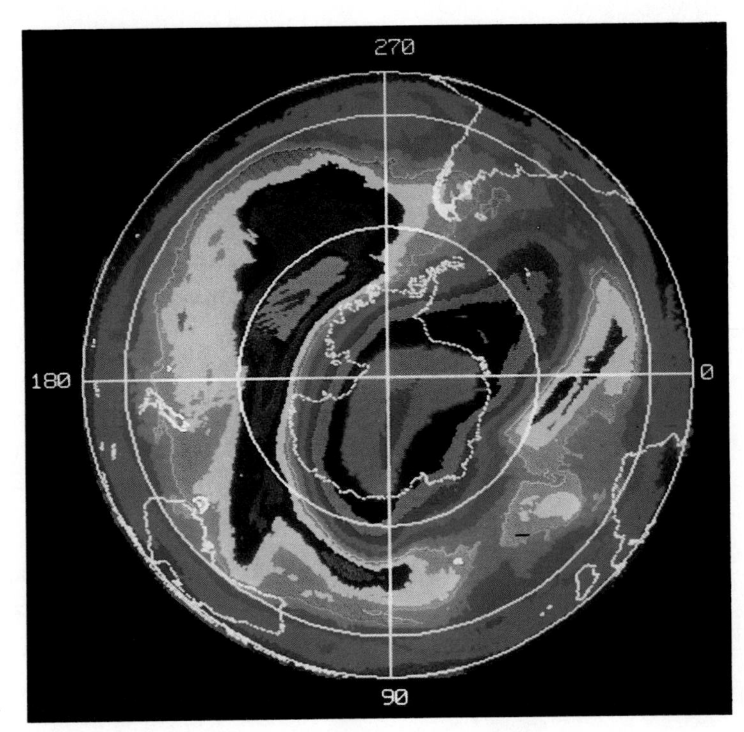

Scientists believe that the ozone destruction is largely due to compounds called chlorofluorocarbons. **Chlorofluorocarbons (CFCs)** are a group of compounds of chlorine, fluorine, and carbon. Some CFCs are used in refrigerators and air conditioners. When CFCs are released into the air, they move into the upper atmosphere. There, UV radiation causes the CFCs to break down and release atoms of chlorine. A chlorine atom destroys an ozone molecule, forming chlorine monoxide and oxygen:

$$Cl(g) + O_3(g) \rightarrow ClO(g) + O_2(g)$$

The chlorine monoxide, ClO, then breaks apart, setting free the chlorine atom, which repeats the process. In this way, a single chlorine atom can destroy 100 000 ozone molecules. The governments of 25 countries hope to totally stop the use of CFCs by the year 2000. But CFCs already in the atmosphere may continue to destroy the ozone for hundreds of years.

SECTION REVIEW

1. Why is the ozone layer in the atmosphere important?
2. Write an equation to show how a chlorine atom from a CFC destroys ozone.

You Decide!

Many businesses are calling for CFC recycling programs to prevent the CFCs from getting into the atmosphere. Will recycling solve the problem?

16-3 Chemical Equations

New Science Words

balanced chemical equation

Objectives

- Explain what is meant by a balanced chemical equation.
- Demonstrate how to write balanced chemical equations.

Checking for Balance

Where does the tarnish on silver come from? As you read in Chapter 11, tarnish is silver sulfide, Ag_2S. It forms when sulfur-containing compounds in the air or food react with the silver. Suppose you write this chemical equation for tarnishing:

$$Ag(cr) + H_2S(g) \rightarrow Ag_2S(cr) + H_2(g)$$

Now, examine the equation. Remember that matter is never created or destroyed in a chemical reaction. Notice that one silver atom appears in the reactants, $Ag + H_2S$. However, two silver atoms appear in the products, $Ag_2S + H_2$. As you know, one silver atom can't just become two. The equation must be balanced so it shows a true picture of what takes place in the reaction. A **balanced chemical equation** has the same number of atoms of each element on both sides of the equation. To find out if this equation is balanced, make a chart like that shown in Table 16-2.

Table 16-2

ATOMS IN UNBALANCED EQUATION				
Kind of Atom	Number of Atoms $Ag + H_2S \rightarrow Ag_2S + H_2$			
	Ag	H_2S	Ag_2S	H_2
Ag	1		2	
H		2		2
S		1	1	

The number of hydrogen and the number of sulfur atoms are balanced. However, there are two silver atoms on the right side of the equation and only one on the left side. This equation isn't balanced. Never change subscripts of a correct formula to balance an equation. Instead, place whole number coefficients to the left of the formulas of the reactants and products so that there are equal numbers of silver atoms on both sides of the equation. If no number is present, the coefficient is one.

Choosing Coefficients

How do you find out which coefficients to use to balance an equation? This decision is a trial-and-error process. With practice, the process becomes simple to perform.

In the chemical equation for tarnishing, you found that both the sulfur atoms and the hydrogen atoms were already balanced. Putting a coefficient before those formulas that contain these atoms might make matters worse. So, look at the formulas containing silver atoms: Ag and Ag_2S. There are two atoms of silver on the right side and only one on the left side. If you put a coefficient of two before Ag, the equation is balanced, as shown in Table 16-3.

$$2Ag(cr) + H_2S(g) \rightarrow Ag_2S(cr) + H_2(g)$$

Table 16-3

ATOMS IN BALANCED EQUATION				
Kind of Atom	Number of Atoms $2Ag + H_2S \rightarrow Ag_2S + H_2$			
	$2Ag$	H_2S	Ag_2S	H_2
Ag	2		2	
H		2		2
S		1	1	

Writing Balanced Chemical Equations

When a piece of magnesium ribbon burns in a flask of oxygen, a white powder called magnesium oxide is formed. To write a balanced chemical equation for this and most other reactions, follow these four steps:

Step 1 Describe the reaction in words, putting the reactants on the left side and the products on the right side.

magnesium plus oxygen produces magnesium oxide

Step 2 Write a chemical equation for the reaction using formulas and symbols. Review how to write formulas for compounds in Section 11-3. The formulas for elements are generally just their symbols. However, as you read in Chapter 12, some elements ordinarily exist as diatomic molecules as shown in Table 16-4. Oxygen is a diatomic molecule.

Table 16-4

DIATOMIC MOLECULES	
Name	Formula
Hydrogen	H_2
Oxygen	O_2
Nitrogen	N_2
Fluorine	F_2
Chlorine	Cl_2
Bromine	Br_2
Iodine	I_2

$$Mg(cr) + O_2(g) \rightarrow MgO(cr)$$

Step 3 Check the equation for balance. Set up a chart like Table 16-5 to help you.

Table 16-5

ATOMS IN UNBALANCED EQUATION			
Kind of Atom	Number of Atoms $Mg + O_2 \rightarrow MgO$		
	Mg	O_2	MgO
Mg	1		1
O		2	1

The magnesium atoms are balanced, but the oxygen atoms are not. Therefore, this equation isn't balanced.

Step 4 Choose coefficients that balance the equation. Remember, never change subscripts of a correct formula to balance an equation. Try putting a coefficient of two before MgO to balance the oxygen.

$$Mg(cr) + O_2(g) \rightarrow 2MgO(cr)$$

Now there are two Mg atoms on the right side and only one on the left side. So a coefficient of two is needed next to Mg also.

$$2Mg(cr) + O_2(g) \rightarrow 2MgO(cr)$$

Table 16-6 indicates that the equation is now balanced.

Table 16-6

ATOMS IN BALANCED EQUATION			
Kind of Atom	Number of Atoms $2Mg + O_2 \rightarrow 2MgO$		
	$2Mg$	O_2	$2MgO$
Mg	2		2
O		2	2

Table 16-7

ATOMS IN AgCl FORMATION				
Kind of Atom	Number of Atoms			
	$AgNO_3$ +	NaCl →	AgCl +	$NaNO_3$
Ag	1		1	
N	1			1
O	3			3
Na		1		1
Cl		1	1	

Work through the following example

The photo to the right shows that when a silver nitrate solution is mixed with a sodium chloride solution, a white, insoluble solid is formed. This solid is silver chloride. The sodium nitrate formed remains in solution. Write a balanced equation for this reaction.

Step 1 Describe the reaction in words:

aqueous silver nitrate plus aqueous sodium chloride produces solid silver chloride plus aqueous sodium nitrate

Step 2 Write the chemical equation:

$$AgNO_3(aq) + NaCl(aq) \rightarrow AgCl(cr) + NaNO_3(aq)$$

Step 3 Check the equation for balance:

There are already equal numbers of each element on both sides of the equation. This equation is balanced.

Step 4 Choose coefficients:

This equation is balanced, so no coefficients other than one are needed.

MINI-Lab

Must the sums of reactant and product coefficients be equal?

Obtain a marked card from your teacher. With others in the class, assemble the cards to represent a basketball team. Written as a chemical equation, the result would appear as: 2 guards + 2 forwards + 1 center = 1 team. Why aren't the sums of the coefficients on each side of the equation equal? How is this equation like a typical chemical equation?

SECTION REVIEW

1. What are two reasons for balancing equations for chemical reactions?
2. Write balanced chemical equations for the following reactions: (a) copper metal plus sulfur produces copper(I) sulfide, (b) sodium metal plus water produces aqueous sodium hydroxide plus hydrogen gas.
3. **Apply:** Rust, iron(III) oxide, is formed when iron is exposed to oxygen in the air. Write a balanced equation for this reaction.

Observing and Inferring

Hard water contains ions of calcium, magnesium, and/or iron. When Na_2CO_3 is added to hard water, it is softened because these ions are removed as a white solid. For Mg, this reaction may occur:

$$MgCl_2(aq) + Na_2CO_3(aq) \rightarrow MgCO_3(cr) + 2NaCl(aq)$$

Write an equation showing how water containing $Ca(NO_3)_2$ could be softened. If you need help, refer to Observing and Inferring in the **Skill Handbook** on page 678.

Types of Chemical Reactions

16-4

Objectives

- Describe four types of chemical reactions using their generalized formulas.
- Classify various chemical reactions by type.

New Science Words

synthesis reaction
decomposition reaction
single displacement reaction
precipitate
double displacement reaction

Classifying Chemical Reactions

There are hundreds of kinds of chemical reactions. Rather than try to memorize them, it is easier to group reactions by their similarities. When you have classified a reaction in this way, you can then learn a great deal about it by comparing it to others in the group.

Scientists have developed a system of classification based upon the way the atoms rearrange themselves in a chemical reaction. Most reactions can be placed in one of four groups: synthesis, decomposition, single displacement, or double displacement reactions.

Synthesis Reactions

The easiest reaction to recognize is a synthesis reaction. In a **synthesis reaction,** two or more substances combine to form another substance. The generalized formula for this reaction type is:

$$A + B \rightarrow AB$$

The reaction in which hydrogen burns in oxygen to form water is an example of a synthesis reaction:

$$2H_2(g) + O_2 \rightarrow (g)\ 2H_2O(g)$$

This reaction between hydrogen and oxygen occurs between two elements. It takes place very rapidly and it is explosive. One type of rocket fuel is hydrogen, which burns in oxygen when the rocket is fired.

Sulfuric acid is one of the most important manufactured chemicals. The final step in making sulfuric acid

Did You Know?

The novocaine that dentists use to deaden pain is a stable, easy-to-synthesize isomer of cocaine with few side effects.

What type of reaction is the burning of hydrogen in oxygen?

Figure 16-4. Because sulfuric acid is used to manufacture so many different products, more of it is produced than any other chemical.

is a synthesis reaction between two compounds, sulfur trioxide and water:

$$SO_3(g) + H_2O(l) \rightarrow H_2SO_4(aq)$$

In the next chapter you will learn more about the importance of this acid and others.

Decomposition Reactions

The opposite of a synthesis reaction is a decomposition reaction. The drawing below illustrates this

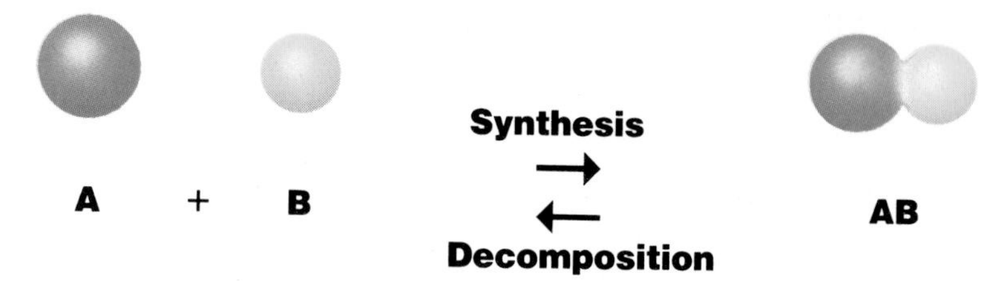

relationship. In a **decomposition reaction,** one substance breaks down, or decomposes, into two or more simpler substances. The generalized formula for this type of reaction is:

$$AB \rightarrow A + B$$

Most decomposition reactions require the use of heat, light, or electricity.

The decomposition of water by an electric current produces hydrogen and oxygen.

$$2H_2O(l) \xrightarrow[\text{current}]{\text{electric}} 2H_2(g) + O_2(g)$$

Displacement Reactions

A **single displacement reaction** occurs when one element replaces another in a compound. There are two generalized formulas for this type of reaction.

In the first case, A replaces B as follows:

$$A + BC \rightarrow AC + B$$

In the second case D replaces C as follows:

$$D + BC \rightarrow BD + C$$

Figure 16-5. Copper in a wire replaces silver in silver nitrate, forming a blue solution. The silver precipitates onto the wire.

In Figure 16-5, a copper wire is put into a solution of silver nitrate. Because copper is a more active metal than silver, it replaces the silver, forming a blue copper(II) nitrate solution. The silver forms an insoluble solid, or **precipitate.**

If a zinc strip is put into a copper(II) nitrate solution, the copper precipitates out.

$$Zn(cr) + Cu(NO_3)_2(aq) \rightarrow Zn(NO_3)_2(aq) + Cu(cr)$$

Zinc replaced the copper, so zinc must be a more active metal than copper. Table 16-8 summarizes the activity of some metals.

A **double displacement reaction** takes place if a precipitate, water, or a gas forms when two ionic compounds in solution are combined. In a double displacement reaction, the positive ion of one compound replaces the positive ion of the other compound to form two new compounds. The generalized formula for this type of reaction is:

$$AB + CD \rightarrow AD + CB$$

The reaction of silver nitrate with sodium chloride is an example of this type of reaction. As shown in the picture on page 412, a precipitate—silver chloride—is formed. The chemical equation is:

$$AgNO_3(aq) + NaCl(aq) \rightarrow AgCl(cr) + NaNO_3(aq)$$

You have seen just a few examples of chemical reactions classified into types. Many more reactions of each type occur around you.

Table 16-8

ACTIVITY SERIES OF METALS	
Lithium	Most active
Potassium	
Barium	
Calcium	
Sodium	
Magnesium	
Aluminum	
Zinc	
Iron	
Nickel	
Tin	
Lead	
(Hydrogen)	
Copper	
Mercury	
Silver	
Gold	Least active

SECTION REVIEW

1. Classify the following reactions by type:
   (a) $2KClO_3(cr) \rightarrow 2KCl(cr) + 3O_2(g)$
   (b) $CaBr_2(aq) + Na_2CO_3(aq) \rightarrow CaCO_3(cr) + 2NaBr(aq)$
   (c) $Zn(cr) + S(cr) \rightarrow ZnS(cr)$
   (d) $2Li(cr) + FeBr_2(aq) \rightarrow 2LiBr(aq) + Fe(cr)$
2. **Apply:** The copper bottoms of some cooking pans turn black after being used. The copper reacts with oxygen forming black copper(II) oxide. Write a balanced chemical equation for this reaction.

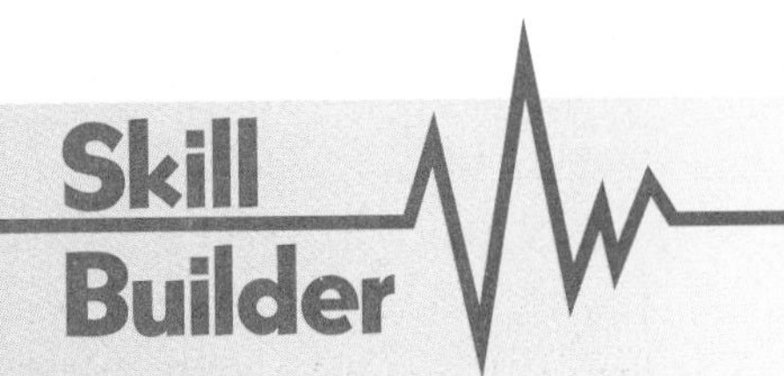

Hypothesizing

Group 1 metals replace hydrogen in water in reactions that are often very violent. A sample equation for one reaction is: $2K(cr) + 2HOH(l) \rightarrow 2KOH(aq) + H_2(g)$.

Use Table 16-8 to help you hypothesize about why these metals are often stored in kerosene. If you need help, refer to Hypothesizing in the **Skill Handbook** on page 682.

ACTIVITY 16-1
Displacement Reactions

Problem: *Which metals can displace hydrogen from an acid?*

Materials   

- 3 test tubes
- test-tube stand
- small pieces of copper, Cu; zinc, Zn; and magnesium, Mg
- 15 mL dilute hydrochloric acid, HCl
- graduated cylinder
- wooden splint

CAUTION: *Handle acid with care. If spillage occurs, rinse area with plenty of water.*

Procedure

1. Copy the data table and use it to record your observations.
2. Set three test tubes in a test tube stand. Carefully pour 5 mL of dilute hydrochloric acid into each tube.
3. Place a small piece of metal in each test tube: copper in the first tube, zinc in the second tube, and magnesium in the third tube.

Data and Observations

Tube	Substances Mixed	Observations
1	HCl + Cu	
2	HCl + Zn	
3	HCl + Mg	

Analyze

1. What evidence of chemical reaction did you observe? In which tubes did a reaction occur?
2. When ignited, hydrogen burns rapidly. With your teacher's permission, trap some of the gas from tube 3. Bring a lighted splint near the gas. What happens? What do you infer about the identity of the gas?
3. Write a balanced equation for the reaction in tube 3. Magnesium reacts with an oxidation state of 2+.

Conclude and Apply

4. Examine your balanced equation in 3. What happens to an element that is displaced by another element?
5. From the activity series of metals, Table 16-8, on page 415, select another element that would have the same behavior as copper. Select another element that would have the same behavior as zinc and magnesium.
6. An outstanding physical property of hydrogen gas is its low density—about 1/15th of the density of air. Although hydrogen is used to fill weather balloons, it is not used to fill blimps. What chemical property of hydrogen that you observed in this activity prevents its use in blimps?

Energy and Chemical Reactions

16-5

Objectives

- Differentiate between an exothermic reaction and an endothermic reaction.
- Describe the effects of catalysts and inhibitors on the speed of chemical reactions.

New Science Words

endothermic reactions
exothermic reactions
catalyst
inhibitor

Energy Changes in Chemical Reactions

Did you ever watch the explosion of dynamite at a construction site? An explosion results from a very violent chemical reaction. In all chemical reactions energy is either released or absorbed. This energy can take many forms. It might be in the form of heat, light, sound, or even electricity. The explosion of dynamite produces heat, light, and sound.

Where does the energy to be released or absorbed come from? Whenever a chemical reaction takes place, some chemical bonds in the reactants must be broken. To break chemical bonds, energy must be provided. In order for products to be produced, new bonds must be formed. Bond formation releases energy.

Figure 16-6. The explosion of dynamite produces heat, light, and sound.

What is one kind of evidence that heat is absorbed in a reaction?

Endothermic Reactions

Sometimes, more energy is required to break bonds than to form new ones in a chemical reaction. In these reactions, called **endothermic reactions,** energy must be provided for the reaction to take place.

When some endothermic reactions proceed, so much heat is absorbed that their containers feel cold to the touch. In other endothermic reactions, so little heat is absorbed that you would need a thermometer to determine that a temperature change has occurred.

Have you ever been at an athletic event where a player was injured and then applied a cold pack to the injury? Cold packs take advantage of an endothermic reaction.

Figure 16-7. When the inner capsule in a cold pack is broken, the chemicals mix, and a lower temperature results.

The cold pack contains ammonium chloride sealed in a container inside a larger plastic bag filled with water. When you break the inner container, the ammonium chloride mixes with the water. The reaction absorbs so much heat from the water that the pack feels very cold.

Figure 16-8. The burning of wood is an example of an exothermic reaction. Energy is released in the form of heat and light.

Exothermic Reactions

Most chemical reactions aren't endothermic. In most chemical reactions, less energy is required to break old bonds than to form new ones. In these reactions, called **exothermic reactions,** energy is given off by the reaction. The heat given off causes the reaction mixture to feel hot.

The burning of wood and the explosion of dynamite are exothermic reactions. They are exothermic because they give off energy as the reaction proceeds. Rusting is also exothermic, but the reaction proceeds so slowly that it is difficult to detect the temperature change caused by the release of energy.

Catalysts and Inhibitors

Some reactions are so slow that you would have to wait for a long time for the desired product to be formed.

To speed up these reactions you can add a catalyst. A **catalyst** is a substance that speeds up a chemical reaction without itself being permanently changed. When you add a catalyst to a reaction, you end up with the same amount of the catalyst that you started with.

How do enzymes affect reactions in living oranisms?

Certain proteins known as enzymes act as catalysts in living organisms. Enzymes allow reactions to occur at faster rates and lower temperatures than would otherwise be possible. Without these enzymes, life as we know it would not be possible.

Some reactions need to be slowed down. The food preservations BHT and BHA slow down the spoilage of certain foods. BHT and BHA are inhibitors. Any substance that slows down a reaction is called an **inhibitor.**

TECHNOLOGY

Catalytic Converters

The exhaust systems of cars today are equipped with catalytic converters that use rhodium and platinum as the catalysts. These catalysts speed up reactions of three types of toxic compounds given off by cars. These compounds are unburned hydrocarbons, carbon monoxide, and nitrogen oxides. Catalytic converters change these compounds into harmless compounds.

Two types of reactions are catalyzed. In one type of reaction, oxygen is added. Adding oxygen converts carbon monoxide to carbon dioxide, and unburned hydrocarbons to carbon dioxide and water. In the other type of reaction, oxygen is removed. Removing oxygen converts nitrogen oxides to nitrogen, water, and carbon dioxide.

Think Critically: Why is it not necessary to add more rhodium and platinum to a catalytic converter as these substances are used?

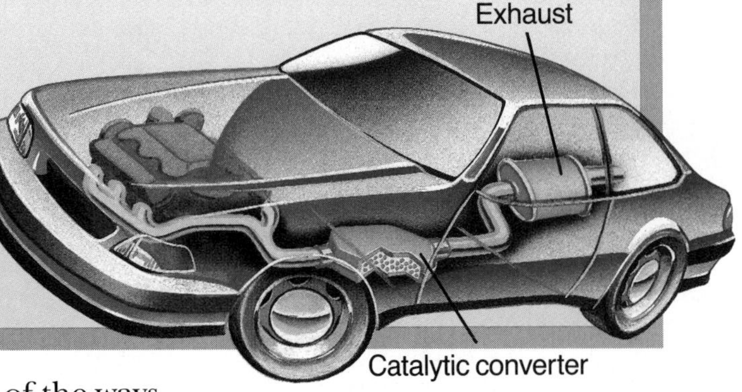

Using catalysts and inhibitors are just a few of the ways scientists control chemical reactions. With further research, scientists will learn more about these very useful chemicals.

SECTION REVIEW

1. What is the difference between exothermic and endothermic reactions?
2. Rusting takes place much faster in the presence of water. What role does water play in this reaction?
3. **Apply:** Suppose you wanted to develop a product for warming people's hands at outdoor winter events. Would you choose an exothermic reaction or an endothermic reaction to use in your device? Why?

Science and WRITING

The development of the chemical accelerator was a major factor in the making of new materials through chemical reactions. Explain how it works.

Concept Mapping

Construct a concept map to show the relationship between energy and bond formation and bond breakage. If you need help, refer to Concept Mapping in the **Skill Handbook** on pages 684 and 685.

ACTIVITY 16-2
Catalyzed Reaction

Problem: *How does a catalyst affect hydrogen peroxide?*

Materials   

- 3 medium-sized test tubes
- test-tube stand
- 15 mL hydrogen peroxide, H_2O_2
- graduated cylinder
- small plastic spoon
- sand
- manganese dioxide, MnO_2
- wooden splint
- hot plate
- beaker of hot water

CAUTION: *Hydrogen peroxide can irritate skin and eyes. Wear goggles and apron.*

Procedure

1. Set three test tubes in a test-tube stand. Pour 5 mL of hydrogen peroxide into each tube.
2. Place about 1/4 spoonful of sand in tube 2 and the same amount of manganese dioxide in tube 3.
3. In the presence of some substances that act as catalysts, H_2O_2 decomposes rapidly, producing oxygen gas,O_2. A glowing splint placed in O_2 will relight. Test the gas produced in any of the tubes as follows. Light a wooden splint, blow out the flame, and insert the glowing splint into the tube.
4. Place all three tubes in a beaker of hot water. Heat on a hot plate until all the remaining H_2O_2 is driven away and there is no liquid left in the tubes.

Analyze

1. What changes did you observe when the solids were added to the tubes?
2. In which tube was oxygen produced rapidly, and how do you know?
3. Which substance, sand or manganese dioxide, caused the rapid production of gas from the hydrogen perioxide?
4. How did you identify the gas produced?
5. What remained in each tube after the hydrogen peroxide was driven away?

Conclude and Apply

6. What are the two characteristics of a catalyst? Which substance in this activity has both characteristics?
7. The word *catalyst* has uses beyond chemistry. If a person who is added to a basketball team acts as a catalyst, what effect is that person likely to have on the team?

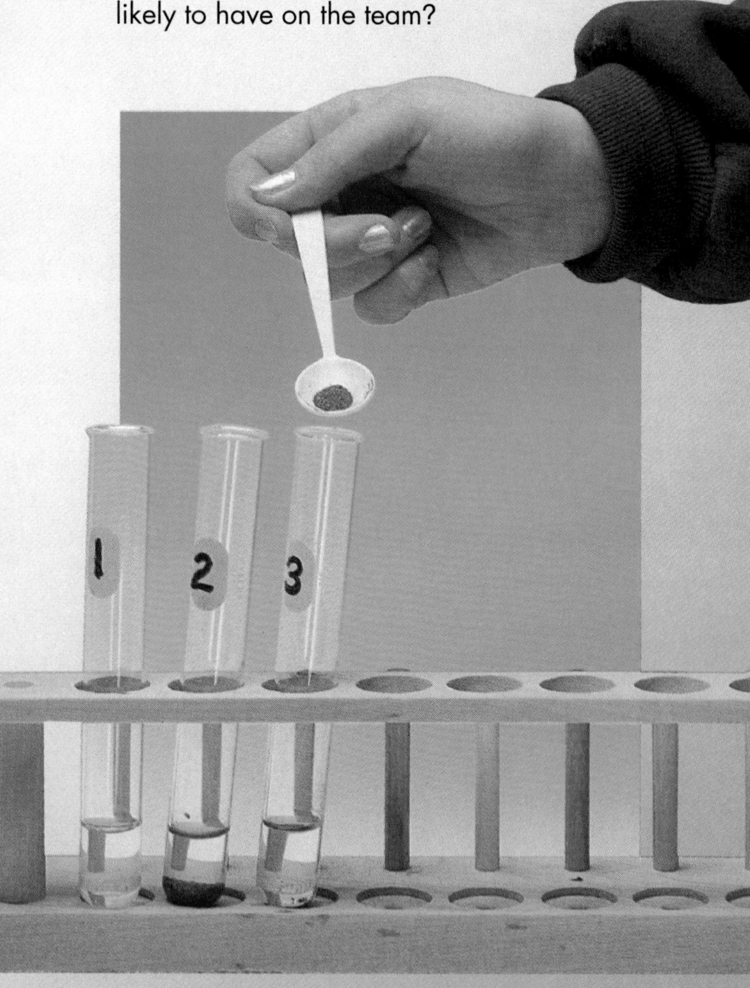

CHAPTER

REVIEW

SUMMARY

16-1: Chemical Changes in Matter

1. In a chemical reaction, the reactants are changed into the products, which are different substances.

2. According to the law of conservation of mass, the mass of the reactants in a chemical reaction equals the mass of the products.

3. A chemical equation is a shorthand way of describing a chemical reaction using symbols, coefficients, and formulas.

16-2: Science and Society: The Hole in the Ozone Layer

1. The ozone layer helps protect life on Earth by absorbing much of the ultraviolet radiation from the sun.

2. In the upper atmosphere, CFCs release atoms of chlorine that destroy ozone molecules.

16-3: Chemical Equations

1. A balanced chemical equation has the same number of atoms of each element on both sides of the equation.

2. The final step in the process of balancing a chemical equation is the choice of the correct coefficients.

16-4: Types of Chemical Reactions

1. Generalized formulas are used to describe four reaction types—synthesis, decomposition, single displacement, and double displacement.

2. Many specific chemical reactions can be classified as one of four types.

16-5: Energy and Chemical Reactions

1. In an exothermic reaction, energy is released; in an endothermic reaction, energy is absorbed.

2. A catalyst increases the speed of a chemical reaction; an inhibitor decreases the speed of a chemical reaction.

KEY SCIENCE WORDS

a. **balanced chemical equation**
b. **catalyst**
c. **chemical reaction**
d. **chlorofluorocarbons (CFCs)**
e. **coefficients**
f. **decomposition reaction**
g. **double displacement reaction**
h. **endothermic reactions**
i. **exothermic reactions**
j. **inhibitor**
k. **precipitate**
l. **products**
m. **reactants**
n. **single displacement reaction**
o. **synthesis reaction**

UNDERSTANDING VOCABULARY

Match each phrase with the correct term from the list of Key Science Words.

1. energy is given off
2. has same number of atoms on both sides
3. energy is absorbed
4. an element replaces another in a compound
5. slows down a reaction rate
6. substance breaks down into simpler substances
7. two ionic compounds are in solution and precipitate forms
8. two or more substances combine
9. group of compounds that contains chlorine, fluorine, and carbon
10. well-defined example of chemical change

CHAPTER

REVIEW

CHECKING CONCEPTS

Choose the word or phrase that completes the sentence.

1. An example of a chemical reaction is ______.
   a. bending **c.** melting
   b. evaporation **d.** photosynthesis
2. Lavoisier's experiments gave examples of the law of ______.
   a. chemical reaction
   b. conservation of mass
   c. coefficients
   d. gravity
3. An element that is more ______ will replace another element in a compound.
   a. active **c.** inhibiting
   b. catalytic **d.** soluble
4. In the expression $4Ca(NO_3)_2$, the 4 is a ______.
   a. coefficient **c.** subscript
   b. formula **d.** symbol
5. BHA is an example of a(n) ______.
   a. catalyst **c.** inhibitor
   b. formula **d.** product
6. If a substance is dissolved in water, ______ follows its formula in an equation.
   a. (*aq*) **c.** (*g*)
   b. (*cr*) **d.** (*l*)
7. In tarnishing, Ag_2S is a(n) ______.
   a. catalyst **c.** product
   b. inhibitor **d.** reactant
8. In the burning of hydrogen, O_2 is a(n) ______.
   a. catalyst **c.** product
   b. inhibitor **d.** reactant
9. ______ is a substance that absorbs UV radiation.
   a. O_2 **b.** O_3 **c.** Cl **d.** Cl_2
10. If a substance is a solid, ______, follows its formula in an equation.
    a. (*l*) **b.** (*g*) **c.** (*cr*) **d.** (*aq*)

UNDERSTANDING CONCEPTS

Complete each sentence.

11. A(n) ______ speeds up a reaction without being permanently changed.
12. ______ represent the relative number of units taking part in a reaction.
13. An insoluble product of a reaction that comes out of solutions is a(n) ______.
14. When nitrogen and oxygen react to form nitrogen dioxide, nitrogen and oxygen are ______.
15. The new substances formed in a chemical reaction are the ______.

THINK AND WRITE CRITICALLY

16. Write a balanced chemical equation and use it to explain the law of conservation of mass.
17. If a strip of Zn is placed in a solution of $Cu(NO_3)_2$, and a strip of Cu is placed in a $Zn(NO_3)_2$ solution, what reaction takes place? Explain.
18. $PbCl_2$ and Li_2SO_4 react to form LiCl and what other substance?
19. Why should subscripts not be changed to balance an equation?
20. Write a balanced equation for the decomposition of copper(II) oxide.

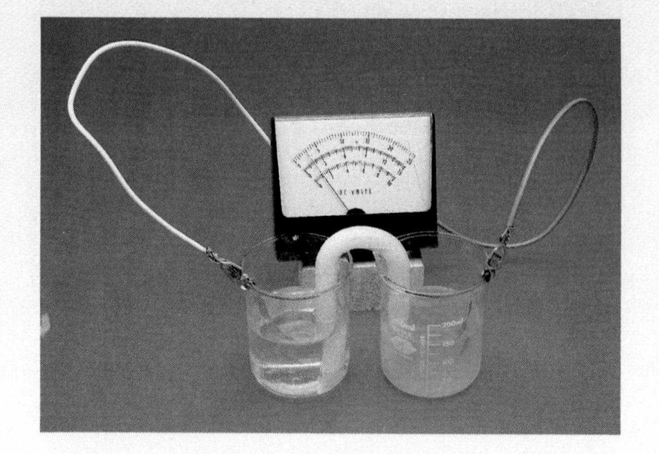

APPLY

21. Chromium is produced by reacting its oxide with aluminum. If 76 g of Cr_2O_3 and 27 g of Al react to form 51 g of Al_2O_3 how many grams of Cr are formed?
22. Propane, $C_3H_8(g)$, burns in oxygen to form carbon dioxide and water vapor. Write a balanced equation for burning propane.
23. $Cl(g) + O_3(g) \rightarrow ClO(g) + O_2(g)$ plays a role in ozone destruction. What is the source of the monatomic chlorine, Cl?
24. In one reaction of a catalytic converter, nitrogen(II) oxide reacts with hydrogen to form ammonia and water vapor. Write a balanced equation for this reaction.
25. If lye, NaOH, is put in water, the solution gets hot. What kind of reaction is this?

MORE SKILL BUILDERS

If you need help, refer to the Skill Handbook.

1. **Observing and Inferring:** What belongs in the parentheses in the following double displacement reaction?

   $BaCl_2(aq) + K_2CO_3(aq) \rightarrow BaCO_3(\ ) + 2KCl(aq)$
2. **Recognizing Cause and Effect:** Sucrose, table sugar, is a disaccharide. This means that sucrose is composed of two simple sugars chemically bonded together. Sucrose can be separated by digestion or by heating it in a sulfuric acid solution. Find out what products are formed by breaking sucrose. What role does the acid play?
3. **Interpreting Data:** When 46 g of sodium were exposed to dry air, 62 g of sodium oxide formed over a period of time. How many grams of oxygen from the air were used?
4. **Outlining:** Make an outline with the general heading "Chemical Reactions." Include the four types of reactions, with a description and example of each.
5. **Concept Mapping:** The arrow in a chemical equation tells the reaction direction. Some reactions are reversible, because they don't go in only one direction. Sometimes the bond formed is weak, and a product breaks apart as it's formed. A double arrow used in the equation indicates this reaction. Fill in the cycle, using the words *product(s)* and *reactant(s)*. In the blanks in the center, fill in the formulas for the substances appearing in the reversible reaction:

   $H_2(g) + I_2(g) \rightleftarrows 2HI(g)$

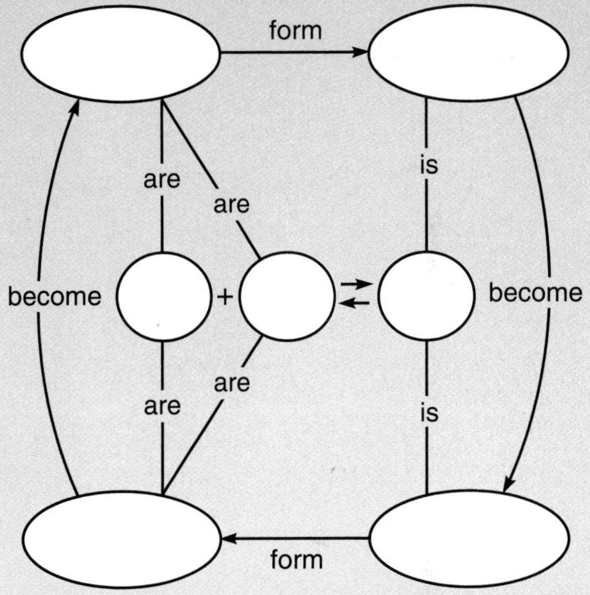

PROJECTS

1. Research common chemical reactions that occur safely in your home. Demonstrate one of these reactions. Tell what type of reaction it is and how it is used. Write a balanced equation for the reaction.
2. Investigate the label on a package of cold cuts. Research as many of the chemicals added as possible. Is anything added as an inhibitor? Report on your findings.

CHAPTER

17 Acids, Bases, and Salts

Do you know what is causing this marble statue to deteriorate at an alarming rate?

FIND OUT!

Do this simple activity to find out how a solution can change a rock.

Marble is mostly calcite, $CaCO_3$, a mineral found in many rocks. Normal rainwater does not have much effect on calcite. However, in places where there is a lot of air pollution, certain chemical pollutants dissolve in rainwater and change its chemical makeup. This rainwater-pollutant solution reacts with calcite, causing it to weaken and eventually crumble.

Let's simulate this reaction. Weigh out exactly 5.0 g of marble chips and place them in a beaker. Next add about 50 mL of soda water, which is similar in some ways to the rain-water-pollutant solution. Observe the mixture for several minutes. Then stir the mixture vigorously and let it sit until it stops moving. Pour the mixture through a filter paper. Dry the marble chips and mass them again. Has their mass changed? How do your conclusions relate to acid rain?

Gearing Up

Previewing the Chapter

Use this outline to help you focus on important ideas in the chapter.

Section 17-1 Acids and Bases
- Properties of Acids
- Common Acids
- Properties of Bases
- Common Bases
- Solutions of Acids and Bases

Section 17-2 Strength of Acids and Bases
- Strong and Weak Acids and Bases
- pH of a Solution
- Determining pH

Section 17-3 Science and Society
Acid Rain
- What Is Acid Rain?

Section 17-4 Acids, Bases, and Salts
- Neutralization
- Salts
- Titration
- Soaps and Detergents
- Organic Acids and Esters

Previewing Science Skills

- In the **Skill Builders,** you will compare and contrast, make a concept map, and interpret data.
- In the **Activities,** you will use models, hypothesize, measure, observe, and predict.
- In the **MINI-Lab,** you will observe and infer.

What's next?

You have seen that contact with some solutions can produce a change in a mineral. Now find out what kinds of solutions produce such changes.

17-1 Acids and Bases

New Science Words

acid
indicator
dehydrating agent
pickling
base
hydronium ion

Objectives

- Define *acid* and *base.*
- Describe the characteristic properties of acids and bases.
- List the names, formulas, and uses of some common acids and bases.
- Relate the processes of ionization and dissociation to the formation of acids and bases.

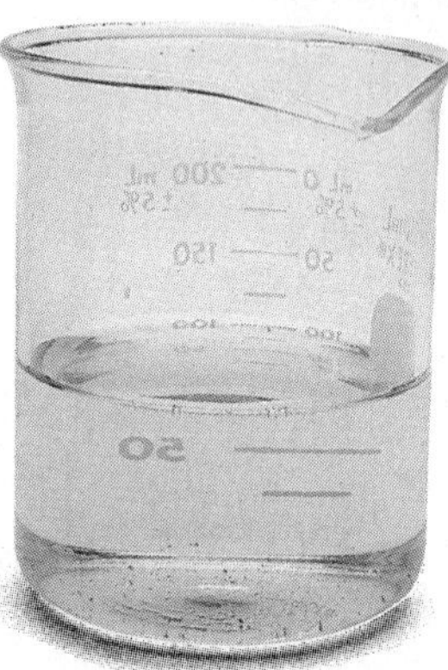

Figure 17-1. This indicator turns red in the presence of an acid.

Properties of Acids

What comes to mind when you hear the word *acid*? Do you think about something that has a sour taste? Do you think of a substance that can burn your skin, or even burn a hole through a piece of metal? Although many acids are not strong enough to burn through metal, or even burn your skin, these characteristics are, indeed, properties of acids.

Acids make up a very important group of compounds. All of these compounds contain hydrogen. When an acid is dissolved in water, some of the hydrogen is released as hydrogen ions (H^+). Thus, an **acid** is a substance that produces hydrogen ions (H^+) in solution. It is the presence of the H^+ ions that gives acids their characteristic properties. A brief description of these acid properties follows.

Acids taste sour. The familiar sour taste of such foods as citrus fruits and tomatoes is due to the presence of acids. *However, taste should **NEVER** be used to test for the presence of acids.* Some acids can produce painful burns and damage to tissues.

Acids are electrolytes. Because they always contain some ions, acid solutions conduct electricity.

Acids are corrosive. Some acids react strongly with certain metals, seeming to "eat away" the metals as metallic compounds and hydrogen gas are produced.

Acids react with certain compounds, called indicators, to produce a predictable change in color. An **indicator** is an organic compound that changes color in an acid or a base.

Common Acids

Many familiar items that you use every day contain acids. Acids are components of many foods. The gastric juices in your stomach contain acid that helps to break down food during digestion. Car batteries, some flashlight batteries, and some household cleaners also contain acids. Table 17-1 gives the names and formulas of a few common acids and tells where they are found.

In addition to these acids that you come in contact with every day, certain acids are vital to industry. The four most important industrial acids are sulfuric acid, phosphoric acid, nitric acid, and hydrochloric acid.

Sulfuric acid, H_2SO_4, is the most widely used chemical in the world. Almost 30 billion kilograms of this acid are produced in the United States annually. More than half of this acid is used by industries in this country. The rest is exported.

Sulfuric acid is a thick, oily liquid. Because of its use in automobile storage batteries, sulfuric acid is sometimes called battery acid. Most sulfuric acid produced is

Did You Know?

In the 8th century, a mixture of nitric acid and hydrochloric acid was known as *aqua regia,* meaning "kingly water," because it was able to dissolve gold.

Table 17-1

SOME COMMON ACIDS		
Name	**Formula**	**Where Found**
Acetic acid	CH_3COOH	Vinegar
Acetylsalicylic acid	$HOOC–C_6H_4–OOCCH_3$	Aspirin
Ascorbic acid (vitamin C)	$C_5H_9O_5–COOH$	Citrus fruits, tomatoes, veteta-bles
Boric acid	H_3BO_3	Eyewash solutions
Carbonic acid	H_2CO_3	Carbonated drinks
Hydrochloric acid	HCl	Gastric juices in stomach
Nitric acid	HNO_3	Making fertilizers, explosives (TNT)
Phosphoric acid	H_3PO_4	Making detergents, fertilizers
Sulfuric acid	H_2SO_4	Car batteries, making fertilizers

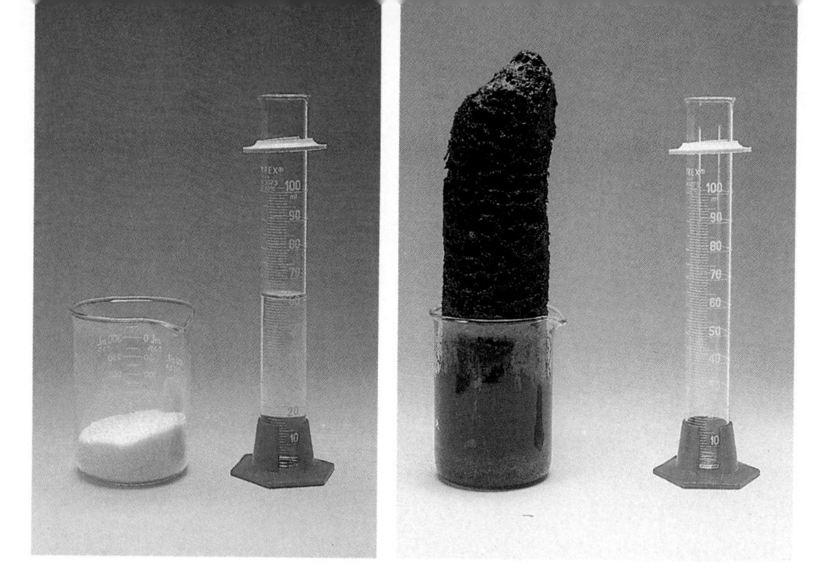

Figure 17-2. Sulfuric acid reacts with the hydrogen and oxgyen in sugar, removing them as water and leaving only carbon.

used in the manufacture of fertilizer. It is also used in petroleum refining, steel manufacture, and in the production of plastics, drugs, dyes, and other acids.

What is a dehydrating agent?

Another important use for sulfuric acid is as a dehydrating agent. A **dehydrating agent** is a substance that can remove water from materials. As Figure 17-2 illustrates, organic compounds are dehydrated by removing hydrogen and oxygen in the form of water from the compounds, leaving only carbon. When sulfuric acid comes in contact with human tissue, this dehydrating action produces painful burns.

Phosphoric acid, H_3PO_4, is another acid important to industry in the United States. Eighty percent of the phosphoric acid produced is used to make fertilizers.

Dilute phosphoric acid has a slightly sour but pleasant taste and is used in soft drinks. It is also used to make phosphates, which are added to detergents to enhance their cleaning power. Unfortunately, these phosphates cause pollution problems in lakes and streams.

Nitric acid, HNO_3, is best known for its use in making explosives. However, like sulfuric and phosphoric acids, most of the nitric acid produced is used in the manufacture of fertilizers. Concentrated nitric acid is a colorless liquid. When exposed to light, the acid slowly changes to a yellow liquid. This change in color occurs because some of the nitric acid decomposes into nitrogen dioxide, NO_2, which is a brownish gas. Nitric acid can cause serious burns on human skin. Contact with light-colored skin causes yellow stains. This yellow color is a test for protein.

MINI-Lab

Do acids and bases conduct an electric current?

What term is used to describe a substance that, when dissolved in water, conducts an electric current? Carefully place the electrodes of a conductivity tester into a glass of orange juice. Did the juice conduct electricity? What acids are present in orange juice? (**CAUTION:** *Do not taste the juice.*) Try the same condictivity procedure with an ammonia cleaner. Did this solution conduct electricity? What base is present in the cleaner? What are the most important ions formed in aqueous solutions of acids? of bases?

Hydrogen chloride is a colorless gas. When this gas is dissolved in water, hydrochloric acid, HCl, is formed. The HCl fumes given off by the hydrochloric acid can harm the lungs, eyes, and skin.

Hydrochloric acid, which is commonly called muriatic acid, is used in industry to clean surfaces of materials. Large quantities of the acid are used by the steel industry for pickling. **Pickling** is a process in which oxides and other impurities are removed from metal surfaces by dipping the metals in hydrochloric acid.

Figure 17-3. Pickling removes impurities from metal surfaces.

TECHNOLOGY

Book Decay

New technologies often bring new problems. When paper made from flax or cotton was replaced by paper made from wood fiber, the life expectancy of the paper was severely reduced. Paper made from wood fiber must be treated with sizing. When this paper is exposed to heat and humidity, the sizing reacts to form an acid. The acid then decomposes the wood fiber in the paper. If the acid is not neutralized or removed, the paper will last only about 50 years.

The Library of Congress currently contains 16 million books and manuscripts that are in danger of acid decay. Several technologies are being developed to remove acid from paper. One involves vacuum drying the books and adding a magnesium compound to neutralize the acid. A second method dips books in a mixture of Freon and magnesium oxide. The most exotic technique exposes the books to diethylzinc (DEZ) gas for neutralization. DEZ, however, is explosive, making the process hard to engineer. Recently, manufacturers have started to produce paper that is alkaline and, therefore, more durable.

Think Critically: What could be done to reduce the rate of paper deterioration while scientists search for an efficient and inexpensive neutralization technique?

EcoTip

Many detergents and household cleaners contain phosphates which pollute lakes, streams, and groundwater when released in wastewater. Read labels carefully and select cleansing agents that do not contain phosphates.

There are several methods for making phosphoric, nitric, and hydrochloric acids. But one general method can be used to make all three acids. This method involves reacting concentrated sulfuric acid with a compound containing the negative ion of the desired acid.

$$Ca_3(PO_4)_2(cr) + 3H_2SO_4(aq) \rightarrow 2H_3PO_4(aq) + 3CaSO_4(cr)$$

$$NaNO_3(cr) + H_2SO_4(aq) \rightarrow HNO_3(g) + NaHSO_4(aq)$$

$$NaCl(cr) + H_2SO_4(aq) \rightarrow HCl(g) + NaHSO_4(aq)$$

Properties of Bases

What properties do acids and bases have in common?

Like acids, bases are an important group of chemical compounds. Although acids and bases seem to have some features in common, the two groups are actually quite different.

A **base** is a substance that produces hydroxide ions (OH^-) in solution. Does this OH combination look familiar? You may recall from Chapter 13 that an alcohol has a hydroxyl group, $-OH$, as part of its molecule. This hydroxyl group is not an ion and should not be confused with the OH^- ions that are present in all bases. Alcohols are not bases.

The hydroxide ions present in all basic solutions are negative ions, whereas the hydrogen ions present in acid solutions are positive ions. This difference in charge accounts for some of the differences between acids and bases.

In the pure, undissolved state, most bases are crystalline solids. In solution, bases feel slippery and have a bitter taste. Like acids, strong bases are corrosive, and contact with the skin may result in severe burns and tissue damage. *Therefore, taste and touch should **NEVER** be used to test for the presence of a base.* Basic solutions are electrolytes. This property is due to the presence of ions in the solutions. Finally, bases react with indicators to produce predictable changes in color.

Figure 17-4. Many household materials contain bases.

Common Bases

Many household products contain bases. Most soaps, for example, contain bases, which explains their bitter taste and slippery feel. Table 17-2 contains the names and formulas of some common bases and tells how the bases are used.

Table 17-2

COMMON BASES AND THEIR USES		
Name	**Formula**	**Uses**
Aluminum hydroxide	$Al(OH)_3$	Deodorant, antacid
Ammonium hydroxide	NH_4OH	Household cleaner
Calcium hydroxide	$Ca(OH)_2$	Leather production, manufacture of mortar and plaster
Magnesium hydroxide	$Mg(OH)_2$	Laxative, antacid
Sodium hydroxide	$NaOH$	Drain cleaner, soap making

Although you won't find it listed in the table, the most widely used base is ammonia, NH_3. Pure ammonia is a colorless gas with a very distinctive, irritating odor. When ammonia gas is dissolved in water, some of its molecules react with water molecules, forming ammonium ions (NH_4^+) and hydroxide ions.

$$NH_3(g) + H_2O(l) \rightarrow NH_4^+(aq) + OH^-(aq)$$

The solution containing ammonium ions and hydroxide ions is called ammonium hydroxide, or ammonia water. However, ammonium hydroxide exists as a solid compound only at temperatures below $-79°C$. Ammonia water is an excellent household cleaning agent. Ammonia is also used as a fertilizer and in the production of rayon, nylon, and nitric acid.

Another widely used base is calcium hydroxide, $Ca(OH)_2$. Commonly called caustic lime, this base is a white crystalline powder that is only slightly soluble in water. Calcium hydroxide is used in the production of mortar and plaster and to "sweeten" acidic soils.

Sodium hydroxide, NaOH, is a strong, very corrosive base. This compound, commonly called lye, dissolves readily in water. Its corrosive nature makes sodium hydroxide an effective oven cleaner and drain cleaner. It reacts with such organic materials as oils and fats to produce soap and glycerine.

Figure 17-5. Ammonia is an important ingredient of these products.

Solutions of Acids and Bases

It is important to understand that the compounds that produce acids or bases when dissolved in water are not, themselves, acids or bases. The terms *acid* and *base* refer to aqueous (water) solutions. Solutions that contain H^+ ions are acids; those that contain OH^- ions are bases.

What is a hydronium ion?

All compounds that produce acids when dissolved in water are made up of polar molecules. When such a compound is dissolved in water, the molecules are pulled apart, forming positive and negative ions. Recall from Chapter 15 that this process is called ionization. The positive hydrogen ion is attracted to and held by the negative end of a water molecule, forming a new ion, as shown in Figure 17-6. The ion formed by the bonding of a hydrogen ion, H^+, to a water molecule is called a **hydronium ion,** H_3O^+.

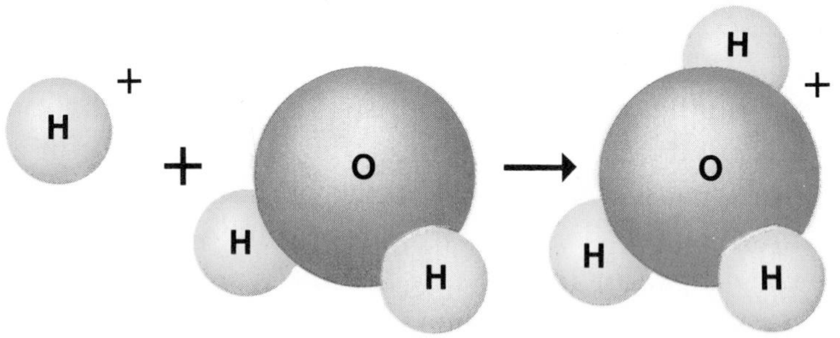

Figure 17-6. When an acid dissolves in water, hydrogen ions from the acid combine with water molecules to produce hydronium ions.

Figure 17-7 shows what happens when hydrogen chloride gas dissolves in water. Because the solution contains H^+ ions, it is an acid—hydrochloric acid, HCl. As described earlier, the H^+ ions bond with water molecules to form H_3O^+ ions.

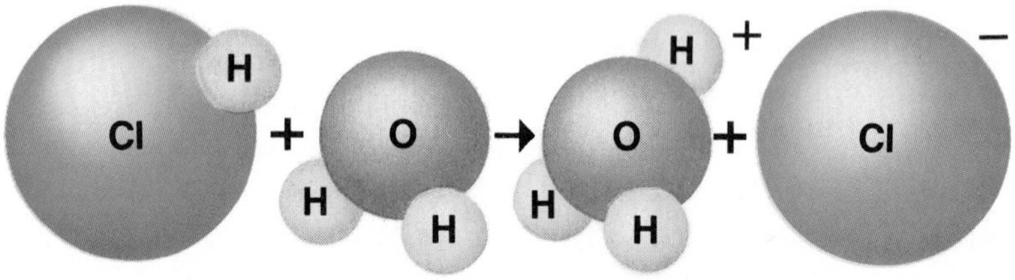

Figure 17-7. When hydrogen chloride gas dissolves in water, it ionizes to produce H^+ ions and Cl^- ions.

$$HCl + H_2O \rightarrow H_3O^+ + Cl^-$$

The equation below shows the ionization of acetic acid, CH_3COOH, which is an organic acid.

$$CH_3COOH(l) + H_2O(l) \rightarrow H_3O^+(aq) + CH_3COO^-(aq)$$

As the equation shows, when an organic acid ionizes, the H at the end of the –COOH group combines with water to form the hydronium ion.

Except for ammonia, nearly all compounds that produce bases in aqueous solution are ionic compounds. That is, they are already made up of ions. As the equation below shows, when such a compound dissolves, the ions dissociate, or pull apart, and exist as individual ions in solution.

$$NaOH(cr) \xrightarrow{H_2O} Na^+(aq) + OH^-(aq)$$

Ammonia is a polar compound. In solution, ionization takes place when the ammonia molecule attracts a hydrogen atom from a water molecule, as shown in Figure 17-8.

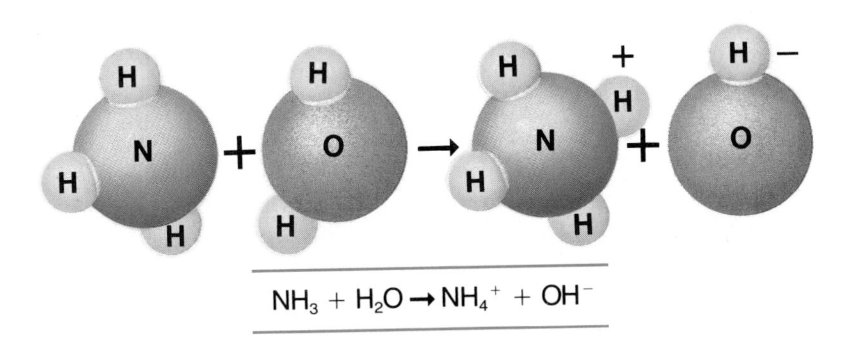

Figure 17-8. Even though ammonia is not a hydroxide, it reacts with water to produce some OH^- ions.

The next time you sip a soft drink, wash your hands with soap, or use any of the products described in this section, stop and think for a minute. Think about what properties the product has and why it has them.

SECTION REVIEW

1. Why are acids and bases electrolytes?
2. Name three important acids and three important bases and describe some uses of each.
3. **Apply:** When you are stung by a bee or a wasp, it injects formic acid, HCOOH, into your body. What kind of acid is formic acid? How do you know? Write an equation showing how formic acid ionizes.

Comparing and Contrasting

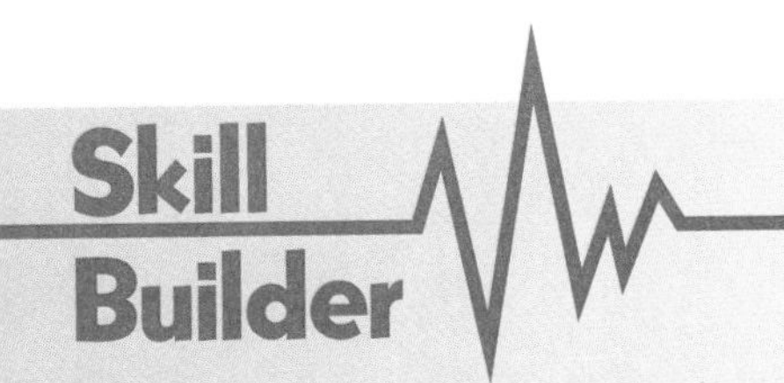

List as many ways as you can think of that acids and bases are similar. Make a second list of the ways in which they are different. If you need help, refer to Comparing and Contrasting in the **Skill Handbook** on page 679.

17-2 Strength of Acids and Bases

New Science Words

strong acid
weak acid
strong base
weak base
pH

Objectives

- Explain what determines the strength of an acid or a base.
- Differentiate between strength and concentration.
- Define *pH.*
- Describe the relationship between pH and the strength of an acid or a base.

Strong and Weak Acids and Bases

You have learned that all acids have certain properties in common. Yet, some acids are safe enough to swallow or put in your eyes, whereas other acids destroy human tissue and corrode metal. Obviously, all acids are not alike. Some acids are stronger than others. The same is true of bases. Table 17-3 lists some strong and weak acids and bases.

How do strong acids differ from weak acids?

The strength of an acid or base depends on how completely a compound is pulled apart to form ions when dissolved in water. An acid that ionizes almost completely in solution is a **strong acid.** Conversely, an acid that only partly ionizes in solution is a **weak acid.**

Strong acids contain large numbers of hydronium ions. Look at the equations for the ionization of hydrochloric acid, a strong acid, and acetic acid, a weak acid.

$$HCl(g) + H_2O(l) \rightarrow H_3O^+(aq) + Cl^-(aq)$$

$$CH_3COOH(l) + H_2O(l) \rightleftarrows H_3O^+(aq) + CH_3COO^-(aq)$$

In the equation for the formation of hydrochloric acid, note that no HCl molecules are present in solution. All of the HCl ionizes, and the H^+ ions produced combine with water to form H_3O^+ ions. In the equation for acetic acid, not all of the CH_3COOH molecules ionize. Some of the molecules remain intact in solution. Thus, only a few H^+ ions are produced to form H_3O^+ ions.

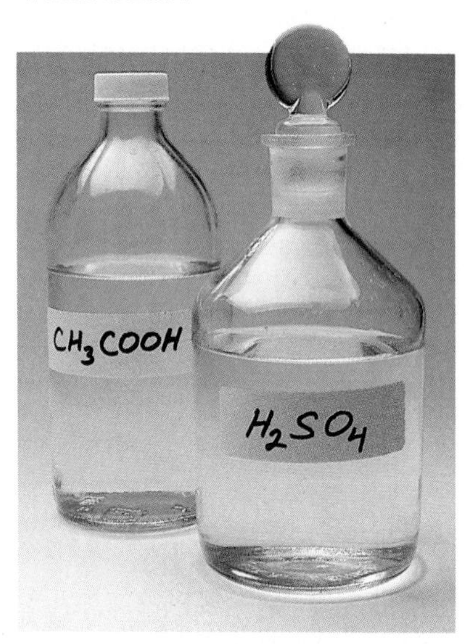

Figure 17-9. H_2SO_4 is a strong acid; CH_3COOH is a weak acid.

The strength of a base is determined by its solubility in water. Remember, most bases are ionic compounds that dissociate to produce individual ions when they dissolve. Thus, the more soluble an ionic compound is, the greater will be its degree of dissociation.

A **strong base** is one that dissociates almost completely in solution. Strong bases are very soluble, and their water solutions contain large numbers of hydroxide ions. A **weak base** is one that only partly dissociates in solution. Weak bases are only slightly soluble in water. The equations show the dissociation of sodium hydroxide, a strong base, and magnesium hydroxide, a weak base.

Table 17-3

STRENGTHS OF SOME ACIDS AND BASES		
Acid	**Strength**	**Base**
Hydrochloric, HCl Sulfuric, H_2SO_4 Nitric, HNO_3	STRONG	Sodium hydroxide, $NaOH$ Potassium hydroxide, KOH Magnesium hydroxide, $Mg(OH)_2$
Phosphoric, H_3PO_4	MODERATE	Calcium hydroxide, $Ca(OH)_2$
Acetic, CH_3COOH Carbonic, H_2CO_3 Boric, H_3BO_3	WEAK	Ammonium hydroxide, NH_4OH Aluminum hydroxide, $Al(OH)_3$ Iron(III) hydroxide, $Fe(OH)_3$

$$NaOH(cr) \xrightarrow{H_2O} Na^+(aq) + OH^-(aq)$$

$$Mg(OH)_2(cr) \rightleftarrows Mg^{2+}(aq) + 2OH^-(aq)$$

Often, the *strength* of an acid or base is confused with its *concentration*. As you learned in Chapter 15, *dilute* and *concentrated* are terms used to indicate the concentration of a solution.

The concentration of an acid or base has nothing to do with its strength. Strong acids and bases are always strong; weak acids and bases are always weak. It is possible to have dilute concentrations of strong acids or bases and concentrated solutions of weak acids or bases.

Did You Know?

The pH of human blood is 7.4. The lungs, kidneys, and circulatory system itself help to maintain that basic level.

pH of a Solution

If you have a pool or keep tropical fish, you know that the pH of the water must be controlled. **pH** is a measure of the concentration of hydronium ions in a solution. It indicates acidity. To determine pH, a scale ranging from 0 to 14 has been devised, as shown in the diagram below.

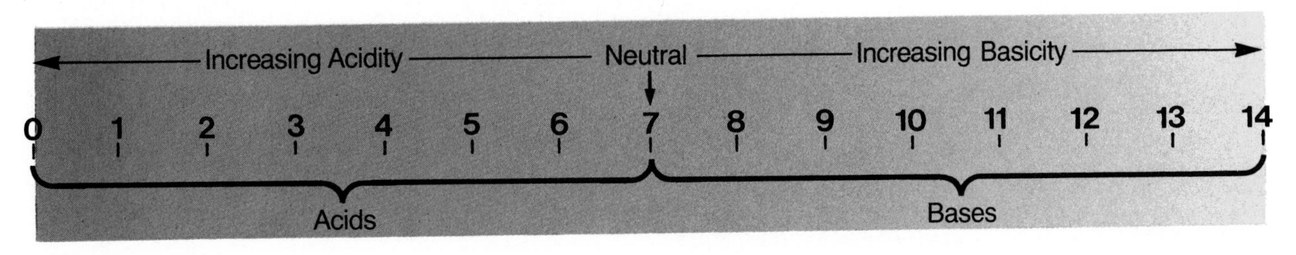

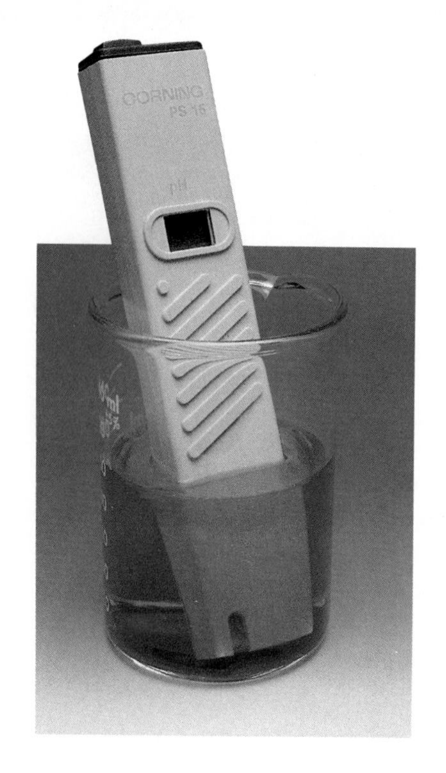

As the diagram shows, solutions with a pH lower than 7 are acidic. The lower the value, the more acidic the solution. Solutions with pH greater than 7 are basic, and the higher the pH, the more basic the solution. A solution with a pH of exactly 7 is neutral—neither acidic nor basic. Pure water has a pH of 7.

Strong acids will have lower pH values—be more acidic—than weak acids of the same concentration. This is because strong acids ionize more completely, thus forming larger numbers of H_3O^+ ions. Similarly, strong bases, which contain large numbers of OH^- ions, will have higher pH values than weak bases of the same concentration.

Determining pH

A pH meter like the one shown can be used to determine the pH of a solution. This meter is operated by simply immersing the electrodes in the solution to be tested and reading the dial. Small, battery-operated pH meters with digital readouts make measuring the pH of materials even more convenient.

If a pH meter is not available, a universal indicator or pH paper can be used. Both of these undergo a color change in the presence of H_3O^+ ions and OH^- ions in solution. The final color of the solution or the pH paper is matched with colors in a chart to find the pH, as shown in Figure 17-10.

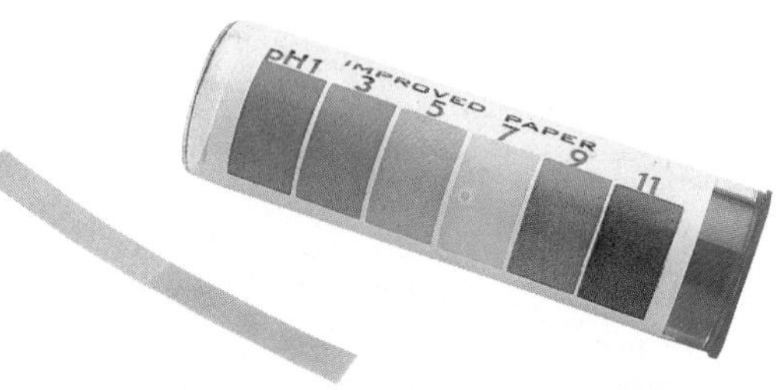

Figure 17-10. When matched with a color chart, the color of the pH paper will show that the solution being tested is a base.

SECTION REVIEW

1. What determines the strength of an acid? a base?
2. How can you make a dilute solution of a strong acid? Include an example as part of your explanation.
3. **Apply:** What does the pH of each of the solutions indicate about the solution? Rainwater, 5.8; soda water, 3.0; drain cleaner, 14.0; seawater, 8.9; pure water, 7.0.

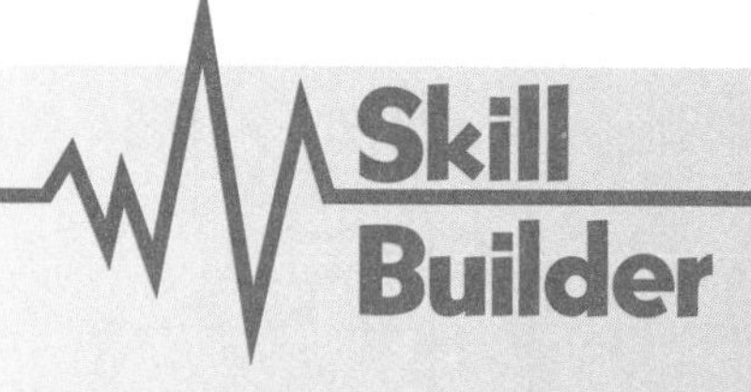

Concept Mapping

Make a concept map of pH values. Start with three boxes labeled acidic, neutral, and basic and indicate the pH range of each box. Below each box, give some examples of solutions that belong in each pH range and give the pH of each. If you need help, refer to Concept Mapping in the **Skill Handbook** on pages 684 and 685.

ACTIVITY 17-1
Strong and Weak Acids

Problem: *How do strong acids differ from weak acids?*

Materials:  

- typing paper (22 cm x 28 cm), marked with rectangles
- thick cardboard (22 cm x 28 cm), marked with rectangles
- scissors
- test tubes (2)
- medicine droppers (2)
- graduated cylinder
- dilute hydrochloric acid (HCl)
- dilute acetic acid (CH_3COOH)
- pH paper
- timer, with second hand

Procedure

1. Prepare a data table like the one shown.
2. Make sure your paper and cardboard are marked with equal numbers of rectangles. Mark every other rectangle with a plus sign (+) to represent hydronium ions. Then mark the blank rectangles with a minus sign (−) to represent negative ions.
3. Using scissors, cut the typing paper into as many of its individual rectangles as possible in ten seconds.

4. Repeat Step 3 with the piece of cardboard.
5. Obtain 2 mL each of dilute HCl and dilute CH_3COOH in test tubes. **CAUTION:** *Handle these acids with care. Avoid contact with the skin or clothing. Report any spills to your teacher immediately.*
6. Using a different dropper for each acid, add two drops of each to separate strips of pH paper. Determine their respective pH values and record them in the data table.

Data and Observations

____	**ions removed from typing paper**	____	**pH of HCl solution**
____	**ions removed from cardboard**	____	**pH of acetic acid solution**

Analyze

1. Which was easier to "separate" into ions, the typing paper or the cardboard?
2. Which acid separated into ions most easily? How do you know?

Conclude and Apply

3. Which acid is stronger, HCl or CH_3COOH? How do you know?
4. Which represents the stronger acid, the typing paper or the cardboard? Explain your answer.
5. Which has the stronger bonds between fibers, the typing paper or the cardboard? Explain your answer.
6. Which acids have stronger bonds within their molecules, strong acids or weak acids? Explain your answer.

17-3 Acid Rain

New Science Words

acid rain
plankton

Objectives

- Describe the factors contributing to the formation of acid rain.
- Discuss the problems acid rain is causing and how these problems might be solved.

What Is Acid Rain?

Fish are disappearing from lakes. The surfaces of sculptures and buildings are wearing away. Crops are growing more slowly, and forests are dying. What is the cause of all these problems? The answer could be acid rain. You might be surprised to learn that the term *acid rain* was first used in 1872 by Angus Smith. Smith wrote a book about the polluted air and rain near large cities in England. In the 1970s, people first started to regard acid rain as a serious problem in the northeastern United States and Canada. Now acid rain seems to be a problem in all industrialized countries.

Normal rain has a pH of 5.6. This acidity is due to the reaction of carbon dioxide gas with rainwater to form carbonic acid.

$$CO_2(g) + H_2O(l) \rightarrow H_2CO_3(aq)$$

Carbonic acid is weak. Thus, the carbon dioxide in the air does not contribute very much to the problem of acid rain.

Any form of precipitation having a pH lower than 5.6 is called **acid rain.** Scientists think that acid rain forms when oxides of sulfur and nitrogen in the atmosphere react with rainwater. These oxides are released when fossil fuels are burned. Oxides of sulfur and nitrogen can combine with rainwater to produce strong acids such as sulfuric acid and nitric acid. Although these acids are quite dilute, they can harm the environment. The problem becomes particularly bad in densely populated industrial regions where large quantities of gasoline and high-sulfur fuels are burned.

Figure 17-11. This tree shows the effects of acid rain.

When acid rain falls to Earth, the soil and water become increasingly acidic. Among the first organisms to suffer are plankton. **Plankton** are tiny aquatic plants and animals. These organisms form the base of the food chain for small fish. When the plankton die, the fish that depend on them as a food source soon die also.

Acid rain also has a harmful effect on soil and land plants. As acid rain moves through the soil, it dissolves important mineral nutrients and carries them away. Plants deprived of these nutrients will not grow at a normal rate. Crops and forests are damaged.

Acid rain also causes rapid weathering of buildings and statues made of limestone and marble. For example, the Parthenon in Greece has survived for more than 2000 years. Today, it is rapidly being destroyed by acid rain.

Figure 17-12. The deterioration of this building is due to the chemical reaction of acid rain with calcite, the principal mineral in marble and limestone.

SECTION REVIEW

1. What are the main causes of acid rain?
2. What are the effects of acid rain?

You Decide!

Assume you live in an area whose main industry is mining high-sulfur coal. The coal is burned by the local power company. A law is passed requiring the local company to reduce its sulfur dioxide emissions. Plant owners are faced with two choices: (1) They can buy low-sulfur coal from a neighboring state, which would not result in increased electric rates. (2) They can use local coal and increase electric rates ten percent to cover the costs of removing sulfur and sulfur compounds. Which choice would you support?

17-4 Acids, Bases, and Salts

New Science Words

neutralization
salt
titration
soaps
saponification
detergents
ester

Objectives

- Describe a neutralization reaction.
- Explain what a salt is and how salts form.
- Differentiate between soaps and detergents.
- Explain how esters are made and what they are used for.

Neutralization

You have probably seen television commercials for antacids that describe how effectively these products neutralize excess stomach acid. Would the pH of such a product be higher or lower than 7? If you answered higher, you are correct. Only a base can neutralize the effects of an acid.

What is neutralization?

Neutralization is a chemical reaction between an acid and a base. During a neutralization reaction, hydronium ions from the acid combine with hydroxide ions from the base to produce water.

$$H_3O^+(aq) + OH^-(aq) \rightarrow 2H_2O(l)$$

As the reactive ions are removed from the solution, the acidic and basic properties of the reactants are cancelled, or neutralized.

The equation above accounts for only half of the ions present in the solution. What happens to the remaining ions? They react to form a salt. A **salt** is a compound formed when the negative ions from an acid combine with the positive ions from a base.

Neutralization reactions are ionic. The following equations show what happens to all of the ions during a neutralization reaction:

$$HCl(aq) + NaOH(aq) \rightarrow H_3O^+(aq) + Cl^-(aq) + Na^+(aq) + OH^-(aq)$$

$$\text{Water Formation: } H_3O^+(aq) + OH^-(aq) \rightarrow 2H_2O(l)$$

$$\text{Salt Formation: } Na^+(aq) + Cl^-(aq) \rightarrow NaCl(cr)^*$$

*Note: The formation of crystalline NaCl occurs only if the water is removed by boiling or evaporation.

Did You Know?

In 1990, a ten-year-long study of acid rain costing 500 million dollars was completed. The study concluded with a 15 000 page report indicating that scientists on both sides of the controversy had overstated their cases.

PROBLEM SOLVING

Julio's Experiment

Julio went to the doctor with stomach pains. The doctor told Julio that he had excess stomach acid and advised him to purchase an over-the-counter antacid and take it according to the directions on the package.

Julio wants to determine the best antacid to use. He thinks the best antacid will neutralize the greatest amount of hydrochloric acid.

He went to the drugstore and purchased several antacids that he had seen advertised on television. His science instructor said he would allow Julio to conduct his experiment during study hall and advised Julio to use bromothymol blue as his indicator because it turned pale green at pH 7. What was Julio's hypothesis?

Think Critically: How could Julio design an experiment to determine which antacid is most effective in neutralizing stomach acid?

Salts

Many substances that you come in contact with every day are salts. Of course, the most familiar salt is sodium chloride—common table salt. Table 17-4 on page 442 contains information about some common salts. As the table shows, most salts are composed of a metal and a nonmetal other than oxygen, or a metal and a polyatomic ion. Ammonium salts contain the polyatomic ammonium ion, NH_4^+, rather than a metal. Salts also form when acids react with metals. Hydrogen gas is released during such reactions.

How do salts form?

$$\text{Acid} + \text{Metal} \rightarrow \text{Salt} + \text{Hydrogen}$$

$$H_2SO_4(aq) + Zn(cr) \rightarrow ZnSO_4(aq) + H_2(g)$$

$$6HCl(aq) + 2Fe(cr) \rightarrow 2FeCl_3(aq) + 3H_2(g)$$

Reactions between metals and acids are replacement reactions in which the metal displaces hydrogen from the acid and replaces it.

Table 17-4

SOME COMMON SALTS			
Name	**Formula**	**Common Name**	**Uses**
Sodium chloride	$NaCl$	Salt	Food preparation; manufacture of chemicals
Sodium hydrogen carbonate	$NaHCO_3$	Sodium bicarbonate (baking soda)	Food preparation; in fire extinguishers
Calcium carbonate	$CaCO_3$	Calcite (chalk)	Manufacture of paint and rubber tires
Potassium nitrate	KNO_3	Saltpeter	In fertilizers; manufacture of explosives
Potassium carbonate	K_2CO_3	Potash	Manufacture of soap and glass
Trisodium phosphate	Na_3PO_4	TSP	In detergents
Ammonium chloride	NH_4Cl	Sal ammoniac	In dry cells

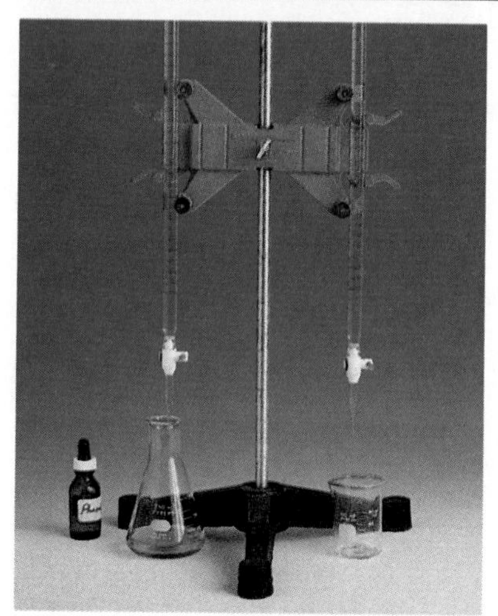

Figure 17-13. The apparatus is set up to perform a titration of a base.

Titration

It is sometimes necessary to find the concentration of an acidic or basic solution. This can be accomplished by titration. **Titration** is the process in which a solution of known concentration is used to determine the concentration of another solution. Most titrations involve acid-base neutralizations.

In a titration, a solution of known concentration, called the standard solution, is added drop by drop to a solution of unknown concentration to which an indicator has been added. If the solution of unknown concentration is a base, a standard acid solution is used, and vice versa.

As an example, assume that you need to find the concentration of an acid solution. First, you would add a few drops of phenolphthalein (feen ul THAYL een) indicator to a carefully measured amount of this solution. Phenolphthalein is colorless in an acid, but is pink in a base.

A standard base solution is added to this acid one drop at a time. At some point, one drop of the base just begins to turn the acid solution pink. This is known as the endpoint of the titration. Just enough standard solution has been added to neutralize the acid. The volume of the base used to neutralize the known volume of acid is determined, and the concentration of the acid can be calculated.

Soaps and Detergents

Soaps are organic salts. Soaps are made by reacting fats or oils with sodium hydroxide or potassium hydroxide. One formula for soap made using sodium hydroxide is $C_{17}H_{35}COONa$. The structural formula for this soap is provided below.

```
    H   H   H   H   H   H   H   H   H   H   H   H   H   H   H   H   H
    |   |   |   |   |   |   |   |   |   |   |   |   |   |   |   |   |
H — C — C — C — C — C — C — C — C — C — C — C — C — C — C — C — C — C — COONa
    |   |   |   |   |   |   |   |   |   |   |   |   |   |   |   |   |
    H   H   H   H   H   H   H   H   H   H   H   H   H   H   H   H   H
```

A soap made using potassium hydroxide might have the formula $C_{15}H_{31}COOK$. Below is the structural formula for this soap.

```
    H   H   H   H   H   H   H   H   H   H   H   H   H   H   H
    |   |   |   |   |   |   |   |   |   |   |   |   |   |   |
H — C — C — C — C — C — C — C — C — C — C — C — C — C — C — C — COOK
    |   |   |   |   |   |   |   |   |   |   |   |   |   |   |
    H   H   H   H   H   H   H   H   H   H   H   H   H   H   H
```

Sodium hydroxide produces solid soaps. Potassium hydroxide makes liquid soaps. Another product of this reaction is glycerin, which is a softening agent in hand creams.

The process of making soap is called **saponification.** Soaps increase the cleaning action of water. When soap is put into water, it ionizes as follows:

$$C_{17}H_{35}COONa(cr) \rightarrow C_{17}H_{35}COO^-(aq) + Na^+(aq)$$

The negative ion consists of two parts: an ionic head and a long, nonpolar hydrocarbon tail. Remember that grease is composed of hydrocarbon molecules. These molecules are similar in structure to the long hydrocarbon tail of the soap molecule.

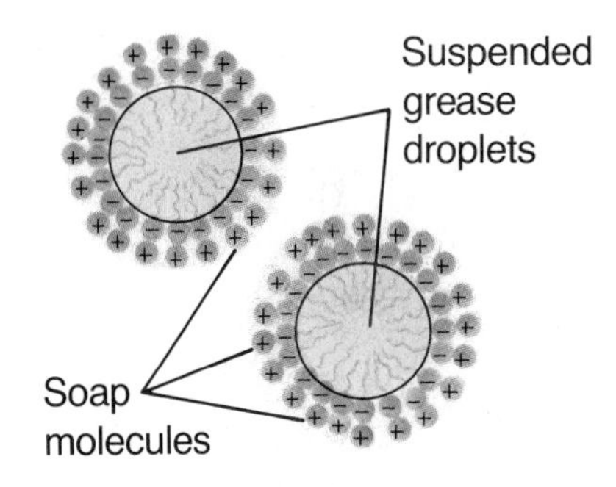

Figure 17-14. Soap removes grease by breaking it up into tiny droplets.

```
    H   H   H   H   H   H   H   H   H   H   H   H   H   H   H   H   H
    |   |   |   |   |   |   |   |   |   |   |   |   |   |   |   |   |
H — C — C — C — C — C — C — C — C — C — C — C — C — C — C — C — C — C — COO⁻
    |   |   |   |   |   |   |   |   |   |   |   |   |   |   |   |   |   ionic head
    H   H   H   H   H   H   H   H   H   H   H   H   H   H   H   H   H
                        nonpolar hydrocarbon tail
```

When you use soap to wash your hands, the nonpolar hydrocarbon tail dissolves any fat or grease that may be on them. The ionic head dissolves in the water and carries the dirt away.

Detergents are organic salts having structures similar to those of soaps. The most common detergent in use today has the following structural formula:

```
                              negative ion
   H  H  H  H  H  H  H  H  H
   |  |  |  |  |  |  |  |  |
H--C--C--C--C--C--C--C--C--C--H
   |  |  |  |  |  |  |  |  |
   H  H  H  H  H  H  H  H  |
                        H--C--H
                           |
                        H--C--H  H  H  H  H  H
                           |     |  |  |  |  |
                        H--C-----C--C--C--C--C--(benzene ring)--S--O⁻  Na⁺
                           |     |  |  |  |  |
                           H     H  H  H  H  H                ionic   positive
                                                              head     ion
                    nonpolar hydrocarbon tail
```

Like soap, the negative ions of detergents have a nonpolar hydrocarbon tail and an ionic head. Detergents enhance the cleaning action of water in a manner similar to that of soap.

When soap is used in hard water, it forms soap scum, or "bathtub ring." This scum forms because hard water contains compounds of calcium, magnesium, and iron. The calcium, magnesium, and iron ions react with the soap to form a precipitate, which is the undesirable scum. Detergents do not form this scum. Therefore, most laundry products are detergents, not soaps.

Organic Acids and Esters

What is an ester?

An **ester** is an organic compound formed by the reaction of an organic acid with an alcohol. The reaction is different from neutralization in that it needs a compound that will split a molecule of water out of the organic acid and alcohol. In Section 17-1 you learned that concentrated sulfuric acid is a powerful dehydrating agent. So this acid must be present for the organic reaction to take place. Figure 17-15 shows the reaction of acetic acid and methyl alcohol to produce an ester—methyl acetate—and water.

Esters are responsible for the many wonderful odors and flavors of flowers, fruits, and other foods. Sometimes esters are added to gelatin desserts or candy to give the characteristic flavors of strawberry, banana, or apple.

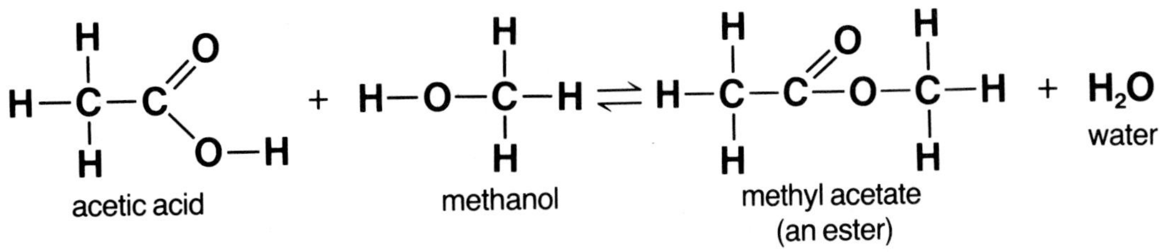

acetic acid + methanol ⇌ methyl acetate (an ester) + H_2O water

Synthetic fibers known as polyesters are made from an organic acid that has two –COOH groups and an alcohol that has two –OH groups. Because the two compounds form long chains with the ester linkage, a polymer results.

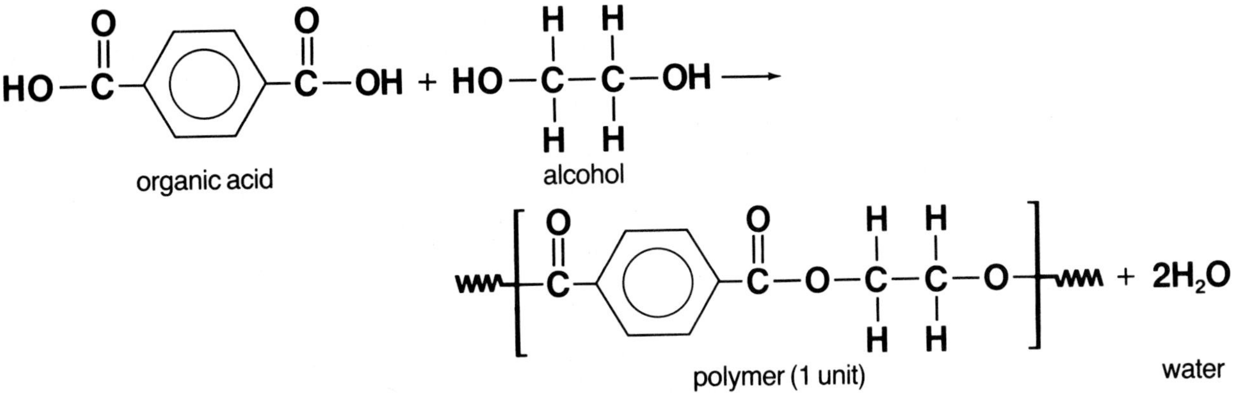

Figure 17-15. This structural equation shows the formation of an ester, methyl acetate, by the reaction of an organic acid and an alcohol.

organic acid + alcohol →

polymer (1 unit) + $2H_2O$ water

SECTION REVIEW

1. What is a neutralization reaction? What are the products of such reactions?
2. When doing laundry, what advantage does using a detergent have over using a soap?
3. **Apply:** Give the names and formulas of the salt that will form in these neutralizations:
   a. hydrochloric acid and ammonium hydroxide
   b. nitric acid and potassium hydroxide
   c. carbonic acid and aluminum hydroxide

Interpreting Data

Skill Builder

Three salts — calcium sulfate, sodium chloride, and potassium nitrate — were obtained in reactions of the acid-base pairs shown here. Match each salt with the acid-base pair that produced it. If you need help, refer to Interpreting Data in the **Skill Handbook** on page 683.

$HCl + NaOH$ $HNO_3 + KOH$ $H_2SO_4 + Ca(OH)_2$

ACTIVITY 17-2
Acid-Base Reactions

Problem: *What happens when a base is added to an acid?*

Materials  

- test tube
- medicine dropper (2)
- graduated cylinder
- carbonated beverage, colorless
- dilute sodium hydroxide (NaOH)
- phenolphthalein indicator, 1%

Procedure

1. Prepare a data table like the one shown.
2. Open a container of a colorless carbonated beverage. Measure 5 mL of the beverage and pour it into a test tube.
3. Add 2 drops of 1% phenolphthalein to the test tube.
4. Using a clean dropper, add dilute NaOH solution to the test tube, one drop at a time. **CAUTION:** *Handle the NaOH solution carefully. Avoid contact with your skin or clothing and report any spills to your teacher immediately.*
5. Count the drops as you add them, gently swirling the solution in the test tube after each drop is added. Stop adding NaOH to the test tube as soon as the solution turns pink and the color remains.
6. Discard the solution as directed by your teacher. Rinse the test tube and droppers thoroughly, dry them, and repeat Steps 1- 4. Find the average number of drops of NaOH used in the two trials.

Data and Observations

	Trial 1	Trial 2	Average
Number of drops of NaOH solution needed			

Analyze

1. What name is used to identify the type of reaction that takes place between the NaOH and the carbonated beverage?
2. Phenolphthalein turns pink in a solution of pH 8 or higher. Why didn't the carbonated beverage turn pink as soon as the phenolphthalein was added? Why did the solution turn pink after NaOH was added?
3. One of the acids present in the carbonated beverage is carbonic acid, H_2CO_3. Write a chemical reaction to show how this acid reacts with NaOH.

Conclude and Apply

4. How many drops of NaOH were needed to neutralize the 5-mL sample of the carbonated beverage? Suppose a solution of NaOH half as concentrated as the one used were added to the carbonated beverage. About how many drops would be needed to cause the same effect?
5. Describe how you might use this experimental design to compare acid levels of several different carbonated beverages.

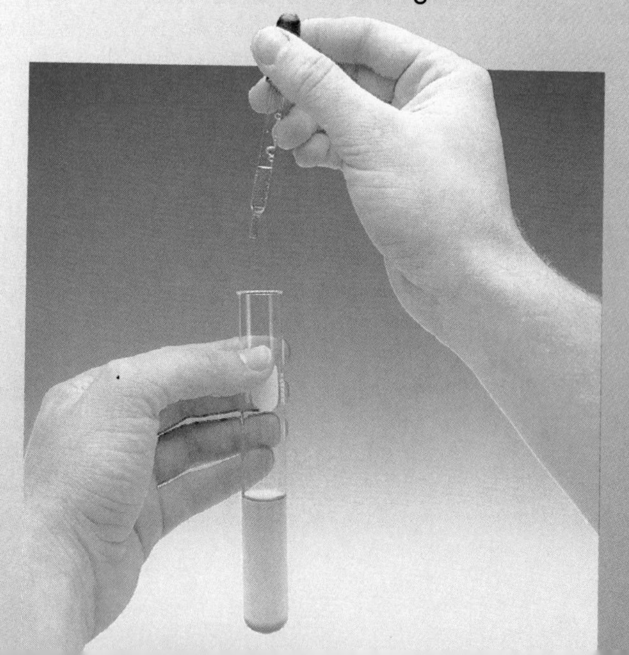

CHAPTER

REVIEW

SUMMARY

17-1: Acids and Bases

1. An acid is a substance that produces hydrogen ions (H^+) in solution. A base produces hydroxide ions (OH^-) in solution.
2. Acids and bases have characteristic properties that are due, in part, to the presence of the H^+ and OH^- ions.
3. Common acids include hydrochloric acid, sulfuric acid, nitric acid, and phosphoric acid. Common bases include sodium hydroxide, calcium hydroxide, and ammonia.
4. Acids form when certain polar compounds ionize as they dissolve in water. Except for ammonia, bases form when certain ionic compounds dissociate upon dissolving in water.

17-2: Strength of Acids and Bases

1. The strength of an acid or base is determined by the number of ions present in solution.
2. Strength and concentration are not related. Concentration involves the relative amounts of solvent and solute in a solution.
3. pH is a measure of the hydrogen ion concentration of a solution.
4. For acid solutions of equal concentration, the stronger the acid, the lower its pH; for basic solutions of equal concentration, the stronger the base, the higher the pH.

17-3: Science and Society: Acid Rain

1. Acid rain is produced when substances in the air react with rainwater to make it acidic. Acid rain production is increased by the release of certain oxides into the air when fossil fuels are burned.
2. Acid rain is harmful to plants and animals and increases the rate of weathering of some building materials.

17-4: Acids, Bases, and Salts

1. In a neutralization reaction, the H_3O^+ ions from an acid react with the OH^- ions from a base to produce water molecules. The products of neutralization are a salt plus water.
2. Salts form when the negative ions from an acid combine with the positive ions from a base.
3. Soaps and detergents are organic salts. Unlike soaps, detergents do not react with compounds in hard water to form scum deposits.
4. Esters are organic compounds formed by the reaction of an organic acid and an alcohol.

KEY SCIENCE WORDS

a. **acid**
b. **acid rain**
c. **base**
d. **dehydrating agent**
e. **detergents**
f. **ester**
g. **hydronium ion**
h. **indicator**
i. **neutralization**
j. **pH**
k. **pickling**
l. **plankton**
m. **salt**
n. **saponification**
o. **soaps**
p. **strong acid**
q. **strong base**
r. **titration**
s. **weak acid**
t. **weak base**

UNDERSTANDING VOCABULARY

Match each phrase with the correct term from the list of Key Science Words.

1. a hydrogen ion bonded to a water molecule
2. a reaction between an acid and a base
3. acid that ionizes completely in solution
4. base that partly dissociates in solution
5. can remove water from materials
6. formed when negative ions from an acid combine with positive ions from a base
7. removes impurities from metal surfaces
8. measures the concentration of H_3O^+ ions
9. produces hydrogen ions in solution
10. the process of making soap

CHAPTER REVIEW

CHECKING CONCEPTS

Choose the word or phrase that completes the sentence.

1. HF reacts strongly with metals; CH_3COOH does not. HF is more ______.
   a. acidic c. corrosive
   b. basic d. sour
2. Sulfuric acid is also known as ______.
   a. battery acid c. stomach acid
   b. citric acid d. vinegar
3. Most sulfuric acid is used to produce ______.
   a. batteries c. petroleum products
   b. fertilizer d. plastics
4. ______ is used to make phosphoric, nitric, and hydrochloric acids.
   a. Dehydration c. Pickling
   b. A base d. Sulfuric acid
5. The most widely used base is ______.
   a. ammonia c. lye
   b. caustic lime d. milk of magnesia
6. Carrots have a pH of 5.0, so carrots are ______.
   a. acidic c. neutral
   b. basic d. an indicator
7. Pure water has a pH of ______.
   a. 0 c. 7
   b. 5.2 d. 14
8. Certain materials can act as indicators because they change ______.
   a. acidity c. pH
   b. color d. taste
9. KBr is an example of a(n) ______.
   a. acid c. indicator
   b. base d. salt
10. You might use a solution of ______ to titrate an oxalic acid solution.
   a. HBr c. NaOH
   b. $Ca(NO_3)_2$ d. NH_4Cl

UNDERSTANDING CONCEPTS

Complete each sentence.

11. The process in which a solution of known concentration is used to determine the concentration of another solution is ______.
12. ______ forms when a fat or oil reacts with sodium or potassium hydroxide.
13. When an organic acid and an alcohol react in the presence of sulfuric acid, a(n) ______ and water are formed.
14. A substance that produces hydroxide ions in solution is a(n) ______.
15. Tiny plant and animals that live in water and may be killed by acid rain are ______.

THINK AND WRITE CRITICALLY

16. When hydrogen chloride, HCl, is dissolved in water to form hydrochloric acid, what happens to the HCl?
17. Explain how the hydroxide ion differs from the –OH group in an alcohol.
18. Why is ammonia considered a base, even though it contains no hydroxide ions?
19. Explain why a concentrated acid is not necessarily a strong acid.
20. Ashes from a wood fire are basic. Explain how early settlers used this fact when making soap.

APPLY

21. Explain why you should never use taste to test for an acid, even though acetic, citric, and dilute phosphoric acids are in things you eat and drink.
22. How would the pH of a dilute solution of HCl compare with the pH of a concentrated solution of the same acid? Explain.
23. Acid rain containing sulfuric acid, H_2SO_4, will react with iron objects. What products will result from this reaction?
24. Chalk, $CaCO_3$, is a salt. What acid and what base react to form this salt?
25. Suppose you have hard water in your home. Would you use a soap or a detergent for washing your clothes and dishes? Explain your answer.

MORE SKILL BUILDERS

If you need help, refer to the Skill Handbook.

1. **Making and Using Tables:** Make a table that lists the chemical and physical properties of acids and bases.
2. **Recognizing Cause and Effect:** Complete the following table by describing the cause and effect of each change listed in the left-hand column.

Process	Cause	Effect
Saponification		
Esterification		
Acid rain		
Neutralization		
Corrosion		

3. **Comparing and Contrasting:** Compare and contrast the reactions that would be produced by pouring sulfuric acid on a piece of paper and burning a marshmallow.
4. **Observing and Inferring:** You have equal amounts of three colorless liquids, A, B, and C. You add several drops of phenolphthalein to each liquid. A and B remain colorless, but C turns pink. Next you add some of liquid C to liquid A and the pink color disappears. You add the rest of C to liquid B and the mixture remains pink. What can you infer about each of these liquids? Which liquid probably has a pH of 7?
5. **Interpreting Data:** A soil test indicates that the pH of the soil in a field is 4.8. To neutralize the soil, would you add a substance containing H_3PO_4 or one containing $Ca(OH)_2$? Explain your answer.

PROJECTS

1. Make a display and write a report on common household acids and bases, how they are used, and cautions to be taken.
2. Do research to find out how acids are used in making fertilizer. Name several acids and tell why each is needed and how their proportions may vary from fertilizer to fertilizer. Conduct an investigation by growing seedlings using different fertilizers. Describe your results in a report.

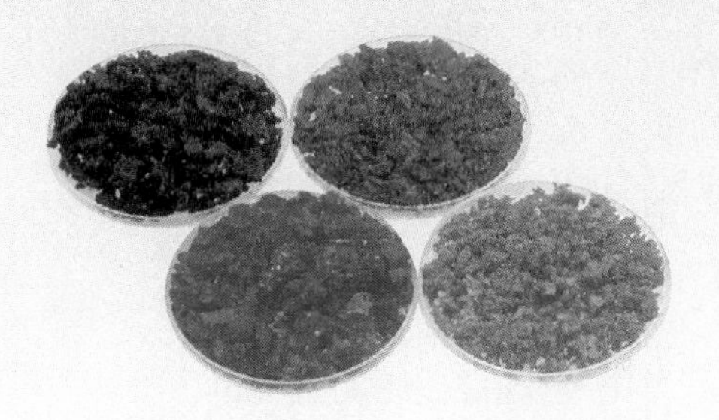

UNIT 5

GLOBAL CONNECTIONS

Interactions of Matter

In this unit, you studied how matter interacts in solutions, chemical reactions, and acids and bases. Now find out how the interactions of matter are connected to other subjects and places around the world.

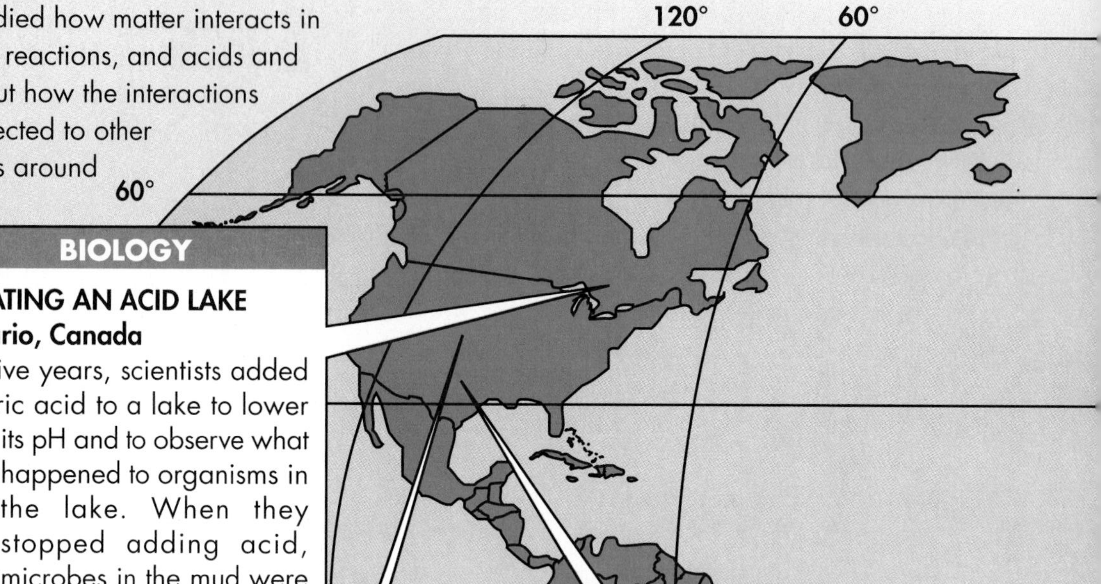

120° 60° 60°

BIOLOGY

CREATING AN ACID LAKE
Ontario, Canada

For five years, scientists added sulfuric acid to a lake to lower its pH and to observe what happened to organisms in the lake. When they stopped adding acid, microbes in the mud were able to start neutralizing the acid. Why do you think the scientists did this experiment?

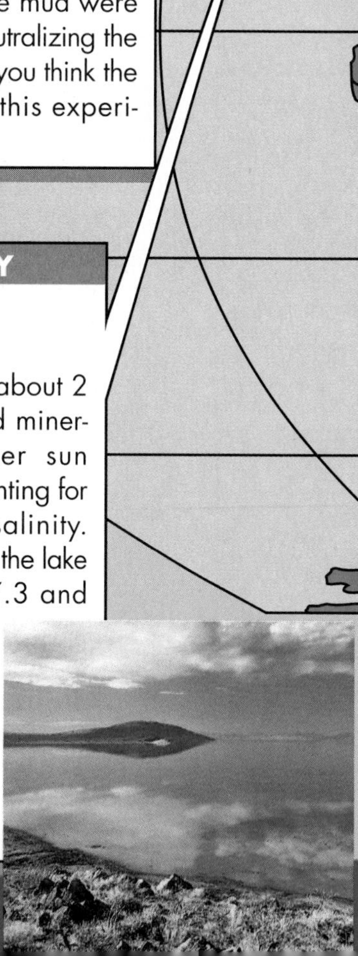

GEOLOGY

CAVE FORMATION
Carlsbad Caverns, New Mexico

Over 200 million years ago, corals built a reef in a sea. As the area was raised above sea level, acidic groundwater entered cracks in the reef and dissolved limestone, forming caverns. Water containing dissolved minerals continued to drip into the caverns. As the water evaporated, mineral deposits formed stalactites and stalagmites. How do stalactites and stalagmites differ?

METEOROLOGY

INLAND OCEAN
Great Salt Lake, Utah

Spring runoff brings in about 2 million tons of dissolved minerals, while the summer sun evaporates water, accounting for the Great Salt Lake's salinity. Since 1843, the depth of the lake has ranged between 7.3 and 13.7 meters and the salinity ranged from 20% to 6%. How would wet winters and cool, cloudy summers affect the salinity of the lake?

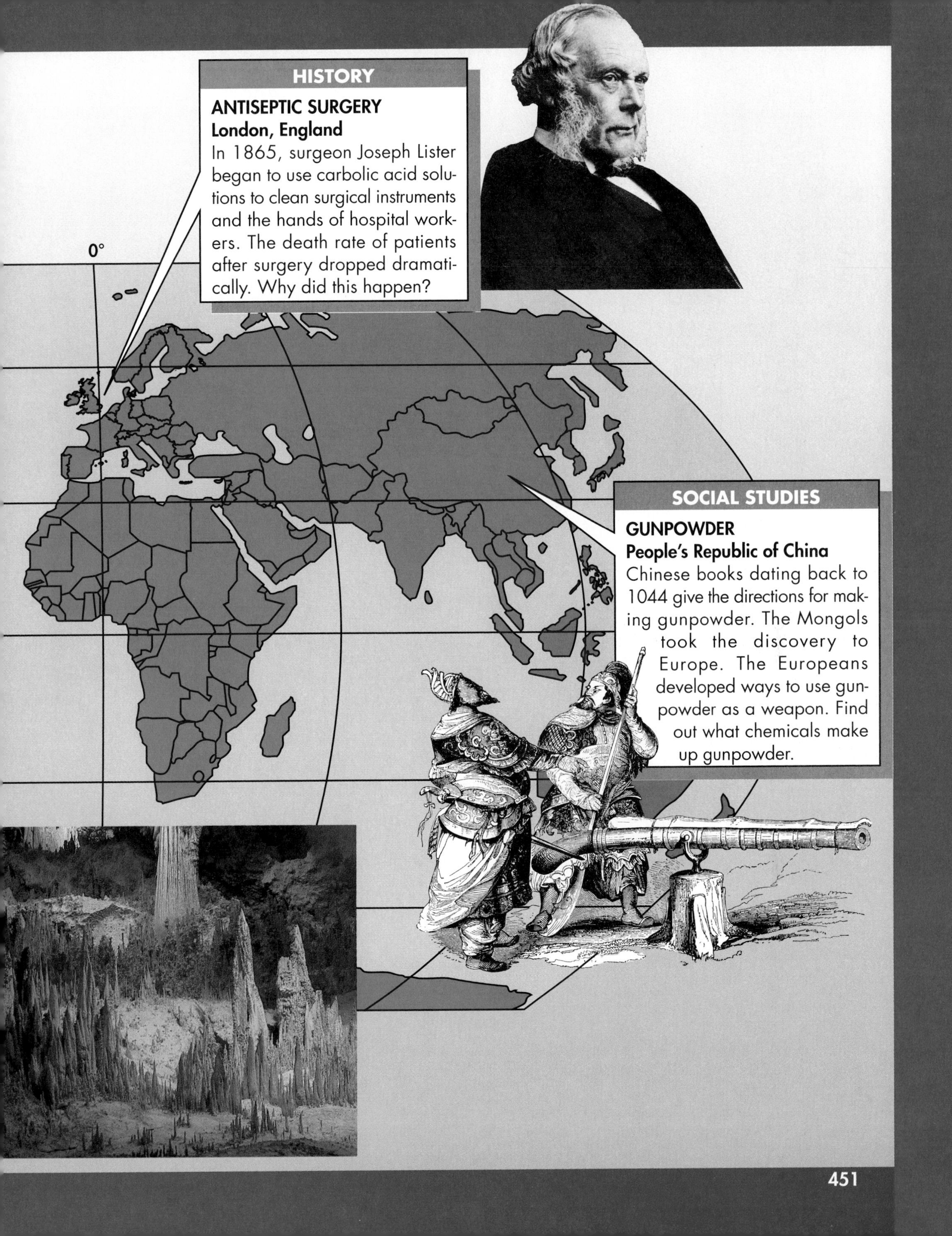

HISTORY

ANTISEPTIC SURGERY
London, England

In 1865, surgeon Joseph Lister began to use carbolic acid solutions to clean surgical instruments and the hands of hospital workers. The death rate of patients after surgery dropped dramatically. Why did this happen?

SOCIAL STUDIES

GUNPOWDER
People's Republic of China

Chinese books dating back to 1044 give the directions for making gunpowder. The Mongols took the discovery to Europe. The Europeans developed ways to use gunpowder as a weapon. Find out what chemicals make up gunpowder.

CAREERS

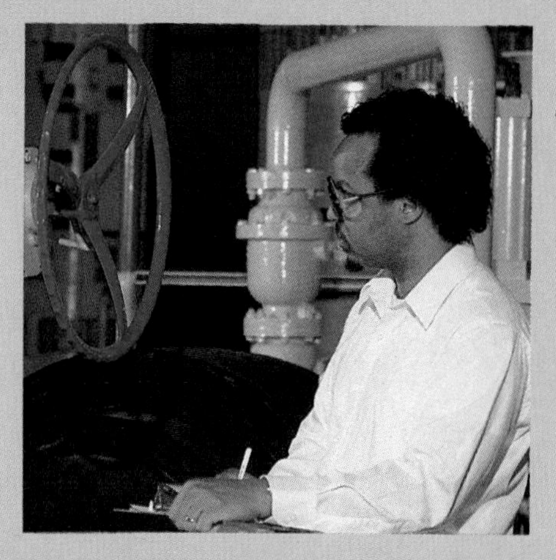

WATER TREATMENT TECHNICIAN

A *water treatment technician* works wherever there is a possibility of water contamination. The technician collects and prepares water samples for laboratory examination.

Some technicians test drinking-water supplies from municipal water plants or wells to make sure the water is safe to use and drink. They add chemicals, such as chlorine or fluorides to the water supply. Other technicians work in waste-water plants, making sure the waste is clean enough to be released back into the environment.

If you're interested in becoming a water treatment technician, you should take high school classes in chemistry, mathematics, and biology. Since some technicians in smaller communities also perform maintenance duties, such as repairing pumps, you should also have mechanical aptitude. Most technicians complete a two-year course at a technical school.

For Additional Information

Contact the National Environmental Training Association, 148 S. Napoleon Street, Valparaiso, IN 46383.

PAINT ANALYST

Paint analysts develop new colors of paints. They mix together basic colors to create hundreds of different colors. You have probably seen these on paint chips in paint or hardware stores. Once you have selected the color you want, a worker at the store mixes the paint according to directions that were provided by the paint analyst.

If you're interested in becoming a paint analyst, you should have good color vision and artistic skills. High school classes in art and chemistry are also helpful. Although some paint analysts receive on-the-job training, most have college degrees in chemistry.

For Additional Information

Contact the American Chemical Society, 1155 16th Street NW, Washington, DC 20036.

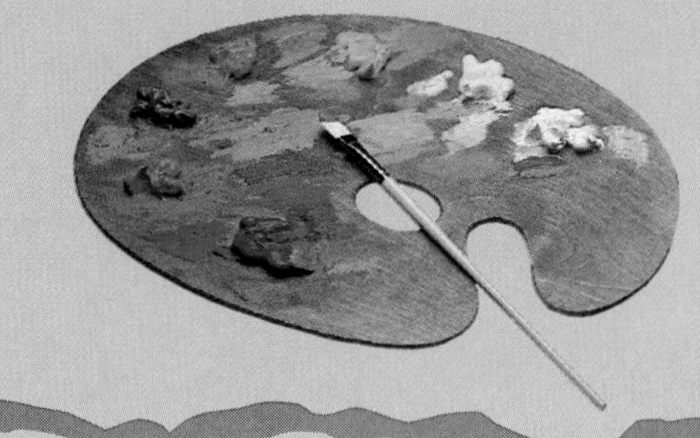

UNIT READINGS

- Cobb, Vicki. *Chemically Active!* Philadelphia: Lippincott, 1985.
- Mohnen, Volker A. "The Challenge of Acid Rain." *Scientific American*, August, 1988, pp. 30-38.
- Whyman, Dathryn. *Chemical Changes*, Danbury, CT: Gloucester, 1986.

SCIENCE & LITERATURE

Snow

by Ruth Kirk

The passage that follows gives Ruth Kirk's perspective on the use of salt for snow control on roads.

Tests show salt damage as far as one hundred feet from the edge of pavement. It harms soil structure and by upsetting osmotic balance causes water to be drawn out of plants' roots instead of into them. (The flow is toward the greater salt concentration, which normally is in the root sap.) Gardeners at Arlington National Cemetery have reported the loss of privet hedges and bluegrass lawns because of salt, and at Walter Reed Hospital street maples and parking lot hemlocks have died because of salt-laden snow piled up outside curbing where its melt seeped into the ground. In New Hampshire, Massachusetts, Vermont, and Connecticut, tests of afflicted and dying trees indicate excess sodium in leaf tissue and a high total salt concentration in sap. Maples seem the most affected, sugar maples more so than red maples. The New Hampshire tests noted damage along state roads, which are salted, but not along roads of the same area where de-icing salts are not used.

Animals and human life suffers too. The death of pheasants, pigeons, quail and rabbits have been traced to salt poisoning in the Madison, Wisconsin, region. Deer drawn to roads to lick salt have been struck by cars. Dog owners protest damage to pets' feet. Doctors in several areas of high winter salt use recommend the purchase of distilled water by patients with congestive heart failure, certain kidney problems, or hypertension, and for many pregnant women. Widespread contamination of municipal wells has become commonplace and a few communities have been forced to close water supplies that had served for generations. Some of the trouble comes from snow scraped off streets and roads and dumped into rivers, lakes, and ponds; some is from seepage through the soil. Improper storage causes a high proportion of the problem. Salt piles should rest on an impermeable footing and be covered as protection from rain and snow, but often no effort at containment is made.

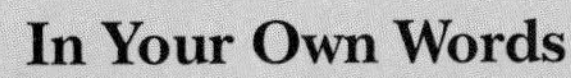

In Your Own Words

▶ Write an informative essay on the importance of finding alternatives to snow control, based on Ruth Kirk's writings.

UNIT

6 WAVES, LIGHT, AND SOUND

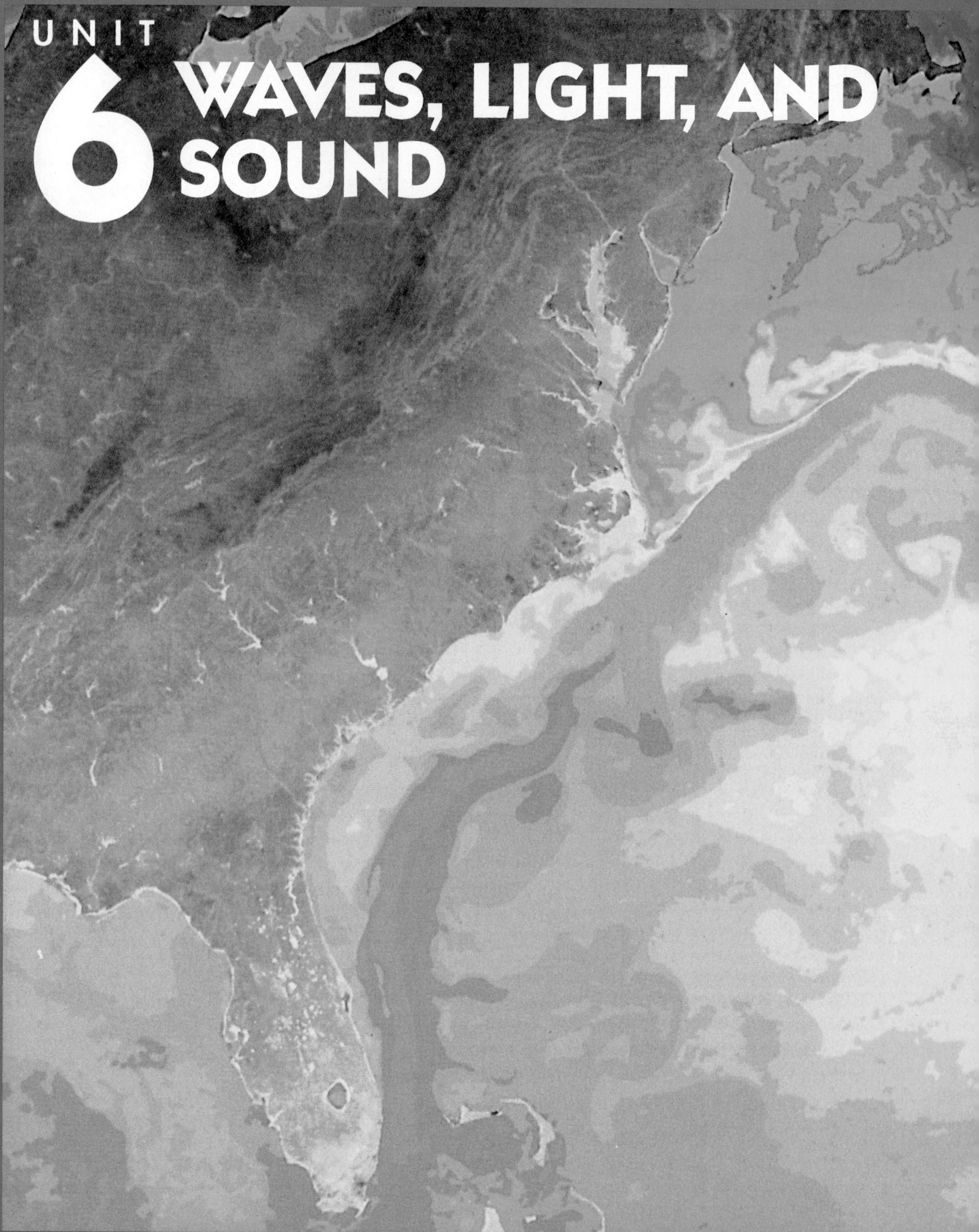

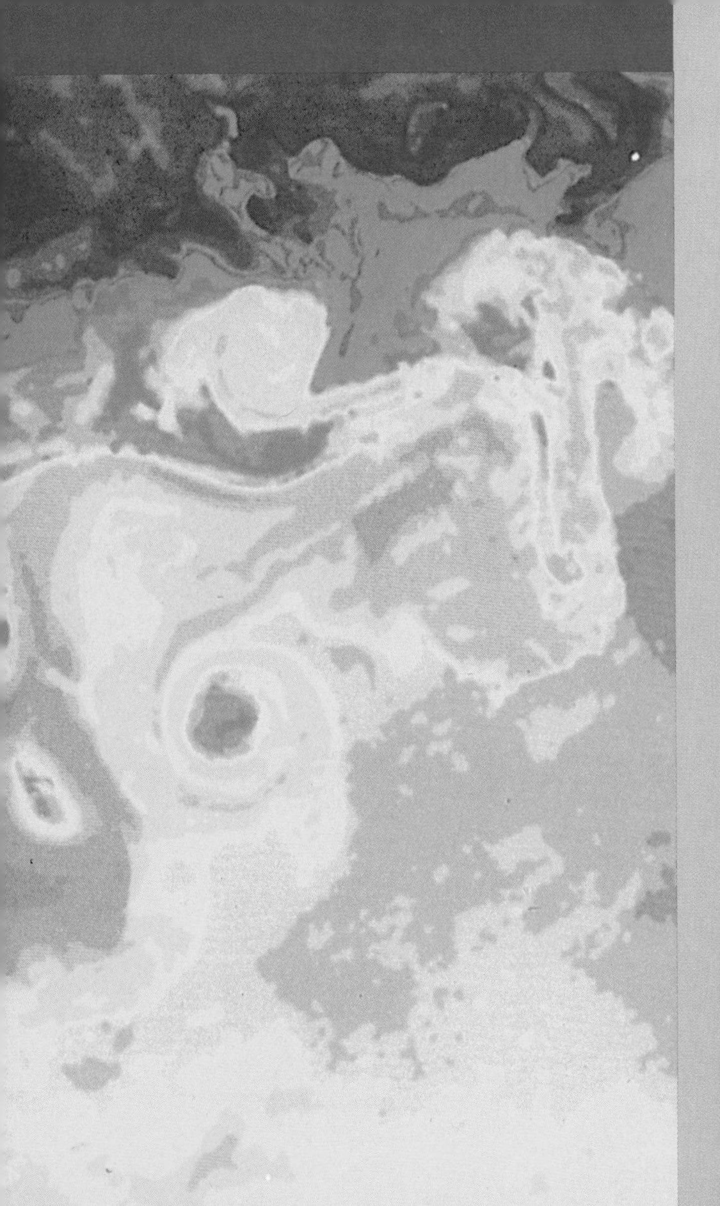

What's Happening Here?

What colors would you choose to show hot and cold? Why do we think of "red hot" and "cool blue"? This color-enhanced satellite photo of the Atlantic Ocean uses red for hot and blue for cold. The orange-red area is the Gulf Stream, a major warm-water current. Satellites detect warm water by measuring waves of electromagnetic radiation. Although we think of red as hot and blue as cool, you'll discover that blue light actually has more energy than red. In this unit, you'll learn about how your experience of heat, light, color, sound, and music depends on waves.

UNIT CONTENTS

CHAPTER 18 Waves and Sound

Have you ever played a musical instrument? Perhaps you plucked the strings on a guitar, or made music by blowing air into a harmonica or a clarinet. Did you know you can even make music with a soda pop bottle?

FIND OUT!

Do this simple activity to find out how you can make music with a soda pop bottle.

You need a clean, empty soda pop bottle. First, place the empty bottle just below your lower lip so it touches your lip lightly. Take a big breath and blow a steady stream of air across the top of the bottle. Did you hear a musical tone? Fill the bottle halfway with water and make another musical tone. Did it sound lower or higher than the first tone you made? Pour some water out of the bottle. How do you expect the tone to sound now? It should be lower. Could you play a song with several other soda pop bottles with different water levels? Try it!

Gearing Up

Previewing the Chapter

Use this outline to help you focus on important ideas in this chapter.

Section 18-1 Wave Characteristics
- Transverse Waves
- Wave Frequency
- Wave Velocity

Section 18-2 The Nature of Sound
- Compressional Waves
- Media and the Speed of Sound
- Frequency and Pitch
- Intensity and Loudness
- The Doppler Effect

Section 18-3 Science and Society Noise Pollution
- What Is Noise Pollution?

Section 18-4 Musical Sounds
- What Is Music?
- Musical Sounds
- Interference
- Acoustics

Previewing Science Skills

- In the Skill Builders, you will make a concept map and determine cause and effect.
- In the Activities, you will observe, measure, and hypothesize.
- In the MINI-Labs, you will observe, interpret, and hypothesize.

What's next?

Now that you know how to make music with a soda pop bottle, you can learn how sound waves are made. You can also find out how changing the length of the air column in the bottle affects the musical tone as you read this chapter.

18-1 Wave Characteristics

New Science Words

waves
medium
transverse wave
crests
troughs
wavelength
amplitude
frequency

Objectives

- Sketch a transverse wave and identify its characteristics.
- Discuss the relationship between the frequency and wavelength in a transverse wave.
- Using the relationship between wavelength, frequency, and velocity, find one variable when two are given.

Transverse Waves

Have you ever seen stadium waves created by enthusiastic fans at a baseball game? What do you think stadium waves have in common with water waves, microwaves, sound waves, and radio waves? These and all other types of waves transfer energy from one place to another. In this lesson, you will read about some of the characteristics of waves.

Figure 18-1. The energy of a water wave does work on anything in its path.

Water waves are probably the easiest type of wave to visualize. If you've been in a boat on a lake, you know that approaching waves bump against the boat but do not carry the boat along with them. The boat just moves up and down as the waves pass by. Like the boat, the water molecules on the surface of the lake move up and down, but not forward. Only energy carried by the waves moves forward.

What are waves?

Waves are rhythmic disturbances that carry energy through matter or space. Water waves transfer energy through the water. Earthquakes transfer energy in powerful shock waves that travel through Earth. Both types of waves travel through a **medium,** a material through which a wave can transfer energy. This medium may be a solid, a liquid, a gas, or a combination of these. Radio waves and light waves, however, are types of waves that can travel without a medium.

Two types of wave motion can carry energy. In one type, a **transverse wave,** the medium moves at right angles to the direction the wave travels. Figure 18-2 shows how you can make transverse waves by snapping the end of a rope up and down while your friend holds one end.

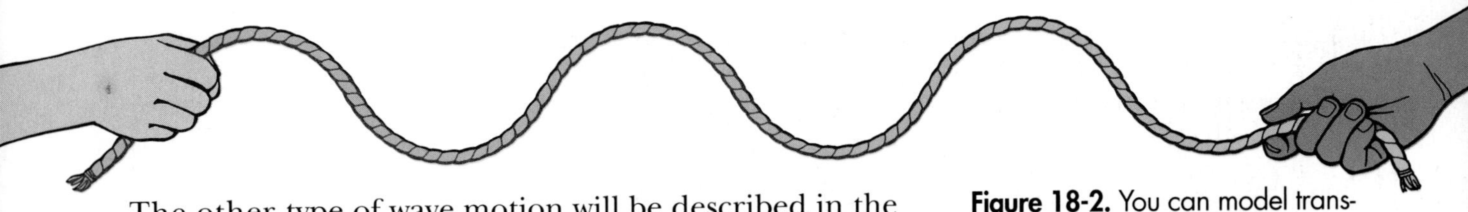

Figure 18-2. You can model transverse waves with a rope.

The other type of wave motion will be described in the discussion of compressional waves in the next lesson.

The wave you made with the rope can be described by its characteristics. When you snapped the rope up and down, you may have noticed that high points and low points formed. The highest points of a wave are called the **crests,** and the lowest points are called the **troughs.** Waves are measured by their wavelength. **Wavelength** is the distance between a point on one wave and the identical point on the next wave, such as from crest to crest, or trough to trough. The wavelength between two crests is labeled on Figure 18-3. How could you measure the wavelength on other parts of the wave?

What are the high points and low points of a wave called?

Ocean or lake waves can be described by how high they appear above the normal water level. Amplitude describes wave height. **Amplitude** is the distance from the crest (or trough) of a wave to the rest position of the medium, as shown in Figure 18-3. The amplitude corresponds to the amount of energy carried by the wave. Waves that carry great amounts of energy have large heights or amplitudes, and waves that carry less energy have smaller amplitudes.

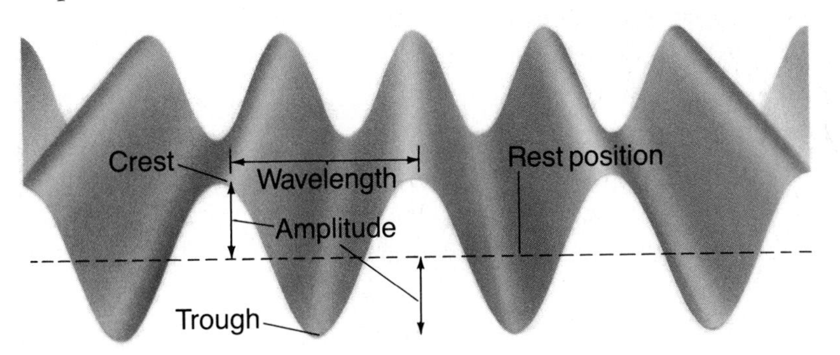

Figure 18-3. Parts of a Transverse Wave

Wave Frequency

Do you know the frequency of your favorite radio station? When you tune your radio to a station, you are actually looking for waves of a certain frequency. The **frequency** of a wave is the number of wave crests that pass one place each second. Frequency is expressed in hertz (Hz). One hertz is the same as one wave per second.

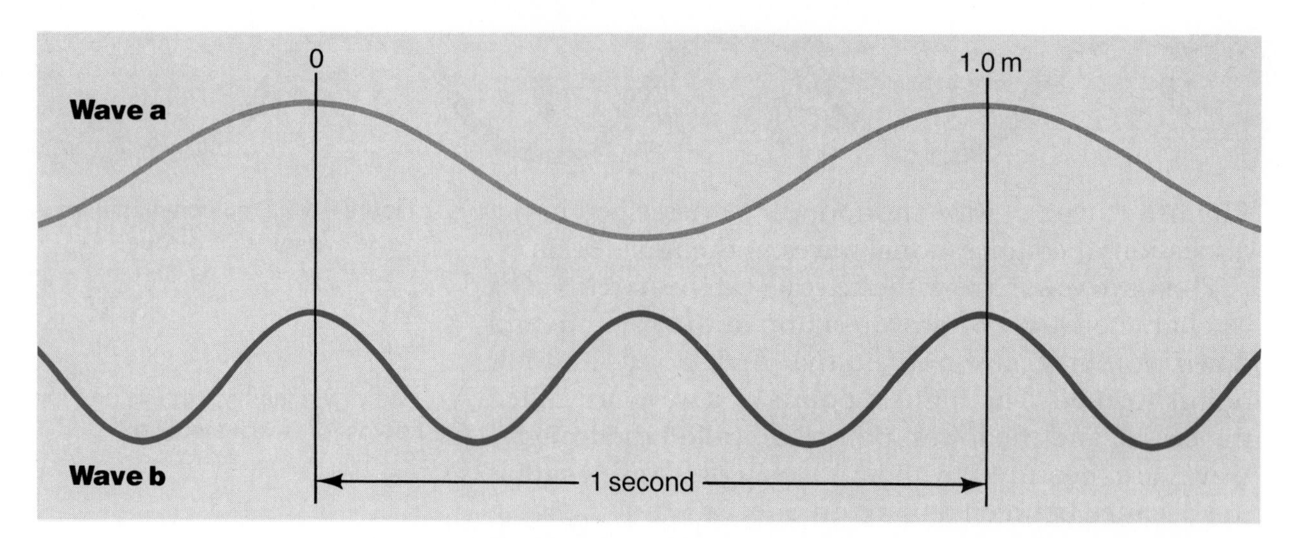

Figure 18-4. Wave a has a longer wavelength and a lower frequency than wave b. Both waves are traveling at the same speed.

What happens to the wavelength of a wave as the frequency increases?

How do you increase the frequency of a wave? To do this with a rope, you simply move the rope up and down faster, so you create more crests each second. Then, if the speed of the waves does not change, the frequency of the waves increases. As a result, the wavelengths must become shorter. In other words, as the frequency increases, the wavelength decreases. Using a rope, you can demonstrate this principle as shown in Figure 18-4. This relationship between wavelength and frequency will be discussed further in the next section and in Chapter 19.

Wave Velocity

Sometimes you may want to know how fast a wave is traveling. For example, earthquakes below the ocean can produce giant tidal waves. You would want to know how soon a tidal wave would reach you, if you needed to seek shelter. Wave velocity, v, describes how fast the wave crests move.

Wave velocity can be determined by multiplying the wavelength and frequency as shown below. Wavelength is represented by the Greek letter lambda, λ. If you know any two variables in the following equation, you can find the unknown variable.

$$\text{velocity} = \text{wavelength} \times \text{frequency}$$

$$v = \lambda \times f$$

The examples that follow show how you can use this equation to solve for the unknown variable.

Did You Know?

Lightning flashes move at speeds up to 140 000 km/s and last about 0.003 s, with temperatures of about 30 000°C (or 5 times greater than the temperature on the surface of the sun).

EXAMPLE PROBLEM: Calculating the Velocity of a Wave

Problem Statement:

A wave is generated in a wave pool at a water amusement park. The wavelength is 3.2 m. The frequency of the wave is 0.60 Hz. What is the velocity of the wave?

Known Information:

Strategy Hint: Another way to express Hertz is 1/second, therefore, m × 1/s = m/s.

wavelength, $\lambda = 3.2$ m
frequency, $f = 0.60$ Hz

Unknown Information:

velocity (v)

Equation to Use:

$v = \lambda \times f$

Solution:

$v = \lambda \times f = 3.2\ \text{m} \times 0.60\ \text{Hz} = 1.92\ \text{m/s}$

PRACTICE PROBLEM

Strategy Hint: Make sure all units correspond.

1. A wave moving along a rope has a wavelength of 1.2 m and a frequency of 4.5 Hz. How fast is the wave traveling along the rope?

EXAMPLE PROBLEM: Calculating the Frequency of a Wave

Problem Statement:

Earthquakes can produce three types of waves. One of these is a transverse wave called an S wave. A typical S wave travels at 5000 m/s. Its wavelength is about 417 m. What is its frequency?

Known Information:

Strategy Hint: Remember, Hz = 1/s, so m/s ÷ m = 1/s = 1 Hz

velocity, $v = 5000$ m/s
wavelength, $\lambda = 417$ m

Unknown Information:

frequency (f)

Equation to Use:

$v = \lambda \times f$

Solution:

$v = \lambda \times f$, so $f = v/\lambda$
$= (5000\ \text{m/s})/(417\ \text{m}) = 12\ \text{Hz}$

PRACTICE PROBLEM

Strategy Hint: What formula do you use to find frequency?

1. A tuning fork produces a sound wave with a wavelength of 0.20 m and a velocity of 25.6 m/s. What is the frequency of the tuning fork?

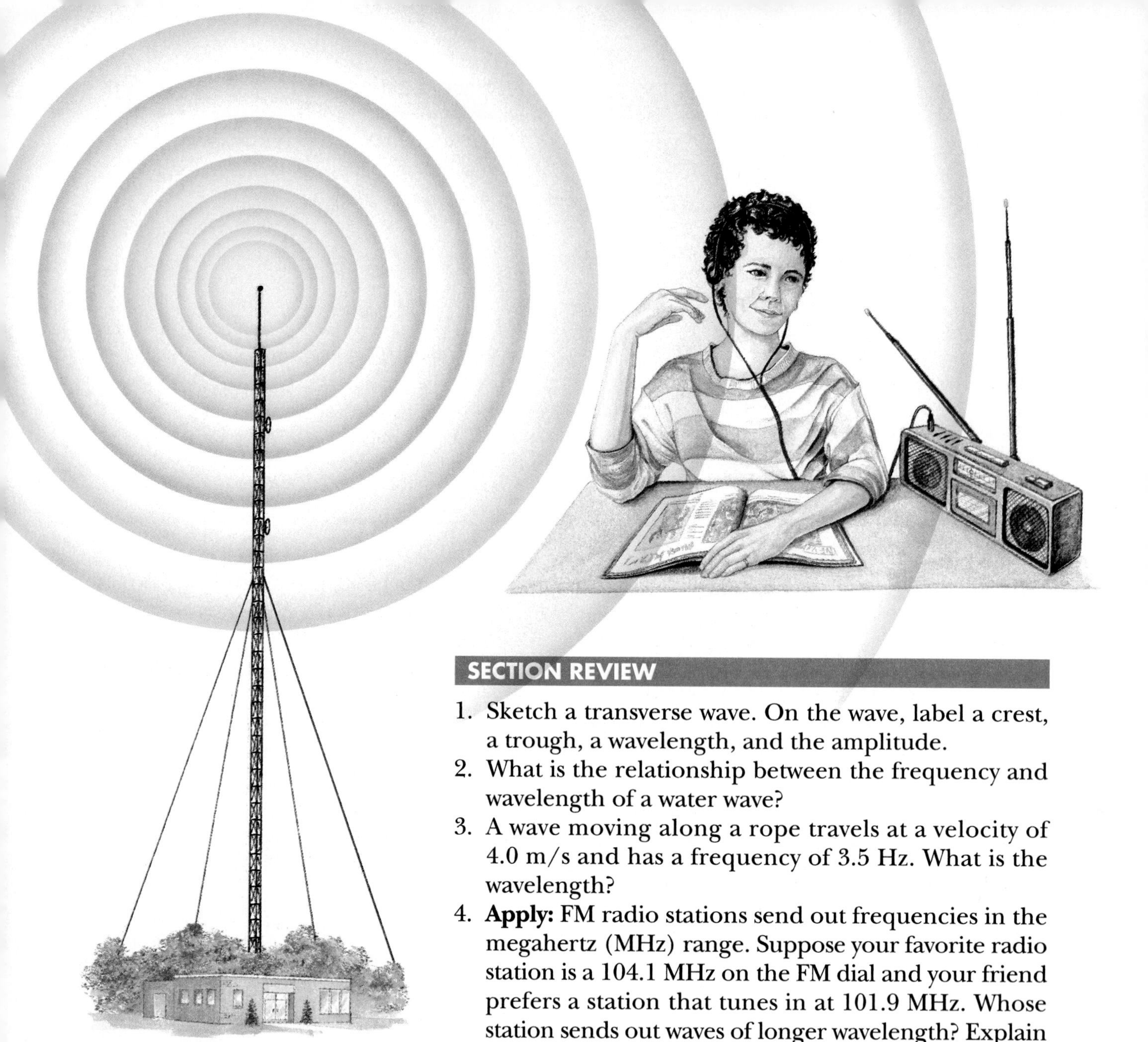

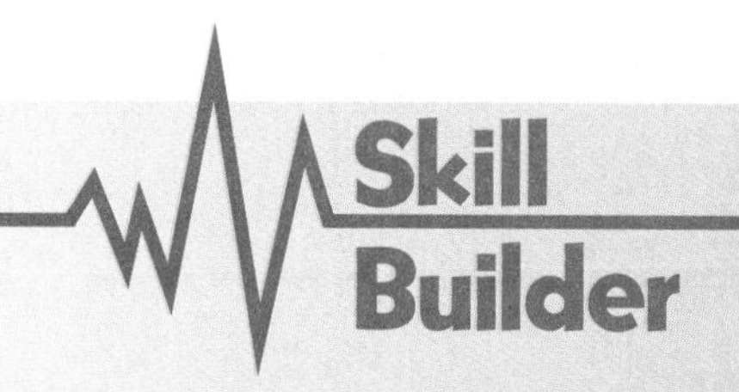

SECTION REVIEW

1. Sketch a transverse wave. On the wave, label a crest, a trough, a wavelength, and the amplitude.
2. What is the relationship between the frequency and wavelength of a water wave?
3. A wave moving along a rope travels at a velocity of 4.0 m/s and has a frequency of 3.5 Hz. What is the wavelength?
4. **Apply:** FM radio stations send out frequencies in the megahertz (MHz) range. Suppose your favorite radio station is a 104.1 MHz on the FM dial and your friend prefers a station that tunes in at 101.9 MHz. Whose station sends out waves of longer wavelength? Explain your answer.

Skill Builder

Comparing and Contrasting

Use Figure 18-3 and information from this section to compare the frequency, amplitude, and wavelength of a wave. Which of these measurements depends on energy? Which is measured in meters? Which depends on the number of waves? If you need help, refer to Comparing and Contrasting in the **Skill Handbook** on page 679.

ACTIVITY 18-1
Transverse Waves

Problem: *How can wave energy be stored?*

Materials 

- small Slinky
- stopwatch

Procedure

1. You and a partner should pull on each end of the Slinky until it is stretched about 1 meter.
2. Hold one end of the Slinky motionless and shake the other end to make the slinky vibrate in one segment.
3. Count the number of vibrations the spring makes in 10 seconds.
4. Make a second wave by moving the end of the spring from side to side twice as fast as before. Look for the spring to vibrate in two equal segments. Each segment will move in opposite directions.
5. Try to make the spring vibrate in three equal segments.

Analyze

1. Draw pictures of the spring for each of the three forms of waves you made. How many transverse waves does each picture represent?
2. The spring can store energy when the wave is the right size to exactly "fit" onto the spring. How many wavelengths fit onto the spring for each of the three forms of waves produced?

Conclude and Apply

3. If wave energy is to be stored in the spring, how must the length of the spring and the length of the wave compare?
4. Why could you store short wave energy in a long spring but are not able to store long wave energy in a short spring?

18-2 The Nature of Sound

New Science Words

compressional wave
pitch
intensity
loudness

Objectives

- ▶ Describe the transmission of sound through a medium.
- ▶ Recognize the relationships between amplitude and loudness and frequency and pitch.
- ▶ Illustrate the Doppler effect with a practical example.

Compressional Waves

Think of all the sounds you've heard since you awoke this morning. Did you hear a blaring alarm, honking horns, human voices, and lockers slamming? Your ears allow you to recognize these different sounds, but do you know what they all have in common? These sounds are all produced by the vibrations of objects. For example, your voice is produced by the vibrations of your own vocal cords. The energy produced by these vibrations is carried to your friend's ears by sound waves.

The waves discussed in the last section were described as transverse waves because the matter moved at right angles to the direction the wave was traveling. You could produce this type of wave in a rope or spring by moving one end from side to side or up and down. Sound waves carry energy by a different type of wave motion. You can model sound waves with a coil spring. If you hold one end of a spring, squeeze the coils together, and then release the coils while holding the end of the spring, you will produce a compressional wave. Matter vibrates in the same direction as the wave travels in a **compressional wave.** Figure 18-5 shows how the compressional wave you made should look.

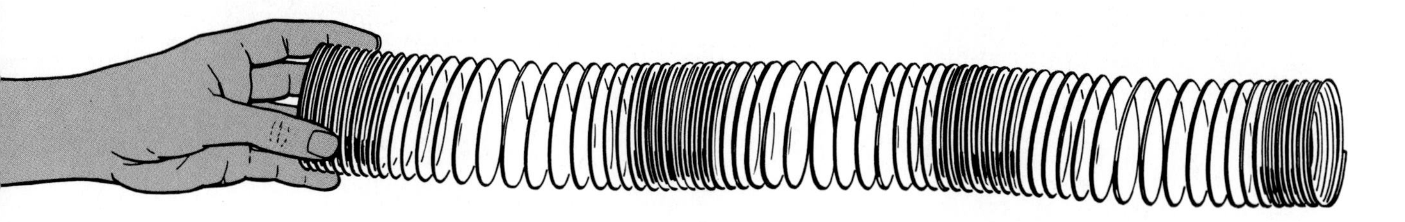

Figure 18-5. You can demonstrate how compressional waves form with a spring.

Notice that as the wave moves, some of the coils are squeezed together just as you squeezed the ones on the end of the spring. This crowded area is called a compression. The compressed area then expands, spreading the coils apart, creating a less dense area. This less dense area of the wave is called a rarefaction. Does the whole spring move forward? Tie a piece of string on one of the coils and observe its motion. The string moves back and forth with the coils. Therefore, the matter in the medium does not move forward with the wave. Instead, the wave carries only the energy forward.

Recall that transverse waves have wavelengths, frequencies, amplitudes, and velocities. Compressional waves also have these characteristics. A wavelength in a compressional wave is made of one compression and one rarefaction as shown in Figure 18-7. Notice that one wavelength is the distance between two compressions or two rarefactions of the same wave. The frequency is the number of compressions that pass a place each second. If you repeatedly squeeze and release the end of the spring three times each second, you will produce a wave with a frequency of 3 Hz. The amount of compression is like the amplitude of the transverse wave, and it depends on the energy content of the wave. Think about what you would do to increase the amount of compression in the coil spring. You would have to squeeze harder, and you would be putting more energy into the wave.

Figure 18-6. The sound of this porpoise's voice travels slower in air than it does in water.

Media and the Speed of Sound

Perhaps while you were making compressional waves on a spring, you spoke to your friend. The vibrations generated by your vocal cords produced compressional waves that traveled through the air to your friend. This process is very similar to what you saw when you made compressional waves on a spring. Your voice causes compressions and rarefactions among the particles in the air.

Figure 18-7. The spring vibrates back and forth, but the energy of this compressional wave moves forward.

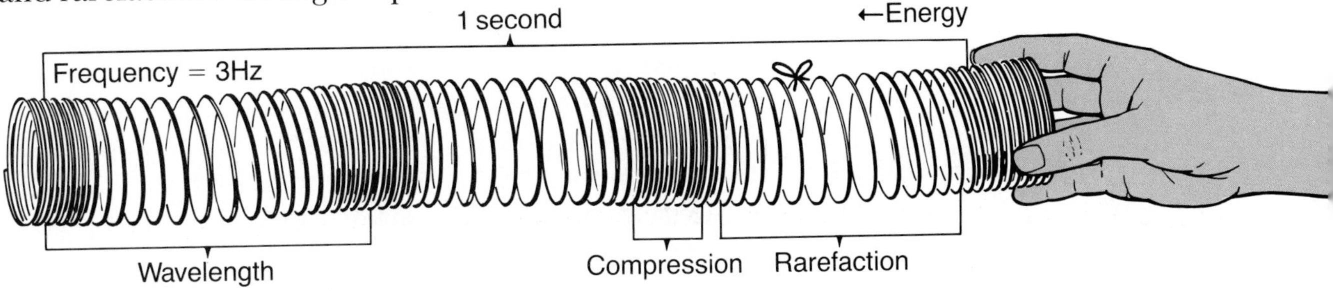

←Energy
1 second
Frequency = 3Hz
Wavelength
Compression
Rarefaction

The speed of sound waves depends on the medium through which the waves travel and its temperature. Air is the most common medium you hear sound waves through, but sound waves can be transmitted through any type of matter. Liquids and solids are even better conductors of sound than air because the individual particles in a liquid or solid are much closer together than the particles in air, making the transmission of energy easier. Sound waves transmit energy faster in substances with smaller spaces between the particles. Can sound be transmitted if there is no matter? Astronauts on the moon would find it impossible to talk to each other without the aid of modern electronic communication systems. Since the moon has no atmosphere, there is no air to compress and expand.

Science and MATH

The timer at a track meet starts the watch when he hears the sound of the gun rather than when he sees the smoke. If the gun is 200 m away from him, how much faster or slower would the recorded time be than the actual time?

MINI-Lab

How is sound different when it travels through solids?

Tie a metal object to the center of a piece of string. Wrap each of the two ends of the string around one finger on each hand. Place the fingers holding the string in your ears. Let the object swing until it bumps against the edge of a chair or table and listen to the sound. Compare this to the sound you hear from the object when your fingers are not in your ears. Which frequencies, high or low, seem to travel best through the string? What kinds of objects produce the most interesting sounds?

The temperature of the medium is also an important factor in determining the speed of sound waves. As the temperature of a substance increases, the molecules move faster and therefore collide more frequently. This increase in molecular collisions transfers more energy in a shorter amount of time. This allows the sound waves to be transmitted faster. Sound travels through air at 344 m/s if the temperature is 20°C, but at only 332 m/s when the temperature is 0°C.

The speed of sound is much slower than the speed of light. Have you ever tried to guess how far away a lightning bolt is by counting the time interval between when you see a lightning flash and when you hear the thunder? Have you seen fireworks explode in the sky before you heard the boom? You see the light before you hear the sound because light waves travel through air about one million times faster than sound waves.

Frequency and Pitch

What is pitch?

If you have ever taken a music class, you are probably familiar with the scale "do re mi fa so la ti do." As you sing this scale, your voice starts low and becomes higher with each note. You hear a change in pitch. **Pitch** is the highness or lowness of a sound. The pitch you hear depends on the frequency of the sound waves. The higher the frequency, the higher the pitch, and the lower the frequency, the lower the pitch. A healthy human ear can hear sound frequencies from about 20 Hz to 20 000 Hz.

As people age, they often have more trouble hearing high frequencies.

Most people can't hear sound frequencies above 20 000 Hz, which are called ultrasonic waves. Bats, however, can detect frequencies as high as 100 000 Hz. Ultrasonic waves are used in sonar as well as in medical diagnosis and treatment. Sonar, or sound navigation ranging, is a method of using sound waves to estimate the size, shape, and depth of underwater objects. Infrasonic waves have frequencies below 20 Hz. These are produced by sources such as heavy machinery and thunder. Although you probably can't hear them, you may have sensed these sound waves as a disturbing rumble inside of your body.

Science and WRITING

You have just formed a new company, Ultrasonics Unlimited. Develop an advertisement for a product that uses this energy.

TECHNOLOGY

Window on the Deep?

Over 130 years ago, a side-wheel steamer, the *Central America,* disappeared in a hurricane off the coast of South Carolina. In its hold lay three tons of newly minted gold coins and bars worth over 50 million dollars in today's market. In 1987 the application of a sophisticated new sonar technology opened a window on the deep for a group of scientifically trained treasure hunters. The group found the wreck of the *Central America* and her rich cargo under more than 2800 m of water.

The treasure hunters used a low frequency sonar system to conduct their search. It could scan a 3-mile-wide section of ocean in a single pass. Signals from the sonar were processed by a computer which displayed images on its screen. When set to a narrower focus, the sonar can spot an object as small as 25 cm at a depth of 7000 m. This method of merging computer and sonar technologies can revolutionize the ways scientists investigate the oceans.

Think Critically: In what other ways do you think these technologies can help scientists study the ocean?

Intensity and Loudness

Have you ever been told to turn down your stereo? If so, you probably adjusted the volume. The music still had the same notes, so the frequencies didn't change, but the amplitude of each sound wave was reduced. The **intensity** of a sound wave depends on the amount of energy in each wave. This, in turn, corresponds to the wave's amplitude. Intensity of a sound wave increases as its amplitude increases.

Loudness is the human perception of sound intensity. The higher the intensity and amplitude, the louder the sound. People vary in sensitivity to different frequencies. What seems loud to one person may not seem loud to you. The intensity of a sound is measured in units called decibels, abbreviated dB. On this scale, the faintest sound that can be heard by most humans is 0 dB. Sounds with intensities above 120 dB may cause pain and hearing loss. Sounds of this intensity occur during some rock concerts. Table 18-1 shows some familiar sounds and their intensities in dB.

Did You Know?

Prolonged noise above 150 dB can cause permanent deafness. The roar of racing cars can be 125 dB, amplified music 130 dB, and some toy guns 170 dB.

Table 18-1 DECIBEL SCALE

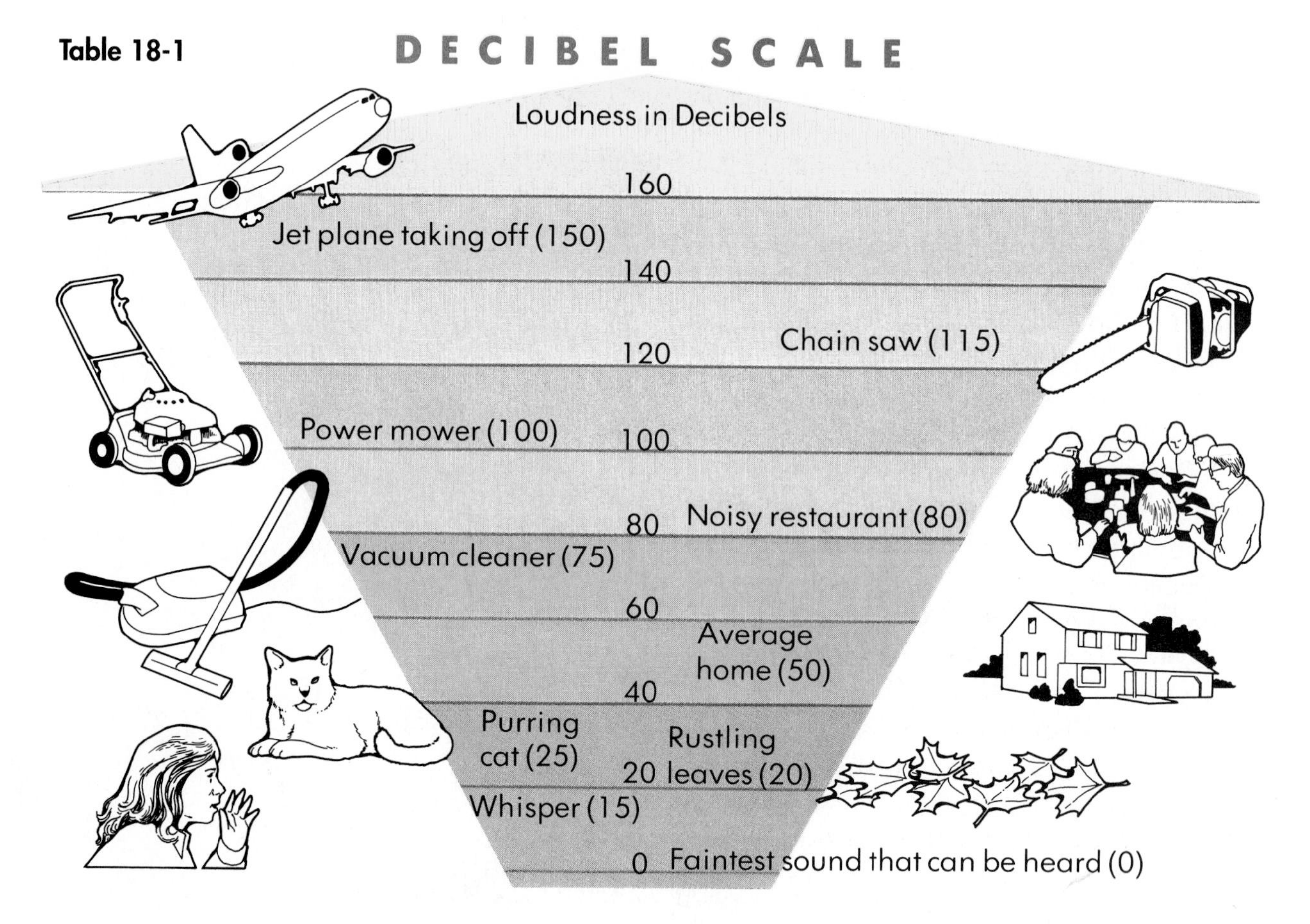

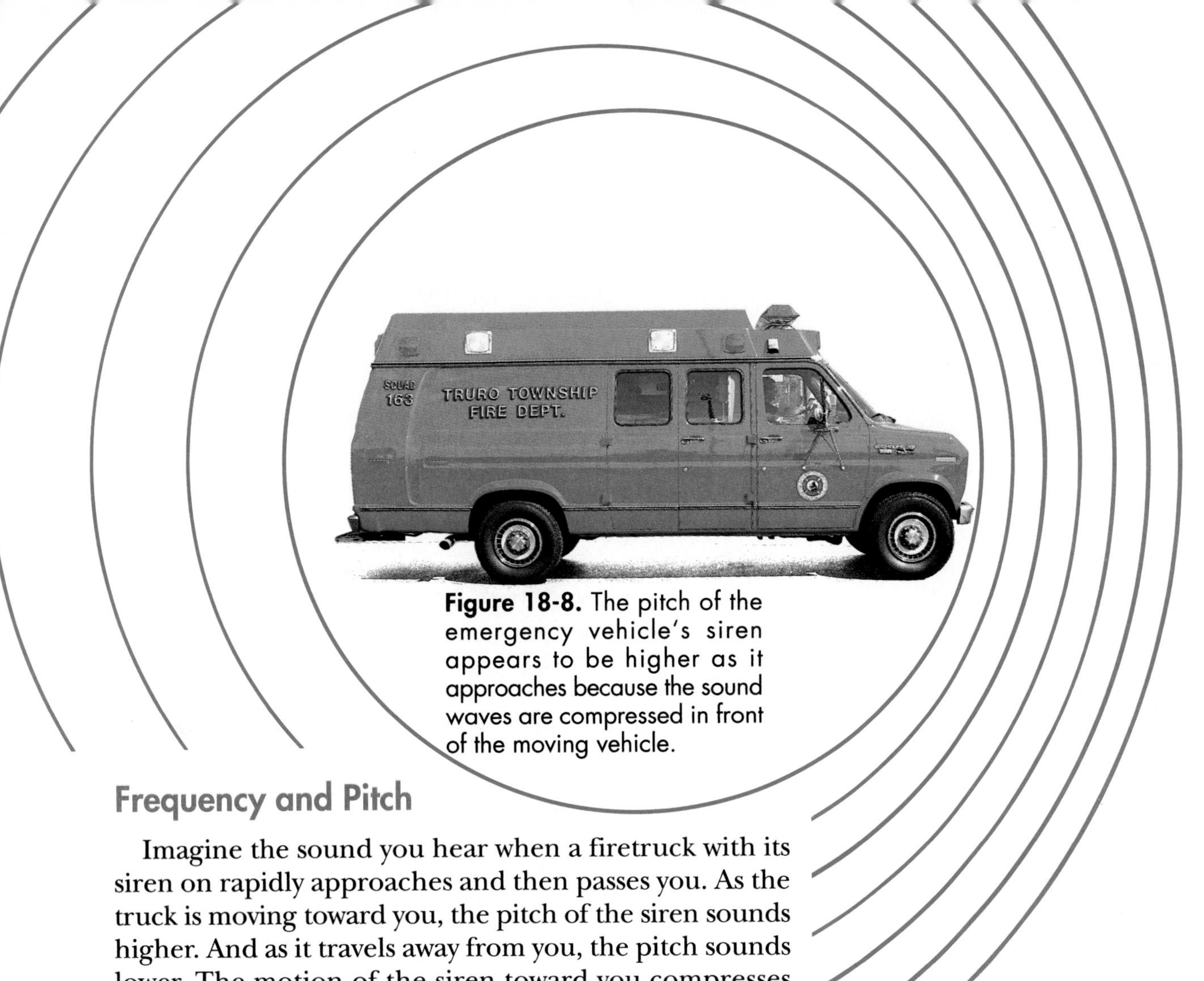

Figure 18-8. The pitch of the emergency vehicle's siren appears to be higher as it approaches because the sound waves are compressed in front of the moving vehicle.

Frequency and Pitch

Imagine the sound you hear when a firetruck with its siren on rapidly approaches and then passes you. As the truck is moving toward you, the pitch of the siren sounds higher. And as it travels away from you, the pitch sounds lower. The motion of the siren toward you compresses the sound waves closer together. This increases the frequency of the sound waves striking your ear. As a result, the pitch you hear is higher. As the siren moves away, the waves are pulled farther apart. This decreases the frequency and you hear a lower pitch. This apparent change in wave frequency is called the Doppler effect. Figure 18-8 illustrates this effect.

What would you expect would happen if you were moving past a stationary sound source? Suppose you were riding a school bus and passed by a building with a ringing alarm bell. The pitch would sound higher as you approached the building and lower as you rode away from it. The Doppler effect is observed when the source of sound is moving or when the observer is moving.

When can the Doppler effect be observed?

Think again of the alarm clock that woke you up this morning. Can you describe how the rhythmic vibrations of the clock produced compressional waves in the air?

The sound waves carried energy to your ears through a series of compressions and rarefactions of air molecules. If your clock gives off high frequency vibrations, you hear a high pitch. The more intense the waves, or the more energy they carry, the louder your clock sounds.

SECTION REVIEW

1. What type of waves are sound waves and how do they transfer energy?
2. How does the temperature of the medium affect the speed of sound waves?
3. While on your way to school, you turned up the volume on the car radio. Which of the following quantities change as a result: velocity of sound, intensity, pitch, amplitude, frequency, wavelength, loudness?
4. While watching a "Star Trek" rerun, you hear the roaring approach of another ship in space. Is this possible? Explain your answer.
5. **Apply:** A bat in a dark cave sends out a high frequency sound wave and detects an increase in frequency after the sound reflects off the prey. Describe the possible motions of the bat and the prey.

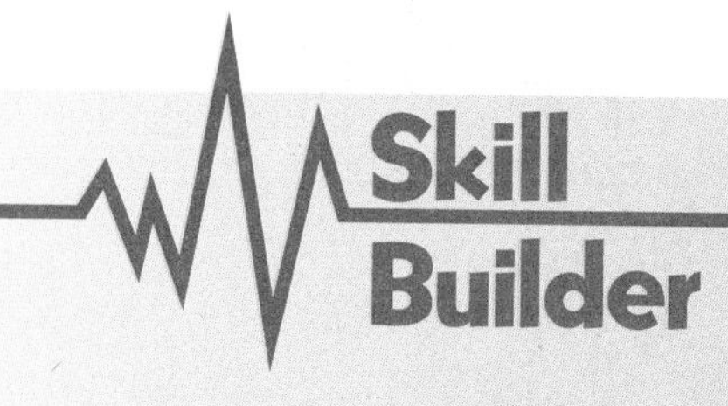

Concept Mapping

Prepare a concept map that shows the series of events that occur to produce sound. Include the terms *rarefaction, vibration,* and *compression.* If you need help, refer to Concept Mapping in the **Skill Handbook** on pages 684 and 685.

ACTIVITY 18-2
Frequency of Sound Waves

Problem: *What is the frequency of a musical note?*

Materials
- plastic pipe
- rubber band
- metric ruler

Procedure
1. Measure the length of the pipe and record it on the data table.
2. Stretch one end of a rubber band across the open end of the pipe and hold it firmly in place as shown. **CAUTION:** *Be careful not to release your grip on the ends of the rubber band.*
3. Hold the rubber band close to your ear and pluck it.
4. Listen for a *double* note.
5. Slowly relax the tightness of the rubber band. Listen for one part of the double note to change and the other part to remain the same.
6. Continue to adjust the tightness until you hear only one note.
7. Exchange pipes with another group and repeat the experiment.

Data and Observations

Sound Frequencies Produced by Open Pipes		
Length of pipe	Length of wave	Frequency of sound

Analyze
1. The wavelength you obtained in Step 6 is twice the length of the pipe. Calculate the wavelength.
2. Assume the velocity of sound to be 34 200 cm/s. Use the equation

   frequency = velocity/wavelength

   to calculate the frequency of the note.
3. What was the wavelength and frequency of the sound waves in the second pipe?

Conclude and Apply
4. How does the length of a pipe compare with the frequency and wavelength of the sound it can make?
5. A pipe organ uses pipes of different lengths to produce various notes. What other musical instruments use lengths of pipe to produce musical notes?
6. If you listen closely, you can hear longer pipes produce certain higher frequency sounds. How is this possible?

18-3 Noise Pollution

New Science Words

noise pollution

Objectives

- Analyze the role of noise as one type of pollution.
- Suggest three ways noise pollution can be reduced.

What Is Noise Pollution?

Are you aware that you can be fined for littering on a highway or in a public place? Littering is one of the most obvious types of pollution. There are other types of pollution which may not seem so obvious. One of these is noise pollution. **Noise pollution** includes sounds that are loud, annoying, or harmful to the ear. These sounds can come from sources such as a jackhammer, a jet engine, or highly amplified music. Noise pollution is becoming a problem that sometimes requires legal intervention.

Noise pollution can be harmful in several ways. Recall the way in which sound waves transfer energy through compressions and rarefactions. If the intensity of the sound waves is high enough, the energy carried can actually shatter windows and crack plaster. However, most laws that govern sound levels were created because loud sounds can damage the human ear.

When sound waves reach the human ear, the vibrations pass through its various parts. Extremely intense vibrations can rupture the eardrum, but loudness-related hearing loss usually develops gradually. Your brain perceives sound when the auditory nerve carries a nerve impulse to the brain. This nerve is composed of many tiny nerve fibers surrounded by a fluid inside your ear. Hearing loss occurs when intense compressional waves traveling through the fluid destroy these nerve fibers. Loud sounds in the frequency range of 4000 to 20 000 Hz cause most of the damage to these nerve fibers. Amplified music, motorcycles, and machinery are sources of sound in this frequency range that often cause hearing loss.

Can you suggest how the amount of noise pollution could be decreased? One way would be to reduce the intensities of the sound waves from sources that cause noise pollution. Some scientists and engineers work on making quieter machinery and cars. Another way to reduce noise exposure is to insulate the loud areas with sound barriers. Giant walls are built along the sides of highways to keep some of the sound from reaching residential areas. You can put the sound barriers over your own ears by wearing ear protection.

Think about the other kinds of pollution you are familiar with. Littering, air pollution, and water pollution might come to mind. Now add noise pollution to the list. Rank your list from the most serious pollution problem to the least serious problem. Where does noise pollution rank? Can you explain your reasoning?

SECTION REVIEW

1. What is noise pollution?
2. How can loud sounds damage your hearing?
3. List at least two things that can be done to reduce the harmful effects of noise pollution.

You Decide!

Sometimes a noise can be irritating without being harmful. In one community, some teens built a large skateboarding ramp in the front yard of a house. Their neighbors have complained to the city officials about the ongoing noise the skating makes. The city officials have determined that the sound levels don't exceed the maximum intensities allowed in the city ordinance. Can this still be considered noise pollution? How might this problem be solved?

18-4 Musical Sounds

New Science Words

music
noise
resonance
quality
interference
reverberation
acoustics

Objectives

- Distinguish between music and noise.
- Describe why different instruments produce sounds of different quality.
- Explain three types of wave interference.

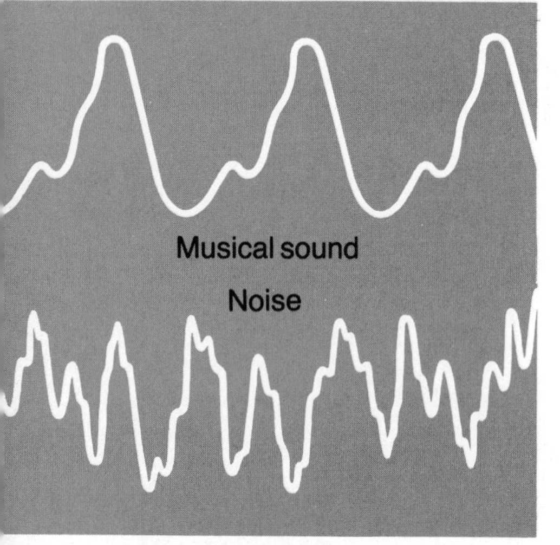

Figure 18-9. Music follows a pattern; noise does not.

How do music and noise differ?

What Is Music?

Has anyone ever commented that the music you were listening to sounded like a jumble of noise? Both music and noise are caused by vibrations, but there are some important differences. You can easily make a noise by just speaking a word or tapping a pencil on a desk, but it takes some deliberate actions to create music. Of course, you may be able to create music with your voice or your pencil if you try. **Music** is created using specific pitches and sound quality and by following a regular pattern. The most common kind of sound is **noise,** which has no set pattern and no definite pitch. Figure 18-9 shows a comparison of noise and music patterns.

A stringed musical instrument, such as a guitar, generates a sound when you pluck a string. Plucking a string creates waves in the string. Because the ends of the string are fastened, the waves reflect back and forth between the ends causing the string to vibrate. The guitar string, like most objects, has a natural frequency of vibration. Plucking it causes the string to vibrate at its natural frequency.

What kind of sound would be produced if you held a guitar string tightly between your hands while a friend plucked it? You would hear a sound, but it would be much quieter than if the string was fixed on a guitar. Because the string is attached to the guitar, the guitar frame and the air inside the instrument absorb energy from the vibrating string. The vibration of the guitar and the air inside it is called a forced vibration. As a result of forced vibration, the sound of the string is made louder.

If the sound that reaches an object is at the same frequency as the natual frequency of the object, the object will begin to vibrate at this frequency. This type of vibration is called **resonance.** As a result of resonance, the sound is amplified.

PROBLEM SOLVING

The Piano That Played Itself

Alan had started piano lessons in elementary school. After many years of practice, he became a member of a local rock band.

One afternoon as he was practicing for a gig, several friends stopped by. He decided to use the piano to play a trick on them. He said, "I bet this piano can play itself. I won't even touch a key." Ralph voiced everyone's reaction when he replied, "No way."

First, Alan pushed a pedal that released all the strings in the piano and left them free to vibrate. Then he asked his friends to join in as he sung a note. When everyone stopped singing, they heard the same note coming from the piano. How could the group cause a different note to come from the piano?

Think Critically: How did the piano play the note? Would this trick have worked if Alan hadn't released the piano strings? Explain why or why not.

Musical Sounds

If you were to play a note of the same pitch and loudness on a flute and on a piano, the sound wouldn't be the same. These instruments have a different quality of sound. This quality does not refer to how good or bad the instrument sounds. Sound **quality** describes the differences among sounds of the same pitch and loudness. All sounds are produced by vibrations of matter, but most objects vibrate at more than one frequency. Distinct sounds from musical instruments are produced by different combinations of these wave frequencies.

Define sound quality.

Imagine producing a tone by plucking a guitar string. The tone produced when the string vibrates in one piece is called the fundamental frequency. At the same time, each half of the string can vibrate in one piece. This produces the first overtone. Its frequency is twice the fundamental frequency. Overtones have frequencies that are multiples of the fundamental frequency. The intensity and number of overtones vary with each instrument to form a distinct quality of sound. Figure 18-10 illustrates the fundamental frequency and the first three overtones.

Music is written and played based on a musical scale of notes. The musical scale has eight notes, each of which has a characteristic frequency. The eight notes span a frequency range called an octave. The first and last notes in an octave are designated by the same letter. The highest note in an octave has exactly twice the frequency of the lowest note in that octave.

Did You Know?

The housefly hums at a pitch equivalent to the middle octave F on the piano.

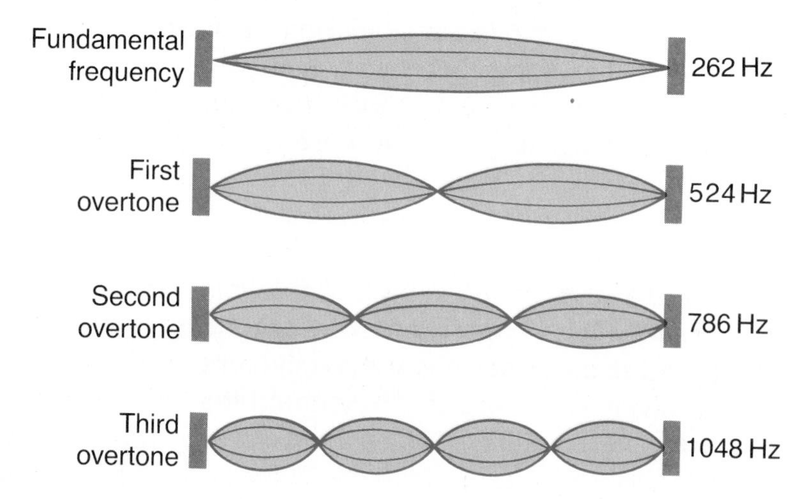

Figure 18-10. This diagram illustrates some of the ways a string can vibrate to produce overtones. A string can vibrate in all these ways at once.

Interference

In a band performance you may have heard several instruments playing the same notes at the same time. What is the purpose of having more than one instrument creating the same sound? The waves are combining to form a new wave. **Interference** is the ability of two or more waves to combine and form a new wave. Because the musicians are simultaneously playing the same note, their compressions overlap to form a greater compression. As a result, the music sounds much louder. Constructive interference occurs when the compressions of different waves arrive at the same place at the same time.

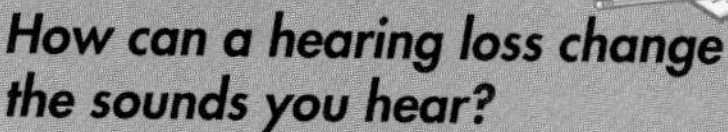

MINI-Lab

How can a hearing loss change the sounds you hear?

To simulate a hearing loss, tune a radio to a news or talk station. Turn the volume down to the lowest level you can hear and understand. Turn the bass to maximum and the treble to minimum. If the radio does not have these controls, mask out the higher frequency sounds with heavy pads over your ears. Which voices are hardest to understand, men's or women's? What letter sounds are the most difficult to hear, vowels or consonants? How could you help a person with a hearing loss understand what you say?

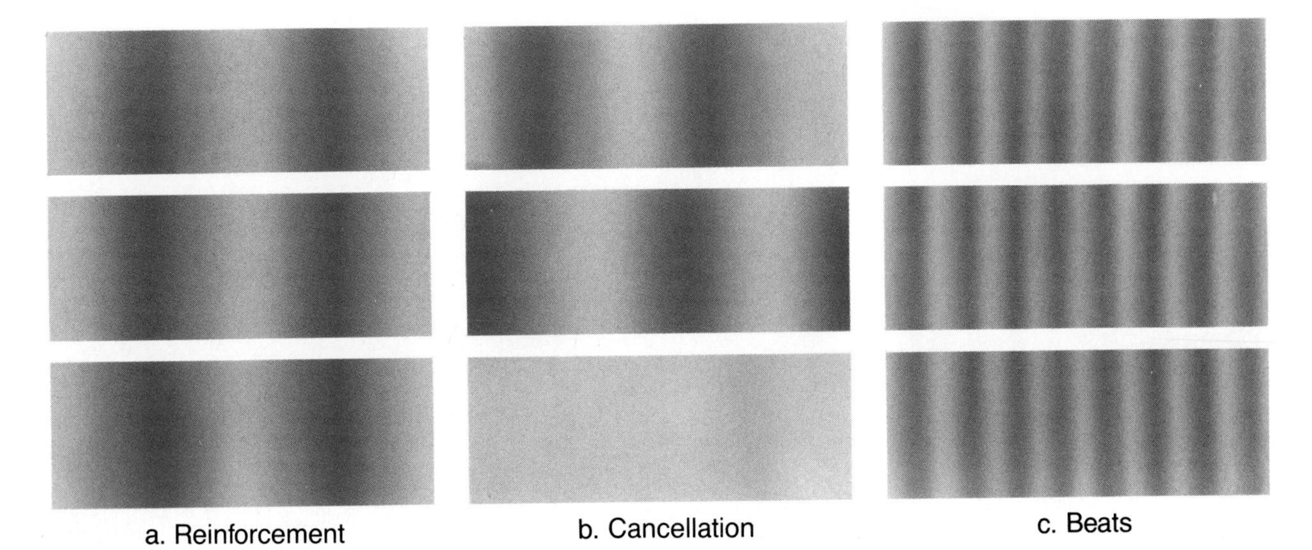

Figure 18-11. In (a) the sound compressions reinforce and produce a louder sound. In (b) compressions and rarefactions combine to cancel the sound waves. In (c) two different frequencies produce loud and soft beats.

Sometimes the compression of one wave will arrive with the rarefaction of another wave. They cancel each other, resulting in a decrease in loudness. This is an example of destructive interference.

If a tuning fork with a frequency corresponding to middle C is used to tune a piano, the piano frequency of middle C should blend perfectly with the tuning fork. If the piano produces a slightly different frequency than middle C, the compressions from the fork can't continue to arrive at the same time as the compressions from the piano. The musician will hear variations of sound intensity called beats. The sum of the amplitudes of the waves causes the loudness to regularly rise and fall. Have you ever heard two flutes play the same note when they weren't properly tuned? You could clearly hear the beats until the musicians correctly adjusted their instruments. The beats slowed and then stopped when the flutes were tuned. Figure 18-11 shows a comparison of the types of sound wave interference.

What are beats?

Acoustics

At a concert or a school assembly where a speaker sound system is used, someone usually speaks into the microphone to test the system. Sometimes you hear the sound linger for a couple of seconds. Perhaps you hear echoes of the sound. The sound reaches your ears at different times because it has been reflected off different walls and objects around you. This effect produced by many reflections of sound is called **reverberation.**

EcoTip

When is sound noise? Not when it comes from birds and insects. Plant sunflowers and other plants that attract these musical friends to your yard.

Concert halls and theaters are designed by scientists and engineers who specialize in **acoustics,** the study of sound. You will often see carpets and draperies lining the walls of concert halls. Soft, porous materials and special room shapes can reduce excess reverberation. Acoustic scientists also work on understanding human hearing and speaking processes.

SECTION REVIEW

1. Compare and contrast music and noise.
2. If you were to close your eyes and listen to middle C played both on a flute and on a cello, what musical property would enable you to distinguish one instrument from the other?
3. Explain the difference between constructive and destructive interference.
4. **Apply:** Intense high frequency sound can actually cause glass to shatter. What might be happening to the glass that causes it to break?

Recognizing Cause and Effect

What is the effect when waves interact by constructive interference? Describe the cause and effect sequence for destructive interference. If you need help, refer to Recognizing Cause and Effect in the **Skill Handbook** on page 679.

CHAPTER

REVIEW

SUMMARY

18-1: Wave Characteristics

1. The medium moves at right angles to the direction a transverse wave travels. Wave characteristics include crests, troughs, wavelength, and amplitude.

2. If the speed of the waves doesn't change, and the frequency increases, the wavelength decreases.

3. The velocity of a wave can be found by multiplying its wavelength by its frequency.

18-2: The Nature of Sound

1. Sound begins as a vibration that is transferred through a medium in a series of compressions and rarefactions of the matter in the medium, called compressional waves.

2. The pitch of a sound becomes higher as the frequency increases, and lower as the frequency decreases. Both amplitude and intensity increase as energy is added to a wave. Loudness is the human perception of sound intensity.

3. The Doppler effect is an apparent change of frequency and pitch of a sound as a result of either the observer or the sound source or both moving with respect to each other.

18-3: Science and Society: Noise Pollution

1. Noise pollution includes sounds that are loud, annoying, or harmful to the ear.

2. Noise pollution can be reduced by producing less noise, building barriers, or by using protective wear over the ears.

18-4: Musical Sounds

1. Music is created using specific pitches, sound quality, and a regular set pattern. Noise has no definite pitch, or set pattern.

2. Musical instruments each have their own unique sound quality. Sound quality describes the differences among sounds of the same pitch and loudness.

3. Interference is the ability of two or more waves to combine and form a new wave.

KEY SCIENCE WORDS

a. **acoustics**
b. **amplitude**
c. **compressional wave**
d. **crests**
e. **frequency**
f. **intensity**
g. **interference**
h. **loudness**
i. **medium**
j. **music**
k. **noise**
l. **noise pollution**
m. **pitch**
n. **quality**
o. **resonance**
p. **reverberation**
q. **transverse wave**
r. **troughs**
s. **wavelength**
t. **waves**

UNDERSTANDING VOCABULARY

Match each phrase with the correct term from the list of Key Science Words.

1. distance between identical points on two waves
2. sounds that are loud, annoying, or harmful
3. the study of sound
4. matter vibrates in the same direction as the wave travels
5. the highness or lowness of a sound
6. material through which a wave travels
7. expressed in Hertz
8. the highest point of a transverse wave
9. distance from the rest position of a medium to the trough or crest of a wave
10. human perception of sound intensity

CHAPTER REVIEW

CHECKING CONCEPTS

Choose the word or phrase that completes the sentence.

1. Waves carry ______.
   a. matter **c.** matter and energy
   b. energy **d.** the medium
2. A wave that carries a large amount of energy will always have a ______.
   a. large amplitude **c.** high frequency
   b. small amplitude **d.** short wavelength
3. A sound with a low pitch always has a low ______.
   a. amplitude **c.** wavelength
   b. frequency **d.** wave velocity
4. As ______, sound intensity decreases.
   a. wave velocity decreases
   b. wavelength decreases
   c. quality decreases
   d. amplitude decreases
5. Sounds with the same pitch and loudness may differ in ______.
   a. frequency **c.** quality
   b. amplitude **d.** wavelength
6. Sound cannot travel through ______.
   a. solids **c.** gases
   b. liquids **d.** empty space
7. Variations in the loudness of sound that are caused by wave interference are called ______.
   a. beats **c.** reverberations
   b. standing waves **d.** forced vibrations
8. ________ is shown when a window pane vibrates at the same frequency as a thunderclap.
   a. The Doppler effect
   b. Resonance
   c. Reverberation
   d. Destructive interference
9. Wave frequency is measured in ______.
   a. hertz **c.** meters
   b. decibels **d.** meters/second
10. When a sound source passes by you, the sound's ______.
    a. velocity decreases
    b. loudness increases
    c. pitch decreases
    d. frequency increases

UNDERSTANDING CONCEPTS

Complete each sentence.

11. _____ interference causes a sound to become softer.
12. Particles of a medium move ______ to the direction of the wave in transverse waves.
13. A sound that does not have a definite pitch or a definite pattern is called ______.
14. Sound quality is determined by ______.
15. As the frequency of a wave ______, its wavelength decreases.

THINK AND WRITE CRITICALLY

16. Describe how amplitude, frequency, and wavelength are determined in transverse and compressional waves.
17. What do constructive interference, destructive interference, and the formation of beats have in common? How are they different?
18. Explain how different combinations of wave frequencies make a guitar and a trumpet sound different even when the same note is played.
19. In what ways can noise pollution be reduced?
20. Why does the ringing of an alarm clock enclosed in an airtight container become softer as the air is drawn out of the container?

APPLY

21. A wave has a wavelength of 6 m and a wave velocity of 420 m/s. What is its frequency?
22. A bus driver is rounding a curve approaching a railroad crossing. She hears a train's whistle and then hears the whistle's pitch become lower. What assumptions can she make about what she will see when she rounds the curve and looks at the crossing?
23. When a little boy blows a dog whistle, his dog comes even though the boy can't hear the whistle. Explain why the boy can't hear the whistle, but his dog can.
24. An earthquake beneath the middle of the Pacific Ocean produces a tidal wave that hits a remote island. Is the water that hits the island the same water that was above the earthquake? Explain.
25. Explain how a stethoscope helps a doctor listen to someone's heart.

MORE SKILL BUILDERS

If you need help, refer to the Skill Handbook.

1. **Hypothesizing:** Sound travels slower in air at high altitudes than at low altitudes. State a hypothesis to explain this observation.
2. **Observing and Inferring:** Infer the effect of increasing wave velocity on the wavelength of a compressional wave that has a constant frequency.
3. **Interpreting Scientific Illustrations:** Look at the two transverse waves in Figure 18-4 on page 460. Compare the frequencies, wavelengths, amplitudes, and energies of these waves. Draw another wave that has twice the frequency and energy of the bottom wave.
4. **Making and Using Graphs:** Construct a bar graph to analyze the following data. Order the substances from most to least dense. Does this graph indicate any differences in the speed of each substance's particles?

Substance	Speed of Sound 25°C
air	343 m/s
brick	3650 m/s
cork	500 m/s
water	1498 m/s
steel	5200 m/s

5. **Making and Using Tables:** You have started a lawn mowing business during summer vacation. Your family's power lawn mower has a sound level of 100 decibels. Using the table below, determine how many hours a day you can safely work mowing lawns. If you want to work longer hours, what can you do to protect your hearing? If your family purchases a new lawn mower with a sound level of 95 dB, how will your business be affected?

OSHA RECOMMENDED NOISE EXPOSURE LIMITS	
Sound Level (decibels)	Time Permitted (hours per day)
90	8
95	4
100	2
105	1
110	0.5

PROJECTS

1. Research the uses of sonar and of ultrasonic waves in medicine. Prepare a written report.
2. Using materials you have at home, make a musical instrument. Play your instrument for your classmates and explain how you can change the pitch of your instrument.

CHAPTER

19 Light

Color is a very important part of our lives. How would you describe things around you without using color?

FIND OUT!

Do the following activity to find out how it feels not to use color.

Get together with a partner. Each of you should pick an object and form a clear picture of it in your own mind. Next, one of you should close your eyes. The other person must describe his or her object as completely as possible without using colors. Can you guess what it is? Switch roles and try it again. Why is it so difficult to describe or identify objects without the use of colors? You depend on light and color to see and describe everything in the world around you, from the food you eat to the clothes you wear.

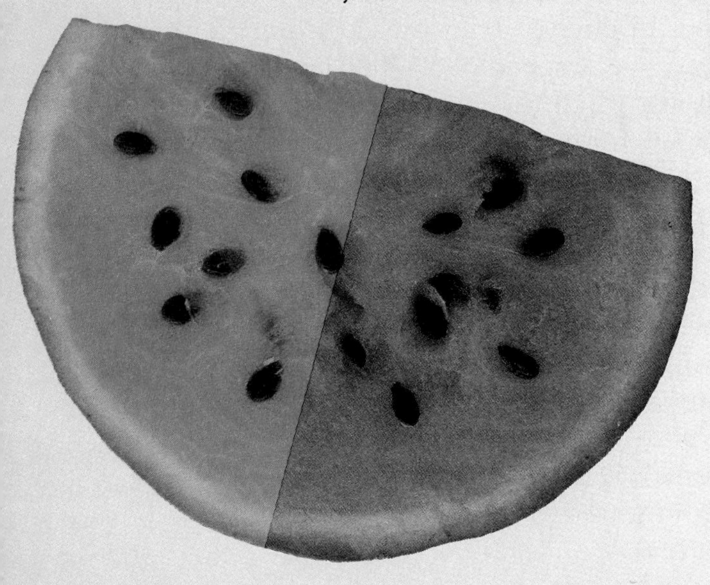

Gearing Up

Previewing the Chapter

Use this outline to help you focus on important ideas in this chapter.

Section 19-1 Electromagnetic Radiation
- The Electromagnetic Spectrum
- Radio Waves
- Infrared Radiation
- Visible Radiation
- Ultraviolet Radiation
- X Rays and Gamma Rays

Section 19-2 Light and Color
- Light and Matter
- Colors
- Pigments

Section 19-3 Science and Society
Battle of the Bulbs
- Do Light Bulbs Make a Difference?

Section 19-4 Wave Properties of Light
- Reflection
- Refraction
- Diffraction and Interference

Previewing Science Skills

- In the Skill Builders, you will outline, make a concept map, and observe and infer.
- In the Activities, you will observe, communicate, predict, and formulate models.
- In the MINI-Lab, you will observe, interpret, and measure.

What's next?

Now that you have thought about how much you depend on light and color to see and describe objects around you, learn why objects have colors. Learn how light affects the color of objects, as well as the characteristics of light, as you read the following pages.

19-1 Electromagnetic Radiation

New Science Words

radiation
electromagnetic spectrum
photons
radio waves
modulation
microwaves
infrared radiation
visible radiation
ultraviolet radiation
X rays
gamma rays

Objectives

- Contrast electromagnetic waves with other kinds of waves.
- Describe the arrangement of electromagnetic waves on the electromagnetic spectrum.
- Explain at least one application of each type of electromagnetic wave.

The Electromagnetic Spectrum

Do you listen to the radio, watch television, play video games, or use a heat lamp or a microwave oven? These devices all make use of different kinds of electromagnetic waves. Light, radio waves, and microwaves are all examples of electromagnetic waves.

Electromagnetic waves are transverse waves produced by the motion of electrically charged particles. These waves radiate from the particles, so we often call them *electromagnetic radiation.* Therefore, the transfer of energy by electromagnetic waves is called **radiation.** One way these waves differ from those you learned about in Chapter 18 is that electromagnetic waves do not need a medium to transfer energy. They travel through a vacuum—empty space—at a speed of 300 000 km/sec. These waves travel slower when they pass through any type of matter, but they still travel very fast compared to the speed of sound waves or water waves.

Figure 19-1. Electromagnetic waves travel at the same speed but at different wavelengths and frequencies.

Electromagnetic waves all travel at the same constant speed in each particular medium, but their frequencies and wavelengths may vary. The shorter the wavelength of a wave, the higher its frequency. Electromagnetic waves are classified according to their wavelengths on the **electromagnetic spectrum.** Figure 19-2 shows the range of the electromagnetic spectrum, which includes and lists all forms of energy—from low frequency, long wavelength radio waves to high frequency, short wavelength gamma rays.

Scientists have observed that radiation not only carries energy, but also that it has momentum. This suggests that electromagnetic radiation has particle-like behavior. In 1905, Albert Einstein suggested that light is composed of tiny particles. These tiny bundles of radiation that have no mass are called **photons.** The photons with the highest energy correspond to light with the highest frequency. Very high energy photons can actually damage matter such as the cells in your body.

Did You Know?

If the sun quit shining in the past eight minutes, you wouldn't know it yet because it takes that long for light from the sun to reach Earth.

Radio Waves

When you tune your radio to a station, you are adjusting it to respond to radio waves of a certain wavelength. Even though radio waves are all around you right now, you can't feel them. **Radio waves** are the kind of electromagnetic radiation with very long wavelength and very low frequency. Thus, radio waves have the lowest photon energy. Locate radio waves on the electromagnetic spectrum in Figure 19-2.

Describe the wavelength and frequency of radio waves.

Figure 19-2. All electromagnetic waves are classified by their wavelengths on the electromagnetic spectrum.

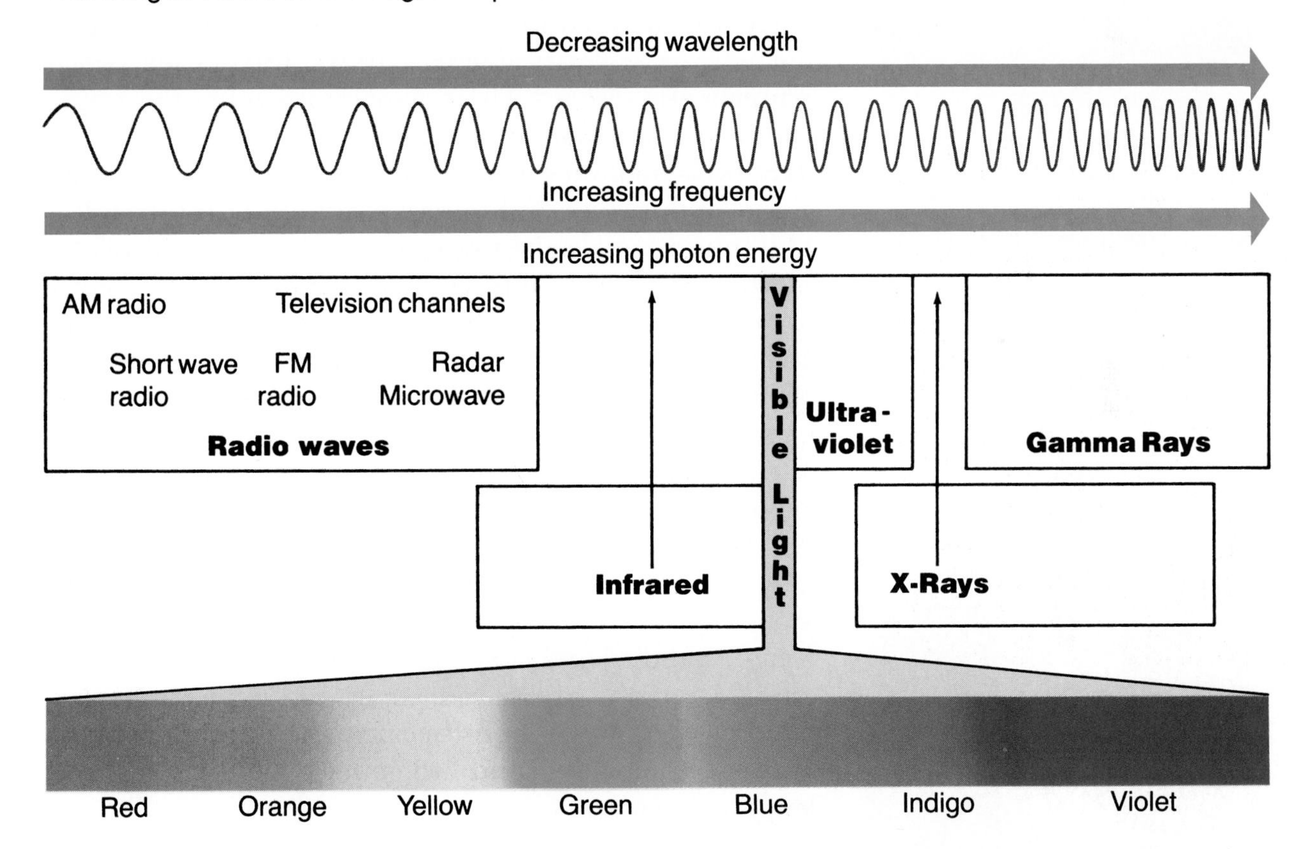

In addition to radio communications, radio waves are used in television, cellular telephones, and cordless telephones. How is your voice transmitted by radio waves on a cordless telephone? The sound waves produced by your voice are changed to varying electrical currents. These currents act as electrical signals that represent your speech patterns and pitches. These signals vary either the amplitudes or frequencies of radio waves that are transmitted. This process of varying radio waves is called **modulation**. Besides your voice, light images, computer information and music can also be used to modulate radio waves.

The radio waves of the highest frequency and energy are called **microwaves.** They are used in communications, but you are probably most familiar with microwaves for their speedy cooking abilities. Have you ever popped popcorn in a microwave oven? Do you wonder how the kernels pop so quickly? Microwaves carry energy into the molecules of the popcorn. When they receive this energy, the molecules vibrate faster and rotate. As a result, the kinetic energy and temperature of the molecules increases. The water inside the popcorn kernel turns to steam, and the kernel explodes due to the increased pressure. Materials such as glass, paper, and some plastics are used in microwave ovens because the microwaves pass through them easily and little energy is wasted in heating the container.

Infrared Radiation

Have you ever napped in a comfortable lawn chair on a hot summer day? Even with your eyes closed, could you feel when clouds moved in front of the sun? When the sunlight wasn't blocked by the clouds, you may have felt its warmth on your skin. This warm feeling is caused by the infrared radiation from the sun. **Infrared radiation** has a wavelength slightly longer than visible light, as you can see by its location on the electromagnetic spectrum. Your skin feels warm because it is actually absorbing some of the infrared radiation from the sun. This causes the molecules in your skin to vibrate more, increasing their kinetic energy and temperature.

What objects give off infrared radiation?

Warmer objects, such as your body, give off more infrared radiation than do cooler objects. Some parts of your body are warmer than others and, as a result, give off more infrared radiation. Measurement of the body's emission of infrared radiation helps doctors make some medical diagnoses. A thermogram, such as the one shown in Figure 19-3b, can be produced by measuring the infrared radiation given off by different body parts. Tumors can sometimes be detected in a thermogram because they are warmer than the healthy tissue around them.

People using infrared-sensitive binoculars can see humans and animals in complete darkness. These binoculars can detect the infrared waves given off by warm bodies. Some home security systems are designed to

a

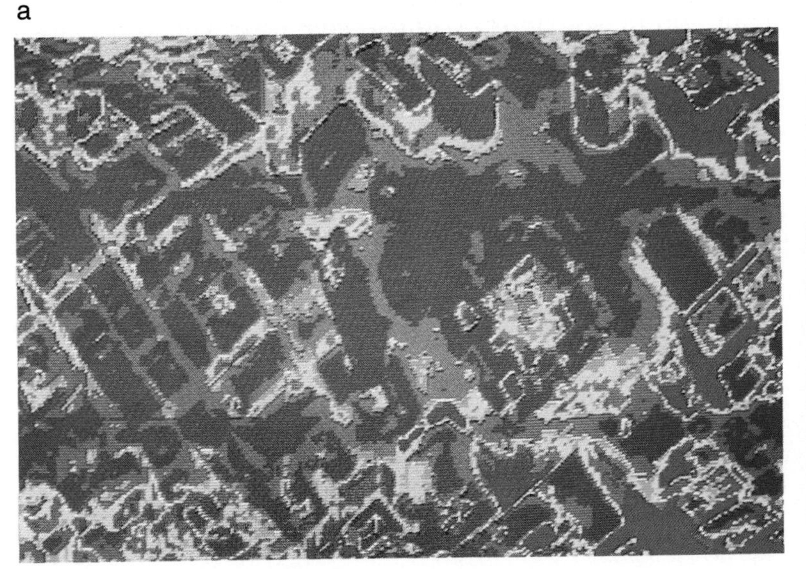

b

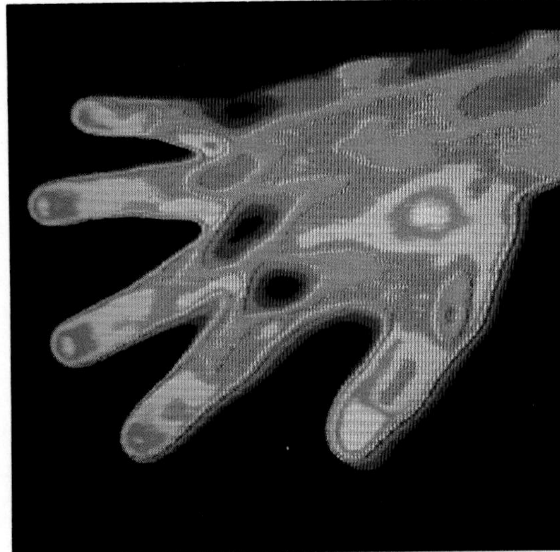

Figure 19-3. Heat loss in your home can be decreased by infrared radiation (a). A thermogram of a hand can help detect circulation problems (b).

Figure 19-4. You may have seen infrared lamps, like these, in restaurants keeping food warm until it is served.

detect objects giving off infrared radiation, and to respond by activating light or an alarm.

What are some uses of infrared radiation?

Because infrared radiation raises the temperature of matter, it can be used to warm and dry objects. Infrared lamps are used in some restaurants to keep cooked food hot until it is served. Some auto paint shops use infrared radiation to dry car finishes. Can you think of any other uses of this form of radiant energy?

Visible Radiation

Visible radiation, or light, is the only part of the electromagnetic spectrum you can see. Can you find visible radiation on the electromagnetic spectrum diagram in Figure 19-2? Notice it covers a very small range of the spectrum compared to the other types of radiation.

Hot objects, such as the sun, radiate a great deal of electromagnetic energy. Much of this energy is in the visible range of the electromagnetic spectrum. Sunlight is a combination of light of all the different colors, and it appears white. Light and color will be discussed in Section 19-2.

Light can stimulate chemical reactions. It provides the energy for the process of photosynthesis in which green plants make their own food through a series of chemical reactions. Light also stimulates chemical reactions in your eyes that allow you to see.

Science and READING

Advertisers write their ads to appeal to a certain audience. Look through magazines and newspapers to see if you can find different kinds of ads for some of the everyday products mentioned in this chapter. Then, write an ad of your own.

Ultraviolet Radiation

Why do you wear sunglasses or use sunscreen when you're in the sunlight for several hours? These two products are designed to protect you from large doses of ultraviolet radiation. Where is ultraviolet radiation located with respect to visible light on the electromagnetic spectrum in Figure 19-2? **Ultraviolet radiation** has a higher frequency than visible light, and as a result its photons are more energetic and have greater penetrating power. Exposure to ultraviolet radiation enables the skin cells to produce vitamin D, which is needed for healthy bones and teeth. However, overexposure to ultraviolet radiation kills healthy cells. Prolonged and frequent overexposure can lead to sagging, dry skin, and even skin cancer. For this reason, it is important to use a sunscreen regularly if you spend a lot of time outdoors. Sunscreens absorb many of the ultraviolet rays before they penetrate your skin.

Earth's atmosphere has a natural filter, ozone, that blocks most of the sun's ultraviolet rays. Three oxygen atoms combine to make each ozone molecule. Therefore, ozone is a form of oxygen. Ozone molecules filter out much of the damaging ultraviolet radiation in the radiant energy from the sun. A reduction in the amount of ozone in Earth's atmosphere will result in an increase of the ultraviolet radiation reaching Earth's surface. Some chemicals can break down ozone molecules. Our use of spray-can propellants and refrigerants, which contain these chemicals, may be breaking down this layer, so we should limit our use of these compounds.

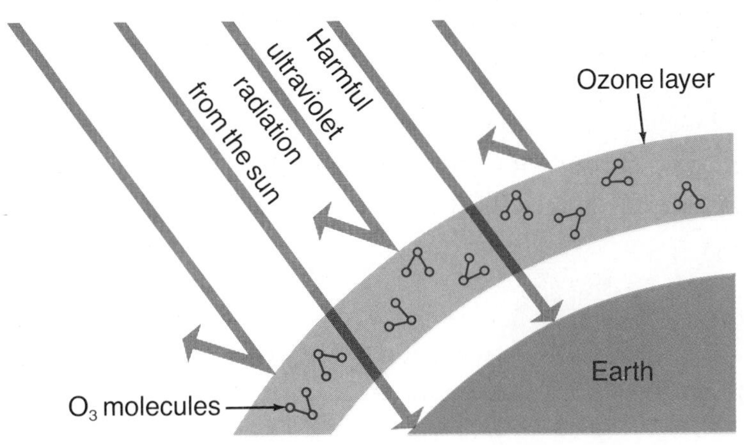

Figure 19-5. A layer of ozone molecules in Earth's atmosphere blocks most of the sun's ultraviolet rays.

MINI-Lab

Is fluorescent light hot?

Use an incandescent light and a fluorescent light of identical wattage. Make a heat collector by covering the top of a plastic foam cup with a plastic food wrap "window." Push a thermometer through the side of the cup. Hold the window of the tester one centimeter from each light for two minutes. Determine the temperature change inside the "heat collector" for exposure to each bulb. What was the temperature change inside the cup for each bulb? Which bulb appears to give off more heat?

Because ultraviolet rays can penetrate cells, they can also be used to kill germs in food processing and in hospitals. Some minerals become fluorescent when exposed to ultraviolet light. Fluorescence occurs when a material absorbs ultraviolet radiation and changes some of the radiation into visible light.

X Rays and Gamma Rays

If you ever had a bad fall, you probably had to have an X ray taken to check for broken bones. **X rays** have a shorter wavelength and higher frequency than ultraviolet radiation. X-ray photons carry higher energy and have a greater penetrating power than any of the forms of electromagnetic radiation discussed so far. This higher energy allows X rays to travel through some types of matter, such as your skin and muscles. When X rays hit a more dense material, such as bone, they are absorbed. If you saw the X ray of your broken bone, it probably looked similar to the one in Figure 19-6. An X-ray photograph is a negative; thus, the bones appear much brighter than the surrounding tissues because they absorb most of the X rays.

Gamma rays have the highest frequency of all the electromagnetic waves. They are located at the opposite end of the electromagnetic spectrum from radio waves. Gamma rays are emitted from the nuclei of radioactive atoms. Earth receives some gamma radiation from space as well. Gamma rays are the most penetrating kind of electromagnetic radiation. Concentrated gamma rays are very destructive to human cells and are used to kill cancerous cells. People who undergo gamma radiation therapy for cancer frequently suffer side effects from the therapy because healthy cells are damaged.

Doctors and technicians who give gamma radiation therapy or take X-ray pictures protect themselves from this penetrating radiation by standing behind lead shields. These shields

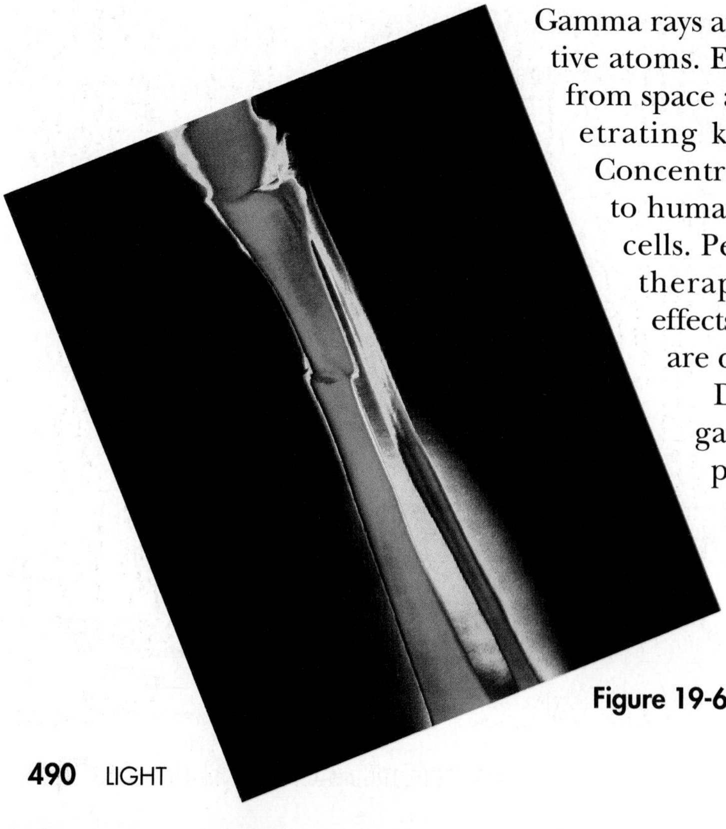

Figure 19-6. X rays can help locate the break in a bone.

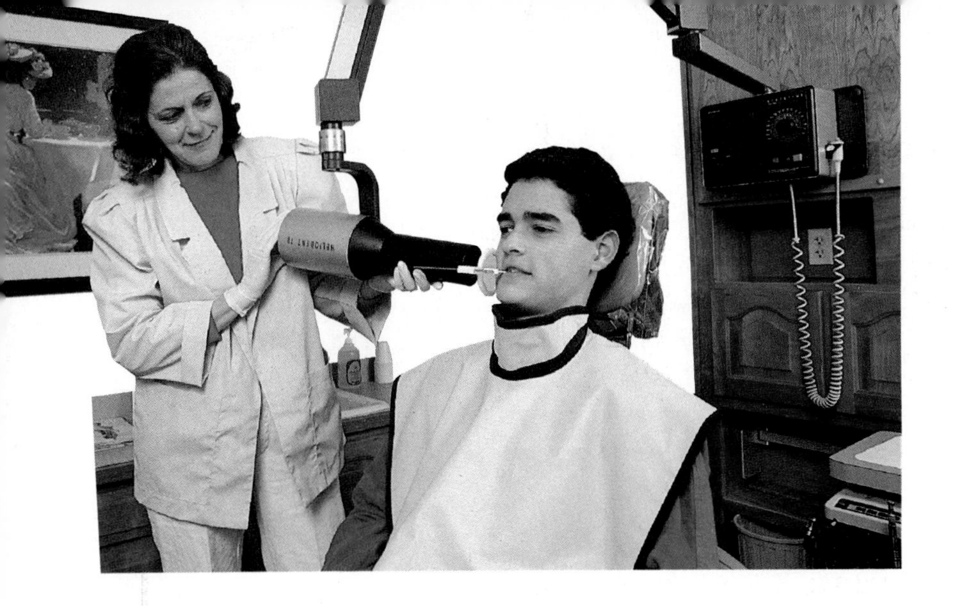

Figure 19-7. Exposure to X rays and gamma radiation can be harmful to workers if they don't use protective measures.

absorb the high-energy photons. Excess exposure to X rays and gamma radiation is even more harmful to your body than overexposure to ultraviolet radiation.

Think of all the uses of the waves of the electromagnetic spectrum that you read about in this section. Can you think of some uses that weren't mentioned? In the next section, you will learn more about the visible part of the spectrum, visible light.

SECTION REVIEW

1. Describe at least three ways electromagnetic waves differ from sound waves.
2. Arrange the following waves in order of decreasing wavelength: radio waves, gamma rays, ultraviolet rays, visible light, infrared radiation.
3. Explain how X rays can be used to photograph your bones.
4. How do microwaves cook food?
5. **Apply:** If someone told you that you were being exposed to radio waves and gamma radiation, which would you be the most concerned about? Explain your choice.

Outlining

Outline the major types of electromagnetic radiation discussed in this section. Include at least two uses for each type listed. If you need more help, refer to Outlining in the **Skill Handbook** on page 677.

19-2 Light and Color

New Science Words

opaque materials
transparent materials
translucent materials

Objectives

- Describe the differences among opaque, transparent, and translucent materials.
- Explain how you see color.
- Describe the difference between light color and pigment color.

Light and Matter

Have you ever been asleep in a dark room when someone suddenly opened the curtains and bright, white light came bursting into the room? You probably groaned as your eyes adjusted to the light. As you looked around, you could clearly see all the objects in the room and their colors. When no light was in the room, your eyes couldn't distinguish those objects or their colors. What you actually see depends on the amount and color of light the objects you are looking at are reflecting or absorbing. In order for you to see an object, it must reflect at least a little bit of light.

The type of matter in an object determines the amount of light it absorbs and reflects. For example, the curtains at the window kept the room dark when they were completely closed. The curtains are opaque. **Opaque materials** absorb or reflect all light and you cannot see objects through them. When the curtains were opened, bright sunlight came shining through the glass window panes. Most glass windows are transparent. **Transparent materials** allow light to pass through and you can clearly see objects through them. Other materials, such as frosted glass and wax paper, allow light to pass through but you cannot clearly see objects through them. These materials are **translucent materials.**

Figure 19-8. The lenses in the glasses are transparent, the vase is translucent, and the flowers are opaque.

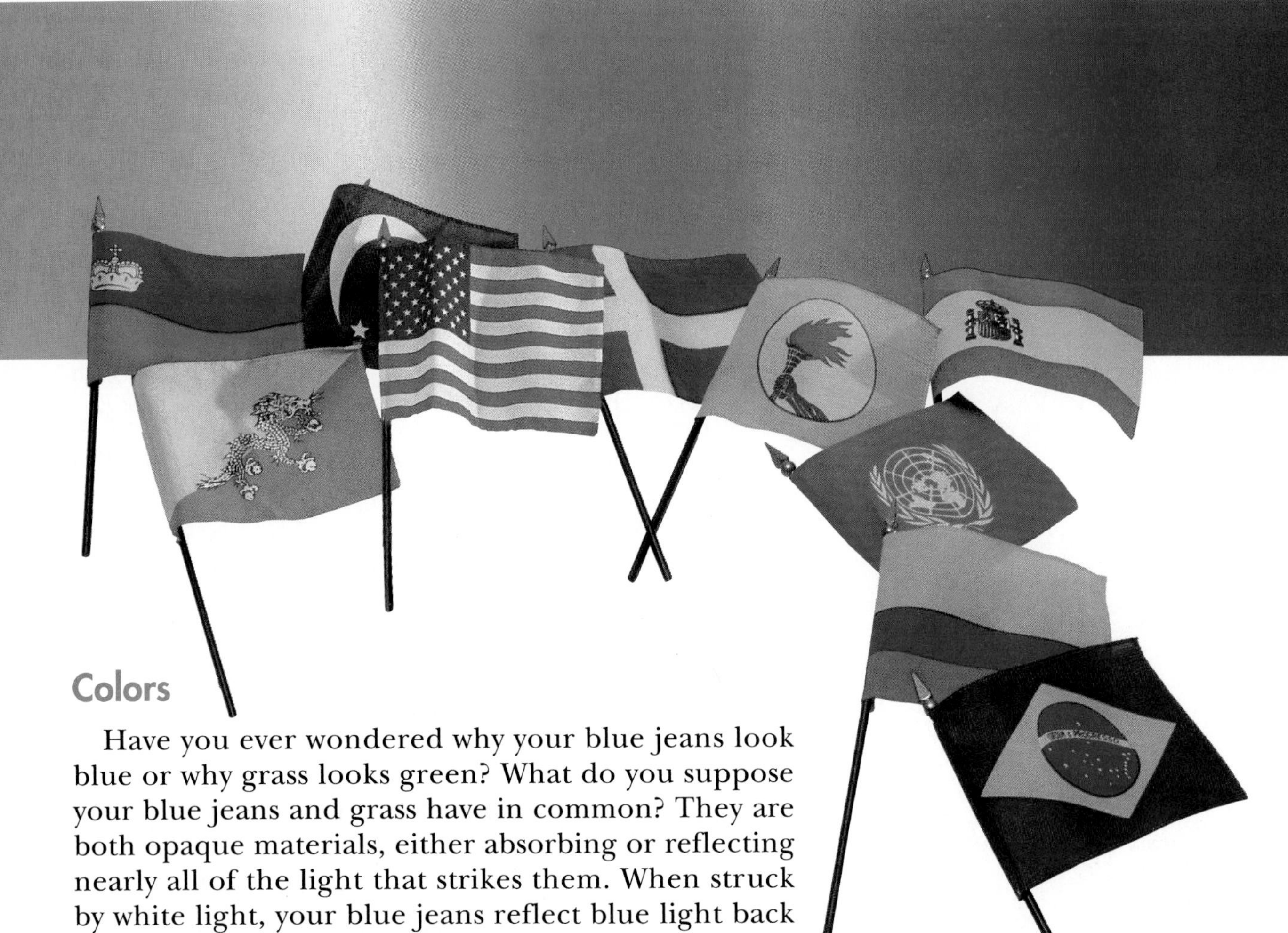

Colors

Have you ever wondered why your blue jeans look blue or why grass looks green? What do you suppose your blue jeans and grass have in common? They are both opaque materials, either absorbing or reflecting nearly all of the light that strikes them. When struck by white light, your blue jeans reflect blue light back to your eyes and absorb all of the other colors. What color of light do you think a blade of grass reflects? White objects appear white because they reflect all colors of light in the visible spectrum. The colors of the spectrum, arranged in order of decreasing wavelengths, are red, orange, yellow, green, blue, indigo, and violet. Infrared radiation lies just outside of the red end of visible light on the electromagnetic spectrum. Infrared lamps often appear red because their filaments produce light with a range of wavelengths that include those of a red light and infrared radiation. Where do you think ultraviolet light is located on the spectrum with respect to visible light? When you see an object that is reflecting all colors of the spectrum, it appears white. Objects that appear black absorb all colors of light and reflect little or no light back to your eye. Why do you think colorful objects appear to be black in a dark room?

Figure 19-9. The colors of the flags depend on the wavelengths they absorb and reflect.

Why do some objects appear black?

a

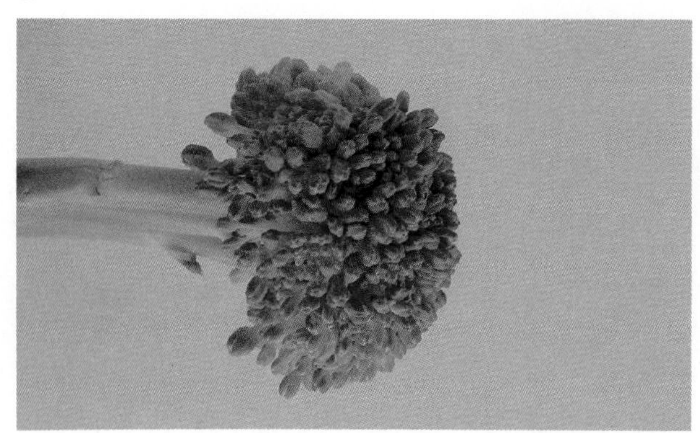

b

Figure 19-10. The broccoli appears green when viewed through a green filter (a) and black when viewed through a red filter (b).

Did you ever look at a white egg through a piece of colored plastic wrap? If you did, you know that the egg appeared the same color as the wrap. The plastic wrap is a filter. A filter is a transparent material that transmits one or more colors of light but absorbs all others. The color of a filter is the same as the color of light it transmits. What happens when you look at colored objects through colored filters? In white light, broccoli looks green because it reflects only the green light in the white light striking it. It absorbs light of all other colors. If you look at the broccoli through a green filter, the broccoli still looks green because the filter transmits the reflected green light. Figure 19-10b shows how the broccoli looks when you look at it through a red filter. Why does it appear this way? Red, green, and blue light, are called the primary colors of light. They can be mixed in different amounts to produce any color of light. Figure 19-11 shows how all three primary colors form white light.

Figure 19-11. White light is produced when the three primary colors of light are mixed.

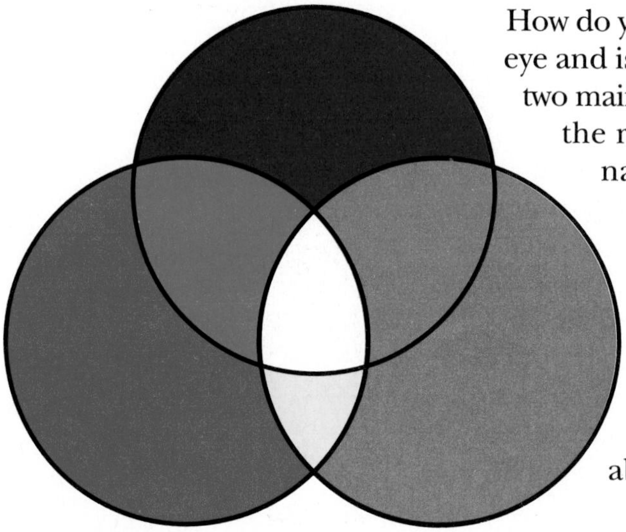

How do you actually see colors? First, light enters your eye and is focused on the retina, which is made up of two main types of nerve cells. When these nerve cells, the rods and cones, absorb light, they send signals to your brain. The rods allow you to see dim light because they are more sensitive than the cones. The cones allow you to distinguish colors. There are three types of cones, each of which absorbs a different range of wavelengths. "Red" cones absorb mostly red and yellow, "green" cones absorb mostly yellow and green, and "blue" cones absorb mostly blue and violet.

What happens when you look at pure yellow

light? Both your red and green cones respond, and your brain interprets the combined signal as yellow. Your brain would get the same signal if a mixture of red light and green light reached your eye. Again, your red and green cones would respond, and you would "see" yellow light because your brain can't perceive the difference.

You "see" white light when a mixture of all visible wavelengths of light enter your eye because all of your cones are stimulated. If a mixture of red, green, and blue light, the primary colors, reaches your eye, you would also see white light.

Did You Know?

Most school buses are yellow because yellow is the most visible of all colors.

Pigments

What is a pigment?

A pigment is a colored material that absorbs some colors and reflects others. Pigments are used by artists to make various colors of paints. Paint pigments are usually made of powered insoluble chemicals such as titanium (IV) oxide, a bright white pigment, and lead (II) chromate, used in painting yellow lines on highways. Few people have exactly the same skin color because the amount of pigmentation in the skin varies.

You can make any pigment color by mixing different amounts of the three primary pigments—yellow, magenta, and cyan. A primary pigment's color depends on the color of light it reflects. For example, in white light the yellow pigment appears yellow because it reflects red and green light but absorbs blue light. The color of a mixture of two primary pigments is deteremined by the primary color of light that both pigments can reflect.

Look at Figure 19-12. Its center appears black because the three blended primary pigments absorb all the primary colors of light. Note that the primary colors of light combine to produce white light; they are called additive colors. But the primary pigment colors combine to produce black. Because black results from the absence of reflected light, the primary pigments are called subtractive colors.

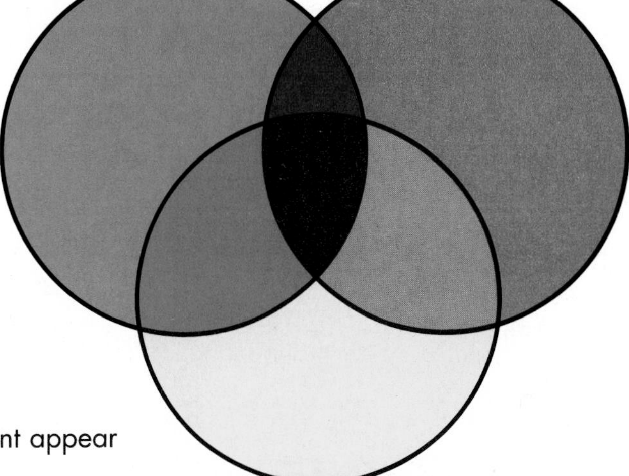

Figure 19-12. The three primary colors of pigment appear black when they are mixed.

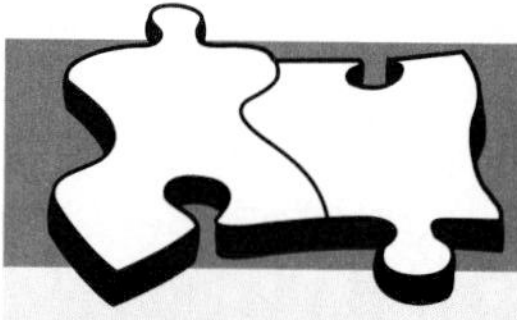

PROBLEM SOLVING

Color in the Sunday Comics

Becky looked forward to Sunday mornings because she liked to read the comics in the Sunday newspaper. One morning, as she was reading the comics, she wondered how color was produced in them. She decided to take a closer look, so she dug through her closet and located a hand lens.

She remembered from science class that the primary colors of pigments were magenta, cyan, and yellow. First, she examined the primary colors in the comics. The red areas were made of magenta dots, the blue areas of cyan dots, and the yellow areas of yellow dots. Next, she examined the other colors in the comics. She saw that an illustration of an orange school bus was made up of a mixture of cyan and yellow dots and one of a purple box was composed of a mixture of magenta and cyan dots. In the next cartoon frame, she examined a field of green grass.

Think Critically: What color dots do you think she found? How can you explain the reflection of green?

SECTION REVIEW

1. Contrast opaque, transparent, and translucent materials. Give at least one example of each.
2. If white light shines on a red shirt, what colors are reflected and what colors are absorbed?
3. What is the difference between blue light and blue pigment?
4. Explain how your eye sees color.
5. **Apply:** What color would your brain perceive if you were looking at a mixture of yellow and blue light? Explain your answer.

Concept Mapping

Design a concept map to show the chain of events that must happen for you to see a blue object. Work with a partner. If you need help, refer to Concept Mapping in the **Skill Handbook** on pages 684 and 685.

ACTIVITY 19-1
Analysis of a Spectrum

Problem: *What colors have the highest frequency and energy?*

Materials  

- diffraction grating
- power supply with rheostat
- clear, tubular light bulb
- socket
- red, yellow, and blue colored pencils
- rope (5 m)

Procedure

1. Set the light bulb in an upright position and plug it into the power supply.
2. Adjust the light to its brightest setting.
3. Look toward the light through the diffraction grating. Look for a spectrum to the right and left of the light bulb.
4. Slowly turn down the power supply to the light. Notice which end of the spectrum (red or blue) disappears first.
5. Next, stretch the rope between you and another student. Hold one end of the rope still and make waves at the other end.
6. Make some waves as long as possible and others as short as possible. Notice which kind of waves need the most energy to produce.

Analyze

1. Make a drawing of the color spectrum you observed using red, yellow, and blue colored pencils.
2. Make a second drawing showing the spectrum with the power of the light turned down.
3. Draw the rope with a long wavelength. Make another drawing showing the rope with short wavelengths. Label one of these drawings "high frequency" and the other "low frequency."

Conclude and Apply

4. Which end of the light spectrum, red or blue, requires the highest energy to produce?
5. What wavelength on the rope requires the highest energy to produce, long or short?
6. What wavelength, long or short, has the highest frequency?
7. Use these observations to decide which end of the light spectrum represents the highest energy. Which end represents the longest wavelength?

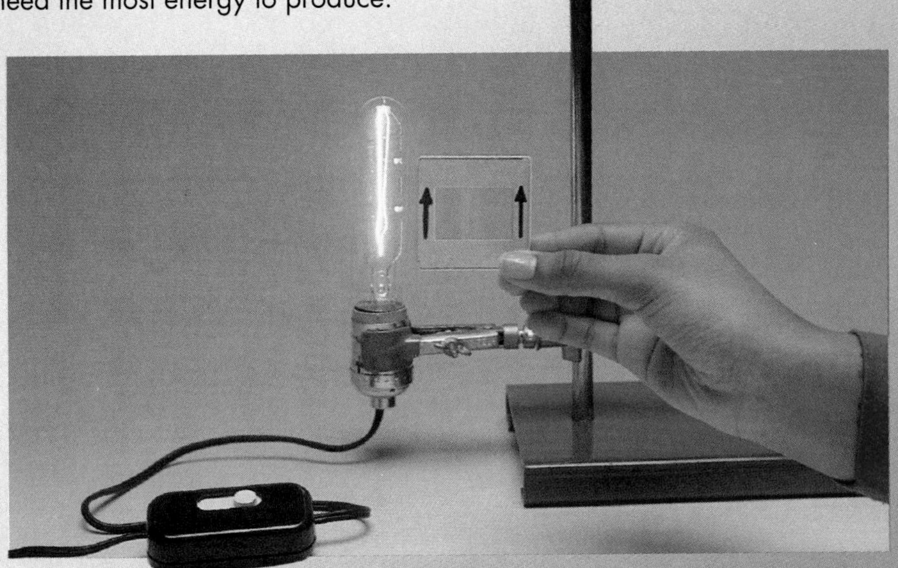

19-3 Battle of the Bulbs

New Science Words

incandescent light
fluorescent light

Objectives

- **Explain how incandescent and fluorescent bulbs work.**
- **Analyze the advantages and disadvantages of different light sources.**

Do Light Bulbs Make a Difference?

Are you using light from a light bulb to illuminate this page as you read it? Have you ever thought about what actually produces this light?

If you touch a light bulb after it has been on for a while, it may feel hot. If it feels hot, it is an incandescent light. **Incandescent light** is produced by heat. If you look into an incandescent light bulb, you will see a thin wire called a filament. It is usually made of the element tungsten. When you turn on the light, electricity flows through the filament. The filament heats up. When it gets hot, tungsten gives off visible light. Over half of the energy given off by incandescent bulbs is heat.

Fluorescent lighting is an alternative to incandescent lighting. A fluorescent bulb is filled with gas at a low pressure. The inner side of the bulb is coated with phosphors, fluorescent materials that give off visible light when they absorb ultraviolet light. When the electricity is turned on, electrons collide with the gas molecules to make them give off ultraviolet radiation. You can't see the ultraviolet light, but the phosphors absorb the ultraviolet radiation and glow to give off visible light that you can see.

A **fluorescent light** produces light without excessive loss of energy due to heat. These bulbs use as little as one-fifth the energy of ordinary incandescent bulbs. This energy difference can save you from $25 to $60 over the life of the fluorescent bulb.

The electricity used by a light bulb has been generated at a power plant. Whenever you turn on a light at home or at school, the electric company measures the amount of energy that the light bulb uses while it is on. The electric company then charges a fee for the energy that is used. By turning a light off when you leave a room, you are saving money as well as electricity.

About 20 percent of all electricity consumed in the United States is used for lighting. A great deal of this energy is wasted by lighting unoccupied rooms and using inefficient lighting sources. How efficient is the lighting in your home? You can find out.

SECTION REVIEW

1. Explain how light is produced in an ordinary incandescent bulb.
2. What are the advantages and disadvantages of using a fluorescent bulb instead of an incandescent bulb?

You Decide!

You are at the store to purchase a new study lamp. The fluorescent and incandescent lamps cost about the same, but the fluorescent bulb costs about ten times as much as the incandescent bulb. The fluorescent bulb is also guaranteed to last ten times longer than the incandescent bulb. Which would you buy? Explain your reasoning.

19-4 Wave Properties of Light

New Science Words

reflection
refraction
diffraction
diffraction grating

Objectives

- State and give an example of the law of reflection.
- Explain how refraction is used to separate the colors of the spectrum in white light.
- Describe how diffraction and interference patterns demonstrate the wave behavior of light.

Reflection

Just before you left for school this morning you might have glanced in a mirror one last time to make sure you looked okay. In order for you to see your reflection in the mirror, light had to reflect off you, hit the mirror, and be reflected off the mirror into your eye. **Reflection** occurs when a wave strikes an object and bounces off.

Reflection occurs with all types of waves: electromagnetic waves, sound waves, and water waves. Look at the water wave striking a barrier in Figure 19-14. The waves striking the barrier are called incident waves. The waves that bounce off the barrier are called reflected waves.

Notice that in Figure 19-14 a line is drawn perpendicular to the surface of the barrier. This line is called the *normal.* The angle formed by the incident wave and the normal is the angle of incidence, labeled *i.* The angle formed by the reflected wave and the normal is the angle of reflection, labeled *r.* Any reflected light, whether it is reflected from a mirror, a piece of foil, or the moon, follows the law of reflection. The law of reflection states that the angle of incidence is equal to the angle of reflection.

If you took a smooth piece of aluminum foil and looked into it, you would see a slightly distorted image of yourself. What if you crumpled up the foil and then unfolded it again? What would you see? The creases in the foil have created an uneven surface. Could you draw lines normal to every surface? These lines would go in many different

Figure 19-13. You can't see a clear image reflected from an uneven surface such as this one.

EcoTip

Turn out lights in your home when they are not needed. Exchange 100 watt bulbs with 60 watt bulbs to save energy.

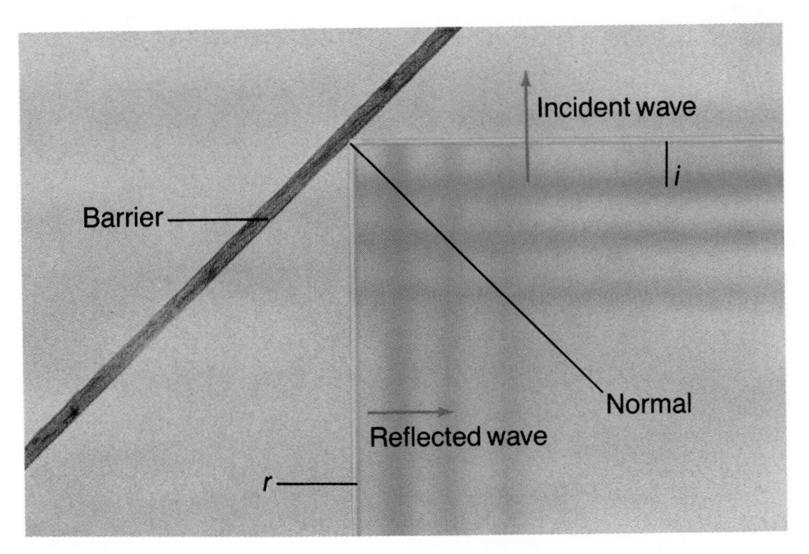

Figure 19-14. The water waves striking the barrier are incident waves and those bouncing off are reflected waves.

directions. You can't see an image of yourself because the reflected light, like the normal lines, is also scattered in different directions. Smooth surfaces reflect light in one direction, but rough surfaces scatter light in many directions.

Refraction

Stick your finger at an angle halfway into a glass of water and look at it through the side of the glass. Do you notice anything bizarre? Your finger appears to be bent or even split into two pieces once it enters the water. This happens because light waves bend when they move from air to water. They bend because the speed of light changes when light waves move from one medium to another.

Refraction is the bending of waves caused by a change in their speed. The amount of bending that occurs depends on the speed of light in both materials. The greater the difference between the speeds of light in two mediums, the more the light is bent as it passes at an angle from one medium to another. When light is passing into a material that will slow it down, the light is refracted (bent) toward an imaginary line drawn perpendicular to the surface of the medium. This imaginary line is called the normal. When light passes into a material in which light travels faster, it will be refracted (bent) away from the normal.

Figure 19-15. The ruler looks bent because of the refraction of the light waves as they change speed when they pass from the water to the air.

The amount of refraction also depends on the wavelength of the light. In the visible spectrum, the wavelengths of light vary from the longer red waves to

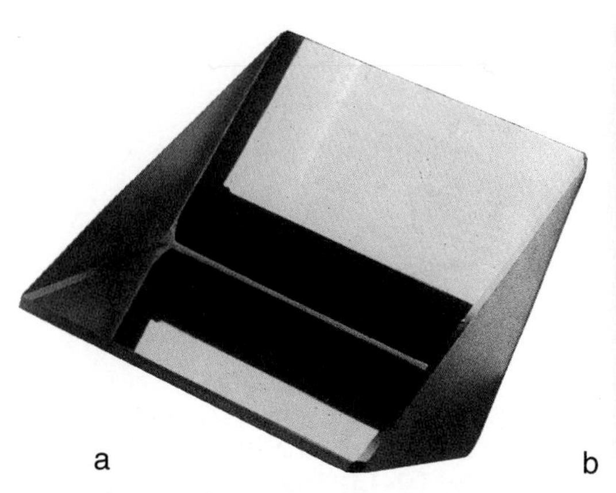

a

b

Figure 19-16. A prism is an angular transparent object (a). White light is refracted into the colors of the visible spectrum as it passes through a prism (b).

the shorter violet waves. Figure 19-16 shows what happens when white light passes through a prism. The triangular prism refracts the light twice, once when it enters the prism and again when it leaves the prism and reenters the air. Because the shorter wavelengths of light are refracted more than the longer wavelengths, violet light is bent the most. Which color of light would you expect to bend the least? As a result of this varied refraction, the different colors are separated as they emerge from the prism.

Does the light leaving a prism remind you of a rainbow? If the sun shines during a rain shower, you might see a rainbow. Like prisms, rain droplets also refract light. The refraction of the different wavelengths can cause white light from the sun to separate into the individual colors of the visible light spectrum. Isaac Newton recognized that white light actually includes all of the seven colors of the rainbow. In order of decreasing wavelength, the colors you should see in the rainbow are red, orange, yellow, green, blue, indigo, and violet—the same order as the colors of the electromagnetic spectrum. Have you noticed that the reddish colors are always on top and the bluish colors are always on the bottom of a rainbow? Can you explain why this is so?

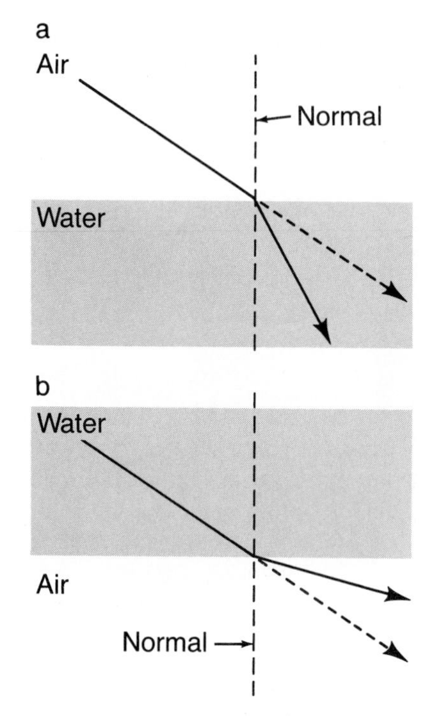

Figure 19-17. Light slows down and refracts toward the normal as it passes into a more dense medium (a), and light speeds up and bends away from the normal as it passes into a less dense medium (b).

Diffraction and Interference

Have you heard bells or music played by vendors selling ice cream as they drive their trucks through your neighborhood? Or maybe you have heard cars drive by your home with blasting stereos. You can hear these sounds even when buildings or hills separate you from

Figure 19-18. Water waves diffract around a barrier.

the sound. This happens because sound waves can bend around corners to reach you. **Diffraction** is the bending of waves around a barrier. In the 1600s, an Italian physicist, Francesco Grimaldi, observed light and dark areas on the edge of a shadow. If you observe the shadow formed when light passes through an open door, you'll notice no clearly defined boundary between light and dark. Instead, you will see a gradual transition. Grimaldi explained this phenomenon by suggesting that light could be bent around the edges of barriers.

What waves can be diffracted?

Electromagnetic waves, sound waves, and water waves can all be diffracted. You can see water waves bend around you as you swim. The pattern of the waves changes as the waves are diffracted. Diffraction is important in the transfer of radio waves. Longer wavelengths, such as those used by AM radio stations, are easier to diffract than short FM waves. That is why AM reception is often better than FM reception around tall buildings and hills.

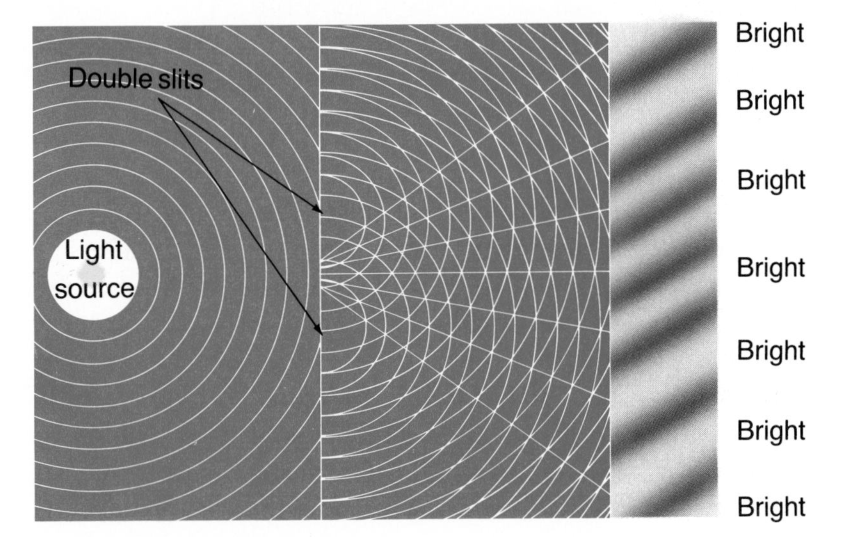

Figure 19-19. Wave interference demonstrates how light behaves like waves.

TECHNOLOGY

Holograms—The Key to 3-D

A hologram is a vivid three-dimensional image that appears to float in space. As you walk around a hologram you see the image from a slightly different angle.

Holograms are produced by illuminating the object you wish to make an image of with light from a laser. Laser light reflected from the object shines on photographic film simultaneously with light from a second laser of the same wavelength. The pattern created on the photographic film produces a hologram image when laser light shines through it.

A hologram conveys more information to your eye than a conventional two-dimensional photograph by controlling both the intensity and direction of the light that departs from the image. As a result, these vivid three-dimensional objects are very difficult to copy. For this reason, holographic images are used on credit cards and on the labels of some clothing to help prevent counterfeiting. Scientists are working on ways of displaying computer information on a three-dimensional screen. How would you like to play video games in 3-D?

Think Critically: What are some situations where a three-dimensional image or display would be a significant advantage over a two-dimensional image?

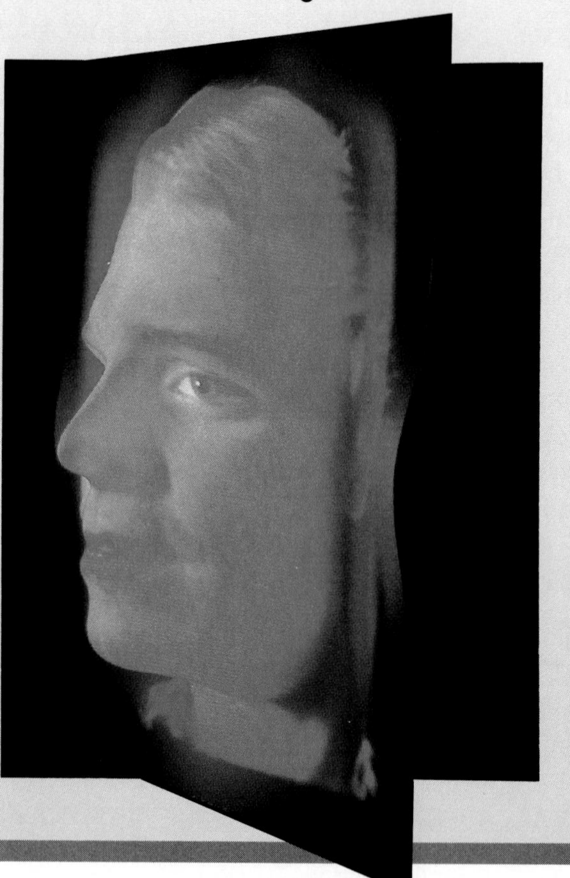

Recall from Section 18-4 that sound waves can interfere with each other to form constructive and destructive interference. In the early 1800s, Thomas Young, an English scientist, expanded the diffraction theory Grimaldi had developed. In a famous experiment, he passed light of a uniform wavelength through a narrow slit. The new diffraction pattern of the light waves then passed through a barrier with two slits. You can see the results, wave interference, in Figure 19-19. The wave crests are shown by the semicircles. The light from these slits was projected on a screen. Young observed light bands where two crests or two troughs combined, and dark areas where a crest and a trough crossed paths. This experiment shows how light behaves as a wave. Only waves have interference; particles do not.

You know that one way to separate colors of white light is by refraction in a prism. Colors can also be separated by interference using many slits. A **diffraction grating** is a piece of glass or plastic made up of many parallel slits. Diffraction gratings commonly have as many as 12 000 slits per centimeter. When white light shines through a diffraction grating, the colors are separated by the interference pattern. Reflective materials can be ruled with closely spaced grooves to produce diffraction patterns. For example, shiny bumper stickers sometimes diffract light into a wide array of colors. You can also see the dazzling results of simple diffraction gratings by looking at the reflection of light provided from the grooves in a compact disc.

Recall that throughout this chapter, we have referred to light as both waves and particles. That is because, as you have read in this lesson, light demonstrates properties of both waves and particles. Do you recall the wave properties of light? What properties of light support the particle theory?

Figure 19-20. Compact discs can produce diffraction patterns.

SECTION REVIEW

1. Explain the law of reflection.
2. When light moves from air into glass at an angle, is the light refracted toward or away from the normal?
3. Explain how you could use a prism to separate the colors of the spectrum from white light.
4. **Apply:** Scientists say that light has both particle and wave properties. Explain why observations of diffraction and interference patterns conflict with the idea that light consists of particles.

Observing and Inferring

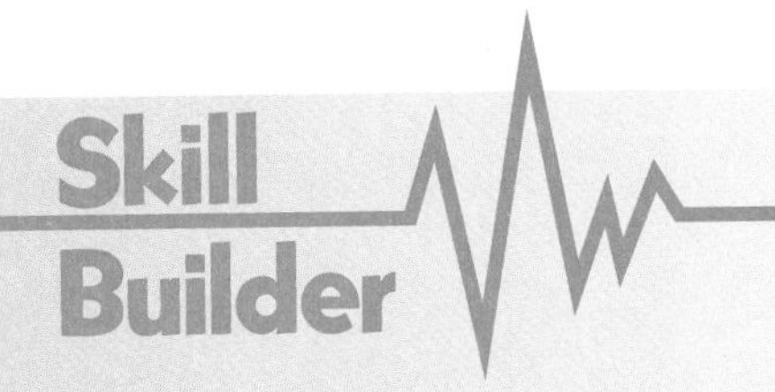

Imagine you are at the ocean shore and see waves moving toward you from behind a cliff. Waves are leaving the cliff at a slightly different angle than that of their approach. What would you infer is happening? If you need help, refer to Observing and Inferring in the **Skill Handbook** on page 678.

ACTIVITY 19-2
Refraction and Reflection

Problem: *How do light rays refract and reflect?*

Materials  

- light source
- pencil
- plastic box
- water
- notebook paper
- clay

Procedure

1. Fill the plastic box with water and place it on a sheet of notebook paper.
2. Outline the box on the paper.
3. Stand the pencil on end in the clay and place it on the paper in front of the box.
4. Place the lamp in an upright position near the paper and turn it on.
5. Adjust the position of the paper and the pencil so the pencil's shadow on the paper goes completely through the box.
6. Draw lines on the shadow where it enters and leaves the box. Draw a line on the shadow that reflects from the surface of the box.
7. Move the box. Connect the lines to show the shadow through the box.

Analyze

1. Draw a reference line (normal) at right angles to the box from the point where the shadow touches its surface. As the shadow enters the box, does it refract toward the reference line or away from it? What happens when the shadow leaves the other side of the box?
2. Alter the xperiment by changing the angle between the reference line and the shadow. What happens to the reflected and refracted shadows?

Conclude and Apply

3. Compare the angles of reflection and refraction for light striking the flat surface of water.
4. Would the angles of reflection or refraction change in Question 3 if the surface of the water was curved? Explain your answer.

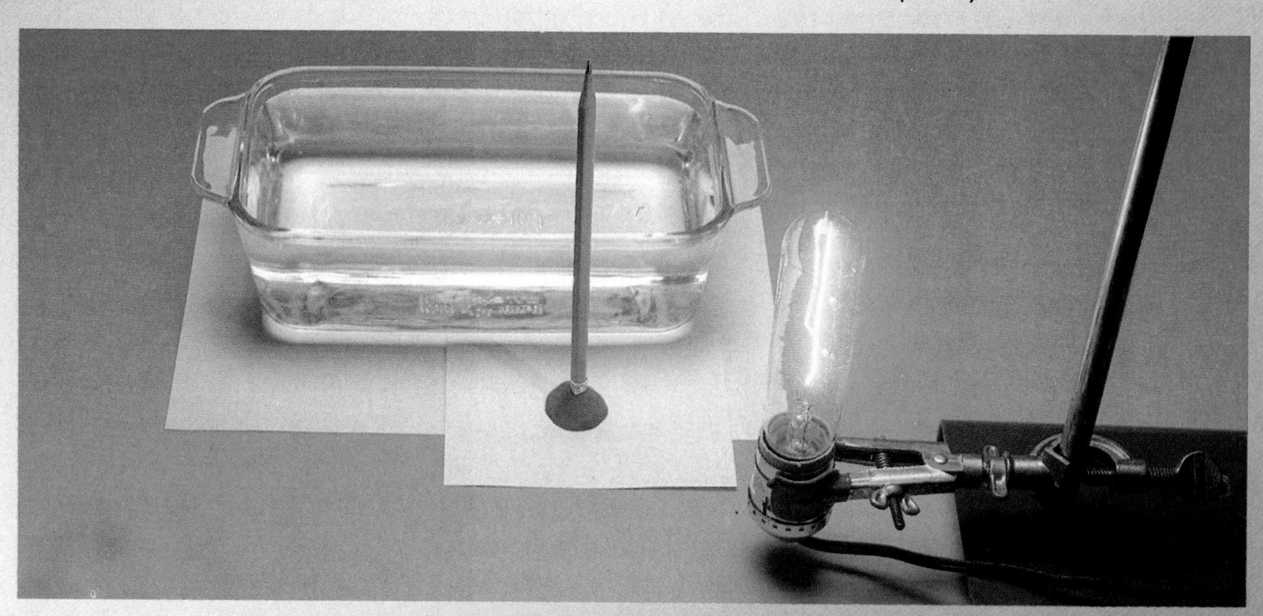

CHAPTER

REVIEW

SUMMARY

19-1: Electromagnetic Radiation

1. Electromagnetic waves differ from other types of waves because they do not need a medium to transfer energy.
2. Electromagnetic waves are arranged on the electromagnetic spectrum in order of decreasing wavelengths.
3. Radio waves and microwaves are used in communications. Infrared radiation is used to detect tumors. Visible light is produced by light bulbs for illumination. Ultraviolet radiation causes fluorescent bulbs to glow. X rays are used for medical diagnosis. Gamma rays can be used to destroy cancer cells.

19-2: Light and Color

1. You can't see through opaque materials. You can see clearly through transparent materials. You can't see clearly through translucent materials.
2. You see color when light is reflected off objects and into your eye. Inside your eyes color cones respond to certain wavelengths.
3. Colored light can be made by mixing the three primary colors of light. Pigment colors can be made by mixing the three primary pigments.

19-3: Science and Society: Battle of the Bulbs

1. Incandescent bulbs produce light by heat. Fluorescent bulbs give off light when ultraviolet radiation produced inside the bulb causes a fluorescent coating inside the bulb to glow.
2. Although expensive to purchase, fluorescent bulbs waste less energy, last longer, and cost much less to use than incandescent bulbs.

19-4: Wave Properties of Light

1. The law of reflection states that the angle of incidence is equal to the angle of reflection.
2. White light can be separated into the colors of the visible spectrum because each wavelength refracts at a different angle as it passes into a medium.
3. Diffraction and interference patterns demonstrate wave patterns of light by showing that the waves bend around a barrier, and that they have crests and troughs.

KEY SCIENCE WORDS

a. **diffraction**
b. **diffraction grating**
c. **electromagnetic spectrum**
d. **fluorescent light**
e. **gamma rays**
f. **incandescent light**
g. **infrared radiation**
h. **microwaves**
i. **modulation**
j. **opaque materials**
k. **photons**
l. **radiation**
m. **radio waves**
n. **reflection**
o. **refraction**
p. **translucent materials**
q. **transparent materials**
s. **visible radiation**
t. **X rays**

UNDERSTANDING VOCABULARY

Match each phrase with the correct term from the list of Key Science Words.

1. energy transfer by electromagnetic waves
2. bundles of radiation with no mass
3. electromagnetic radiation that is felt as heat
4. objects that can't be seen through
5. light produced by heat
6. occurs when a wave strikes an object and then bounces off
7. the bending of waves around a barrier
8. contains many parallel slits that can separate white light into colors
9. highest frequency electromagnetic waves
10. radio waves with the greatest energy

CHAPTER

REVIEW

CHECKING CONCEPTS

Choose the word or phrase that completes the sentence.

1. Electromagnetic waves are different from other types of waves in that they do not ______.
   a. have amplitude **c.** transfer energy
   b. have frequency **d.** need a medium
2. When radiation passes through matter, it ____.
   a. slows down
   b. speeds up
   c. travels at 300 000 km/sec
   d. stops
3. A contact lens is ______.
   a. transparent **c.** opaque
   b. translucent **d.** all of these
4. Electromagnetic waves with the longest wavelengths are ______.
   a. radio waves **c.** X rays
   b. visible light **d.** gamma rays
5. The process of changing the frequency or amplitude of radio waves in order to send a signal is ______.
   a. diffraction **c.** reflection
   b. modulation **d.** refraction
6. When food molecules absorb microwaves, they vibrate faster and their ______.
   a. kinetic energy decreases
   b. kinetic energy increases
   c. temperature decreases
   d. temperature remains constant
7. Your body gives off ______.
   a. radio waves **c.** infrared radiation
   b. visible light **d.** ultraviolet radiation
8. Fluorescence occurs when a material glows as it absorbs ______.
   a. microwaves **c.** infrared radiation
   b. gamma rays **d.** ultraviolet radiation
9. X rays are best absorbed by ______.
   a. bone **c.** muscle
   b. hair **d.** skin
10. Objects that partially scatter light that passes through them are called ______.
    a. reflective **c.** translucent
    b. opaque **d.** transparent

UNDERSTANDING CONCEPTS

Complete each sentence.

11. An object that absorbs all colors of light appears ______.
12. An ______ filter transmits blue light.
13. Fluorescent lights are more efficient than incandescent lights because they lose less energy as ______.
14. The angle of incidence of a wave is ______ its angle of reflection.
15. When light travels into a medium in which its speed _____, it will be bent from the normal.

THINK AND WRITE CRITICALLY

16. Explain how sound waves are converted to radio waves. Give some examples of uses of this process.
17. What is the difference between light color and pigment color?

18. How is the reflection of light off a white wall similar to the reflection of light off a mirror? How is it different?
19. Explain how a rainbow is produced.
20. Describe the evidence that light behaves both as a wave and a particle and note the scientists who studied both behaviors.

APPLY

21. Heated objects often give off light of a particular color. Explain why an object that glows blue is hotter than one that glows red.
22. How would a blue shirt appear if a blue filter were placed in front of it? A red filter? A green filter?
23. What color cones in your eye would transmit signals to your brain as you looked at the purple shirt through each of the three filters described in Question 22?
24. Which color of visible light slows down the most when it passes through a prism? Explain.
25. Explain why you can hear a fire engine coming around a street corner but cannot see it.

MORE SKILL BUILDERS

If you need help, refer to the Skill Handbook.

1. **Sequencing:** List the types of radiation in the electromagnetic spectrum in order of decreasing penetrating power. Use Figure 19-2, the electromagnetic spectrum, as a reference.
2. **Making and Using Tables:** Construct a table to show the applications of each type of electromagnetic wave. Which type would an electronics engineer be most interested in? A doctor?
3. **Observing and Inferring:** Most mammals, such as dogs and cats, can't see colors. Infer how a cat's eye might be different from your eye.
4. **Concept Mapping:** Use the blank concept map below to show the five steps in the production of fluorescent light.

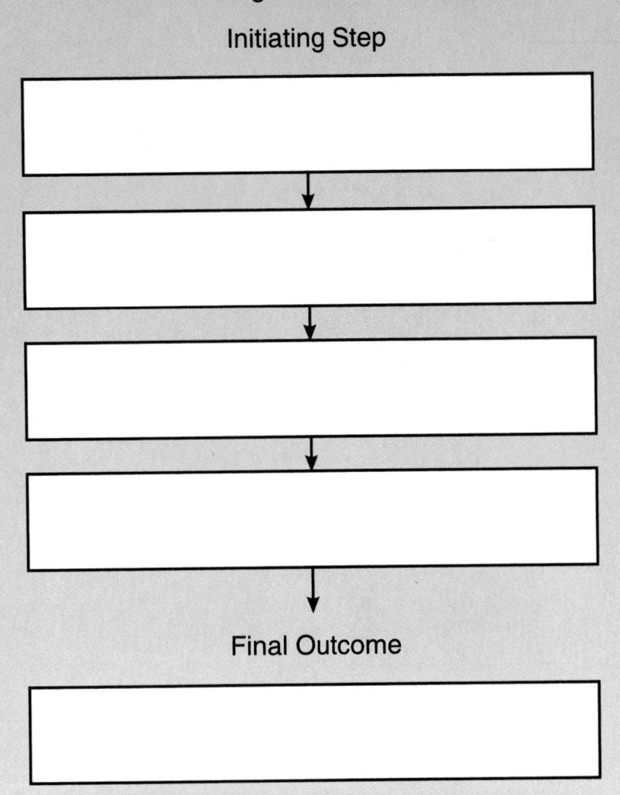

5. **Outlining:** Make an outline of Section 19-1. Be sure to include the types of energy on the electromagnetic spectrum and give one example of how each type of energy is used.

PROJECTS

1. Make a scrapbook of newspaper and magazine articles describing the dangers of ultraviolet radiation and the damage they cause to Earth's ozone layer. Write a short summary of each article.
2. Make a poster to show how the three primary pigments are combined to produce common colors such as blue, red, yellow, green, purple, brown, and black.

CHAPTER

20 Mirrors and Lenses

Have you ever seen a magnified or distorted reflection of yourself? What kinds of objects cause this reflection?

FIND OUT!

Do the following activity to find out how light reflecting off surfaces of different shapes can produce different images.

Obtain a flat mirror and a shiny metal spoon. First look at your reflection in the flat mirror. What do you see? Is the reflection the same size as your face? Is it right side up? Now look at your image in the back of the spoon. Move the spoon close to your face and then far away. How does the image change? Turn the spoon over and look into the inside of the spoon. Move it back and forth. How do the images produced by these three shiny surfaces differ?

Gearing Up

Previewing the Chapter

Use this outline to help you focus on important ideas in this chapter.

Section 20-1 The Optics of Mirrors
- ▶ Plane Mirrors
- ▶ Concave Mirrors
- ▶ Convex Mirrors

Section 20-2 The Optics of Lenses
- ▶ Convex Lenses
- ▶ Concave Lenses
- ▶ Lenses and Vision

Section 20-3 Optical Instruments
- ▶ Telescopes
- ▶ Microscopes
- ▶ Cameras

Section 20-4 Science and Society
The Hubble Space Telescope
- ▶ Is It Worth It?

Section 20-5 Applications of Light
- ▶ Polarized Light
- ▶ Lasers
- ▶ Optical Fibers

Previewing Science Skills

- ▶ In the **Skill Builders,** you will recognize cause and effect, make a concept map, hypothesize, and sequence.
- ▶ In the **Activities,** you will observe, measure, predict, and infer.
- ▶ In the **MINI-Labs,** you will hypothesize, infer, and measure.

What's next?

You've seen how your reflection can change, depending on the shape and distance of the mirror you are looking into. As you read the next section, you'll find out how images are formed in three types of mirrors.

20-1 The Optics of Mirrors

New Science Words

plane mirror
virtual image
concave mirror
focal point
focal length
real image
convex mirror

Objectives

- Explain how an image is formed in two types of mirrors.
- Identify examples and uses of plane, concave, and convex mirrors.

Plane Mirrors

Recall the wave properties of light from Chapter 19—reflection, refraction, and diffraction. In this chapter, you will examine the properties of reflection and refraction more closely. First, you will read about how mirrors reflect light and lenses refract light to form images. Next you will study some of the practical applications of these concepts.

Now, close your eyes and picture your own face. You know what you look like because you have seen your reflection. In what objects have you seen your reflection? The most obvious answer is a mirror, but you probably have seen your reflection in objects such as windows and pieces of aluminum foil also. Any smooth object that reflects light to form an image is a mirror.

You are probably used to seeing your image in a **plane mirror,** one with a flat surface. What happens if you stand in front of the mirror and snap your fingers on your right hand? Your reflection seems to snap its left fingers because the left and right sides of the image appear to be reversed. Notice your reflection is also upright and the same size as you. Figure 20-1 shows how your image is formed by a plane mirror. The mirror is a piece of glass with a reflective coating on the front or the back. Light is reflected off of you toward the mirror. Then, the light rays are reflected by the mirror back to your eyes.

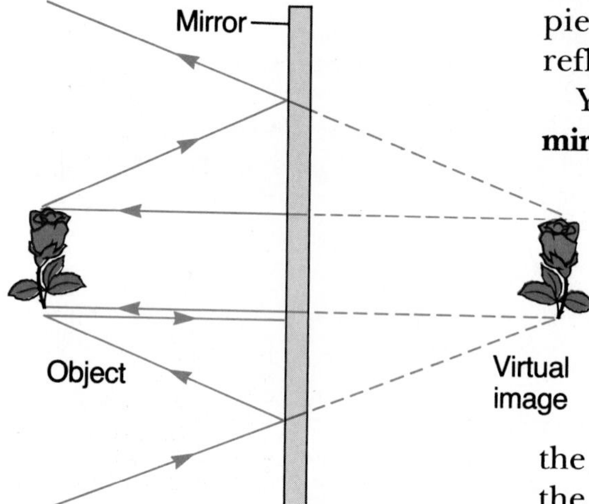

Figure 20-1. A plane mirror forms an upright, virtual image.

Your image appears to be behind the mirror because you perceive that the light forming the image is coming from somewhere beyond the mirror. Figure 20-1 shows how rays reflected from a plane mirror appear to form an image. Remember, reflected light rays do not exist *behind* the mirror because the mirror is opaque. The image you see in a plane mirror is called a virtual image. A **virtual image** is an image in which no light rays pass through the image. The virtual image formed by a plane mirror is erect and appears as far behind the mirror as the object is in front of it.

When can a virtual image be seen?

Concave Mirrors

Mirrors are not always flat. If the surface of a mirror is curved inward, like the inside of a spoon, it is a **concave mirror.** Look for your reflection in the bowl of a shiny spoon. Concave mirrors form images differently than plane mirrors do. The way an image is formed depends on the position of the object in front of the mirror. Figure 20-2 shows one way an image can be formed in a concave mirror. The straight line drawn through the center of the mirror is the optical axis. Light rays parallel to the optical axis approaching a concave mirror are all reflected to pass through one point on the optical axis, called the **focal point.** The distance from the center of the mirror to the focal point is called the **focal length.**

Suppose that the distance from the object to the mirror is a little greater than the focal length, as in Figure 20-2. Then, you can locate the image by following two rays. One ray is drawn through the focal point to the mirror. All rays that pass through the focal point on the way to the mirror are reflected parallel to the optical axis. From the same point on the object, a second ray is drawn parallel to the optical axis. This ray is reflected through the focal point. Find the point where these two reflected rays meet. This image is enlarged and upside down. Because

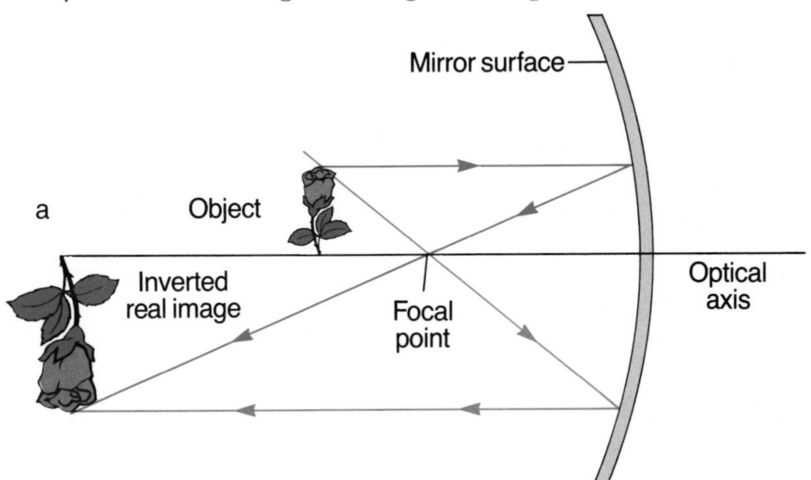

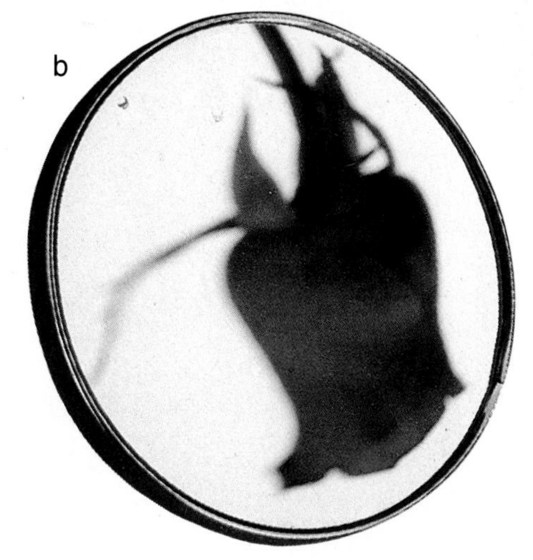

Figure 20-2. When the distance from the object to the concave mirror is a little greater than the focal length (a), you see an enlarged, inverted, real image (b).

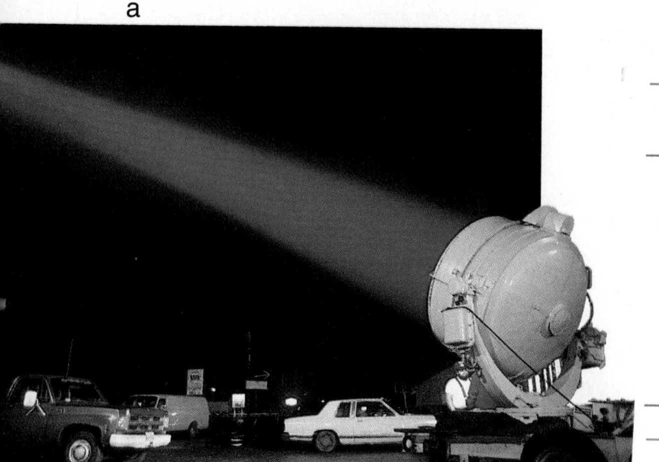

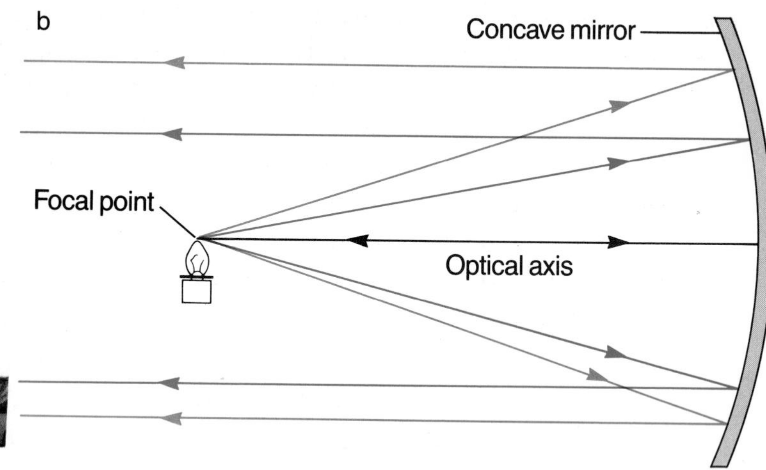

Figure 20-3. A beam of light forms (a) when a light is placed at the focal point of a concave mirror (b).

the light rays actually converge at this point in front of the mirror, you could hold a screen there and see the inverted, or **real image.**

What if you placed an object at the focal point of the concave mirror? Figure 20-3 shows that if the object is at the focal point, all light rays are reflected parallel to the optical axis. No image can be seen because the rays do not converge. However, a light placed at the focal point can be reflected in a beam. In devices such as car headlights, flashlights, and spotlights, the light bulb is placed at the focal point of a concave mirror to create a concentrated light beam of nearly parallel light rays. The light isn't exactly parallel because not all of the light bulb can be exactly at the focal point.

You may own a hand mirror that magnifies reflections. This, like the inside of the shiny spoon, is a concave mirror also. When you hold the mirror close to your face, your face is between the focal point and the mirror. Again,

Figure 20-4. The image of the rosebud is magnified (a) when the rosebud is placed between the focal point and the surface of a concave mirror (b).

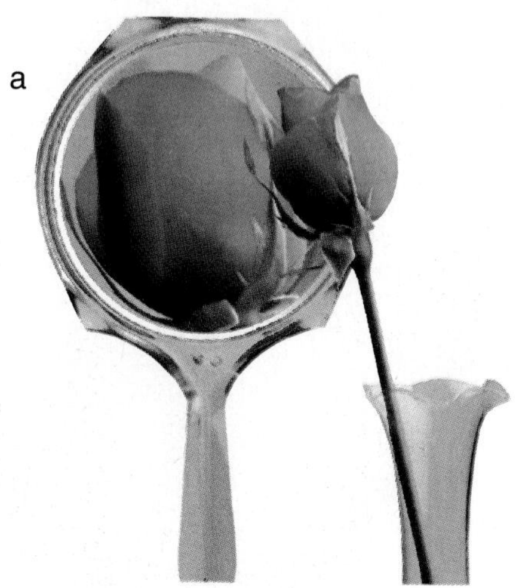

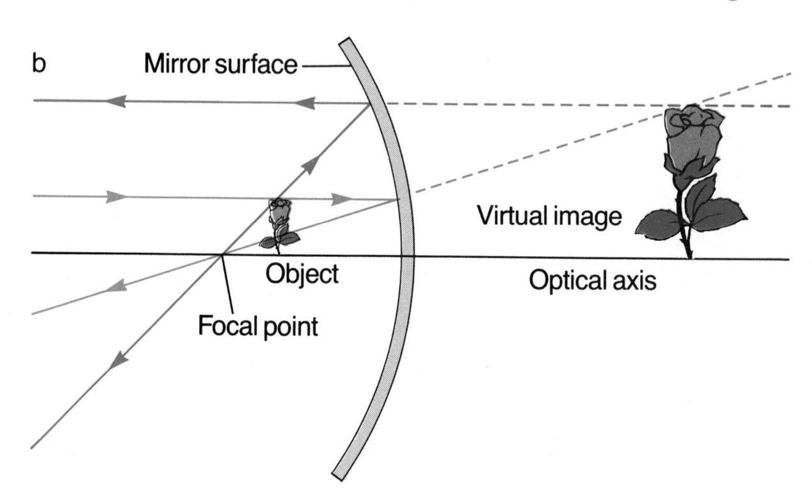

two rays leave the object from the same point. One ray is drawn toward the mirror as if it had come through the focal point. It is reflected parallel to the optical axis. The second ray leaves the object parallel to the optical axis and reflects through the focal point. These rays never meet to form a real image. Instead, they appear to come from a single point behind the mirror. Rays from various points on the object form a virtual image that appears upright, enlarged, and behind the mirror.

Convex Mirrors

Have you ever seen a large mirror mounted above the aisles in a store? This type of mirror that curves outward is called a **convex mirror.** No matter where the object is, the convex mirror diverges, or spreads the rays. Figure 20-5 shows how convex mirrors produce an image. The reflected rays never meet, so the image is always virtual. The image is upright and smaller than the actual object.

What kind of image does a convex mirror form?

Because convex mirrors spread out the reflected light, they allow large areas to be viewed. In addition to increasing the field of view in places like grocery stores and factories, convex mirrors can widen the view of traffic that can be seen in rear or side-view mirrors of automobiles. Your perception of distance can be distorted, however, because objects are always closer than they appear in a convex mirror.

So far, you have read about three ways that light can be reflected and form images. Can you recall the three types of mirrors and describe the image that each mirror produces? In Section 20-2, you will find out the ways in which light can be refracted to form images.

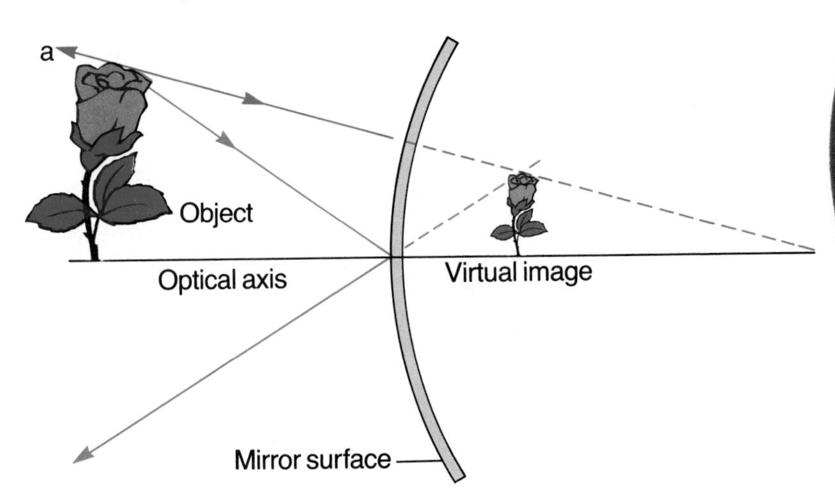

Figure 20-5. A convex mirror diverges reflected rays (a) to form a virtual image that is always upright and smaller than the object (b).

PROBLEM SOLVING

Mirrors on the New Car

Joel and his father visited car dealerships for two weeks looking for a new car. They finally found one that had the features they both wanted.

When they went to pick up the new car, Joel's father disappeared with the salesman to complete the paperwork.

Joel decided to give the new car a quick once-over while he was waiting. He noticed that the mirror on the passenger side of the car was stamped with a warning stating "OBJECTS IN MIRROR ARE CLOSER THAN THEY APPEAR." He thought that was strange and looked at the driver's side mirror. It didn't have the warning. Joel compared his image in both mirrors and decided that the mirror on the driver's side was a plane mirror and the mirror on the passenger side was a convex mirror. Describe the images Joel saw in the two mirrors.

Think Critically: Explain why convex mirrors are sometimes used as outside rear view mirrors on cars. Why are they stamped with a warning?

SECTION REVIEW

1. Describe the image formed by a concave mirror when the object is beyond the focal point.
2. What are convex mirrors used for? Explain.
3. Contrast the differences between the surfaces of plane, concave, and convex mirrors.
4. **Apply:** If you were going to use a mirror to gather the light entering a telescope, what kind of mirror would you use to focus it? Explain.

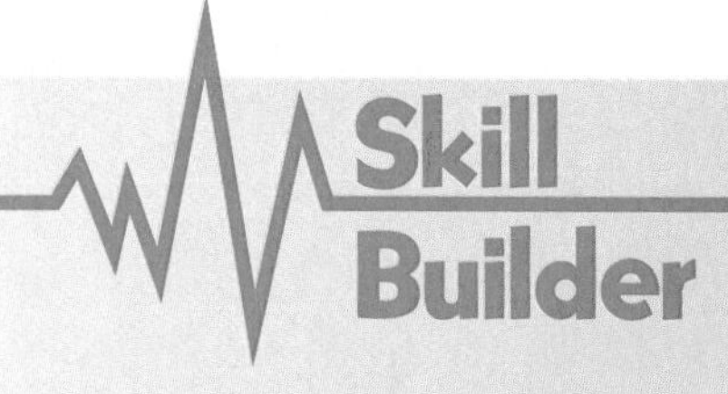

Recognizing Cause and Effect

Suppose you drop a flashlight that has a concave mirror in it. When you turn the flashlight on, you notice the light is less intense than it was before you dropped it. What may have happened? If you need help, refer to Recognizing Cause and Effect in the **Skill Handbook** on page 679.

ACTIVITY 20-1
Reflections of Reflections

Problem: *How do plane mirrors make images?*

Materials   

- 2 plane mirrors
- cellophane tape
- masking tape
- protractor
- paper clip
- light source

Procedure

1. Lay the two mirrors side by side and tape them together so they will open and close. Label them *R* and *L* as shown.
2. Place the mirrors on a sheet of paper and using the protractor, close the mirrors to an angle of 72°. Mark the position of the *R* mirror on the paper.
3. Bend one leg of a paper clip up 90° and place it close to the front of the *R* mirror.
4. Count the number of paper-clip *R* and *L* images you see in the mirrors. Don't move the clip.
5. Count the images as you slowly open the mirrors to 90° and then to 120°.
6. Place the light behind the paper clip to form a shadow that extends from the surface of the *R* mirror to the *L* mirror. Look into each mirror along the paths of the reflected shadows.
7. Make a data table to record the number of images you can see when the mirrors are at 72°, 90°, and 120°.

Data and Observations

Angle of Mirrors	Number of Paper Clip Images	
	R	L
72°		
90°		
120°		

Analyze

1. How does the direction of the shadow help you predict where the image of the paper clip will seem to be?
2. How is the number of paper-clip images affected by increasing the angle between the mirrors in Step 5?

Conclude and Apply

3. Considering that there are 360° in a circle, into how many "wedges" of space does each of the angles divide the circle?
4. What angle would divide space into six segments? How many images do you think would be produced by it?
5. Which is the best predictor of paper-clip images, numbers of mirror images, or numbers of space segments?

20-2 The Optics of Lenses

New Science Words

convex lenses
concave lenses

Objectives

- Describe the types of images formed in convex and concave lenses.
- Cite examples of how these lenses are used.
- Explain how lenses are used to correct vision.

Did You Know?

The fastest camera, built for laser research, registers images at the rate of 33 million per second.

Convex Lenses

Do you wear glasses or contact lenses? If so, you use lenses to improve your ability to see. Like curved mirrors, lenses are described as convex or concave, depending on their shape.

Convex lenses are thicker in the middle than at the edges. Light rays approaching the lens parallel to the optical axis are refracted toward the center of the lens. They converge at the focal point, so they are capable of forming real images that can be projected on a screen.

The amount of refraction depends on the change in the speed of light as it passes through a material, and the amount of refraction also depends on the shape of the object. Thick lenses with very curved surfaces bend light a great deal more than thin ones with less curved surfaces. The focal length of the thick convex lens in Figure 20-6

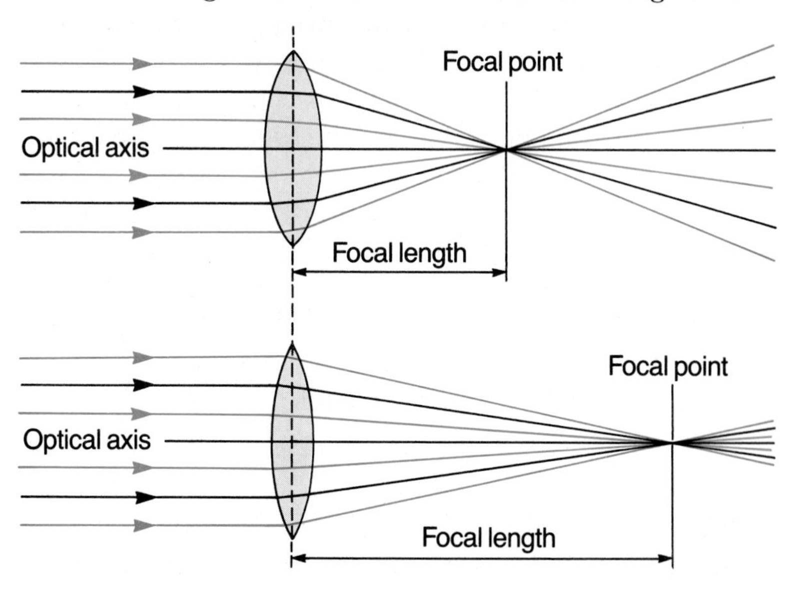

Figure 20-6. A thick convex lens bends light more than a thin convex lens. Notice that the focal length is shorter for the thick lens.

is shorter than that of the thin convex lens. Convex lenses are capable of producing many kinds of images, both real and virtual, upright, inverted, enlarged, or smaller. The type of image formed depends on the position of the object and the focal length of the lens.

Have you ever photographed a faraway object? If so, it's likely the object was more than two focal lengths from the lens. If you follow the light paths in Figure 20-7a, you'll notice that the real image is smaller than the object, and inverted. The lens in your eye forms images in the same way.

If an object is between one and two focal lengths from the lens, as in Figure 20-7c, the real image is inverted and larger than the object. This is the method used to project a movie from a small film to the large screen of the theater. Can you think of other examples in which producing a larger, inverted image is desired?

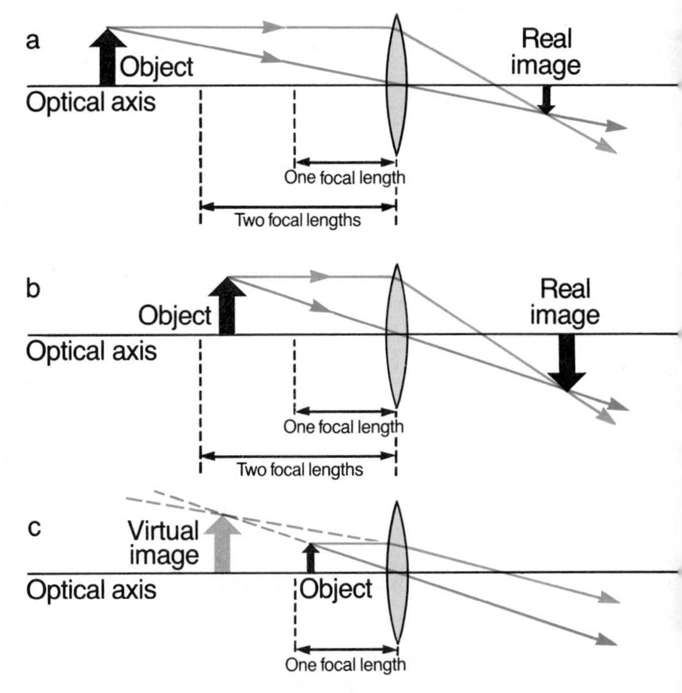

Figure 20-7. The image formed by a convex lens depends on the location of the object in relation to the focal length of the lens.

Have you ever used a magnifying glass to closely examine an object? A magnifying glass is a convex lens, so you must hold it less than one focal length from the object. The light rays can't converge and an enlarged and upright virtual image is formed. Look at the position of the image in Figure 20-7c. Notice the object seems farther away than it really is.

Concave Lenses

Concave lenses are thinner in the middle and thicker at the edges. Light passing through a concave lens bends toward the edges. The rays diverge and never form a real image. The virtual image is upright and smaller than the actual object. The image formed by a concave lens is similar to the image produced by a convex mirror because they both diverge light to form virtual images.

Concave lenses are usually used in combination with other lenses. They can be used with convex lenses in telescopes and cameras to extend the focal length so you can see a clear image of a faraway object. Concave lenses are also used to correct nearsighted vision.

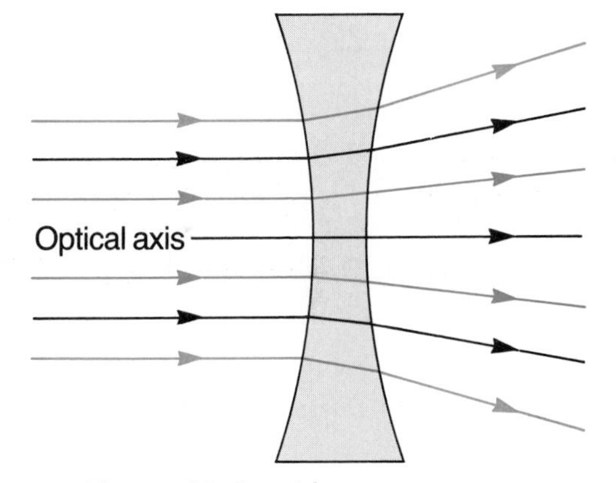

Figure 20-8. Light rays passing through a concave lens diverge and form a virtual image.

Lenses and Vision

What determines how well you can "see" the words on this page? Your ability to focus on these words depends

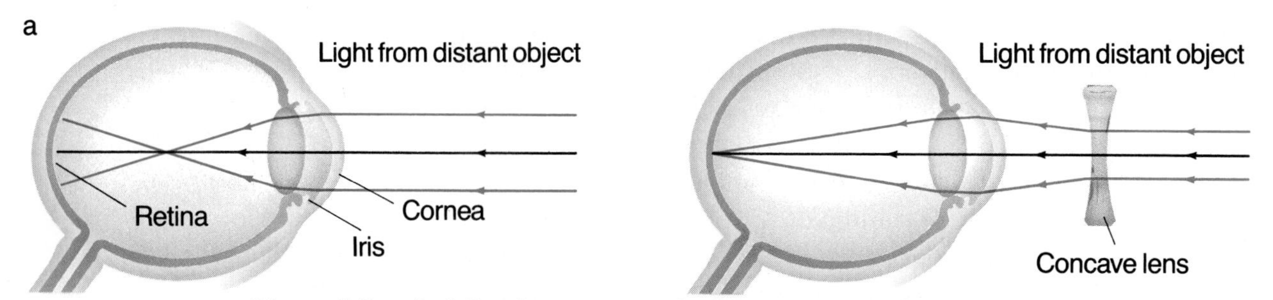

Nearsighted vision is corrected with a concave lens.

Farsighted vision is corrected with a convex lens.

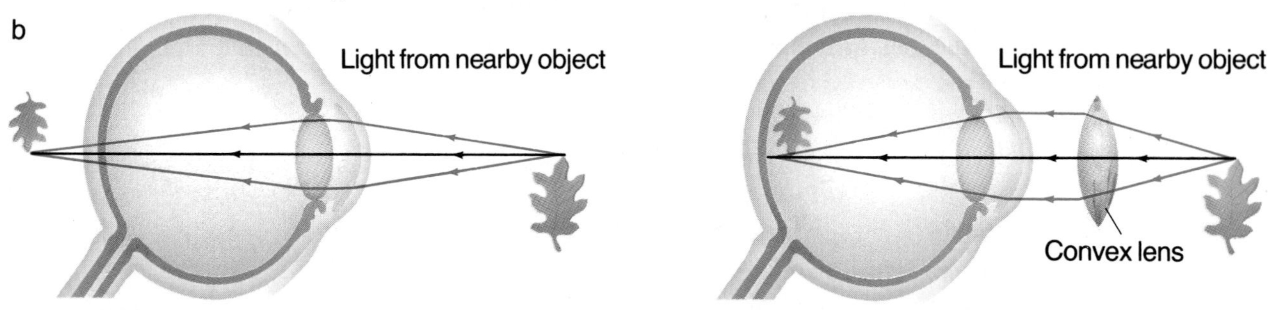

Figure 20-9. Some vision problems can easily be corrected with concave and convex lenses.

on the way your eye is designed. Light enters your eye through the transparent covering of your eye, the cornea. The light then passes through an opening called the pupil. The colored part of your eye, the iris, adjusts the pupil size to control how much light can pass through a convex lens behind the pupil. The light then converges to form an inverted image on your retina. The lens in your eye is soft; and flexible muscles in your eye can change its shape. When you look at a distant object, you need a longer focal length than that needed to look at nearby objects. Your eye muscles adjust your lens to a less convex shape. When you focus on a nearby object, the eye muscles will tighten to increase the curvature of the lens.

If you have healthy vision, you should be able to clearly see objects from a focal length of about 25 cm or more. Many people need their vision corrected with lenses to enjoy normal vision. To have normal vision, the image of an object should focus on the retina inside your eye. A nearsighted person has difficulty seeing distant objects clearly. The eyeball is too long or the cornea bulges out, causing the image to focus in front of the retina. Figure 20-9a illustrates how concave lenses correct this problem by diverging the light rays before they enter the eye.

Farsighted people can see faraway objects, but they can't focus clearly on nearby objects. Their eyeballs are

MINI-Lab

Can lenses be made of liquids?

Make a water-drop lens holder by cutting a round hole in the bottom of a plastic bowl. Make the hole about 2 cm across. Stretch a piece of plastic wrap over the hole and tape it in place. Put a drop of water on the plastic window and look at this print through the drop. Look at other small objects. What kind of lens does the drop form? How can your lens make two kinds of images?

either too short or their corneas are too flat. Their lenses aren't convex enough to converge the rays on the retina. As a result, the image is focused behind the retina. Figure 20-9b shows how this condition can be corrected if an additional convex lens is used.

Another vision problem is astigmatism. Blurry vision from astigmatism is caused when the surface of the cornea is curved unevenly. Corrective lenses for this condition have an uneven curvature as well.

There are currently several ways to correct poor vision caused by lens problems in the eye. Artificial lenses in the form of eyeglasses or contacts can be worn. These prescription lenses are shaped to refract light before it enters the eye, so that the light will focus on the retina. As a result, the wearer will see clear images. Contact lenses can actually be worn over the cornea. Another way to correct the lens in the eye is by using surgery. Eye surgeons often use lasers to reshape the cornea.

Can you recall what all lenses have in common? They all refract light that passes through them. Convex lenses refract light toward the center of the lens, and concave lenses refract light away from the center of the lens. As you read the next section, you'll see how these two kinds of lenses are used in cameras, microscopes, and telescopes.

EcoTip

Collect and videotape all the trash your school throws away in one day. Classify the trash as recyclable or non-recyclable. Show the video to your classmates.

What do all lenses have in common?

SECTION REVIEW

1. Distinguish between the characteristics of convex and concave lenses.
2. When using a slide projector, you put the slides in the projector upside down. Why must they be inserted this way?
3. What type of lens would you use to examine a tiny spider on your desk?
4. **Apply:** If you have difficulty reading the chalkboard from the back row, what is most likely your vision problem? How could it be corrected?

Concept Mapping

Mirrors and lenses are the simplest optical devices. Design a network tree concept map to show some uses for each shape of mirror and lens. If you need help, refer to Concept Mapping in the **Skill Handbook** on pages 684 and 685.

20-3 Optical Instruments

New Science Words

refracting telescope
reflecting telescope
microscope
wide-angle lenses
telephoto lenses

Objectives

- Compare refracting and reflecting telescopes.
- Explain how a camera creates an image.

Figure 20-10. The moon can be seen in greater detail when viewed through a telescope as in the lower photo.

Telescopes

There are many uses for lenses and mirrors. They are important components in optical instruments—devices that are designed to aid the human eye in making observations. In this section you'll read about three common optical instruments that you are probably familiar with. The first of these is the telescope.

Have you ever looked at the moon through a telescope? It appears to be very different from the moon you see when you glance at the night sky, doesn't it? With a good telescope, you should be able to clearly see the craters and other features on the moon's surface. Telescopes are designed to magnify objects that are very far away. Much of the information we have today about the moon, the planets, and our galaxy and others has been gathered by viewing these celestial bodies through telescopes.

Early telescopes, like those used today, were built from lenses and mirrors. Around the year 1600, lensmakers in Holland constructed a telescope to view distant objects. In 1609, Galileo built and used his own telescope to discover the moons of Jupiter, the phases of Venus, and details of the Milky Way galaxy. Today, scientists use several kinds of telescopes with many design improvements.

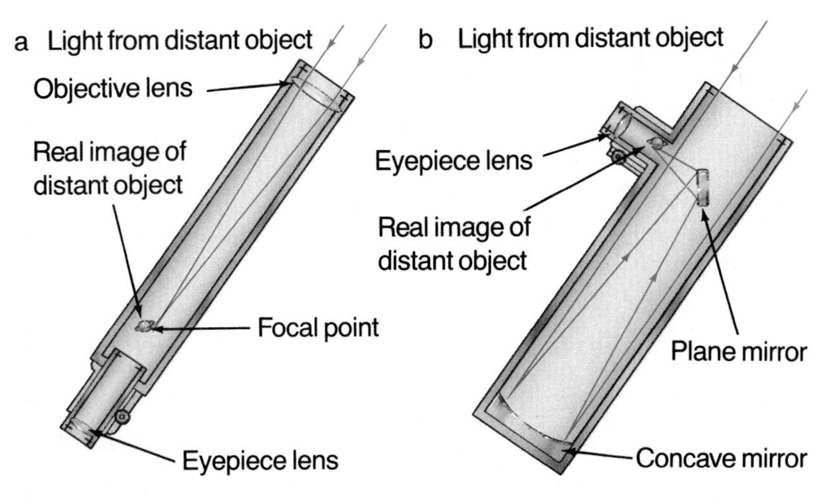

Figure 20-11. A refracting telescope (a) and a reflecting telescope (b) magnify the images of distant objects.

One common telescope is the **refracting telescope.** A simple refracting telescope uses two convex lenses to gather and focus light from distant objects. Figure 20-11a is a diagram of a refracting telescope. Notice how light enters the telescope through a convex lens with a long focal length. This lens is called the objective lens. The real image formed by this lens is magnified by a second convex lens, called the eyepiece, with a shorter focal length. What you view through the eyepiece is an enlarged, virtual image of the real image. The image you see is also inverted.

There are several problems with refracting telescopes that may make another type of telescope more desirable to use. First of all, the objective lens must be quite large to allow enough light in to form a bright image. These heavy glass lenses are hard to make and quite costly. Their own weight can cause them to sag and distort the image. As a result, most large telescopes are reflecting telescopes. A **reflecting telescope** uses a concave mirror, a plane mirror, and a convex lens to magnify distant objects. Figure 20-11b shows how light enters the telescope and is reflected by the concave mirror onto a plane mirror inside the telescope. The plane mirror reflects the rays to form an inverted real image in the telescope. The convex lens in the eyepiece then magnifies this image. The eyepiece can be replaced by a camera to photograph the real image.

Sometimes you might want to view distant objects so they appear upright. Imagine trying to watch a baseball game through binoculars if the image were upside down. Binoculars work on the same principle as a refracting telescope, except there are two lenses—one for each eye.

MINI-Lab

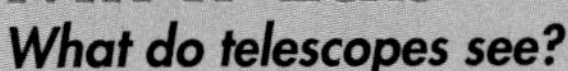

What do telescopes see?

Punch two closely spaced holes in a piece of aluminum foil with a needle. Have a friend hold it in front of a light bulb. Move away from the light bulb until you can barely see both holes. Make a tiny hole in a second piece of foil. Make two slightly larger holes in the second piece of foil. Hold the foil close to your eye and look through each hole at the two "stars." How does the image of the "stars" compare as seen through each of the three holes?

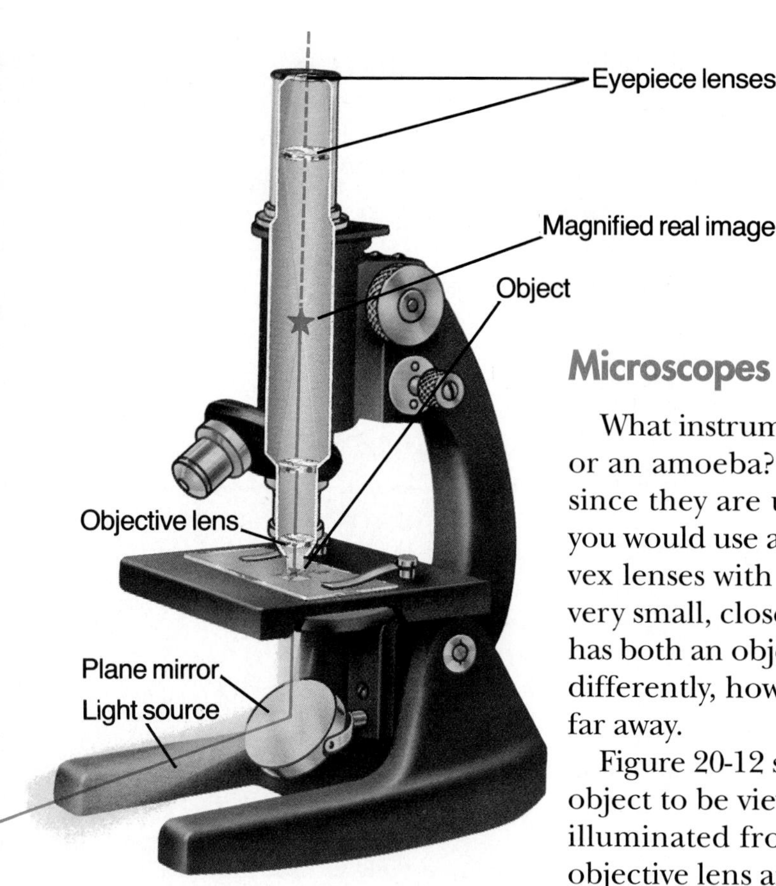

Figure 20-12. A microscope contains two convex lenses so it can magnify very small objects.

A third lens or a pair of reflecting prisms has been added to binoculars to invert the upside-down image so it appears upright. Terrestrial telescopes, such as those used for bird watching, are also designed to produce an upright image.

Microscopes

What instrument would you use to look at a cell, a hair, or an amoeba? You obviously wouldn't use a telescope since they are used to look at faraway objects. Instead, you would use a microscope. A **microscope** uses two convex lenses with relatively short focal lengths to magnify very small, close objects. A microscope, like a telescope, has both an objective lens and an eyepiece. It is designed differently, however, because the objects viewed are not far away.

Figure 20-12 shows the operation of a microscope. The object to be viewed is placed on a transparent slide and illuminated from below. The light travels through the objective lens and a real, enlarged image is formed. It is enlarged because it is farther from the lens than the object. The real image is magnified again by the eyepiece. The image you see is actually a virtual, enlarged image of the already magnified real image. This results in an image up to several hundred times larger than the actual object.

Did You Know?

The most powerful microscope is the IBM 1981 scanning tunneling microscope with the magnifying ability of 100 million X. This instrument resolves down to 1/100 the diameter of an atom and the tip of its probe is a single atom.

Cameras

Do you keep a photograph album with your favorite pictures? Have you ever wondered how these pictures were made? Of course, they were made with a camera, but have you ever wondered how a camera transfers an image onto film? A camera gathers light through a lens and projects an image on light-sensitive film.

When you take a picture with a camera, the light reflected off the subject of the photograph enters an opening in the camera called the aperture. A shutter on the aperture opens to allow light to enter the camera.

The light passes through the lens of the camera, which focuses the image on the photographic film. The image is real, inverted, and smaller than the actual object. The size of the image depends on the focal length of the lens and how close the lens is to the film.

Imagine you and a friend are going to photograph the same object at the same distance, but with different types of cameras. Your picture would look different from that of your friend if the cameras had different lenses. Some lenses have short focal lengths that produce a relatively small image of the object but include much of its surroundings. These lenses are called **wide-angle lenses,** and they must be placed close to the film to focus the image with their short focal length. **Telephoto lenses** have longer focal lengths and are located farther from the film than wide-angle lenses. Telephoto lenses are easy to recognize because they protrude out from the camera to increase the distance between the lens and the film. The image seems enlarged and closer than the object actually is. These lenses are preferred when photographing people's faces from a distance.

Telescopes, microscopes, and cameras are just a few examples of instruments that contain mirrors and lenses and help you to make observations. What are some other types of optical instruments? See how many you can name.

Figure 20-13. The upper photo was taken with a wide-angle lens, and the lower photo was taken with a telephoto lens.

SECTION REVIEW

1. Compare and contrast reflecting and refracting telescopes.
2. If you wanted to photograph a single rose on a rosebush, what kind of lens would you use? Explain why you chose this lens.
3. Why are maps of the moon upside down?
4. **Apply:** Which optical instrument—a telescope, a microscope, or a camera—forms images in a way most like your eye? Explain.

Hypothesizing

You've noticed that all the objects in a photograph you've taken are blurry. Use your knowledge of lenses and focal lengths to form a hypothesis that could explain why the photo was blurred. If you need help, refer to Hypothesizing in the **Skill Handbook** on page 682.

20-4 The Hubble Space Telescope

Objectives

- **Describe the development and goals of the Hubble Space Telescope.**
- **Evaluate the need for a space telescope.**

Is It Worth It?

Imagine trying to read a sign from the bottom of a swimming pool. The water distorts your view of objects beyond the water. In a similar way, Earth's atmosphere blurs our view of many stars, planets, and other objects in space. Not even powerful telescopes positioned at high elevations can allow us to see distant objects clearly. On April 20, 1990, the National Aeronautics and Space Administration (NASA) launched the Hubble Space Telescope. The telescope has produced images sharper than powerful telescopes on Earth by allowing us to view the planets, stars, and distant galaxies from an orbit beyond Earth's atmosphere. It is designed to detect infrared and ultraviolet light in space that is usually blocked by Earth's atmosphere.

The Hubble Space Telescope was placed into an orbit almost 600 kilometers above Earth by the space shuttle *Discovery*. The 13 m, 11 300 kg telescope is named after Edwin P. Hubble, an astronomer. Hubble is famous for his observations of many other galaxies beyond the Milky Way, and evidence that the universe appears to be expanding.

Look at the diagram of the Hubble Space Telescope on the opposite page. The solar panels provide electrical power to the system. A 2.4 m primary and a smaller secondary mirror collect and focus light to form an image. Various instruments on the telescope interpret the data and communicate it to scientists on Earth.

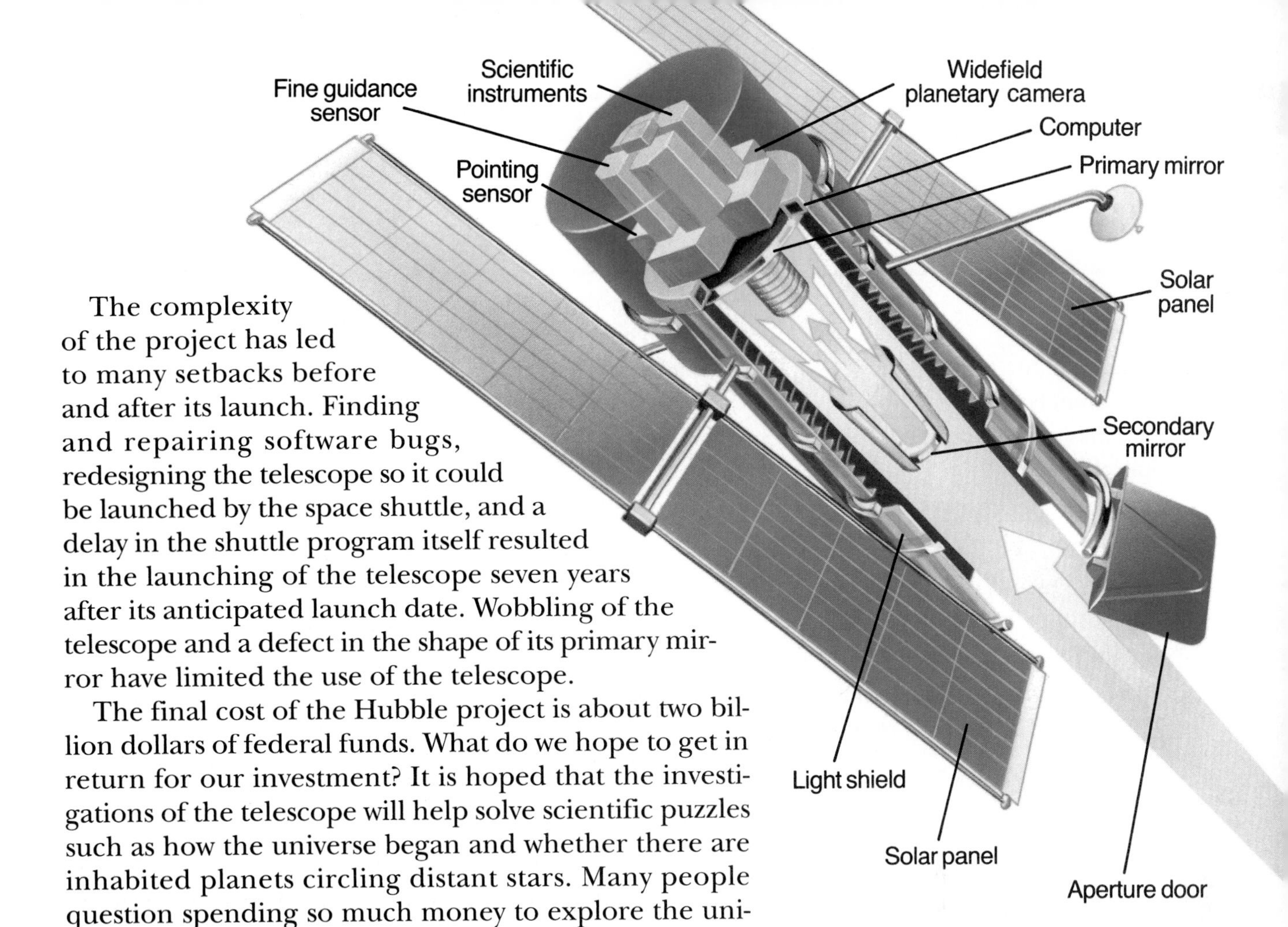

The complexity of the project has led to many setbacks before and after its launch. Finding and repairing software bugs, redesigning the telescope so it could be launched by the space shuttle, and a delay in the shuttle program itself resulted in the launching of the telescope seven years after its anticipated launch date. Wobbling of the telescope and a defect in the shape of its primary mirror have limited the use of the telescope.

The final cost of the Hubble project is about two billion dollars of federal funds. What do we hope to get in return for our investment? It is hoped that the investigations of the telescope will help solve scientific puzzles such as how the universe began and whether there are inhabited planets circling distant stars. Many people question spending so much money to explore the universe when they believe there are so many unsolved problems on Earth. What do you think?

SECTION REVIEW

1. Why can a telescope in orbit above Earth form clearer images than a telescope on Earth?
2. What knowledge do we hope to gain from the Hubble Space Telescope?

You Decide!

Make a list of the major unsolved problems and questions our society faces today. Consider the future benefits from solving these problems. Where do you rank exploring the universe on your list? Do you think we should spend more billions of dollars to answer these questions about the universe? Some people are even in favor of launching more space telescopes. Do you think we need more?

20-5 Applications of Light

New Science Words

polarized light
laser
coherent light
incoherent light
total internal reflection
optical fibers

Objectives

- Describe polarized light and the uses of polarizing lenses.
- Explain how a laser produces coherent light and how it differs from incoherent light.
- Apply the concept of total internal reflection to the uses of optical fibers.

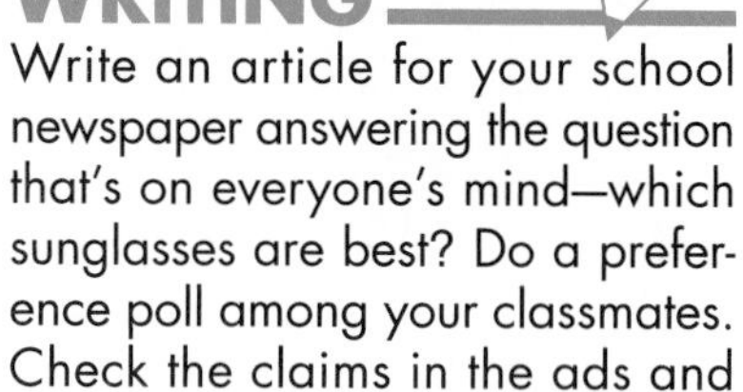

Science and WRITING

Write an article for your school newspaper answering the question that's on everyone's mind—which sunglasses are best? Do a preference poll among your classmates. Check the claims in the ads and see what research magazines, such as *Consumer Reports*, have to say.

Polarized Light

Have you ever purchased a new pair of sunglasses? You may have tried on dozens of pairs of sunglasses before you found the pair you wanted. Did you notice that some of them had a sticker on them that said *polarized*? What makes them different from other kinds of sunglasses?

Recall modeling a transverse wave on a rope in Chapter 18. You could make the waves vibrate in any direction—horizontal, vertical, or anywhere in between. Most light sources, such as incandescent lamps and the sun, emit light that also vibrates in many directions. If this light passes through a special filter, called a polarizing filter, the light becomes polarized. In **polarized light**, the transverse waves vibrate only on one plane. A polarizing filter consists of chains of long, thin molecules lined up in parallel rows. Only light waves vibrating in the same direction as these molecular chains are allowed to pass through

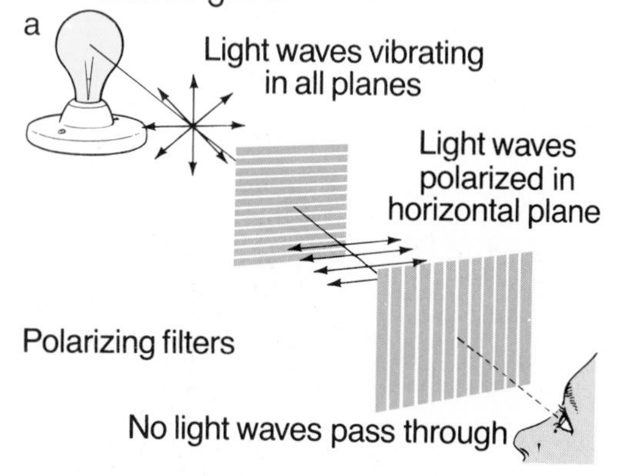

Figure 20-14. Very little light passes through two polarized filters that are aligned at right angles to each other (a). A polarizing filter is used in the left photo (b) to reduce glare.

them. If a second polarizing filter is aligned so its molecules are oriented at right angles to the first filter, very little light is passed through, as illustrated in Figure 20-14(a).

Light that is reflected from horizontal surfaces, such as a lake or a car's hood, is partially polarized horizontally. This annoying reflection is called glare. Polarizing sunglasses are made with vertically polarizing filters. They block out most of the glare while allowing vertically polarized light through. In addition, the lenses are darkly colored to absorb even more light. Polarizing filters can also be placed over camera lenses to reduce the glare when taking pictures.

Figure 20-15. Polarizing filters are often used by photographers to reduce glare.

Have you ever watched a 3-D movie? Did you wear special glasses to see the effects? The characters seemed like they were right in front of you, didn't they? In three dimensional (3-D) glasses, one filter is aligned vertically and one filter is aligned horizontally. The movie is shown through two projectors, one with a horizontally polarizing filter and the other with a vertically polarizing filter. As a result, your right eye sees a slightly different picture than your left eye. This creates the impression of depth, or three dimensions.

Next time you shop for sunglasses, you will know why some are polarized. They are designed to reduce glare, while sunglasses that aren't polarized don't reduce glare. What kind do you think you would prefer?

Lasers

The narrow beams of light that zip across the stage and through the auditorium during a rock concert are produced by **lasers.** Beams of laser light do not spread out as does light from other light sources because laser light is coherent. **Coherent light** is electromagnetic energy of only one wavelength which travels with its crests and troughs aligned. The beam does not spread out because all the waves travel in the same direction. Light from an ordinary light bulb is incoherent because it lacks the characteristics of coherent light. **Incoherent light** may contain more than one color and its electromagnetic waves do not travel in the same direction, causing the beam to spread out.

Science and READING

How can a laser be used in such a wide range of activities as welding, performing surgery, transmitting communications signals, printing, etc.?

Photons in a beam of coherent light are identical and travel in the same direction. Such photons can be produced by a laser. A laser's light begins when a photon is spontaneously emitted from an atom. This photon is reflected back and forth between two facing mirrors at opposite ends of the laser. One mirror is partially coated to allow some light to leave that end of the laser. If the emitted photon travels perpendicular to one of the mirrors it will be reflected between them many times. As it moves back and forth, it can stimulate other atoms to emit identical photons as well. The continual production of photons travelling perpendicularly to the mirror by *other* photons produces a coherent beam of laser light.

What is laser light?

Figure 20-16. A laser produces a coherent beam of visible light of the same wavelengths.

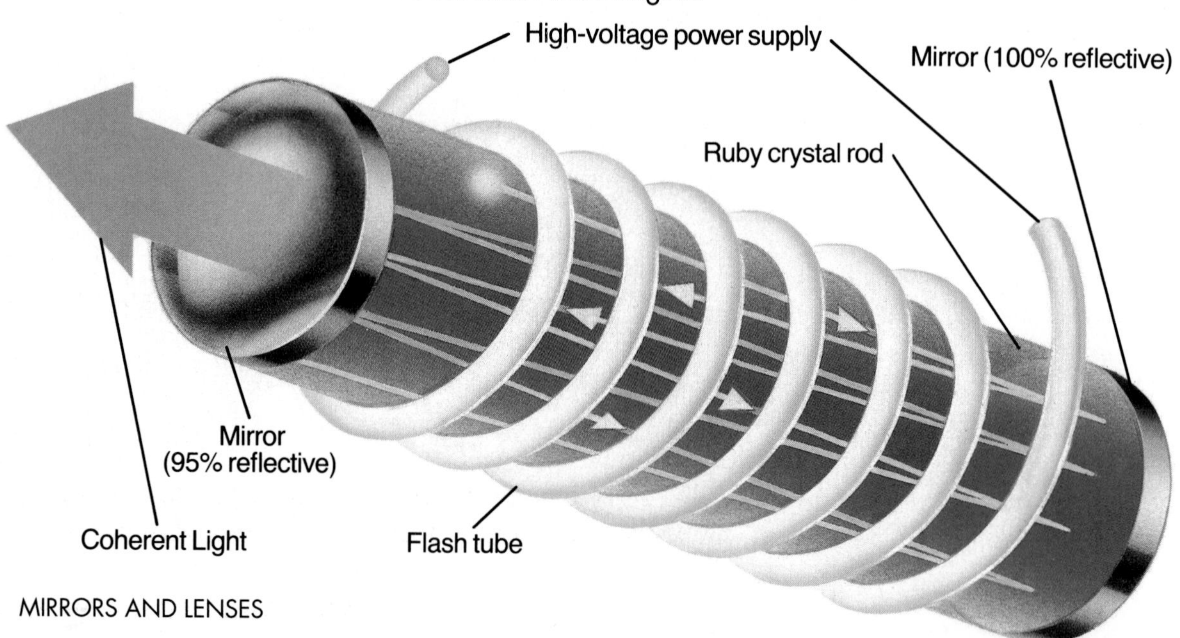

Figure 20-17. There are many practical uses for laser light.

Lasers can be made with many different materials, including gases, liquids, and solids. One of the most common lasers is the helium-neon laser, which produces a beam of red light. As the name implies, a mixture of helium and neon gases is sealed in a tube with mirrors at both ends. An electric spark is used to excite the atoms in the gases.

What materials can lasers be made from?

Laser light has many applications. Perhaps you have seen lasers used in grocery stores to read the bar codes on packages. One reason that compact discs maintain high sound quality is that the laser used to read the disc doesn't scratch the disc's surface. Surgeons can use lasers in place of a scalpel to cut cleanly through body tissues. The energy from the laser can seal off some blood vessels in the incision to reduce bleeding. Lasers are routinely used to remove cataracts and repair the retina in the eye. Powerful lasers are used for cutting and welding materials in industry. Surveyors and builders use lasers for measuring and leveling. Lasers beamed at the moon allow us to measure the moon's orbit with great accuracy. The beam is reflected from mirrors placed on the moon by astronauts. Lasers also provide a coherent light source for fiber-optic communications.

Optical Fibers

Did you ever dangle your legs from the side of a swimming pool and watch your feet disappear as you raised them in the water? The disappearance of your feet is an example of total internal reflection. **Total internal reflection** occurs when light striking a surface between two transparent materials reflects totally from that surface, back into the first material. As you know, to see your feet in

Figure 20-18. Total internal reflection causes gems to sparkle.

the pool, light must reflect from your feet to your eyes. As you raise your feet in the pool, the light reflecting from your feet strikes the surface between the water and the air and reflects back into the water. Your feet seem to disappear because light reflecting from your feet never reaches your eyes. Total internal refelection depends on the speed of light in the two materials and the angle at which the light strikes the surface. The speed of light in the first materials must be less than it is in the second. Also, the angle at which the light strikes the surface of the first material must be large.

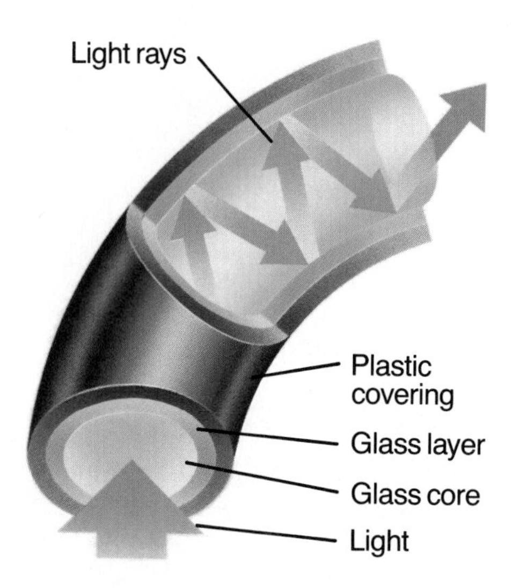

Figure 20-19. An optical fiber is designed to reflect light so that it is piped through the fiber without leaving it, except at the ends.

Total internal reflection makes light transmission in optical fibers possible. **Optical fibers** are transparent glass fibers that can pipe light from one place to another. As shown in Figure 20-19, light entering one end of the fiber is continuously reflected from the sides of the fiber until it emerges from the other end. Very little light is lost or absorbed in optical fibers.

Optical fibers are most comonly used in communications. Telephone conversations, television programs, and computer information can be used to modulate light beams into optical signals. The signals are transmitted by a laser through the optical fibers with far less loss of signal than if similar electric signals were transmitted though copper wires. Because of total internal reflection, signals can't leak from one fiber to another and interfere with other messages. As a result, the signal is clearly transmitted. One optical fiber can carry thousands of phone conversations at one time because the signals can be produced quite rapidly and travel at high speeds through the fiber.

Figure 20-20. Just one of these optical fibers can carry thousands of phone conversations at the same time.

TECHNOLOGY

The Light Scalpel

Optical fibers piping laser energy deep inside the human body may replace some conventional surgical procedures. The effect of the laser on human tissue depends on wavelength and intensity of the laser light, and the color of the body tissue. As a result of varying wavelength and intensity of a laser, it can target a particular kind of tissue for surgery.

Low-power lasers are used to seal soft tissue, and to treat ulcers in the stomach, intestine, and colon. Many other surgical applications, however, require high-power lasers. One of the most exciting applications of a high-power laser and optical fiber system would be in the treatment of cardiovascular diseases. An optical fiber-conducted laser may be used to treat a patient with a blocked artery. The optical fiber would be used to deliver pulses of high-powered laser light to blast the artery clear.

Think Critically: What problems might arise in using a high-power laser to blast an artery clear of an obstruction?

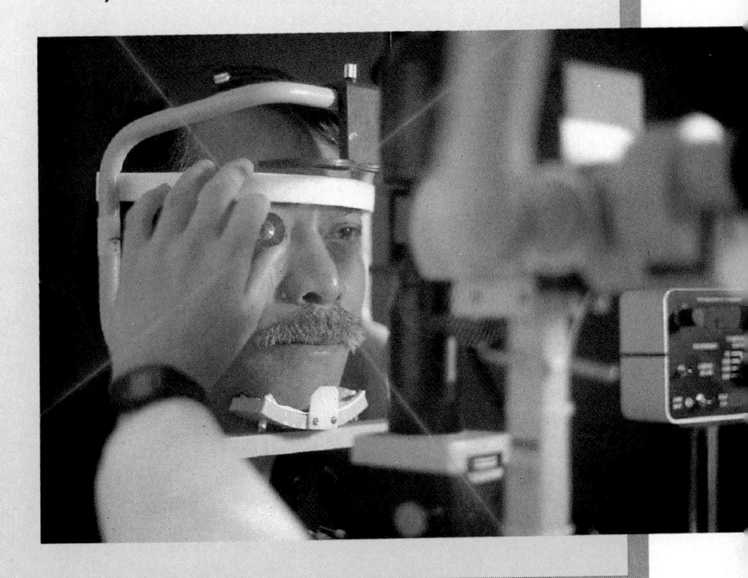

SECTION REVIEW

1. What is polarized light?
2. Distinguish between coherent and incoherent light.
3. Explain how an optical fiber transmits light.
4. **Apply:** Which of the following materials could possibly be substituted for the glass in an optical fiber: clear plastic, wood, or water? Explain your answer.

Sequencing

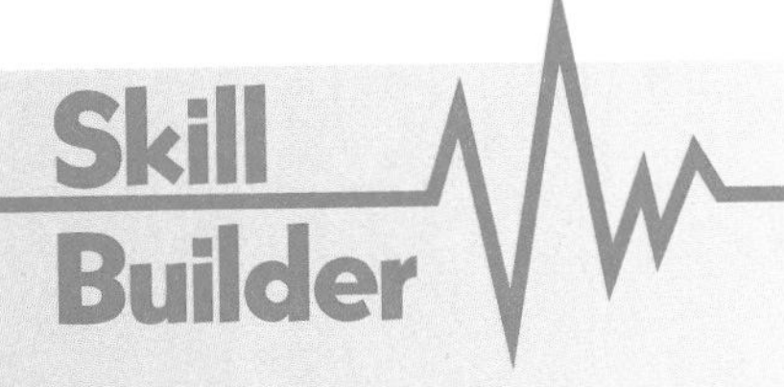

Sequence the events that occur in a laser in order to produce coherent light. Begin with the emission of a photon from an atom. If you need help, refer to Sequencing in the **Skill Handbook** on page 676.

ACTIVITY 20-2
Polarized Light

Problem: *How can polarized light be identified?*

Materials  

- two polarizing filters
- light source
- objects with flat, hard surfaces

Procedure

1. Turn one filter against the other while looking through them. When the maximum light can be seen, mark the edges of the filters "X" and "Y" as shown.
2. Hold an object with its flat surface horizontal. Reflect light from its surface. Look at the reflection through one filter and turn it until the glare disappears.
3. Turn the object so that light reflects from a vertical surface and repeat Step 2.
4. Light from the sky which is 90° from the sun is polarized. Look through the filter at this part of the sky and rotate the filter to make the sky darken.

Analyze

1. How many degrees must you turn one filter from the other to change the light from brightest to darkest?
2. When the light glare from the horizontal surface disappears, which filter edge is up, "X" or "Y"? Is this also true for glare from the vertical surface?
3. If there are clouds in the sky, how do they appear as the filter darkens the sky?

Conclude and Apply

4. LCD or digital calculators and watches are polarized. Why does it matter which way a digital watch's polarizing filter is oriented?
5. Would your polarizing sunglasses work as well if you turned them sideways?
6. Photographs look best if taken in polarized light. What is the best time of day to take pictures?

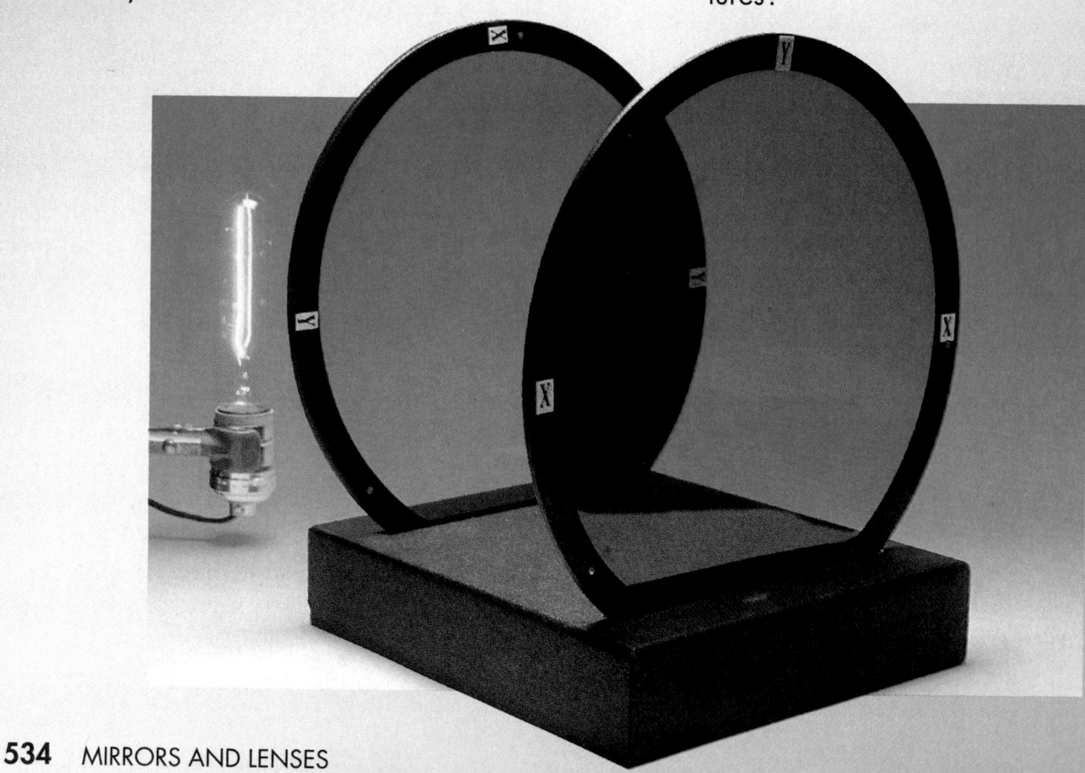

CHAPTER

REVIEW

SUMMARY

20-1: The Optics of Mirrors

1. Plane mirrors and convex mirrors produce virtual images. Concave mirrors produce real images.

2. A concave mirror is like the inside of a shiny spoon, and a convex mirror is like the outside of a shiny spoon.

20-2: The Optics of Lenses

1. Convex lenses form real images; concave lenses form virtual images.

2. Convex lenses converge light rays and can form images on a screen. Concave lenses diverge light rays and are used in combination with other lenses to extend the focal length.

3. Corrective lenses can be used in combination with the lens in your eye to focus images on the retina. Farsighted people must wear convex lenses, and nearsighted persons must wear concave lenses.

20-3: Optical Instruments

1. A refracting telescope uses convex lenses to magnify distant objects; a reflecting telescope uses concave and plane mirrors, and a convex lens to magnify distant objects.

2. Light passing through the lens of a camera is focused on photographic film inside the camera. The image on the film is real, inverted, and smaller than the object being photographed.

20-4: Science and Society: The Hubble Space Telescope

1. The Hubble Space Telescope produces sharper images than telescopes on Earth; in addition, it can detect infrared and ultraviolet radiation.

2. Scientists hope space telescopes will provide information that will answer our questions about the universe.

20-5: Applications of Light

1. Polarized light consists of transverse waves that only vibrate along one plane. Polarized lenses act as filters to block light waves that aren't polarized in the same plane as the filter.

2. A laser produces coherent light by emitting a beam of photons that travel in the same phase and direction. Light that spreads out from its source is incoherent.

3. Optical fibers can "pipe" light rays because the fibers are made of a material that allows the light rays to reflect totally inside the fibers.

KEY SCIENCE WORDS

a. **coherent light**
b. **concave lenses**
c. **concave mirror**
d. **convex lenses**
e. **convex mirror**
f. **focal length**
g. **focal point**
h. **incoherent light**
i. **laser**
j. **microscope**
k. **optical fibers**
l. **plane mirror**
m. **polarized light**
n. **real image**
o. **reflecting telescope**
p. **refracting telescope**
q. **telephoto lenses**
r. **total internal reflection**
s. **virtual image**
t. **wide-angle lenses**

UNDERSTANDING VOCABULARY

Match each phrase with the correct term from the list of Key Science Words.

1. mirror with a flat surface
2. image that cannot be projected onto a screen
3. image formed where light rays actually meet
4. curved mirror that diverges reflected light
5. lenses that converge light at their focal point
6. a telescope that uses two convex lenses
7. an instrument used to study very small objects
8. light waves that vibrate in only one plane
9. light produced by lasers
10. often used to transmit telephone signals

CHAPTER

REVIEW

CHECKING CONCEPTS

Choose the word or phrase that completes the sentence.

1. Images formed by plane mirrors are not ____.
   a. upright c. enlarged
   b. reversed d. virtual
2. An object that reflects light and curves inward is called a ______.
   a. plane mirror c. convex mirror
   b. concave mirror d. concave lens
3. Mirrors that can magnify a reflection are ___.
   a. convex c. concave
   b. plane d. all of these
4. The light bulb in a headlight, flashlight, or spotlight is placed at the focal point of a ____.
   a. concave lens c. concave mirror
   b. convex lens d. convex mirror
5. Lenses form images by ______.
   a. reflecting light c. diffracting light
   b. refracting light d. interfering with light
6. A concave lens bends light towards its _____.
   a. focal point c. center
   b. optical axis d. edges
7. Farsighted people must wear _______.
   a. flat lenses
   b. convex lenses
   c. concave lenses
   d. unevenly curved lenses
8. Reflecting telescopes don't contain a ______.
   a. plane mirror c. convex lens
   b. concave mirror d. concave lens
9. Sunglasses and 3-D glasses use _______.
   a. concave lenses c. telephoto lenses
   b. convex lenses d. polarizing lenses
10. Lasers are often used in ______.
    a. cutting and welding c. surgery
    b. reading bar codes d. all of these

UNDERSTANDING CONCEPTS

Complete each sentence.

11. The image of a girl five meters in front of a plane mirror appears to be ______ meters behind the mirror.
12. Images formed by ______ mirrors are virtual, small, and upright.
13. Camera lenses with short focal lengths that include much of the surroundings in their images are ______ lenses.
14. Optical fibers can transmit light around corners because light undergoes ______ within the fiber.
15. The Hubble Space Telescope can detect infrared and ultraviolet radiation that is usually blocked out by Earth's ______.

THINK AND WRITE CRITICALLY

16. Describe how a concave mirror reflects light rays that approach it parallel to its optical axis. How does such a mirror reflect approaching light rays that pass through its focal point?
17. Why was the Hubble Space Telescope built?
18. Convex lenses are often called converging lenses while concave lenses are often called diverging lenses. Explain these different names by describing how each type of lens refracts light.
19. Compare and contrast the uses of telescopes and microscopes. Which type of telescope is built most like a microscope?
20. Explain how a laser produces coherent light.

APPLY

21. Magicians often make objects disappear by using "trick" mirrors. How might a magician seem to make an object disappear by using a concave mirror?
22. What would happen if a movie projector's lens was less than one focal length from the film?
23. If you were an optician, what type of lens would you prescribe for a patient who can't focus clearly on close objects?
24. Would a reflecting telescope work properly if its concave mirror were replaced by a convex mirror? Explain.
25. You only have enough money to buy one lens for your camera. What type of lens would be most useful? Explain.

MORE SKILL BUILDERS

If you need help, refer to the Skill Handbook.

1. **Outlining:** Summarize in an outline the different types of images formed by plane, concave, and convex mirrors.
2. **Observing and Inferring:** Infer the effects of a hard, rigid eye lens on human vision. Would this make the eye more or less like a simple camera?
3. **Recognizing Cause and Effect:** Distinguish between and describe the causes and effects of the following vision problems: nearsightedness, farsightedness, and an astigmatism.
4. **Hypothesizing:** Rough, uncut diamonds lack the sparkle of diamonds that have been cut by a gem cutter. Propose a hypothesis to explain this observation.
5. **Concept Mapping:** Below is a concept map summarizing characteristics of coherent and incoherent light. Use the following terms to complete the map (terms may be used more than once): wavelength(s), frequency(ies), color(s), sun, lasers, coherent light, incoherent light.

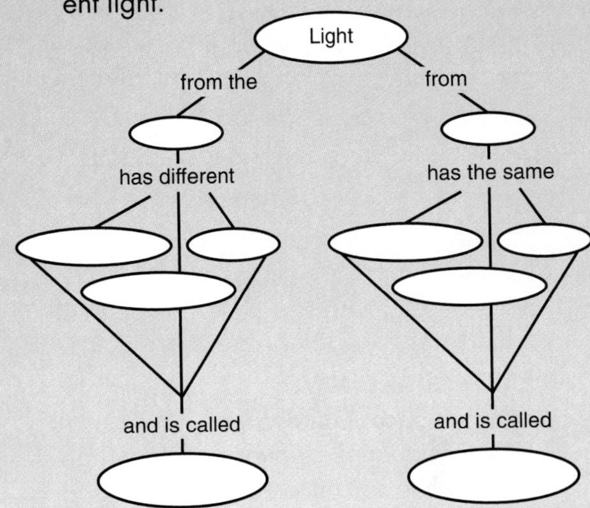

PROJECTS

1. Write a report tracing the development of the telescope from the time of Galileo to the Hubble Space Telescope.
2. Investigate the types of mirrors used in funhouses. Explain how these mirrors give distorted images and report your findings to the class.

GLOBAL CONNECTIONS

Waves, Light, and Sound

In this unit, you studied about waves, light, and sound. Now find out how waves, light, and sound are connected to other subjects and places around the world.

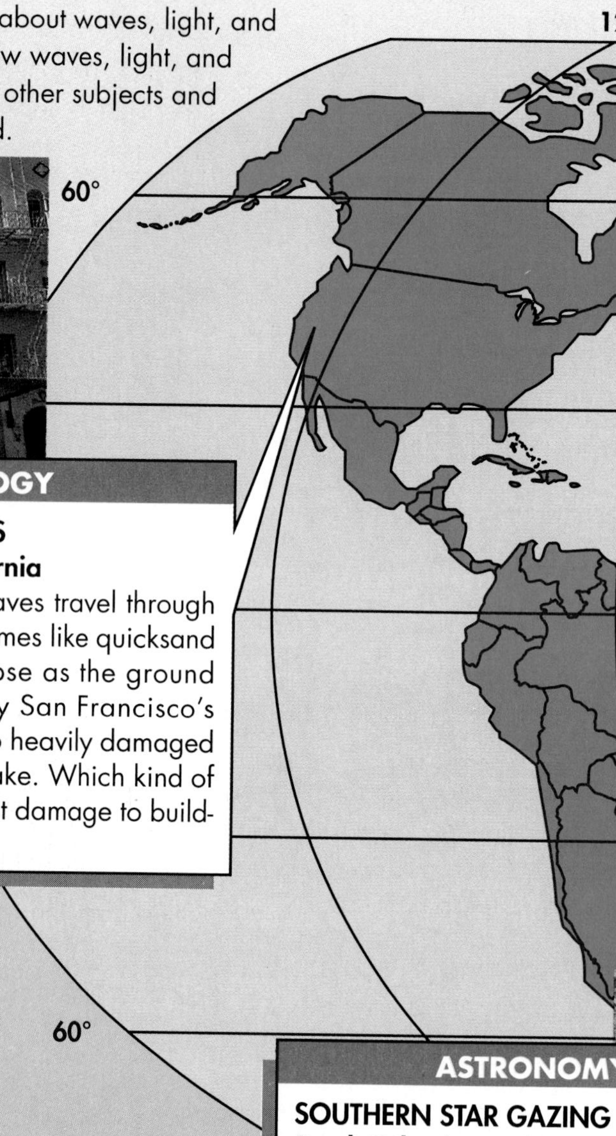

120° 60° 60° 30° 60°

GEOLOGY

EARTHQUAKE WAVES
San Francisco, California

When earthquake waves travel through soft soil, the soil becomes like quicksand and structures collapse as the ground shakes. Find out why San Francisco's Marina district was so heavily damaged by the 1989 earthquake. Which kind of waves causes the most damage to buildings?

ASTRONOMY

SOUTHERN STAR GAZING
South Pole, Antarctica

At the Amundsen-Scott South Pole Station, astronomers have an especially clear view of the sky through their telescopes. One reason for the clear view is the unpolluted atmosphere. Why is it also helpful to have telescopes located far from the lights of cities?

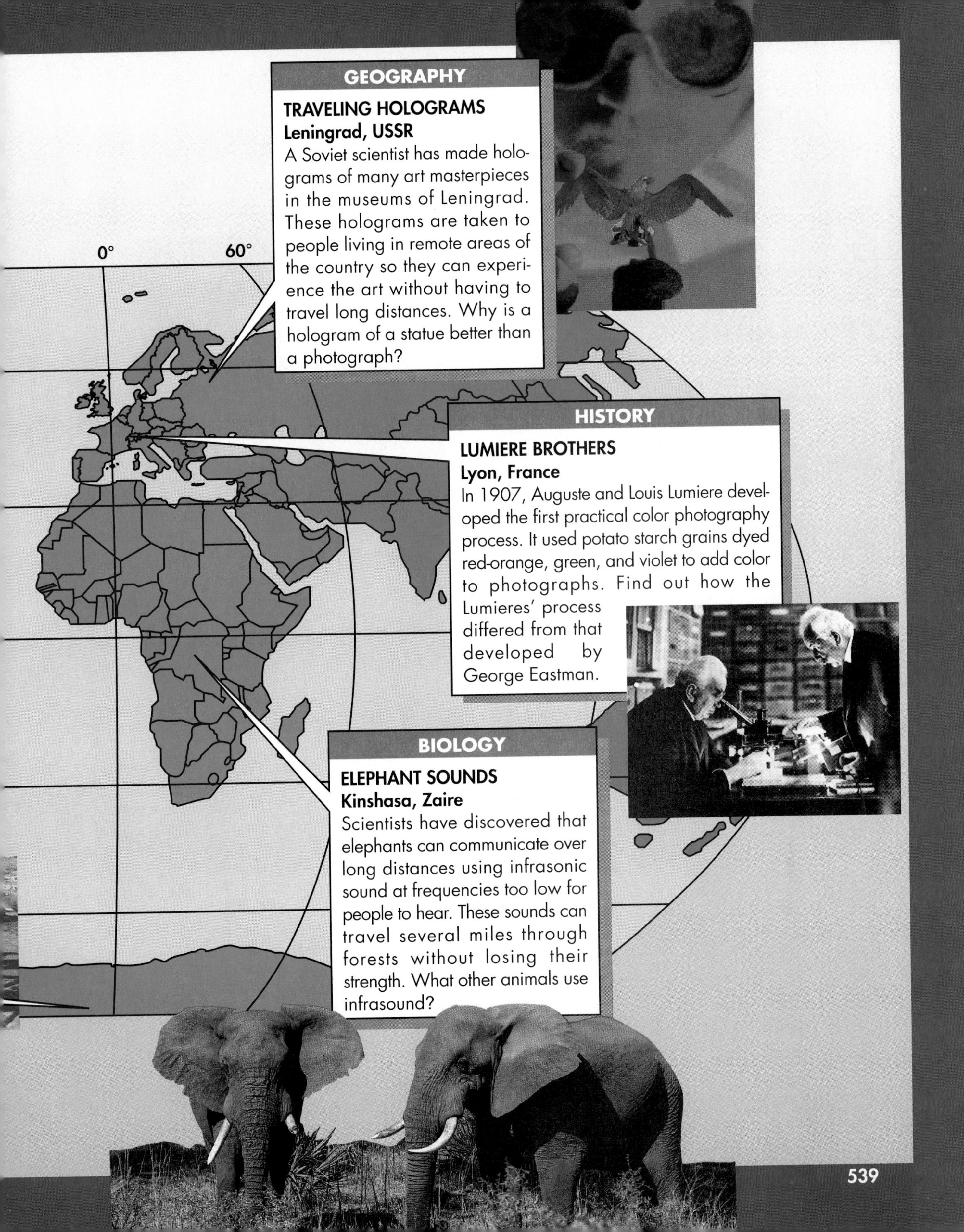

GEOGRAPHY

TRAVELING HOLOGRAMS
Leningrad, USSR

A Soviet scientist has made holograms of many art masterpieces in the museums of Leningrad. These holograms are taken to people living in remote areas of the country so they can experience the art without having to travel long distances. Why is a hologram of a statue better than a photograph?

HISTORY

LUMIERE BROTHERS
Lyon, France

In 1907, Auguste and Louis Lumiere developed the first practical color photography process. It used potato starch grains dyed red-orange, green, and violet to add color to photographs. Find out how the Lumieres' process differed from that developed by George Eastman.

BIOLOGY

ELEPHANT SOUNDS
Kinshasa, Zaire

Scientists have discovered that elephants can communicate over long distances using infrasonic sound at frequencies too low for people to hear. These sounds can travel several miles through forests without losing their strength. What other animals use infrasound?

CAREERS

OPTICAL MECHANIC

An *optical mechanic* uses special equipment to grind and polish lenses. Some optical mechanics make lenses for cameras and binoculars, while others make lenses for eyeglasses. Each pair of eyeglass lenses is made according to a prescription written by an optometrist or ophthalmologist. The optical mechanic makes sure each lens is correctly ground and then fits them into the eyeglass frames.

Most optical mechanics receive on-the-job training for about three years. If you're interested in becoming an optical mechanic, you should take courses in biology and physics.

For Additional Information

Contact the Optical Laboratories Association, 6935 Wisconsin Avenue, Suite 200, Chevy Chase, Maryland 20816.

PHOTOGRAPHER

A *photographer* uses light meters, lights, and cameras to take photographs. Some photographers work in commercial studios, photographing products or people. Others work for magazines or newspapers. Many photographers are self-employed.

A person interested in photography should have good color vision and artistic skills. High school classes in art, chemistry, and physics are helpful. If you're interested in becoming a photographer, there are several options for training. He or she can work as an assistant and receive on-the-job training for two or three years, or attend an art school or college that offers special programs in photography. A photographer who wants to specialize in medical or scientific subjects needs additional college classes in science.

For Additional Information

Contact the Professional Photographers of America, Inc., 1090 Executive Way, Des Plaines, Illinois 60018.

UNIT READINGS

▶Heckman, Philip. *The Magic of Holography.* New York: Atheneum, 1986.

▶Ward, Alan. *Experimenting With Light and Illusions.* London, England: Batsford, 1985.

▶Wolkomir, Richard and Joyce. "When Animals Sound Off." *National Wildlife,* April - May, 1990, pp. 48-50.

Alma Woodsey Thomas — Color Field Painter

Alma Thomas was a black artist who achieved prominence in the mainstream art community. She worked in the modern tradition of Color Field painting.

She was born in 1892 in Columbus, Georgia. Because her aunts were teachers, she decided at an early age that teaching could be her way to a better life, too. Her family moved to Washington, D.C., in 1907. In 1924, she was the first graduate of the new art department at Howard University.

She taught art in the Washington schools for 35 years. During that time, she earned an M.A. at Teachers College of Columbia University. During her teaching years, she exhibited realistic paintings in shows of Afro-American artists. But in the 1950s, she took painting classes at American University and became interested in color and abstract art.

By 1959, her paintings had become abstract. By 1964, she had discovered a way to create an image through small dabs of paint laid edge to edge across the painting's surface. In *Iris, Tulips, Jonquils, and Crocuses,* the color bands move vertically and horizontally across the canvas to represent a breeze moving over a sunlit spring garden. In *Autumn Leaves Fluttering in the Wind,* rust-colored patches move in patterns like those of swirling autumn leaves. The spaces between show glimpses of blue, yellow, and green, representing the sky and the land.

Thomas's paintings are mosaics of patches of color that she said, "represent my communion with nature." She wrote, "Color is life. Light reveals to us the spirit and living soul of the world through colors."

In Your Own Words

► Alma Thomas wrote that she was "intrigued with the changing colors of nature as the seasons progress." Describe how you would paint a natural scene using the Color Field painting style.

UNIT 7 ELECTRICITY AND ENERGY RESOURCES

What's Happening Here?

When the sun goes down, New York City's lights go on. New York City generates electricity for lighting by burning fossil fuels, harnessing water power, and controlling nuclear reactions. What does it mean to "generate" electricity? How do solar collectors like the ones shown below generate electricity? Why is it important to develop alternatives to fossil fuels? In this power-packed unit, you'll learn the answers to these questions. You'll also learn about magnetism, nuclear reactions, and computers.

UNIT CONTENTS

CHAPTER 21 Electricity

Throughout the day you see examples of electricity and its uses. All of us have come to depend on electricity on a daily basis. Electricity provides us with entertainment, transportation, and convenience. So where does electricity come from? What is it? How does it affect matter?

FIND OUT!

Do this simple activity to find out how matter can be affected by electric charges.

Get a thin plastic ruler. Tear some tissue paper into tiny pieces less than 1 cm^2 and scatter them on your desk top. Rub the plastic ruler briskly across your hair several times and slowly lower it near the paper. What happens? Touch the ruler with your other hand and lower it to the paper again. What happens now?

Gearing Up

Previewing the Chapter

Use this outline to help you focus on important ideas in this chapter.

Section 21-1 Electric Charge
- ▶ Static Electricity
- ▶ Conductors and Insulators
- ▶ The Electroscope

Section 21-2 Science and Society
Lightning—Its Causes and Effects
- ▶ Should Lightning-induced Forest Fires Be Left to Burn?

Section 21-3 Electric Current
- ▶ Flowing Electrons
- ▶ Batteries
- ▶ Resistance
- ▶ Ohm's Law

Section 21-4 Electrical Circuits
- ▶ Series Circuits
- ▶ Parallel Circuits
- ▶ Household Circuits

Section 21-5 Electrical Power and Energy
- ▶ Electrical Power
- ▶ Electrical Energy

Previewing Science Skills

- ▶ In the **Skill Builders,** you will observe and infer, hypothesize, and make a concept map.
- ▶ In the **Activities,** you will measure in SI, predict, and formulate models.
- ▶ In the **MINI-Labs,** you will observe, hypothesize, and interpret data.

What's next?

Now you may wonder what electric charges are and where they come from? As you read on, you will find out more about electric charges and electricity.

21-1 Electric Charge

New Science Words

static electricity
electric field
conductor
insulator
electroscope

Objectives

- Describe the effects of static electricity.
- Distinguish between conductors and insulators.
- Recognize the presence of charge in an electroscope.

Static Electricity

Have you ever walked across a carpeted floor and were stung by a spark as you reached out to touch something? If you immediately touched the object a second time, you might have felt a very small spark, or none at all. If you shuffled your feet on the carpet again, you might've felt a larger spark again. What caused this startling and sometimes painful phenomenon?

When your feet rubbed on the carpet, some of the atoms in the carpet were disturbed. Recall from Chapter 10 that atoms contain protons, neutrons, and electrons. Neutrons have no charge, protons are positively charged, and electrons are negatively charged. An atom is electrically neutral if it has an equal number of protons and electrons. Sometimes electrons are not held tightly in the atom. For example, as you walked on the carpet some electrons that were loosely held by the atoms rubbed from the carpet onto your shoes. As a result, your shoes gained electrons, and they were no longer neutral, but instead had a negative charge. The carpet lost electrons, leaving it positively charged. The excess electrons, stored in your body, gave you an overall negative electric charge. This is an example of static electricity. **Static electricity** is the accumulation of electric charges on an object. Can you think of any other examples of static electricity?

Figure 21-1. When charges are brought together, opposite charges attract and like charges repel.

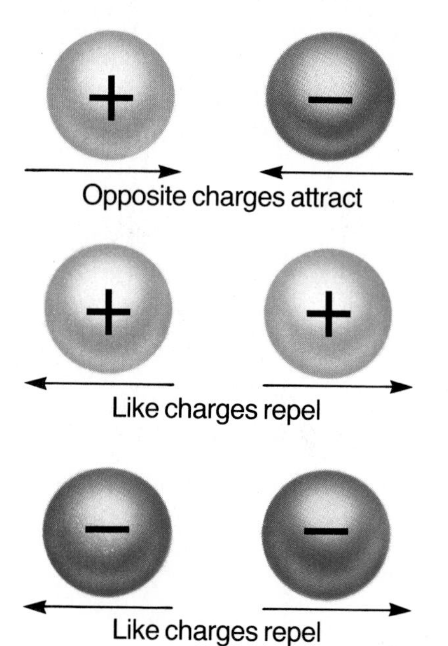

Have you noticed how a sock will cling to your shirt when you remove them from the dryer? Electrons can be rubbed off some clothes while they are tumbling around inside the dryer. Clothes that gain electrons become negatively charged, whereas those that lose electrons become positively charged. Clothes with opposite charges cling together, but clothes with the same charge repel each other. Electrically charged objects obey the following rule: opposite charges attract, and like charges repel.

Charged objects can cause electrons to rearrange their position on a neutral object. For example, suppose you charge a balloon by rubbing it with a cloth. If you bring the negatively charged balloon near your sleeve, the extra electrons on the balloon will repel the electrons in the sleeve. The electrons near the surface will move away from the balloon, leaving a positively charged area on the surface of the sleeve. As a result, the negatively charged balloon will attract the positively charged area of the sleeve. The rearrangement of electrons on a neutral object caused by a charged object is called charging by induction.

How can an electron exert a force on a particle that is some distance away? It does this by setting up an **electric field** in space. This electric field exerts a force on anything that has an electric charge. The electric field is strongest near the electron and becomes weaker as distance from the electron increases.

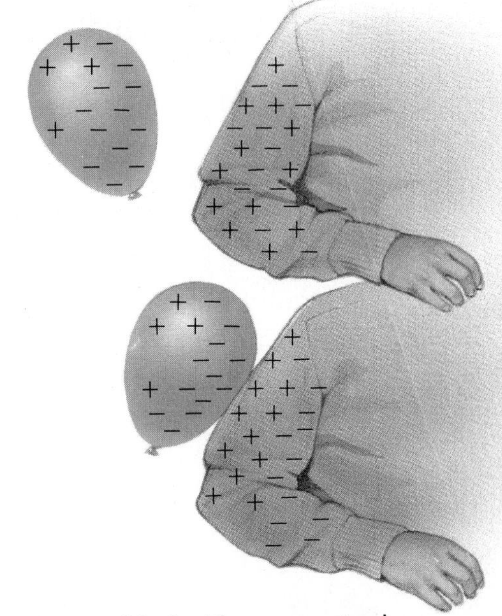

Figure 21-2. The negatively charged balloon induces a positive charge in the sleeve by repelling its electrons.

Conductors and Insulators

You now know you can build up a negative charge by walking across a carpet. Suppose you then could touch either a wooden door or a metal doorknob. Which one would you prefer to touch? If your choice was the metal doorknob, be prepared to feel a spark.

When you put your finger near the doorknob, the electric field between your finger and the knob became so strong that it pulled electrons out of molecules in the air. These molecules became positively charged ions. Movement of these ions and the electrons created the spark that you saw and felt.

The electrons can move through your body to the metal doorknob because both your body and the metal are conductors. A **conductor** is a material that allows electrons to move easily through it. Metals such as copper and silver are made of atoms that don't hold their electrons tightly, so electrons can move easily through materials made up of these kinds of atoms. For this reason, electric wires are usually made of copper, a good conductor. Silver wire also conducts electricity very well, but silver is much more costly to use than copper.

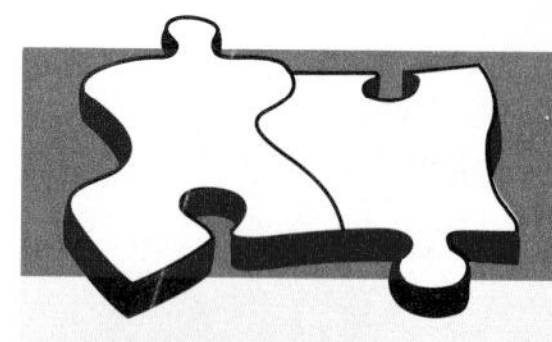

PROBLEM SOLVING

How Can Birds Perch on Power Lines?

As Maria was watching television one evening, she saw an advertisement on the dangers of electric power lines. The advertisement showed a man climbing an aluminum ladder to saw off some tree branches near some power lines. Near the top of the ladder, he reached for the branches and the ladder began to wobble. Unbalanced, he reached out toward the power lines for support

Just before he grasped the power lines, the man turned into a chimpanzee and the television screen went blank. A message then appeared on the screen warning people not to monkey around power lines.

The next day, Maria noticed several sparrows perching on a high voltage power line. She thought about the advertisement she had seen on television and wondered how the birds could safely perch on a power line. Explain how the advertisement inferred that the chimpanzee was injured by electric current when he grabbed the power lines.

Think Critically: How could the sparrows perch on the power line without getting injured?

MINI-Lab

Can static charge move things?

Get a piece of plastic food wrap, about 30 cm by 30 cm. Lay it on a table top and smooth it down flat with a cotton cloth. Use a paper punch to make round chips of aluminum foil. Put the foil chips in a pile in the center of the plastic wrap. Lift the plastic wrap slowly from the table and observe the response of the aluminum. How do the aluminum chips react to the plastic? How do they react to each other? Would paper chips respond the same way? How would you summarize the behavior of electrically charged objects?

What covers the metal wires in cords attached to telephones and other household appliances? They are usually coated with some type of plastic, an insulating material. An **insulator** is a material that doesn't allow electrons to move through it easily. In addition to plastic, wood, rubber, and glass are good insulators. Would you expect static discharge to occur if you touched the wooden door instead of the metal doorknob?

The largest object you touch is Earth. Earth contains a large supply of electrons and functions as a conductor of electricity. It is sometimes desirable to provide a path for the static discharge to reach Earth. An object connected to Earth, or the ground, by a good conductor is said to be grounded. Look around you. Do you see anything that might act as a path to the ground? Plumbing fixtures, such as metal faucets, sinks, and pipes, often provide a convenient ground connection.

The Electroscope

The presence of electric charges can be detected by an **electroscope.** An electroscope is made of two thin metal leaves attached to a metal rod with a knob at the top. The leaves are allowed to swing freely from the metal rod. When the device is not charged, the leaves hang straight down.

Suppose a negatively charged balloon touches the knob. Because the metal is a good conductor, electrons travel down the rod into the leaves. Both leaves become negatively charged as they gain electrons. Because the leaves have similar charges, they repel each other.

If a glass rod is rubbed with silk, electrons leave the glass rod and build up on the silk. The glass rod becomes positively charged. When the positively charged glass rod is touched to the metal knob, electrons are conducted out of the metal leaves and onto the rod. The leaves repel each other because each leaf becomes positively charged as it loses electrons.

Can you think of any other effects of static electricity you have seen? Can you explain them in terms of like or opposite charges. How do objects become charged, and what happens when they discharge? In Section 21-3, you will find out how electrons can move continuously to keep a light bulb glowing or make a tape player play music.

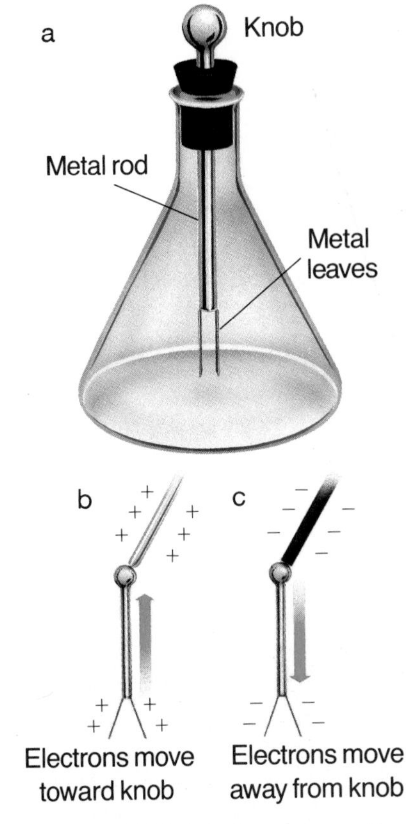

Figure 21-3. Notice the position of the leaves on the electroscope when they are uncharged (a), positively charged (b), and negatively charged (c).

SECTION REVIEW

1. What is static electricity?
2. Distinguish between electrical conductors and insulators and give an example of each.
3. **Apply:** Assume you have already charged an electroscope with a positively charged glass rod. Hypothesize what would happen if you touched the knob again with another positively charged object.

Observing and Inferring

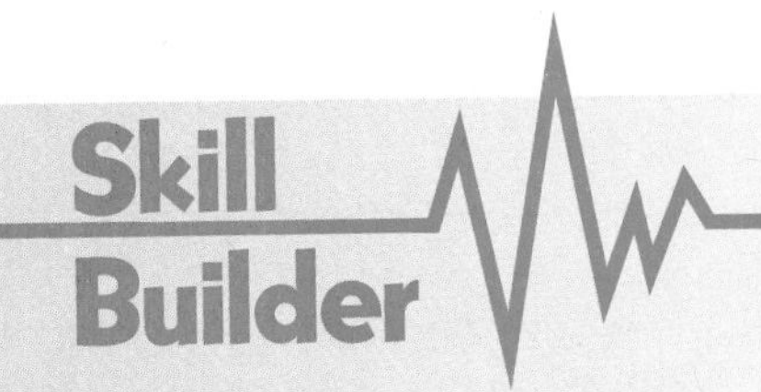

Suppose that you observe the individual hairs on your arm rise up when a balloon is placed near them. Using the concept of induction and the rules of electricity, what could you infer about the cause of this phenomenon? If you need help, refer to Observing and Inferring in the **Skill Handbook** on page 678.

21-2 Lightning—Its Causes and Effects

New Science Words

lightning rod

Objectives

- Explain the occurrence of lightning in terms of induction and static discharge.
- Evaluate the positive and negative aspects of lightning-induced forest fires.

Should Lightning-induced Forest Fires Be Left to Burn?

Have you ever seen lightning strike Earth? Lightning is actually a very large discharge of static electricity. The moving air currents in a storm cause charged particles to move about. Sometimes the charged particles become separated to form areas of positive and negative charge within a cloud. If the bottom portion of a cloud has a negative charge, it can induce a positive charge on Earth's surface. As the difference in charge increases, electrons may be attracted toward the positively charged ground. A lightning bolt occurs when many electrons are transferred at the same time. Each lightning bolt that strikes Earth may carry several billion billion electrons!

Much of the lightning you see doesn't strike Earth's surface. Electrons can also move through lightning bolts from the negative area of one cloud to the positive area of another cloud. The electrical energy in a lightning bolt produces great amounts of heat. The heat causes the air in the clouds to expand very rapidly, producing thunder. Have you ever tried to time the difference between the flash of light and the loud crack of lightning in a thunderstorm? Because sound travels much slower than light, you see the lightning flash before you hear the crack or rumble of the thunder.

The sudden discharge of so much electricity can be quite dangerous. Lightning strikes Earth many times each day. If it strikes a populated area, it can cause power outages, fires, or even injury or loss of life. One way to prevent lightning damage is to provide a path for the electrons to travel to the ground. Many buildings have lightning rods. A **lightning rod** is a pointed metal rod that extends above the highest part of a structure with a cable that connects the rod to the ground. Electric charges leak from the clouds to the lightning rod, which carries them safely into the ground.

Lightning is also responsible for an important cycle in Earth's forests. You have probably seen news reports about huge forest fires burning out of control in dry regions. Many of these fires were started by lightning. Often, the flames creep along the ground and don't destroy large healthy trees. In order to protect the beauty of our national parks and wilderness areas, these fires usually were promptly extinguished. However, it became evident to ecologists that nature's cycle of growth and renewal might not be consistent with the human version of natural beauty. Therefore, laws were passed in the 1970s to allow fires started by lightning to burn naturally unless they threaten people or property.

Many people were upset in 1989 when one-third of Yellowstone National Park was burned. Suppressing fires can allow dead debris to accumulate in the forest, and increase the risk of a rapidly spreading natural fire. In addition, when the ground is covered with debris, fires don't burn holes in the shade covering of the forest, so the plant life changes. Perhaps protecting the forest by putting out fires from lightning doesn't preserve a forest as well as allowing nature to take its course.

SECTION REVIEW

1. How are lightning and thunder produced?
2. What is the purpose of a lightning rod?

You Decide!

Suppose a lightning storm has started a large fire in Yosemite National Park in California. Should it be allowed to burn along its natural course, or should it be put out to preserve areas for human and wildlife use? Would your decision be different if the fire was caused by careless campers?

21-3 Electric Current

New Science Words

potential difference
circuit
current
dry cell
wet cell
resistance
Ohm's law

Objectives

- Describe how the potential energy of an electron changes as it moves through a simple circuit.
- Explain how a dry cell is a source of electricity.
- Conceptually and mathematically relate potential difference, resistance, and current.

Flowing Electrons

You read in Section 21-1 that if you touch a conductor after building up a negative charge in your body, electrons will move from you to the conductor. Could you light a lamp in this manner? Probably not, because the static discharge occurs for an instant and then stops. The lamp needs a continuous flow of electrons to stay lit. Why does the static discharge stop so suddenly?

How does the electric potential energy of a negatively charged object compare to that of an uncharged object?

Recall from Chapter 5 that heat flows from objects with higher temperatures to objects with lower temperatures. Heat ceases to flow when the temperatures of the objects become the same. Similarly, a negatively charged object has electrons with more potential energy to move and do work with than those of an uncharged object. This difference in potential energy causes the electrons to flow from places of higher potential energy to those with lower potential energy. In a static discharge, the potentials quickly become equal and electron flow stops.

The potential energy difference per unit of charge is called the electrical potential. The difference in potential between two different places is the **potential difference.** Potential difference is measured in volts, (V). Potential difference, often called voltage, is measured by a voltmeter. The voltage doesn't depend on the number of electrons flowing, but on a comparison of the energy carried by electrons at different points.

How can you get electrons to flow through a lamp continuously? You must connect it in an electric circuit. A **circuit** is a closed path through which electrons can flow. Because the lamp is part of a circuit, there is a potential

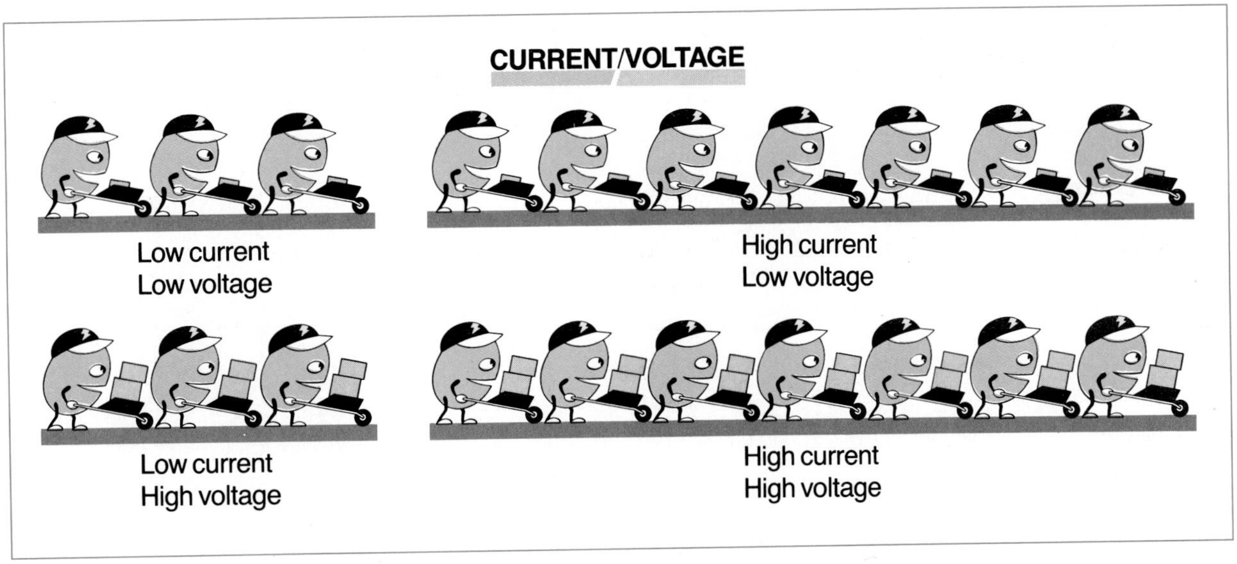

CURRENT/VOLTAGE

Low current
Low voltage

High current
Low voltage

Low current
High voltage

High current
High voltage

Figure 21-4. The amount of energy delivered each second in a circuit, or the rate of electron flow, depends on the number of electrons and how much energy each electron carries.

difference across it. If the lamp is turned on, electrons will move through it causing it to produce light. The electrons will continue to flow in the circuit as long as there is a potential difference and the path of the flowing electrons is unbroken.

What is current?

The flow of electrons through a wire or any conductor is called **current.** The amount of electric current depends on the number of electrons passing a point in a given time. The rate of flow of electrons in a circuit is measured in amperes (A). One ampere is one coulomb of charge flowing past a point in one second. One coulomb is the charge carried by 6.24 billion billion electrons. Current is measured with an ammeter.

What keeps current moving through a circuit?

In order to keep the current moving through a circuit, there must be a device that maintains a potential difference. One common source of potential difference is a battery. Unlike a static discharge from your finger to a doorknob, a battery can light a lamp by maintaining a potential difference in the circuit.

Batteries

Have you ever noticed how a tape begins to drag in a portable tape player after using it for several hours? Perhaps you decided the batteries were dead and replaced them. Do you know why batteries are required to operate your tape player?

You probably have the option of plugging your tape player into a wall outlet, or using batteries to supply the

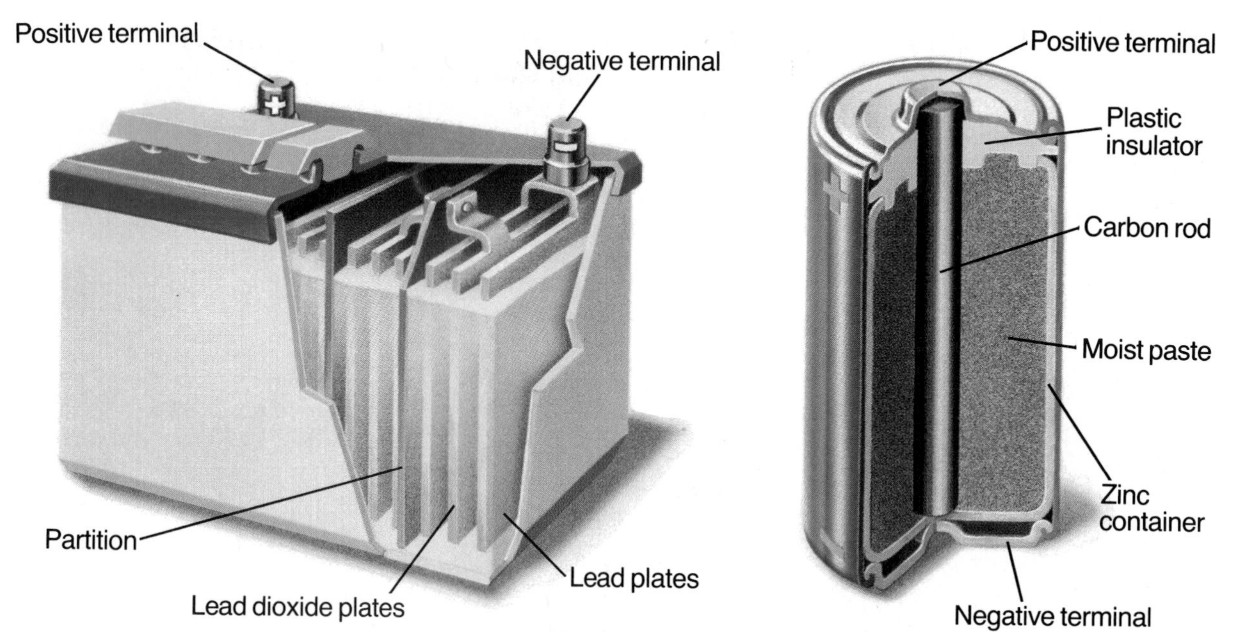

Figure 21-5. The car battery on the left is a series of wet cells, and the dry cell on the right can be connected in series with other dry cells to form a battery.

energy it needs to operate. If you want to take the tape player outside, you will have to use batteries, or dry cells. Look at the dry cell shown in Figure 21-5. Can you locate the positive and negative terminals of the dry cell in the diagram? They are located at opposite ends. Notice that the zinc container of the dry cell contains a moist chemical paste with a solid carbon rod suspended in the middle. The carbon rod forms the positive terminal of the dry cell, and the zinc can forms the negative terminal. A **dry cell** can act as an electron pump because it has a potential difference between the positive and negative terminals. Batteries are usually combinations of dry cells.

When the two terminals of the battery are connected in a circuit, electrons are released from the carbon rod as a chemical reaction occurs between the zinc and the chemical paste. The carbon rod becomes positive, forming the positive (+) terminal of the battery. Extra electrons accumulate on the zinc cell, making it negative. The potential difference between these two terminals causes current to flow through the closed circuit. As long as the chemical reaction continues, electrons are pumped from the negative to positive terminals of the dry cell. Two or more cells can be connected together to produce a higher voltage. How many dry cells does your tape player or camera require?

Another way to operate your tape player is by plugging it into a wall socket. The potential difference between

Science and READING

Read an automobile owner's manual to see if it explains how to "jump start" a car with a discharged battery. Explain this process to your classmates.

two holes in a wall socket is 120 V. The electricity coming out of the wall socket is provided by an electric generator, instead of a battery.

Batteries can also be made up of a series of wet cells. A **wet cell** contains two connected plates made of different metals or metallic compounds in an electrolyte solution. One of the most common wet cell batteries is a car battery. Most car batteries contain wet cells made up of lead and lead dioxide plates in a sulfuric acid solution, as shown in Figure 21-5. As a chemical reaction occurs between lead and sulfuric acid inside the battery, electrons move from the lead plates through the conductor to the lead dioxide plates. As a result, a negative terminal with an excess of electrons and a positive terminal with a shortage of electrons form. This potential difference produces a current in the circuit between the battery and various parts of the car. Can you think of any other situations where wet cell batteries are used?

How does a car battery maintain a potential difference in a circuit?

Resistance

One function of the car battery mentioned earlier is to light various light bulbs in the car's electric circuits. Do you know what makes a light bulb glow? Look at the light bulb in Figure 21-6. Part of the circuit through the bulb contains a filament. As a current flows through the filament, electrical energy is converted by the filament into light and heat. The current loses electrical energy as it moves through the filament because the filament, as do most materials, resists the flow of electrons through it.

Resistance is the tendency for a material to oppose the flow of electrons. With the exception of a few substances called superconductors, all conductors have some resistance. The amount of resistance varies with each conductor. Resistance is measured in ohms (Ω).

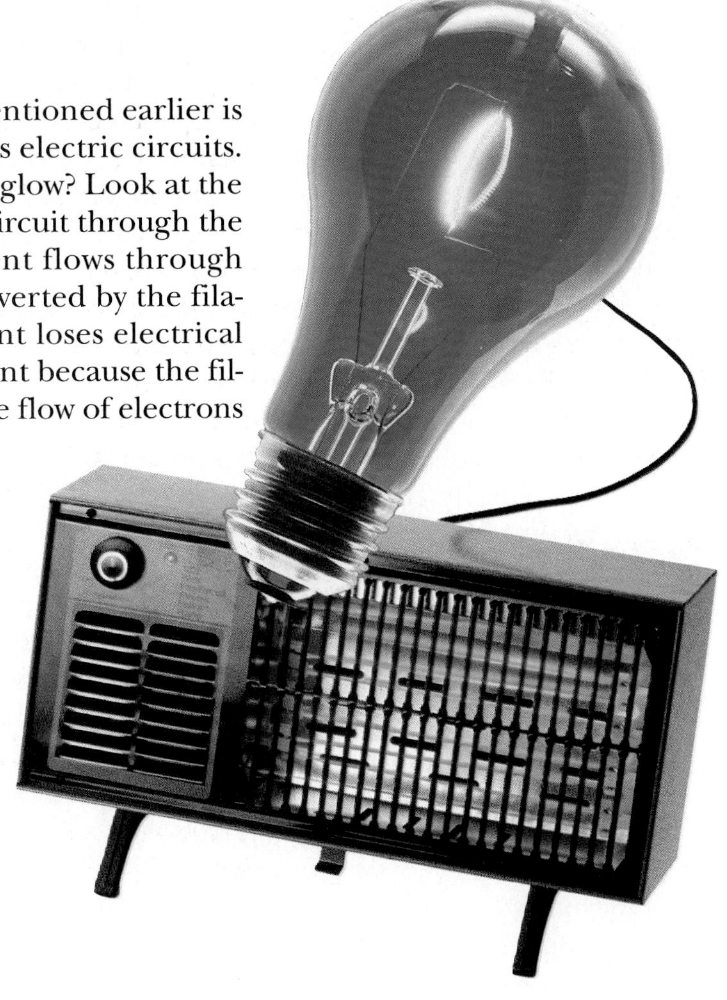

Figure 21-6. The light bulb and the heater glow and give off heat as current moves through them because they each have a high resistance to the flow of electrons.

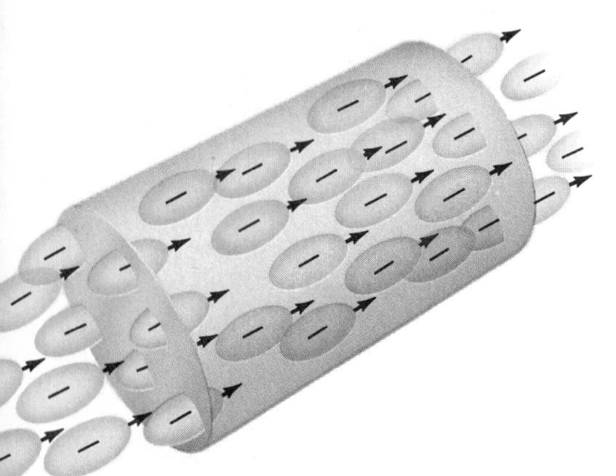

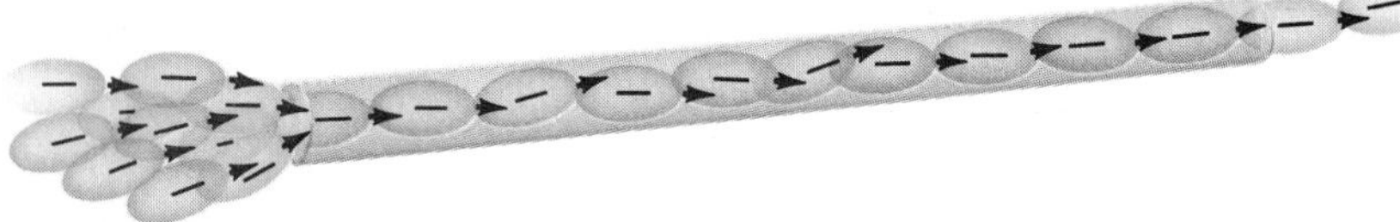

Copper is an excellent conductor; it has low resistance to the flow of electrons. Copper is used in household wiring because very little electrical energy is converted to thermal energy as current passes through the wires. In contrast, tungsten wire glows white-hot as current passes through it. Tungsten's high resistance to current makes it very suitable for use as filaments in light bulbs.

Figure 21-7. A short, thick piece of wire has less resistance than a long, thin piece of wire.

The size of wires also affects their resistance. Figure 21-7 illustrates how electrons have more room to travel through thick wires than thin wires. In wires of the same

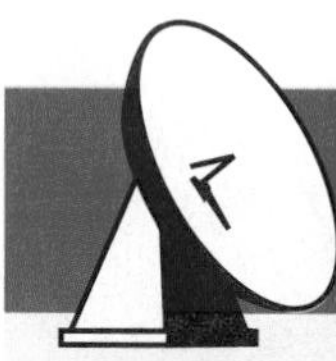

TECHNOLOGY

Shake and Bake Superconductors

Mix together some oxides of lanthanum, barium, and copper, grind them up, and bake them in a furnace with some oxygen and, presto, you have made your own superconductor. After you cool your superconductor to its critical temperature, it will offer very little resistance and produce very little heat as electrons flow through it. The first superconductors were cooled to temperatures near absolute zero (273°C) to achieve these results. However, your "shake and bake" compound will become superconductive at a comparatively warm 178°C. In other words, your superconductor can be cooled easier and with less expense than the first superconductors.

The future of these new superconductive materials is promising and challenging. First, however, we must find ways to fashion these brittle superconducting materials into wires and thin films. The rewards of solving these problems are tremendous. For example, high powered electric cars, magnetically levitated trains, super fast computers, and extremely efficient power transmission might become realities.

Think Critically: Even though superconductive materials lose very little energy as heat, a power transmission system using these new superconductors would not be energy-loss free. Where would these energy losses occur?

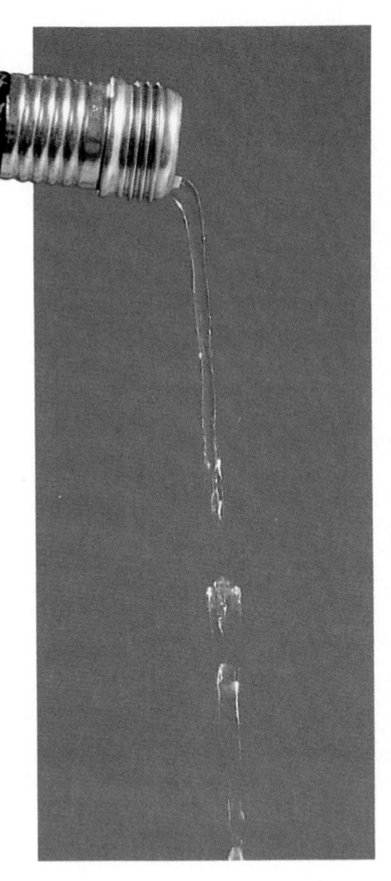

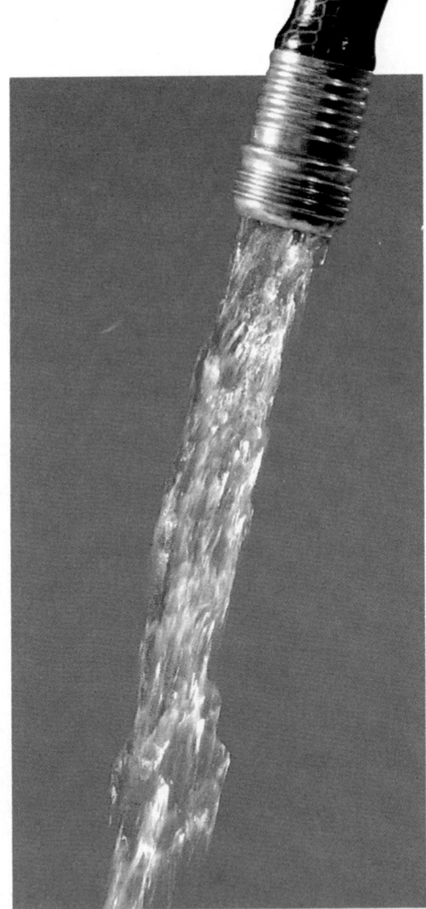

Figure 21-8. As the height of the hose increases, the potential difference increases and water flows at a faster rate. Electrons also flow at a faster rate when the potential difference in a circuit is increased.

length and material, thinner wires have greater resistance to electron flow. Likewise, if the diameters of two wires of the same material are the same, the longer wire offers a greater resistance. In most conductors, the resistance also increases as the temperature increases.

Ohm's Law

When you try to understand the relationship between voltage, current, and resistance, it is helpful to think of the way water behaves in a pipe. If one end of the pipe is higher than the other, there is a difference in the potential energy of the water due to gravity. This causes a stream, or current, of water to flow. If the height difference increases, the current increases. In a similar way, a greater potential difference in a circuit also causes the electric current to increase. Also, just as the walls and any obstructions in the pipe resist the flow of water, so do atoms in a wire resist the flow of electricity. As a result, the current in a circuit depends on both the voltage and the resistance.

This relationship is expressed mathematically in Ohm's law. **Ohm's law** states that the current is equal to the potential difference divided by the resistance.

$$\text{current (amperes)} = \frac{\text{potential difference (volts)}}{\text{resistance (ohms)}}$$

$$I = V/R$$

Did You Know?

The highest synthetic potential difference ever achieved was more than 30 million volts.

EXAMPLE PROBLEM: Calculating Current

Problem Statement:

Strategy Hint: Make sure the decimal is correctly placed.

A light bulb with a resistance of 160 Ω is plugged into a 120-V outlet. What is the current flowing through the bulb?

Known Information:

resistance, $R = 160\ \Omega$
voltage, $V = 120$ V

Unknown Information:

current (I)

Equation to Use:

$I = V/R$

Solution:

$I = V/R = 120\ \text{V}/160\ \Omega = 0.75$ A

PRACTICE PROBLEMS

Strategy Hint: Your answer will be in amperes.

1. Find the current flowing through a wire if its resistance is 20 Ω and it is connected to a 12-V battery. What if it was connected to a 6-V battery?

Strategy Hint: Your answer will be in ohms. Use $R = V/I$.

2. The current flowing through a lamp is 1.5 A. It is plugged into a 120-V outlet. What is the resistance of the lamp?

SECTION REVIEW

1. How does a current traveling through a circuit differ from the static discharge that may occur when you touch a metal doorknob?
2. Briefly describe how a carbon-zinc dry cell supplies electricity for your tape player.
3. Calculate the potential difference across a 25-Ω resistor if a 0.3-A current is flowing through it.
4. **Apply:** How is the current in a circuit affected if the resistance is doubled? What if both the voltage and resistance are doubled?

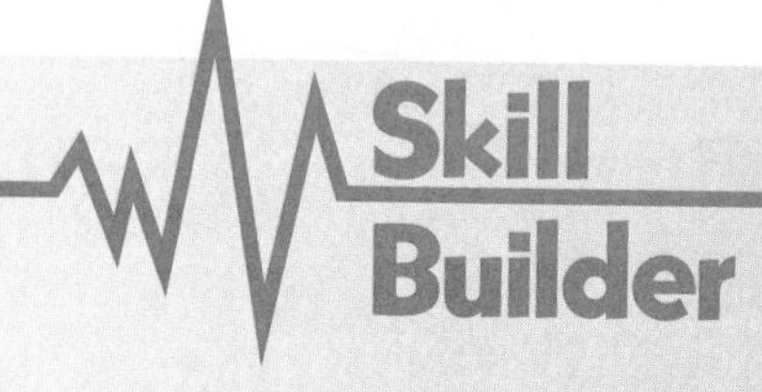

Making and Using Tables

Suppose you individually connect three copper wires of unequal length to a 1.5-V dry cell and an ammeter. The following currents were obtained: wire #1, 1.2 A; wire #2, 1.4 A; wire #3, 1.1 A. Make a table showing current (given) and resistance (use Ohm's law). If you need help, refer to Making and Using Tables in the **Skill Handbook** on page 686.

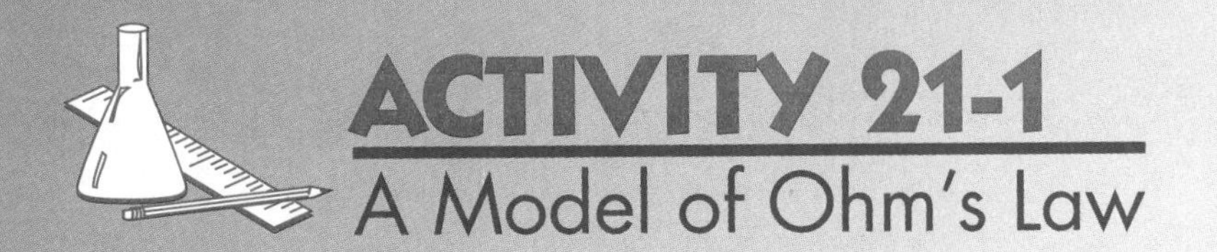

ACTIVITY 21-1
A Model of Ohm's Law

Problem: *How is flowing water like flowing electrons?*

Materials
- plastic funnel
- ring stand with ring
- rubber tubing (1 m)
- meterstick
- 2 beakers (250 mL)
- stopwatch or clock

Procedure
1. Copy the data table below.
2. Assemble the apparatus as shown. Place the funnel as high as possible.
3. Measure the height from the top of the funnel to the outlet end of the rubber tubing, in meters. Record your data on the table.
4. Pour 200 mL water into the funnel fast enough to keep it full, but not overflowing.
5. Measure the time for 0.10 L water to flow into the lower beaker, and record it on the table.
6. Repeat Steps 2 through 4 at least three more times, lowering the funnel for each trial.

Data and Observations

Trial	Height (m)	Time (s)	Rate (L/s)
1			
2			
3			

Analyze
1. Gravity causing water to move can be compared to voltage causing electrons to move. Which trial can represent a circuit with the highest voltage?
2. The rate (L/sec) of flow of water from the tubing can be compared to current. Which trial can represent the highest current?
3. If voltage is increased, what happens to current?

Conclude and Apply
4. According to Ohm's law, what should happen to the current if the voltage stays the same but the resistance is reduced?
5. If a long tube has more resistance, what should happen to rate of flow of water if the tube is shorter?

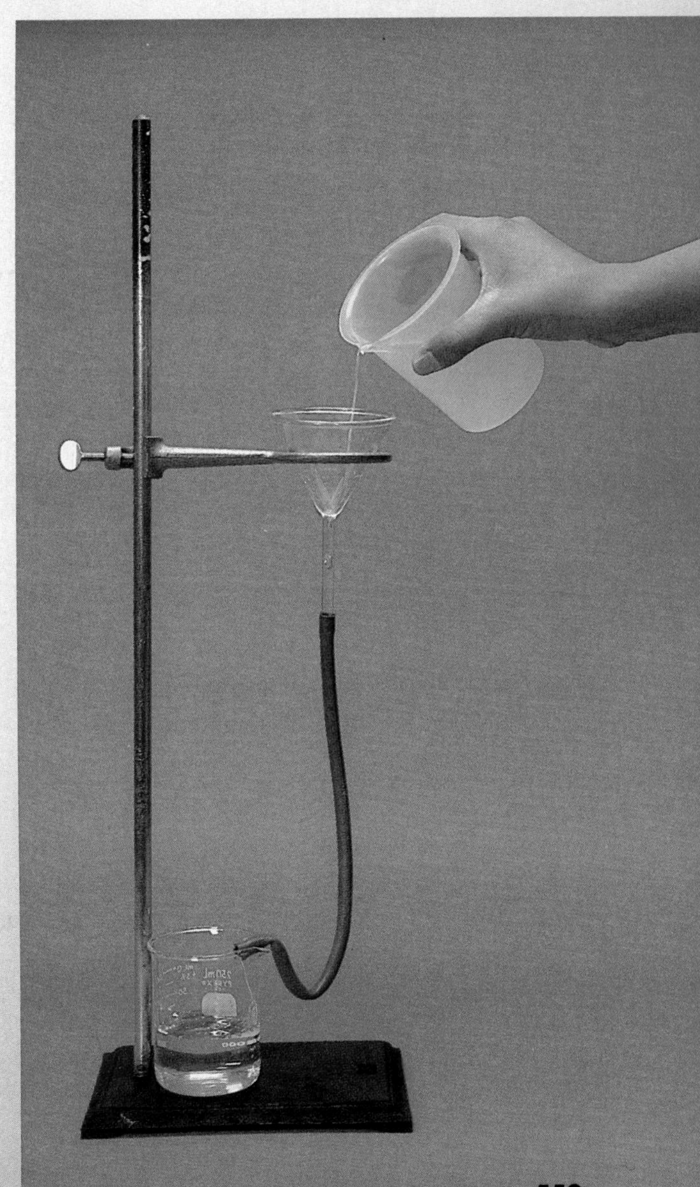

21-4 Electrical Circuits

New Science Words

series circuit
parallel circuits

Objectives

- Sketch a series and a parallel circuit, and list applications of each type of circuit.
- Recognize the function of circuit breakers and fuses.

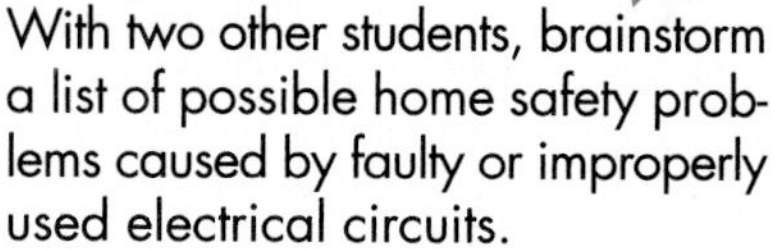

With two other students, brainstorm a list of possible home safety problems caused by faulty or improperly used electrical circuits.

Series Circuits

Look around you. How many electrical devices, such as lights, alarm clocks, stereos, and televisions, do you see that are plugged into wall outlets? These devices all rely on circuits to supply electricity where it is needed. Most circuits include a voltage source, a conductor, and one or more devices that use the electricity to do work.

Consider, for example, a circuit that includes an electric hair dryer. The dryer must be plugged into a wall outlet to receive current. The dryer and the circuit in the house both contain conducting wires to carry the current. A generator at a power plant probably produces a potential difference in the circuit, causing the electrons to move. The hair dryer turns the electricity into thermal and mechanical energy to do work. When you unplug the hair dryer, or turn off its switch, you are opening the circuit and breaking the path of the current. When this happens, does the dryer still operate?

Figure 21-9. There is only one path for electrons to follow in a series circuit.

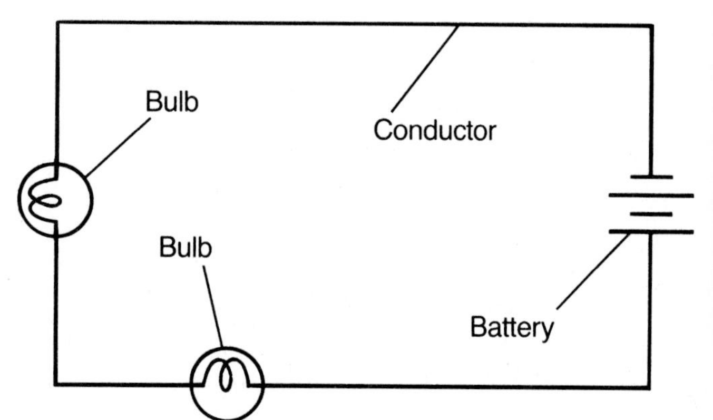

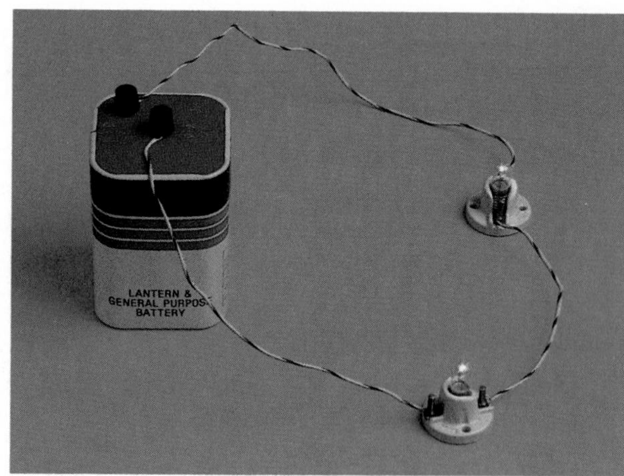

There are several kinds of circuits. One kind of circuit is called a series circuit. Some holiday lights are wired together in a series circuit. In a **series circuit**, the current has only one path it can travel along. Look at the diagram of the series circuit in Figure 21-9. If you have ever decorated a window or a tree with a string of lights, you may have had the frustrating experience of trying to find one burned out bulb. How can one faulty bulb cause the whole string to be out? Because the parts of a series circuit are wired one after another, the amount of current is the same through every part. When any part of a series circuit is disconnected, no current can flow through the circuit. This is called an "open" circuit. The electrons require a closed path or they won't move at all. Does this explain how a broken bulb can ruin a whole string of lights?

Figure 21-10 shows the symbols used in diagramming electric circuits. Notice how the switch must be closed for the circuit to be continuous.

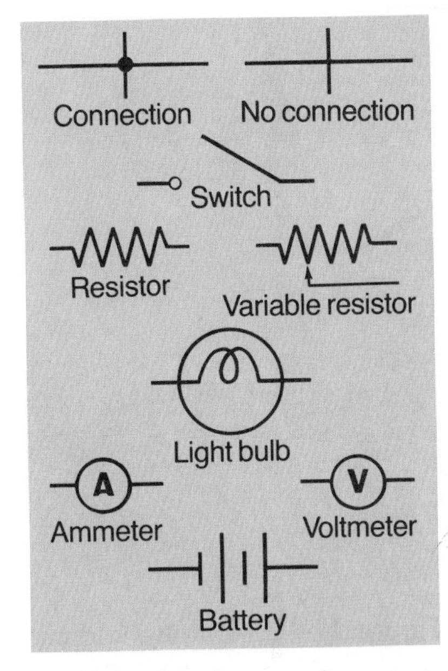

Figure 21-10. A circuit diagram is very easy to draw when you use these symbols.

Parallel Circuits

What would happen if your home was wired in series and you turned off a light? All other lights and appliances in your home would go out too! Fortunately, houses, and some holiday lights, are wired in parallel. **Parallel circuits** contain separate branches for current to move through. Look at the parallel circuit in Figure 21-11. The current splits up to flow through the different branches. More current flows through the paths of lowest resistance. Because all branches connect the same two points

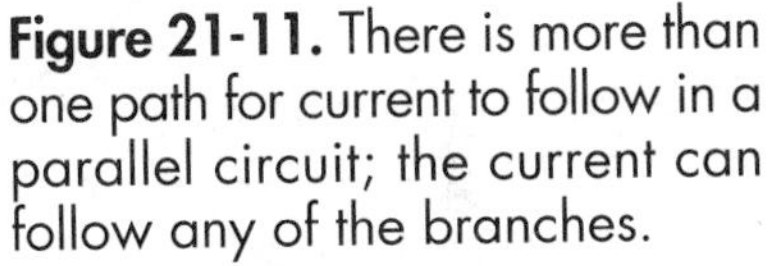

Figure 21-11. There is more than one path for current to follow in a parallel circuit; the current can follow any of the branches.

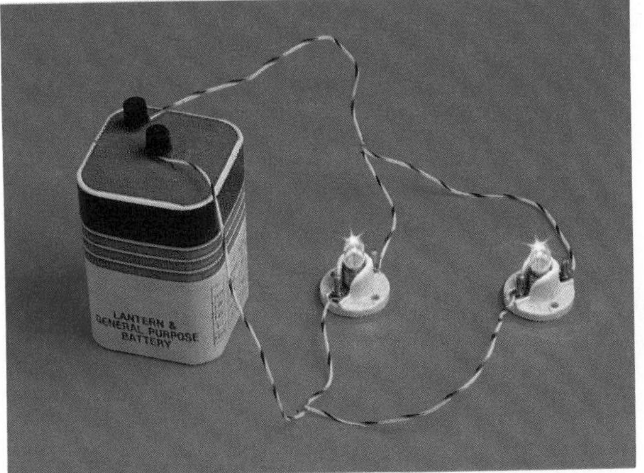

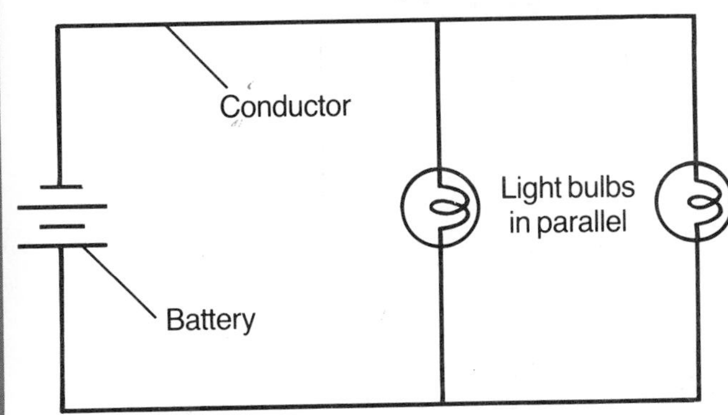

of the circuit, the potential difference is the same in each branch.

Parallel circuits have the advantage that when one branch of the circuit is opened, such as when you turn a light off, the current continues to flow through the other branches. Think again of the example of the hair dryer. Would you expect it to be part of a series or parallel circuit?

Household Circuits

Try to count how many different things in your home require electricity. Do you leave many appliances plugged in all the time for convenience? You don't see the wires in the circuits because most of the electrical wiring in your house or apartment is hidden behind the walls, ceilings, and floors. This wiring is composed mostly of a combination of parallel circuits connected in a very organized and logical network. Electrical current enters your home from overhead or underground wires. Figure 21-12 shows how electrical current passes through a meter to monitor your energy use. The main switch and circuit breaker box serves as a sort of electrical headquarters for your home. Parallel circuits branch out from the breaker box to wall sockets, major appliances, and lights.

Figure 21-12. A household circuit is a complex combination of parallel circuits.

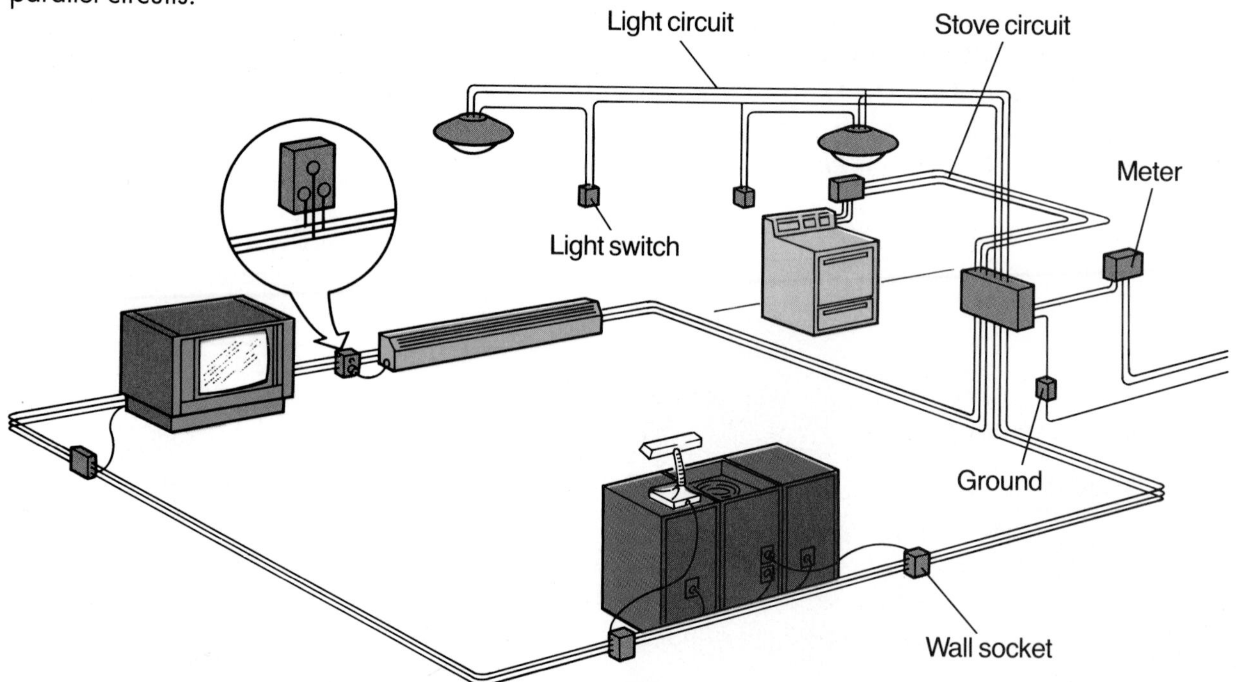

Many appliances can draw current from the same circuit, so protection against overheating must be built in. If a great amount of current is drawn through the wires, the wires can actually become hot enough to start a fire. Either a fuse or a circuit breaker is wired between every parallel circuit and the main switch box as a safety device.

What does it mean to say somebody has "blown a fuse"? Usually it refers to somebody losing his or her temper. This expression comes from the function of an electrical fuse. A fuse contains a small piece of metal that melts if the current causes the circuit wire to heat up too much. When it melts, it causes a break in the circuit and prevents more current from flowing through the overloaded circuit. To complete the circuit, you must replace the damaged fuse with a new one.

A circuit breaker is another guard against overheating a wire. A circuit breaker contains a piece of metal that bends when it gets hot. The bending causes a switch to open the circuit, preventing the flow of more current. Circuit breakers can usually be reset by flipping the switch. Before you reset a circuit breaker or replace a blown fuse, you should unplug some of the appliances from the overloaded circuit.

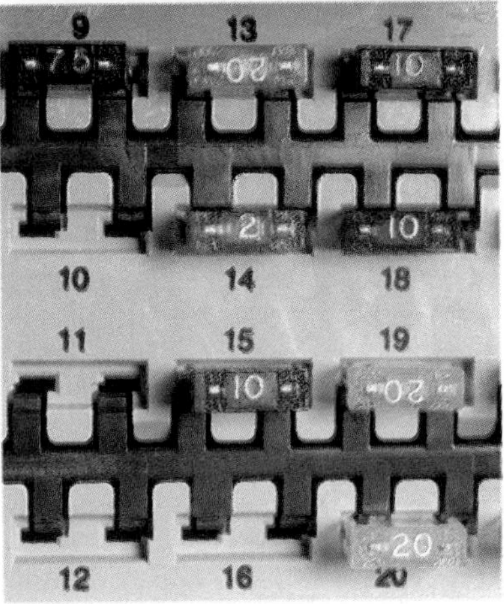

Figure 21-13. The circuit breaker (above) and fuses (below) prevent circuits from overheating.

SECTION REVIEW

1. Use symbols to draw a series circuit containing a battery, an open switch, a resistor, and a light bulb.
2. Use symbols to draw a parallel circuit with a battery and two resistors wired in parallel.
3. Compare and contrast fuses and circuit breakers. Which is easier to use?
4. **Apply:** Explain why buildings are wired in parallel instead of series circuits.

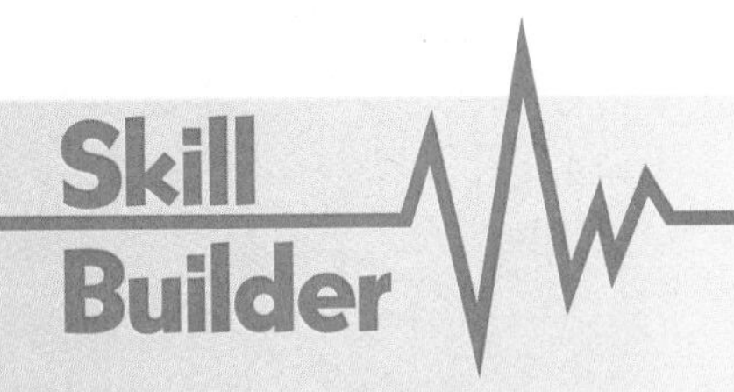

Hypothesizing

You are walking by a sign made of lighted bulbs. One of the lights begins to flicker and goes out. All other bulbs are still lit. Use your knowledge of circuits to form a hypothesis to explain why only one bulb went out instead of the entire sign. If you need help, refer to Hypothesizing in the **Skill Handbook** on page 682.

ACTIVITY 21-2
Electric Circuits

Problem: *How do parallel and series circuits work?*

Materials  

- aluminum foil
- cellophane tape
- scissors
- 3 lights with sockets
- 6 paper clips
- battery (6 or 9 volt)

Procedure

1. On a sheet of paper, draw a series circuit of three lights and a battery as shown.
2. Make conductors by taping a 30-cm piece of cellophane tape to a sheet of aluminum foil. Use scissors to cut this into three narrow strips.
3. Tape the conductor strips over the conductor lines on your drawing. Leave loose ends of about 3 cm at the lights and battery.
4. Connect the lights to the circuit with the paper clips.
5. Test the circuit by touching the remaining two conductor ends to the poles of the battery.
6. Draw a three-light parallel circuit on another sheet of paper and repeat the procedure.

Analyze

1. If one light is removed from the series circuit, will the other lights still work? Is this also true of the parallel circuit?
2. In which kind of circuit do the lights shine the brightest?
3. Mark your circuit diagram with (+) and (−) to identify the battery poles.
4. Mark your circuit diagram with arrows to show the flow of electrons through the circuit.

Conclude and Apply

5. Where in the parallel circuit would you place a switch to control all three lights? Where would a switch be placed to control only one light?
6. How do you know that your house lights are connected in parallel to each other?
7. How can you make a switch that will work in your circuit?

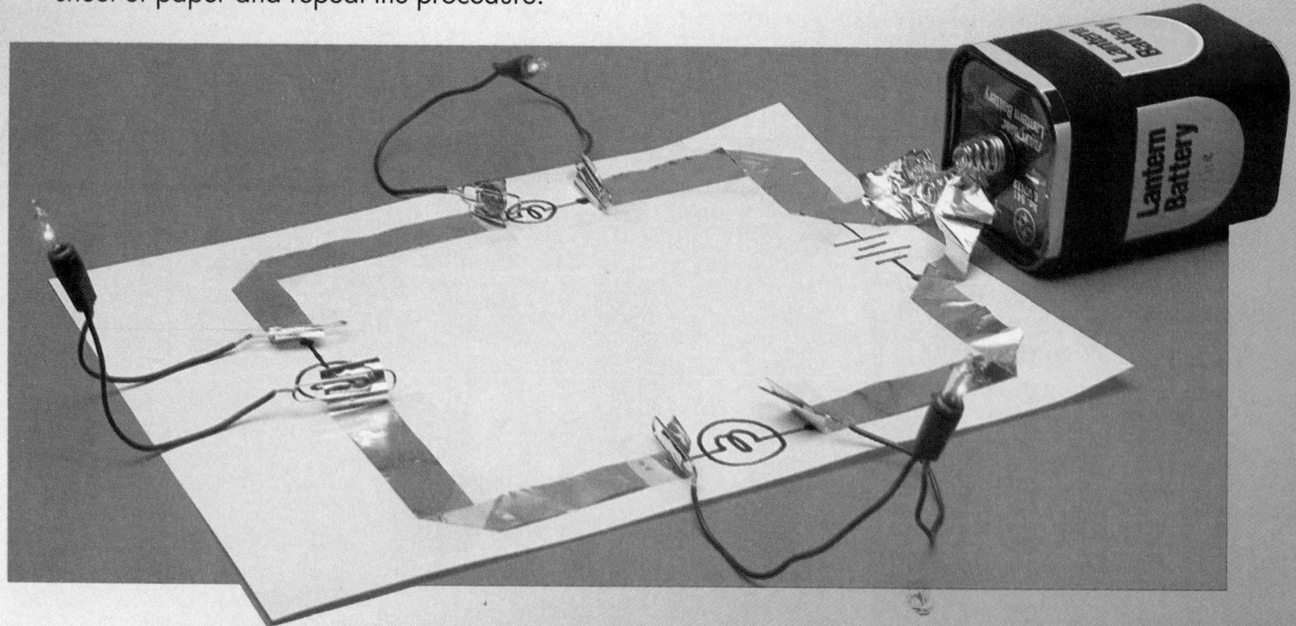

Electrical Power and Energy

21-5

Objectives

- Explain and calculate electric power.
- Calculate the amount of electrical energy in kilowatt-hours.

New Science Words

electrical power
kilowatt-hour

Electrical Power

How does electrical energy do work?

What do you think of when you hear the word *power?* The word *power* has many different meanings. Earlier, in Chapter 7, you read that power is the rate at which work is done. Electricity can do work for us. Electrical energy is easily converted to other types of energy to do work. For example, the blades of a fan can rotate and cool you as electrical energy is changed into mechanical energy. An iron changes electrical energy into heat. **Electrical power** is the rate at which electrical energy is converted to another form of energy.

Table 21-1

ENERGY USED BY HOME APPLIANCES

Appliance	Time of Usage (hours/day)	Power Usage (watts)	Energy Usage (kWh/day)
Hair dryer, blower	0.25	1000	0.25
Microwave oven	0.5	1450	0.73
Radio/record player	2.5	109	0.27
Range (oven)	1	2600	2.60
Refrigerator/freezer (15 cu ft, frostless)	24	615	14.76
Television (color)	3.25	200	0.65
Electric toothbrush	0.08	7	0.0006
100-watt light bulb	6	100	0.60
40-watt fluorescent light bulb	1	40	0.04

Remove dust from light bulbs regularly, and you might be able to user lower wattage bulbs and save energy.

The rate at which different appliances use energy varies. Appliances are often advertised with their power rating, which depends on the amount of electrical energy each appliance needs to operate. Table 21-1 shows the power requirements of some appliances.

Electrical power is expressed in watts (W), or kilowatts, (kW). The amount of power used by an appliance can be calculated by multiplying the potential difference by the current.

$$\text{power} = \text{current} \times \text{voltage}$$
$$\text{watts} = \text{amperes} \times \text{volts}$$
$$P = I \times V$$

One watt of power is produced when one ampere of current flows through a circuit with a potential difference of one volt. Look again at Table 21-1. Which appliance requires the most electrical power to operate? You can tell by looking at the number of watts listed for that appliance under the power usage column. Now see which appliance requires the least amount of electrical power to operate. The example problem below shows you how to calculate the electrical power usage for an appliance. This can be easily done as long as you know the values of the current and voltage.

EXAMPLE PROBLEM: Calculating Power

Problem Statement:

A calculator has a 0.1-A current flowing through it. It operates with a potential difference of 9 V. How much power does it use?

Known Information:

Strategy Hint: Remember that electrical power is measured in watts.

current, $I = 0.1$ A
potential difference, $V = 9$ V

Unknown Information:

power (P)

Equation to Use:

$P = I \times V$

Solution:

$P = I \times V = (0.1 \text{ A})(9 \text{ V}) = 0.9 \text{ W}$

PRACTICE PROBLEMS

Strategy Hint: Be sure your decimal is correctly placed after you multiply.

1. A lamp operates with a current of 0.625 A and a potential difference of 120 V. How much power does the lamp use?

Strategy Hint: Your answer should be in amperes.

2. A microwave oven uses 1000 W of power. The voltage source is 120 V. What is the current flowing through the microwave?

Electrical Energy

Why is it important that you not waste electricity? Most electrical energy is produced from natural resources, which are limited in supply. Electrical energy also costs you money. All the electricity you use in your home is measured by a device called an electrical meter. You have probably noticed that the meter for your home has a wheel that spins quickly when you are using a great deal of electricity and is stopped when no electricity is being used. The amount of electrical energy you use depends on the power required by appliances in your home and how long they are used. For example, you can calculate the amount of energy a refrigerator uses in a day by multiplying the power required by the amount of time it uses that power.

$$\text{energy} = \text{power} \times \text{time}$$
$$\text{kWh} = \text{kW} \times \text{h}$$
$$E = P \times t$$

The unit of electrical energy is the **kilowatt-hour** (kWh). One kilowatt-hour is 1000 watts of power used for one hour. The electric utility company charges you periodically for each kilowatt-hour you use. You can figure your electric bill by multiplying the energy used by the cost per kilowatt-hour. Table 21-2 shows some sample costs of running electrical appliances.

MINI-Lab

How much power operates an electric toy?

Remove the battery from an electric toy. Fasten wires to the battery with tape or rubber bands. Attach one wire to the proper battery connection in the toy. Attach the other wire to an ammeter. Connect the other pole of the ammeter to the other connection in the toy. Turn on the toy and read the amperage on the ammeter. Determine the voltage from the battery size. Use voltage and amperage to calculate the electric power in watts. Does power usage change if the toy is allowed to run on different speeds? When is power usage the highest?

Table 21-2

MONTHLY COSTS OF USING APPLIANCES

	APPLIANCE		
	Hair dryer	Stereo	Color television
Average power in watts	600	109	200
Hours used daily	.25	3.0	2.5
Hours used monthly	7.5	90.0	75.0
Monthly watt hours	4500	9810	15 000
kWh used a month	4.5	9.81	15.000
Rate charged	$0.09	$0.09	$0.09
Monthly cost	$0.41	$0.88	$1.35

EXAMPLE PROBLEM: Calculating Electrical Energy

Problem Statement:

A refrigerator is one of the major users of electrical power in your home. If it uses 700 W and runs 24 hours each day, how much energy (in kWh) is used in one day?

Known Information:

Strategy Hint: Convert W to kW before you multiply.

power, $P = 700$ W
time, $t = 24$ h

Unknown Information:

energy (E)

Equation to Use:

$E = P \times t$

Solution:

Convert W to kW, 700 W/1000 W/kW = 0.7 kW
$E = P \times t = (0.7 \text{ kW})(24 \text{ h}) = 16.8 \text{ kWh}$

PRACTICE PROBLEMS

Strategy Hint: Remember to convert watts to kilowatts.

Strategy Hint: Use the equation $P = E/t$; convert minutes to hours.

1. A 100-W light bulb is left on for 5.5 hours. How many kilowatt-hours of energy is used?
2. How much power is used by an electric hair dryer that uses 0.15 kWh of energy during 6 minutes of use?

To get an idea of energy costs in your home, you can make a list of all the appliances you use and add together their monthly energy costs. How do you think this value would compare to your electric bill?

SECTION REVIEW

1. What is electrical power?
2. A television uses a current of 1.5 A at 120 V. The television is used for 2 hours. Calculate the power used in kW and the energy used in kWh.
3. **Apply:** Assume your 110-W stereo is used 3 hours each day. If electricity costs 9 cents per kilowatt-hour, find the cost of listening to your stereo for one day.

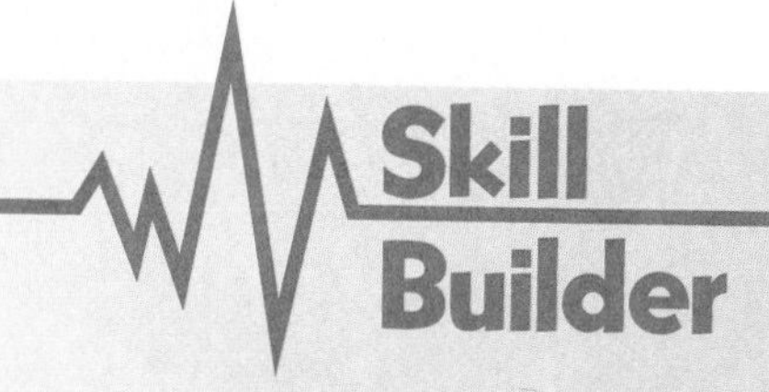

Concept Mapping

Prepare a concept map that shows the steps in calculating the energy used in operating an electrical device with known voltage and current for a known amount of time. If you need help, refer to Concept Mapping in the **Skill Handbook** on pages 684 and 685.

CHAPTER

REVIEW

SUMMARY

21-1: Electric Charge

1. Static electricity is the accumulation of electric charges on an object.

2. An electrical conductor is a material that allows electrons to move through it easily. An electrical insulator is a material that doesn't allow electrons to move through it easily.

3. An electroscope contains two suspended metal leaves in a jar that move apart when induced with an electrical charge.

21-2: Science and Society: Lightning—Its Causes and Effects

1. Clouds often contain areas of positively and negatively charged particles and can cause nearby objects to become charged by induction. A static discharge, lightning, occurs when excess electrons flow between the cloud and the charged object.

2. Some lightning-caused forest fires are allowed to burn as part of the natural processes in the forest.

21-3: Electric Current

1. The potential energy stored in an electron decreases as it moves through a circuit.

2. A dry cell creates a potential difference in a circuit, causing the electrons to flow.

3. Ohm's law states that the current in a circuit is equal to the potential difference divided by the resistance.

21-4: Electrical Circuits

1. Current only has one path along which it can travel in a series circuit. Parallel circuits provide more than one path for current to follow.

2. Circuit breakers and fuses are safety devices that open a circuit if the current becomes too great.

21-5: Electrical Power and Energy

1. Electrical power is the rate at which electrical energy can be transformed into other kinds of energy.

2. A kilowatt-hour is a thousand watts of power used for one hour.

KEY SCIENCE WORDS

a. **circuit**
b. **conductor**
c. **current**
d. **dry cell**
e. **electrical power**
f. **electric field**
g. **electroscope**
h. **insulator**
i. **kilowatt-hour**
j. **lightning rod**
k. **Ohm's law**
l. **parallel circuits**
m. **potential difference**
n. **resistance**
o. **series circuit**
p. **static electricity**
q. **wet cell**

UNDERSTANDING VOCABULARY

Match each phrase with the correct term from the list of Key Science Words.

1. buildup of electric charges on an object
2. exerts a force on an electric charge
3. a material through which electrons can move
4. a device that is used to detect electric charges
5. closed path through which electrons flow
6. composed of two connected plates made of different metals or metallic compounds in an electrolyte solution
7. opposes the flow of electrons in a conductor
8. electric current has at least two separate paths
9. the rate at which electrical energy is converted to a different form of energy
10. relates voltage and resistance to current

CHAPTER REVIEW

CHECKING CONCEPTS

Choose the word or phrase that completes the sentence or answers the question.

1. An object becomes positively charged when it ______.
   a. loses electrons **c.** gains electrons
   b. loses protons **d.** none of these
2. When two negative charges are brought close together, they will ______.
   a. repel **c.** neither attract nor repel
   b. attract **d.** ground
3. As the distance from a charged particle increases, the strength of the electric field ____.
   a. varies **c.** increases
   b. remains the same **d.** decreases
4. An example of a good insulator is ______.
   a. copper **c.** wood
   b. silver **d.** salt water
5. Connecting a charged object to Earth in order to discharge the object into Earth is called ______.
   a. charging **c.** conduction
   b. grounding **d.** induction
6. The difference in potential energy per unit charge between two electrodes is measured in ______.
   a. amperes **c.** ohms
   b. coulombs **d.** volts
7. The difference in energy carried by electrons at different points in a circuit will determine the ______.
   a. voltage **c.** current
   b. resistance **d.** power
8. Resistance in an electrical wire causes electrical energy to be converted to ______.
   a. chemical energy **c.** heat
   b. nuclear energy **d.** sound
9. Which of the following wires would tend to have the least amount of electrical resistance?
   a. long **c.** hot
   b. fiberglass **d.** thick
10. Electrical energy is measured in ______.
   a. volts **c.** kilowatts
   b. newtons **d.** kilowatt-hours

UNDERSTANDING CONCEPTS

Complete each sentence.

11. The number of protons is equal to the number of ______ in an electrically neutral atom.
12. ______ occurs when a charged object causes electrons on a second object to rearrange without touching it.
13. In a battery, ______ energy is converted into electrical energy.
14. When any part of a ______ circuit is disconnected, no current can flow.
15. ______ open a circuit when too much current flows through it.

THINK AND WRITE CRITICALLY

16. Compare and contrast static electricity and current electricity.
17. How are the atoms of conductors different from the atoms of insulators?
18. What causes electrons to move through a circuit? What happens to the electrons' potential energy as they pass through an electrical appliance?
19. How does lightning occur?
20. How are resistance and potential difference related to the amount of current flowing through a circuit?

APPLY

21. Lightning rods are conductors on roofs of buildings that are grounded. How do they protect buildings from lightning?

22. Explain how an electroscope could be used to detect a negatively charged object.

23. A toy car has a 1.5-A current and its internal resistance is 2 ohms. How much voltage does the car require?

24. The current flowing through an appliance connected to a 120-V electron source is 2 A. How many kilowatt-hours of electrical energy does the appliance use in 4 hours?

25. You are asked to connect a stereo, a television, a VCR, and a lamp in a single, complex circuit. Would you connect these appliances in parallel or in series? How would you prevent an electrical fire? Explain your answers.

MORE SKILL BUILDERS

If you need help, refer to the Skill Handbook.

1. Making and Using Graphs: The resistance in a 1-cm length copper wire at different temperatures is shown below.

Resistance in Microohms	Temperature in °C
2	50
3	200
5	475

Construct a line graph for the above data. Is copper a better conductor on a cold day or a hot day?

2. Interpreting Data: Look at the power usage of the appliances in Table 21-1 and calculate the current each appliance pulls from a 120-V electron source. Which appliance draws the most current?

3. Concept Mapping: List the events that occur when an electroscope is brought near a positively charged object and a negatively charged object. Be sure to indicate which way electrons flow and the charge and responses of the leaves.

4. Using Variables, Constants, and Controls: Design an experiment to test the effect on current and voltage in a circuit when two batteries of equal voltage are connected in parallel and in series. What is your hypothesis? What are the variables and control?

PROJECTS

1. Research the origin and history of lightning rods. Relate your findings in a written report.

2. Obtain information from your electric company about safety rules of using electricity and make a poster to display.

CHAPTER

22 Magnetism and Its Uses

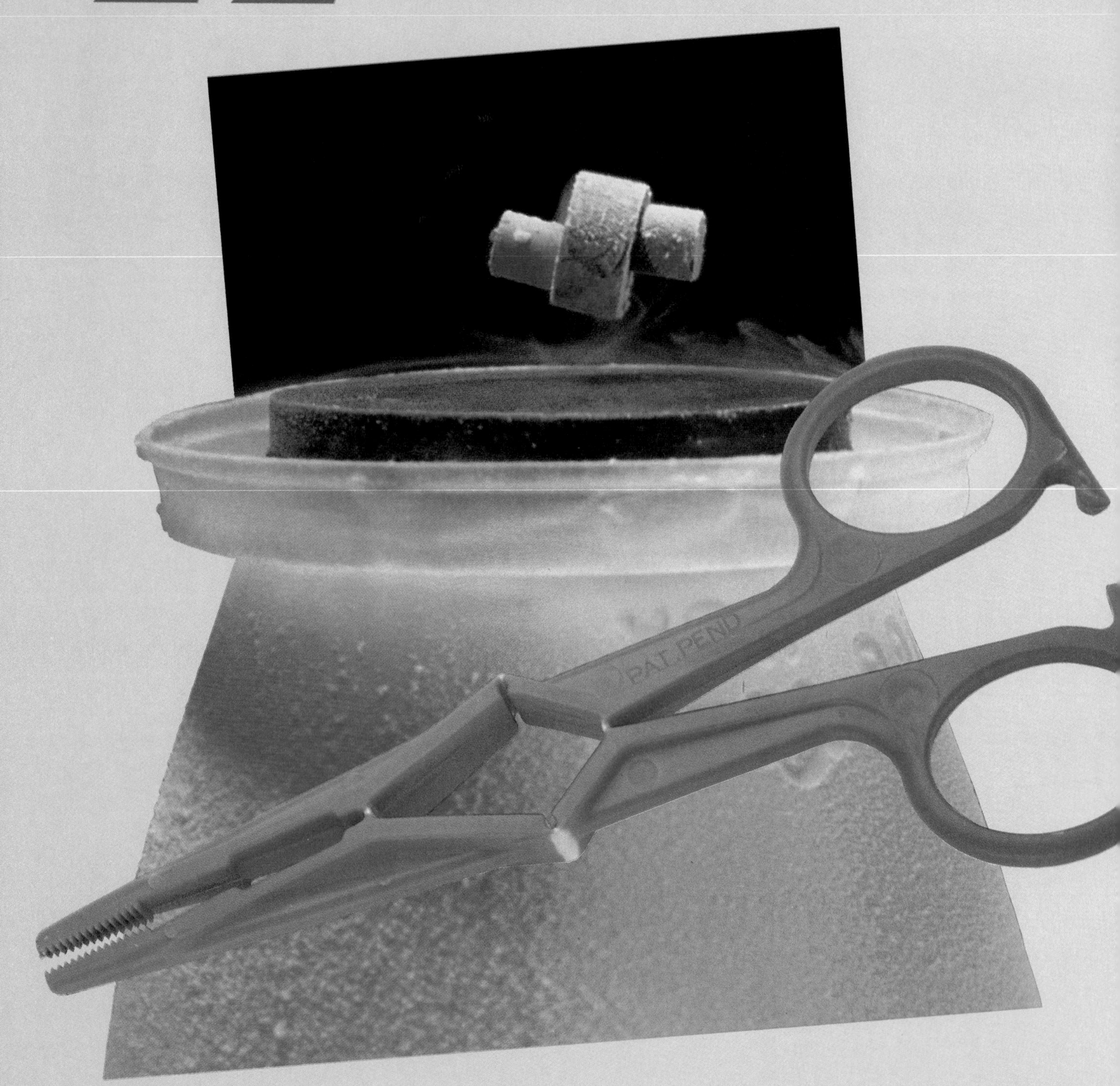

Did you ever get lost on your first day in a new school? Perhaps your homeroom teacher gave you a map of the building, or you had to ask an older student to help you find your way.

How do you think sailors found their way across the ocean hundreds of years ago? Maybe they had maps, but they couldn't stop for directions. They used a compass to show them which way was north.

FIND OUT!

Make and use a compass in this simple activity.

Magnetize a sewing needle by stroking it in one direction with a magnet. Then tie a piece of thread around the needle and let it hang. It will line up in a north-south direction. Which end points north? Use your needle compass to make a map from your science classroom to the library. Let a friend use your map and compass to find the library.

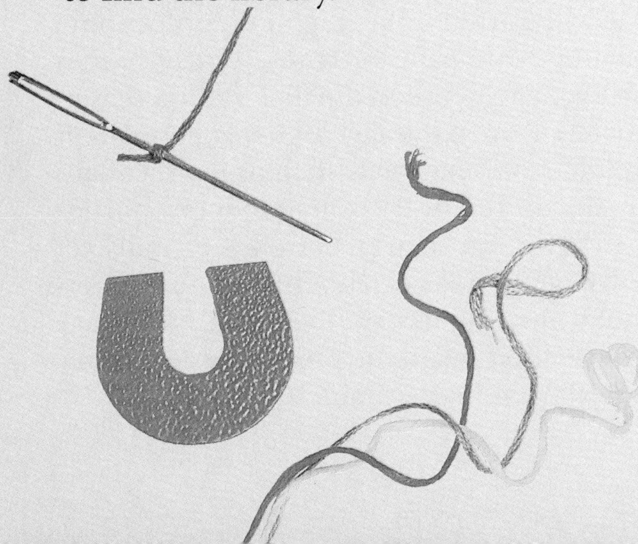

Gearing Up

Previewing the Chapter

Use this outline to help you focus on important ideas in this chapter.

Previewing Science Skills

- In the **Skill Builders**, you will hypothesize, compare and contrast, and make a concept map.
- In the **Activities**, you will observe, predict, interpret, and formulate models.
- In the **MINI-Lab**, you will hypothesize, observe, and interpret data.

What's next?

You have already discovered one important use of magnets. Technology has advanced by leaps and bounds since the first compass was used. We have learned how magnets work, and we have found many applications for them. As you read this chapter, think about all the ways you use magnets.

22-1 Characteristics of Magnets

New Science Words

magnetism
magnetic poles
magnetic field
magnetic domains

Objectives

- Explain the properties of magnets.
- Define the region of force around a magnet.
- Model magnetic behavior using domains.

Magnets

Have you ever stuck two magnets together? The Greeks were experimenting with magnetic materials more than 2000 years ago. They found a mineral that pulled iron objects toward it. If this mineral dangled freely on a string, it always pointed north. They described this mineral as being magnetic. Today we know that magnetism is related to electricity. Together, magnetic and electric forces can generate electricity and operate electric motors.

What is magnetism?

Magnetism is a property of matter in which there is a force of repulsion or attraction between like or unlike poles. Bring two magnets close together and they will either attract or repel. The magnetic forces are strongest near the ends, or **magnetic poles**, of the magnets. All magnets have two magnetically opposite poles, north (N), and south (S). If a bar magnet is suspended so it turns freely, the north end will point north.

Figure 22-1. Magnetite is a mineral with natural magnetic properties.

When you bring the north ends of two magnets close together, they repel. However, the north and south ends of two magnets will attract. Like magnetic poles repel and opposite magnetic poles attract. These forces decrease as the distance between the magnets increases.

Only a few materials are naturally magnetic. Permanent magnets are made from materials such as iron, cobalt, and nickel, which can retain their magnetic properties for a long time. Have you seen paper clips or nails act like magnets? By being near or rubbing against a permanent magnet, these objects can become temporary magnets. They lose their magnetic properties soon after they are separated from the permanent magnet.

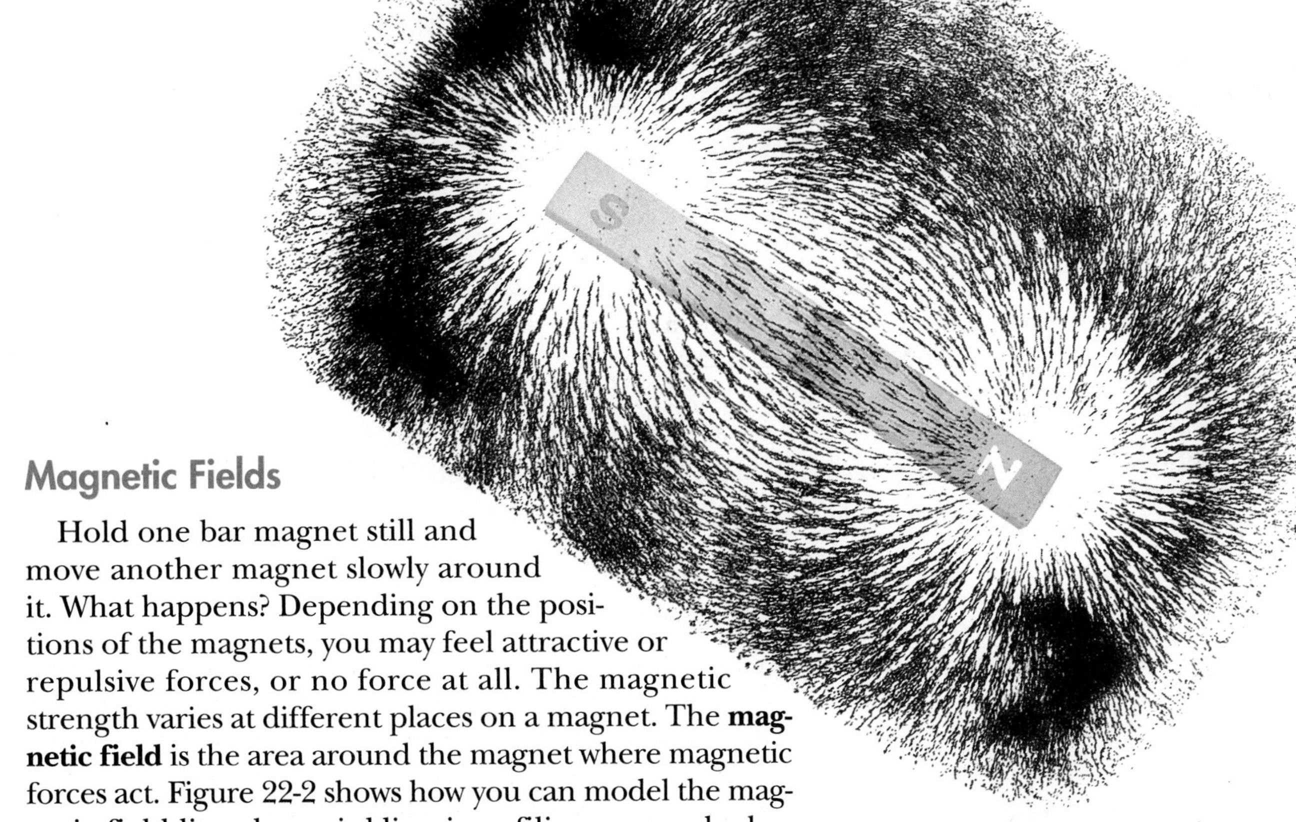

Magnetic Fields

Hold one bar magnet still and move another magnet slowly around it. What happens? Depending on the positions of the magnets, you may feel attractive or repulsive forces, or no force at all. The magnetic strength varies at different places on a magnet. The **magnetic field** is the area around the magnet where magnetic forces act. Figure 22-2 shows how you can model the magnetic field lines by sprinkling iron filings around a bar magnet. The filings line up along the magnetic field lines of the magnet. Notice that these magnetic lines of force are most dense around the poles of the magnet. Figure 22-3 shows how magnetic field lines differ when two poles repel or attract.

Figure 22-2. The magnetic lines of force around this bar magnet can be modeled with iron filings.

Have you used a compass to find out which way was north? A compass contains a magnetic needle that freely rotates in a circle and always points north. This happens because Earth is like a giant magnet surrounded by a magnetic field that extends beyond the atmosphere. The compass aligns with Earth's magnetic lines of force.

Figure 22-3. Notice the magnetic lines of force when like poles repel (a) and unlike poles attract (b).

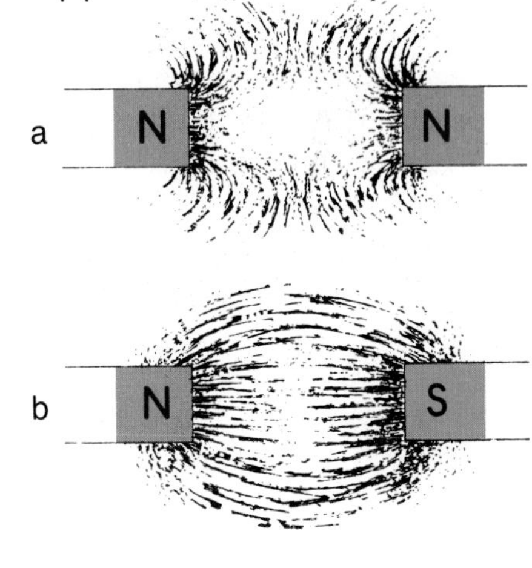

A Model for Magnetism

Many magnets are made of iron. What happens if you hold an iron nail close to a refrigerator door and let go? It falls to the floor. Why doesn't it stick to the refrigerator? Why is it that many substances can't become magnets? Because you can't see magnetism, a model or mental picture will help you answer these questions.

Electrons in most atoms exist in pairs, with each electron spinning in an opposite direction. Each moving electron causes a magnetic field to form around it. In most materials, the magnetic field of one electron is can-

PROBLEM SOLVING

A Magnetic Puzzle

When Shantelle came to physical science class today, Mrs. Kline placed the students in groups. She gave each group three magnets and a long piece of string. Mrs. Kline then told the students to work with the other members of their group to determine the polarity of the three magnets.

Shantelle suggested, "Since Earth is magnetic, we can hang one of the magnets from a string to make a compass. The north pole of the magnet will swing to point to the North Pole."

The group tried Shantelle's suggestion with a red and silver magnet. As a result of their findings, they labeled the red end North and the silver end South. Next, they determined the polarity of a green and yellow magnet. The green end of the magnet pushed the red end away, and yellow end attracted the red end.

They tested a blue and pink magnet last. The blue end was attracted to the red end of the hanging magnet. They were surprised when the pink end was also attracted to the red end.

How did Shantelle's group label the green and yellow magnet?

Think Critically: What should Shantelle's group infer from the results of testing the blue and pink magnet?

celled by an opposite magnetic field produced by the other electron in the pair. The atoms in materials such as iron, cobalt, and nickel have unpaired electrons, so they don't cancel the electrons' magnetic fields. As a result, each atom of these elements acts like a very small magnet.

The magnetic field created by each iron atom exerts force on the other atoms, causing groups of atoms to align their magnetic poles so that all like poles are facing the same direction. These groups of atoms are called **magnetic domains.** Figure 22-5b shows how the domains are randomly arranged in an ordinary, unmagnetized nail. If a permanent magnet strokes the nail or comes near it, the domains rearrange to orient themselves in the direction of the nearby magnetic field, as in Figure 22-5a. The

Figure 22-4. Elements with paired electrons aren't magnetic, but those elements with unpaired electrons are magnetic.

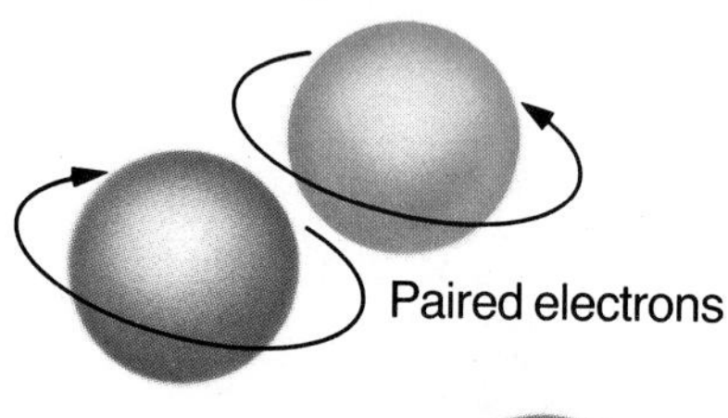

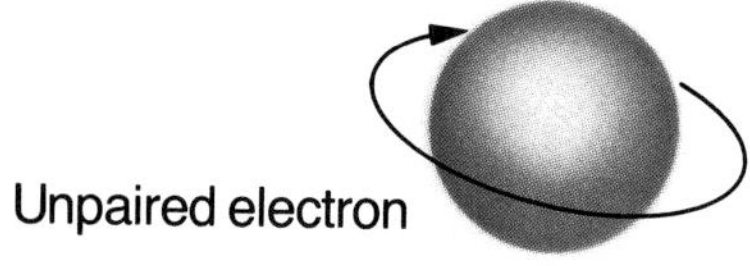

nail now acts as a magnet itself. When the strong magnet is removed, the magnetic domains in the nail soon return to their random arrangement. For this reason, the nail is a temporary magnet. Even permanent magnets can lose some of their magnetic properties if they are dropped or heated. Their magnetic domains would be rattled or melted out of alignment.

What happens when a magnet is broken in two? Would you expect one piece to be a north pole and one piece to be a south pole? Look again at the domain model in Figure 22-5. Because each magnet is actually made of many aligned smaller magnets, even the smallest pieces of a magnet have both a north and south pole.

Although people have been observing magnets since the Greeks first discovered them, and the magnetic domain model explains many observations about magnets, some questions about magnets and magnetic fields are still unanswered. For example, one of the most puzzling questions involves Earth's own magnetic field. We know Earth's magnetic poles have reversed, or flip-flopped north and south, more than 170 times during Earth's history. Scientists are unable to explain why the magnetic field reverses. They have, however, found many uses and applications for magnetism. As you read the next section, you will find out more about these applications.

Figure 22-5. Magnetic domains are magnetized (a) and unmagnetized (b).

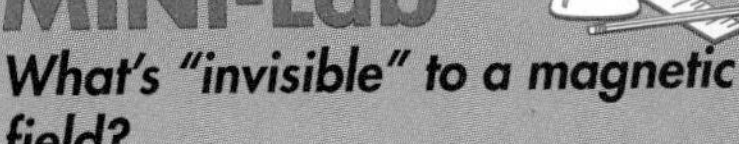

What's "invisible" to a magnetic field?

Clamp a magnet to a ring stand. Thread a needle. Stick the needle on the magnet and tape the thread to the table and pull the thread until the needle is suspended below the magnet. Slip some paper between the needle and magnet. The needle doesn't fall; therefore, the paper is "invisible." Repeat the experiment with aluminum foil, coins, and other solids. If the needle falls, the substance is "seen" by the field.

SECTION REVIEW

1. Describe what happens when you bring two magnetic poles together.
2. What is a magnetic field and where is it strongest?
3. **Apply:** You have a bar magnet dangling horizontally from a string. Explain two ways you could use another magnet to rotate the suspended magnet without touching it.

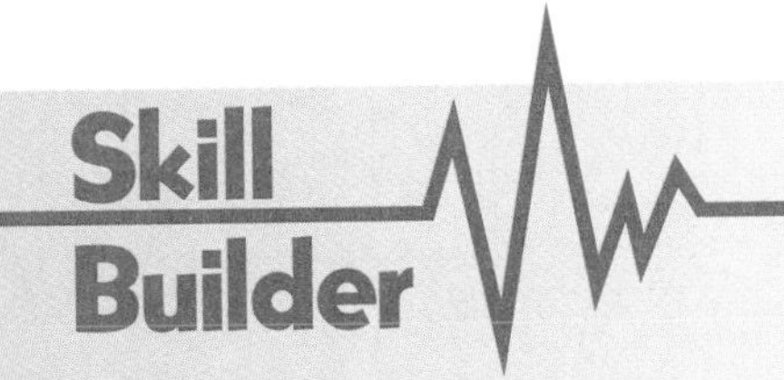

Hypothesizing

Suppose you had a strong bar magnet and allowed your younger brother or sister to play with it. When you got the magnet back, it was barely magnetic. Write a hypothesis to explain what might have happened to your magnet. How could you fix it? If you need help, refer to Hypothesizing in the **Skill Handbook** on page 682.

22-2 Uses of Magnetic Fields

New Science Words

electromagnet
ammeters
voltmeters
commutator

Objectives

- Explain how a coil carrying electric current can induce a magnetic field.
- Compare and contrast ammeters and voltmeters.
- Describe the function of an electric motor.

Electromagnets

In 1820, Hans Christian Oersted, a Danish physics teacher, observed that a current moving through a wire moved the needle on a nearby compass. When the current was reversed, the compass needle was deflected in the opposite direction. These magnetic effects ceased when the current in the wire stopped. Therefore, Oersted hypothesized, the electric current must produce a magnetic field around the wire, causing the direction of the field to change with the direction of the current.

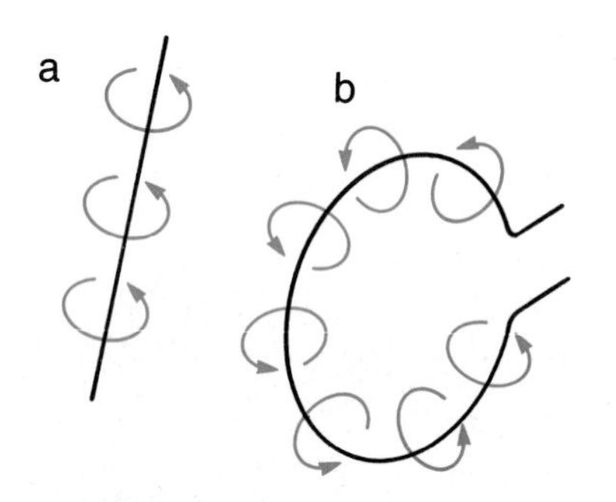

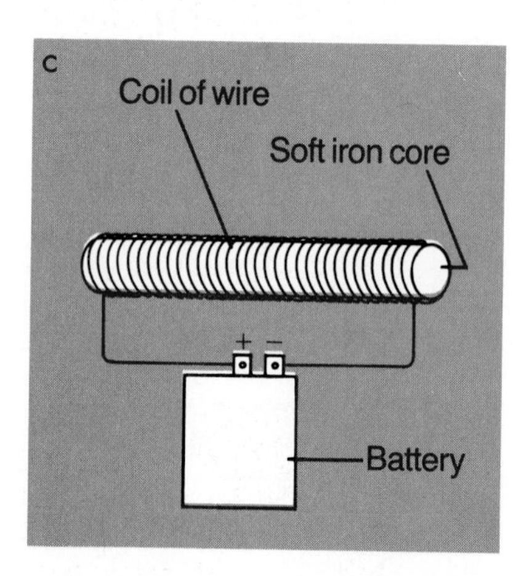

Figure 22-6. Magnetic fields form around any wire that is conducting current (a) (b); that is the principle behind the electromagnet (c).

Figure 22-6a shows magnetic field lines going around a straight wire with current in it. Figure 22-6b shows how the magnetic field lines bunch up when the wire is looped. Even more loops can be bent in the wire to form a coil, Figure 22-6c. Adding turns of the wire to the coil causes more overlapping of the magnetic field lines, and, as a result, the magnetic field grows stronger. When a current is passed through such a coil, a strong temporary magnet called an **electromagnet** is formed. One end of the coil acts as the north pole and the other end as the south pole of the electromagnet. The strength of the magnetic field can be increased by adding more turns to the wire coil and by increasing the amount of current passing through the wire. The electromagnet can also be made stronger by inserting an iron core inside the coil of wire. The iron core becomes a magnet and its magnetic field is aligned with that of the electromagnet.

Electromagnets operate doorbells and loudspeakers and lift large metal objects in construction machines.

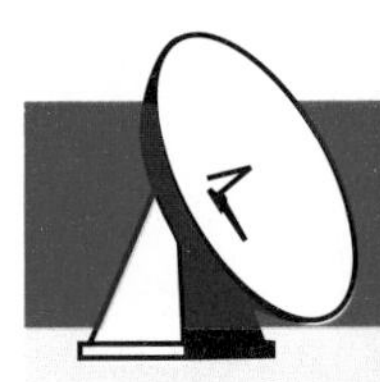

TECHNOLOGY

Flying Trains

Can you imagine flying over the ground at speeds of more than 500 kilometers per hour without an airplane? German and Japanese firms are currently developing high-speed trains that ride on magnets instead of rails.

One such magnetically levitated train, called a maglev, is being built by a German company. This train will run from the airport to downtown in Las Vegas, Nevada. The undercarriage of this train is lined with strong permanent magnets. These magnets are attracted to steel guide tracks above them, thus providing lift. Electric current is delivered at just the right time to devices mounted on the guide track so they will produce magnetic fields that pull and push the train along at speeds up to 90 km/h.

A high-speed prototype in Japan uses superconductive magnets mounted on the underside of the vehicle. These magnets interact with nonelectric coils in the guide track to produce lift and with electric coils in the guide track to produce the push and pull. This maglev will travel between cities at speeds of 500 km/h.

Think Critically: Compare the advantages and disadvantages of magnetically levitated trains versus standard rail transportation.

They change electrical energy to mechanical energy to do work. Another important feature of electromagnets is that they can be turned on and off by controlling the flow of current through the coil. What would happen if the magnetic field in the doorbell was permanent?

Meters

The sensitivity of electromagnets to electrical currents makes them useful in detecting electric current. An instrument used to detect currents is called a galvanometer. It is made of a coil of wire connected to a circuit and suspended so it can rotate in the magnetic field of a permanent magnet. When current flows through the coil, the magnetic force causes the coil to rotate against a spring. A needle is attached to the coil and turns with it to provide a reading on a scale.

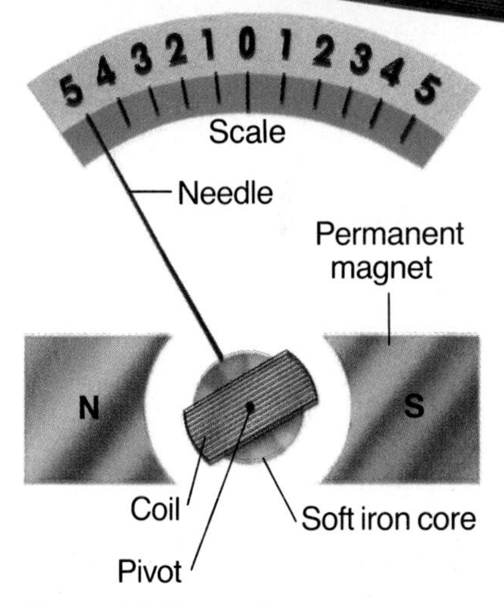

Figure 22-7. A galvanometer uses an electromagnet to detect electric currents.

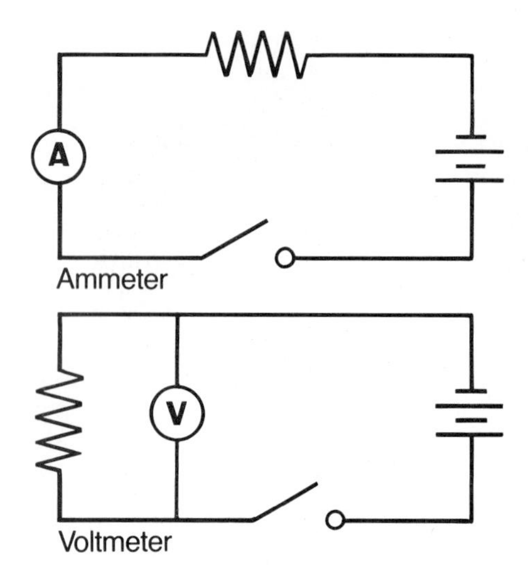

Galvanometers can be calibrated to measure current or electrical potential depending on whether they are contained within an ammeter or a voltmeter. **Ammeters** measure the electrical current of a circuit in amperes. An ammeter should be connected in series with a circuit to measure the current passing through it.

Voltmeters measure the potential difference of a circuit in volts. Unlike ammeters, voltmeters should be placed in parallel across a part of a circuit. The readings in volts depend on the amount of current passing through the voltmeters. The higher the current in the voltmeter, the larger the potential difference across that part of the circuit.

Electric Motors

Do you ever use a fan to keep cool during periods of hot weather? Your fan has an electric motor in it that changes electric energy into mechanical energy, which then turns the blades of your fan. The turning blades push air toward you so your skin feels cooler.

Use a magnet to separate aluminum and tin cans for recycling.

Like a galvanometer, the electric motor in your fan contains an electromagnet that is free to rotate. It rotates between opposite poles of a permanent, fixed magnet. When a current flows through the moveable electromagnet, a magnetic field is induced. This causes enough attraction and repulsion with the permanent magnet to force the coil to turn. But the rotation would stop when opposite poles of the magnet were near each other. How could you make the coil turn again?

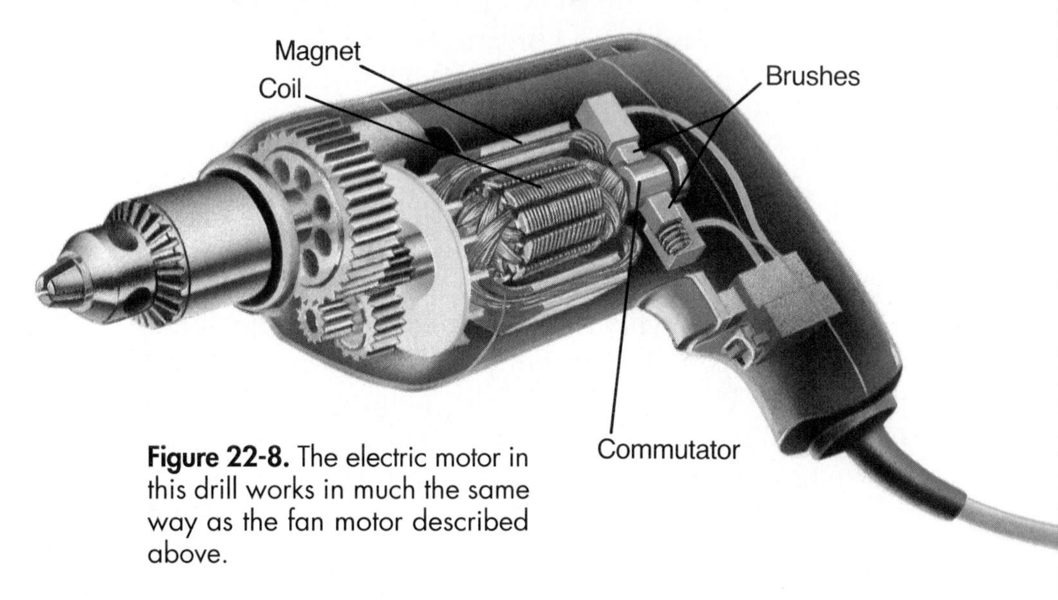

Figure 22-8. The electric motor in this drill works in much the same way as the fan motor described above.

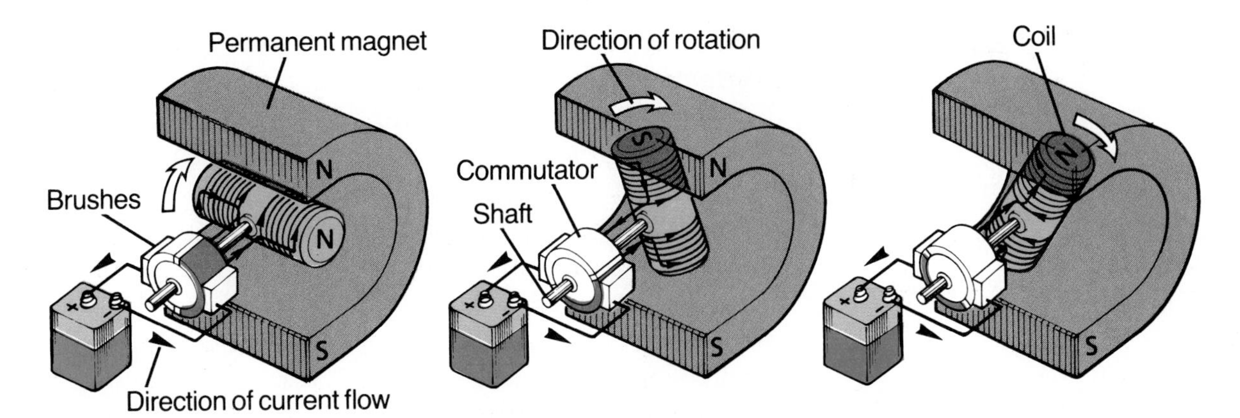

Figure 22-9. The commutator in a motor switches the direction of the current so the coil will turn continuously.

To make the coil in the fan motor spin steadily, the direction of the current through the coil must be reversed after each half revolution. This causes the poles of the rotating electromagnet to switch and turn toward the opposite pole of the permanent magnet. A fan's electric motor operating on direct current must have a device to change the direction of the current. A **commutator** is a reversing switch that rotates with the electromagnet. Electric current reaches the commutator through fixed electrical contacts called brushes. The continual rotation of the electromagnet in your fan's motor keeps the fan's blades turning.

Did You Know?

Lightning can magnetize objects so strongly that they are capable of lifting objects as much as three times their own weight.

SECTION REVIEW

1. Does a straight wire or a looped wire have a stronger magnetic field when both carry the same amount of current? Explain your answer.
2. What is a galvanometer?
3. Why is it important that the current in an electric motor change its direction frequently?
4. **Apply:** Why does the magnetic field inside a current-carrying coil increase if a piece of iron is placed in the coil?

Comparing and Contrasting

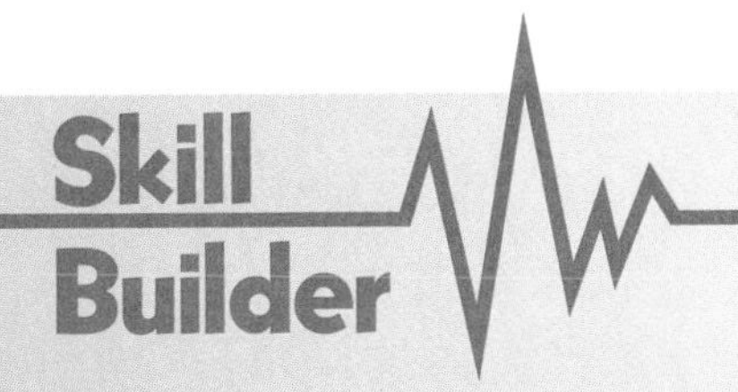

Compare and contrast ammeters and voltmeters. Discuss what they measure, how they are connected, and the relative resistance each meter has. If you need help, refer to Comparing and Contrasting in the **Skill Handbook** on page 679.

ACTIVITY 22-1
Electric Motors

Problem: *How does an electric motor work?*

Materials  

- paper cup or beaker
- nail
- magnet wire, 22 ga
- magnet wire, 32 ga
- bare copper wire, 16 ga
- soda straw
- tape
- 6-volt batteries (2)
- sandpaper
- magnetic compass

Procedure

1. Construct the field as shown by wrapping wire around the top of the plastic cup.
2. Sandpaper the coating from 3 cm of each end of the wire.
3. Test the field coil by holding the compass inside the coil and connecting its wires to a battery. The compass should respond.
4. Construct the armature as shown. Make the direction of wrap of wire the same on both sides of the armature.
5. Scrape the coating from one side of the ends of the armature wire which extend from each end of the straw.
6. Assemble as shown. Attach the batteries and start the motor.

Analyze

1. When testing the field coil, what does the movement of the compass tell you about the field?
2. The armature is designed to turn on and off as it spins. What test could you use to see if it is working?
3. As the armature spins, what is the best position for it to turn on? At what position should it turn off?

Conclude and Apply

4. Would the motor work if the field coil were replaced by a permanent magnet?
5. Why would the motor not work if the armature were replaced by a permanent magnet?

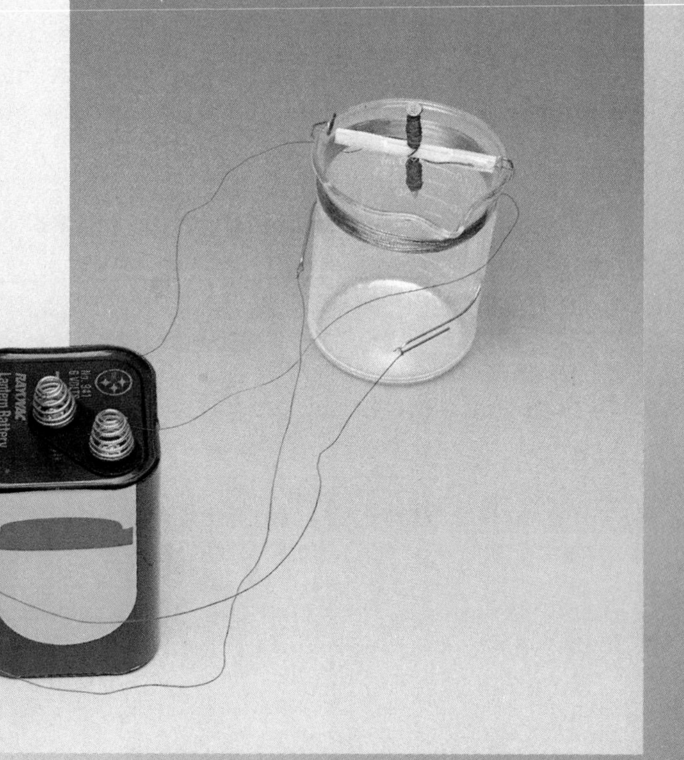

Producing Electric Current

22-3

Objectives

- ▶ Describe how a generator produces an electric current using electromagnetic induction.
- ▶ Distinguish between alternating current and direct current.
- ▶ Explain how a transformer can step up or step down the voltage of an alternating current.

New Science Words

electromagnetic induction
generator
direct current (DC)
alternating current (AC)
transformer

Generators

After Oersted discovered that magnetism could be produced from electric currents, scientists tried to produce an electric current using magnets. Working independently in 1831, a British scientist, Michael Faraday, and an American scientist, Joseph Henry, found that moving a wire through a magnetic field induced an electric current in that wire. **Electromagnetic induction** is the process in which the motion of a wire through a magnetic field produces a current. Moving a magnet in and out of a coil of wire also produces a current. This important discovery led to numerous applications. Most of the electrical energy you use has been converted to useful electricity by electromagnetic induction.

Have you wondered what produces the electricity that comes to your home and school? Most of the electricity you use each day was electromagnetically induced in generators. A **generator** produces electric current by rotating a loop of wire in a magnetic field. The wire loop is connected to a source of mechanical energy and placed between the poles of a magnet, as shown in Figure 22-10. The design of the generator is very much like that of an electric

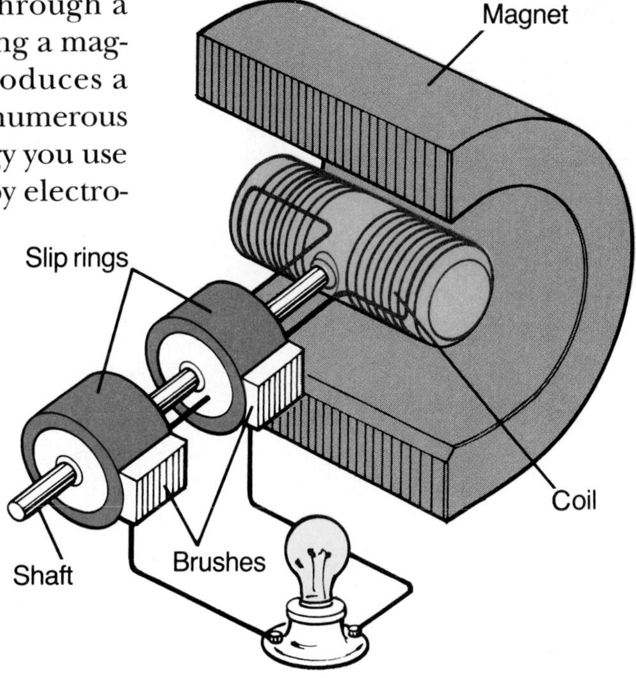

Figure 22-10. Electric current is produced in a generator when a loop of wire is rotated in a magnetic field.

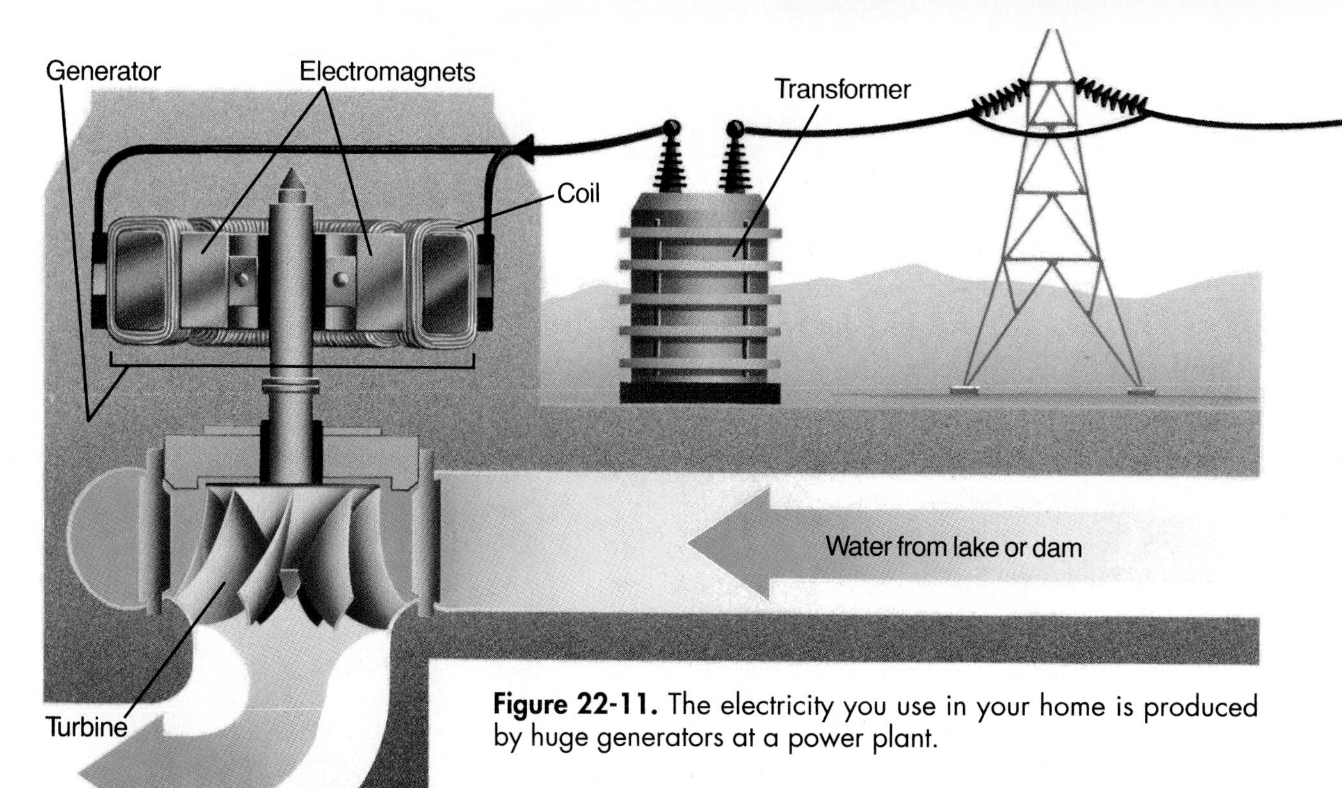

Figure 22-11. The electricity you use in your home is produced by huge generators at a power plant.

motor. The wire loop, however, is made to rotate by externally supplied forces. When it rotates, an electric current is produced. This is the opposite of how a motor acts. In a generator, the wire crosses through the magnetic lines of force as it rotates, causing electrons to move along the wire in one direction. After one-half revolution of the wire loop, the current changes direction. As a result, the direction of the current changes twice with each revolution. The rotation speed of generators is regulated so the current always changes direction with the same frequency.

Do you have a generator in your home that supplies all the electricity you need to watch television or wash your clothes? Probably not! You get your electricity from huge generators at a local power plant. These generators are more complex than the ones discussed here. The electromagnets in these generators are made of many loops of wire wrapped around iron cores. A source of mechanical energy is needed to rotate the loop in the generator. One such source, a turbine, is a large wheel that rotates when pushed by water, wind, or steam. Potential energy released by the burning of fossil fuels or from nuclear reactions can heat water to produce steam. The thermal energy of the steam changes to mechanical energy in the turbine. The generator then changes this mechanical energy into an electric current that is easily conducted to your home.

What is a turbine?

Direct and Alternating Currents

Do you have a tape player that operates on batteries or the electric current in your home? Is the electric current you use in your home that's been produced by a generator the same as the current produced by a dry cell? Both devices cause the electrons to move through a wire and to operate appliances. However, the currents produced by these electric sources are not the same.

Are electric currents produced by a dry cell and a generator the same?

When you use a dry cell or battery to run your tape player, you are using direct current. **Direct current (DC)** flows only in one direction through a wire. Electrons always move out of the negative terminal toward the positive terminal. Whenever direct current flows, it always flows in the same direction.

When you plug your tape player into the wall outlet, you are using alternating current. **Alternating current (AC)** reverses its direction in a regular pattern. In North America, generators produce alternating current at a frequency of 60 cycles per second (60 Hz). Because current in a generator changes direction twice during each rotation of the shaft, 60-Hz alternating current changes direction 120 times each second.

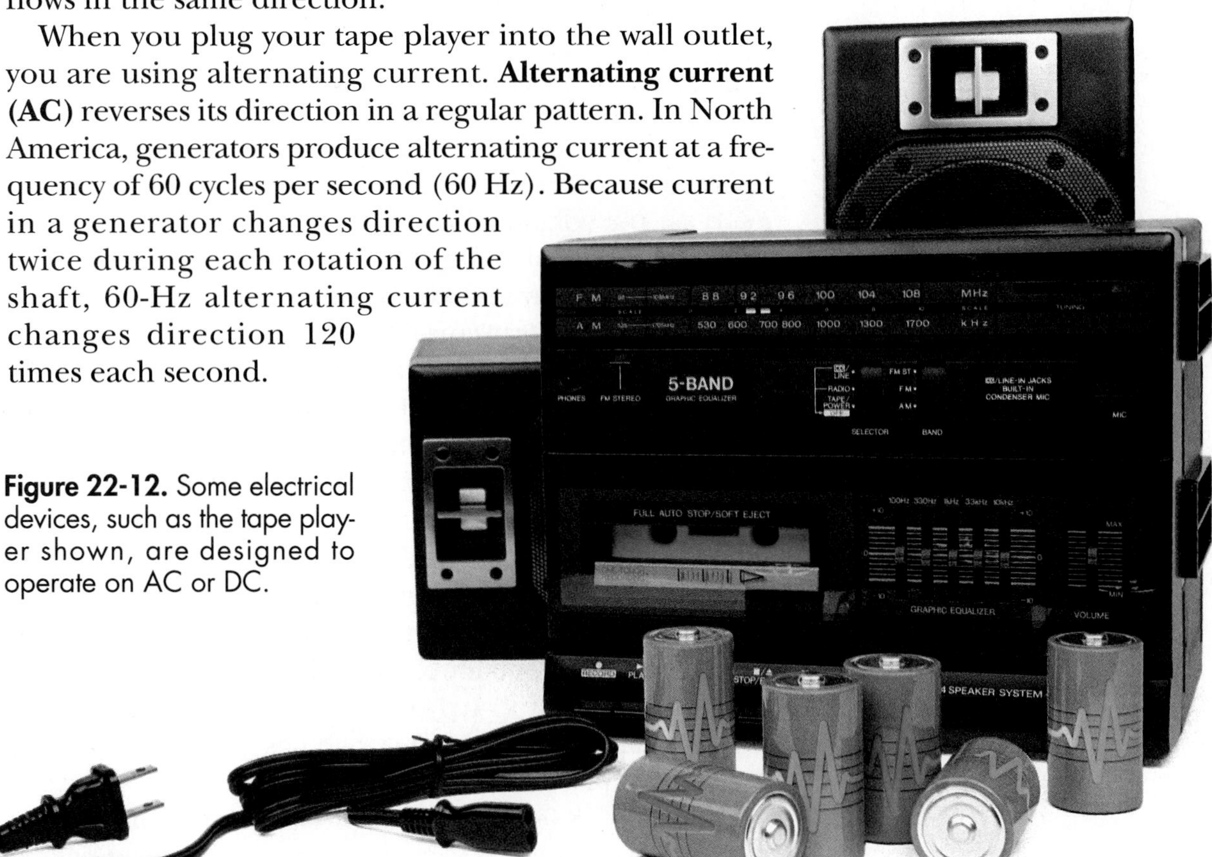

Figure 22-12. Some electrical devices, such as the tape player shown, are designed to operate on AC or DC.

Transformers

The alternating current traveling through power lines is at an extremely high voltage. Before alternating current from the power plant can enter your home, its voltage must be decreased. The current must flow

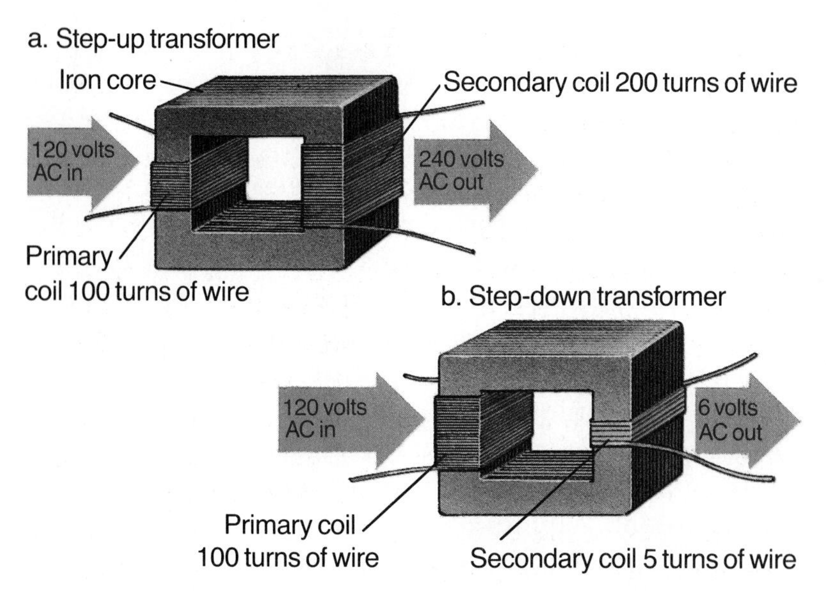

Figure 22-13. A step-up transformer increases voltage (a), and a step-down transformer decreases voltage (b).

What is a transformer?

through a device called a transformer so the voltage is lowered to a useful level. A **transformer** can increase or decrease the voltage of an alternating current. The operation of a transformer involves principles of both electromagnetism and electromagnetic induction.

A simple transformer is made of two coils of wire called the primary and secondary coils. These coils are wrapped around an iron core, as shown in Figure 22-13. As an alternating current passes through the primary coil, the iron core becomes an electromagnet with its own magnetic field. Because the current varies in direction, the magnetic field also changes its direction. The changing magnetic field electromagnetically induces an alternating current in the secondary coil. The number of turns of wire on the secondary coil in the transformer can determine if it is a step-up transformer or a step-down transformer. If the secondary coil has more turns of wire than the primary coil, then it increases voltage. If the secondary coil has fewer turns of wire than the primary coil, it decreases voltage.

Science and WRITING

Write to your local electric company and find out how your electricity is generated. How does this method of generating electricity compare with others?

What kind of transformer decreases voltage?

Transformers are used to reduce the voltage of the alternating current entering your home from several thousand volts to 120 volts. A transformer that reduces voltage is called a step-down transformer. Figure 22-13 shows how the output voltage of a transformer will be decreased if the number of turns in the secondary coil is less than the number of turns in the primary coil.

Suppose the secondary coil of a transformer has half as many turns as the primary coil. If the input voltage is 120 V, the output voltage will be half the input voltage, or 60 V. Step-down transformers allow you to operate devices such as tape players, model trains, and doorbells with 120-V household current.

Power plants commonly produce alternating current because its voltage can be increased or decreased with transformers. To transmit alternating current efficiently over long distances, power plants increase their voltages to very high values. In a step-up transformer the output voltage is greater than the input voltage because the secondary coil has more turns than the primary coil. For example, the secondary coil of a step-up transformer at a generating plant may have 100 times the number of turns as the primary coil. That means that an input voltage of 2000 V would increase to 200 000 V—high voltage indeed!

Think back over this section. Could you describe how electromagnetic induction, generators, alternating current, and transformers all affect your tape player? See if you can recall the series of steps in which AC current is produced, transported, and delivered to your home in a form that you can safely use.

SECTION REVIEW

1. How does a generator use electromagnetic induction to produce a current?
2. A transformer in a neon sign contains 20 turns in the primary coil and 80 turns in the secondary coil. Will the output voltage be greater or less than the input voltage?
3. Compare and contrast alternating current and direct current.
4. **Apply:** Explain why a transformer can't be used to step up the voltage in a direct current.

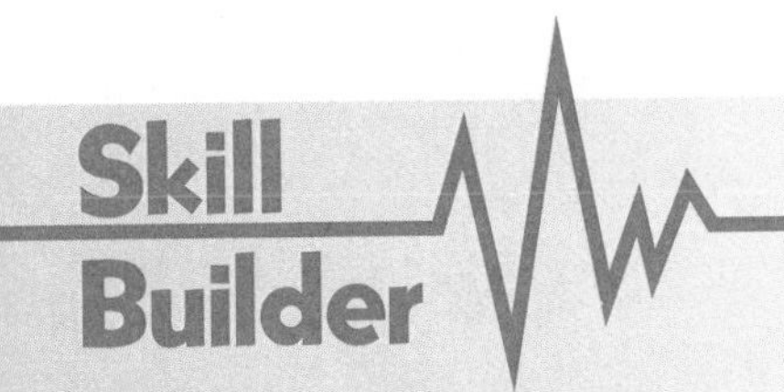

Concept Mapping

Prepare an events chain concept map to show how electricity is produced by a generator, as discussed on pages 583 aand 584. If you need help, refer to Concept Mapping in the **Skill Handbook** on pages 684 and 685.

22-4 Superconductivity

New Science Words

superconductors

Objectives

- Describe the characteristics of superconductors.
- Consider various applications of superconductivity.

Are Superconductors Important?

What do you think about the idea of having train systems that would be levitated, or suspended over magnets, instead of running on rails? Is this a realistic idea? How is this possible?

Recall that conducting materials all have some resistance to electron flow. Some of the electricity moving through the conductor is lost as heat due to this resistance. Likewise, as the temperature of a material increases, the resistance of the material also increases. Ideally, the most efficient transfer of electricity would occur if conducting materials had no electrical resistance.

Superconductors are materials that have no electrical resistance. In 1911, a Dutch physicist, Heike Kamerlingh Onnes, discovered that some materials lose all electrical resistance when cooled to temperatures near absolute zero (0 K), −273°C. The temperature at which a material becomes superconducting is called the critical temperature.

One way to cool a material to superconducting temperatures is to submerge it in liquid helium. Helium is normally a gas, but it liquefies at 4.2 K. In 1986, Bednorz and Muller received a Nobel prize for making a ceramic material that became a superconductor at 30 K. This opened a new field of research to find "high temperature" superconductors. New materials have been developed that are superconducting at more than 120 K.

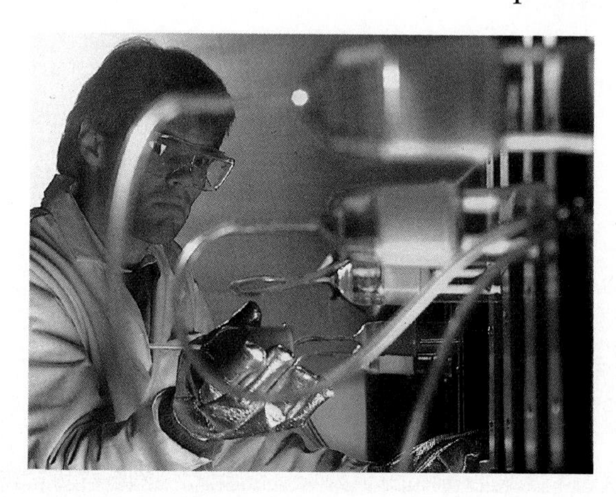

Because superconductors have no electrical resistance, a current can flow indefinitely through them without losing energy. In one experiment, a current traveled through a superconducting loop for more than two years without losing energy. This characteristic of superconductors gives them potential for many different uses.

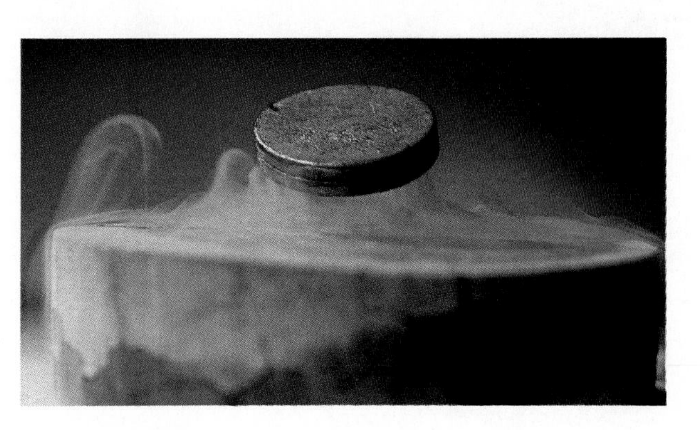

The use of superconductors could eliminate much of the electrical energy waste that we experience today. Ten percent of the energy transmitted through electrical power lines is lost as heat. For similar reasons, superconductors could make electric motors, generators, and computer parts more efficient as well. One problem to be resolved is that superconducting materials are often brittle, and therefore hard to shape into wires.

The picture at the right shows the spectacular levitation effects of magnets over superconductors. Recall that a magnet moving toward a conductor induces a current in the conductor. The current, in turn, produces a magnetic field around the conductor. If the conductor is a superconductor cooled to its critical temperature, the current will move continuously through it. The magnetic forces of these currents moving through the superconductor repel the magnet. This repulsion causes the magnet to float, or levitate, above the superconductor. This is the principle behind levitated trains. If a train had a powerful magnet beneath it and the rails were made of a superconducting material, the train would move on a pocket of air above the rails without friction. It would not lose energy to the environment and would not give off pollutants. What do you think it would be like to ride on a superconducting train?

SECTION REVIEW

1. How do superconductors differ from ordinary conductors?
2. Explain how a magnet can be levitated over a superconductor.

You Decide!

What would be the advantages and disadvantages of developing superconducting trains? Use information in this section to determine what the difficulties of perfecting this system might be. Do you think superconducting trains would be one part of the solution to energy shortages?

ACTIVITY 22-2
Transformers

Problem: *Can electricity move between unconnected wires?*

Materials  

- battery, 6 V
- AC power supply, low voltage
- light, low voltage
- insulated wire, 32 ga
- soda straw, cut to length of nail
- large nail
- knife
- paper clip

Procedure

1. Construct a transformer as shown.
2. Insert nail in straw. Wrap 300 turns of the insulated wire in a tight coil at one end of the straw. Make an identical coil at the other end.
3. Scrape the insulation off the wire ends with the knife.
4. Connect the battery to one coil and the light to the other coil. Gently touch the nail with a paper clip.
5. Connect the AC source in place of the battery. Observe the light and notice the reaction of the paper clip.
6. Observe the light as you slide the nail out of the straw.

Analyze

1. Does the battery produce a magnetic field in the nail? Does its energy reach the light?
2. Does an AC current produce a magnetic field in the nail? Does its energy reach the light?
3. How does the battery magnetism differ from the AC magnetism?
4. What happens when the nail is removed?

Conclude and Apply

5. What kind of current transfers energy by magnetic fields?
6. How is a transformer like a DC generator?
7. What is the purpose of the nail?

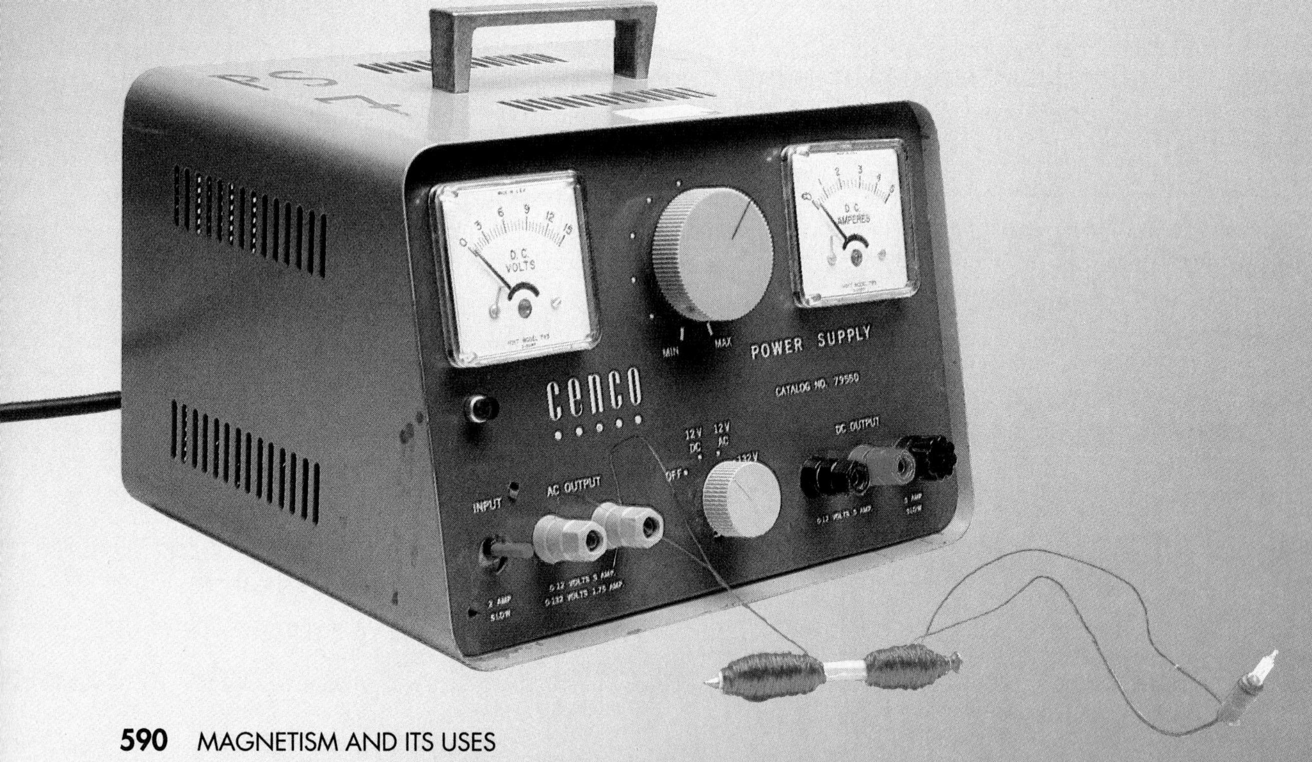

CHAPTER

REVIEW

SUMMARY

22-1: Characteristics of Magnets

1. Opposite poles of magnets attract; like poles repel.

2. The magnetic field is the area around the magnet where magnetic forces act.

3. Groups of atoms with aligned magnetic poles are called magnetic domains.

22-2: Uses of Magnetic Fields

1. An electric current passing through a coil of wire can produce a magnetic field around the wire. The coil becomes an electromagnet; one end of the coil forms the magnet's north pole, and the other end forms the south pole.

2. Ammeters measure electrical current in amperes and should be connected in series. Voltmeters measure the potential difference in volts and should be connected parallel.

3. An electric motor contains a rotating electromagnet that converts electrical energy to mechanical energy.

22-3: Producing Electric Current

1. A generator produces electric current by rotating a loop of wire in a magnetic field.

2. Direct current flows in one direction through a wire; alternating current reverses its direction in a regular pattern.

3. The number of turns of wire in the primary and secondary coils of a transformer determine whether it increases or decreases voltage.

22-4: Science and Society: Superconductivity

1. Superconductors are materials that have no electrical resistance.

2. The use of superconductors can eliminate electrical energy waste in the form of heat. Magnets used with superconductors could provide alternatives to current transportation methods.

KEY SCIENCE WORDS

a. **alternating current (AC)**
b. **ammeters**
c. **commutator**
d. **direct current (DC)**
e. **electromagnet**
f. **electromagnetic induction**
g. **generator**
h. **magnetic domains**
i. **magnetic field**
j. **magnetic poles**
k. **magnetism**
l. **superconductors**
m. **transformer**
n. **voltmeters**

UNDERSTANDING VOCABULARY

Match each phrase with the correct term from the list of Key Science Words.

1. area around a magnet in which a magnetic force acts
2. a property of matter in which there is a force of repulsion or attraction between like or unlike poles
3. a temporary magnet made of a wire coil through which an electric current passes
4. measure electric current
5. a device that reverses the direction of a direct current in an electric motor
6. the production of an electric current by moving a wire through a magnetic field
7. current that flows in only one direction
8. a device that changes the voltage of an alternating current
9. materials with no electrical resistance
10. regions of magnets where magnetic lines of force are most dense

CHAPTER REVIEW

CHECKING CONCEPTS

Choose the word or phrase that completes the sentence or answers the question.

1. A magnet's force is strongest at its ______.
   a. north and south poles c. north pole
   b. south pole d. center
2. As the distance between two magnetic poles decreases, the magnetic force ______.
   a. remains constant c. increases
   b. changes unpredictably d. decreases
3. Atoms at the north pole of a bar magnet have ______.
   a. north magnetic poles only
   b. south magnetic poles only
   c. no magnetic poles
   d. both north and south magnetic poles
4. Which of the following would not change the strength of an electromagnet?
   a. increasing the amount of current
   b. changing the current's direction
   c. inserting an iron core inside the loop
   d. increasing the number of loops
5. Ammeters should be ______.
   a. designed to have high resistance
   b. designed without magnets
   c. connected in parallel
   d. calibrated in amperes
6. A device containing a wire coil suspended in a magnetic field that measures potential difference is called a(n) ______.
   a. transformer c. ammeter
   b. electromagnet d. voltmeter
7. The direction of the electric current in an AC circuit ______.
   a. remains constant c. changes regularly
   b. is direct d. changes irregularly
8. Before current in power lines can enter your home, it must pass through a ______.
   a. step-up transformer c. commutator
   b. step-down transformer d. voltmeter
9. Some materials lose all electrical resistance when they are ______.
   a. at room temperature
   b. at their critical temperatures
   c. below absolute zero
   d. heated
10. Superconductors can levitate magnets because the continuous electric current through the superconductor produces ______.
   a. a repulsive magnetic force
   b. an attractive magnetic force
   c. an anti-gravity force
   d. a mechanical force

UNDERSTANDING CONCEPTS

Complete each sentence.

11. ______ magnetic poles attract one another.
12. When the poles of atoms containing unpaired electrons are aligned, ______ is produced.
13. The direction of the magnetic field produced by an electric current will change when the ______ changes.
14. In a(n) ______, a loop of wire is mechanically rotated in a magnetic field in order to produce a current.
15. In order for a transformer to increase voltage, its secondary coil must have ______ turns than its primary coil.

THINK AND WRITE CRITICALLY

16. Describe the magnetic domain model.
17. Describe the basic device used in both galvanometers and electric motors. What additional device does an electric motor have? Why is this device necessary?
18. Explain how a generator produces an electric current.
19. Explain how a transformer works. How do step-up and step-down transformers differ?
20. How might superconductors help conserve energy resources?

APPLY

21. If a magnetic compass needle points north, what is the actual polarity of Earth's northern magnetic pole? Explain.
22. Explain why dropping or heating a permanent magnet causes its magnetic domains to shift out of alignment.
23. Why must an ammeter be connected in series with a circuit? Why must a voltmeter be connected in parallel across a circuit?
24. A step-down transformer reduces a 1200 V current to 120 V. If the primary coil has 100 turns, how many must its secondary coil have?
25. You are developing a superconducting train. On what two problems will you concentrate your research? Why?

MORE SKILL BUILDERS

If you need help, refer to the Skill Handbook.

1. **Comparing and Contrasting:** Compare and contrast electric and magnetic forces.
2. **Comparing and Contrasting:** Compare and contrast AC generators and DC motors.
3. **Recognizing Cause and Effect:** Earth's magnetic field has reversed itself many times in the past. What would be the likely effect of this switching of Earth's magnetic poles on the alignment of magnetic minerals deposited in Earth?
4. **Hypothesizing:** Some metals are strongly attracted by a magnetic field; others such as zinc are not. Propose a hypothesis about the arrangement of electrons in zinc.
5. **Concept Mapping:** Complete the following events chain map by supplying the name and function of devices used to convert the mechanical energy of a turbine at an electrical power plant into the mechanical energy of an electric fan in your home.

Initiating Step

↓

↓

↓

Final Outcome

PROJECTS

1. Research the most recent developments in superconductors. Write a brief paper stating whether or not the government should spend more money on superconductor research. Give reasons supporting your position.
2. Invent a new device that uses an electric motor. Make a poster diagram of the device.

CHAPTER 23 Electronics and Computers

Have you ever received a greeting card from a friend that made you feel especially happy? Did you ever get a card that played a song when you opened it? How can a greeting card play music? A small electronic device located inside the card actually plays the song you hear.

FIND OUT!

Observe a simple application of electronics as you do this activity.

Get a musical greeting card and examine the electronic device inside. Notice that the music plays only when the card is opened. Do you see the tiny metal disc inside the card? The disc is a type of electronic device containing a small speaker. The music is created from electric signals within the disc that are amplified and turned into sound waves within the tiny speaker. Carefully examine the parts inside the disc with a powerful hand lens. What do you see?

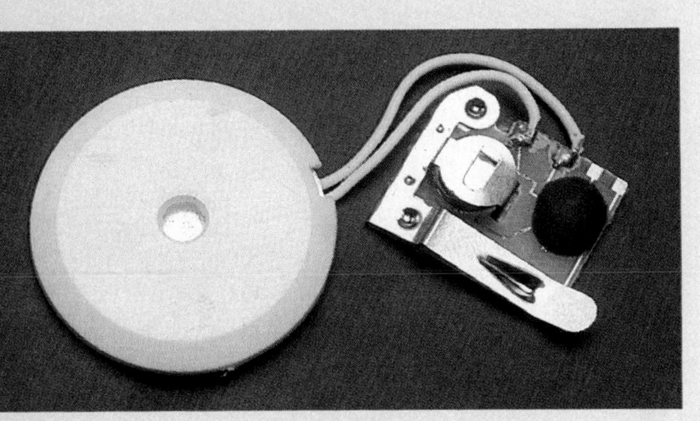

Gearing Up

Previewing the Chapter

Use this outline to help you focus on important ideas in this chapter.

Previewing Science Skills

- In the Skill Builders, you will interpret scientific illustrations, make a concept map, and compare and contrast.
- In the Activities, you will observe, infer, classify, and communicate.
- In the MINI-Labs, you will observe, infer, and interpret.

What's next?

You've examined one type of simple electronic device. Read on to find out how this and other electronic devices are actually applications of the principles of electricity and magnetism you studied in Chapters 21 and 22.

23-1 Semiconductor Devices

New Science Words

rectifier
diode
transistor
amplification
integrated circuit

Objectives

- ▶ Describe how the two types of doped semiconductors conduct a current.
- ▶ Explain the device that changes AC into DC.
- ▶ Realize the practical benefits of an integrated circuit.

Semiconductors

Do you use a calculator when you do your homework, average your grades, or add up the amount of money you've saved? You probably use a calculator to work a math problem every day. Your calculator is only one of thousands of complex electronic devices made possible by advances in the applications of electricity and magnetism. If you carefully removed the front of your calculator, you would see tiny circuits with all sorts of unusual parts inside. You might see several kinds of semiconductor devices: a diode, a rectifier, and a transistor.

To understand what a semiconductor is, and how it works, you must first think about the periodic table you studied in Chapter 10. Recall that the elements on the left side and center of the table are metals. These metals are conductors of electricity. Nonmetals—poor conductors of electricity—are found on the right side of the table. They are electrical insulators. How would you classify the elements found along the staircase-shaped border between the metals and nonmetals? Would you call these conductors or insulators?

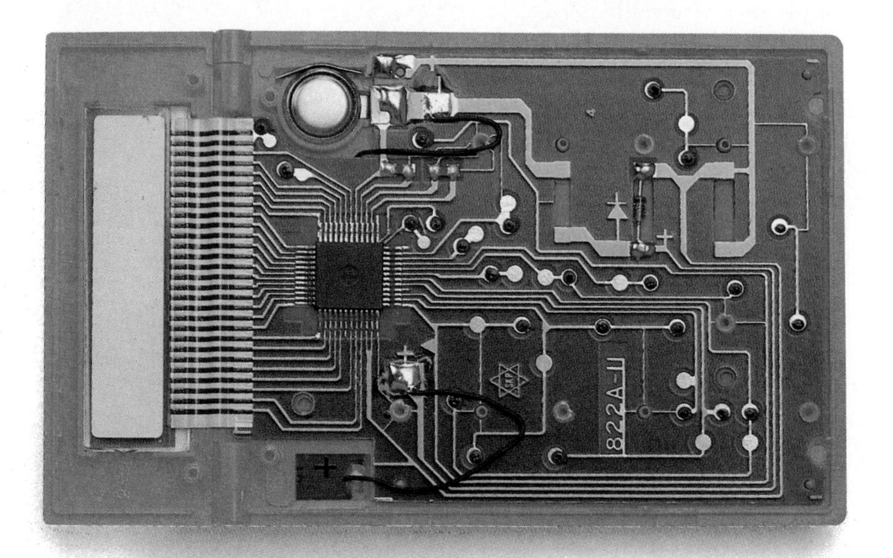

Figure 23-1. A calculator contains several different types of semiconductor devices.

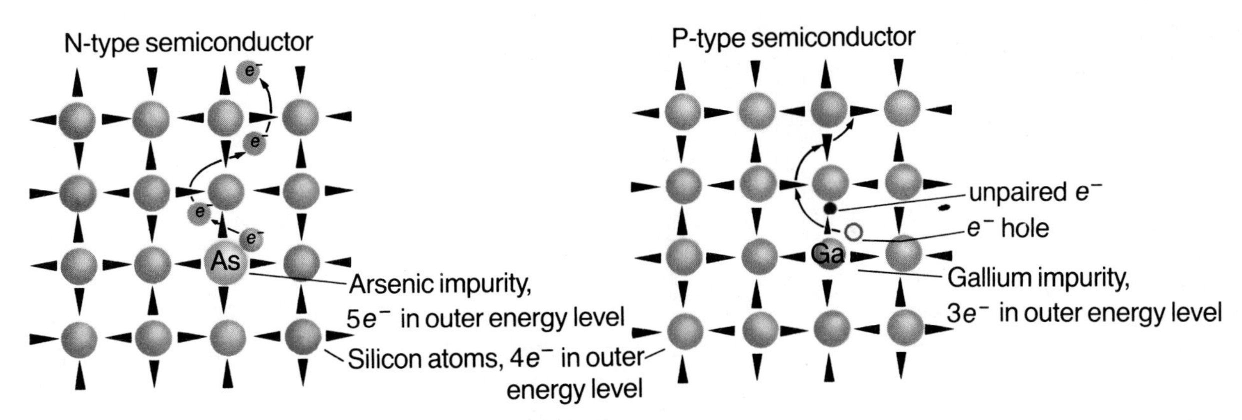

Figure 23-2. Doping semiconductor crystals with impurities can change their resistance and conductivity.

The elements located between the metals and nonmetals on the periodic table are metalloids. Some metalloids, such as silicon and germanium, are semiconductors. Semiconductors are less conductive than metals, but more conductive than nonmetal insulators. Your calculator and other electronic devices in your home that use semiconductors use less current to operate than similar devices that don't use semiconductors.

What is doping?

The conductivity of semiconductor crystals can be increased by adding impurities. This process is called doping. Doped silicon is a commonly used semiconductor. Silicon atoms have four electrons in their outer energy level. If small amounts of another element with more than four electrons in its outer energy level are added, the semiconducting crystal will have a few additional electrons. These extra electrons can move easily through the crystal to increase its conductivity. For this reason, silicon is often doped with arsenic as shown in Figure 23-2a. Notice that arsenic has five electrons in its outer energy level. Arsenic-doped silicon has more negative electrons and is called an *n*-type (negative-type) semiconductor.

What is an *n*-type semiconductor?

Silicon semiconductors can also be doped with a material, such as gallium, that has fewer than four electrons in its outer energy level. Because gallium-doped silicon has fewer electrons in its crystal than does pure silicon, the doping creates "holes" in the electron structure of the silicon crystal. You can picture these holes as imaginary positive charges throughout the silicon crystal. Gallium-doped silicon is an example of a *p*-type semiconductor. When a potential difference is applied across a *p*-type semiconductor, electrons move to fill the holes as if they were attracted to the imaginary positive charges. Figure 23-2b illustrates how moving electrons create more holes in the crystal. The process produces a current in the semiconductor.

What is a *p*-type semiconductor?

ACTIVITY 23-1
Semiconductors

Problem: *How can diodes be used to change AC to DC?*

Materials 

- diode
- two LEDs, different colors
- hook-up wire
- resistor, 1000 ohms
- battery, 6 volt
- AC power supply, 6 volts

Procedure

1. Attach the resistor to one of the LEDs before connecting it to the battery. Reverse battery connections until the LED lights.
2. Mark the positive side of the LED.
3. Repeat Steps 1 and 2 with the second LED.
4. Twist the positive wire of one LED with the negative wire of the other. Attach the resistor to the other two wires.
5. Connect the assembly to the poles of the battery and notice which LED light works. Reverse the connections and observe.
6. Connect the assembly to 6 volts AC and observe.
7. Attach the diode in series with the assembly and connect it to 6 volts AC.
8. Reverse the direction of the diode and reconnect to the AC current. Notice the response of the LEDs.

Analyze

1. A battery sends current in one direction. How does the LED assembly show this?
2. How does the LED assembly detect an alternating current?
3. What does the addition of a diode do to an alternating current?
4. What does reversing the direction of the diode accomplish?

Conclude and Apply

5. In an AC circuit, are the LEDs "on" all the time? How about in the DC circuit?
6. The resistance of a diode is very high in one direction and low in the other. How did this experiment show that to be true?

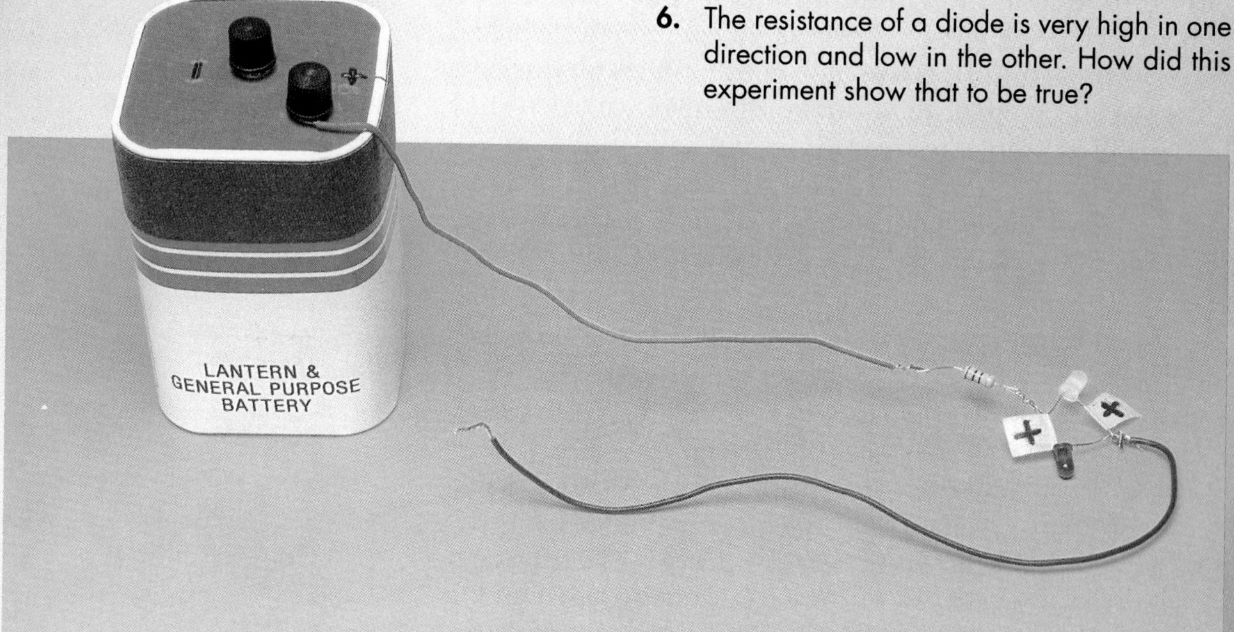

Diodes

Have you noticed that some portable radios have adapters that plug into wall sockets? Why do they need an adapter? Radios operate on low-voltage direct current. For the radio to operate with household alternating current, the voltage of the current must be lowered and the current must be changed to flow in one direction. A radio adapter contains a transformer, which reduces the voltage, and a rectifier. A **rectifier** is a device that changes alternating current into direct current.

Many household devices are built to operate on direct current. Some, such as smoke detectors and clocks, can easily be supplied with current from batteries. Other appliances that use large amounts of electricity, such as your television or computer, would not be practical to operate with batteries. Therefore, transformers and rectifiers are wired into the circuits inside of radios, televisions, computers, and other appliances to supply them with low-voltage direct current from a source of alternating current.

A diode is one type of rectifier. A **diode** allows current to flow only in one direction. A diode can be made by doping the ends of a crystal with different elements to make one end a *p*-type semiconductor and the other end an *n*-type semiconductor. Electrons can easily flow from the *n*-type end to fill the electron holes in the *p*-type end, but it is more difficult to make them flow in the other direction. This device is called a *pn*-diode. Your radio's adapter plug probably contains a *pn*-diode rectifier.

Figure 23-3. Diodes and rectifiers change alternating current into direct current.

Transistors and Amplification

What is a transistor?

Have you wondered why some radios are called transistor radios? They contain electrical devices called transistors. A **transistor** is a semiconductor that amplifies an electric signal. The signal in an electronic device is the varying electric current that represents a sound, picture, or some other piece of information. Transistors can be made by doping both sides of a thin *p*-type semiconductor with arsenic. This process sandwiches a *p*-type semiconductor between the two *n*-type semiconductors

Figure 23-4. These transistors are used to amplify electric signals.

producing an *npn*-transistor. An *npn*-transistor can amplify a weak electric signal. **Amplification** is the process of increasing the strength of an electric signal.

Another type of transistor can be made by placing a thin *n*-type semiconductor between two *p*-type semiconductors, forming a *pnp*-transistor. They differ slightly in operation, but both types of transistors can be used to amplify an input signal or current. Like diodes, these electronic components are very small and lightweight.

The signal that travels many kilometers from a broadcast station to your stereo and television receivers is too weak to reproduce the information it carries into picture or sound. In other words, the signal produced by the radio waves received by your stereo does not have a large enough amplitude to vibrate the loudspeaker and create sound that can be heard. An *npn*-transistor in the electric circuit of the stereo uses a small current from a weak incoming signal to control a large current provided by a power source. The varying current produced by the radio signals flows between the center *p*-type area to an *n*-type area of the transistor This produces a large varying current through the two *n*-type areas of the transistor which are connected in series with a speaker to a power source. Thus, the small input signal supplied to the transistor results in a large, varying output current which can vibrate the speaker.

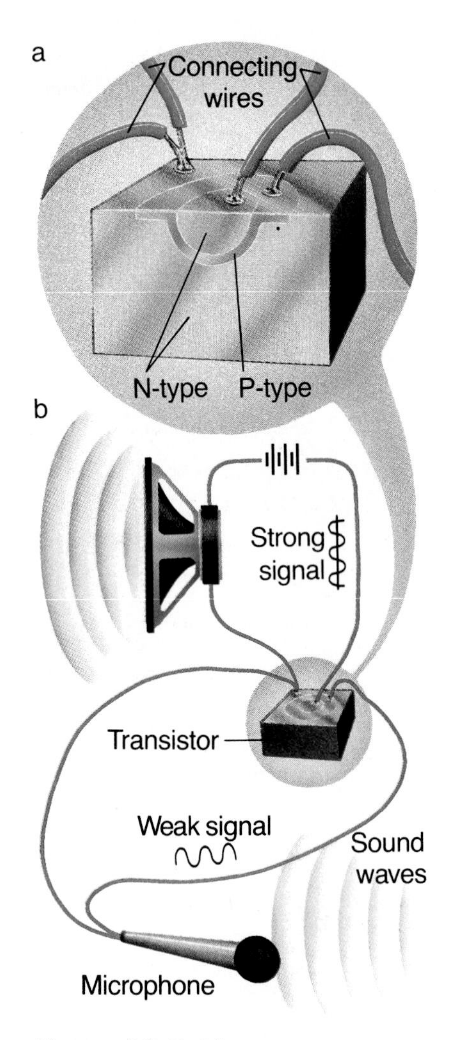

Figure 23-5. The *npn*-transistor shown above uses a weak input current to control the flow of a much larger current.

Your school PA (public address) system contains several transistors. When someone speaks over the system, the sound wave is converted to an electrical signal by a microphone and amplified by transistors within the circuit of the system. The amplified signal is then changed back into sound waves by a speaker. Transistors and their ability to amplify signals make it possible for you to use tape players, bullhorns, hearing aids, and televisions. They are also used in medical diagnoses to amplify tiny electrical signals given off by the heart and brain so these signals can be detected. None of these electronic devices or their applications would be possible without the transistor. It is considered the most fundamental part of an electronic circuit.

Integrated Circuits

Before transistors were invented, devices called vacuum tubes were used to amplify electric signals. These low-pressure glass or metal tubes regulated the electron flow of a circuit's current as it went through each tube. Your grandparents probably owned a television or radio that used these tubes to amplify signals. Televisions and radios today have semiconductor components instead of vacuum tubes. After the development of the transistor, integrated circuits became a reality. As a result of this electronics breakthrough, today's televisions and radios are much smaller than the older ones.

An **integrated circuit** can contain thousands of resistors, diodes, and transistors on a thin slice of silicon. These thin silicon slices, called chips, can be smaller than 1 cm on a side. The miniature circuit components in an integrated circuit are made by doping the silicon chip with small amounts of impurities. The conductors between the components are made by painting tiny aluminum wires on the silicon chip. Having circuit components so close together reduces the time required for a current to travel through a circuit. As a result, the integrated circuit is a very effective design for rapid information processing, which is essential in devices such as microcomputers.

Figure 23-6. Vacuum tubes, such as the one above, were used to amplify electric signals in early electronic devices.

Did You Know?

The integrated circuit concept was developed in 1952, but the actual product was not produced for 20 more years.

SECTION REVIEW

1. Describe two ways the conductivity of a semiconductor can be improved.
2. What device can you use to change AC to DC? How does it work?
3. How are integrated circuits made?
4. **Apply:** Would carbon atoms be useful in doping a silicon semiconductor? Explain.

Interpreting Scientific Illustrations

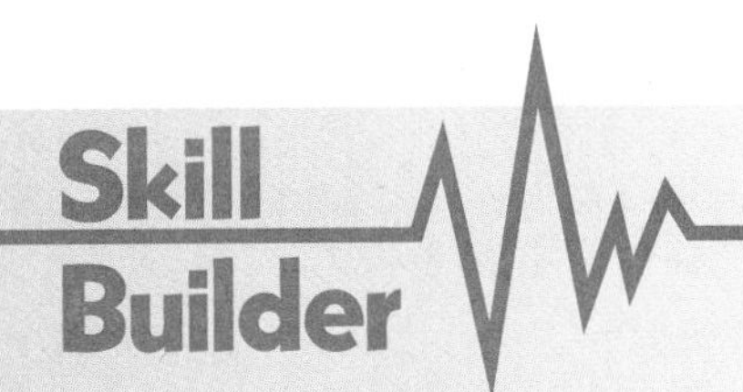

Look at the periodic table of the elements on pages 258 and 259. List the metals, nonmetals, and metalloids. Classify each of these as a conductor, an insulator, or a semiconductor. If you need help, refer to Interpreting Scientific Illustrations in the **Skill Handbook** on page 689.

23-2 Radio and Television

New Science Words

cathode-ray tube (CRT)

Objectives

- Describe how radio and television programs are transmitted.
- Explain the operation of a cathode-ray tube.

Radio Transmission

Now that you've studied sound, electromagnetic waves, and electricity, you should be comfortable with the concepts that explain how a radio works. Radios operate by changing transverse radio waves into vibrations that produce compressional sound waves. Recall that radio waves are the kind of electromagnetic radiation with the longest wavelength and shortest frequency. Radio waves travel at the speed of light, like all electromagnetic radiation. However, the conversion to sound waves is not possible without first converting the radio waves to electrical signals.

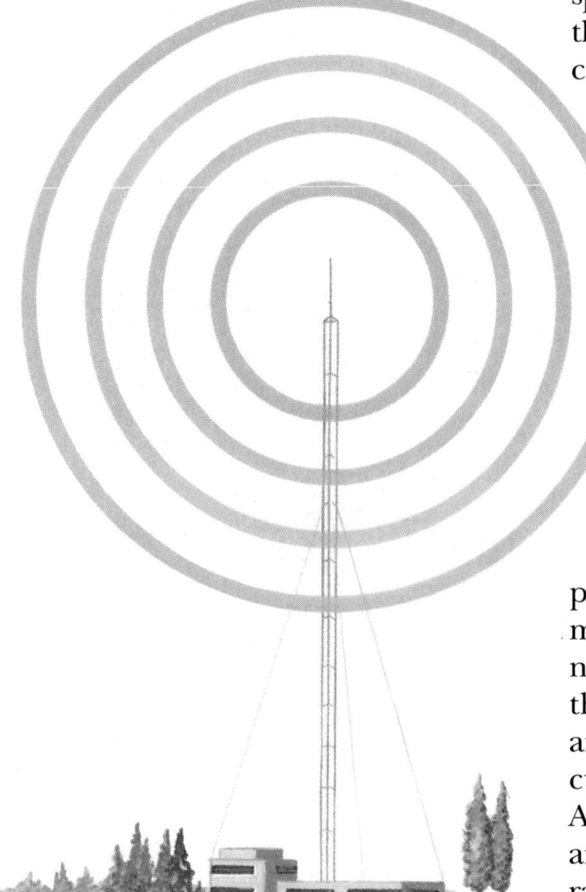

At the radio station, a microphone collects the compressional waves created by musical sounds. The microphone changes the sound waves into electrical signals. The electric current vibrations vary according to the sound vibrations. These signals are then amplified and passed through the modulator. Modulation was discussed in Chapter 19. The type of modulation varies in AM and FM radio stations. When the electrical signals are used to produce variations in the amplitude of the radio waves, they are called amplitude-modulated, or AM, waves. When the electrical signals are used to produce variations in the frequency of the radio waves, they are called frequency-modulated, or FM, waves. The electric currents are amplified and sent to an antenna, where they are transformed into radio waves.

Your receiving radio has an antenna that collects these radio waves and transforms them into electric currents. If the radio is tuned to the same frequency as the radio waves, the waves will be amplified again. The carrier wave—the wave of the frequency to which the radio is tuned—is removed. This leaves only the waves that correspond to the original sound waves. The radio's loudspeaker vibrates to cause sound waves like those of the original music to leave the radio. As a result, you hear music!

EcoTip

Save energy by turning off radios and televisions when you are not using them.

Look at the radio dial pictured below. Notice that a set of numbers on the top of the dial corresponds to the FM range and a separate set of numbers on the bottom corresponds to the AM range. Every radio station, AM or FM, operates at a specific frequency and wavelength. FM stations broadcast at carrier frequencies ranging from 88 to 108 megahertz. AM stations broadcast at carrier frequencies between 540 and 1600 kilohertz. Do AM stations operate at a higher frequency than FM stations?

Television Transmission

What do radios have in common with television sets? Both have tuners that tune the circuits to the frequency of the radio waves. Both have a loudspeaker to vibrate and produce sound and an antenna to collect radio signals. The antennas on modern radios and television sets are often hidden in the circuits of these devices. Televisions not only turn the radio waves into sound, but they also use these signals to create a visual image. Television is like a radio with pictures.

The audio, or sound, signal for television programs is sent and received like an FM radio signal. The video images are sent by AM carrier waves. Just as a microphone is used to change sound waves into varying electric currents, a television camera is used to change light into electric currents that represent the images. This electric video signal then amplitude-modulates a carrier wave. A television station simultaneously transmits the audio and video signals from its antenna.

Tuning into a television station is much like tuning a radio. When you select a channel, only a certain carrier frequency is picked up and amplified within the set. The audio portion of the television program is changed to sound by a loudspeaker. The picture you see on the screen is created by a more complex process. You may have heard that if the picture tube inside your television goes

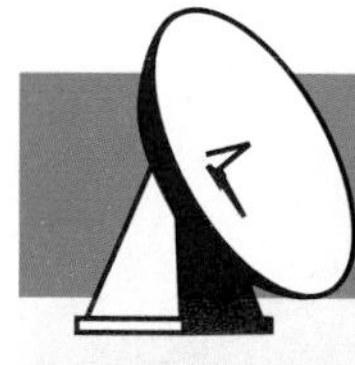

TECHNOLOGY

HDTV

Would you like to have a large-screen TV with pictures as clear as a 35-millimeter photograph and the sound quality of a compact disc? This is the pledge of a new generation of television referred to as "high-definition television" (HDTV). HDTV sets will provide images by constructing a picture from 1 125 individual horizontal lines rather than the 525 horizontal lines you have on your current TV set. This means that you can see a clear picture even if you are close to an HDTV screen that is four or five feet across.

The technology for the design and construction of the new TV sets is relatively simple to achieve. Problems arise, however, in trying to move from the United States' current broadcast system to the new broadcast system without making TV sets that aren't HDTV obsolete. Because the HDTV signals encode much more information than conventional TV signals, broadcasting HDTV signals could interfere with conventional TV broadcasts. Japan, the United States, and some European countries are competing to set the standard for these new HDTV signals. This competition could result in the development of other forms of delivering HDTV signals such as direct broadcast satellites or fiber-optic cables.

Think Critically: How are TV signals currently broadcast? What form of broadcasting do you think would be best for HDTV signals that would not interfere with other TV signals?

out, you are faced with a major repair bill or should probably buy a new television. That's because this picture tube is the most expensive component in your TV set. The picture tube is a type of cathode-ray tube. A **cathode-ray tube (CRT)** uses electrons and fluorescent materials to produce images on a screen.

Look at the CRT in the television set at the right. A CRT is a sealed glass vacuum tube. When power is applied to the components in the tube, electrons come off a negative cathode and are focused into a beam. They move toward the screen, which is coated on the inside with materials that glow when struck by the electrons. The direction of the beam is changed by electromagnets outside of the CRT. This allows the beam of electrons to sweep the surface of the screen many times each second.

The cathode-ray tube of a color TV contains a screen lined with different materials that give off light in one of the three primary colors: red, blue, or green. The radio waves that carry the picture signal are changed into electrical signals in the television. These electrical signals control the intensity and position of the electron beams, which determine the colors and patterns of the image that forms on the screen. If you look closely at your television screen, you can see the tiny dots of red, blue, and green that make up each image. How is this process similar to the way your eye forms color images?

Figure 23-7. A television set contains a CRT.

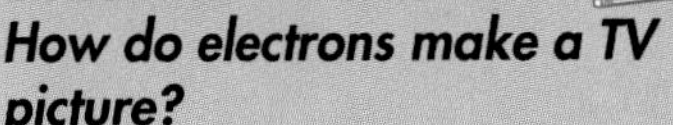

MINI-Lab

How do electrons make a TV picture?

Electrons are guided to the screen of a CRT by electrical and magnetic fields. A chemical inside the screen reacts to the electrons by flashing a color of the light. Place a small magnet on the glass surface of an operating CRT and observe the response. Do both poles of the magnet produce the same reaction? What happens to the colors on the screen?

SECTION REVIEW

1. Explain what happens inside your radio when you tune in to a particular radio station.
2. How does a cathode-ray tube produce an image?
3. **Apply:** How might a cathode-ray tube that produces a color image differ from one with a black and white image?

Concept Mapping

Make a concept map that shows the steps involved in radio broadcasts. Begin with the voice at the microphone and end with the radio waves leaving the transmitter. If you need help, refer to Concept Mapping in the **Skill Handbook** on pages 684 and 685.

23-3 Microcomputers

New Science Words

microprocessor
RAM
ROM

Objectives

- **Identify the basic parts of a microcomputer.**
- **Describe the role of the microprocessor.**
- **Distinguish between RAM and ROM.**

Microcomputer Components

How often do you use microcomputers? You may use them to play computer games, practice math problems, or locate a book in the library. A computer is a device you can program to carry out calculations and make logical decisions. How many simple addition problems can you do in ten seconds? Computers can store large amounts of information and perform up to several million calculations in each second. This ability makes them very efficient at processing and storing large amounts of information.

What are the three main capabilities of microcomputers?

Microcomputers must have three main capabilities. First, they must be capable of storing the data or information needed to solve a problem. Next, microcomputers must be able to follow instructions to perform tasks in a logical way. Finally, microcomputers must communicate their information to the outside world. These requirements can be fulfilled with a combination of hardware and software components.

Computer hardware refers to the major permanent components of the microcomputer. When you think of a computer you probably think of the input and output devices. Output devices usually include a screen, part of the video display terminal, and a printer. The video screen in most computers is a cathode-ray tube similar to the one in your television set. Input devices allow you to communicate your ideas to the computer. Keyboards, joysticks, and mouses are common input devices. Disk drives can both input and output information. The main circuit board inside the computer holds the central processing unit (CPU) and the main memory.

Name three output devices.

Microprocessors

The first computers were very large and slow compared to the computers you are familiar with. The United States built several of the first computers shortly after World War II, between 1946 and 1951. These early computers operated on complex circuits composed of thousands of vacuum tubes. They used a lot of energy and were large enough to fill entire rooms. The

Figure 23-8. The computerized video game on the opposite page can hold more memory and perform more operations than this early computer.

invention of the integrated circuit rapidly improved the efficiency of computers.

A **microprocessor** serves as the brain of the computer. A microprocessor is an integrated circuit on the main circuit board. It receives electrical input from the user and tells other parts of the computer how to respond, just as your brain tells your hand to move when you touch a hot pan. It might store information using a disk drive, change a video display, or make a sound. The microprocessor contains the CPU, which is the circuitry that actually carries out the arithmetic and logical operations. CPUs are different among various kinds of microcomputers. The details of the CPU in the microprocessor determine how "user friendly" a computer is.

Science and WRITING

If you are "computer wise" you may be able to help novices by developing a dictionary of computer terms. Start with the terms in computer ads.

Table 23-1

BINARY CODE		
Number	Binary	Switch
0	0	○
1	1	●
2	10	●○
3	11	●●
4	100	●○○
5	101	●○●
6	110	●●○
7	111	●●●
8	1000	●○○○
9	1001	●○○●
10	1010	●○●○

Computer Memory

Information is collected and stored in the memory of the computer. The memory contains thousands of tiny circuits which have switches with two positions: open (off) or closed (on). Recall that a switch must be closed for current to flow. All computer information is processed with combinations of just two numbers, zero and one, to represent these situations. This is called a binary number system. Each 0 (off) or 1 (on) represents one binary digit and is called a bit. Numbers, letters, and symbols are grouped in your computer in arrangements of eight bits called bytes. Often computer memory is expressed in terms of larger units, such as kilobytes and megabytes. How many bytes of information can be stored in 30 kilobytes of memory?

There are several kinds of memory in a microcomputer. Temporary memory stores documents and data while they are being used. The computer can send information to the memory by turning certain bits on or off. Similarly, the computer can read information from the memory by determining whether certain bits are on or off. This temporary memory is called random-access memory, or **RAM,** because any bit can be used in storing information. Because information is electronically stored in RAM, the information is lost when the computer is turned off. However, using information stored in RAM is much faster than pulling it from mechanical disk drives.

When you purchase a computer, it comes with some information already stored in permanent memory. This information contains instructions required by the microprocessor to operate the computer. The computer can read this memory, but information can't be added to it. For this reason, it is called read-only memory, or **ROM.** Information in ROM is permanently stored inside the computer and, therefore, isn't lost when the computer is turned off. Neither RAM nor ROM is useful in helping you store your work between uses.

MINI-Lab

What makes a calculator "user friendly"?

Examine a pocket-sized calculator and see how easy it is to use. Are the keys large enough for your fingers? Can you tell by the feel of pressing a key when the contact has been made? Is the display large enough to be seen from any angle? Does it work by normal rules of arithmetic, or must you use special rules to multiply and divide? How would you change the design of this calculator to make it more "friendly"?

Data Storage

One of the main advantages of using computers is that you can save information and then come back later to make changes to it. Because RAM is lost when you turn off the computer, and you can't save information in ROM, the information must be stored in another way. Disk drives are used to record information magnetically. This process is similar to the way music is recorded on cassette tapes, but much more information can be stored on formatted computer disks. There are two main kinds of disks used for data storage.

Most computers have at least one disk drive for storing information on a "floppy" disk. A floppy disk is a thin, round, plastic disk coated with a magnetic material, such as iron oxide. The disk is encased in a thicker plastic case for protection. Information can be saved on the disk, and the disk can be removed from the disk drive for storage. Floppy disks can be used in different computers if they have compatible systems. Floppy disks can be used to transfer data or programs from one computer to another computer.

Hard disk drives are found inside the main part of some computers. Hard disks are rigid metal disks that stay inside the computer. The disks spin continuously when the computer is on. Hard drives are useful because they hold many times more information than do floppy disks. They also retrieve information much faster. A hard drive is a costly, but helpful, addition to a computer system.

Figure 23-9. A hard disk, like the one at the far right, is a permanent part of some computers. It is used to store data.

PROBLEM SOLVING

Computer Art

Emilio spent most of his spare time drawing and painting. His teachers and friends liked his artwork and they thought it was very creative.

Emilio used the family computer to write reports for school, but he really wanted to use the computer to create artwork. He visited a computer store at the mall to see what hardware was available that he could use for this purpose.

He found a graphic tablet and a light pen that allowed him to draw on the CRT screen. First, he tried the graphic tablet. He drew on a special pad with a stylus, and his design appeared on the computer screen. To use the light pen, he drew directly on the CRT. Because the graphic tablet was less expensive and easier to use, he decided to buy it. If Emilio was creating a design and the power went off, what would happen to the design?

Think Critically: How could Emilio save a design he was working on to finish at some other time?

Uses for Computers

What is a program?

Computers can't complete a task without guidelines for carrying out a series of operations. A program is a group of instructions that tells a computer what to do. Programs are sometimes referred to as software. Computer programmers use special languages that convert your language into instructions the CPU can understand. BASIC, Pascal, and Fortran are examples of computer languages. Whenever you play a computer game, use a word processor, or solve mathematical problems, a computer program is instructing the computer to perform in a certain way.

Microcomputers are becoming useful in more and more applications. You often use them in situations where a computer screen is not visible. For example, computers are regularly used to regulate mechanical processes in cars, to monitor heating and cooling systems in build-

Figure 23-10. Look closely at the computer screen above and you will see this two-page spread. Computers are commonly used for desktop publishing.

ings, and to enter inventory bar codes in grocery stores. Many calculators can now be programmed as well. Even some kitchen appliances contain simple small computers to enhance their operations. Microcomputers wouldn't exist without advances in electronics, such as the transistor and the integrated circuit. Can you imagine going through one week without using a microcomputer of some sort? How do you think we'll use microcomputers of the future?

SECTION REVIEW

1. What are three main functions of a computer?
2. Describe the function of a microprocessor.
3. What is the difference between RAM and ROM?
4. **Apply:** If you wanted to transfer a computer program from your computer to a friend's computer, how would you do it?

Comparing and Contrasting

Compare and contrast the advantages and disadvantages of floppy disk drives and hard disk drives. If you need help, refer to Comparing and Contrasting in the **Skill Handbook** on page 679.

23-4 Computer Crimes

New Science Words

computer virus

Objectives

- Discuss the types of crimes that can be committed by computer misuse.
- Predict the possible consequences of computer crimes.

How Serious Are Computer Crimes?

What do you think of when you hear the word *crime*? You probably think of stealing, vandalism, or violence. Would you believe an increasingly common type of crime is being committed by the misuse of computers?

You may have copied a friend's cassette tape onto a blank tape for your own personal use. Computer programs can also be copied from one floppy disk to another. When you purchase a program, the software company usually intends for you to make one backup copy in case the original one becomes damaged. The companies don't intend for you to copy the program to give to your friends. These programs are protected by copyright laws. However, some programs are free and can be copied legally for distribution. Sharing of illegal copies of software is probably the most common of computer crimes, as well as the most difficult computer crime to safeguard against.

In recent years, computer viruses have become a problem. Some computer viruses can be deliberately planted in a computer. A **computer virus** is a type of program that can multiply inside a computer and use so much memory that it harms the system. Like a virus in your body, it can remain inactive in the computer until something causes it to spread. As a result of the virus attack, data in memory might be lost, and a strange message might appear on the screen. The infected computer might even just stop functioning. Viruses can be sent through phone lines linking computers, or can spread from infected software shared between computers. Sometimes antivirus programs can find and destroy viruses before they spread, or even fix the damage already done. Do you think it is a crime to purposefully spread a computer virus?

Perhaps the most controversial computer crime is "hacking." People who break into closed computer systems without permission are called hackers. They may have several motives. Some hackers may just find hacking challenging, but others are looking for specific restricted information.

Hacking is an invasion of privacy. For example, a hacker might be able to find out about your parents' financial history without permission. A hacker could break into your school's computer to alter his or her grades. Do you think this is the same type of crime as breaking into someone's house?

We are very dependent on computers. Make a list of the activities in your life that involve computers. How do computer crimes affect these activities? Stealing software can cause the price of software programs to go up. If a virus were to shut down a major computer system, such as the system at your bank, how would you be affected?

1. How does a computer virus interfere with a computer?
2. What is computer hacking?

You Decide!

Suppose a computer hacker broke into a secret government computer system. Should this be considered a criminal offense, such as treason, or should it be considered a misdemeanor crime, such as breaking and entering? Do you think the hacker should be punished in the same manner as someone who broke into a building and took secret files? Explain your point of view.

ACTIVITY 23-2
Information Storage

Problem: *Can you store information in a magnetic field?*

Materials
- disk magnets, 12
- cardstock paper, 2 sheets and a thin strip
- transparent tape
- metric ruler

Procedure
1. Divide one sheet of the cardstock into four rows of squares as shown.
2. Put all the magnets in a single stack. Mark the top side of each magnet with the number 1 and the bottom with number 0.
3. Invent a code using only the numbers 1 and 0 to represent the letters of the alphabet. Make a code table as shown.
4. Choose a three or four letter word to "write" with eleven magnets.
5. Tape the magnets, code number side up, to the "message sheet" made in Step 1. Tape one magnet to a square so that each row shows the code of a particular letter.
6. Cover the magnets with a second sheet marked with the location of squares on the message sheet.
7. Tape a magnet to the end of a strip of cardstock. Holding the other end of the strip, slide the magnet over the top sheet and "read" its response to the message magnets.
8. Write down the operating rules for "reading" your word. Trade your rules and magnetic message with another team.

Analyze
1. How do you know what kind of letter is underneath the "reading" message.
2. How many letters can be made with two magnets each?
3. How much of the alphabet can be made if no letter can have more than four magnets?

Conclude and Apply
4. Why are the operating rules for reading as important as knowing the code number?
5. Why are there only two numbers in the code?

LETTER CODES	
A — 0	**F** — 11
B — 1	**G** — 000
C — 00	**H** — 001
D — 01	**I** — 011
E — 10	**J** — 111

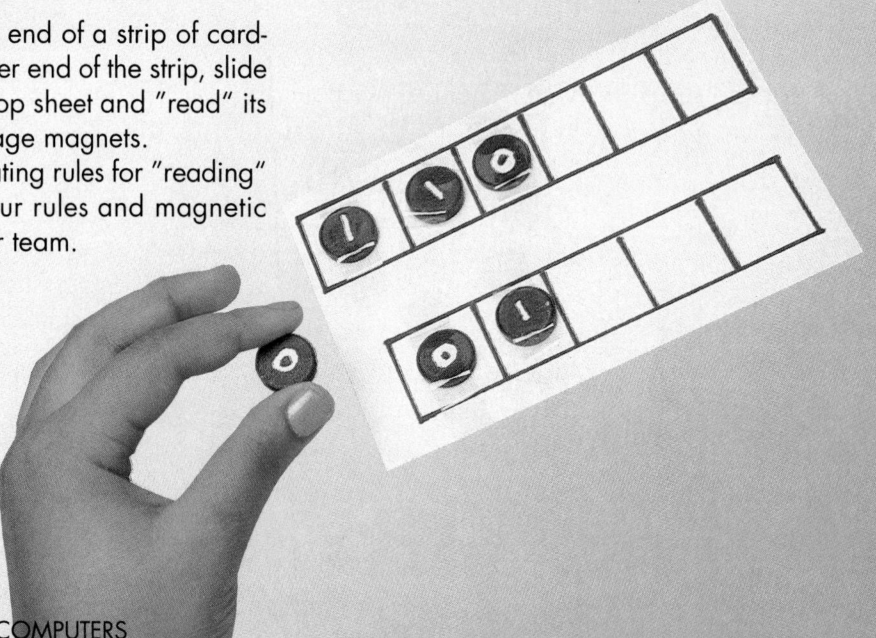

CHAPTER

REVIEW

SUMMARY

23-1: Semiconductor Devices

1. The conductivity of semiconductors can be increased by adding impurities to them.

2. A rectifier changes alternating current into direct current.

3. Electronic devices containing integrated circuits are much smaller than those that don't contain these circuits.

23-2: Radio and Television

1. Radio and television signals are transmitted by changing electrical signals into electromagnetic radiation.

2. A cathode-ray tube uses electrons and fluorescent materials to produce pictures on a television screen.

23-3: Microcomputers

1. The basic parts of a microcomputer include the input devices, the output devices, disk drives, and the main circuit board.

2. The microprocessor receives input and tells the computer how to respond.

3. RAM is the temporary memory in a computer. ROM is memory that is permanently stored inside the computer.

23-4: Science and Society: Computer Crimes

1. Computer crimes include illegally copying software, planting computer viruses, and hacking.

2. Some computer crimes can involve stealing restricted information or altering records.

KEY SCIENCE WORDS

a. **amplification**
b. **cathode-ray tube (CRT)**
c. **computer virus**
d. **diode**
e. **integrated circuit**
f. **microprocessor**
g. **RAM**
h. **rectifier**
i. **ROM**
j. **transistor**

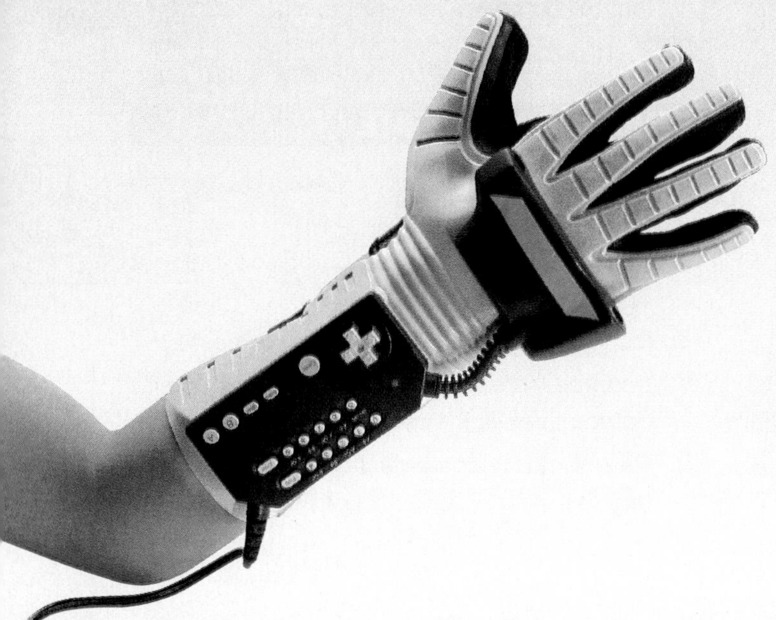

UNDERSTANDING VOCABULARY

Match each phrase with the correct term from the list of Key Science Words.

1. miniature components on a slice of silicon
2. converts AC to DC
3. amplifies an electric signal
4. the process of making an electric current stronger
5. a TV picture tube
6. transfers a user's commands to other parts of the computer
7. a computer's temporary memory
8. a computer program that multiplies and causes a computer's memory to be lost
9. contains stored information needed by a microprocessor to operate a computer
10. a type of rectifier

CHAPTER REVIEW

CHECKING CONCEPTS

Choose the word or phrase that completes the sentence.

1. Elements that are semiconductors are located on the periodic table ______.
   a. between metals and nonmetals
   b. on the right side
   c. at the bottom
   d. on the left side
2. Solid-state electronic devices use ______.
   a. low current **c.** no current
   b. high current **d.** vacuum tubes
3. Rectifiers are used in ______.
   a. adapter plugs **c.** computers
   b. televisions **d.** all of these
4. The signal in an electronic device that represents sound and images is a ______.
   a. varying current **c.** radio wave
   b. constant current **d.** sound wave
5. Transistors are used in all of the following except ______.
   a. medical diagnoses **c.** hearing aids
   b. TV vacuum tubes **d.** tape players
6. Integrated circuits consist of ______.
   a. silicon chips with painted aluminum wires
   b. transistors
   c. resistors
   d. all of these
7. The video images for a television program are transmitted to your home as ______.
   a. frequency-modulated radio waves
   b. amplitude-modulated radio waves
   c. cathode rays
   d. electric current
8. Computer hardware consists of all of the following except ______.
   a. video display terminal **c.** disk drives
   b. programs **d.** keyboards
9. A computer represents information using ____.
   a. a binary number system
   b. sequences of numbers
   c. arrangements of 4 bits
   d. the numbers 1 through 10
10. Computer data and programs both can be stored permanently and transferred to other computers using ______.
    a. RAM **c.** floppy disks
    b. ROM **d.** hard disks

UNDERSTANDING CONCEPTS

Complete each sentence.

11. Both *p*-type and *n*-type semiconductors are used in the construction of ______.
12. An electric signal is amplified by a sandwich of three alternating semiconductors in a(n) ______.
13. ______ are the most fundamental components of modern electronic circuits.
14. Cathode-ray tubes use ______ to produce images on their screens.
15. A computer ______ is a group of instructions that tells a computer what to do.

THINK AND WRITE CRITICALLY

16. How are semiconductors used in diodes and transistors?
17. Describe the advantages and disadvantages of integrated circuits.
18. Identify three functions of a microcomputer.
19. Describe three types of computer crime. Which do you think is the most serious? Why?
20. Describe how computers affect you in everyday life.

APPLY

21. Could a diode work properly if *both* of its ends were either *p*-type or *n*-type semiconductors? Explain your answer.
22. You have connected your new compact disc player directly to your stereo speakers, but when you turn on the CD, you hear nothing. Should you return the CD player to the store? Why or why not?
23. Which would do more harm to the operation of a computer, the loss of its random-access memory or the loss of its read-only memory? Explain your answer.
24. You need to store information on your computer that you can retrieve rapidly whenever you use your computer. What is the best way to store this information?
25. Why might your school keep written records even when it has computers that can store these records much more efficiently?

MORE SKILL BUILDERS

If you need help, refer to the Skill Handbook.

1. **Recognizing Cause and Effect:** Complete the following table by identifying either the cause or effect of problems associated with cathode-ray tubes.

Cause	Effect
1. Inside of tube coated with a non-fluorescent material.	1.
2.	2. Electron beam doesn't sweep the entire screen.
3. Incoming electrical signals are garbled.	3.

2. **Comparing and Contrasting:** Compare and contrast *n*-type and *p*-type semiconductors. Discuss the purpose of each semiconductor, how each functions, and what elements each uses and why.
3. **Making and Using Tables:** Construct a table to organize what you know about the parts of the microcomputer and the function of each part.
4. **Interpreting Scientific Illustrations:** Look at the two diagrams of doped silicon crystals in Figure 23-2 on page 597. Read the statements below and separate them into two columns. Label these columns N-type Semiconductor and P-type Semiconductor. Be sure to place the statements in each column in the correct order. Some statements can be used twice.
   - **a.** Electrons move to fill holes, creating more holes in the crystal.
   - **b.** Current flows through the doped crystal.
   - **c.** The extra electrons move through the crystal.
   - **d.** A silicon crystal is doped with gallium.
   - **e.** A silicon crystal is doped with arsenic.
   - **f.** Voltage is applied across the crystal.
   - **g.** An electron hole is near each gallium atom in the crystal.
   - **h.** The crystal has extra electrons that are free to move.

PROJECTS

1. Find out how microphones convert sound and turntable needles convert mechanical vibrations into electrical signals. Make a poster illustrating how each works.
2. Learn one of the basic computer languages and write a simple program.

CHAPTER

24 Radioactivity and Nuclear Reactions

Have you ever watched a news report about the disposal of radioactive materials? Have you wondered how long these materials remain radioactive? Why are so many problems associated with radioactive materials?

FIND OUT!

Do the following activity to find out how radioactive materials decay into nonradioactive materials.

Put 32 marbles in a jar. Let these marbles represent radioactive atoms that will decay into nonradioactive atoms. Use a stopwatch or a second hand to time one-minute intervals. During the first minute, take half of the 32 marbles out of the jar and put them aside. These marbles represent atoms that have decayed into another element. During the second and third minutes, remove half of the remaining marbles from the jar. What happens to the radioactive atoms during each one-minute interval? What's the rate of decay of this radioactive element? Predict how many minutes it would take for all of the radioactive sample to decay.

Gearing Up

Previewing the Chapter

Use this outline to help you focus on important ideas in this chapter.

Previewing Science Skills

- ▶ In the **Skill Builders**, you will compare and contrast, interpret scientific illustrations, observe and infer, and make a concept map.
- ▶ In the **Activities**, you will predict, interpret, and formulate models.
- ▶ In the **MINI-Labs**, you will observe and infer.

What's next?

If you predicted it would take about six minutes for the radioactive atoms in the Find Out activity to decay, you were correct. Some radioactive elements decay in less than one second; others take thousands of years. As you read this chapter, you will learn more about the many radioactive elements and how they decay.

24-1 Radioactivity

New Science Words

radioactivity
nuclide

Objectives

- ▶ Discuss the discovery of radioactivity.
- ▶ Contrast properties of radioactive versus stable nuclides.

Radioactive Elements

Do you have a smoke detector in your home to alert you if there's a fire? If it is an ionizing smoke detector, it probably contains a small amount of a radioactive element called americium-241. How do you feel about having a radioactive element in your home?

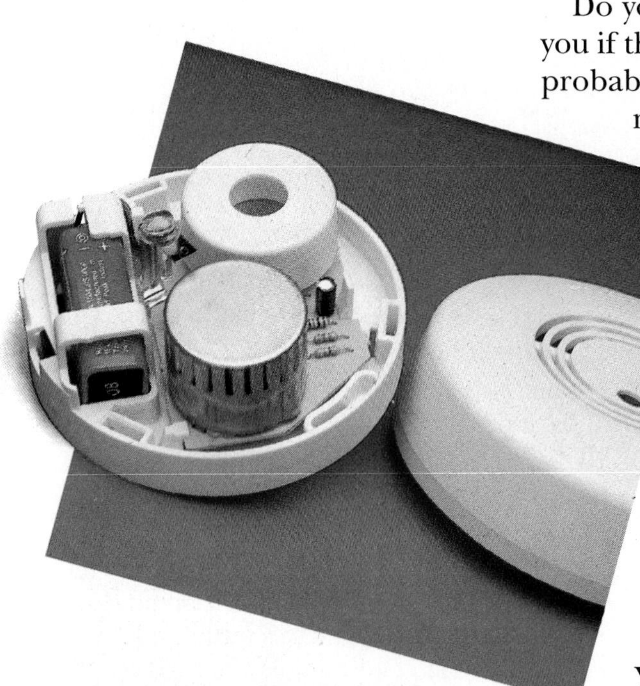

Figure 24-1. Many smoke detectors, such as this one, contain a small amount of a radioactive element.

The discovery of radioactivity about 100 years ago has led to major advances in medical diagnoses and treatments, the use of nuclear energy, and the designing of nuclear weapons. Do you consider radioactivity to be helpful or harmful? It's certainly easy to see why some uses of radiation and nuclear energy are so controversial.

Look around the room. Can you detect any evidence of radioactivity? Did you know there are small amounts of radioactivity all around you? You can't see, hear, taste, touch, or smell it. You even have small amounts of radioactivity inside your body.

You may wonder how radiation was first discovered if it can't be detected by your senses. Henri Bequerel accidentally discovered radioactivity in 1896 when he left some uranium salt in a desk drawer with a photographic plate. When he later removed the plate and developed it, he found an outline of the uranium salt. He hypothesized that the uranium had given off some invisible energy and exposed the film. This process is called radiation, and the particles given off by the uranium are sometimes referred to as "radiation." Marie Curie and her husband Pierre took interest in Bequerel's discovery. They began looking for other radioactive elements in a uranium ore called pitchblende. Two years after

Bequerel's discovery, they discovered the elements polonium and radium. These elements are even more radioactive than uranium.

Notice where these three elements are found on the periodic table. These elements all have high atomic numbers and therefore are located near the bottom of the chart. All elements that have an atomic number greater than 83 are radioactive. Some other elements are also radioactive.

You know that all elements are made of atoms, and that atoms are made up of protons, neutrons, and electrons. The protons and neutrons are held together in the nucleus by what scientists call the strong force. This force is strong enough to prevent the positive protons from pushing each other out of the nucleus of the atom; however, this force only acts across very small distances. As a result, those elements with high atomic numbers—many protons and neutrons—are held together less securely than, say, an oxygen atom. Particles or energy can escape from all nuclei with atomic numbers of 84 or higher. This process is called radioactive decay. These nuclei are considered to be unstable. **Radioactivity,** therefore, is the emission of high energy radiation or particles from the nucleus of a radioactive atom.

Find the elements with atomic numbers 93 to 109 on the periodic table. Elements with these atomic numbers don't exist naturally on Earth. They have been produced in labs and are called synthetic elements. All these synthetic elements are very unstable. Why might these elements be difficult to study?

Nuclides

Recall that most elements have isotopes. Isotopes of an element differ in their number of neutrons and in their atomic mass, but they have the same number of protons. Some isotopes are radioactive and others are not. Why is this so? The nucleus of an isotope with a certain atomic number and mass is called a **nuclide.** In many nuclides, the strong force is enough to keep the nucleus permanently together, creating a stable nuclide. However, the strong force is not sufficient to hold unstable nuclides together permanently. These unstable nuclides are radioactive because they decay to give off matter and energy.

MINI-Lab

Does radiation change film?

Radiation was discovered as a result of placing a radioactive source near a photographic plate. Today, some workers that are in danger of being exposed to radiation wear photographic film badges. Obtain one of these badges or some undeveloped film and a weak source of radiation. Place the source near the film or badge for ten minutes and observe the film. Describe the changes you observed.

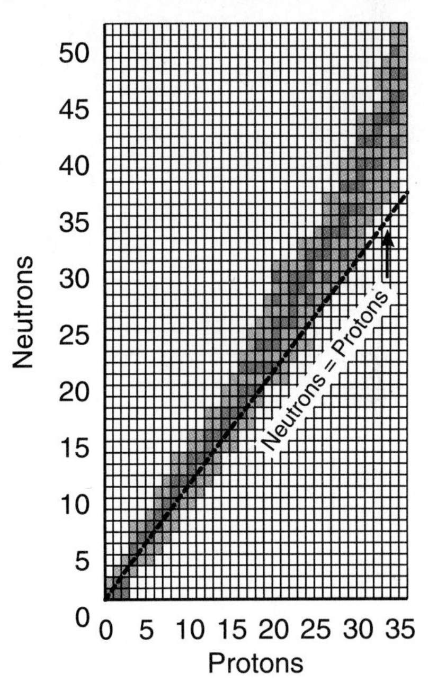

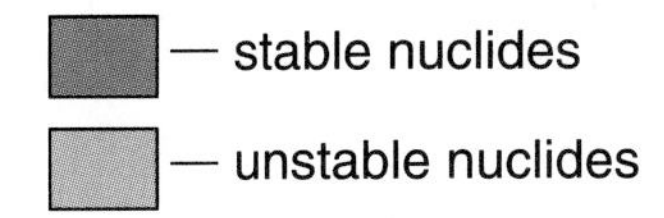

Figure 24-2. Elements with low atomic numbers have stable nuclides when the numbers of protons and neutrons are close.

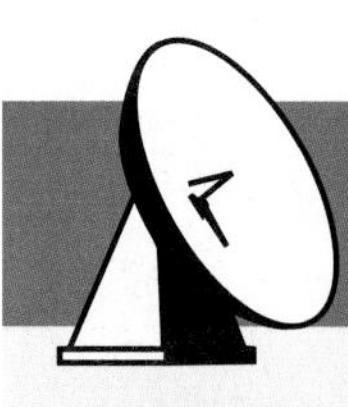

TECHNOLOGY

Super Atom Smasher

Probing the structure of the nucleus is a difficult task. As a result, construction of the largest and most expensive scientific instrument ever produced is under way. This instrument, called the superconducting super collider—or SSC—will improve our understanding of nuclear structure. The SSC is a particle accelerator that is designed to smash atomic particles together to produce a shower of basic particles that will provide clues to nuclear structure.

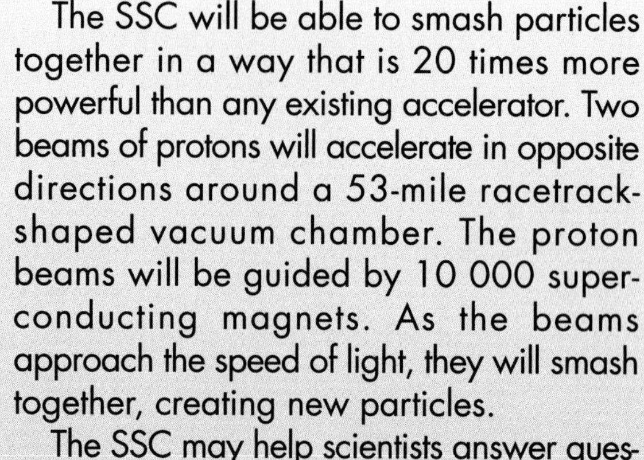

The SSC will be able to smash particles together in a way that is 20 times more powerful than any existing accelerator. Two beams of protons will accelerate in opposite directions around a 53-mile racetrack-shaped vacuum chamber. The proton beams will be guided by 10 000 superconducting magnets. As the beams approach the speed of light, they will smash together, creating new particles.

The SSC may help scientists answer questions about the structure of matter that are so fundamental that many other fields will benefit. A totally new and unexpected understanding of the laws of nature may emerge from the knowledge gained from the SSC.

Think Critically: Why do you think the proton beams need to be smashed with such great force? How will this help us learn more about matter?

Isotopes of elements differ in the ratio of neutrons to protons. This ratio affects the stability of the nucleus. An isotope of a less massive element is stable if the ratio is about 1 to 1. An isotope of a heavier element is stable when the ratio of neutrons to protons is about 3 to 2. However, the nuclei of isotopes of both lighter and heavier elements that differ much from these ratios are unstable. That is, nuclei with too many or too few neutrons are radioactive.

What isotopes are unstable?

How can you distinguish one isotope from another of the same element? A nuclide can be represented by a symbol that gives the atomic number, mass number, and element symbol. You know the atomic number is the same as the number of protons in the element, and the mass

Table 24-1

RADIOACTIVE NUCLIDES OF SOME ELEMENTS

Element	Nuclide	Atomic mass number	Protons	Neutrons
Hydrogen	$^{3}_{1}H$	3	1	2
Helium	$^{5}_{2}He$	5	2	3
Lithium	$^{8}_{3}Li$	8	3	5
Carbon	$^{14}_{6}C$	14	6	8
Nitrogen	$^{16}_{7}N$	16	7	9
Potassium	$^{40}_{19}K$	40	19	21

number is the total number of protons and neutrons in the nucleus. The nucleus of the stable isotope of potassium is shown below.

$$\begin{matrix}\text{mass number} \rightarrow \\ \text{atomic number} \rightarrow\end{matrix} \; ^{39}_{19}K \leftarrow \text{element symbol}$$

Now compare the stable isotope of potassium to the radioactive isotope below.

$$\begin{matrix}\text{mass number} \rightarrow \\ \text{atomic number} \rightarrow\end{matrix} \; ^{40}_{19}K \leftarrow \text{element symbol}$$

The stable isotope is called potassium-39. This isotope has 19 protons and 20 neutrons. The radioactive isotope is potassium-40. How many neutrons does potassium-40 have?

EcoTip

Radon is an odorless, colorless, radioactive gas that comes from underground rocks. Keep radon out of your house by sealing cracks in the basement floor and walls, and spaces around water pipes and drains.

SECTION REVIEW

1. Identify the contributions of the three scientists who discovered the first radioactive elements.
2. What is the range of atomic numbers in which all isotopes are radioactive? Which of these are synthetic?
3. **Apply:** What is the ratio of protons to neutrons in lead-214? Explain whether you would expect this isotope to be radioactive or stable.

Comparing and Contrasting

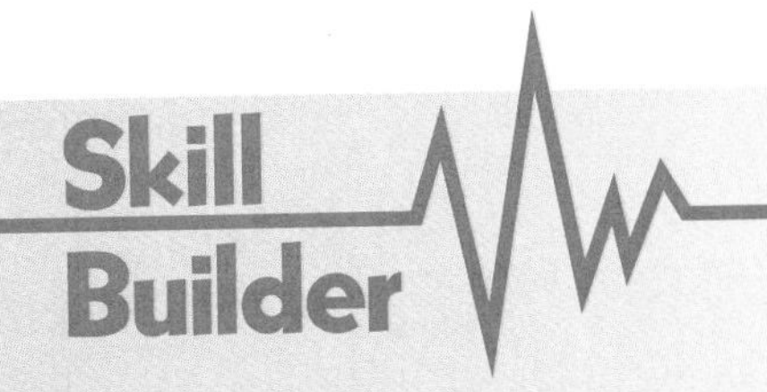

Compare and contrast stable and unstable isotopes of potassium. What do they have in common? How do they differ? If you need help, refer to Comparing and Contrasting in the **Skill Handbook** on page 679.

24-2 Nuclear Decay

New Science Words

alpha particles
transmutation
beta particle
gamma rays
half-life

Objectives

- Distinguish between alpha, beta, and gamma radiation.
- Calculate the amount of a radioactive substance remaining after a time based on its half-life.
- Relate half-life to the process of radioactive dating.

Nuclear Radiation

You've heard the terms *radiation* and *radioactive* ever since you were a young child. Maybe you didn't know what these words meant then, but now you know they refer to unstable, radioactive nuclei that emit radiation composed of small particles or energy. There are three main types of nuclear radiation—alpha, beta, and gamma radiation. Figure 24-3 shows the path that each type of nuclear radiation follows as it moves through a magnetic field. As you can see, each type of radiation is affected differently. Which type of radiation is most affected by a magnetic field?

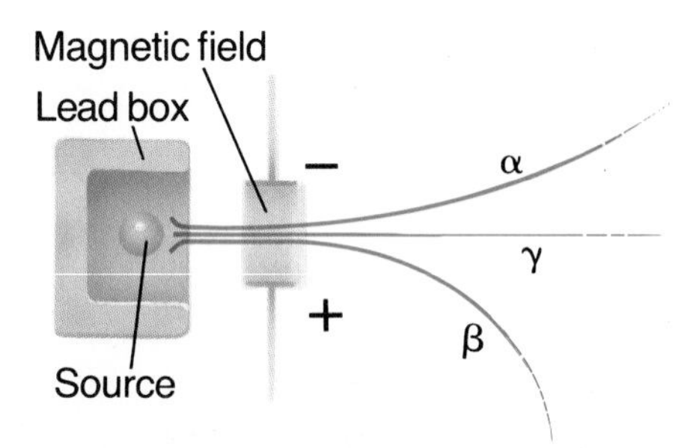

Figure 24-3. Notice how alpha and beta particles are deflected by a magnetic field.

Radiation in the form of **alpha particles** is given off when a nucleus releases two protons and two neutrons. Notice that the alpha particle is the same as a helium nucleus, as shown in Table 24-2. An alpha particle has a charge of +2 and an atomic mass of 4. It is the largest and slowest form of radiation, so it is also the least penetrat-

Table 24-2

THREE TYPES OF NUCLEAR RADIATION

Type	Symbol	Charge	Mass	Can be stopped by
alpha	He	+2	4	Paper
beta	e	−1	0	Aluminum
gamma	none	none	0	Lead or concrete

ing. Alpha particles can be stopped by a sheet of paper, but they can be deadly if they are released by atoms inside your body.

The smoke detector mentioned earlier in this chapter gives off alpha particles that ionize the surrounding air. An electric current flows through the ionized air, but the circuit is broken when smoke particles enter the ionized air. When the circuit is broken, the alarm is set off.

Isotopes that give off alpha or beta particles undergo transmutation. **Transmutation** is the process of changing one element to another through nuclear decay. The nuclear equation below shows a nuclear transmutation. Because two protons are lost from the nucleus in alpha decay, the new element formed has an atomic number two less than that of the original element. The atomic mass number of the new element is four less than the original element. In a transmutation, the atomic mass number of the decayed nuclide equals the sum of the mass numbers of the newly formed nuclide and the emitted particle.

$$^{218}_{84}\text{Po} \rightarrow ^{214}_{82}\text{Pb} + ^{4}_{2}\text{He}$$

Sometimes a neutron inside a nucleus decays spontaneously into a proton and an electron. The electron is emitted from the nucleus at very high speed and is called a **beta particle**. The proton formed by the decaying neutron stays in the nucleus, forming an element with an atomic number one greater than the original element. Because the beta particle has such a tiny mass, the atomic mass number of the new element is the same as that of the original element. A proton can also decay into a neutron and a positron. A positron is similar to an electron, but has a positive charge. Positrons are also considered to be beta particles. In a transmutation, the charge of the original nuclide equals the sum of the charges of the nuclide and particle formed, as shown in the equation below.

$$^{214}_{82}\text{Pb} \longrightarrow ^{214}_{83}\text{Bi} + ^{0}_{-1}\text{e}$$

Did You Know?

The first person whose death was attributed to radiation exposure was Marie Curie.

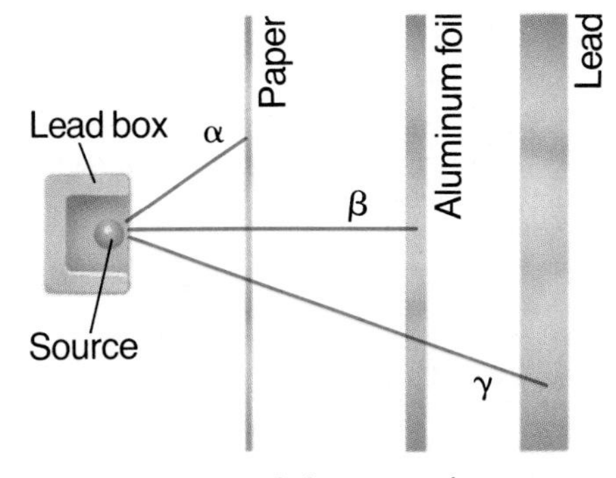

Figure 24-4. Alpha particles can be stopped by paper, beta particles by aluminum foil, and gamma rays by lead.

Beta particles are much faster and more penetrating than alpha particles. However, they can be stopped by a sheet of aluminum foil.

The most penetrating and potentially dangerous form of radiation is not made of particles at all. **Gamma rays** are electromagnetic waves with very high frequency and energy. They have no mass, no charge, and they travel at the speed of light. They are usually released along with alpha or beta particles. Gamma rays are the most penetrating form of radiation, and thick blocks of materials with dense nuclei are required to stop them. Lead and concrete are commonly used barriers for gamma rays. Compare the symbols and the relative penetrating powers of the three kinds of radiation shown in Table 24-2.

Science and MATH

How long does it take for strontium-90, with a half-life of 28 years, to be reduced to less than one percent of its rate of decay?

Half-life

Safe disposal of a some radioisotopes is not a problem because their nuclides decay to stable nuclides in less than a second. However, nuclides of other radioactive isotopes may require millions of years to decay. A mea-

PROBLEM SOLVING

The Radioactive Clock

Kristine had a difficult time waking up for school. Her mother had to call to her to wake her up several times each morning.

Kristine found an old alarm clock in the attic. Now she can wake up without her mother calling her.

During the night Kristine awoke. She was startled by a greenish-white glow next to her bed. Then she realized that the glow was coming from the hands of the alarm clock. She wondered what caused the hands to glow.

The next day, she did some research in the school library and found that the hands of the clock were coated with a paint containing radium and zinc sulfide. The zinc sulfide emits little flashes of light when excited by radiation. These tiny flashes of light make the hands of the clock appear to glow. Why does the zinc sulfide in the paint appear to glow?

Think Critically: Explain why the glow of the hands will become dimmer over time.

sure of the time required by the nuclides of an isotope to decay is called half-life. The **half-life** of an isotope is the amount of time it takes for half the nuclides in a sample of a given radioactive isotope to decay. Half-lives vary widely among the radioactive isotopes. For example, polonium-214 has a half-life of about a thousandth of a second; but uranium-238 has a half-life of 4.5 billion years.

You can determine the amount of a radioactive sample that will remain after a given amount of time if you know the half-life of the sample. The half-lives of some radioactive elements are listed in Table 24-3. Look at the problem below to see how to calculate the amount of remaining sodium-24, which has a half-life of 15 hours.

Table 24-3

SAMPLE HALF-LIVES	
Isotope	Half-life
$^{3}_{1}H$	12.3 years
$^{14}_{6}C$	5730 years
$^{131}_{53}I$	8.07 days
$^{212}_{82}Pb$	10.6 hours
$^{194}_{84}Po$	0.7 second
$^{235}_{92}U$	7.1×10^8 years

EXAMPLE PROBLEM: Calculating the Quantity of a Radioactive Element

Problem Statement: How much of a 20-g sample of sodium-24 would remain after decaying for 15 hours?

Known Information:
Strategy Hint: Find the half-life of sodium-24 above.

Amount of original sample of sodium-24 = 20 g
Time elapsed = 15 hours
Half-life of sodium-24 = 15 hours

Unknown Information: amount of remaining sodium-24

Equation to Use:

$$\text{amount remaining} = \frac{\text{amount of original sample}}{2^n}$$

n = number of half-lives elapsed

Solution:

$$\frac{20\text{ g}}{2^1} = \frac{20\text{ g}}{2} = 10\text{ g}$$

PRACTICE PROBLEM

Strategy Hint: Determine how many half-lives of sodium-24 elapse in 45 hours.

1. How much of a 20-g sample of sodium-24 would remain after 45 hours?

Radioactive Dating

It was mentioned earlier that you have some radioactive materials inside your body. One of these is a radioactive isotope of carbon, carbon-14. This isotope is in some of the carbon dioxide molecules plants take in as they respire. As a result, you have carbon-14 inside of you from the plants and animals you eat. Carbon-14 emits a beta particle and decays into nitrogen.

All living things contain a somewhat constant amount of carbon-14. Decaying carbon-14 is constantly replaced by new carbon-14 in a living organism, but when the organism dies, its carbon-14 decays without replacement. The half-life of carbon-14 is 5730 years. By measuring the amount of carbon-14 remaining in a fossil or skeleton, scientists can determine the approximate age of the material. This process is called carbon-14 dating.

How does the age of a rock compare with fossils in it?

Do you think carbon-14 dating could be used to determine the age of a dinosaur skeleton? No, it wouldn't work, because the last dinosaur species died out well over 50 million years ago. Only remains of plants and animals that lived within the last 50 000 years contain enough carbon-14 to measure.

You may wonder how the ages of fossils more than 50 000 years old and rocks can be determined. If the rock contains some amount of a radioactive element, such as uranium-238 with a half-life of 4.5 billion years, the time of the rock's formation can be determined. If the rock contains fossils, it is assumed that the age of the fossils is the same as that of the rock.

SECTION REVIEW

1. Describe each of the three types of radiation and compare their penetrating power.
2. Write a nuclear equation to show how radon-222 decays to give off an alpha particle and another element. What is the other element?
3. The half-life of iodine-131 is about eight days. How much of a 40-g sample will be left after eight days? After 16 days? After 32 days?
4. **Apply:** Is it possible for an isotope to decay to an element with a higher atomic number? Explain.

Interpreting Scientific Illustrations

Use Figure 24-3 on page 624 to explain why the alpha particle appears to curve up, the beta particle curves down, and the gamma particle travels straight through the magnet. If you need help, refer to Interpreting Scientific Illustrations in the **Skill Handbook** on page 689.

ACTIVITY 24-1
Half-life

Problem: *What is a half-life?*

Materials
- rubber stopper
- graph paper

Procedure
1. Copy the data table.
2. Hold a rubber stopper and stand an equal distance from nearby classmates.
3. When the teacher says "go," *gently* toss your stopper to a nearby student and catch the stopper tossed to you.
4. If you drop the stopper, *don't* pick it up.
5. If you catch the stopper, immediately toss it to someone other than the person who threw it to you.
6. When the teacher says "stop," hold your stopper up. Count the stoppers that are held up and record the number on your data table.
7. Repeat Steps 3 through 6 for three more time intervals.
8. Plot the data from the table on a graph. Connect the points with a smooth curve.

Data and Observations

Interval	Total Time	Atoms Remaining
0		
1		
2		
3		
4		

Analyze
1. Assume each stopper is an atom of a radioactive element. The stoppers that hit the floor represent atoms that have changed into another element. During which time interval were most of the "atoms" changed?
2. Were all the "atoms" changed during the experiment? If not, how long do you think it would take for all of them to change?
3. According to your graph, how long did it take for half the atoms to change? How many atoms changed in twice that amount of time?

Conclude and Apply
4. According to your graph, if 20 stoppers are still "unchanged," how many seconds ago did the class start throwing stoppers?
5. What would the half-life curve look like for a class of 40 students if the half-life time was the same as for your class?

24-3 Detecting Radioactivity

New Science Words

cloud chamber
bubble chamber

Objectives

- Describe how radioactivity can be detected.
- Explain how a Geiger counter can determine the quantity of nuclear radiation present.

Radiation Detectors

Because you can't feel a single proton or gamma ray, you must use instruments to detect their presence. Methods of detecting radioactivity depend on radiation forming ions by removing electrons from matter it passes through. The newly formed ions can be detected in several ways.

Have you ever seen clouds formed in a cloud chamber? A **cloud chamber** can be used to detect charged nuclear particles as they leave cloud tracks. It contains supersaturated water or ethanol vapor. When a charged particle from a radioactive sample moves through the chamber, it leaves a path of ions behind as it knocks electrons off the atoms in the air. The vapor condenses around these ions to provide a visible path of droplets along the track of the particle. Do you think the trail of a beta particle might differ from the trail of an alpha particle? Beta particles leave long, thin trails, and alpha particles leave shorter and thicker trails.

How does a cloud chamber detect nuclear particles?

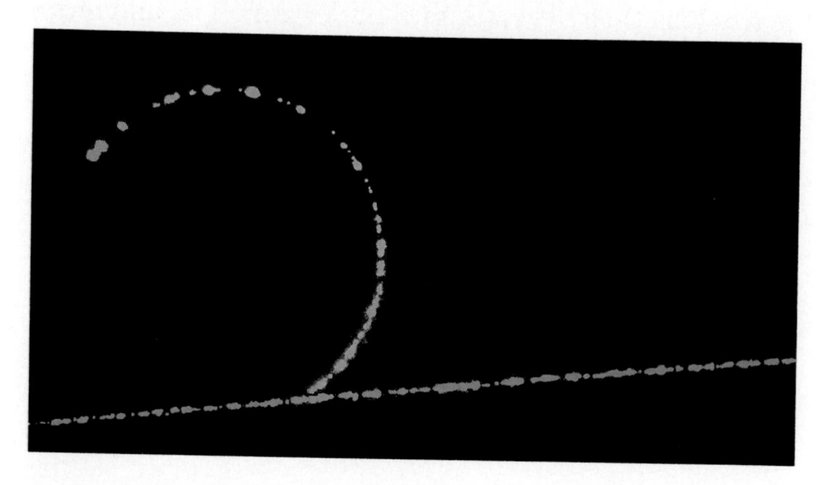

Figure 24-5. A cloud chamber is a device used to detect particles of nuclear radiation.

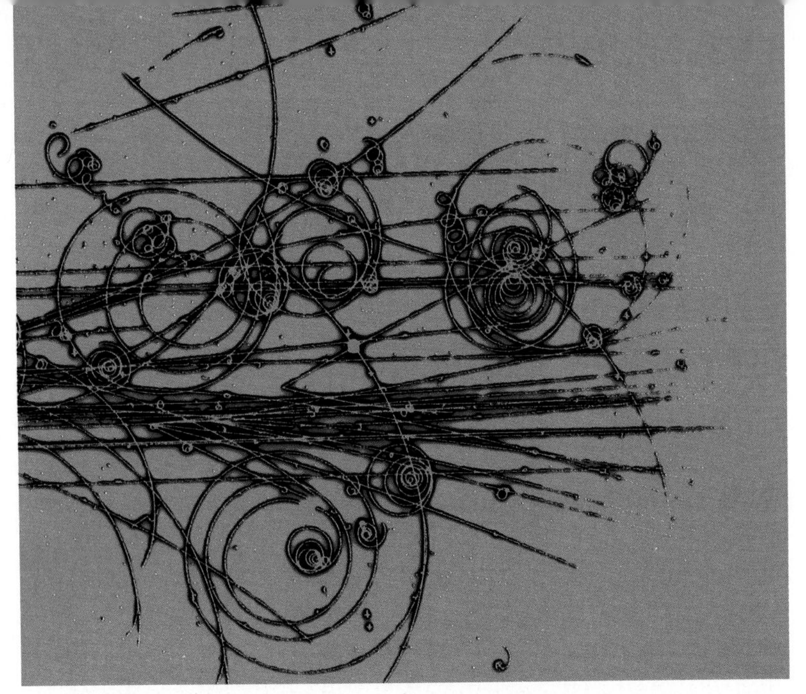

Figure 24-6. Particles of nuclear radiation can be detected as they leave trails of bubbles in a bubble chamber.

Another way to detect and monitor the paths of nuclear particles is by using a bubble chamber. A **bubble chamber** holds a superheated liquid, which doesn't boil even though it's hot enough. When a moving particle leaves ions behind, the liquid boils along the trail. The path shows up as tracks of bubbles.

Do you remember how an electroscope was used to detect electric charges in Chapter 21? When an electroscope is given a negative charge, the leaves repel each other and spread apart. They will remain apart until the extra electrons have somewhere to go and discharge the electroscope. A nuclear particle moving through the air will remove electrons from air molecules, leaving them positively charged. When this occurs near an electroscope, the positively charged air molecules will attract the electrons from the leaves. As these negatively charged leaves lose their charges, they no longer repel and move together again.

MINI-Lab

What senses atomic radiation?

A dosimeter measures atomic radiation. It is a type of electroscope that discharges when the gases around it are ionized. Hold a lighted match so the stream of ionized air from the flame will pass near a charged electroscope. Observe the change. Bring a source of beta radiation near a charged electroscope. How does the rate at which the electroscope discharges compare with its distance to the radiation source?

Counting Radioactivity

You constantly receive small doses of radiation from your environment. It is not known whether this radiation is harmful to your body tissues. Larger doses of radiation, however, can be harmful to living tissue. If you worked or lived in an environment that could result in exposure to high levels of radiation—a nuclear testing facility, for example—you might want to know exactly how much radiation you were being exposed to. The simplest

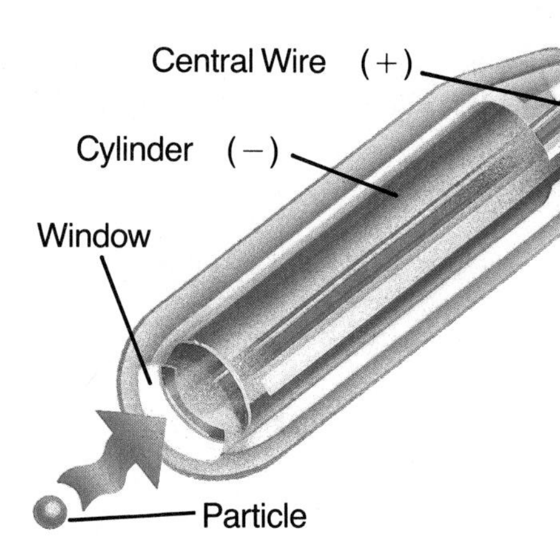

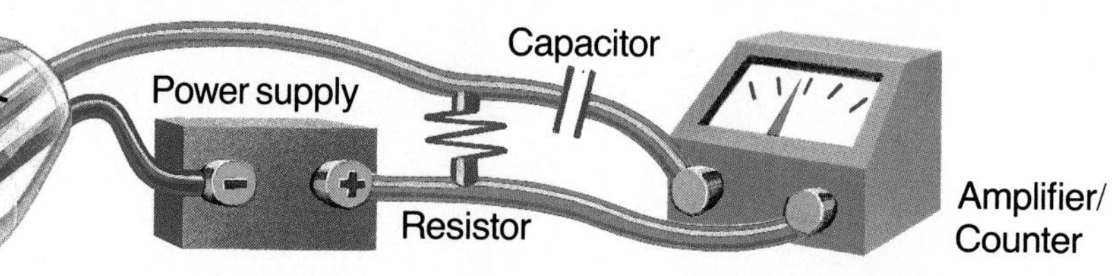

Figure 24-7. A Gieger counter can be used to measure the intensity of nuclear radiation.

method of counting radioactivity is to use a Geiger counter. A Geiger counter is a device that produces an electric current when radiation is present.

Figure 24-7 illustrates the parts of a Geiger counter. The tube is filled with gas at a low pressure. A positively charged wire runs through the center of a negatively charged copper cylinder. These are connected to a voltage source. Radiation enters the tube at one end, stripping electrons from the gaseous atoms. The electrons are attracted to the positive wire. They knock more electrons off the atoms in the gas and an "electron avalanche" is produced. A large number of electrons reach the wire, producing a short, intense current in the wire. This current is amplified to produce a clicking sound or flashing light. The intensity of radiation present is determined by the number of clicks in each second.

Geiger counters can be made very small and portable. They are often used to test the radioactivity at job sites where workers can be exposed to radioactive materials. For example, workers in a hospital radiation lab or at a nuclear power plant could actually wear small Geiger counters to monitor their exposures.

SECTION REVIEW

1. What are four ways radioactivity can be detected?
2. Explain the basic function of a Geiger counter.
3. **Apply:** Suppose you needed to check the level of radioactivity in the laboratory of a hospital. Which method would you use? Explain your choice.

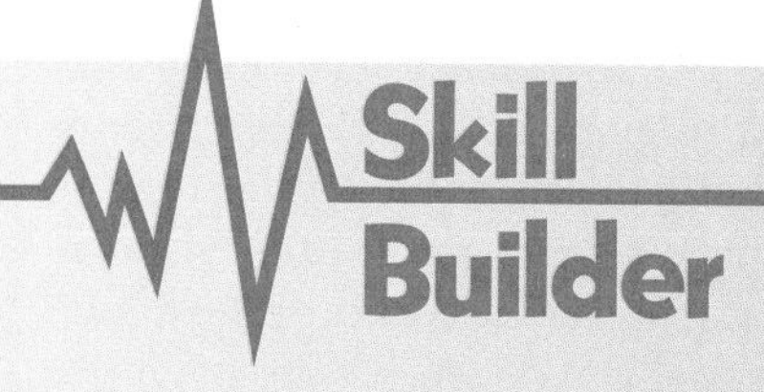

Observing and Inferring

Suppose that you are observing the presence of nuclear radiation with a bubble chamber. You see two kinds of trails. Some trails are short and others are long and thin. What type of nuclear radiation might have caused each trail? If you need help, refer to Observing and Inferring in the **Skill Handbook** on page 678.

Nuclear Reactions

24-4

Objectives

- ▶ Distinguish between nuclear fission and fusion.
- ▶ Explain how nuclear fission can begin a chain reaction.
- ▶ Discuss how nuclear fusion occurs in the sun.

New Science Words

nuclear fission
chain reaction
nuclear fusion

Nuclear Fission

Have you ever played a game of pool? What happens when you shoot the cue ball into an area of densely packed balls? They split apart, or "break" the pack. In 1938, physicists Otto Hahn and Fritz Strassmann found that a similar result occurs when a neutron is shot into the large nucleus of a U-235 atom. Earlier, another physicist, Enrico Fermi, had tried to bombard large nuclei with neutrons in an effort to make larger nuclei than uranium. Splitting an atomic nucleus wasn't the expected outcome of this process.

Did You Know?

An estimated one million gallons of radioactive liquid will need to be disposed of daily by the year 2000.

Lise Meitner was the first to offer a theory to explain this process. She concluded that the neutron fired into the nucleus disturbs the already unstable nucleus and causes it to split into two nuclei of nearly equal mass. The process of splitting a nucleus into two nuclei with smaller masses is called **nuclear fission.** You may have heard of the fission that occurs in cells, or of fissures in the Earth's surface. In all of these cases, fission means to divide. Typically, large nuclei with atomic numbers above 90 can undergo nuclear fission.

What is nuclear fission?

In addition to splitting into two new nuclei, a fission reaction usually emits two or three individual neutrons as well. For example, the U-235 nucleus is easily split by bombarding it with a neutron. It forms a barium-141 nucleus and a krypton-92 nucleus and releases three neutrons.

$$^{1}_{0}n + ^{235}_{92}U \longrightarrow ^{141}_{56}Ba + ^{92}_{36}Kr + 3^{1}_{0}n$$

The total mass of the products is somewhat less than the mass of the U-235 nucleus and the neutron. This reaction releases a tremendous amount of energy because some of the mass has been converted to energy.

Do you think the energy released in the fission of a single nucleus would be dangerous? Probably not by itself. However, the three neutrons produced in the fission reaction can bombard other nuclei in the sample to split three more nuclei. These reactions will each release more neutrons, and so on. If there is not some stable material present to absorb these neutrons, a chain reaction may result. A **chain reaction** is an ongoing series of fission reactions. This can cause billions of reactions to occur in each second, resulting in the release of tremendous amounts of energy. In the next chapter, you will read about ways scientists control nuclear fission and use the energy to produce electricity.

What is a chain reaction?

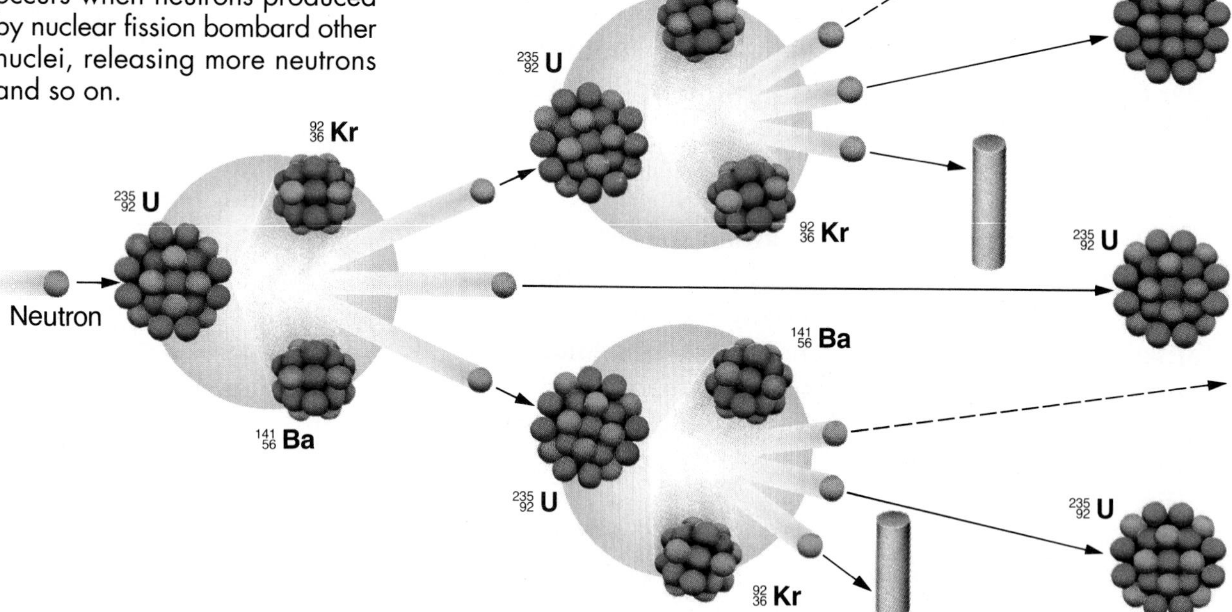

Figure 24-8. A chain reaction occurs when neutrons produced by nuclear fission bombard other nuclei, releasing more neutrons and so on.

Nuclear Fusion

You read in the last section how tremendous amounts of energy can be released in nuclear fission. In fact, splitting one U-235 nucleus produces several million times more energy than exploding one molecule of dynamite. Even more energy can be released in another type of nuclear reaction. This process is caused by the fusing together of nuclei, so it is the opposite of fission. **Nuclear fusion** is the combining of two nuclei with low masses to form one nucleus of larger mass. Nuclear fusion is difficult to induce in a controlled situation because extremely high temperatures are required for this process to occur.

These extremely high temperatures do exist in the stars, including the sun. The sun is a star of medium internal temperature, averaging about 20 million degrees Celsius. At these high temperatures, the atoms have so much kinetic energy that positive nuclei and electrons exist separately. Matter in this state is called plasma. This kind of fusion is called thermonuclear fusion, because such tremendous thermal conditions must exist.

When the sun first formed, most of its nuclei were hydrogen nuclei. As thermonuclear fusion occurs, four hydrogen nuclei are fused to become a helium nucleus. This process is still occurring, and about one percent of the mass of the sun's original nuclei is changed to energy and released in the form of electromagnetic radiation. As the star ages, the percentage of helium nuclei gradually increases and the amount of hydrogen nuclei decreases until there is no more for the reaction to occur. Scientists estimate that the sun has enough hydrogen to keep this reaction going for another five billion years.

As you will read in Chapter 25, scientists are searching for a way to induce and control nuclear fusion in the laboratory. If they achieve this goal in the future, many of our current energy problems will be solved. Can you think of other applications of nuclear fusion?

Science and READING

Find out what happens to the by-products of fission-produced electricity.

SECTION REVIEW

1. Compare and contrast nuclear fission and fusion.
2. Why does a chain reaction often occur when a U-235 nucleus is split?
3. **Apply:** Account for the mass of the four hydrogen nuclei that undergo fusion to form a helium nucleus within the sun.

Concept Mapping

Skill Builder

Make a concept map to show how a chain reaction occurs when U-235 is bombarded with a neutron. Show how each of the three neutrons given as products begins another fission reaction. If you need help, refer to Concept Mapping in the **Skill Handbook** on pages 684 and 685.

24-5 Nuclear Medicine

New Science Words

tracers

Objectives

- Describe how radioactive tracers can be used to diagnose medical problems.
- Discuss how radioactive isotopes can aid in the treatment of cancers.

Are Radioactive Isotopes Useful in Medicine?

Did you know that radioactive isotopes can help locate and even kill cancerous tumors in the body? The rapidly growing field of nuclear medicine involves the use of radioactive isotopes in the diagnosis and treatment of many medical problems.

Just as wildlife conservationists tag animals to make them easy to follow, scientists can tag molecules with radioactive isotopes. Within the body, these radioactive isotopes behave like any other atom of the same element. However, they emit radiation as they move and can be followed with a radiation detector. Radioisotopes that are put in the body to monitor a bodily process are called **tracers.** Tracers typically have a relatively short half-life so they are constantly emitting a fair amount of radiation.

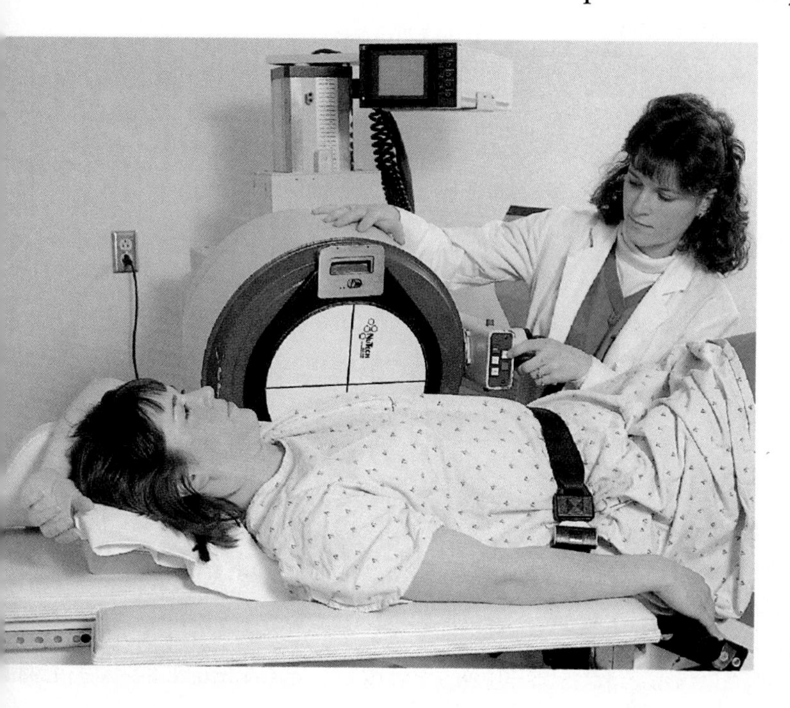

Certain parts of your body need specific elements, so the tracer is attached to a particular element that will travel to a desired location. For example, your thyroid gland, which regulates body growth and other processes, requires a certain amount of iodine to function normally. A doctor can examine the way the thyroid uses iodine by having the person drink a solution containing a radioactive isotope of iodine called I-131. The amount of this isotope in the thyroid can be determined by a detector. A thyroid problem is detected if the rate at which iodine is used in the gland is abnormal.

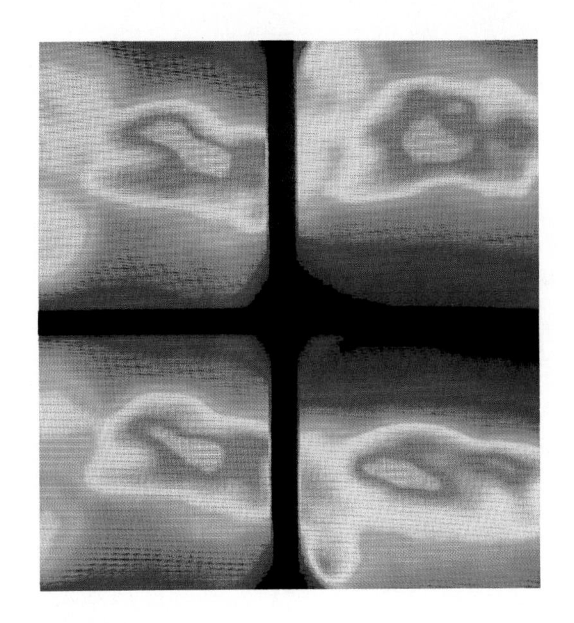

Tumors can also be found with radioactive isotopes. Cancerous cells reproduce very rapidly, so more of the radioactive isotope gathers in these cells than in those of healthy tissues. For example, technetium-99 is one element that is rapidly absorbed in brain tumors. The exact location of the tumor can be determined by using tracers, thus eliminating the need for risky exploratory surgery.

Tracing techniques are helpful in diagnosing cancer, but the problem of treating the cancer remains. There are many kinds of cancer treatment. One treatment, therapy with ionizing radiation, often complements or replaces surgery. This radiation can be given either internally or externally. I-131 is sometimes given internally to treat thyroid cancer. Cobalt-60 is often used as an external source of ionizing radiation. A beam of this radiation is aimed at the cancerous spot to destroy the cancerous cells. This treatment can shrink, and even eliminate, some cancerous tumors. Unfortunately, healthy tissue can also be damaged by radiation therapy. This treatment may produce unpleasant side effects, such as hair loss, fatigue, and nausea.

Although the use of radiation in medicine does have some risks associated with it, the risks are often smaller than the possible complications of surgery or even medication. The decision to take any kind of medical treatment involves a certain amount of risk. Nuclear medicine is responsible for saving many lives. Do you know anyone who has had medical testing or treatment with radioactive isotopes?

SECTION REVIEW

1. How does a radioactive tracer work?
2. Describe two ways radioactive isotopes can be used in the treatment of cancerous tumors.

You Decide!

Radioactive isotopes used in medicine produce radioactive wastes that are potentially hazardous to people and the environment for many years. Should radioactive isotopes continue to be used in medical treatments? Explain your position.

ACTIVITY 24-2
Nuclear Fusion

Problem: *Can you simulate thermonuclear fusion?*

Materials
- 6 balls of green clay
- 6 smaller balls of white clay

Procedure
1. Make six hydrogen nuclei (protons) by sticking one small white positron to each large green neutron.
2. Refer to Step 1 of the table and make two particles of $^{2}_{1}H$.
3. Refer to Step 2 of the table and make two particles of $^{3}_{2}He$.
4. Refer to Step 3 of the table and make one particle of $^{4}_{2}He$.

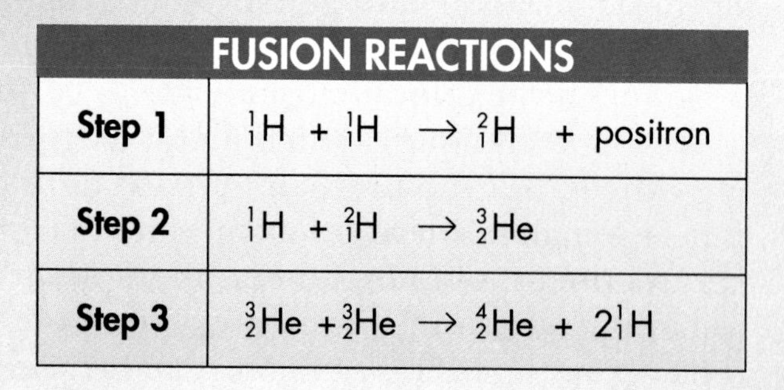

FUSION REACTIONS	
Step 1	$^{1}_{1}H + ^{1}_{1}H \rightarrow ^{2}_{1}H$ + positron
Step 2	$^{1}_{1}H + ^{2}_{1}H \rightarrow ^{3}_{2}He$
Step 3	$^{3}_{2}He + ^{3}_{2}He \rightarrow ^{4}_{2}He + 2^{1}_{1}H$

Analyze
1. Describe the steps necessary to change $^{1}_{1}H$ into $^{4}_{2}He$.
2. In this process, what is lost and what is left over?
3. How many atoms of hydrogen does it take to make one atom of helium?

Conclude and Apply
4. What can the leftover hydrogen be used for?
5. Refer to the periodic table on pages 258-259. Compare the mass of one helium atom to the mass of four hydrogen atoms. If leftover mass changes to energy, where does the energy of the sun come from?

CHAPTER
REVIEW

SUMMARY

24-1: Radioactivity

1. Radioactivity was accidentally discovered by Henri Bequerel about 100 years ago.

2. Radioactive nuclides are unstable and therefore decay. Stable nuclides don't decay.

24-2: Nuclear Decay

1. The three types of radiation that can be emitted from a decaying nucleus are alpha particles, beta particles, and gamma rays.

2. The amount of a remaining radioactive substance can be determined if you know the amount of the original sample and the number of half-lives that have elapsed.

3. The ages of rocks and fossils can be determined by a process called radioactive dating.

24-3: Detecting Radioactivity

1. Radioactivity can be detected with a cloud chamber, a bubble chamber, an electroscope, or a Geiger counter.

2. A Geiger counter can indicate the intensity of radiation present by producing a clicking sound or a flashing light that increases in frequency as more radiation is present.

24-4: Nuclear Reactions

1. Atomic nuclei are split during fission and combined during fusion.

2. Subatomic particles released from a nucleus during fission can split other nuclei.

3. Hydrogen atoms in the sun undergo fusion, and as a result, form helium atoms and electromagnetic radiation.

24-5: Science and Society: Nuclear Medicine

1. Radioactive tracers can go to certain areas of the body to indicate abnormalities.

2. Some radioactive isotopes can kill cancer cells.

KEY SCIENCE WORDS

a. **alpha particles**
b. **beta particle**
c. **bubble chamber**
d. **chain reaction**
e. **cloud chamber**
f. **gamma rays**
g. **half-life**
h. **nuclear fission**
i. **nuclear fusion**
j. **nuclide**
k. **radioactivity**
l. **tracers**
m. **transmutation**

UNDERSTANDING VOCABULARY

Match each phrase with the correct term from the list of Key Science Words.

1. emission of high-energy particles from an unstable nucleus
2. a particle of nuclear radiation with a charge of +2 and an atomic mass of 4
3. nuclear decay that results in the formation of a new element
4. the time for one-half of a sample of a radioactive isotope to decay
5. detects nuclear particles as they leave a trail of condensed water or ethanol vapor
6. splitting a nucleus into two smaller masses
7. radioactive isotopes that are used to monitor human body functions
8. the nucleus of a specific isotope
9. radiation in the form of electromagnetic waves
10. two nuclei combining into a larger nucleus

CHAPTER REVIEW

CHECKING CONCEPTS

Choose the word or phrase that completes the sentence.

1. Radioactivity can be ______.
   a. found in your classroom **c.** seen
   b. found with a tracer **d.** smelled
2. Elements that have been produced artificially through nuclear reactions have atomic numbers ______.
   a. greater than 92 **c.** between 83 and 92
   b. greater than 83 **d.** none of these
3. When a neutron decays by turning into a proton and an electron, it emits ______.
   a. an alpha particle **c.** gamma radiation
   b. a beta particle **d.** both a and c
4. The time for half the nuclides in a sample of a radioactive isotope to decay ______.
   a. is constant **c.** increases with time
   b. varies **d.** decreases with time
5. Carbon-14 dating could be used to date ______.
   a. an ancient Roman scroll
   b. an ancient marble column
   c. dinosaur fossils
   d. Earth's oldest rocks
6. Radiation in a nuclear laboratory could best be measured with ______.
   a. a cloud chamber **c.** an electroscope
   b. a Geiger counter **d.** a bubble chamber
7. A ______ is an ongoing series of fission reactions.
   a. chain reaction
   b. decay reaction
   c. transmutation reaction
   d. fusion reaction
8. The sun is powered by ______.
   a. nuclear decay **c.** thermonuclear fusion
   b. nuclear fission **d.** combustion
9. A radioisotope that acts as an external source of ionizing radiation in the treatment of cancer is ______.
   a. cobalt-60 **c.** iodine -131
   b. carbon-14 **d.** technetium-99
10. Disadvantages of using radiation to treat cancer include ______.
    a. hair loss **c.** fatigue
    b. nausea **d.** all of these

UNDERSTANDING CONCEPTS

Complete each sentence.

11. The ______ in an atom's nucleus weakens across small distances and prevents protons from repelling one another.
12. As nuclear particles move through the superheated liquid in a(n) ______, they ionize the liquid in their path and cause it to boil.
13. Some mass is converted to ______ in both nuclear fission and nuclear fusion.
14. The splitting of one heavy nucleus can result in a(n) ______ if individual neutrons are released and split nearby nuclei.
15. Nuclear fusion releases ______ energy than nuclear fission.

THINK AND WRITE CRITICALLY

16. Briefly discuss the history of nuclear science.
17. Explain why certain nuclides decay.
18. Describe the basic principles of carbon-14 dating.
19. Discuss the similarities and differences in the devices that detect radioactivity.
20. Discuss the use of radioactive tracers. How do they detect cancer cells?

APPLY

21. Can a radioactive isotope of sodium combine with chlorine to form table salt? If so, would its chemical and physical properties be the same as ordinary table salt? Explain your answer.
22. Copper-66 releases a beta particle as it decays, and radium-226 releases an alpha particle. Write a nuclear equation for each of these transmutations.
23. Nitrogen-13 has a half-life of about 10 minutes. How much of a 320-g sample of nitrogen-13 would remain after decaying for 40 minutes?
24. Explain the presence of heavy elements such as carbon, oxygen, magnesium, and iron in stars.
25. Explain how radioisotopes are used to preserve foods and to study how plants take up nutrients from the soil.

MORE SKILL BUILDERS

If you need help, refer to the Skill Handbook.

1. **Concept Mapping:** Complete the following concept map summarizing how a Geiger counter works.

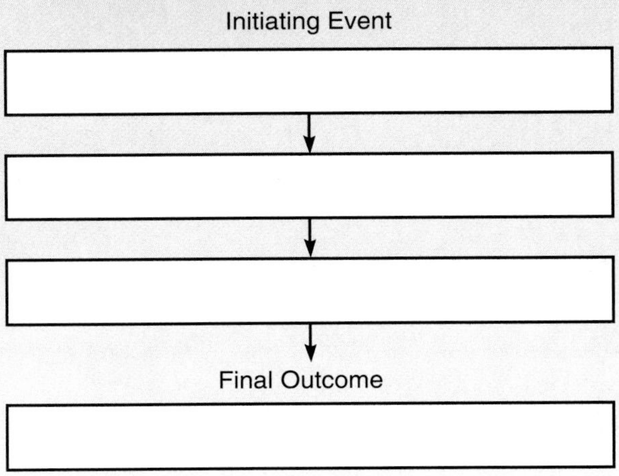

Initiating Event

↓

↓

↓

Final Outcome

2. **Making and Using Tables:** Construct a table summarizing the characteristics of each of the three types of radiation.
3. **Observing and Inferring:** Another type of particle of nuclear radiation is a positron which has a charge of +1 and essentially no mass. This particle is given off when a proton spontaneously changes into a neutron. Infer what type of radiation will be emitted from each of the following radioisotopes:
   a. Boron-8 which is unstable due to an extra proton.
   b. Thorium-232 which is unstable due to its large nucleus containing too many protons and neutrons.
   c. Potassium-40 which is unstable due to an extra neutron.
4. **Making and Using Graphs:** Using the data below, construct a graph plotting the mass numbers vs. the half-lives of radioisotopes. Plot mass numbers to the nearest ten. Is it possible to use your graph to predict the half-life of a radioisotope given its mass number?

Radio Isotope	Mass Number	Half-life
Radium	222	4 days
Thorium	234	25 days
Iodine	131	8 days
Bismuth	210	5 days
Polonium	210	138 days

PROJECTS

1. Write a biography of a person who made an important contribution to nuclear science.
2. Research the causes and effects of radon pollution in the home. Report your findings to the class.

CHAPTER

25 Energy Sources

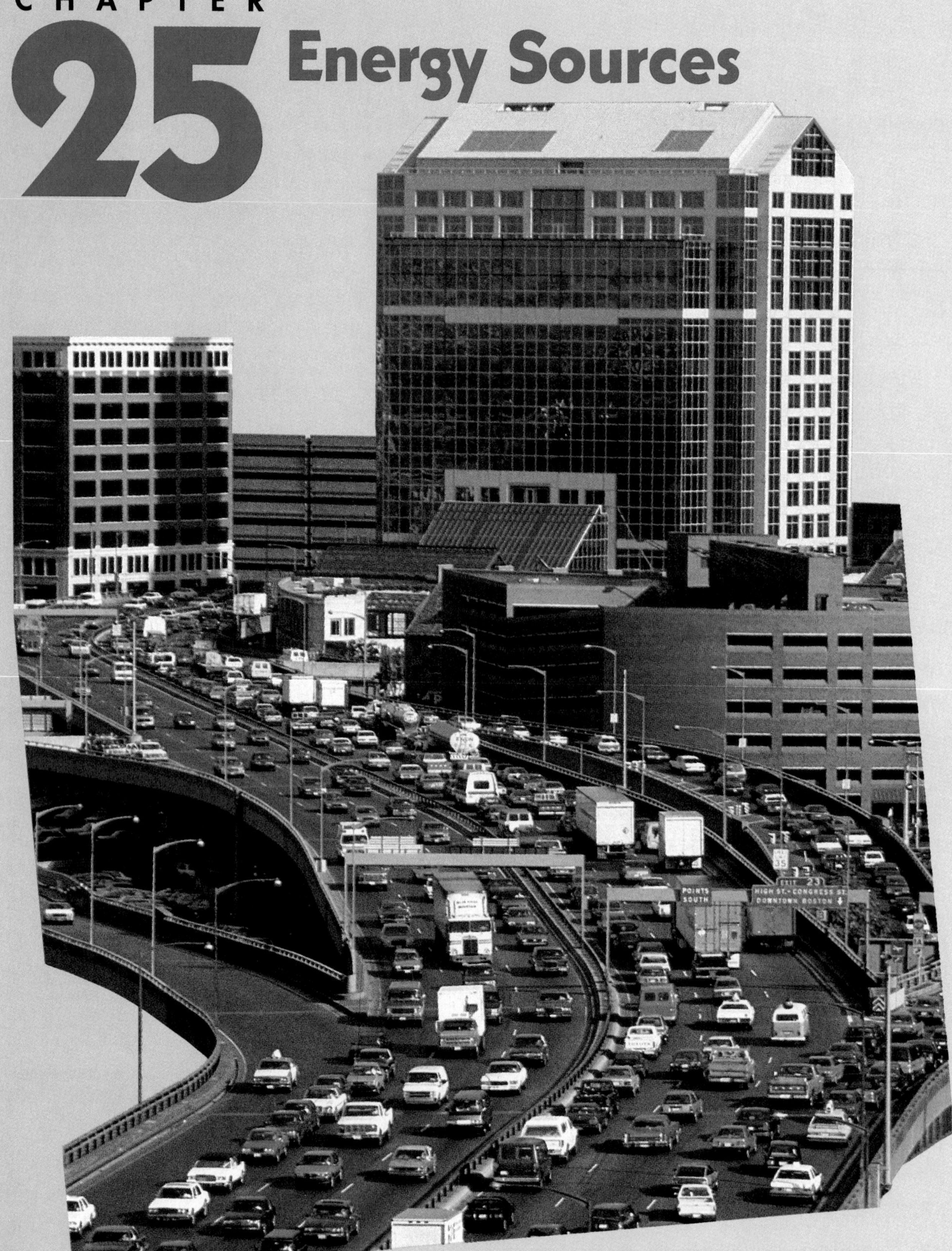

How many times do you ride in a car or bus in one week? Is that car or bus powered by a gasoline engine? It probably is, because most automobiles are fueled by gasoline. If you live in a large city, you may often see a layer of smog all around you. Smog is a type of pollution that forms from the exhausts of thousands of cars.

FIND OUT!

Do the following activity to find out about automobile emissions.

Have an adult help you with this activity. Hold a microscope slide, on which you have smeared a thin layer of petroleum jelly, near the opening of an automobile's exhaust pipe. Have the adult start the car and let it idle IN PARK. Be careful not to touch the exhaust pipe or breathe the vapors. Remove the slide after two minutes and observe it under a microscope or with a powerful hand lens. What do you see?

Gearing Up

Previewing the Chapter

Use this outline to help you focus on important ideas in the chapter.

Previewing Science Skills

- In the **Skill Builders**, you will compare and contrast, make a concept map, and outline.
- In the **Activities**, you will formulate models, hypothesize, and make observations.
- In the **MINI-Lab**, you will measure, observe, and make conclusions.

What's next?

Did you observe some dark particles on the slide in the Find Out activity? Tons of particles like these are released into the atmosphere daily when gasoline and other fossil fuels are burned for energy. Consider some of the energy alternatives mentioned as you read this chapter.

25-1 Fossil Fuels

New Science Words

petroleum
fractional distillation
nonrenewable resources

Objectives

- Discuss the origin and characteristics of the three main types of fossil fuels.
- Describe the need and methods for energy conservation.

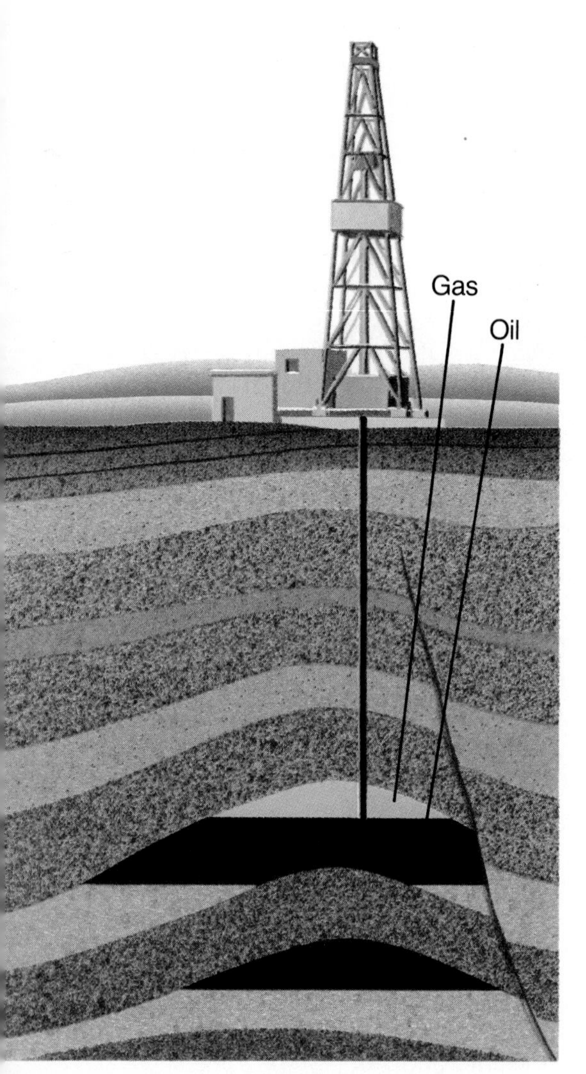

Petroleum

Do you own a sweater made of synthetic fibers such as polyester, rayon, or nylon? If so, are you aware that your sweater has something in common with the gasoline used for fuel in cars and buses? Synthetic fibers are made with chemicals that come from crude oil, and gasoline is refined from crude oil.

Crude oil, or **petroleum,** is a liquid source of energy made from the remains of plants and animals that lived several hundred million years ago. Petroleum, along with natural gas and coal, is called a fossil fuel. When ancient plants and animals died, they were covered with layers of sand, mud, volcanic ash, and other matter that collected on the surface of Earth over many years. Great pressure, heat, and bacterial action acted on these buried organisms, forming fossil fuels. Petroleum and natural gas are probably made from this process acting on the remains of sea organisms.

Have you ever seen oil wells pumping in a field as you rode along a highway? Petroleum is pumped to the surface from wells drilled deep down into the ground. The crude oil that comes from these wells contains a variety of different chemicals that originated in plants and animals. Because plants and animals contain large amounts of hydrogen and carbon, petroleum is composed mostly of compounds containing these elements. As a result, petroleum compounds are called hydrocarbons.

These various hydrocarbon compounds must be separated to make use of the chemical energy stored in petroleum. If you have ever seen an oil refining plant, you may have noticed several tall towers. These towers are called fractionating towers. Fractionating towers use a process called **fractional distillation** to separate hydrocarbon compounds. First, crude oil is pumped into the bottom of the tower and heated. The chemical compounds in the crude oil, called fractions, boil and evaporate according to their individual boiling points. Those materials with the lowest boiling points rise to the top of the column as vapor and are separated and collected. When the vapor cools below its boiling point, it again turns to a liquid. Hydrocarbons with very high boiling points may remain as liquid and be drained off through the bottom of the tower. Notice all the different products made from petroleum fractions that are shown in Figure 25-1.

Oil can be carried through pipelines, such as the Alaskan pipeline, or it can be carried in fuel tankers. You use petroleum every day for electricity and transportation. You probably know that burning petroleum has serious side effects on the environment. When petroleum is burned in cars and at electric power plants, it gives off smoke as well as carbon monoxide and other chemical compounds. These particles and compounds affect the quality of the air you breathe.

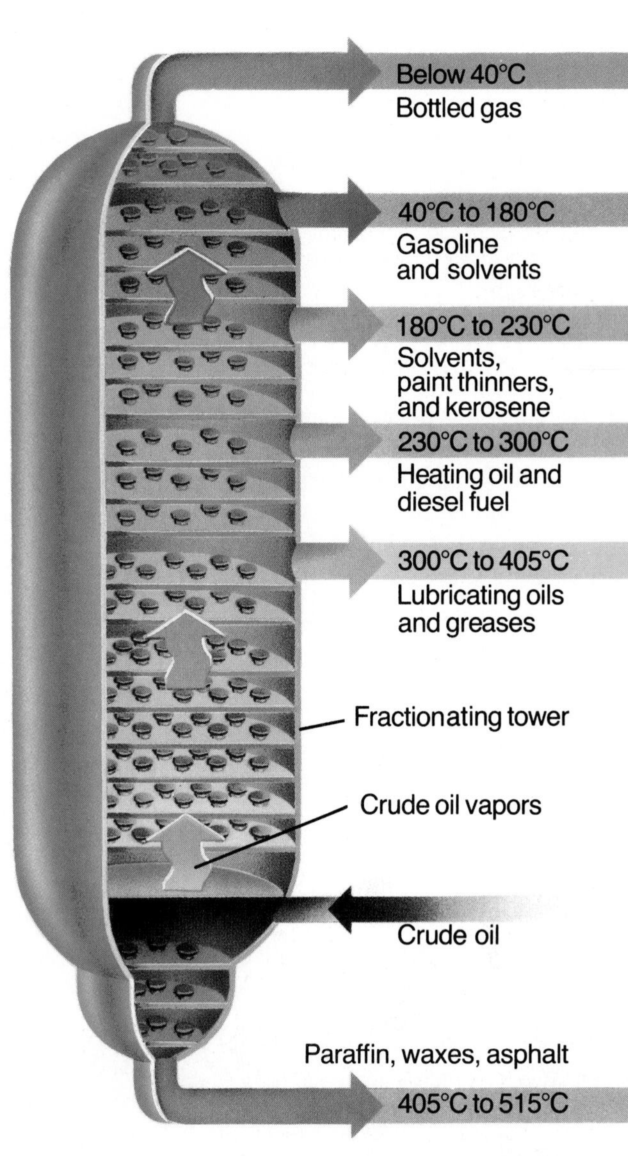

Figure 25-1. Fractional distillation is used to separate the hydrocarbon components in petroleum.

Other Fossil Fuels

Do you cook on a gas stove at home? If so, you burn natural gas to get energy to cook your food. Natural gas, like petroleum, is a fossil fuel. Natural gas most likely originated from plants and animals that lived in Earth's oceans. It is often found lying above liquid petroleum reservoirs below Earth's surface; it is extracted with the petroleum.

Natural gas is composed mostly of methane, CH_4, but it also contains smaller amounts of hydrocarbon gases such as propane, C_3H_8 and butane, C_4H_{10}. When natural gas or petroleum is burned, it combines with oxygen, and heat is given off. During this process, carbon dioxide and water are formed as chemical by-products. This is a combustion reaction. Natural gas is burned to provide energy for cooking, heating, and manufacturing.

Did You Know?

Energy consumption per household decreased in the United States by more than 25 percent between 1978 and 1987.

MINI-Lab

Can efficient use conserve fuel?

Use a candle to increase the temperature of 50 mL of water 10 degrees Celsius. Measure the mass of the candle before and after so you know how much was used. Design a chimney out of aluminum foil that will help transfer the heat of the candle to the water. Repeat the experiment to find out how much fuel you can save while heating the water the same amount.

When natural gas is used properly, it doesn't pollute the environment with the compounds that result from burning petroleum. However, the carbon dioxide that it produces can cause Earth's atmospheric temperature to rise. Natural gas is like petroleum, in that it can be transported long distances by large underground pipelines.

Coal is a solid fossil fuel made from the remains of plants. About one-fourth of the world's supply of coal is in the United States. It is sometimes mined near the surface, but is more commonly mined several hundred feet underground. The quality of a coal sample depends on its age and on the type of plant life from which it formed.

When used as a fuel, coal must be cleaned to remove sulfur and other impurities that would be released into the air when the coal is burned. Sulfur compounds can be removed from unburned coal or from the smoke from burning coal to prevent the formation of compounds in the air that cause acid rain. Harmful nitrogen oxides often form when coal is burned at high temperatures. Therefore, it is desirable to find ways to burn coal at lower temperatures.

Because coal is mined from Earth, digging coal mines can disturb the natural environment. Today, laws exist to require that the environment is returned to something close to its original state when a coal mine is closed.

TECHNOLOGY

Gas Instead of Gasoline

One fuel that is an alternative to gasoline is natural gas. Cars, buses, and other vehicles that currently run on gasoline can be modified to use natural gas instead. Natural gas vehicles (NGVs) appear to contribute less than gasoline to the problems of pollution and global warming. That's because NGVs don't release as much carbon monoxide, carbon dioxide, and other pollutants as gasoline. It is estimated that 30 000 NGVs are already in use on our nation's highways.

Think Critically: The cost of converting a vehicle that runs on gasoline to an NGV can be offset by fuel cost savings. What other problems might NGV owners encounter?

Fuel Conservation

Think of how many times you ride in a car, turn on a light, or use an electric appliance. Each time you do one of these things, you probably use some type of fossil fuel as a source of energy. We depend on fossil fuels to meet a large percentage of our energy needs. Fossil fuel reserves are decreasing as our population and industrial energy demands are increasing. At our current rate of consumption, the United States may be out of oil in less than 80 years. Coal is more plentiful, but like petroleum, it is a nonrenewable resource. All fossil fuels are **nonrenewable resources**—they cannot be replaced after they are used.

We must conserve nonrenewable energy resources that we do have. Conservation can be as simple as turning off a light when you leave a room, avoiding unnecessary speeding when driving a car, or riding a bike instead of driving the car at all. Insulating your home and using energy-efficient appliances can conserve energy within your home. Trees around your home can keep it cooler in summer and reduce the use of air conditioning. We need to develop some alternative energy sources to help us conserve now and to prepare for the time when fossil fuels may not be readily available.

SECTION REVIEW

1. Describe the three main types of fossil fuels.
2. Which type of fossil fuel is the most abundant in the United States? What are the advantages and disadvantages of using this fuel?
3. **Apply:** As the plants and animals living on Earth today die, they will decay and be buried to form the fossils of tomorrow. If the formation of fossil fuels is a continuous cycle, why are they considered to be *nonrenewable* resources?

Science and WRITING

Many of our energy conservation techniques refer to what we can do in the home, but most of us spend at least half of our waking hours outside of the home. What can you do to conserve energy at school?

Figure 25-2. Find ways to conserve energy at home, such as caulking around windows.

Comparing and Contrasting

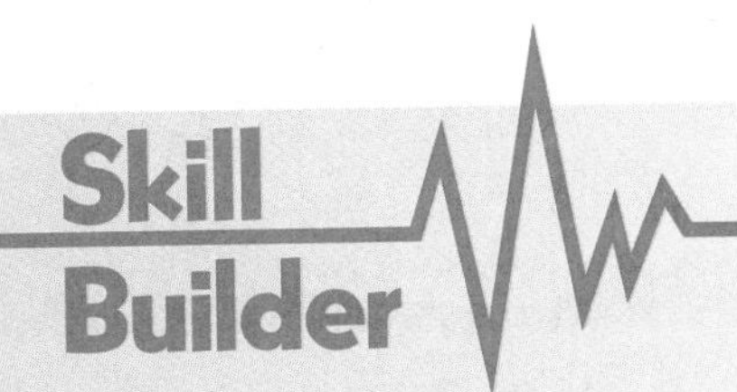

Compare and contrast the different fossil fuels. Include the advantages and disadvantages of using each as a source of energy. If you need help, refer to Comparing and Contrasting in the **Skill Handbook** on page 679.

25-2 Nuclear Energy

New Science Words

nuclear reactor
nuclear wastes

Objectives

- Outline the operation of a nuclear reactor.
- Describe the problems and methods associated with nuclear waste disposal.
- Discuss nuclear fusion as a possible energy source.

Nuclear Reactors

In the last chapter you learned that nuclear fission chain reactions give off a great deal of energy. A **nuclear reactor** uses the energy from a controlled nuclear fission chain reaction to generate electricity. Nuclear reactors can vary in design. Most fission reactors have several parts in common, including fuel, control rods, and cooling systems. The actual fission of the radioactive fuel occurs in a relatively small part of the reactor, the core.

Once the core of the reactor contains fuel, uranium oxide, a chain reaction starts from a single uranium atom that spontaneously splits into two parts, releasing two or more neutrons. If two of these neutrons reached U-235 atoms and made them split, releasing two neutrons each, there would now be four neutrons. These four could produce eight, then sixteen. This happens so fast that in one millisecond there could be 1000 neutrons. Each of those would produce 1000 more in the next millisecond, make one thousand thousand (or one million neutrons) in two milliseconds, then one thousand million (one billion) in three milliseconds. The reactor would be out of control.

To control the reaction, rods containing boron or cadmium are used to absorb some of the neutrons. Moving these control rods deeper into the reactor allows them to capture more neutrons and slow down the chain reaction. Eventually only one neutron per fission is able to react with a U-235 atom to produce another fission, and energy is released at a constant rate.

The nuclear fission reaction inside the core generates tremendous amounts of thermal energy. The core is surrounded by water that cools it. The water also carries

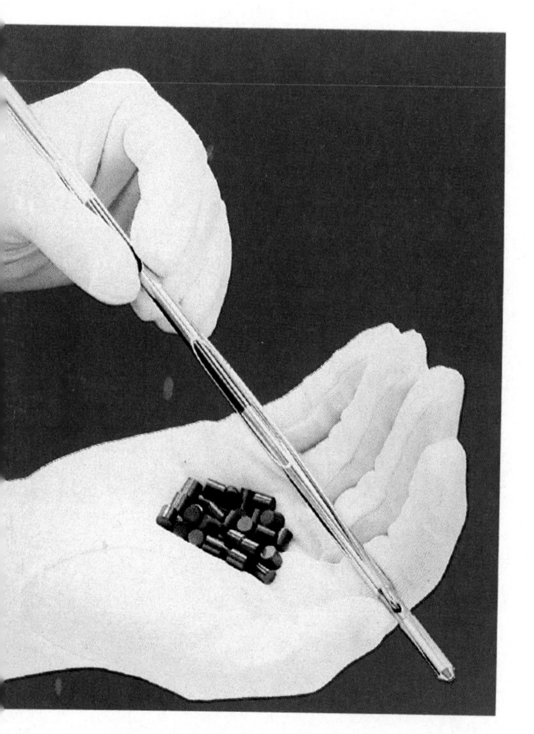

Figure 25-3. Uranium oxide pellets are used to fuel nuclear reactors.

thermal energy away from the core. The superheated water is pumped through a heat exchanger, where the thermal energy released boils a separate system of water to produce steam. The core and cooling system are surrounded by a barrier of thick concrete. The entire building is also built with steel-lined concrete to prevent the escape of radiation from the reactor.

Nuclear Generation of Electricity

How much of our nation's energy is supplied by fission reactors?

Nuclear fission reactors currently supply over 20 percent of our nation's electricity. One advantage of using nuclear energy is that it's less harmful to the environment than the use of fossil fuels. The fission process produces no air pollution, whereas the burning of coal and petroleum creates nearly 20 000 metric tons of pollutants each day. Nuclear fission doesn't produce carbon dioxide that will escape into the atmosphere and contribute to the problem of global warming. On the other hand, the mining of uranium and extraction of U-235 does cause environmental damage.

Using nuclear fission to generate electricity also has other disadvantages. The water that circulates around the core of the reactor must cool before it goes back into streams and rivers. If it is released into those waterways while still warm, the excess heat could harm fish and other plants and animals in the water. The most serious risk of nuclear fission is the escape of harmful radiation from the power plant. There is an elaborate system of safeguards in nuclear reactors to ensure that this doesn't happen. Strict safety precautions and highly trained workers can prevent most accidents.

After the chain reaction has occurred, however, the fuel rods contain fission products that are highly radioactive. These products must be contained in insulated surroundings while they decay so no

Figure 25-4. Many safeguards are taken to prevent accidents in nuclear fission reactors.

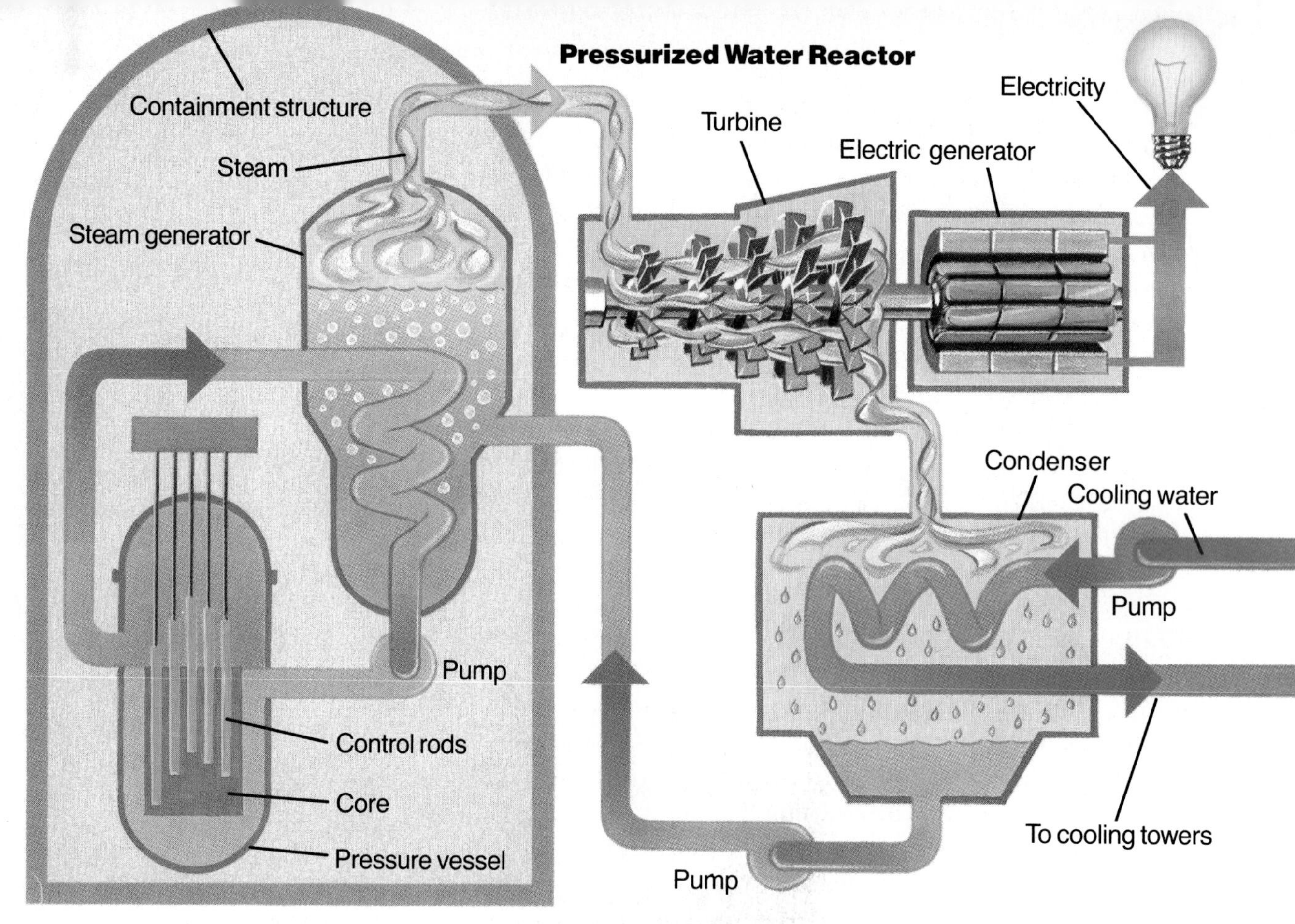

Figure 25-5. The coolant water and the water used to produce the steam that turns the turbines are not the same in a water-cooled nuclear power plant.

radiation will escape into the environment. Because these fission products have long half-lives, they must be stored in containers that will last the duration of the period of radioactive decay, which can be as long as tens of thousands of years.

Another problem is the disposal of the reactor itself when it no longer runs as it should. Every nuclear reactor has a limited useful life span of a few decades. After that time the reactor's efficiency is severely reduced by the presence of large amounts of fission products that can't be cleaned up. The reactor is then shut down or "decommissioned."

Nuclear Waste Disposal

Has your watch ever run down because the battery was too old? The battery wasn't able to produce enough energy to allow your watch to keep correct time. Once you replaced the battery, your watch worked. A similar thing happens to the fuel source in a nuclear reactor. After about three years, there is not enough fissionable U-235 left in the fuel pellets to sustain the chain reaction. These used fuel pellets are called "spent" fuel. The spent fuel contains the radioactive fission products in addition to the remaining uranium. This is an example of nuclear waste. **Nuclear wastes** are radioactive by-products that result when radioactive materials are used. They are usually classified as high-level and low-level wastes for disposal.

Radiation is around you all the time. Low-level nuclear waste usually contains a small amount of radioactive material diluted by a large amount of nonradioactive material. Products of some medical and industrial processes are low-level wastes. They may include items used in handling radioactive materials such as protective gloves. These low-level wastes are usually buried in sealed containers in locations licensed by the federal government. When dilute enough, they are sometimes released into the air or water.

Figure 25-6. A solid capsule of nuclear waste, can be made by mixing the wastes with molten glass. These capsules are buried in sealed containers.

High-level nuclear waste is generated in nuclear power plants and by defense research. After spent fuel is removed from a reactor, it is stored in a deep, heavily insulated pool of water. Many of the radioactive materials in high-level nuclear waste have short half-lives. Almost half of the radiation will have been emitted in several months. But the spent fuel also contains materials that will continue to decay for thousands of years. For this reason, the waste must be disposed of in extremely durable and stable containers.

Fusion Power

Imagine the amount of energy the sun must give off to heat Earth 93 million miles away. In Chapter 24, thermonuclear fusion was explained as the process that releases this energy. Recall that thermonuclear fusion is the joining together of small nuclei at high temperatures. Fusing the nuclei in one gram of heavy hydrogen gives off about the same amount of energy as burning more than eight million grams of coal. If we could make thermonuclear fusion happen in a laboratory, we would likely have the answer to Earth's energy problems.

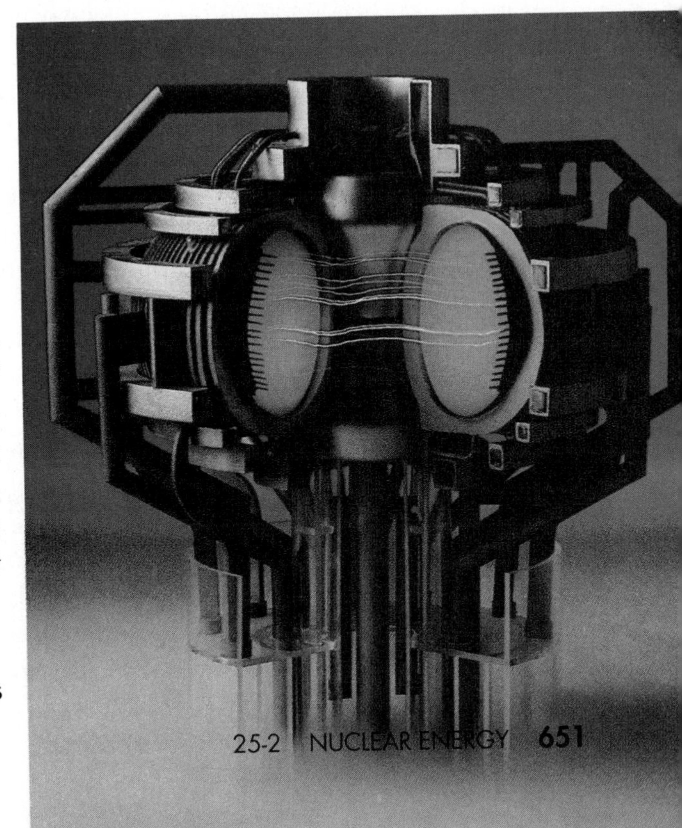

Figure 25-7. Two nuclei fuse to form a larger nucleus in this experimental fusion reactor.

Science and READING

The energy that reaches us from the sun is 50 000 times as much as the whole world uses. In light of this fact, why do you think we continually have energy shortages?

The challenge lies in creating and containing nuclear fusion. The temperature needed to carry out a nuclear fusion reaction is over one million degrees Celsius. The plasma containing the hydrogen nuclei can't be contained by any material at this temperature. However, it can be contained for a short time in a "magnetic bottle" which uses a magnetic field to keep the particles in a small volume. Unfortunately, the energy required to maintain the high temperatures needed for the fusion reaction is greater than the energy output from the fusion of the nuclei.

What is the source of energy for nuclear fusion?

Let's examine the benefits of nuclear fusion as a source of energy. Hydrogen nuclei, such as those found in water, are the source of energy for nuclear fusion. Hydrogen is the most abundant element in the universe. Unlike those in nuclear fission, the products of nuclear fusion are not radioactive. Some neutrons released by the fusion reactions, however, can react with the walls of a fusion reactor to make the walls radioactive. Helium, the gas commonly used to fill balloons, is the main product of hydrogen fusion. Someday nuclear fusion may provide a permanent and economical way to generate electricity.

SECTION REVIEW

1. How is the rate of fission in a nuclear reactor controlled?
2. What do the nuclear generation of electricity and the burning of fossil fuels to generate electricity have in common?
3. Explain the major obstacles in controlling nuclear fusion.
4. **Apply:** Suppose that in a research project, you have generated a 10-gram sample of nuclear waste. Some of the materials have a fast half-life and some will decay for thousands of years. How would you classify it and how will it likely be disposed of?

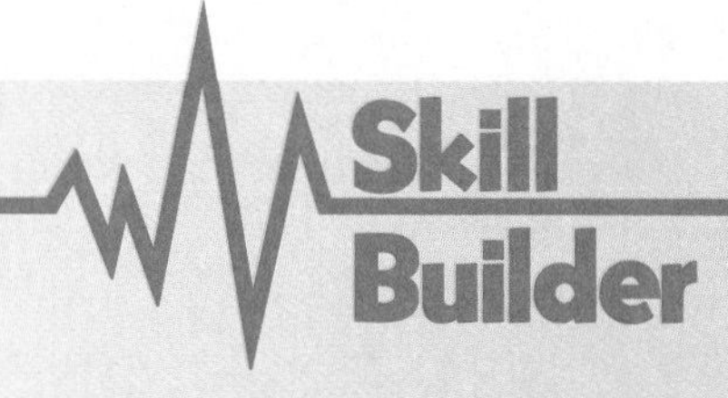

Concept Mapping

Design an events chain concept map for the generation of electricity in a nuclear fission reactor. Begin with the bombarding neutron and end with electricity in overhead lines. If you need help, refer to Concept Mapping in the **Skill Handbook** on pages 684 and 685.

ACTIVITY 25-1
Nuclear Waste Disposal

Problem: *Can you design a safe storage method?*

Materials  

- sodium hydroxide pellets (4)
- 100 mL beakers (4)
- phenolphthalein solution
- plastic food wrap
- aluminum foil
- rubber bands (3)
- twist ties (2)
- modeling clay
- forceps
- goggles

Procedure

1. Copy the data table.
2. Let the sodium hydroxide pellets represent pellets of nuclear waste. Your job is to test materials that may be able to keep unwanted chemicals from leaking into the environment.
3. **CAUTION:** *Do not touch the sodium hydroxide pellets or solution with your hands. Always wear goggles when handling sodium hydroxide. Wipe up all spills.*
4. Fill all four beakers with water and add 3 or 4 drops of phenolphthalein to each.
5. Using the forceps, place one pellet in one of the beakers. Record your observations.
6. Wrap each of the remaining pellets; one in aluminum foil, one in plastic wrap, and one in clay. Secure the plastic with twist ties.
7. Drop the wrapped pellets into the remaining three beakers and cover them with food wrap.
8. Make observations each day for three days to determine if there is leakage from the containers. Record your observations in the data table.
9. After the last observations, pour the solutions into a container provided by your teacher.

Data and Observations

Beaker Containing Pellets	Observations		
	Day 1	Day 2	Day 3
Unwrapped			
Wrapped in aluminum foil			
Wrapped in plastic wrap			
Embedded in clay			

Analyze

1. Was red color seen in any of the beakers after the first day?
2. After three days, which, if any, of the beakers show no red color?

Conclude and Apply

3. What kind of wrapping appears to be the most leak proof?
4. Why do you think storing and disposing nuclear wastes is a major concern of society?

25-3 Breeder Reactors

New Science Words

breeder reactor

Objectives

- Distinguish between breeder reactors and normal nuclear fission reactors.
- Assess the advantages and disadvantages of operating breeder reactors.

Are Breeder Reactors Really Such a Good Idea?

You read about using nuclear fission as a way of generating electricity in the last section. Do you remember the isotope that is commonly used as a fuel source in a fission reactor? The fuel rods are made of a small amount of U-235 in a larger sample of unfissionable U-238. The fissionable U-235 isotope is not plentiful in nature. It is a nonrenewable resource that may be depleted in less than 100 years. If nuclear energy is to be a long-lasting energy source, other nuclear fuels must be developed.

A **breeder reactor** is a nuclear reactor that produces, or "breeds," new fuel as it operates. In a breeder reactor, some of the neutrons produced by the fission of U-235 are absorbed by the U-238 nuclei while other neutrons cause fission of U-235. This requires that more neutrons be captured in the fuel rods, and it leads to difficulties in the reactor design. The new U-239 nuclei decays in several days to form Pu-239, as illustrated in the picture equation shown below.

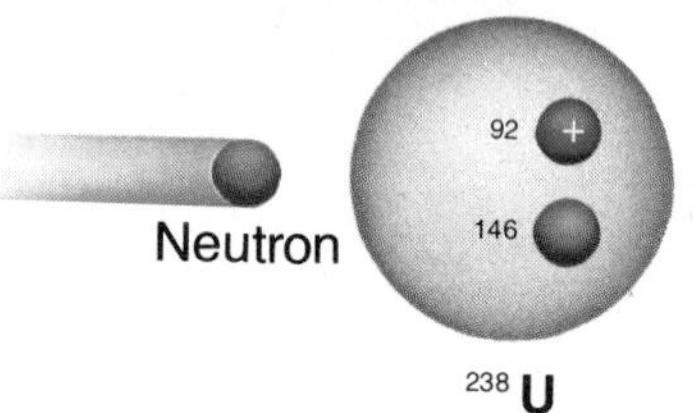

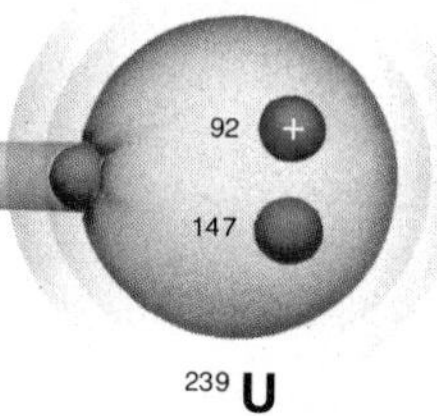

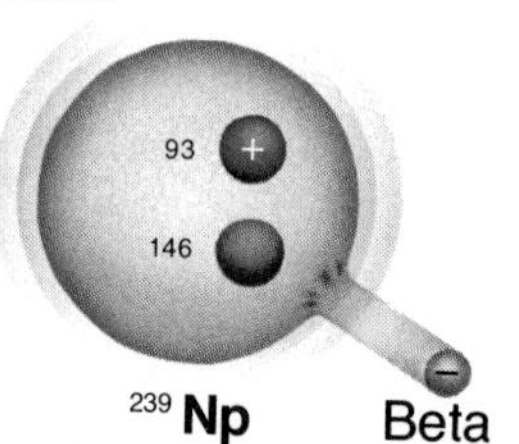

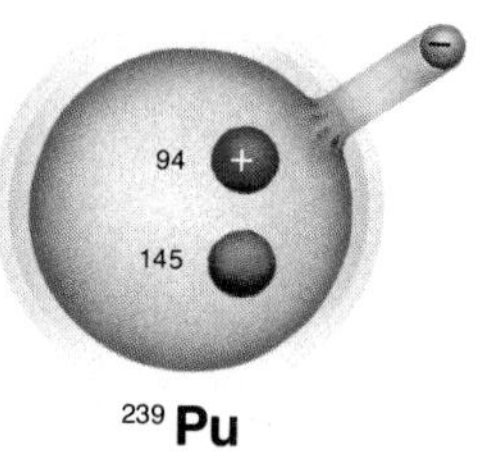

This isotope of plutonium is fissionable. Thus, a large supply of new Pu-239 fuel can be produced from the otherwise useless U-238 nuclei. Three new plutonium atoms are formed for every two plutonium atoms that under-

go fission. As a result, more fuel is present after fission has occurred in the reactor than was present before the fission occurred. After operating for several years, a breeder reactor can produce twice as much fissionable fuel as it started with.

Breeder reactors have obvious efficiency advantages. The Pu-239 can be chemically separated from the remaining uranium and used in another reactor. So, breeder reactors can prolong the life of nuclear energy as an energy resource. This process decreases our burning of fossil fuels and the resulting pollution.

Breeder reactors can cause several hazards for society. As with nuclear fission reactors, safe radioactive waste disposal is still a problem. There is a risk of releasing low-level radioactive materials into the air and water. The plutonium fuel produced in a breeder reactor has a half-life of 24 000 years. Elemental plutonium is chemically poisonous in addition to being radioactive, but it usually combines with oxygen to form inert compounds.

SECTION REVIEW

1. How does a breeder reactor differ from a nuclear fission reactor?
2. List the advantages and disadvantages of using breeder reactors.

You Decide!

Breeder reactors produce Pu-239. This is an important component of nuclear fission weapons. How do you think breeder reactors should be regulated? Explain your point of view.

25-4 Alternative Energy Sources

New Science Words

photovoltaic cell
hydroelectricity
tidal energy
geothermal energy

Objectives

- Analyze the need for alternative energy sources.
- Discuss the methods of generating electricity with several energy sources.
- Describe the advantages and disadvantages of several alternative energy sources.

Keep the outside of your family car clean and waxed. Also make sure the tires are properly inflated. These measures will increase gas mileage and help to conserve gasoline.

The Need for Alternatives

Can you name any sources of energy other than fossil fuels and nuclear energy? Although we have enough of these energy sources to fill our energy demands today, there is a great need to develop alternative sources of energy for the future. As you have already discovered, using fossil fuels and nuclear fission for our energy needs has many disadvantages.

Nuclear fission and the burning of fossil fuels are both processes used to boil water to produce steam. Other materials can be burned to give off energy as well. Biomass is renewable organic matter, such as wood, sugar cane fibers, rice hulls, and animal manure. It can be burned in the presence of oxygen to convert the stored chemical energy to thermal energy. Biomass burning is probably the oldest use of natural resources for human needs.

Have you ever seen gasohol advertised at a gas station? How does this fuel differ from normal gasoline? Corn and other plant fibers can be fermented to produce alcohol, another combustible fuel source. In fermentation, yeast converts the sugar and starch in the grain to ethanol. The ethanol is combined with fossil fuels in gasoline. This product, commonly called gasohol, is combusted inside your car engine.

Biomass and gasohol are just two examples of many energy alternatives that reduce our consumption of fossil fuels. The energy alternatives discussed in this section make use of processes that occur naturally on Earth. What natural processes do you see around you which could be used to generate electricity or provide heat?

Solar Energy

The sun is Earth's only source of new energy. Have you ever seen an automobile powered by sunlight? The solar panels on the car collect and use solar energy to power the car. Methods of collecting and using solar energy are usually divided into two categories, passive and active solar energy.

What is passive solar heating?

Passive solar heating is the direct use of the sun's energy in maintaining comfortable indoor temperatures. Passive solar heating was used centuries ago by the Romans to heat their bath houses. Efforts in energy conservation have renewed interest in this method of heating. Buildings constructed with strategically-placed windows can be heated by the sun. On warm days, these windows can be covered with blinds to prevent excessive heating.

In active solar heating, solar panels collect and store solar energy. Solar panels are made of large, darkly colored trays covered with transparent glass or plastic. Large mirrors are sometimes used to focus the sun's radiation into these solar collectors. The panels absorb the sun's energy and use it to heat water. The heated water can be used directly, or it can be stored to give off thermal energy. Solar energy can even be used to drive electric power generators in solar thermal power plants.

A device used to convert solar energy into electricity is the **photovoltaic cell,** also called the solar cell. Do you own a solar-powered calculator? It contains a solar cell. Photovoltaic cells are made of a semiconductor lined on both surfaces with a conducting metal. As light strikes the surface of the cell, electrons flow between the two metal layers. If these metal layers are connected into a circuit, an electric current moves through the solar cell. Many cells connected in a circuit can provide significant amounts of electricity.

Figure 25-8. Solar cells can be used to supply the electricity to operate an automobile.

This method of producing electricity is more expensive on a large scale than the use of fossil fuels, but it can be less expensive in isolated areas, when the cost of building transmission lines to those areas is considered. Solar energy is a pollution-free resource that is becoming more economical as our solar technology develops.

Hydroelectricity

One way to produce electricity is with water. Water flowing in rivers carries tremendous amounts of kinetic and potential energy. Dams are built to store vast amounts of water. Right behind a dam, the water is very deep. Near the base of a hydroelectric dam, water is allowed to rush out through tunnels. The rushing water spins a turbine. The turbine rotates the shaft of an electric generator, which produces electricity.

Hydroelectricity is electricity produced by the energy of moving water. Hydroelectric power plants are a very efficient way to produce electricity. They produce almost no pollution. The bodies of water held back by dams can provide lakes for recreational uses and irrigation. The ongoing natural water cycle makes hydroelectric power a permanent resource. After the initial cost of building a dam and power plant, the electricity is relatively cheap. However, artificial dams can disturb the balance of natural ecosystems.

Tidal Energy

The gravitational forces of the moon and the sun cause bulges in Earth's oceans. As Earth rotates, the two bulges of ocean water move westward. Each day the level of the ocean on a coast rises and falls continually. A kind of hydroelectric power can be generated by these ocean tides. The moving water can be trapped by building a dam at the opening of a river or bay. The flowing water spins a turbine, which operates an electric generator. Energy generated by tidal motion is called **tidal energy.**

Like producing hydroelectric power, generating electricity from tidal motion is nearly pollution-free. But, there are only a few places on Earth where the difference between high and low tide is large enough to be an efficient source of energy. In the United States the use of tidal energy is being explored in the Cook Inlet in Alaska and Passamaquoddy Bay in Maine. The ocean environment will possibly make construction and maintenance of these plants difficult. Salt water corrodes metals, so corrosion-resistant building materials will have to be used. Ocean storms can also be violent and damaging. Tidal energy probably will be a limited source of energy in the future.

Wind Energy

You may have seen a windmill on a farm. Or, in a windy region you may have seen several hundred windmills. A windmill is a turbine that is turned by the wind instead of steam or water. The windmill spins and rotates an electric generator to produce electricity. Obviously, electricity cannot be produced when there is very little wind.

Only a few places on Earth consistently have enough wind to rely on wind power to meet energy needs. Improved design of wind generators can increase their efficiency, so new methods of using the wind's energy are being researched. Wind generators do not actually use up any resources. They do not pollute the atmosphere or water. However, they do change the appearance of a landscape.

Geothermal Energy

Where is most of Earth's geothermal energy found?

Look down at the ground. What do you see and feel underneath your feet? Although you may think of the Earth as a solid sphere, hot gases and molten rock lie far beneath the surface. The inner parts of Earth contain a great deal of thermal energy, called **geothermal energy.** You do not usually notice this energy because most of it is far below Earth's crust.

In some places, Earth's crust has cracks or thin spots in it. These areas allow some of the geothermal energy to rise up near the surface of Earth. Active volcanoes permit hot gases and molten lava from deep within Earth to escape. Perhaps you have seen a geyser shoot steam and hot water from Earth. Have you ever visited or seen pictures of the famous geyser, Old Faithful, in Yellowstone National Park? This water was heated by hot rocks in contact with geothermal energy. Wells can be drilled deep within Earth to pump out this hot water. The temperature of this water and steam ranges from 150°C to 350°C, and the steam can be used to rotate turbines and turn electric generators. Use of geothermal energy can release some sulfur compounds from gases within Earth. This pollution can be controlled by pumping the water and steam back into Earth.

As with wind and tidal energy, there are only certain places on Earth where geothermal energy is accessible as an economical energy resource. For example, in Iceland, all power plants are run by geothermal energy.

What similarities can you identify between all of the alternative energy sources discussed in this chapter? Which ones do you think would be the most useful in your area?

Figure 25-9. Geothermal power plants, like the one below, supply Iceland with most of its energy.

PROBLEM SOLVING

Renewable Energy Sources for Beachtown

Rosa and her family live on the coast in Beachtown. Rosa enjoys the recreation opportunities offered by living on an ocean coast. During the hot, sunny summer, Rosa enjoys cool swims in the ocean and the strong breezes blowing on the beach. She also enjoys fishing at an inlet close to her house.

Like Rosa, many other people think Beachtown is a great place to live and are moving there. Lots of new businesses are being built all over town. The mayor and city council are concerned because the growth of the city is exceeding the production capability of the old fossil-fueled power plant.

Think Critically: What alternative energy sources could the power company consider when planning to increase its output? How do these renewable resources compare with using fossil fuels for energy?

SECTION REVIEW

1. Why is there a need for developing and using alternative energy sources?
2. Describe three main ways to use direct solar energy.
3. Identify some advantages and limitations of using hydroelectric and tidal energy.
4. Explain how geothermal energy is used to generate electricity.
5. **Apply:** What single resource do most of the energy alternatives discussed in this section either directly or indirectly depend on?

Outlining

Make an outline of the energy alternatives discussed in this section. List at least one advantage and one disadvantage of each. If you need help, refer to Outlining in the **Skill Handbook** on page 677.

ACTIVITY 25-2
Energy Alternatives

Problem: *What kind of energy is practical?*

Materials
- large sheet of poster paper
- set of colored flow pens
- miscellaneous construction supplies

Procedure
1. Your team has been appointed by the state legislature to prepare a recommendation for the construction of a new power plant. You will research the problem and prepare an illustrated oral report on the energy source assigned to you by the governor.
2. Your report must describe the energy source. How does it work? What is it best suited for? What are its limitations?
3. Your report must include an illustration or diagram showing at least one important idea about the construction or operation of the power plant.
4. You must construct a model which can be used to demonstrate how some important part of the power plant works.
5. When all reports have been heard, the legislature will vote on the type of power plant to be constructed.

Analyze
1. Listen to the points being made in each report. Consider the appropriateness of the power source for your state. Does your state have enough sunshine for solar, or enough water for hydro?
2. Are the environmental issues acceptable? Are pollution problems involved? Is there suitable space for construction?
3. Will the power plant provide enough power to meet the need? Is it to be a primary power source for an expanding population or a supplementary source for an existing population?

Conclude and Apply
4. Acting as a member of the legislature, determine how you can best serve the present energy needs of the state and preserve the state's environmental qualities.
5. Acting as a member of the study committee, should you try to influence the legislature to vote in favor of your project?

CHAPTER REVIEW

SUMMARY

25-1: Fossil Fuels

1. The three types of fossil fuels are petroleum, natural gas, and coal. They formed from the buried remains of ancient plants and animals.
2. All fossil fuels are nonrenewable energy resources. Supplies will run out soon if they aren't used wisely.

25-2: Nuclear Energy

1. A nuclear reactor uses the energy from a controlled nuclear chain fission reaction to generate electricity.
2. Nuclear wastes must be carefully contained and disposed of so radiation from nuclear decay will not leak into the environment.
3. Nuclear fusion releases greater amounts of energy than nuclear fission, but fusion must occur at temperatures that are too high to be contained in a laboratory.

25-3: Science and Society: Breeder Reactors

1. Breeder reactors make a continuous source of nuclear fuel as a by-product of the chain reaction.
2. Breeder reactors produce plutonium, a fissionable fuel that can be used in nuclear fission reactors or to make nuclear weapons.

25-4: Alternative Energy Sources

1. Alternate energy resources are needed to supplement or replace nonrenewable energy resources.
2. Other sources of energy include hydroelectricity, and solar, wind, tidal, and geothermal energy.
3. Although some alternative energy sources don't pollute the environment and are renewable, their use is often limited to certain regions, as well as being expensive.

KEY SCIENCE WORDS

a. **breeder reactor**
b. **fractional distillation**
c. **geothermal energy**
d. **hydroelectricity**
e. **nonrenewable resources**
f. **nuclear reactor**
g. **nuclear wastes**
h. **petroleum**
i. **photovoltaic cell**
j. **tidal energy**

UNDERSTANDING VOCABULARY

Match each phrase with the correct term from the list of Key Science Words.

1. separates the hydrocarbons in crude oil
2. liquid remains of dead organisms
3. generates electricity from a controlled fission reaction
4. thermal energy inside Earth
5. sources of energy that can't be replaced
6. converts solar energy directly into electricity
7. electricity produced by the energy of moving water
8. energy produced by the rise and fall of ocean levels
9. a fission reactor that produces new reactor fuel
10. by-product of fission reactions

CHAPTER REVIEW

CHECKING CONCEPTS

Choose the word or phrase that completes the sentence.

1. Plant and animal remains that are buried under sediments and acted upon by ______ form fossil fuels.
   a. bacteria **c.** heat
   b. pressure **d.** all of these
2. Hydrocarbons react with ______ during the combustion of fossil fuels.
   a. carbon dioxide **c.** oxygen
   b. carbon monoxide **d.** water
3. Fossil fuels are becoming more scarce as industrial demands increase and ______.
   a. the population increases
   b. the population decreases
   c. the number of nuclear reactors increases
   d. fewer plants and animals die
4. Both burning fossil fuels and nuclear fission must first be used to produce ______ in order to produce electricity.
   a. steam
   b. carbon dioxide
   c. plutonium
   d. water
5. A major advantage of using nuclear fusion reactors is that they ______.
   a. use hydrogen from air as fuel
   b. produce no radioactivity.
   c. produce only helium as a product
   d. produce no air pollutants
6. Nuclear wastes include ______.
   a. products of fission reactors
   b. materials with very short half-lives
   c. products from medical and industrial processes
   d. all of these
7. High-level nuclear wastes are currently disposed of by ______.
   a. releasing them into water
   b. storing them in a deep, insulated pool of water
   c. burying them in unstable areas
   d. releasing them into the air
8. All of Earth's energy resources can ultimately be traced back to ______.
   a. plants **c.** geothermal resources
   b. the sun **d.** fossil fuels
9. Photovoltaic cells must be made ______ before they can be more widely used to produce electricity.
   a. pollution-free **c.** less expensive
   b. nonrenewable **d.** all of these
10. ______ is an alternate source of energy that uses water heated naturally by Earth's internal heat.
    a. Hydroelectricity **c.** Tidal energy
    b. Nuclear fission **d.** Geothermal energy

UNDERSTANDING CONCEPTS

Complete each sentence.

11. The actual fission of uranium occurs in the ______ of a nuclear reactor.
12. Control rods slow the rate of fission in a nuclear reactor by ______.
13. In ______, energy from the sun is collected and stored in solar panels.
14. The major difference between breeder reactors and other fission reactors is that in breeder reactors U-238 nuclei absorb ______ to produce Pu-239.
15. A major disadvantage of ______ is that they make plutonium, which has a very long half-life.

THINK AND WRITE CRITICALLY

16. Most of the energy resources discussed in this chapter produce electricity by means of an electric generator. Briefly discuss how each resource is used to do this.

17. Why is energy conservation important? What are some ways to conserve energy?

18. How great is the possibility of a nuclear explosion in a nuclear reactor?

19. Why isn't fusion being used today as a source of energy?

20. What specific problems have created the need for alternative energy resources? Why aren't these resources more widely used today?

APPLY

21. Which fossil fuel do you think we should use to generate electricity? What are the pros and cons of using this fossil fuel?

22. Match each of the energy resources described in the chapter with the proper type of energy conversion listed below:

a. kinetic energy to electricity
b. thermal energy to electricity
c. nuclear energy to electricity
d. chemical energy to electricity
e. light energy to electricity

23. Evaluate the following disposal methods of high-level nuclear wastes:

a. Bury the wastes in an area of high earthquake and volcanic activity.
b. Place the wastes on the ocean floor.
c. Rocket the wastes into space.

24. Classify the energy resources discussed in this chapter as renewable or nonrenewable.

25. Suppose that new reserves of petroleum were discovered and that a non-polluting way to burn them for energy were found. Why would it still be a good idea to decrease our use of petroleum as a source of energy? (HINT: Consider fractional distillation.)

MORE SKILL BUILDERS

If you need help, refer to the Skill Handbook.

1. Sequencing: The ultimate source of energy for cooking food on an electric stove is the sun. List in order the steps that must occur before you can use the sun's energy in this way.

2. Recognizing Cause and Effect: Complete the following table which describes changes in the normal operation of a nuclear reactor and the possible effects of these changes.

Cause	Effect
1. Uranium oxide pellets containing only U-238	1.
2. Control rods are removed	2.
3.	3. Reactor core overheats; "meltdown"

3. Making and Using Tables: Construct a table to summarize the advantages and disadvantages of each of the energy resources discussed in this chapter.

PROJECTS

1. Research the ways in which scientists are currently trying to contain and control a fusion reaction. Write a report and present it to your classmates.

2. Design a campaign to raise public awareness of current energy problems. Point out possible solutions.

UNIT 7

GLOBAL CONNECTIONS

Electricity and Energy Resources

In this unit, you studied about electricity, magnetism, and energy resources. Now find out how these subjects are connected to other subjects and places around the world.

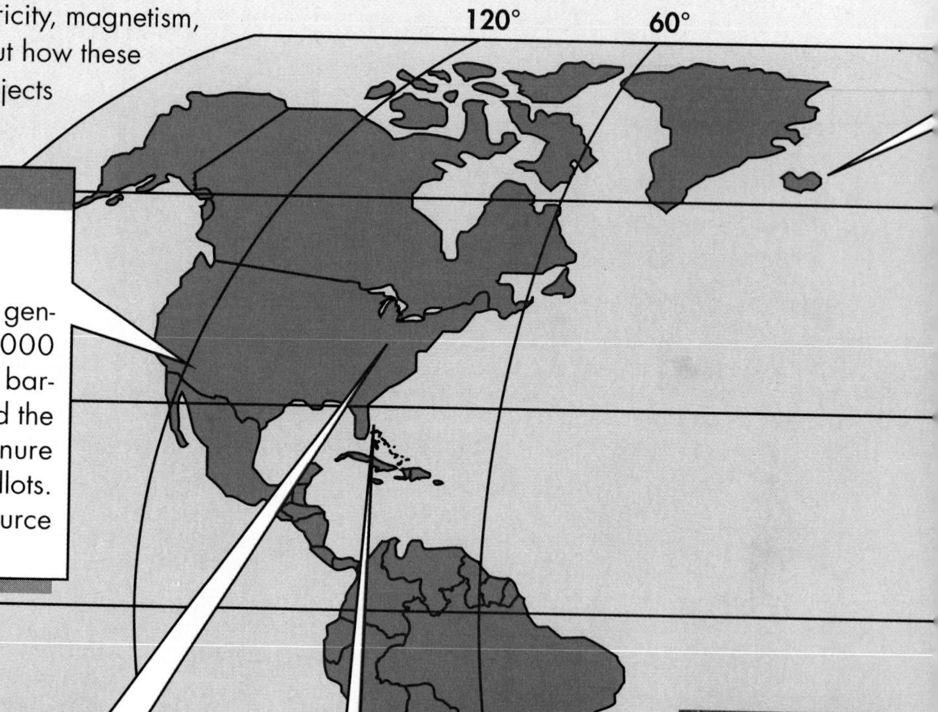

120° 60°

BIOLOGY

MANURE POWER
Imperial Valley, California

A power plant fired by cow manure generates enough electricity for 20 000 homes. Besides saving about 300 barrels of oil a day, the plant has solved the problem of what to do with the manure from 400 000 cattle in nearby feedlots. What type of alternative energy source does this plant use?

HISTORY

RADIO BROADCASTING
Pittsburgh, Pennsylvania

On the evening of November 2, 1920, the first commercial radio station, KDKA, began broadcasting. The first broadcast was of the Harding-Cox presidential election returns. Hundreds of people, from as far away as Kentucky, heard the broadcast. KDKA operates at 1020 kilohertz. Is it an AM or an FM station?

ASTRONOMY

SPACE TECHNOLOGY ON EARTH
Cape Kennedy, Florida

Cordless power tools are now common around many houses. The first cordless power tools were developed for and used on NASA expeditions to the moon. A cordless drill allowed astronauts to take core samples of the moon. Find out how cordless power tools work.

STEAM HEAT
Reykjavik, Iceland

This island of Iceland was formed by volcanic activity. Now Icelanders use that geothermal energy. Water piped underground becomes hot and turns to steam. The steam is then piped into houses and businesses where it is used to heat them. How do Icelanders generate electricity?

PHYSICS

DRIVING SIMULATORS
Berlin, Germany

Car manufacturers are using computer-generated images of an imaginary road to put test models of their cars through road tests. The images are linked to the car's controls and create a realistic driving experience. The computer measures both the driver's and the vehicle's responses to various road conditions. What advantage does this method have over actual road testing?

CAREERS

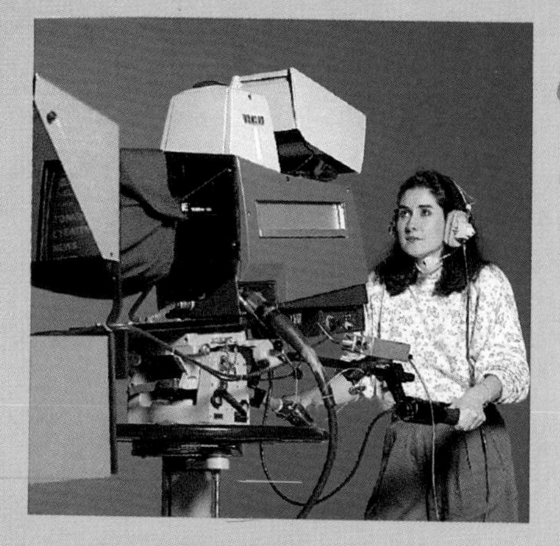

BROADCAST ENGINEER

Broadcast engineers are responsible for a wide variety of electronic equipment used in radio or television transmission. In small stations, they usually set up and operate equipment, as well as keep it working. In larger stations, the jobs are more specialized.

Engineers operate equipment such as microphones, lights, recording equipment, projectors, and cameras. In the control room, engineers also run the equipment that controls the quality of sound and pictures.

If you're interested in becoming a broadcast engineer, you must be flexible and be able to keep a cool head under pressure. High school classes in math and science are helpful. Broadcast engineers must have a license issued by the Federal Communications Commission. Technical schools offer course work designed specifically for preparing you to pass the tests for FCC licensing.

For Additional Information

Contact the Federal Communications Commission, Washington, DC 20036.

COMPUTER PROGRAMMER

A *computer programmer* writes programs that enable a computer to perform particular tasks or functions. The programmer takes a specific problem, studies and analyzes various ways to solve it, then devises a step-by-step procedure in terms that a computer can understand.

Programmers must be problem solvers who have the ability to think logically, yet creatively. They must also learn to use new programming languages as they are needed.

If you're interested in becoming a computer programmer you should take classes in science, mathematics, and computer science. Most computer programmers have college degrees in computer science or mathematics.

For Additional Information

Contact the Electronics Industries Association, 2001 I Street NW, Washington, DC 20006.

UNIT READINGS

►McGowen, Tom. *Radioactivity: From the Curies to the Atomic Age.* Danbury, CT: Watts, 1986.

►Vogt, Gregory. *Electricity and Magnetism.* Danbury, CT: Watts, 1985.

Earthships: Environmental Architecture

The passage that follows describes a house design that solves a number of environmental problems.

Architecture is the art and profession of designing buildings. Architecture is one of the oldest art forms and dates from prehistoric times. It has been said that a society's architecture reflects the values and ideals of its people.

In that context, environmental architecture reflects the growing concern of people for the future of planet Earth with its fragile ecology and disappearing resources. Architect Michael Reynolds' concern for the environment led him to design houses he calls "Earthships."

Reynolds' earthships help solve a number of environmental problems simultaneously. First, they use discarded tires as building materials. The Environmental Protection Agency says that tires are discarded at a rate of 240 million per year in the United States. The interior and exterior walls of the earthships are constructed of tires filled with dirt and laid like concrete blocks. The walls are then covered with a coat of plaster or adobe.

Using tires provides a house with walls that are about one meter thick and gives it a very large mass. Because of this "thermal mass," the house utilizes little or no energy for cooling and heating. The base of the house is built below the frost line, meaning that the temperature of the walls will stay at approximately the temperature of Earth below that point — about 15°C. If a house gets no sun at all, but has this amount of mass, it will never get below 15°C.

Earthships in the Southwest have been built in the mountains where temperatures reach −34° in winter and +38° in summer. These houses are able to maintain a temperature that varies only a few degrees year round with no energy used for heating or cooling. Asked if earthships would work anywhere in the country, Reynolds said yes—even if you put them where there is no sun and you are heating with gas, you will reduce your heating costs by 90 percent.

Some earthships also generate their own electricity with solar panels mounted on the roof. They also are able to grow food year round in the greenhouse that Reynolds incorporated in the earthship design. Even the design of the plumbing system was given environmental consideration. "Black water" from toilets goes into a septic system, but "gray water" from sinks, bathtubs, and the washing machine goes into holding tanks to be used in greenhouse irrigation.

Reynolds stresses that earthships are easy and comparatively inexpensive to build. But more importantly, he said, these are buildings that take care of people. That is why he calls them earthships.

In Your Own Words

▶ Would you like to live in an earthship? Write an essay explaining why or why not.

APPENDIX A

SI Units of Measurement

Table A-1

SI BASE UNITS					
Measurement	**Unit**	**Symbol**	**Measurement**	**Unit**	**Symbol**
length	meter	m	temperature	kelvin	K
mass	kilogram	kg	amount of substance	mole	mol
time	second	s	intensity of light	candela	cd
electric current	ampere	A			

Table A-2

UNITS DERIVED FROM SI BASE UNITS			
Measurement	**Unit**	**Symbol**	**Expressed in Base Units**
energy	joule	J	$kg \bullet m^2/s^2$
force	newton	N	$kg \bullet m/s^2$
frequency	hertz	Hz	$1/s$
potential difference	volt	V	$kg \bullet m^2/(A \bullet s^3)$ or (W/A)
power	watt	W	$kg \bullet m^2/s^3$ or (J/s)
pressure	pascal	Pa	$kg/(m^2 \bullet s^2)$ or (N/m^2)
quality of electric charge	coulomb	C	$A \bullet s$

Table A-3

COMMON SI PREFIXES					
Prefix	**Symbol**	**Multiplier**	**Prefix**	**Symbol**	**Multiplier**
	Greater than 1			Less than 1	
mega-	M	1 000 000	*deci-*	d	0.1
kilo-	k	1 000	*centi-*	c	0.01
hecto-	h	100	*milli-*	m	0.001
deka-	da	10	*micro-*	μ	0.000 000 1

Table A-4

SI/METRIC TO ENGLISH CONVERSIONS			
	When you want to convert:	Multiply by:	To find:
Length	inches	2.54	centimeters
	centimeters	0.394	inches
	feet	0.305	meters
	meters	3.28	feet
	yards	0.914	meters
	meters	1.09	yards
	miles	1.61	kilometers
	kilometers	0.621	miles
*** Mass and Weight**	ounces	28.35	grams
	grams	0.0353	ounces
	pounds	0.454	kilograms
	kilograms	2.205	pounds
	tons	0.9072	tonnes (metric tons)
	tonnes (metric tons)	1.102	tons
	pounds	4.448	newtons
	newtons	0.225	pounds
Volume	cubic inches	16.38	cubic centimeters
	cubic centimeters	0.0610	cubic inches
	cubic feet	0.0283	cubic meters
	cubic meters	35.3	cubic feet
	liters	1.06	quarts
	liters	0.264	gallons
	gallons	3.78	liters
Area	square inches	6.45	square centimeters
	square centimeters	0.115	square inches
	square feet	0.0929	square meters
	square meters	10.76	square feet
	square miles	2.59	square kilometers
	square kilometers	0.386	square miles

*Weight as measured in standard Earth gravity

SI/Temperature Scale Conversions

Table A-5

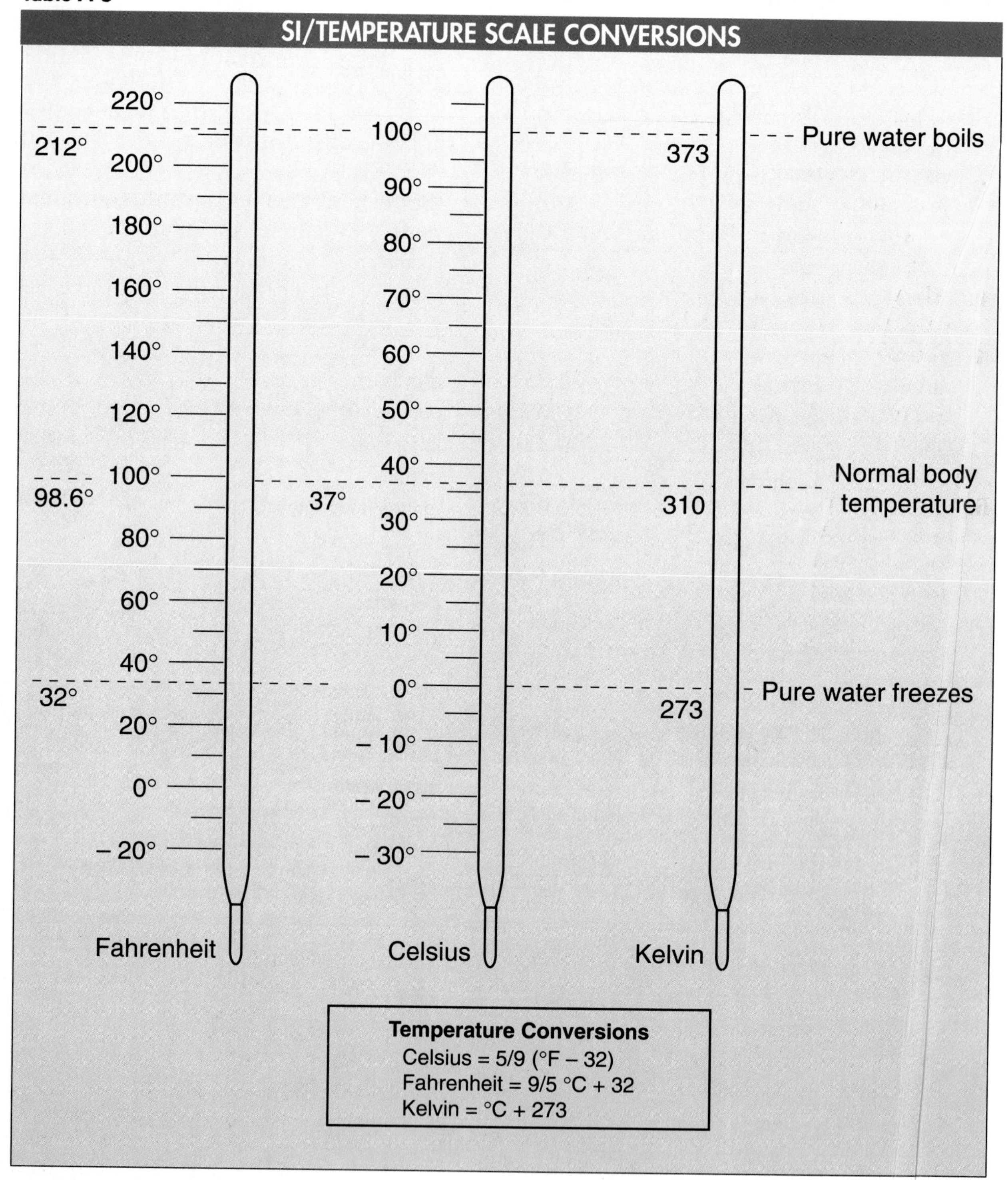

APPENDIX B

Safety in the Classroom

1. Always obtain your teacher's permission to begin an investigation.
2. Study the procedure. If you have questions, ask your teacher. Be sure you understand any safety symbols shown on the page.
3. Use the safety equipment provided for you. Goggles and a safety apron should be worn when any investigation calls for using chemicals.
4. Always slant test tubes away from yourself and others when heating them.
5. Never eat or drink in the lab, and never use lab glassware as food or drink containers. Never inhale chemicals. Do not taste any substances or draw any material into a tube with your mouth.
6. If you spill any chemical, wash it off immediately with water. Report the spill immediately to your teacher.
7. Know the location and proper use of the fire extinguisher, safety shower, fire blanket, first aid kit, and fire alarm.
8. Keep all materials away from open flames. Tie back long hair and loose clothing.
9. If a fire should break out in the classroom, or if your clothing should catch fire, smother it with the fire blanket or a coat, or get under a safety shower. NEVER RUN.
10. Report any accident or injury, no matter how small, to your teacher.

Follow these procedures as you clean up your work area.

1. Turn off the water and gas. Disconnect electrical devices.
2. Return all materials to their proper places.
3. Dispose of chemicals and other materials as directed by your teacher. Place broken glass and solid substances in the proper containers. Never discard materials in the sink.
4. Clean your work area.
5. Wash your hands thoroughly after working in the laboratory.

Table B-1

FIRST AID	
Injury	**Safe response**
Burns	Apply cold water. Call your teacher immediately.
Cuts and bruises	Stop any bleeding by applying direct pressure. Cover cuts with a clean dressing. Apply cold compresses to bruises. Call your teacher immediately.
Fainting	Leave the person lying down. Loosen any tight clothing and keep crowds away. Call your teacher immediately.
Foreign matter in eye	Flush with plenty of water. Use eyewash bottle or fountain.
Poisoning	Note the suspected poisoning agent and call your teacher immediately.
Any spills on skin	Flush with large amounts of water or use safety shower. Call your teacher immediately.

Safety Symbols

This textbook uses the safety symbols in Table B-2 below to alert you to possible laboratory dangers.

Table B-2

SAFETY SYMBOLS	
DISPOSAL ALERT This symbol appears when care must be taken to dispose of materials properly.	**ANIMAL SAFETY** This symbol appears whenever live animals are studied and the safety of the animals and the students must be ensured.
BIOLOGICAL HAZARD This symbol appears when there is danger involving bacteria, fungi, or protists.	**RADIOACTIVE SAFETY** This symbol appears when radioactive materials are used.
OPEN FLAME ALERT This symbol appears when use of an open flame could cause a fire or an explosion.	**CLOTHING PROTECTION SAFETY** This symbol appears when substances used could stain or burn clothing.
THERMAL SAFETY This symbol appears as a reminder to use caution when handling hot objects.	**FIRE SAFETY** This symbol appears when care should be taken around open flames.
SHARP OBJECT SAFETY This symbol appears when a danger of cuts or punctures caused by the use of sharp objects exists.	**EXPLOSION SAFETY** This symbol appears when the misuse of chemicals could cause an explosion.
FUME SAFETY This symbol appears when chemicals or chemical reactions could cause dangerous fumes.	**EYE SAFETY** This symbol appears when a danger to the eyes exists. Safety goggles should be worn when this symbol appears.
ELECTRICAL SAFETY This symbol appears when care should be taken when using electrical equipment.	**POISON SAFETY** This symbol appears when poisonous substances are used.
PLANT SAFETY This symbol appears when poisonous plants or plants with thorns are handled.	**CHEMICAL SAFETY** This symbol appears when chemicals used can cause burns or are poisonous if absorbed through the skin.

APPENDIX C

The Periodic Table
Based on Carbon 12 = 12.0000

Key: Atomic number / Symbol / Element name / Atomic mass

Period	1	2	3	4	5	6	7	8	9	10	11	12	13	14	15	16	17	18 (Noble Gases)
1	1 H Hydrogen 1.00794																	2 He Helium 4.002602
2	3 Li Lithium 6.941	4 Be Beryllium 9.01218											5 B Boron 10.811	6 C Carbon 12.011	7 N Nitrogen 14.0067	8 O Oxygen 15.9994	9 F Fluorine 18.998403	10 Ne Neon 20.179
3	11 Na Sodium 22.98977	12 Mg Magnesium 24.305											13 Al Aluminum 26.98154	14 Si Silicon 28.0855	15 P Phosphorus 30.97376	16 S Sulfur 32.06	17 Cl Chlorine 35.453	18 Ar Argon 39.948
4	19 K Potassium 39.0983	20 Ca Calcium 40.078	21 Sc Scandium 44.95591	22 Ti Titanium 47.88	23 V Vanadium 50.9415	24 Cr Chromium 51.9961	25 Mn Manganese 54.9380	26 Fe Iron 55.847	27 Co Cobalt 58.9332	28 Ni Nickel 58.69	29 Cu Copper 63.546	30 Zn Zinc 65.39	31 Ga Gallium 69.723	32 Ge Germanium 72.59	33 As Arsenic 74.9216	34 Se Selenium 78.96	35 Br Bromine 79.904	36 Kr Krypton 83.80
5	37 Rb Rubidium 85.4678	38 Sr Strontium 87.62	39 Y Yttrium 88.9059	40 Zr Zirconium 91.224	41 Nb Niobium 92.9064	42 Mo Molybdenum 95.94	43 Tc Technetium 97.9072*	44 Ru Ruthenium 101.07	45 Rh Rhodium 102.9055	46 Pd Palladium 106.42	47 Ag Silver 107.8682	48 Cd Cadmium 112.41	49 In Indium 114.82	50 Sn Tin 118.710	51 Sb Antimony 121.75	52 Te Tellurium 127.60	53 I Iodine 126.9045	54 Xe Xenon 131.29
6	55 Cs Cesium 132.9054	56 Ba Barium 137.33	71 Lu Lutetium 174.967	72 Hf Hafnium 178.49	73 Ta Tantalum 180.9479	74 W Tungsten 183.85	75 Re Rhenium 186.207	76 Os Osmium 190.2	77 Ir Iridium 192.22	78 Pt Platinum 195.08	79 Au Gold 196.9665	80 Hg Mercury 200.59	81 Tl Thallium 204.383	82 Pb Lead 207.2	83 Bi Bismuth 208.9804	84 Po Polonium 208.9824*	85 At Astatine 209.98712*	86 Rn Radon 222.017*
7	87 Fr Francium 223.0197*	88 Ra Radium 226.0254	103 Lr Lawrencium 260.1054*	104 Unq Unnilquadium 261*	105 Unp Unnilpentium 262*	106 Unh Unnilhexium 263*	107 Uns Unnilseptium 262*	108 Uno Unniloctium 265*	109 Une Unnilennium 266*									

Transition Elements: groups 3–12

Metallic Properties ← → Nonmetallic Properties

Series														
Lanthanoid Series	57 La Lanthanum 138.9055	58 Ce Cerium 140.12	59 Pr Praseodymium 140.9077	60 Nd Neodymium 144.24	61 Pm Promethium 144.9128*	62 Sm Samarium 150.36	63 Eu Europium 151.96	64 Gd Gadolinium 157.25	65 Tb Terbium 158.9254	66 Dy Dysprosium 162.50	67 Ho Holmium 164.9304	68 Er Erbium 167.26	69 Tm Thulium 168.9342	70 Yb Ytterbium 173.04
Actinoid Series	89 Ac Actinium 227.0278*	90 Th Thorium 232.0381	91 Pa Protactinium 231.0359*	92 U Uranium 238.0289	93 Np Neptunium 237.0482	94 Pu Plutonium 244.0642*	95 Am Americium 243.0614*	96 Cm Curium 247.0703*	97 Bk Berkelium 247.0703*	98 Cf Californium 251.0796*	99 Es Einsteinium 252.0828*	100 Fm Fermium 257.0951*	101 Md Mendelevium 258.986*	102 No Nobelium 259.1009*

Metallic Properties
Nonmetallic Properties
Metalloids
Synthetic Elements

State at Room Temperature: and Solid, Liquid, Gas

*Mass of isotope with longest half-life, that is, the most stable isotope of the element

Organizing Information

Sequencing

Think about going to a grocery store to purchase a loaf of bread. As you walk down the aisles, you notice that canned fruits are in one section, boxed cereals are in another, and the bread you are looking for is in yet another. What would happen if different food items were placed randomly on the shelves? It would be difficult for people to locate the food items they wanted. Just like the grocery store, much of the world around you has been put into order to make it easier to understand. Sequencing and outlining are two methods scientists use to organize information.

One method of organizing information is to create a sequence. A sequence is an arrangement of things or events in a particular order. In some of your classes, the students may have been seated in alphabetical order. By organizing students alphabetically, teachers find it easier to remember students' names and to match papers with names in their grade books.

Think about baking chocolate chip cookies. Certain steps have to be followed for the cookies to taste good. If you skip a step in order, the cookies will not turn out right. Baking chocolate chip cookies is an example of the arrangement of events in a particular order.

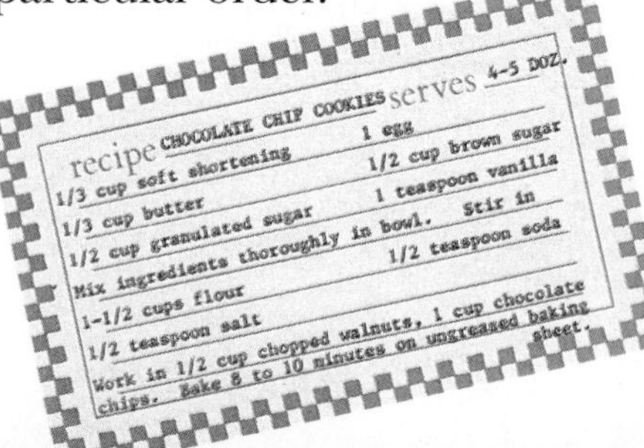

When you are asked to sequence things or events, you must first identify what comes first. You then decide what should come second. Continue to choose things or events until they are all accounted for and in order. Then, go back over the sequence to make sure each thing or event logically leads to the next.

Suppose you wanted to watch a movie that just came out on videotape. What sequence of events would you have to follow to watch the movie? You would first turn the television set to channel 3 or 4. You would then turn the videotape player on, insert the tape, and press the "play" button. Once the tape had started playing, you would adjust the sound and picture. Then, when the movie was over, you would rewind the tape.

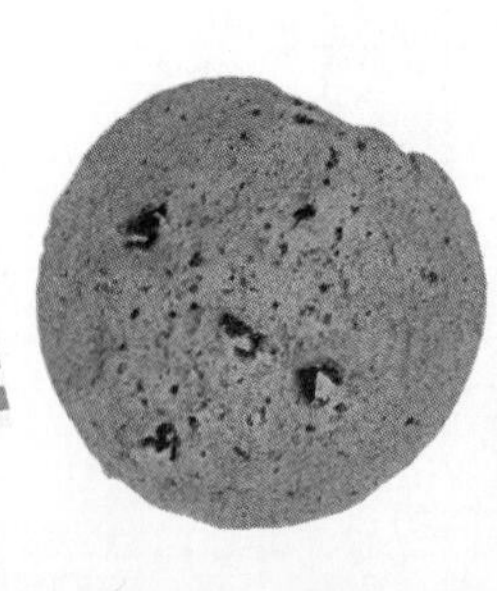

Outlining

Have you ever wondered why teachers ask students to outline what they read? The purpose of outlining is to show the relationships between main ideas and information about the main ideas. Outlining can help you organize, remember, and review written material.

When you are asked to outline, you must first find a group of words that summarizes the main idea. This group of words corresponds to the Roman numerals in an outline. Next, determine what is said about the main idea. Ideas of equal importance are grouped together and are given capital letters. Ideas of equal importance are further broken down and given numbers and letters.

To get an idea how to outline, compare the following outline with Chapter 20 of your textbook.

Chapter 20 Mirrors and Lenses

I. The Optics of Mirrors
- A. Plane Mirrors
  1. has flat surface
  2. reflection of
     - a. left and right sides of image appear reversed
     - b. image upright
     - c. image same size
  3. results in virtual image
     - a. light rays don't form image in front of mirror
     - b. light rays meet to form image that appears like object but reversed
- B. Concave Mirrors
  1. surface curved inward
  2. reflection depends on distance of image from mirror

II. The Optics of Lenses
- A. Convex Lenses

Notice that the outline shows the pattern of organization of the written material. The boldface title is the main idea and corresponds with Roman numerals I and II. The capital letters and numbers and letters that follow divide the rest of the text into supporting ideas.

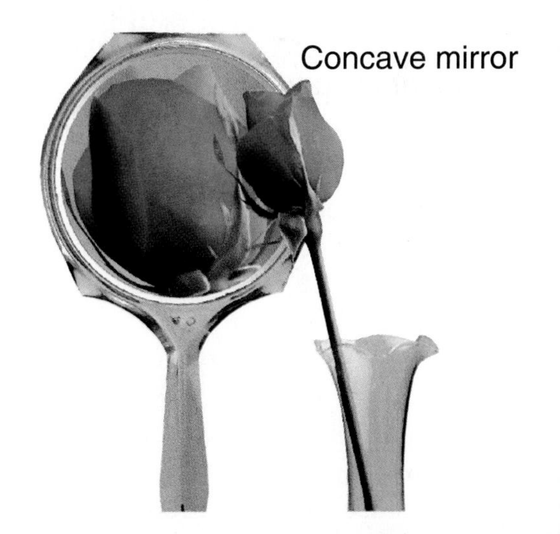

Thinking Critically

Observing and Inferring

Imagine that you have just finished a volleyball game with your friends. You hurry home to get a cold drink. Opening the refrigerator, you see a jug of orange juice at the back of the top shelf. The jug feels cold as you grasp it. "Ah, just what I need," you think. You hear the tone rise as you pour the juice into a tall glass. When you quickly down the drink, you smell the oranges and enjoy the tart taste in your mouth.

As you imagined yourself in the story, you used your senses to make observations. The basis of all scientific investigation is observation. Scientists are careful to make their observations accurate. When possible they use instruments, like microscopes or telescopes, to extend their senses.

Often they use instruments to make measurements. When observations involve measurements, they are called quantitative observations. Because measurements are easy to communicate and provide a concrete means of comparing collected data, scientists use them whenever possible.

When you make observations in science, you may find it helpful to first examine the entire object or situation. Then, look carefully for details using your sense of sight. Write down everything you see before using another sense to make additional observations. Continue until you have used all five senses.

Scientists often use their observations to make inferences. An inference is an attempt to explain or interpret observations or to determine what caused what you observed. For example, if you observed a CLOSED sign in a store window around noon, you might infer the owner is taking a lunch break. But, perhaps the owner has a doctor's appointment or has taken the day off to go fishing. The only way to be sure your inference is correct is to investigate further.

When making an inference, be certain to make accurate observations and to record them carefully. Then, based on everything you know, try to explain or interpret what you observed. If possible, investigate further to determine if your inference is correct.

Comparing and Contrasting

Observations can be analyzed and then organized by noting the similarities and differences between two or more objects or situations. When you examine objects or situations to determine similarities, you are comparing. Contrasting is looking at similar objects or situations for differences.

Suppose you were asked to compare and contrast transverse and compressional waves. You start by examining your observations. You then divide a piece of paper into two columns, listing ways the waves are similar in one column and ways they are different in the other column. After completing your lists, you report your findings in a table or in a paragraph.

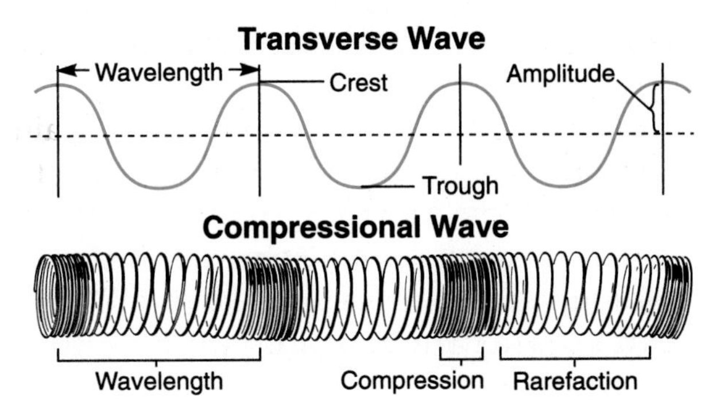

A similarity you would point out is that both transverse and compressional waves carry energy through matter and space. A difference you might list is that matter in transverse waves moves at right angles to the direction the wave travels, but matter in compressional waves moves parallel to the direction the wave travels.

Recognizing Cause and Effect

Have you ever observed something happen and then tried to figure out why or how it might have happened? If so, you have observed an event and have inferred a reason for the event. The event or result of action is the effect, and the reason for the event is the cause.

Suppose that you had a clothesline outside your bedroom window. You look out your window every morning to determine what kind of weather the day will bring forth. You notice one warm fall day that the clothesline is sagging and make a mental note to help pull the line tighter. Another morning upon looking outside, you find the weather is quite cold, and notice the clothesline is no longer sagging. Instead, the line is taut and almost parallel to the ground.

What is the effect and what would you infer to be the cause? The effect is the change of position of the clothesline from sagging to taut. You might infer the cause to be the drop in temperature. In trying to determine cause and effect, you have made a logical inference based on observations.

Perhaps, someone in the family tightened the line while you were at school. When scientists are unsure of the cause for a certain event, they often design controlled experiments to determine what caused their observations. How could you determine what caused the tautness of the clothesline?

Experimentation Skills

Measuring in SI

You are probably familiar with the metric system of measurement. The metric system is a uniform system of measurement developed in 1795 by a group of scientists. The development of the metric system helped scientists avoid problems with different units of measurement by providing an international standard of comparison for measurements. A modern form of the metric system called the International System, or SI, was adopted for worldwide use in 1960.

You will find that your text uses metric units in almost all its measurements. In the activities you will be doing, you'll use the metric system of measurement.

The metric system is easy to use because it has a system for naming of units and a decimal base. For example, meter is the base unit for measuring length, gram for measuring mass, and liter for measuring volume. Unit sizes vary by multiples of ten. When changing from smaller units to larger, you divide by ten. When changing from larger units to smaller, you multiply by ten. Prefixes are used to name larger and smaller units. Look at the following table for some common metric prefixes and their meanings.

METRIC PREFIXES

Prefix	Symbol	Meaning	
kilo-	k	1000	thousand
hecto-	h	100	hundred
deka	da	10	ten
deci-	d	0.1	tenth
centi	c	0.01	hundredth
milli-	m	0.001	thousandth

Do you see how the prefix *kilo-* attached to the unit *gram* is *kilogram,* or 1000 grams, or how the prefix *deci-* attached to the unit *meter* is *decimeter,* or one tenth (0.1) of a meter?

You have probably measured distance many times. The meter is the SI unit used to measure distance. To visualize the length of a meter, think of a baseball bat. A baseball bat is about one meter long. When measuring smaller distances, the meter is divided into smaller units called centimeters and millimeters. A centimeter is one hundredth (0.01) of a meter, which is about the size of the width of the fingernail on your little finger. A millimeter is one thousandth of a meter (0.001), about the thickness of a dime.

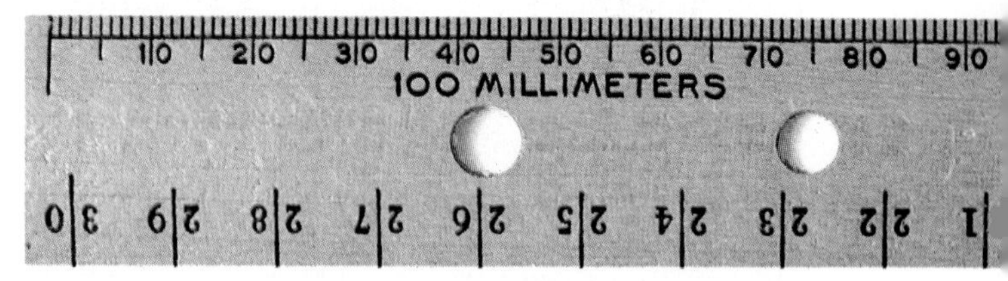

Most metersticks and metric rulers have lines indicating centimeters and millimeters. Look at the illustration. The centimeter lines are the longer numbered lines, and the shorter lines between the centimeter lines are millimeter lines.

When using a metric ruler, you must first decide on a unit of measurement. You then line up the 0 centimeter mark with the end of the object being measured and read the number of the unit where the object ends.

Units of length are also used to measure the surface area. The standard unit of area is the square meter (m^2), or a square one meter long on each side. Similarly, a square centimeter (cm^2) is a square one centimeter long on each side. Surface area is determined by multiplying the number of units in length times the number of units in width.

The volume of rectangular solids is also calculated using units of length. The cubic meter (m^3) is the standard SI unit of volume. A cubic meter is a cube one meter on a side. You can determine the volume of rectangular solids by multiplying length times width times height.

Liquid volume is measured using a unit called a liter. You are probably familiar with a two-liter soft drink bottle. One liter is about one half of the two-liter bottle. A liter has the volume of 1000 cubic centimeters. Because the prefix *milli-* means thousandth (0.001), a milliliter would equal one cubic centimeter. One milliliter of liquid would completely fill a cube measuring one centimeter on each side.

During science activities, you will measure liquids using beakers marked in milliliters and graduated cylinders. A graduated cylinder is a tall cylindrical container marked with lines from bottom to top. Each graduation represents one milliliter.

Scientists use a balance to find the mass of an object in grams. In science class, you will likely use a beam balance similar to the one illustrated. Notice that on one side of the beam balance is a pan and on the other side is a set of beams. Each beam has an object of a known mass called a rider that slides on the beam.

You must be careful when using a balance. When carrying the balance, hold the beam support with one hand and place the other hand under the balance. Also, be careful about what you place on the pan. Never place a hot object on the pan or pour chemicals directly on it. Mass a suitable container and place dry or liquid chemicals into the container to mass.

Before you find the mass of an object, you must set the balance to zero by sliding all the riders back to the zero point. Check the pointer to make sure it swings an equal distance above and below the zero point on the scale. If the swing is unequal, find and turn the adjusting screw until you have an equal swing.

You are now ready to use the balance to mass the object. Place the object on the pan. Slide the rider with the largest mass along the beam until the pointer drops below the zero point. Then move it back one notch. Repeat the process on each beam until the pointer swings an equal distance above and below the zero point. Read the masses indicated on the beams. The sum of the masses will be the mass of the object.

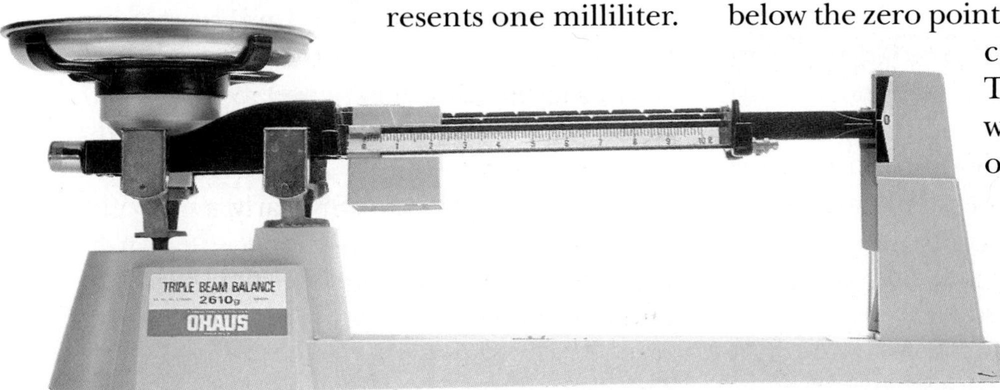

Hypothesizing

What would you do if the combination lock on your locker didn't work? Would you try the combination again? Would you check to make sure you had the right locker? You would likely try several possible solutions until you managed to open the locker.

Scientists generally use experiments to solve problems and answer questions. An experiment is a method of solving a problem in which scientists use an organized process to attempt to answer a question.

Experimentation involves defining a problem and formulating and testing a hypothesis, or testable prediction about how to solve a problem. Each prediction is tested during an experiment, which includes making careful observations and collecting data. After analysis of the collected data, a conclusion is formed and compared to the hypothesis.

Imagine it's after school, and you are changing clothes. You notice a brownish-black spot on a favorite shirt. Your problem is how to remove the stain from the shirt without damaging the shirt. You think that soap and water will remove the stain. You have made a hypothesis regarding the solution to the problem. But, making a hypothesis is not enough—the hypothesis must be tested. You try soap and water, but the stain doesn't budge.

You then observe the stain more carefully and decide that you will need to use a solvent. You have revised your hypothesis based on your observations. The new hypothesis is still only a testable prediction until you test it and examine the results. If the test removes the stain, the hypothesis is accepted. But, if the test doesn't remove the stain, you will have to revise and refine the hypothesis.

Using Variables, Constants, and Controls

When scientists do experiments, they are careful to manipulate or change only one condition and keep all other conditions in the experiment the same. The condition that is manipulated is called the independent variable. The conditions that are kept the same during an experiment are called constants. The dependent variable is any change that results from manipulating the independent variable.

Scientists can know that the independent variable caused the change in the dependent variable only if they keep all other factors constant in the experiment. Scientists also use controls to be certain that the observed changes were a result of manipulation of the independent variable. A control is a sample that is treated exactly like the experimental group except that the independent variable is not applied to the control. After the experiment, the change in the dependent variable of the control sample is compared to the change observed in the experimental group to see the effect of the application of the independent variable.

Suppose you were asked to bring your portable compact disc player on a weekend camping trip. You put in fresh dry cell batteries so that you and your friends can play CDs all weekend. But, the player loses volume about midday Sunday and soon won't play at all. You expected the dry cell batteries to last all weekend. You played the CDs louder than you do at home, so you wonder if the volume of the player affects how long the batteries last and decide to design an experiment to find out. What would be the independent and dependent variables, the constants, and the control in your experiment?

This is how you might set up your experiment. You decide to compare the amount of time the player will operate at different volume settings. You purchase enough fresh dry cell batteries to operate the player at number 6, your normal listening volume, and at lower and higher volume settings. You first set the volume at number 6 and operate the player until you can no longer hear the music. You then repeat the experiment two more times using volume settings of 3 and 9. You record the amount of time the player operates at each volume setting in a data table. Your data table might look like this:

DURATION MUSIC IS HEARD	
Volume	Amount of Time
3	23 h, 46 min
6	18 h, 13 min
9	14 h, 53 min

What are the independent and dependent variables in the experiment? Because you are changing the volume setting of the compact disc player, the independent variable is the volume setting. The dependent variable is any change that results from the independent variable, so the dependent variable is the number of hours and minutes music is heard on the player.

What factors are constants in the experiment? The constants are using identical dry cell batteries, playing the same compact disc, and keeping the compact disc player in the same environment for each test. What was the purpose of playing the compact disc player at your normal setting? The normal setting of the player is the control. The duration that music is heard at the normal volume setting will be used to compare the durations at lower and higher volume settings.

Interpreting Data

After doing a controlled experiment, you must analyze and interpret the collected data, form a conclusion, and compare the conclusion to your hypothesis. Analyze and interpret the data in the table. On which volume setting did the dry cell batteries last the longest? The batteries lasted the longest on number 3, the lowest setting. On which volume setting did the dry cell batteries last the shortest duration? The batteries lasted the shortest duration on volume setting number 9. What conclusion did you form? The data indicate that as the volume increases, the dry cell batteries last for a shorter duration. How does the conclusion compare with your hypothesis for this experiment? Was it supported by the experiment or not?

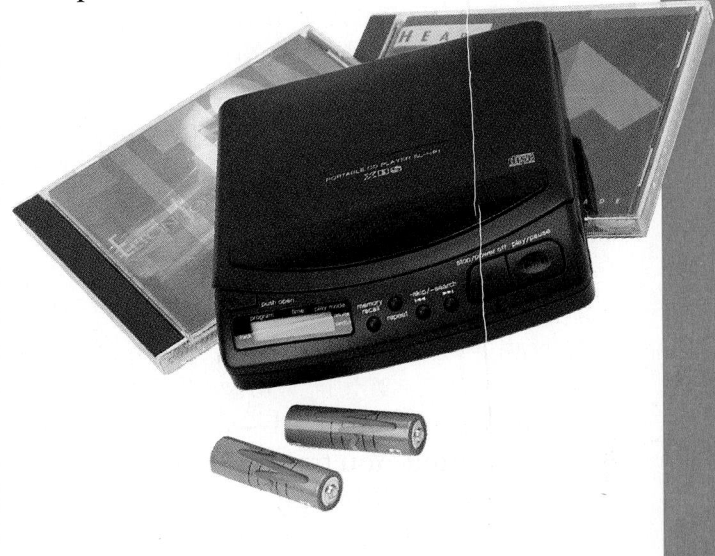

Graphics Organizers

Concept Mapping

If you were taking an automobile trip, you would likely take along a road map. The road map shows your location, your destination, and other places along the way. By examining the map, you can understand where you are in relation to other locations on the map.

A concept map is similar to a road map. But, a concept map shows the relationships among ideas (or concepts) rather than places. A concept map is a diagram that visually shows how concepts are related. Because the concept map shows the relationships among ideas, it can clarify the meanings of ideas and terms and help you to understand what you are studying.

Look at the construction of a concept map called a **network tree.** Notice how some words are circled and others are written on connecting lines. The circled words are science concepts. The lines in the map show relationships between concepts, and the words written on them describe relationships between the concepts.

A network tree can also show more complex relationships between the concepts. For example, a line labeled "affected by" could be drawn from *plants* and *animals* to *chemistry,* because chemical processes occur in plants and animals. Another example of a relationship that crosses branches would be a line labeled "caused by interactions of" connecting *Earth changes* with *matter and energy.* Earth changes are caused by interactions of matter and energy.

When you are asked to construct a network tree, state the topic and select the major concepts. Find related concepts and put them in order from general to specific. Branch the related concepts from the major concept and describe the relationships on the lines. Continue to write the more specific concepts. Write the relationships between the concepts on the lines until all concepts are mapped. Examine the concept map for relationships that cross branches and add them to the concept map.

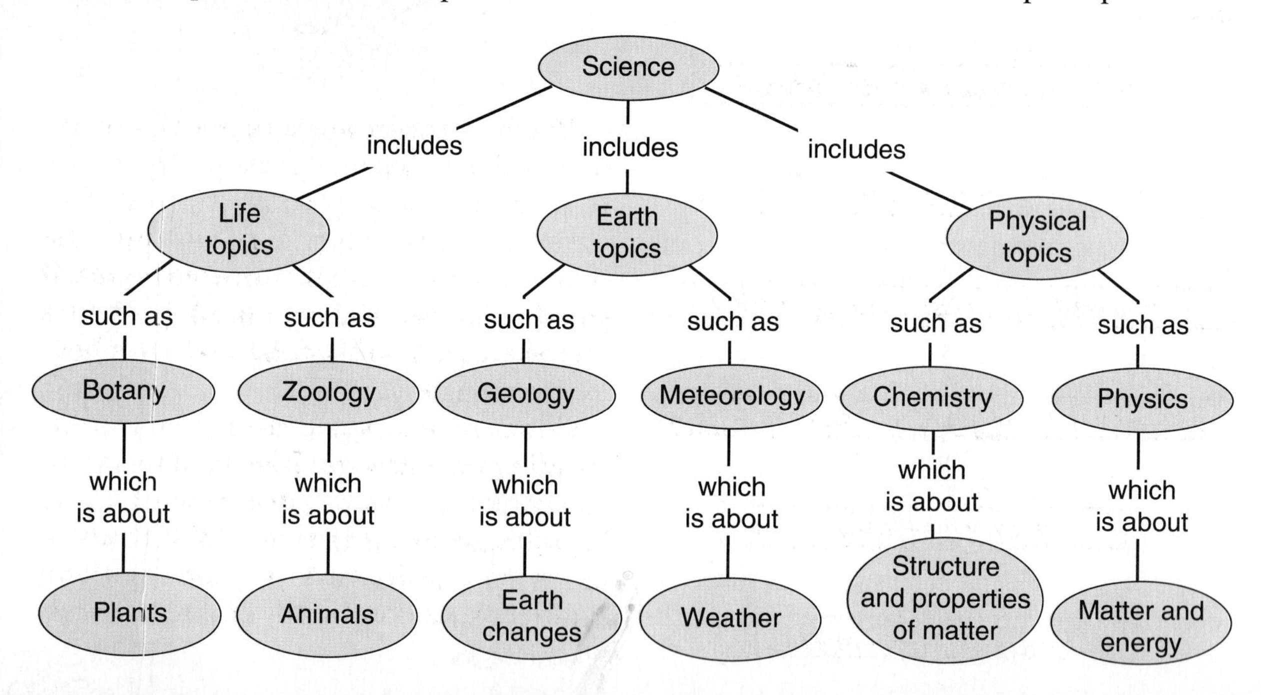

An **events chain** is another type of concept map. An events chain map is used to describe ideas in order. In science, an events chain can be used to describe a sequence of events, the steps in a procedure, or the stages of a process.

When making an events chain, you first must find the one event that starts the chain. This event is called the initiating event. You then find the next event in the chain and continue until you reach an outcome. Suppose your mother asked you to wash the dinner dishes. An events chain map might look like the one below. Notice that connecting words may not be necessary.

Initiating event:

Mother asks you to wash dishes.

↓

Event 2:

You clear the table.

↓

Event 3:

You wash the dishes in soapy water.

↓

Event 4:

You rinse the dishes in hot water.

↓

Event 5:

You dry the dishes.

↓

Final outcome:

You put the dishes away.

A **cycle concept map** is a special type of events chain map. In a cycle concept map, the series of events do not produce a final outcome. The last event in the chain relates back to the initiating event.

As in the events chain map, you first decide on an initiating event and then list each important event in order. Because there is no outcome and the last event relates back to the initiating event, the cycle repeats itself. Look at the cycle map of physical changes of water:

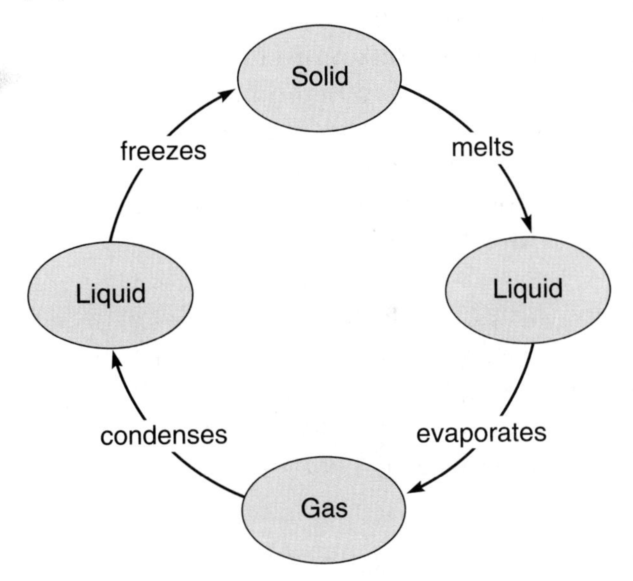

There is usually more than one correct way to create a concept map. As you are constructing a map, you may discover other ways to construct the map that show the relationships between concepts better. If you do discover what you think is a better way to create a concept map, do not hesitate to change it.

Concept maps are useful in understanding the ideas you have read about. As you construct a map, you are constructing knowledge and learning. Once concept maps are constructed, you can use them again to review and study and to test your knowledge.

Making and Using Tables

Browse through your textbook, and you will notice many tables both in the text and in the activities. The tables in the text arrange information in such a way that it is easier for you to understand. Also, many activities in your text have tables to complete as you do the activity. Activity tables will help you organize the data you collect during the activity so that they can be interpreted easily.

Most tables have a title telling you what is being presented. The table itself is divided into columns and rows. The column titles list items to be compared. The row headings list the specific characteristics being compared. Within the grid of the table, the collected data are recorded. Look at the following table:

COMMON BASES AND THEIR USES

Name of base	Formula	Uses
Sodium hydroxide	$NaOH$	Drain cleaner, Soap making
Aluminum hydroxide	$Al(OH)_3$	Antacid, Deodorant
Magnesium hydroxide	$Mg(OH)_2$	Laxative, Antacid
Ammonium hydroxide	NH_4OH	Cleaner

What is the title of this table? The title is "Common Bases and Their Uses." What items are being compared? The uses of common bases are being compared.

What is the use of ammonium hydroxide? To find the answer, you must locate the column labeled *Uses* and the row labeled *ammonium hydroxide*. The information contained in the box where the column and row intersect is the answer. Did you answer "cleaner"? What is the formula for sodium hydroxide? The answer is NaOH. Which two bases are commonly used as antacids? If you answered aluminum hydroxide and magnesium hydroxide, you have an understanding of how to use a table.

RECYCLED MATERIALS

Day of Week	Paper (kg)	Aluminum (kg)	Plastic (kg)
Mon.	4	2	0.5
Wed.	3.5	1.5	0.5
Fri.	3	1	1.5

To make a table, you simply list the items compared in columns and the characteristics compared in rows. Make a table and record the data comparing the masses of recycled materials collected by a class. On Monday, students turned in 4 kg of paper, 2 kg of aluminum, and 0.5 kg of plastic. On Wednesday, they turned in 3.5 kg of paper, 1.5 kg of aluminum, and 0.5 kg of plastic. On Friday, the totals were 3 kg of paper, 1 kg of aluminum, and 1.5 kg of plastic. If your table looks like the one shown, you should be able to make tables to organize data.

Making and Using Graphs

After scientists organize data in tables, they often display the data in graphs. A graph is a diagram that shows a comparison between variables. Because graphs show a picture of collected data, they make interpretation and analysis of the data easier. The three basic types of graphs used in science are the line graph, bar graph, and pie graph.

A line graph is used to show the relationship between two variables. The variables being compared go on the two axes of the graph. The independent variable always goes on the horizontal axis, called the *x*-axis. The dependent variable always goes on the vertical axis, or *y*-axis.

Suppose a school started a peer study program with a class of students to see how it affected their science grades.

AVERAGE GRADES OF STUDENTS IN STUDY PROGRAM	
Grading Period	**Average Science Grade**
First	81
Second	85
Third	86
Fourth	89

You could make a graph of the grades of students in the program over a period of time. The grading period is the independent variable and should be placed on the *x*-axis of your graph. The average grade of a student in the program is the dependent variable and would go on the *y*-axis.

After drawing your axes, you would label each axis with a scale. The *x*-axis simply lists the grading periods. To make a scale of grades on the *y*-axis, you must look at the data values. Because the lowest grade was 81 and the highest was 89, you know that you will have to start numbering at least at 81 and go through 89. You decide to start numbering at 80 and number by twos through 90.

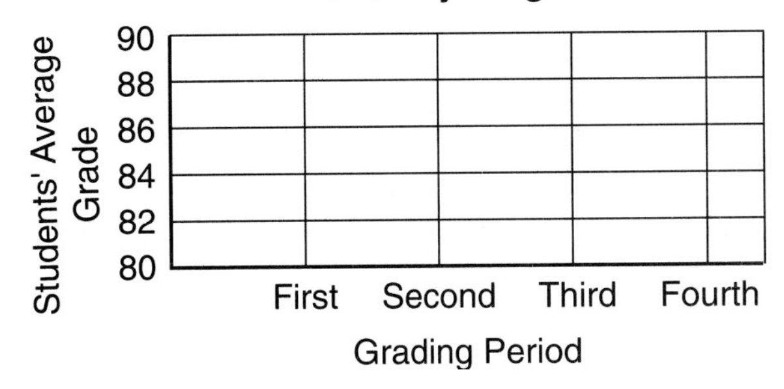

Next you must plot the data points. The first pair of data you want to plot is the first grading period and 81. Locate "First" on the *x*-axis and 81 on the *y*-axis. Where an imaginary vertical line from the *x*-axis and an imaginary horizontal line from the *y*-axis would meet, place the first data point. Place the other data points the same way. After all the points are plotted, connect them with a smooth line.

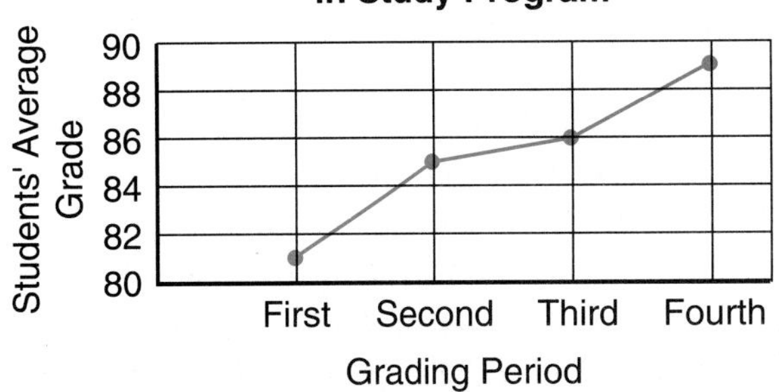

What if you wanted to compare the average grades of the class in the study group with the grades of another science class? The data of the other class can be plotted on the same graph to make the comparison. You must include a key with two different lines, each indicating a different set of data. Also change the title of the new graph to represent the data you are comparing.

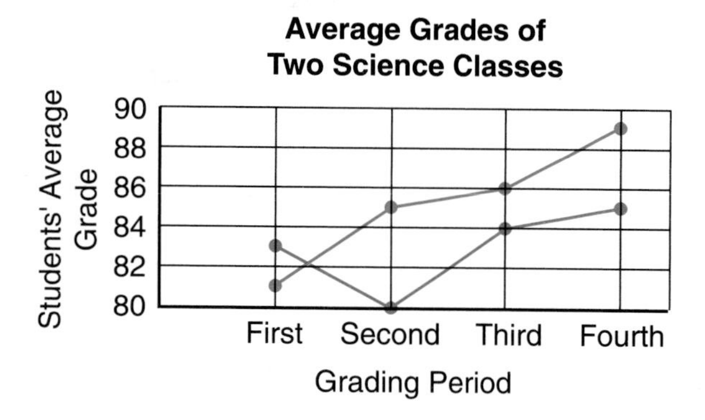

KEY Class or study students ———

Regular class ———

Bar graphs are similar to line graphs, except they are used to compare or display data that do not continuously change. In a bar graph, thick bars show the relationships among data rather than data points.

To make a bar graph, set up the *x*-axis and *y*-axis as you did for the line graph. The data is plotted by drawing thick bars from the *x*-axis up to an imaginary point where the *y*-axis would intersect the bar if it was extended.

Look at the bar graph comparing the masses lifted by an electromagnet with different numbers of dry cell batteries. The independent variable is the number of dry cell batteries, and the dependent variable is the mass lifted. The lifting power of the electromagnet as it changed with different numbers of dry cell batteries is being compared.

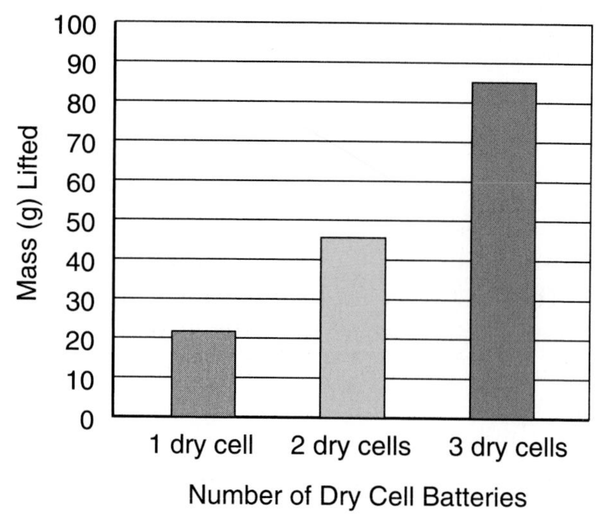

A pie graph uses a circle divided into sections to display data. Each section represents part of the whole. When all the sections are placed together, they equal 100 percent of the whole.

Suppose you wanted to make a pie graph of the periodic table to show how many elements have nonmetallic properties, how many are metalloids, and how many have metallic properties. You would have to determine the total number of elements and the number of elements of each type. Because there are 109 elements, the whole pie will represent this amount.

You count the number of elements of each type and find out there are 17 elements with nonmetallic properties, 8 metalloids, and 84 elements with metallic properties.

To find out how much of the pie each section should take, you must divide the number of elements in each group by the total number of elements. You then multiply your answer by 360, the number of degrees in a circle. Round your answer to the nearest whole number. The percentage of elements with nonmetallic properties would be determined as follows:

$$\frac{17}{109} \times 360 = 56.1, \text{ or about 56 degrees}$$

Use the formula to compute how much of the circle metalloids and elements with metallic properties would fill. Metalloids would take up 26 degrees, and metallic elements would take up 278 degrees.

To plot the groups on the pie graph, you need a compass and protractor. Use the compass to draw a circle. Then draw a straight line from the center to the edge of the circle. Place your protractor on this line and use it to mark a point on the edge of the circle at 56 degrees. Connect this point to the center of the circle with a straight line. This is the part of the circle representing elements with nonmetallic properties. Place your protractor on the line you just made and use it to mark a point on the edge of the circle at 26 degrees. Again draw a straight line from this point to the center of the circle. This part represents the metalloids. The remaining part of the circle represents the percentage of metallic elements. Complete the graph by labeling the sections of your graph and giving the graph a title.

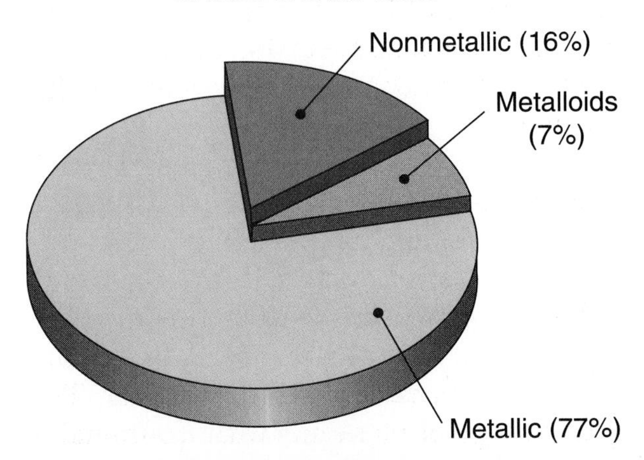

Interpreting Scientific Illustrations

Your science textbook contains many scientific illustrations to help you understand, interpret, and remember what you read. When you are reading the text and encounter an illustration, examine it carefully and relate it to the text you have just read. Also read the caption for the illustration. The caption is a brief comment that explains or identifies the illustration.

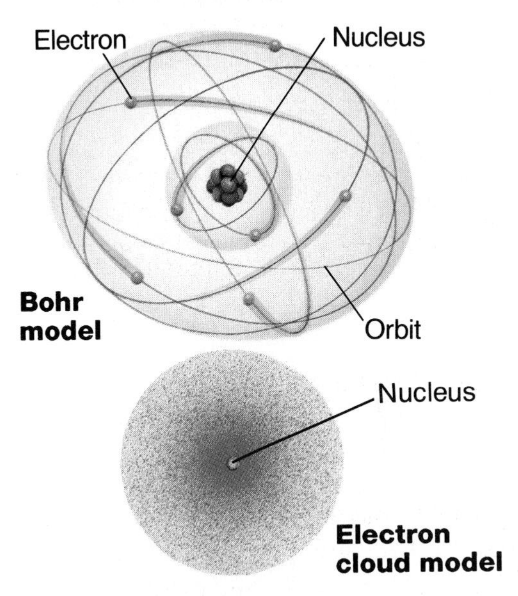

Figure 10-2. The top illustration is an early model of an atom with defined paths for electrons. The lower illustration is a later model showing a region where electrons are likely to be.

Some illustrations are designed to show you how the internal parts of a structure are arranged. Look at the illustrations of atoms. The illustrations are models that with the text will help you understand an atom's internal parts. Notice that a caption briefly describes each illustration. Also, note that the illustrations include labels to help you understand the locations of the internal parts of an atom.

Other illustrations will help you understand how something works. The illustration of the circulation of air in a room of a house shows how a furnace works and how hot and cool air circulate within the room. The arrows indicate the flow of air within the heating system and the room to help you understand the text.

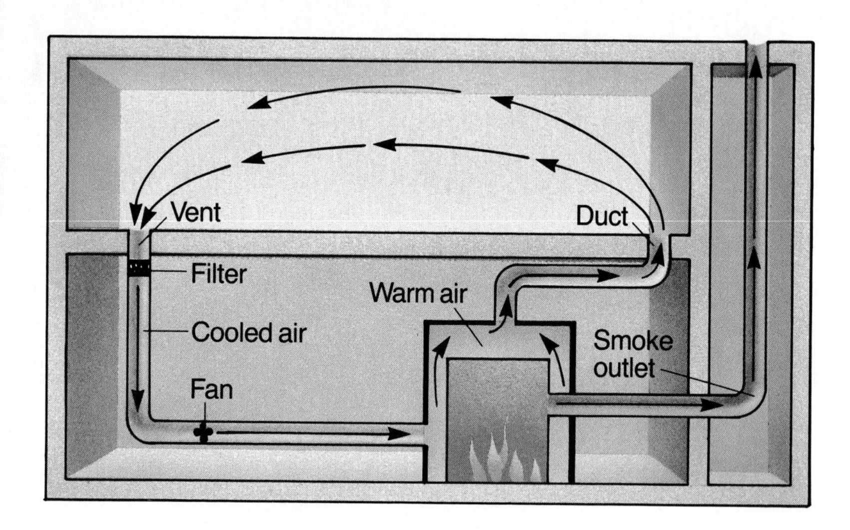

Figure 6-9. In a forced-air heating system, air heated by the furnace is used to heat the rooms of the house.

The illustrations of the house and heating system show what is called a cross section. A cross section is a section that is formed by cutting through an object. The illustration of the cross section is formed by cutting at right angles to the horizontal axis of the house and heating system.

Scientific illustrations similar to that of the heating system of a house are two-dimensional. A two-dimensional illustration has height and width. However, many of the illustrations in this text, such as the model of atoms, are three-dimensional. Three-dimensional illustrations have not only height and width but also depth. An illustration in three dimensions is similar to the way you see the world, so it is even more useful in helping you understand the science ideas you are reading about.

GLOSSARY

This glossary defines each key term that appears in **bold type** in the text. It also shows the page number where you can find the word used. Some other terms that you may need to look up are included, too. We also show how to pronounce some of the words. A key to pronunciation is in the table below.

PRONUNCIATION KEY

a . . . b**a**ck (bak)	oh . . . g**o** (goh)	sh . . . **sh**elf (shelf)
ay . . . d**ay** (day)	aw . . . s**o**ft (sawft)	ch . . . na**t**ure (nay chur)
ah . . . f**a**ther (fahth ur)	or . . . **or**bit (or but)	g . . . **g**ift (gihft)
ow . . . fl**ow**er (flow ur)	oy . . . c**oi**n (coyn)	j . . . **g**em (jem)
ar . . . c**ar** (car)	oo . . . f**oo**t (foot)	ing . . . s**ing** (sing)
e . . . l**e**ss (les)	ew . . . f**oo**d (fewd)	zh . . . vi**s**ion (vihzh un)
ee . . . l**ea**f (leef)	yoo . . . p**u**re (pyoor)	k . . . ca**k**e (kayk)
ih . . . tr**i**p (trihp)	yew . . . f**ew** (fyew)	s . . . **s**eed, **c**ent (seed, sent)
i (i + con + e) . . . **i**dea (i dee uh), l**i**fe (life)	uh . . . comm**a** (cahm uh)	z . . . **z**one, rai**s**e (zohn, rayz)
	u (+ con) . . . flow**er** (flow ur)	

acceleration: the rate of change in velocity (speed and/or direction). (66)

acid: a substance that produces hydrogen ions (H^+) when dissolved in water; this lowers the solution's pH below 7. (426)

acid rain: rain that is more acidic than normal because it contains dilute sulfuric acid (from coal-burning power plants) and dilute nitric acid (from car exhausts). (438)

acoustics: the study of sound. (478)

actinoid: any of the 14 radioactive elements having atomic numbers 89-102; used in nuclear power generation and nuclear weapons.

active solar heating: collecting the sun's energy with solar panels, heating water with that energy, and storing the heated water to use the energy later.

aerosol: a liquid sprayed from a pressurized container; for example, a can of insect spray.

air resistance: the frictional force air exerts on a moving object, opposite in direction to the object's motion. (88)

alchemist: a medieval version of the modern chemist; a practitioner blended primitive chemistry with magic, seeking to turn ordinary metals into gold.

alcohol: a substituted hydrocarbon in which one or more hydrogen atoms have been replaced by an –OH group; for example, ethanol. (335)

allotropes: different molecular structures of the same element; for example, some carbon molecules form soft graphite whereas others form hard diamonds. (317)

alloy: a solid solution of a metal with other metals or nonmetals; for example, brass or steel. (352)

alpha particle: a low-energy particle given off by a radioactive atomic nucleus; it is a helium nucleus (two protons and two neutrons with a positive charge). (624)

alternating current (AC): electrical current that reverses its direction many times each second; the AC in our homes reverses direction 60 times each second. (585)

amalgam: an alloy containing the element mercury; for example, dental fillings are amalgams. (355)

ammeter: a galvanometer that measures the electrical current flowing in a circuit, in amperes. (580)

amorphous: something that has no specific shape; for example, a liquid or gas.

ampere: the unit for measuring the rate of flow of electrons in a circuit; abbreviated *A*; 1 ampere = 1 coulomb of charge flowing past a point in 1 second.

amplification: the process of increasing the strength of an electric current. (600)

amplitude: in a wave, the distance from the resting position to either the crest or trough (they are the same distance). (459)

amplitude-modulated (AM) waves: radio waves whose amplitude is varied with voice, music, video, or data for transmission over long distances.

angle of incidence: in waves, the angle formed by the incident wave and the normal (perpendicular); labeled *i*.

angle of reflection: in waves, the angle formed by the reflected wave and the normal (perpendicular); labeled *r*.

anhydrous: a chemical compound that normally has water molecules attached to its ions, but from which the water has been removed.

antacid: an "anti-acid," or a chemical that changes an acid substance to a neutral substance.

antifreeze: a solute added to a solvent to lower the temperature at which the solvent will freeze; for example, the antifreeze added to water in a car's cooling system.

aqueous: describes a solution made with water; for example, ammonia water is an aqueous solution of ammonia gas.

Archimedes' principle: the Greek mathematician Archimedes stated that the buoyant force that pushes up on an object in a fluid is equal to the weight of the fluid displaced by the object. (210)

aromatic compounds: chemical compounds that contain the benzene ring structure; most have distinctive aromas. (334)

astigmatism: an uneven curvature of the eye's cornea, causing blurry vision.

atomic number: the number of protons in an atom's nucleus; each element has a unique number (hydrogen = 1, helium = 2, and so on). (243)

average atomic mass: the average mass of all isotopes of an element; used as a convenience, because most elements have more than one isotope and therefore more than one mass number. (253)

average speed: a rate of motion determined by dividing the distance traveled by travel time. (61)

B

balance: a device used in laboratories to measure mass; it works by balancing an "unknown" (material whose mass is to be determined) with a standard mass that is known.

balanced chemical equation: a chemical equation that has the same number of atoms of each element on both sides of the equation. (410)

balanced forces: forces that are equal in size and opposite in direction. (70)

bar graph: a type of graph used to show information collected by counting; uses vertical or horizontal bars of different lengths to help people compare quantities.

base: a substance that produces hydroxide ions (OH^-) when dissolved in water; this raises the solution's pH above 7. (430)

Bernoulli's principle: the Swiss mathematician Daniel Bernoulli stated that, as the velocity of a fluid increases, the pressure exerted by the fluid decreases. (212)

beta particle: a high-energy particle given off by a radioactive atomic nucleus; it is a negatively charged electron. (625)

BHA: a food preservative; it is a chemical inhibitor that slows the chemical reactions that spoil food (*Butylated Hydroxyanisole*).

BHT: a food preservative; it is a chemical inhibitor that slows the chemical reactions that spoil food (*Butylated Hydroxytoluene*).

binary compound: a chemical compound composed of two elements; for example, sodium chloride. (283)

biodegradable: describes a material that can be decomposed into a harmless form by the biological action of organisms such as bacteria.

biogas: gas (mostly methane) produced by plant and animal wastes that rot in the absence of air. (338)

biomass: all plant and animal material, both dead and alive; sometimes used as fuel. (338)

boiling point: the temperature at which vapor bubbles form in a liquid and rise to the surface, increasing evaporation.

Boyle's law: English physicist Robert Boyle stated that, if a container of gas is made smaller, the pressure throughout the gas increases (if the temperature stays the same). (205)

breeder reactor: a type of nuclear reactor that breeds new fuel as it operates. (654)

brittleness: a characteristic of certain materials that makes them break easily when stressed.

bubble chamber: a chamber filled with a superheated liquid; used to detect charged nuclear particles, which leave a trail of bubbles as they pass through. (631)

buoyant force: the upward force exerted on an object when it is completely immersed in a fluid. (209)

butane: a flammable gas (C_4H_{10}); a part of natural gas.

byte: a basic unit of computer memory that represents a character (number, symbol, or alphabet letter); consists of 8 bits.

C

calorimeter: an instrument used to measure changes in thermal energy.

carbohydrate: an organic compound characteristically having twice as many hydrogen atoms as oxygen atoms; for example, glucose = $C_6H_{12}O_6$. (343)

carbon-14 dating: age-determining method for carbon-containing objects up to 50 000 years old; works by calculating the half-life of the radioactive carbon-14 remaining in the object.

catalyst: a substance that speeds a chemical reaction without itself being changed. (418)

cathode-ray tube (CRT): a picture tube with an internal electron gun that fires a stream of electrons (cathode rays) at a fluorescent screen to produce pictures. (605)

central processing unit (CPU): the main circuit board inside a computer that performs the calculating and holds the main memory.

centripetal (sen TRIHP uh tuhl) **acceleration:** acceleration (change in speed and/or direction) toward the center of a curve. (92)

centripetal force: the force that causes an object to move toward the center of a curve. (92)

ceramic: a material made from clay or sand, usually baked at a high temperature. (357)

cermet: a synthetic material made to have the properties of both a ceramic and an alloy; for example, some magnets use cermet material (*cer*amic + *met*al). (358)

chain reaction: a continuing series of fission reactions in which neutrons from fissioning nuclei cause other nuclei to split, releasing more neutrons which split more nuclei, and so on. (634)

Charles's law: French scientist Jacques-Alexandre Charles stated that the volume of a gas increases when temperature increases (if the pressure stays the same). (205)

chemical bond: the force that holds together the atoms in a compound. (271)

chemical change: the change of one substance to another substance by changing the elements in it, or by changing their proportions. (232)

chemical formula: a precise statement of the elements in a compound and their ratio; for example, H_2O, CO_2, or $C_{12}H_{22}O_{11}$. (269)

chemically stable: describes an atom whose outermost energy level is filled with electrons, so that it does not form compounds under normal conditions; for example: helium, neon. (270)

chemically unstable: describes an atom whose outermost energy level is not filled with electrons, so it seeks electrons from other atoms and thus forms compounds; for example: sodium, chlorine.

chemical property: a characteristic of a substance that indicates whether it can undergo a certain chemical change. (233)

chemical reaction: a change in which substances are converted to different substances that have different properties. (404)

chemical symbol: a shorthand way to write the name of an element; for example: *O* for oxygen, *Fe* for iron. (242)

chloro- prefix meaning chlorine, as in tetrachloroethylene or chlorofluorocarbon.

chlorofluorocarbon (CFC): a group of chemicals compounded of chlorine, fluorine, and carbon; used as refrigerants and spray propellants; damaging to the atmosphere's ozone layer. (409)

circuit: a closed path through which electrons (electricity) can flow. (552)

circuit breaker: a device that protects an electrical circuit. If too much current flows, the circuit breaker switches off the current flow.

cloud chamber: a chamber filled with water-saturated air; used to detect charged nuclear particles, which leave a vapor trail as they pass through. (630)

coal: a rock formed of ancient decayed plants; burned as a fossil fuel.

coefficient: in a chemical equation, a number to the left of each reactant and product that shows the relative amount of each substance involved in the reaction; for example, the *3* in $3H_2O$. (406)

coherent light: a beam of light in which all rays travel parallel to one another, so that the beam spreads out very little even over thousands of kilometers. (530)

colloid: a heterogeneous mixture containing tiny particles that do not settle; for example, milk and gelatin. (223)

combustion: rapid oxidation, or burning. (148)

commutator: a reversing switch in a direct-current electric motor that changes the polarity of the current with each half-revolution. (581)

composite: a material made by mixing other materials to combine the desirable properties of each. (367)

compound: matter that is a combination of atoms of two or more elements. (220)

compound machine: a combination of two or more simple machines. (174)

compression: in compressional waves, the dense area of the wave.

compressional wave: a wave that vibrates in the same direction in which the wave is traveling. (464)

computer: a device you can program to do calculations, make logical decisions, and manipulate data.

computer virus: a computer program designed to infect a computer and make it "sick"; it can erase data, scramble other programs, or fill up memory so the system won't work right. (612)

concave lens: a lens that is thinner in the middle and thicker at the edges and thus curves inward. (519)

concave mirror: a mirror whose surface curves inward, producing a reflected image that is enlarged. (513)

concentrated solution: a solution in which the amount of solute is near the maximum that the solvent can hold.

concentration: generally, the proportion of a solute dissolved in a solvent; specifically, the milliliters of solute, plus enough solvent to total 100 mL of solution.

condensation: the change of a substance from a gaseous state to a liquid state; for example, water vapor condensing on a cold surface. (201)

condense: to go from the gas state to the liquid state, due to a loss of heat.

conduction: the transfer of energy through matter by direct contact of particles; the movement of heat or electricity through a substance. (134)

conductor: a material that allows heat or electrons to move easily through it. (547)

constant: in an experiment, a factor that cannot change. (21)

constant speed: a rate of motion that does not vary, such as Earth's speed in orbit. (61)

contract: movement of molecules toward one another, so that they occupy a smaller space.

control: in an experiment, the standard for comparison. (20)

convection: the transfer of energy through matter by movement of the matter itself, as in air or water currents. (135)

convex lens: a lens that is thicker in the middle than at the edges and thus curves outward. (518)

convex mirror: a mirror with a surface that curves outward. (515)

cooling tower: a tower-shaped device in which water is cooled by fans or evaporation; used in factories and power plants. (147)

corrosive: describes any substance that attacks and alters metals, human tissue, or other materials; for example, battery acid, bleach, and cleaners for ovens, toilets, and drains. (274)

coulomb: the charge carried by 6.24 billion billion electrons.

covalent bond: A type of chemical bond formed by atoms when they share electrons; this force holds together molecules in gases like oxygen (O_2) and nitrogen (N_2), and in compounds like water (H_2O). (278)

crest: in waves, the highest point of a wave. (459)

critical temperature: in superconductors, the very low temperature at which a material ceases to have any electrical resistance.

critical thinking: the process of using thinking skills to solve problems. (14)

crystal: a solid having a distinctive shape because its atoms are arranged in repeating geometric patterns. (191)

current: the flow of electrons through a conductor, measured in amperes with an ammeter. (553)

D

deceleration: the rate of change in velocity (speed and/or direction) when velocity is decreasing; also called negative acceleration.

decibel: the unit of measure for sound intensity, abbreviated *dB*. The faintest sound most people can hear = 0 dB.

decomposition reaction: a chemical reaction in which a substance breaks down (decomposes) into two or more simpler substances. (414)

dehydrating agent: a substance that removes water from materials; for example, sulfuric acid. (428)

density: how tightly packed a substance's molecules are; expressed as the mass of a substance divided by its volume, in g/cm^3. (39)

dependent variable: in an experiment, the factor that is forced to change because the independent variable is changed. (21)

derived unit: a unit of measurement formed by combining other units of measurement; for example, density is a derived unit formed by dividing an object's mass by its volume. (38)

desalination: removing dissolved salts from seawater to produce fresh, drinkable water. (386)

desalination plant: facility for removing dissolved salts from seawater to produce fresh, drinkable water.

detergent: an organic salt similar to soap, except that detergents do not form "soap scum" in hard water. (444)

diatomic molecule: a molecule made up of two atoms of the same element; for example, hydrogen (H_2) or oxygen (O_2). (311)

diesel engine: an internal combustion engine that compresses a fuel-air mixture so much that it ignites from the heat of compression, without a spark.

diffraction: the bending of waves around a barrier. (503)

diffraction grating: a piece of glass or plastic with many parallel slits that acts like a prism, causing white light that passes through it to separate into its component colors (the spectrum). (505)

dilute solution: a solution in which the amount of solute is much less than the maximum the solvent can hold.

diode: a type of rectifier that allows electric current to flow only in one direction. (599)

direct current (DC): electrical current that flows in only one direction; thus direct current cells (batteries) are labeled + and – so you can install them the right way. (585)

disinfectant: a chemical that kills bacteria, such as alcohol.

dissociation: the breaking apart of an ionic compound (like salt) into positive and negative ions when dissolved in water. (396)

distillation: a water-purifying process in which water is evaporated from a solution, and the vapor is cooled to condense it to a pure liquid. (387)

DNA: *d*eoxyribo*n*ucleic *a*cid, an acid in the nuclei of cells that codes and stores genetic information.

doping: adding an impurity to a semiconductor to increase its electrical conductivity.

Doppler effect: an increase or decrease in wave frequency, caused by motion of the source and/or motion of the observer; applies to all waves (including light, heat, sound, and so on).

dot diagram: a diagram of an atom, using the element symbol with dots to show the electrons in the outer energy level. (257)

double displacement reaction: a chemical reaction in which the positive ions in two or more substances trade places. (415)

dry cell: a power source that generates electric current by a chemical reaction; "dry" because it uses a thick, pasty electrolyte in a sealed container instead of a liquid electrolyte as in a car battery. (554)

ductile: describes metals that can be pulled into thin strands (wire). (300)

E

efficiency: the amount of work put into a machine compared to how much useful work is put out by the machine; always between 0 percent and 100 percent. (175)

effort arm: the part of a lever to which the effort force (F_e) is applied. (163)

effort force (F_e): the force applied to a machine. (159)

electrical power: the rate at which electrical energy is converted to another form of energy, such as heat; measured in kilowatt-hours. (565)

electric field: a force surrounding an electron that affects anything nearby that has an electric charge; is strongest near the electron and weakens with distance. (547)

electric motor: a device that changes electric energy into mechanical energy; for example, the motor in an electric fan.

electrolyte: a substance that forms ions in a water solution, making the water an electrical conductor; for example, sodium chloride and hydrogen chloride. (396)

electromagnet: a temporary magnet formed when an electric current is passed through a wire coil that surrounds an iron core. (578)

electromagnetic induction: electrical current induced in a wire when it is moved through a magnetic field. (583)

electromagnetic radiation: transverse energy waves that radiate in all directions from their source; vary in length from very long radio waves to extremely short X rays and gamma rays.

electromagnetic spectrum: the classification of electromagnetic waves, either by wavelength or frequency. (484)

electron: a negatively charged particle that orbits around the nucleus of an atom. (243)

electron arrangement: in an atom, how the electrons are distributed in the atom's various energy levels.

electron cloud: actually not a cloud, but the space where electrons most probably exist around the nucleus of an atom. (244)

electroscope: a device used to detect the presence of electric charges. (549)

element: matter in which all the atoms are alike; for example, zinc, chlorine, and aluminum. (220)

endothermic reaction: a chemical reaction that requires the addition of heat energy to proceed; thus the reaction absorbs heat from its surroundings. (417)

energy: the ability to cause change. (110)

energy farming: the growing of plants for use as fuel. (338)

energy transfer: the movement of energy from one object to another; for example, thermal energy flowing as heat from a stove to a skillet.

ester: a chemical compound formed by reacting an organic acid with an alcohol; some provide the scents in flowers, fruits, and candy. (444)

evaporation: the change of a substance from a liquid state to a gaseous state. (200)

exothermic reaction: a chemical reaction that releases heat energy. (418)

expand: outward movement of molecules away from one another, so that they occupy a larger space.

experiment: a controlled procedure for testing a hypothesis. (20)

external combustion engine: an engine in which the fuel is burned outside the engine, and energy from it is used to operate the engine; for example, an old-fashioned steam engine. (150)

factor: a condition that affects the outcome of an event.

farsighted: describes a person who sees faraway things clearly, but has trouble focusing on nearby objects.

fiberglass: hairlike strands of glass that make a good insulator when arranged in puffy layers.

filter: in working with light, a device that allows one or more colors to be transmitted while others are absorbed.

flame test: a laboratory test to identify elements by heating a substance in a flame and observing the flame color.

flammable: a chemical characteristic of a substance that allows it to oxidize rapidly; also called burnable.

flash distillation: a desalination process where seawater is pumped into a vacuum chamber so it boils quickly and at a lower temperature (because the normal air pressure is absent).

fluid: any material that can flow, such as air, water, or molten metal. (135)

fluorescence: occurs when a material absorbs ultraviolet radiation, which stimulates it to radiate visible light.

fluorescent light: light produced by phosphors when they are stimulated by ultraviolet light, as in a fluorescent light bulb. (498)

focal length: the distance from the center of a lens or mirror to its focal point. (513)

focal point: a point on the optical axis of a concave mirror or convex lens where the light rays come together. (513)

force: a push or a pull exerted by one body on another. (70)

fractional distillation: a process used in oil refineries to separate petroleum into gasoline, kerosene, and other products. (645)

fractionating towers: towers at oil refineries used for fractional distillation of petroleum.

free-fall: how an object moves in space when it is influenced only by gravity.

freeze distillation: a desalination process in which seawater is frozen to form salt-free ice.

freon: a refrigerant gas used in refrigerators and air conditioners.

frequency: the number of waves that pass a point during one second, expressed as hertz; for example, 60 waves per second = 60 hertz. (459)

frequency-modulated (FM) waves: radio waves whose frequency is varied with voice, music, video, or data for transmission over long distances.

friction: the force that resists motion between two surfaces that are touching each other. (73)

fuel rod: a metal rod filled with uranium pellets, used as the fuel in a nuclear reactor.

fulcrum (FUL krum): the fixed point around which a lever pivots. (163)

fuse: a device that protects an electrical circuit. If too much current flows, the fuse melts, breaking the circuit to stop current flow.

G

galvanometer: an instrument (meter) used to detect electric currents; most electrical meters are galvanometers.

gamma rays: electromagnetic waves given off by a radioactive atomic nucleus; they have very short wavelength (high frequency), high energy, and are very penetrating. (490, 626)

gaseous solution: a homogeneous gas that is composed of two or more gases.

gasohol: a biomass fuel that is about 90 percent gasoline and 10 percent alcohol (ethanol); used in cars and trucks. (339)

gear: a wheel with teeth around its edge, designed to mesh with teeth on another gear, so as to transfer force and motion.

gelatin: a substance obtained by boiling animal bones; used in glues and foods.

generator: a device that uses electromagnetic induction to induce electrical current by rotating loops of wire through a magnetic field. (583)

geothermal energy: thermal energy from the magma underneath volcanoes. (660)

glass: a solid ceramic mixture lacking a crystal structure. (358)

graduated cylinder: a cylinder marked with a volume scale, used in laboratories for measuring liquid volumes.

granite: an igneous rock that is a mixture of crystals of several different compounds.

graph: a visual display of information or data, organized to help people interpret, understand, or quickly find information. (42)

graphite: a mineral made of carbon atoms arranged in layers that easily slide past one another, forming a dry lubricant.

gravity: the attracting force exerted by every object on every other object. The amount of force depends on the masses of the objects and their distance apart. (75)

greenhouse effect: the process by which heat radiated from Earth's surface is trapped and reflected back to Earth by carbon dioxide in the atmosphere. (18)

grounded: electrically connected to Earth (the ground), either directly or through a wire or other metal object.

groundwater: water in the ground that comes from rain and melting snow. Although often pure enough to drink, it is easily polluted by dumps, sewers, and chemical spills.

group: one of the 18 vertical columns in the periodic table. All elements in a group have similar properties. (257)

H

hacker: a person who uses a computer to break into other computer systems without permission.

half-life: the time required for half of the atoms in a radioactive substance to decay. (627)

halogens: highly active elements in periodic table Group 17 (fluorine, chlorine, bromine, iodine, astatine); halogens have seven electrons in their outer shells and readily combine with Group 1 elements such as sodium.

heat: the type of energy that moves from anything having a higher temperature to anything having a lower temperature. (121)

heat engine: a device that converts thermal energy into mechanical energy; for example, an automobile engine. (148)

heat mover: a device that removes thermal energy from one location and transfers it to another location having a different temperature; for example, a refrigerator, air conditioner, or heat pump. (151)

heat of fusion: the amount of energy needed to change a material from the solid state to the liquid state. (201)

heat of vaporization: the amount of energy needed to change a material from the liquid state to the gaseous (vapor) state. (202)

heat pump: a two-way heat mover that pumps heat out of a building in warm weather and into a building in cold weather. (151)
herbicide: a chemical poison that kills undesirable plants.
hertz: the unit of measure for frequency, abbreviated Hz; for example, 440 waves per second = 440 Hz.
heterogeneous mixture: a mixture in which different materials are distributed unevenly, so at any place in the mixture different combinations of materials occur. (222)
high-speed photography: a photographic method that takes clear (not blurred) pictures of fast-moving objects.
homogeneous mixture: a mixture in which different materials are blended evenly, so that the mixture is the same throughout; also called a solution. (222)
horizontal: a direction parallel to Earth's surface.
hydrate: a compound that has water molecules chemically attached to its ions. (287)
hydraulic: describes a system operated by applying pressure to a liquid.
hydrocarbon: a chemical compound containing only carbon and hydrogen atoms; for example, methane gas (CH_4). (329)
hydroelectricity: electricity produced by the energy of moving water. (658)
hydronium ion: the ion (H_3O^+) that makes a solution acidic; formed by the bonding of a hydrogen ion (H^+) to a water molecule (H_2O). (432)
hypothesis: a proposed solution to a problem or explanation of how something works; a hypothesis can be tested to see if it is correct. (16)

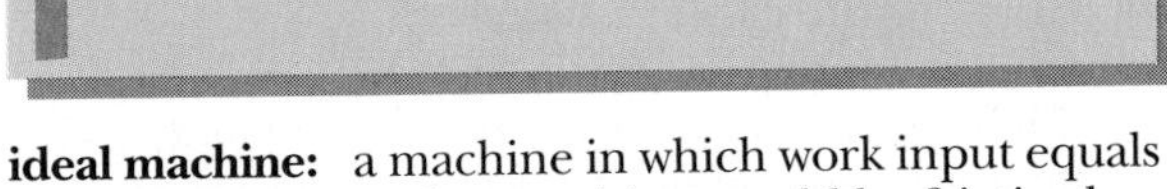

ideal machine: a machine in which work input equals work output; such a machine would be frictionless and 100 percent efficient. (160)
incandescent light: light produced by heat, as from a hot filament in an incandescent light bulb. (498)
inclined plane: a simple machine consisting of a sloping surface (ramp) used to raise objects; it changes the amount of force. (169)
incoherent light: light rays that are nearly parallel, but spread out. (530)
independent variable: in an experiment, the factor changed to see what effect it will have on the dependent variable. (21)
indicator: an organic compound that changes color when in an acid solution or a basic solution; for example, phenolphthalein. (426)
induction: electrically charging an object or creating an electrical current in it, without physically touching it.
inertia (ihn UR shuh): the tendency of an object to resist any change in motion; if motionless, it remains still; if moving, it keeps moving. (71)
infrared radiation: electromagnetic waves that have a wavelength slightly longer (lower frequency) than visible light; commonly known as heat; abbreviated *IR*. (487)
infrasonic waves: waves at frequencies below the limit of human hearing (below 20 Hz).
inhibitor: a substance that slows a chemical reaction. (418)
instantaneous speed: the rate of motion at any given instant, such as that given on a speedometer. (60)
insulator: a material through which heat or electricity cannot move easily. (137, 548)
integrated circuit: a thin slice of silicon, often less than 1 cm on a side, which may contain thousands of resistors, diodes, and transistors, and can perform several electronic functions at once; used in computers and electronic equipment; also called a chip. (601)
intensity: in sound waves, the amount of energy in each wave. (468)
interference: the mixing of two or more waves, which combine to form a new wave. (476)
internal combustion engine: an engine in which fuel is burned inside chambers (cylinders); for example, an automobile engine. (148)
ion: an atom having an electrical charge, either positive or negative; for example, Na^+, Cl^-. (277)
ionic bond: A type of chemical bond that holds together compounds of oppositely charged ions; for example, ionic bonding holds together Na^+ and Cl^- to make salt, NaCl. (277)
ionization: the breaking apart of a molecular polar substance (such as hydrogen chloride) to form ions when dissolved in water. (396)
isomers: compounds that have identical chemical formulas but different molecular structures and shapes. (333)
isometric exercise: exercise in which muscles push against other muscles, instead of pushing or pulling against gravity. (97)
isotopes: atoms of the same element that have different numbers of neutrons; for example, uranium-235 and uranium-238. (251)

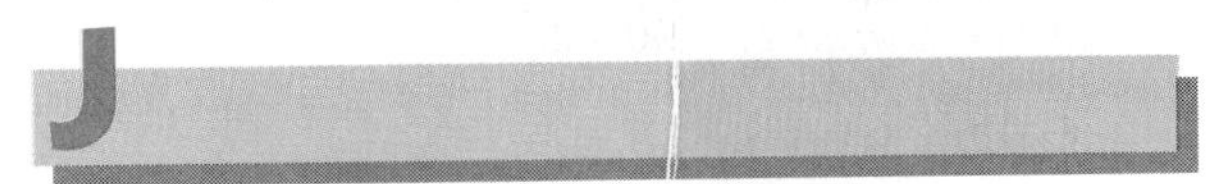

joule (JEWL): the basic unit of energy and work, named for English scientist James Prescott Joule; 1 joule (J) = a force of 1 newton moving through 1 meter.

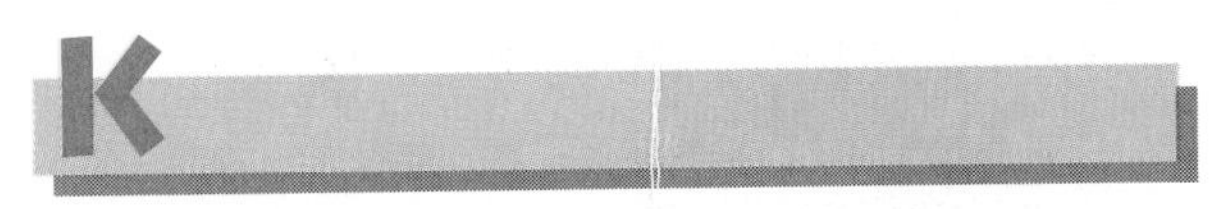

kelvin: the SI unit of temperature; 0 K = absolute zero (the coldest possible temperature) = –273°C. (41)

kilogram: the SI unit of mass; 1000 grams. (39)
kilowatt-hour: the unit of electrical power; 1 kilowatt-hour = 1000 watts of power used for 1 hour. (567)
kinetic energy: energy that causes change in the form of motion, as in a rolling ball. (111)
kinetic theory of matter: the theory that all matter is made up of tiny particles that are in constant motion. (191)

lanthanoid: any of the 14 metallic elements having atomic numbers 57-70; used in magnets, ceramics, and television picture tubes.
laser: a device that generates a beam of coherent light. (530)
law of conservation of energy: a law stating that energy can change form (for example, from potential to kinetic), but it cannot be created or destroyed under ordinary conditions. (115)
law of conservation of mass: a law stating that the mass of all substances involved in a chemical change will be the same after the change; matter is neither created nor destroyed during a chemical change. (234)
law of conservation of momentum: a law stating that the total momentum of a group of objects does not change unless outside forces act on the objects. (102)
lever: a simple machine consisting of a bar that is free to pivot (rotate) around a fixed point (fulcrum); it changes the direction or amount of force. (163)
lightning rod: a metal rod mounted atop a structure and connected to Earth (grounded) to leak off electric charges between the clouds and Earth before they grow strong enough to cause lightning. (551)
line graph: a type of graph used to show trends or continuous change by drawing a line that connects data points.
lipid: an organic compound containing more hydrogen atoms and fewer oxygen atoms than carbohydrates; for example, fats and oils. (344)
liquid solution: a liquid solvent that has dissolved in it a gas, liquid, or solid.
liter: the unit of liquid volume (L). (38)
loudness: the human perception of sound intensity. (468)
lubricant: a substance used to reduce the friction between two surfaces that move together; for example, oil, grease, or graphite.

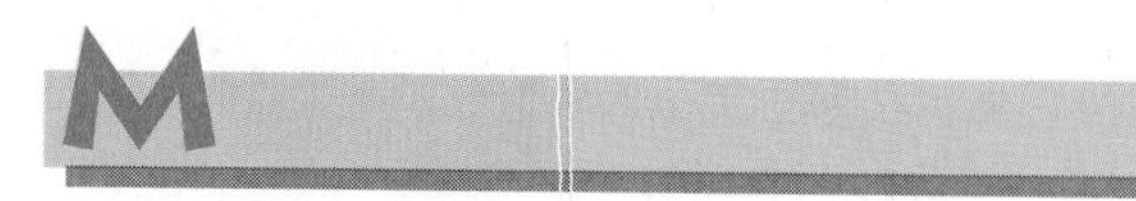

machine: a device that makes work easier by changing the speed, direction, or amount of a force. (158)
magma (MAG muh): hot melted rock originating beneath Earth's surface; it is a potential source of energy for heating and generating electricity. (122)
magnetic: a physical property of matter that causes it to be attracted to a magnet.
magnetic bottle: a powerful magnetic field that creates a container ("bottle") to hold the hydrogen plasma needed for a nuclear fusion reaction.
magnetic domain: a group of aligned atoms in a magnetic material such as iron, caused by the magnetic field around each atom exerting a force on nearby atoms. (576)
magnetic field: the area of magnetic force around a magnet. (575)
magnetic poles: the two ends of a piece of magnetic material where the magnetic forces are strongest, labeled north pole (N) and south pole (S). (574)
magnetism: a property of matter that creates forces of attraction and repulsion between certain substances. (574)
magnifier: a device that makes things appear larger so that more detail can be seen; for example, a magnifying glass or microscope.
malleable: describes metals that can be hammered or rolled into thin sheets, like foil. (300)
mass: the amount of matter in an object; its SI unit is the kilogram (kg). (39)
mass number: total particles in an atom's nucleus; mass number = protons + neutrons; also called atomic mass. (251)
mechanical advantage (MA): the number of times a machine multiplies the effort force (the force applied to it). (160)
mechanical energy: the total kinetic energy and potential energy in a system. (115)
medium: a material (solid, liquid, or gas) through which a mechanical wave can transfer energy. (458)
melt: the changing of a substance from a solid state to a liquid state when heated above the substance's freezing/melting point.
melting point: the temperature at which a solid changes to a liquid.
metal: an element usually having these characteristics: shiny, ductile (can be drawn into wire), and a good conductor of heat and electricity. (260)
metallic bonding: the type of chemical bond that holds metals together; loose electrons and metal ions attract one another, holding the metal atoms together. (301)
metalloid: an element having some properties of both a metal and a nonmetal; for example, boron and silicon. (262)
meter: the SI unit of length (m). (34)
methane: a flammable gas (CH_4); the main gas in natural gas.
microprocessor: an integrated circuit on the main circuit board of a computer; the computer's "brain." (608)

microscope: an optical instrument that uses two convex lenses with relatively short focal lengths to magnify objects that are very small and up close. (524)
microwaves: electromagnetic waves that are very short (very high frequency) and have high energy. (486)
mixture: a substance made of elements or compounds stirred together but not combined chemically.
model: a representation of an idea or process to make it understandable, using a diagram, formula, or physical structure; for example, Ping-Pong balls to model a molecule or a mathematical formula to model a river's flow. (12)
modulation: the process of adding voice, music, video, or other data to radio waves, by varying either their amplitude or frequency. (486)
momentum: a property of any moving object; equals the object's mass times its velocity. (100)
monomers: organic molecules that are strung together to form polymers.
music: sound created using specific pitches, sound quality, and patterns. (474)

nearsighted: describes a person who sees nearby things clearly, but has trouble focusing on distant objects.
net force: the resulting velocity of an object when multiple forces are applied to it. (71)
neutral: (1) electrically neutral: a compound having no overall electrical charge because the total positive charge equals the total negative charge; (2) chemically neutral: a solution that is neither acidic nor basic.
neutralization: a chemical reaction between an acid and a base; the acid's hydronium ions (H_3O^+) combine with the base's hydroxide ions (OH^-) to produce water (H_2O), and the acid's negative ions combine with the base's positive ions to produce a salt. (440)
neutralize: to change an acidic solution or a basic solution so that it is neutral.
neutron: one of the two types of particles (protons and neutrons) that occur in an atom's nucleus; a neutron is neutral and has no electrical charge (neither negative nor positive). (243)
Newton's first law: English physicist Sir Isaac Newton stated that an object moving at a constant velocity keeps moving at that velocity unless a net force acts on it. (72)
Newton's second law of motion: English physicist Sir Isaac Newton stated that an object accelerates in the direction of the net force applied to it. (85)
Newton's third law of motion: English physicist Sir Isaac Newton stated that for every action, there is an equal and opposite reaction. (98)
noise: sound that has no pattern or definite pitch. (474)
noise pollution: sound that is loud, annoying, or harmful to the ear. (472)
nonelectrolyte: a substance that does not form ions in a water solution, so the water does not become an electrical conductor; for example, sugar or alcohol. (396)
nonmetal: an element that usually lacks the characteristics of a metal (shiny, can be drawn into wire, and a good conductor of heat and electricity). (261)
nonpolar molecule: a molecule in which the atoms have an equal attraction for electrons, so the molecule is not polarized into positive and negative ends. (280)
nonrenewable resources: resources such as coal, oil, and natural gas that we are using up faster than natural processes can replace. (647)
normal: in the study of light, an imaginary line drawn perpendicular to a reflecting surface or perpendicular to a medium that light is entering.
nuclear fission: the splitting of an atom's nucleus into two nuclei having smaller masses, with a simultaneous release of particles and energy. (633)
nuclear fusion: the fusing together of two atomic nuclei into a single nucleus of larger mass. (634)
nuclear reactor: a device in which uranium atoms fission to release energy; the energy is used to generate electricity. (648)
nuclear waste: waste products from nuclear power generation, nuclear weapons manufacture, nuclear medicine, and industrial use of radioactive materials. (651)
nucleic acid: an organic polymer that controls the activities and reproduction of cells. (342)
nucleus: the positively charged center of an atom. (243)
nuclide: an isotope having a specific atomic number and atomic mass. (621)

observation: using your senses to gather information; in science we use instruments to help our senses make more accurate and more detailed observations. (16)
ohm: the unit for measuring resistance; symbol Ω.
Ohm's law: German physicist Georg Ohm stated that electric current (I) equals the potential difference or voltage (V) divided by the resistance to current flow (R). (557)
opaque materials: materials you can't see through because they absorb or reflect nearly all light. (492)
optical axis: a line perpendicular to the center of a mirror or lens.
optical fibers: transparent glass fibers that can pipe light from one place to another. (532)

ore: a mineral or rock containing a useful substance that can be mined at a profit; for example, iron ore or silver ore. (356)

organic compound: a chemical compound containing the element carbon; about 90 percent of all compounds are organic. (328)

oxidation number: a positive or negative number that indicates an element's ability to form a compound. (283)

ozone layer: a layer of Earth's atmosphere that contains plentiful ozone, which absorbs ultraviolet radiation from the sun. (18)

P

parallel circuit: an electrical circuit where the current flows in several separate branches. If one branch is interrupted, current still flows through the other branches. (561)

pascal: the international unit of pressure; 1 pascal = 1 newton/square meter. (204)

Pascal's principle: French scientist Blaise Pascal stated that pressure applied to a fluid is transmitted equally throughout the fluid. (211)

passive solar heating: direct use of the sun's energy to heat something, without storing the energy.

petroleum: crude oil, formed by decay of ancient plants and animals; a fossil fuel that is burned and used to make lubricants and plastics. (644)

period: a horizontal row of elements in the periodic table; increasing from left to right is the number of electrons in the atoms' outer shells. (260)

periodic table: a table of the elements, in order by increasing atomic mass, arranged in rows and columns to show their repeated (periodic) properties. (255)

pH: a measure of hydronium ion (H_3O^+) concentration in a water solution, expressed on the pH scale from 0 to 14. From 7 down to 0, a solution is increasingly acidic; at 7 it is neutral (pure water); from 7 up to 14, a solution is increasingly basic. (pH = *p*otential of *H*ydrogen) (435)

phenolphthalein (feen ul THAYL een): a chemical used as a color indicator in titration; colorless in an acidic solution, but turns pink in a basic solution.

photon: a particle of light. (485)

photovoltaic cell: a solar cell; a semiconductor that converts light energy into electrical energy. (657)

physical change: a change in a substance's size, shape, color, or state (solid, liquid, gas). (230)

physical property: any characteristic of a material that you can observe, such as state, shape, size, or color. (228)

physical science: the study of matter and energy. (7)

pickling: a process that removes oxides and other impurities from steel and other metal surfaces by dipping them in hydrochloric acid. (429)

pitch: the highness or lowness of a sound, which is determined by the frequency (wavelength) of the sound. (466)

plane mirror: a mirror with a flat surface. (512)

plankton: tiny plants and animals that live in water and are food for small fish; they are easily killed by acid rain. (439)

plasma: a gaslike mixture of positively and negatively charged particles; it is the commonest state of matter in the universe. (194)

plastic: a material made from synthetic organic polymers that can be easily molded; nylon and polyethylene are examples. (362)

polarized light: light in which the waves vibrate only in one plane. (528)

polarizing filter: a filter made of chains of molecules in parallel rows that will transmit only light waves vibrating in the same direction as the molecular chains.

polar molecule: a molecule in which one atom has a stronger attraction for electrons than the other, giving the molecule a positive end and a negative end. (278)

polluted water: water that is contaminated with substances that may be harmful to living things. (199)

polyatomic ion: a group of covalently bonded atoms in which the whole group has a positive or negative charge, like NH_4^+ or CO_3^{2-} (286)

polymer: a huge molecule made of many smaller organic molecules (monomers) linked together; examples are proteins and plastics. (340)

positron: a positively charged electron.

potential difference: the difference in electric potential energy between two different points. (552)

potential energy: energy that is not causing change right now but is stored for potential use, as in a battery or a wound-up spring. (111)

power: the rate at which work is done; power = work ÷ time. (177)

precipitate: an insoluble solid that settles out of a chemical reaction occurring in a liquid. (414)

pressure: the amount of force exerted per unit of area; pressure = force ÷ area. (204)

principle: a basic rule or law describing how something always works in the natural world; for example, "gravity always pulls objects toward each other."

products: in a chemical reaction, the substances formed by the reaction. (404)

projectile: any object shot or thrown through the air. (90)

propane: a flammable gas (C_3H_8); a part of natural gas.

protein: an organic polymer formed from amino acids; various proteins make up many body tissues. (340)

proton: one of the two types of particles (protons and neutrons) that occur in the nucleus of an atom; a proton has a positive charge. (243)

pulley: a simple machine consisting of a grooved wheel with a rope or a chain running along the groove; it changes the direction and/or amount of force. (166)

Q

quality: in sound, the differences among sounds that have the same pitch and loudness. (475)
quark: a very small particle of matter that makes up protons and neutrons; five or six different quark types may exist. (248)

R

radiation: the transfer of energy through matter or space by electromagnetic waves such as heat, light, radio waves, X rays and gamma rays. (136, 484)
radiator: a device with a large surface area that transfers heat to surrounding air by conduction. (142)
radioactive element: an unstable element (like uranium) that naturally decays to form other elements by radiation (expelling an alpha particle, beta particle, or gamma ray from the atom's nucleus). (302)
radioactivity: the emission of particles or gamma rays from the nucleus of an atom that is unstable and radioactive. (621)
radio waves: electromagnetic waves that have long wavelengths (low frequencies). (485)
radius: the distance from the center of a circle to its circumference.
RAM: *r*andom-*a*ccess *m*emory in a computer; the temporary electronic memory in a chip that "forgets" as soon as the power is turned off. (608)
rarefaction: in compressional waves, the less dense area of the wave.
reactants: in a chemical reaction, the substances you start with before the reaction. (404)
real image: an image produced where light rays converge, as with a concave mirror or convex lens; a real image can be projected on a screen. (514)
rectifier: a device that changes alternating current into direct current. (599)
recycling: reprocessing of waste products into new products; for example, aluminum cans are recycled to make other aluminum cans or foil. (360)
reflecting telescope: an optical instrument that uses a concave mirror and a convex lens to magnify distant objects. (523)
reflection: bouncing of a wave off an object; this includes all types of waves—light, sound, radio, ocean, and so on. (500)
refraction: the bending of waves, caused by changing their speed. (501)
resistance: the opposition to the flow of electrons through a conductor, measured in ohms with an ohmmeter. (555)
resistance arm: the part of a lever that exerts the resistance force (F_r). (163)
resistance force (F_r): the force exerted by a machine to overcome resistance to gravity or friction. (159)
resonance: the tendency of an object to vibrate at the same frequency as a sound source. (475)
reverberation: the echoing effect produced by multiple reflections of sound. (477)
RNA: *r*ibo*n*ucleic *a*cid, a nucleic acid that controls production of proteins that make new cells.
ROM: *r*ead-*o*nly *m*emory in a computer; it is permanent memory stored inside the computer, even when the power is turned off. (609)

S

salt: a compound containing negative ions from an acid combined with positive ions from a base; forms during a neutralization reaction. (440)
saponification: the process of making soap. (443)
saturated hydrocarbon: a hydrocarbon compound in which each carbon atom is joined to four other atoms by single covalent bonds; an example is methane gas (CH_4). (331)
saturated solution: a solution that has dissolved all the solute it can hold at a specific temperature. (390)
scientific law: a rule that describes a pattern in nature and predicts what will happen under specific conditions. (16)
screw: a simple machine consisting of an inclined plane wrapped in a spiral around a cylindrical post; it changes the amount of force. (169)
second: the SI unit of time. (40)
semiconductor: an element that conducts electricity under certain conditions; in the periodic table, semiconductors are between metals and nonmetals. (317)
series circuit: an electrical circuit where the current flows only in one path. If the path is interrupted at any point, it stops current flow in the entire circuit. (561)
SI: International System of Units, the standard worldwide system of measurement used by all scientists; a modern version of the metric system. (31)
simple machine: a device that performs work with only one movement. Simple machines include the lever, pulley, wheel and axle, inclined plane, screw, and wedge. (158)
single displacement reaction: a chemical reaction in which one element replaces another element in a compound. (414)
smog: a form of air pollution; a colloid in which invisible solid particles mix with the air gases that we breathe. (226)
soap: an organic salt made by reacting fats or oils with a strong base such as sodium hydroxide. (443)
solar collector: a device that absorbs radiant energy from the sun. (144)
solar energy: energy from the sun, which includes heat, light, radio, ultraviolet, gamma, and other waves. (144)

solubility: the amount of a substance (solute) that will dissolve in a solvent; scientifically it is how many grams of solute will dissolve in 100 g of a solvent, at a specific temperature. (388)
solute: the substance being dissolved in a solvent; for example, in a sweet drink sugar is the solute and water is the solvent. (381)
solution: a homogeneous mixture containing tiny particles that don't settle and don't scatter light. (222)
solvent: the substance that dissolves a solute; for example, in a sweet drink sugar is the solute and water is the solvent. (381)
specific heat: the amount of energy needed to raise the temperature of 1 kilogram of a material 1 degree Celsius. (124)
speed: the rate of motion, or the rate of change in position. (60)
standard: in measurement, an exact quantity that everyone agrees to use for comparison; for example, a meter, kilogram, liter, kelvin, joule, and so on. (30)
state of matter: any of the four conditions in which matter can exist: solid, liquid, gas, or plasma. (190)
static electricity: the accumulation of electric charges on an object. No current flows because the electricity is static (motionless). (546)
step-down transformer: an electrical transformer that decreases (steps down) the voltage of a power line.
step-up transformer: an electrical transformer that increases (steps up) the voltage of a power line.
strong acid: an acid that ionizes almost completely in water solution, thus containing large numbers of hydronium ions (H_3O^+); for example, hydrochloric acid. (434)
strong base: a base that dissociates almost completely in water solution, thus containing a large number of hydroxide ions (OH^-); for example, sodium hydroxide. (435)
sublimation: a type of evaporation in which a solid changes directly to a gas without going through a liquid state. (313)
submerge: to fully immerse (completely cover) something in a fluid.
substance: matter that is an element or a compound. (221)
substituted hydrocarbon: a hydrocarbon in which one or more hydrogen atoms have been replaced by atoms of other elements. (335)
supercollider: a device to make protons collide at high speed so they break apart into quarks.
superconductor: a supercooled material that has no electrical resistance and so is a "super" conductor of electricity. (588)
supersaturated solution: an unstable solution that contains more solute than the solvent can dissolve at a specific temperature. (392)
suspension: a heterogeneous mixture containing larger particles that eventually settle out. (224)
synthesis reaction: a chemical reaction in which two or more substances combine to form a different substance. (413)
synthetic fiber: a strand of a synthetic polymer; examples are nylon, rayon, and Kevlar fibers. (365)

T

technology: the application of scientific knowledge to improve the quality of human life. (7)
telephoto lens: a lens having a long focal length and producing an enlarged, closeup image of an object. (525)
temperature: a measure of the average kinetic energy of the particles in matter; expressed in degrees kelvin or Celsius. (118)
terminal velocity: the greatest velocity reached by a falling object. (89)
theory: a solution to a problem; a former hypothesis that has been tested with repeated experiments and observations and found always to work. (16)
thermal energy: the total energy of particles in a material, including both kinetic and potential energy. (119)
thermal expansion: a characteristic of matter causing it to expand when heated and contract when cooled. (195)
thermal pollution: pollution caused when waste thermal energy raises the temperature of the environment. (146)
thermonuclear fusion: nuclear fusion that occurs under conditions of enormous heat (millions of degrees), as in a star or our sun.
tidal energy: electricity generated by the ocean tides. (658)
time: the interval between two events; the SI unit is the second. (40)
titration: a method for finding the concentration of an acidic or basic solution, using a solution of known concentration. (442)
total internal reflection: occurs when all the light entering an object is reflected internally, maintaining the intensity of the light. (531)
toxic: describes any substance that can injure living tissue; a poison. (274)
tracer: a radioactive isotope used for medical diagnosis; it allows a doctor to trace the location of tumors and fluid movements in the body.
transformer: a device that transforms electrical current to a higher voltage or a lower voltage. (586)
transistor: a semiconductor that amplifies an electrical signal. (599)
transition element: an element in Groups 3-12 of the periodic table; each is metallic, with one or two electrons in its outer energy level. (304)
translucent materials: materials that can be partially seen through because they allow some light to pass, but not enough for a clear image. (492)

transmutation: changing one element to another through radioactive decay; for example, uranium-238 is transmuted into lead-206 after enough particles and rays have been emitted from its nucleus. (625)

transparent materials: materials that can be seen through because they allow nearly all light to pass through them. (492)

transuranium element: any element beyond uranium in the periodic table (having a higher atomic number than 92); these radioactive synthetic elements are made in laboratories or nuclear reactors. (309)

transverse wave: a wave that vibrates at right angles to the direction the wave is traveling. (458)

trough: in waves, the lowest point of a wave. (459)

Tyndall effect: the scattering of light by particles in a mixture, as occurs with a flashlight beam in the night sky. (226)

U

ultraviolet radiation: electromagnetic waves that have a wavelength slightly shorter (higher frequency) than visible light; abbreviated *UV.* (489)

unsaturated hydrocarbon: a hydrocarbon compound in which each carbon atom is joined to other atoms by double or triple covalent bonds; an example is acetylene. (331)

unsaturated solution: a solution that is capable of dissolving more solute at a specific temperature. (391)

V

velocity: the rate of motion in a specific direction. (65)

virtual image: an image formed of diverging light rays, as in a flat or convex mirror, or seen through a concave lens. A virtual image isn't "real" and can't be projected. (513)

visible radiation: electromagnetic waves in the only part of the electromagnetic spectrum we can see—light. (488)

volt: the unit for measuring electrical potential energy, abbreviated *V.*

voltage: a difference in electrical potential, measured in volts with a voltmeter.

voltmeter: a galvanometer that measures electrical potential differences in a circuit, in volts. (580)

volume: the amount of space occupied by an object; its SI unit is the cubic meter (m^3). (37)

W

Watt (W): the unit of power, one joule per second. (177)

wave: a rhythmic disturbance that carries energy through matter or space. Mechanical waves require a medium to travel in; electromagnetic waves can travel either through a medium or space. (458)

wavelength: the distance between a point on one wave and the identical point on the next wave; for example, the distance between two crests or two troughs. (459)

weak acid: an acid that ionizes only partially in water solution, thus creating a small number of hydronium ions (H_3O^+); for example, acetic acid. (434)

weak base: a base that dissociates only partially in water solution, thus creating a small number of hydroxide ions (OH^-); for example, magnesium hydroxide. (435)

wedge: a simple machine consisting of an inclined plane with one or two sloping sides; examples are a chisel, knife, and axe. It changes the amount of force. (170)

weight: the measure of the force of gravity on an object, usually the force between Earth and an object at its surface. (76)

wet cell: a power source that generates electric current by a chemical reaction; "wet" because it uses a liquid electrolyte, as in an automobile battery. (555)

wheel and axle: a simple machine consisting of two wheels of different sizes that are connected so they rotate together, such as a doorknob or wheel-handled faucet; it changes the amount of force. (167)

wide-angle lens: a lens having a short focal length and producing a relatively small image of an object, but including much of the object's surroundings. (525)

work: the transfer of energy through motion; work = force × distance. (112)

X, Y, Z

X rays: electromagnetic waves having a wavelength shorter (higher frequency) than ultraviolet radiation; often used in medical photography because they can penetrate human tissue. (490)

INDEX

The Index for *Merrill Physical Science* will help you locate major topics in the book quickly and easily. Each entry in the Index is followed by the numbers of the pages on which the entry is discussed. A page number given in **boldface type** indicates the page on which that entry is defined. A page number given in *italic type* indicates a page on which the entry is used in an illustration or photograph. The abbreviation *act.* indicates a page on which the entry is used in an activity.

C

L

W

PHOTO CREDITS

Cover, Osborn Photographic Illustration Inc.; **xviii,** StudiOhio; **xix,** Doug Martin; **xx,** StudiOhio; **iv,** (l)BLT Productions, (r)StudiOhio; **v,** Bud Fowle; **vi,** Ken Frick; **vii,** (t)Doug Martin, (b)Ken Frick; **viii, ix,** Doug Martin; **x,** T. J. Florian/Rainbow; **xi,** Hickson & Associates; **xii,** Mike Brown/Gamma Liaison; **xiii,** Doug Martin; **xiv,** Keith Kent/Peter Arnold Inc.; **xv,** Ken Frick; **2-3,** Ed Degginger; **3,** Tim Courlas; **4,** BLT Productions; **5,** Doug Martin; **6,** (t)Phil Degginger, (b)National Radio Astronomy Observatory; **7,** Ken Frick; **8,** Doug Martin; **9,** NOAA/NESDIS/Satellite Applications Laboratory; **10,** (t)The Bettmann Archive, (b)Lloyd Lemmerman; **11,** Tim Courlas; **12,** (t)Ken Frick, (b)Bruce Frisch/Photo Researchers; **13,** James H. Karales/Peter Arnold Inc.; **14,** Ken Frick; **16,** (tl)Ken Frick, (tr)William E. Ferguson, (b)Tim Courlas; **18,** Dan McCoy/Rainbow; **19,** Will McIntyre/Photo Researchers; **20,** Hickson & Associates; **21,** Doug Martin; **22,** Hickson & Associates; **24,** Doug Martin; **25,** Latent Images; **26,** First Image; **28,** Hickson & Associates, (inset)Ken Frick; **29,** Doug Martin; **30,** StudiOhio; **31,** National Standard of Mass; **32,33,** Doug Martin; **35,** Ken Frick; **37,** NASA; **39,** Doug Martin; **40,** (l)Ken Frick, (r)Courtesy of National Institute of Standards & Technology; **41,** Doug Martin; **46,** (t)Tom McGuire; (b)Al Tielemans/DUOMO; **47,48,** Doug Martin; **49,** Tim Courlas; **51,** File Photo; **52,** (t)Atomic Energy Commission, (b)Phil Degginger; **53,** (t)TSW, (c)Susan McCartney/Photo Researchers, (b)NASA; **54,** (tl)Pictures Unlimited, (tr)Cobalt Productions, (bl)Doug Martin, (br)Ken Frick; **55,** Michael Holford; **56-57,** Geisser/H. Armstrong Roberts; **57,** Robert Daemmrich/TSW; **58,** StudiOhio; **59,** StudiOhio; **60,** Doug Martin; **61,** (t)Bud Fowle, (b)StudiOhio; **64,** StudiOhio; **65,** (t)Scott Camazine/Photo Researchers, (b)Ed Pritchard/TSW; **68,** Doug Martin; **69,** Bud Fowle; **70,** Focus on Sports; **71,** StudiOhio; **72,73,** Doug Martin; **74,** Bud/Fowle/Sonja Welker and the BalletMet Dance Academy of Columbus, Ohio; **75,** Dan Hems/DUOMO; **76,** NASA; **77,** StudiOhio; **78,** Doug Martin; **82,** Cyril Isy-Schwart/The Image Bank; **83,** StudiOhio; **86,** Peticolas/Megna/Fundamental Photographs; **88,** (t)StudiOhio, (b)Chris Hackett/The Image Bank, (br)Runk/Schoenberger from Grant Heilman; **89,** Craig Aurness/Westlight; **90,** Pictures Unlimited; **91** (t), StudiOhio, (b)Richard Magna/Fundamental Photographs; **92,** Doris DeWitt/TSW; **93,** Courtesy of Daniel L. Feicht/Cedar Point; **94,** NASA; **95,** Doug Martin; **97,** NASA; **99,** (t)Bill Ross/Westlight, (b)StudiOhio; **100,** NASA; **101** (t)Bud Fowle, (c)StudiOhio, (b)Lou Jones/The Image Bank; **102,** Ed Degginger; **103,** Gianalberto Cigowni/The Image Bank; **104,** Doug Martin; **106,** TSW; **108,** BLT Productions; **109,** StudiOhio; **110,** Latent Images; **111,** David Dennis; **112,** (t)(c)StudiOhio, (b)Cobalt Productions; **114,** Bud Fowle; **116,** Alan D. Carey; **117,** Doug Martin; **119,** StudiOhio; **120,** Bud Fowle; **122,** Aaron Haupt; **125,** NOAA/NESDIS/Satellite Applications Laboratory; **127,** Hickson & Associates; **128,** Latent Images; **130,** Pictures Unlimited; **132,** BLT Productions; **133,** StudiOhio; **137,** Johnny Johnson; **138,** H. Armstrong Roberts; **139,** Ken Frick; **141,** Doug Martin; **142,** Cobalt Productions; **144,** (l)Paolo Koch/Photo Researchers, (r)John Keating/Photo Researchers; **146,** Grant Heilman; **147,** Phil Degginger/H. Armstrong Roberts; **148,** Hickson & Associates; **150,** (t)Hughes Aircraft Company, (b)Ed Degginger; **152,** Doug Martin; **154,** Ken Frick; **156** Murray Alcosser/The Image Bank; **157,** Ken Frick; **158,** (t)Jim Franck Photography, (bl)Ken Frick, (bc)StudiOhio, (br)Lloyd Lemmerman; **161,** Hickson & Associates; **162,163,** Doug Martin; **165,** (tl)Steve Lissau, (tc)Ken Frick, (tr)(b)StudiOhio; **166,** (t)Doug Martin, (b)BLT Productions; **167,** Hickson & Associates; **169,** (tl)StudiOhio, (tr)W. Geiersperger/The Stock Market, (b)Doug Martin; **170,** (l)Ken Frick, (r)Aaron Haupt; **171,** Doug Martin; **172,** John Barr/Gamma Liaison; **174,** StudiOhio; **175,** Doug Martin; **176,** Tim Courlas; **177,** © University of CA, Berkeley/Peter Arnold Inc.; **182,** (t)Culver Pictures, (b)William E. Ferguson; **183,** (t)Roger Burnard, (bl)Andrea Pistolesi/The Image Bank, (br)Marvin E. Newman/The Image Bank; **184,** (tl)(bl)Hickson & Associates, (tr)Bruno de Hogues/TSW, (br)Pictures Unlimited; **185,** S. J. Krasemann/Peter Arnold Inc.; **186-187,** Josquin Carrillo/Photo Researchers; **187,** StudiOhio; **188,** Doug Martin; **189,** StudiOhio; **190,** Dan McCoy/Rainbow; **191,** Philip A. Harrington/The Image Bank; **192,** (t)Barry Seidman/The Stock Market, (b)StudiOhio; **193,** Chip Clark; **194,** (l)Hansen Planetarium, (r)File Photo; **195,** Cobalt Productions; **196,** StudiOhio; **197,198,** Doug Martin; **199,** (l)Mark Lewis/TSW, (r)Grant Heilman; **200,** (l)Doug Martin, (r)StudiOhio; **201,** StudiOhio; **203,** Doug Martin; **204,** StudiOhio; **206,** NASA; **207,** Pictures Unlimited; **208,209,** Doug Martin; **211,212,** StudiOhio; **213,** Doug Martin; **214,216,** StudiOhio; **218,** Steve Strickland/Westlight; **219,** Doug Martin; **220,** StudiOhio; **221,** (t)StudiOhio, (r)Doug Martin, (b)Hickson & Associates; **222,** (tl)Ed Degginger, (tr)Latent Image, (b)StudiOhio; **223,** (t)StudiOhio, (b)Doug Martin; **224,** StudiOhio; **225,** Doug Martin; **226,** Dan McCoy/Rainbow; **227,228,** StudiOhio; **229,** (t)Ken Frick, (b)Doug Martin; **230,** Doug Wilson/TSW; **231,** John Brennels/© 1990 DISCOVER PUBLICATIONS; **232,** (t)James Westwater; (l)NASA, (r)Ed Degginger; **233,** (l,c)Ken Frick, (r)Ken Frick; **234,** (l)Colin Bell/TSW, (r)Doug Martin; **235,236,** Doug Martin; **237,** Alexander Lowry/Photo Researchers; **238-239,** Pete Saloutos/The Stock Market; **240,** File Photo, (inset)Jet Propulsion Laboratory; **241,** First Image, **242,** (t)StudiOhio; (b)Doug Martin; **243,** (t)Ken Frick, (b)The Smithsonian Institution; **244,** (t)StudiOhio, (b)Doug Martin, (b inset)First Image; **245,** William E. Ferguson; **247,** Doug Martin; **250,** (l)First Image, (r)Doug Martin; **251,252,** Doug Martin; **254,** (t)Ken Frick, (b)First Image; **255,** Stamp from the Collection of Prof. C. M. Lang, Photography by Gary Shulfer, Univ. of Wisconsin-Stevens Point: Russia 3608 (1969); **256,** Ed Degginger; **257,** (t)Doug Martin, (b)First Image; **260,** Lawrence Migdale/Science Source/Photo Researchers; **261,** Courtesy of IBM; **262,** Bill Pierce/Rainbow; **263,264,** Doug Martin; **266,** StudiOhio; **267,** Doug Martin; **268,** StudiOhio; **269,** Doug Martin; **270,273,274,275,** StudiOhio; **276,278,** Doug Martin; **279,** Franklin Bailey and Keith Stormo/© 1990 DISCOVER PUBLICATIONS; **280,** (l)StudiOhio, (r)K. G. Vock/Okapia 1989/Photo Researcher; **281,** Doug Martin; **282,** (l)W. W. Winter Ltd./The Derby Museum, (r)Doug Martin; **285,287,** Doug Martin; **288,** Bud Fowle; **290,** Pictures Unlimited; **292,** (t)Howard Bluestein/Photo Researchers, (b)FPG International; **293,** (t)Culver Pictures, (bl)Ed Degginger, (br)© The Cousteau Society; **294,** Doug Martin; **295,** Culver Pictures; **296-297,** Tim Courlas; **297,** Doug Martin; **298,** Toyofumi Mori/The Image Bank; **299,** Doug Martin; **300,** (t)FPG International, (tc)Light Source, (c)Tom Tracy Photography, (r)Ed Degginger; **301,** Charles Thatcher/TSW; **302,** Doug Martin; **303,** (l)ZEFA-U.K./H. Armstrong Roberts, (c)Doug Martin, (r)StudiOhio; **304,** Doug Martin; **305,** (t)Doug Martin, (b)NASA; **306,** (l)Ken Frick, (r)Doug Martin; **307,** Doug Martin; **308,** Ken Frick; **309,** Martin Bond/Photo Researchers; **311,** Annie Griffiths/Westlight; **312,** (t)Ken Frick, (b)Doug Martin; **313,** (t)Ken Frick, (b)Ben Simmons/The Stock Market; **314,** Dan McCoy/Rainbow; **315,** Doug Martin; **317,** (t)StudiOhio, (c)(r)Doug Martin; **318,** Ken Frick; **319,** Doug Martin; **320,** Manfred Kage/Peter Arnold Inc.; **321,** Ken Frick; **322,** Doug Martin; **324,** Ken Frick; **326,327,328,** Doug Martin; **329,** (t)R. Krubner/H. Armstrong Roberts, (c)Phil Degginger, (b)Doug Martin; **330,** Ken Frick; **331,** (t)Doug Martin, (b)Steve Strickland/Westlight; **332,** (t)StudiOhio, (b)Ken Frick; **334,** (l)Skinnet-Veron/Fig. Mag/Gamma Liaison, (r)Ken Frick; **335,** (t)Ken Frick, (b)Doug Martin; **337,** Doug Martin; **338,** Mark N. Boulton/Photo Researchers; **339,** Bruce Sampsel; **340,** (t)Ken Frick, (l)CNRI/Science Photo Library/Photo Researchers, (r)Lab. of Molecular Biology, MCR/Science Photo Library/Photo Researchers; **341,** (t)Elaine Comer-Shay, (b)Doug Martin; **342,** Nelson Max/CCNL/Photo Researchers; **343,** Ken Frick; **344,** (t)Courtesy of the Simplesse Company, (b)Ken Frick; **345,** Ken Frick; **346,** Doug Martin; **348,** Ken Frick; **350,** ©Terry O'Neill/Woodfin Camp & Associates, (l&r)Ken Frick; **351,** StudiOhio; **352,** FPG International; **353,** Ken Frick; **354,** (t)Ed Degginger, (tr)(c)(br)Doug Martin; **355,** (t)Tim Courlas, (b)Mike Devlin/Science Photo Library/Photo Researchers; **356,** Bill Tronca/Tom Stack & Assoc.; **357,** (t)The Smithsonian Institution, (bl)(br)Ken Frick, (c)BLT Productions; **358,359,** Doug Martin; **360,** William E. Ferguson; **361,** Randall L. Schieber; **362,** Ken Frick; **365,** (t)StereoLithography is a proprietary product of 3D Systems, Inc., (b)Doug Martin; **366,** Doug Martin; **367,** (l)Dan McCoy, (r)Ken Frick; **368,369,** Doug Martin; **370,** Ken Frick; **372,** (t)Michael Doolittle/Rainbow, (b)Carl Frank/Photo Researchers; **373,** (t)Blaine Harrington III/The Stock Market, (c)Courtesy of General Motors, (b)The Bettmann Archive; **374,** (tl)Doug Martin, (tr)Bill Weems/Woodfin Camp & Associates, (bl)Aaron Haupt, (br)Pictures Unlimited; **375,** Photo from the Collection of Michele Tofoya; **376-377,** Hans Pfletschinger/Peter Arnold Inc.; **377,** Jeffrey M. Spielman/Stockphotos; **378,** Steven Burr Williams/The Image Bank; **379,** StudiOhio; **380,** Ken Frick; **381,** (t)Doug Martin, (tc)Ken Frick, (b)Doug Martin; **384,** Bud Fowle; **385,** Ken Frick; **386,** Bill Ross/Westlight; **388,** Doug Martin; **389,** Latent Images; **392,393,394,** Doug Martin; **395,** Ken Frick; **398,399,** Doug Martin; **401,** Bud Fowle; **402,** Guido Alberto Rossi/The Image Bank; **403,** Ken Frick; **404,** Culver Pictures; **405,** Doug Martin; **407,** ZEFZ-U.K./H. Armstrong Roberts; **408,** NASA; **409,** StudiOhio; **412,** Doug Martin; **414,** (t)Ken Frick, (b)Doug Martin; **416,** Doug Martin; **417,** Lawrence Hughes/The Image Bank; **418,** (t)Tim Courlas, (b)Grant Heilman; **420,** Doug Martin; **422,** Ted Rice; **424,** Ron Watts/Westlight; **425,** Doug Martin; **426,** (t)StudiOhio, (b)Doug Martin; **428,** Doug Martin; **429,** (t)First Image, (b)Aaron Haupt; **430,431,** Ken Frick; **434,435,437,** Doug Martin; **438,** Tom McHugh/Photo Researchers; **439,** Runk/Schoenberger from Grant Heilman; **441,** Doug Martin; **442,** (t)Tim Courlas, (b)Doug Martin; **446,** Doug Martin; **448,** Tim Courlas; **449,** Panographics/L. S. Stepanowicz; **450,** (t)Tom Bean/The Stock Market, (b)Phil Degginger; **451,** (t)The Bettman Archive, (c)Culver Pictures, (b)Francis Current/Photo Researchers; **452,** (tl)Doug Martin, (tr)Roger Tully/TSW, (bl)Doug Martin, (br)Steve Weber/TSW; **453,** The Salt Institute; **454-455,** Courtesy of Dr. Otis Brown, Rosentiel School of Marine and Atmospheric Science, University of Miami; **455,** NASA; **456,** Doug Martin; **457,** StudiOhio; **458,** Steve Lissau; **463,** StudiOhio; **465,** Ed Degginger; **467,** Burton McNeely/The Image Bank; **469,** Doug Martin; **471,472,473,** StudiOhio; **475,478**(t), Doug Martin; **478**(inset),**480,** StudiOhio; **482,** Pete Saloutos/The Stock Market; **483,** Shay/Gerard; **484,** File Photo; **486,** (tl)StudiOhio, (r)Tim Courlas, (b)StudiOhio; **487,** (l)Dan McCoy/Rainbow, (r)© Howard Sochurek/The Stock Market; **488,** Bud Fowle; **489,** StudiOhio; **490,** Science Photo Library/Photo Researchers; **491,** Doug Martin; **492,493,494,** StudiOhio; **497,** Doug Martin; **498,499,500,** StudiOhio; **501,** Pictures Unlimited; **502,** (l)Ed Degginger, (r)Kodak; **503,** Vance A. Tucker; **504,505,** Dan McCoy/Rainbow; **506,** Doug Martin; **508,** Allen Zak; **510,** Cobalt Productions; **511,513,** StudiOhio; **514,** (t)Aaron Haupt, (b)Latent Images; **515,516,517,** Doug Martin; **522,** (l)Kurt Thorson, (r)Johnny Johnson; **525,** Doug Martin; **526,** NASA; **528,** Cobalt Productions; **529,** (t)StudiOhio, (b)Doug Martin; **531,** (t)Lou Jones/The Image Bank, (b)Doug Martin; **532,** John Feingersh 1988/The Stock Market; **533,** Tom Tracy Photography; **534,** Doug Martin; **536,** StudiOhio; **538,** (t)Garry Gay/The Image Bank, (b)Michael Parfit; **539,** (t)Chuck O'Rear/Westlight, (c)The Bettmann Archive, (b)William E. Ferguson; **540,** (tl)Ted Kawalerski/The Image Bank, (cl)Ken Frick, (tr)StudiOhio, (br)Ken Frick; **541,** Art Resource; **542-543,** D. W. Hamilton/The Image Bank; **543,** Jean Marc Giboux/Gamma Liaison; **544,** Hank Morgan/Rainbow; **545,547,** StudiOhio; **548,** Steven Burr Williams/The Image Bank; **550,** © Thomas Ives/The Stock Market; **551,** 1986 © Mark Gibson/The Stock Market; **555,** (t)T. J. Florian/Rainbow, (b)StudiOhio; **556,** Sheffield University/Science Photo Library/Photo Researchers; **557,** StudiOhio; **559,** Doug Martin; **560,561,** Tim Courlas; **562,** StudiOhio; **563,** (t)Elaine Comer-Shay, (b)Doug Martin; **564,** Doug Martin; **567,** Mark Burnett; **570,** Ken Frick; **572,** Larry Hamill; **572(inset),** Doug Martin; **573,** Ken Frick; **574,575,576,** Doug Martin; **579,** P&G Bowater/The Image Bank; **582,** Doug Martin; **585,** Ken Frick; **587,** Joe Bator/The Stock Market; **588,** Lou Jones/The Image Bank; **589,** © 1989 Makoto Iwafuji/The Stock Market; **590,** Doug Martin; **592,** StudiOhio; **594,595,** Doug Martin; **596,** StudiOhio; **598,** Doug Martin; **599,** (t)Ken Frick, (b)Doug Martin; **600,** Doug Martin; **601,** StudiOhio; **604,** Hank Morgan/Rainbow; **605,606,** StudiOhio; **607,** The Bettmann Archive; **609,** Hickson & Associates; **610,611,** Doug Martin; **612,** Hickson & Associates; **613,614,** Doug Martin; **615,** StudiOhio; **618,** TSW; **619,** Ken Frick; **620,** Doug Martin; **622,** Hank Morgan/Photo Researchers; **626,** Ken Frick; **628,** Ed Degginger; **629,** Doug Martin; **630,** Science Photo Library/Photo Researchers; **631,** Patrice Loiez, CERN/Science Photo Library/Photo Researchers; **636,637,638,** Doug Martin; **642,** Steve Dunwell/The Image Bank; **643,** Doug Martin; **646,** Randall L. Schieber; **647,** Doug Martin; **648,** D.O.E./Science Source/Photo Researchers; **649,** Light Source; **651,** (t)Y. Arthus-Bertrand/Peter Arnold Inc., (b)Gordon Gahar/Lawrence Livermore Laboratory; **653,** Doug Martin; **654,** Dan McCoy/Rainbow; **655,** Ed Degginger; **657,** Mike Brown/Gamma Liaison; **658,** Coco McCoy/Rainbow; **659,** (b)Spencer Swanger/Tom Stack & Assoc., (r)Ed Degginger; **660,** Barry Griffiths/Photo Researchers; **661,** David W. Hamilton/The Image Bank; **662,664,** Doug Martin; **666,** (tl)David Sailors/The Stock Market, (bl)Courtesy of Westinghouse Electric Corporation, (r)Hickson & Associates; **667,** (t)Blaine Harrington/The Stock Market, (b)First Image; **668,** (tl)Doug Martin, (tr)(br)Hickson & Associates, (bl)Doug Martin; **669,** Coco McCoy/Rainbow.

640 N. Calumet Road
Chesterton, IN 46304